W9-ATN-869

NETWORK TECHNOLOGY & SERVICE INTEGRATION

Taken from:

Telecommunications for Managers, Fifth Edition
by Stanford H. Rowe II

Introduction to Telecommunications
by M.A. Rosengrant

Computer Networking: A Top-Down Approach Featuring the Internet, Third Edition
by James F. Kurose and Keith W. Ross

Taken from:

Telecommunications for Managers, Fifth Edition
by Stanford H. Rowe II

A Pearson Education Company
Upper Saddle River, New Jersey 07458

Introduction to Telecommunications
by M.A. Rosengrant

Published by Prentice-Hall, Inc.

Computer Networking: A Top-Down Approach Featuring the Internet, Third Edition
by James F. Kurose and Keith W. Ross

Published by Addison Wesley
Boston, Massachusetts 02116

This special edition published in cooperation with Pearson Custom Publishing.

Printed in the United States of America

10 9 8

ISBN 0-536-91611-X

2005200056

EM

Please visit our web site at *www.pearsoncustom.com*

PEARSON CUSTOM PUBLISHING
75 Arlington Street, Suite 300, Boston, MA 02116
A Pearson Education Company

CONTENTS

CHAPTER 1

Introduction to Telecommunications

OBJECTIVES

After you complete your study of this chapter, you should be able to

- define telecommunications and data communications;
- describe the basic elements of a telecommunications system and give examples of all of them;
- explain why telecommunications is an integral part of the contemporary business environment;
- explain why it is important to study and understand something about telecommunications;
- explain many of the requirements for voice and data communications systems;
- give several examples of the way telecommunications is used in business;
- summarize telecommunications history;
- explain why it can be difficult to keep your telecommunications knowledge up-to-date.

INTRODUCTION

We are members of the information age and the networked society, and the ability to share and communicate information and knowledge is more important than ever—and it is more possible. Every year brings an accelerating number of new discoveries about every facet of our world and the universe. Although information known only to one person can be very useful to that person for decision making, knowledge and information are most useful when they are shared with others. Sharing means communicating, and communicating can occur in many ways. A raised eyebrow, a shrug, a quizzical expression, a posture, a stance—all are effective ways of *body language* communication in certain situations. Communication can occur in other forms too. Music, art, and dance come immediately to mind as ways of expressing feelings and emotions that sometimes stir and inspire the soul.

Another example is *written* communication. Books, newspapers, magazines, and graffiti scrawled on a wall all exist to convey messages to readers. In some cases, the intent is to convey information that the reader wants to receive; in other cases, the writer wants to express his or her thoughts, ideas, or feelings on a topic of importance to him or her.

Radio and television are two forms of *broadcast* communication that cannot be ignored. Every day, most people around the world are bombarded by broadcasts designed to entertain, sell, or provide information.

Although one can ignore specific broadcasts, it is virtually impossible to deny the strong impact this type of communication has on our daily lives.

The amount of information that is available to us is accelerating rapidly. More books are being published and magazine articles written than ever before, to say nothing of the increasing number of research reports and all of the data generated by computers. Sharing this vast information bank is a staggering proposition, but all over the globe the *networked society* is taking form and growing at an equally staggering pace. At the start of the 1990s an estimated 1 million people were exchanging information through a primitive *Internet*. As joining the Internet became easier its population swelled to several hundred million at the beginning of the twenty-first century.

Internet

People log on to the Internet because it gives them value in the form of access to information that they never dreamed possible. Robert Metcalfe, who invented the Ethernet, a local area network that will be studied, says that the power of a network—how much it can do—is measured by the square of the number of connected machines: $P(n) = n^2$. The implication is that the rapid growth of the Internet has given us an information tool that allows us to access unimaginable amounts of information. To say that the pace is breathtaking is probably an understatement!

DEFINITION OF COMMUNICATION

Communication is defined as "a process that allows information to pass between a sender and one or more receivers" or "the transfer of meaningful information from one location to a second location." *Webster's New World Dictionary* adds, "the art of expressing ideas especially in speech and writing" and "the science of transmitting information, especially in symbols." Each of these definitions has important elements. Communication is a process that is ongoing, and it obviously can occur between a sender and one or more receivers. The word *meaningful* in the second definition is significant. It is clear that communication is not effective if the information is not meaningful. One could also argue that if the information is not meaningful, no communication has occurred at all. There is a strong analogy here to the traditional question: If a tree falls deep in the forest and no one is within earshot, does the tree make a sound as it falls? The answer is that because sound requires a source and a receiver, without the receiver, there is no sound.

The last definition of communication relates most closely to the focus of this book. You will be studying the science of communication using electrical or electromagnetic techniques. The information being communicated will be in coded form so that it is compatible with the transmitting and receiving technologies. For our purposes, the practical applica-

The use of personal computer workstations has become so common throughout industries of all types that most workers use one or work with someone who does. Most of these workstations are connected to others using some form of telecommunications. (Courtesy of Terry Vine/Tony Stone Images)

tion of the communication science in the business environment is essential to the definition and study of communication.

DEFINITION OF TELECOMMUNICATIONS

Webster also tells us that the prefix *tele* means far off, distant, or remote. Practically speaking, the word *telecommunications* means communication by electrical or electromagnetic means, usually (but not necessarily) over a distance. Not long ago, telecommunications meant communication by wire. Although this is still accurate in many situations, it is not complete because telecommunication can also occur using optical fiber or radio waves.

DEFINITION OF DATA COMMUNICATIONS

Data communications is the movement of coded information from one place to another by electrical or electromagnetic means. Data communications is generally considered a subset of telecommunications that excludes voice communications. That distinction was accurate and useful years ago; however, today the notion of a subset is too narrow. In modern communication systems, voice transmissions are usually converted to digital signals. When this occurs, voice and data signals are indistinguishable from each other, and they appear and can be handled by the communications network in the same way. Voice communications can, therefore, be viewed as a subset of data communications, and the terms *data communications* and *telecommunications* can be used interchangeably. That is how they will be used in this book.

Data and Information

Perhaps you are not sure about the difference between *data* and *information*. According to the American National Standards Institute's *Dictionary for Information Systems*, the term *data* means "a representation of facts, concepts, or instructions in a formalized manner suitable for communication, interpretation, or processing by human beings or by automatic means." *Information* is "the meaning that is currently assigned to data by means of the conventions applied to those data." It's the meaning of the

This office worker is checking the status of her company's inventory while talking to a customer on the telephone. She will be able to tell the customer if the part he wants to order is available for immediate shipment. (Courtesy of Chris Marona/Photo Researchers, Inc.)

data that makes it information. The value of the information depends on its relevance to the individual receiving it.

Another way to look at the breadth of telecommunications is to look at the component parts that make up most of industry today.

Voice communications, also known as telephony, which is growing annually between 6 percent and 8 percent.

Data communications, which is the fastest part of the telecommunications industry at nearly 30 percent annually. Data communications is the foundation for computer networking, including local area networks and wide area networks, which you will study.

Video communications, including video monitors for security, information displays, such as the flight information displays you see at the airport, and videoconferencing, which allows people in different locations to have a meeting and see each other.

You'll see, as we begin looking at the technology, the differences between these types of communications are rapidly disappearing. Inside networks, most voice, data and video is transmitted in digital form—a series of binary 1s and 0s. If you just look at the 1s and 0s and don't know how to interpret them, you can't tell whether they represent a voice conversation, a television picture, or a file being transferred between two computers.

Students often ask, "What's the difference between data transmission and text transmission or e-mail?" At the fundamental level of 1s and 0s, the answer is nothing—there is no difference. The difference is mainly in the way we think about what we're sending from one location to another. Usually, we think of text communications or e-mail as being relatively short transmissions, whereas when we say data transmission, we are usually thinking about a moderate or large quantity of data transferred between computers or other devices. The distinction is not solely based on size, however, because we could transfer a very small file between two personal computers, and call that data transmission, or we could send a very long e-mail. If you're feeling confused, don't worry. As you begin studying telecommunications, the distinctions, and the way the terms are used will become clear to you, and it won't be long before you're speaking the language of telecommunications like a pro!

BASIC ELEMENTS OF A TELECOMMUNICATIONS SYSTEM

A telecommunications system contains three basic elements: the *source, medium,* and *sink.* These are illustrated in Figure 1–1. More common terms would be *transmitter, medium,* and *receiver.* Examples of each element in

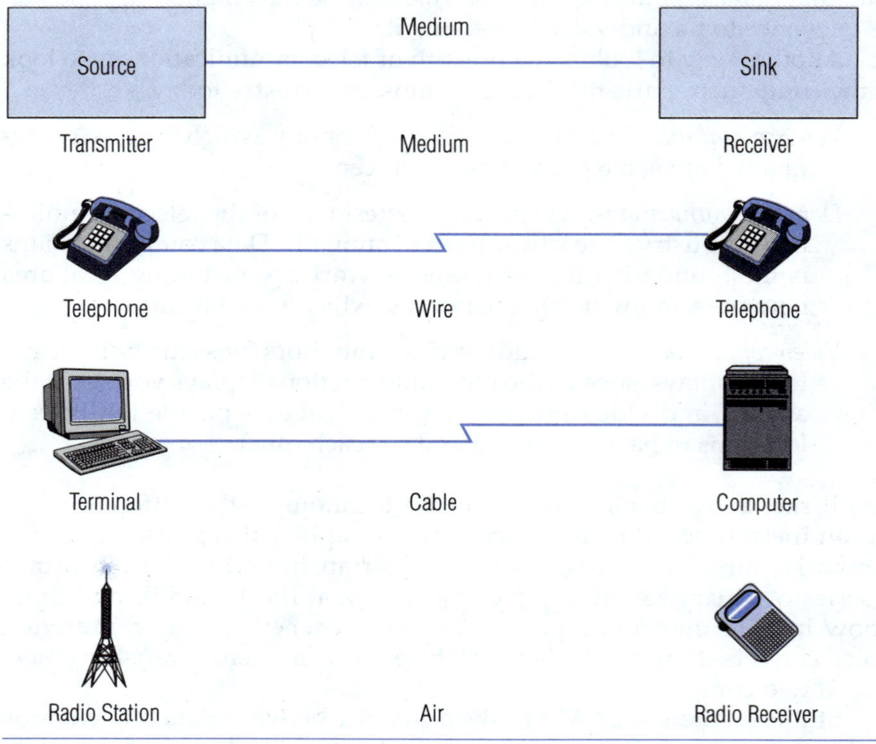

Figure 1–1 Basic elements of a telecommunications system.

the system are abundant: voicebox, air, ear; telephone, telephone lines, telephone; or terminal, data circuit, computer. There are many possible combinations of each of the basic elements.

We will immediately begin referring to the medium as the *communication line*. You can think of it as the telephone wire that comes into your house or office to connect your telephone to the telephone company office. The line can be implemented in many physical forms, such as copper wire or microwave radio, but visualizing it as a copper wire is convenient and not inaccurate.

communication networks

Communication lines are connected in many ways to build *communication networks*. It is easy to think of the telephone network as a series of lines connecting telephones to telephone company offices. As you undoubtedly realize, there are also many lines that connect the telephone company offices with each other. Together, all these lines make up the *telephone network*. In a similar way, businesses frequently build or lease their own networks, which connect all their locations. Lines and networks are precisely defined and more thoroughly discussed in Chapter 9.

To ensure that communications will be successful and effective, rules must guide its progress. Although these rules are not technically a basic

SIDEBAR 1–1

BLOCK DIAGRAMS

Note that in this context, the word *system* means the complete process of communicating. Figure 1–1 is a very simple and high-level type of *block diagram* that is designed to illustrate the communications system. Block diagrams can be used to illustrate any process or flow of work. Perhaps you have seen or used a block diagram showing the process of registering for a class at school. From the diagram you can see what steps have to be performed to complete the process. Block diagrams are usually read left to right and/or top to bottom, and each block represents a step or stage in the overall process. What is sometimes confusing when you are first learning to read block diagrams is that they can exist at any level of detail. Figure 1–1 is called a high-level diagram because it shows very little detail. A low-level block diagram would show much more detail about what actually goes on when a telephone call is made or when a terminal is connected to a computer. You'll see diagrams of that type later in the book.

element of telecommunications, they are absolutely necessary to prevent chaos. For two entities to communicate successfully, they must speak the same language. If you are a person who speaks only Spanish and you try to communicate with someone who speaks only German, you won't be successful. Perhaps, through trial and error, you'll be able to negotiate a compromise, such as both of you speaking English, in which case you'll be at least partially successful in your communication, depending on how well both of you speak your second language.

communication rules

At a different level, there are unwritten rules that guide our use of the telephone. Most of us learned them when we were very young. When receiving a telephone call, the answering party traditionally initiates the conversation by saying "hello" if he is American. The caller and answerer then go through a brief dialogue to identify each other before they launch into the purpose of the call. This is illustrated in Figure 1–2. The process is often shortcut by combining some of the exchanges or when one of the parties recognizes the other's voice. Some examples of this process are shown in Figure 1–3.

In some aspects of a telephone communication, well-defined rules don't exist. For example, what happens if the conversation is cut off due to some fault in the telephone equipment? Who calls whom to reinitiate the conversation? When you have been cut off, have you ever received a busy signal when you redialed the call because the person you were talking to also tried to redial? Eventually one person waits, and the problem is solved.

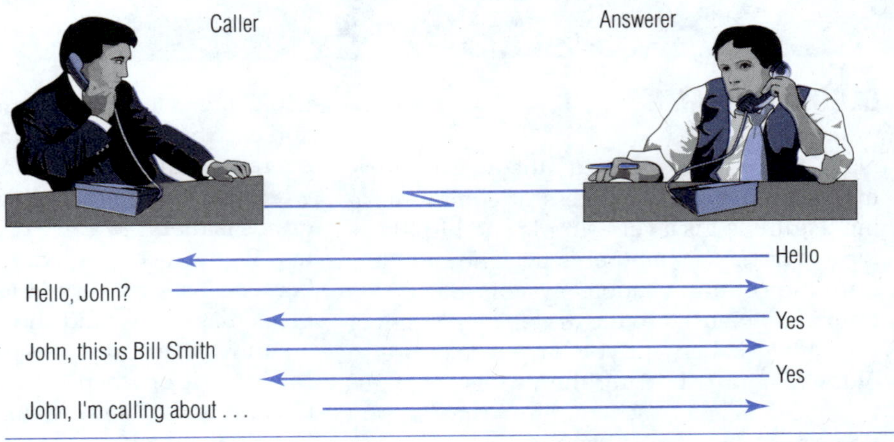

Figure 1–2 Unwritten rules of telephone communication: the initiation of the conversation.

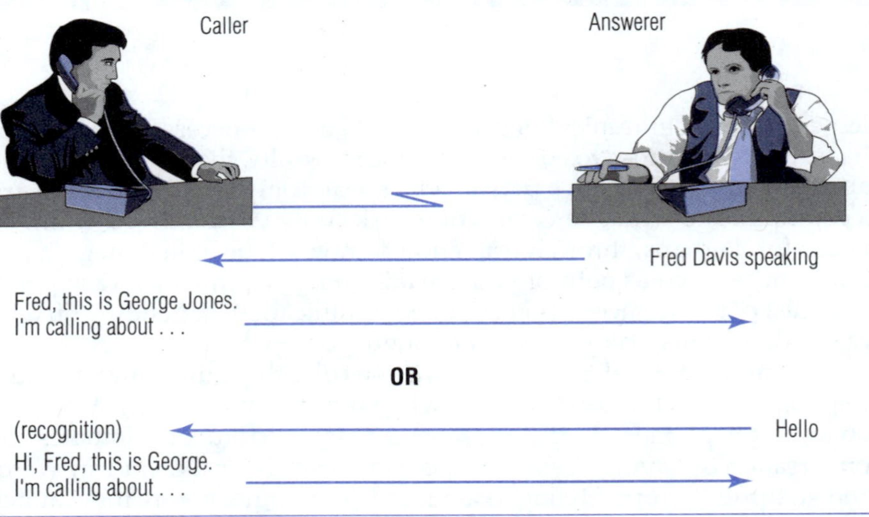

Figure 1–3 Shortcutting the unwritten rules of telephone call initiation.

In a similar way, when two pieces of equipment such as a terminal and a computer communicate, rules are needed to determine which device will transmit first, how the terminal and computer will be identified to each other, what happens if the communication gets cut off, and so forth. Unlike the voice communication example, however, when equipment is communicating automatically, all of the rules must be defined precisely, and they must cover all situations—usual and unusual—that can occur. The rules of communication are called *protocol*.

protocol

SCOPE OF THIS BOOK

For the purposes of this book, telecommunications includes the transmission and reception of information using electrical or electromagnetic means from a transmitter to a receiver over a medium. Various types of transmitters, receivers, and media, and alternative sets of rules that can be used for those communications, will be introduced and described in some detail. The primary focus of this book is the communication of information in commerce or business taken in its broadest sense. Although most of the examples will come from business and industry, the points being made will in most cases apply equally well to governmental, educational, medical, or other not-for-profit institutions. The types of communication that will be discussed involve the transmission and reception of voice, data, text, graphics or images, or combinations of these forms. You will see that when they are reduced to their most basic electrical form, all of these communications look alike. There are no fundamental differences among voice, television and data transmissions. This book does not specifically describe or analyze commercial radio or television; however, most of the principles and techniques described here apply equally well in those settings.

It is important for you to realize that this is an introductory book. Most of the chapters in this book are themselves the subject of other books that delve into far more detail than is appropriate for an introductory course in telecommunications. Furthermore, communications engineering is highly technical and mathematical, and is beyond the scope of this book. You will find, however, that this book gives you an excellent introduction to this complex field and provides a solid foundation for further study if you decide to expand your knowledge of the subject.

IMPORTANCE OF TELECOMMUNICATIONS TO BUSINESS

Melding of Information Systems and Telecommunications

Telecommunications is an important part of the information systems environment in many companies. Certainly, if an organization has more than one location, there is a high potential for data communications. But even if the company has only a single location, it is likely to have multiple personal computers that are candidates to be interconnected on a small, local network so that data and information can be shared. Or, if the company has a mainframe computer, it is likely that data communications is used to connect terminals located more than a few hundred feet from the computer room. Data communications with or between computers is one of the fastest-growing segments in the communication marketplace and the foundation of the Internet.

Furthermore, modern telephone switching equipment is a specialized type of computer, designed to handle voice conversations instead of data. It has many of the same capabilities and physical requirements as the traditional data processing computer. Many companies have realized that they can improve their communication efficiency by managing all of their voice *and* data communication activities together. Communication lines can be shared, costs can be managed, and new technology can be assimilated in ways that provide more effective communication service to the employees of the company.

Having Information Available in the Right Place at the Right Time

Businesses in the information age generate more information faster than ever before. At the same time, most companies realize that information is an increasingly valuable asset that must be managed with the same care and attention as the company's finances, buildings, machines, and people. Having the right information in the right place at the right time can mean the difference between the profitability and unprofitability of the business—and ultimately can determine its success or failure. Having information available to the right people isn't a new requirement of business success. What is new is the amount of information that can be delivered near or far at speeds that were unthinkable a few years ago. For years, companies have had telephones for voice communication, and reports and analyses were hand-generated and mailed to arrive days later. Now, with the marriage of communication and computer techniques, you can make the detail report or summary analysis available anywhere virtually instantaneously. People in widely different locations can look at the data and discuss it soon after it becomes available.

In the world at large, but especially in today's competitive business world, information is power. Organizations that understand what their competitors are doing, and can quickly and efficiently distribute that information to their marketing and sales people in the field, will have a leg up on their competition. Organizations whose employees keep in touch with one another using electronic mail find that their productivity increases dramatically. Transportation companies that can track the location of their vehicles and their customers' shipments have a significant advantage over competitors that don't have similar capabilities. News organizations with a large global presence and sophisticated telecommunications networks dominate their industry. Startup companies have grown to powerhouses in their industry by focusing on doing business entirely on the Internet. The more information you or your company has about a particular subject of interest, the better positioned you are to lead, control, or teach others.

Capturing Basic Data About Business Operations as They Occur

Another reason that telecommunications is increasingly important is that, combined with the computer, it is being used as an input mechanism for capturing data about the basic operations of the business as soon as they occur. Online computer applications, in which a terminal is connected directly to a computer with virtually instantaneous communication, are being used by businesses to enter customer orders, record customer payments, give notification of product shipments, and track inventory. These operations are the *basic business transactions* that are fundamental units of business operations. Once data about the business transaction is captured and stored in a computer, it is available, via telecommunications, to others.

basic business transactions

A classic example is the airline reservation system, in which the traveler's airline representative or travel agent makes a flight reservation. Information about this reservation is recorded in a computer database and has the effect of reducing the number of seats that are available for the particular flight. This reduction of seat inventory is a basic business transaction of the airline. As soon as the database is updated, other airline reservation agents or travel agents in other locations around the country or around the world can check to see if seats are still available on the flight for their customers. Imagine how this was done before computers and telecommunications.

In another case, a customer who wishes to order a product from a company calls the company and talks to an order processing clerk. Through a computer terminal, the clerk can check to see if the required product is available or, if not, when it will be. If the product is available and the customer places the order, shipping instructions can be processed in the warehouse nearest the customer to ensure the most rapid delivery. Later, the reports detailing this and all other sales transactions can be generated and transmitted to analysts who can spot trends or detect inventory problems quickly. These reports often generate follow-up questions that analysts and management confer about over the telephone or through terminals.

In an increasing number of cases, customers might do most of the ordering directly through the Internet. Online shopping for both consumer and industrial products is increasingly widely used, and while the customers do more of the work themselves, they are also in control of the transaction and can seek as much or as little information as they need from the vendor's web site, assuming of course that the web site is properly designed and rich in content.

With online systems, businesses are increasingly dependent on the computing and telecommunications technologies on which those systems are based. In the transportation, insurance, and finance industries, the dependence on telecommunications and computer systems has become critical. If a massive failure occurred, business could not be conducted, and financial failure would follow. As a result, some companies have gone to

Satellite antennas, such as this dish, can transmit many different kinds of telecommunication signals, such as voice, data, and television, at the same time. (Courtesy of Mark Gibson/Corbis)

great lengths to ensure that they have complete backup facilities in place so that major computer and telecommunications "downtimes" cannot occur. Most companies find that whether or not the computer and telecommunications systems are vital to their operation, it is prudent to make contingency plans for how business operations would be conducted if a prolonged outage did occur.

Allowing Geographic Dispersion of Facilities and People

Telecommunications allows people in diverse locations to work together as if they were in close proximity. Branch banking clerks, car rental agents, and insurance agents can all share common information and have most of the same capabilities they would have if they were located in the home office. In some industries, it is much less expensive to do manufacturing offshore in foreign countries such as Malaysia or the People's Republic of China. Companies in these industries need telecommunications to connect their far-flung operations and eliminate the barriers that distance would otherwise impose.

At the same time, companies in industries that are not *required* to have operations in widely separated geographic regions have a relatively inexpensive opportunity and the flexibility to do so, thanks to telecommunications. While corporate headquarters remain in a major metropolitan area, such as New York City, other facilities, such as sales and marketing offices, can be located close to customers, and manufacturing plants can be located close to sources of raw materials or natural resources used in the manufacturing process. With telecommunications, the company can still operate as a single, coordinated entity and, for most purposes, ignore the geographic dispersion.

Internet Marketing

Using the Internet, many companies are making information about their products available to potential customers and selling products directly. This capability, which has only been available on a practical basis since the mid-1990s, has expanded potential markets dramatically for many companies. Small companies especially find that they are able to reach potential customers globally whom they never would have been able to contact in the past. Product descriptions and photographs can be displayed, and sometimes demonstrations can be given online. Software companies can distribute trial copies of their products for prospective customers to try. Payments can be collected by asking customers to submit credit card numbers, which can then be automatically verified. Telecommunications is providing significant new capabilities that were unthought of 10 years ago.

In summary, telecommunications is becoming an integral part of the way companies conduct business because its capabilities provide efficient, effective ways of conducting business. In some cases, the combination of telecommunications and computing allows business to be performed in ways that are impossible using manual techniques. Business can be conducted faster and more accurately, and decisions can be made with more timely information than was previously possible. It is important to point out, however, that making decisions faster and with better information does not necessarily lead to making "better" decisions, although it should contribute to their overall quality.

REASONS FOR STUDYING TELECOMMUNICATIONS

There are several important reasons for learning about telecommunications, its terminology, and its applications.

Telecommunications Is Shrinking the World

In these days of worldwide news organizations, instant financial information from stock exchanges around the world, national paging systems, global electronic mail, and countless other examples, it is apparent that telecommunications, in all forms, is becoming a significant part of all our lives. Only a few years ago, calling grandma across the country on Christmas Day was a big event—and moderately expensive. Now people pick up the phone on a whim and think little about calling or sending a fax halfway around the world to place an order with a mail-order clothing company or to make a travel reservation. People log on to information networks such as America Online to exchange messages, see information, or register complaints with vendors. There is much talk about the "information highway" which will link all of our homes and offices with incredibly fast communications of high capacity and capability. We're inundated with information about new services that are available now. Telecommunications is affecting all of us and, for the most part, improving the quality of our lives.

Direct Use on the Job

In businesses of all types, telecommunications is an integral part of the way work is done. Whether it be the automatic teller machine at a bank, the supermarket checkout scanner that reads bar codes on food products, the wand and computer terminal that the librarian uses to check books out of the public library, or the terminal that the clerk at the Internal Revenue Service uses to enter the income tax information from a tax form into the computer, telecommunications often is involved. More and more people are using computer terminals connected to computers via telecommunications lines.

It has been estimated that as far back as 1989 there was a computer terminal for *every* person in the U.S. workforce. This won't surprise you if you work in the information intense industries, or companies that rely on telecommunications to survive. In fact, today many workers have more than one terminal—perhaps a PC on their desk and a laptop to take when they work at home or when they travel. Scientists often have a PC in their office and one or more in their laboratory. Stockbrokers usually have multiple terminals so that they can keep track of several markets of interest. It is literally true that most workers in the industrialized countries use a terminal on their job in one way or another.

Indirect Use on the Job

Even if your job doesn't deal directly with telecommunications, you will most likely work with people who do. Knowledge of the subject and its vocabulary will help you communicate with "telecommunications workers." In business, it could help you request new information or services and understand problems. In some cases, people find that because of a job change or promotion, they are suddenly thrust into a new job where they work directly with telecommunications terminals or equipment. They are thankful for any telecommunications background they have obtained in the past.

SIDEBAR 1–2

A BIG 10-4 FOR THE INTERNET

E-Mail and Satellite Tracking Revamp Trucking

By Justin Bachman, *International Herald Tribune.* Reprinted with permission.

Atlanta—Ah, the lonely, tedious life of a long-haul trucker. Rest stops and road-stop coffee. Lonely phone calls home and a CB radio on the road.

Times change. Citizens-band radios are giving way to Internet sites. Truckers now punch up an electronic mail rather than wait by the phone. And global positioning systems are used to give traffic advice in a matter of seconds.

"As far as all these computers are concerned, I get directions to everywhere I go," Don Buchta said as he fueled his rig at an Atlanta truck stop on his way to Massachusetts.

Before his company installed a satellite tracking system to manage trucks and communicate with drivers, Mr. Buchta used to spend much of his time sitting by a pay phone—waiting for load orders, directions and "calling back, calling back, calling back," he said.

Now, trucks are wired for e-mail, dispatchers send route changes to a driver's personal video display and an engine diagnosis is as likely to take place while driving on the highway as it is in a maintenance shop.

One company, Park 'n View, provides access to cable, Internet, pay-per-view and telephone services at 125 truck stops nationwide. For $30 per month, subscribers receive a card that allows them to plug in.

Freight companies say that global positioning satellites, which can locate a truck to within a 50-foot (15-meter) radius, have reduced the practice of drivers' visiting girlfriends or hangouts when they should be on the road.

But most importantly to the industry, the technology cuts delays and costs.

"The pace of technology coming to this industry is just unbelievable," said Seth Skydel, editor of Trucking Technology Magazine.

A truck's maintenance schedule used to be posted on a chalkboard in the repair depot, he said. Now, systems that monitor engine performance allow technicians to receive data while the truck is on the road. Technicians can determine whether a quirky noise is cause for immediate repair or can be ignored until the driver returns.

"Computers were unheard of in this industry 10, 12 years ago," Mr. Skydel said. "The accounting people may have had them, but you never saw them in dispatch or maintenance."

Ten years ago, the largest U.S. trucking company, Wisconsin-based Schneider National Inc., became the first of the industry's major players to adopt two-way satellite communications on its 14,000-truck fleet. "It paid for itself years ago," said John Lanigan, president of Schneider's transportation division.

Despite drivers' initial suspicions that satellite tracking meant Big Brother-style surveillance, managers report that the systems have become a recruitment tool in the fierce competition for truckers.

Drivers, and especially their families, appreciate knowing that help is a push of a distress button away, regardless of location, said Andy Dougherty, operations manager at Georgia-based Ready Trucking, which spent $300,000 to wire its 135 trucks.

"They want to know that someone is looking out for them," he said. "Some employees say, 'I don't want to be watched,' but those are probably the ones that need to be."

The satellite also tracks the truck's progress, with an updated arrival time sent directly to the customer. Some haulers post the information on the World Wide Web.

Wide Use at Home

Telecommunications techniques and products are becoming more widely used every day. Nearly everyone has or will have some contact with them. At home, using the telephone is perfectly natural, but we have to make some decisions about the type of telephone service we want. We have the option of purchasing our own telephones rather than renting them from the telephone company. We have to select which company we want to carry our long distance telephone calls.

Being able to use the Internet and the World Wide Web is the reason that many people made their first use of data communications. Whether sending electronic mail, getting assistance with homework by searching for information, tracking the prices of stocks or mutual funds, or for countless other reasons, millions of people are using the Internet every day. Getting started has become so simple that people with no computer or data communications background successfully log on with no help. Making optimal, efficient, and cost-effective use of the myriad of capabilities and tapping the full potential requires some knowledge, however.

Knowledge of telecommunications is also desirable to help us make intelligent decisions about the communications services we want to purchase. Many people have cable television at home, and this is another form of telecommunications. Subscribers can select from a wide variety of available programming, some of which is included in the basic fee paid each month and some of which is available only at extra cost. In most sections of the country, it is possible to do banking using the telephone or a personal computer in the home. In the future, we will be faced with ever-increasing choices, and a knowledge of telecommunications principles and terminology will be even more useful.

A Possible Career in Telecommunications

Another reason for learning about telecommunications is to help you assess whether you might want to consider making telecommunications your career. A partial list of telecommunications jobs is shown in Figure 1–4. As the use of telecommunications grows, so does the need for knowledgeable people to design, install, repair, maintain, and operate telecommunications systems. We can all relate to the job of telephone operator, computer terminal operator, or repairperson because we have seen these people at work.

related careers

Not so obvious, however, are the thousands of people who work "behind the scenes" to sell, design, and install telecommunications systems and keep them operating reliably and properly. Network analysts and designers are people who are knowledgeable about the types of telecommunications hardware and services that are available. They identify the communication requirements for a company and then design a telecommunications solution that will provide the required capabilities. Communication programmers write special computer software that en-

Telephone operator
Terminal operator
Network control operator
Telecommunications administrative support specialist
Communication repair technician
Network analyst
Network designer
Telecommunications programmer
Telecommunications technical support specialist
Network and services sales
Telecommunications management

Figure 1–4
A partial list of telecommunications career opportunities.

ables computers to communicate with one another or with terminals. Network operators monitor the day-to-day operation of a communication network, solve problems when they occur, capture statistics about the network's performance, and assist the users of the network to take advantage of its capabilities.

All of these jobs and others are described in detail in the text. Suffice it to say now that good, well-prepared telecommunications people—who creatively apply technology and techniques to take advantage of new business opportunities or to help solve a company's communications problems—are always in demand. They are especially valuable if they can communicate well with others in the company and have a solid business background with knowledge of finance, accounting, and marketing in addition to their specialized telecommunications knowledge. Several universities offer degrees in the technical and management aspects of telecommunications to help people get the best possible preparation for a career in this exciting field. Well-prepared people can earn a very good income because the value of their skills and the services they provide are recognized by the companies and organizations they serve.

NEW TERMINOLOGY

Like any other subject, telecommunications has its own vocabulary to master. When you first learned about computers, you were probably overwhelmed and mystified by such words as *disk, CPU,* and *file.* After some study, however, these words became a comfortable part of your vocabulary.

It is the same with telecommunications. There are many new words to learn, but your computer background will stand you in good stead and provide a foundation on which to build. Unfortunately, many people assume that since they know the language of computers, they also know and understand the language of telecommunications. This is usually not the case. There are even some words, such as *dataset*, that mean one thing in the computer sense and something entirely different in a telecommunications context. There are also quite a few acronyms to be mastered. Some are directly related to specific vendors' products, but many are used more generally. A list of commonly used telecommunications acronyms can be found in Appendix G.

There are three words used rather generically throughout the book that need to be explained up front. *Business* generically includes the business, education, government, and medical fields. A sentence that begins, "Telecommunications is becoming more widely used in," could end with business, education, government, or medicine and be equally correct.

Company is used generically to mean organization, bureau, hospital, college, or farm. A company is a specific organizational unit within the business field, just as a hospital is a specific organization within the medical field.

Virtually anyplace the pronoun *he* is used, *she* could be substituted. Telecommunications is truly an equal opportunity career field. Both men and women are commonly terminal operators, network designers, repair technicians, salespeople, and telecommunications managers.

COMMON EXAMPLES OF TELECOMMUNICATIONS

You have been exposed to telecommunications in many forms—probably more than you realize. Let's look at some common activities that rely on telecommunications technology and techniques.

Telephone Call

Figure 1–5 is a simplified diagram of the components involved when you make a telephone call. The line that looks like a small lightning bolt con-

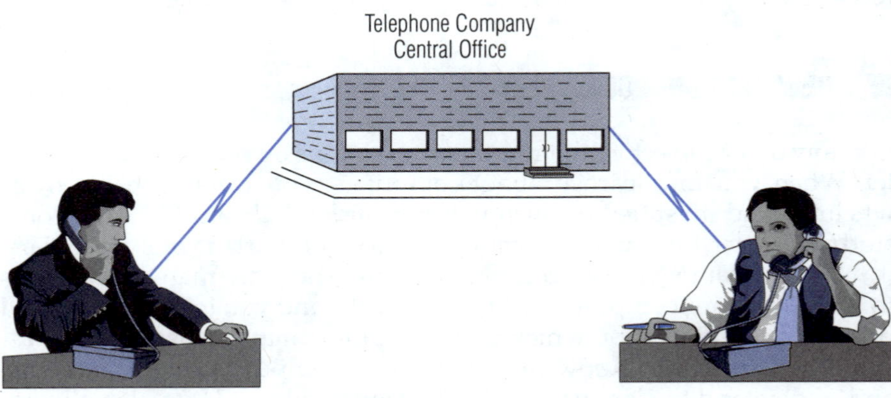

Figure 1–5
Simplified diagram of the components of a standard telephone call.

SIDEBAR 1–3

The symbol in Figure 1–5 that looks like a lightning bolt and connects the people to the telephone company central office is commonly used in telecommunications block diagrams to indicate a communications connection. This connection can be over long or short distances—no distance is implied by the symbol itself. Contrast this with the solid line connecting the computer and modem in Figure 1–6. The solid line is used to indicate a cable connection, usually of short distance, and no telecommunications. Later in the text you'll learn the difference between sending electrical signals over a simple, short cable and telecommunications signals over a longer distance.

necting the telephone to the telephone company is the common symbol used to indicate a telecommunications connection. This connection can take many forms, as you'll see in Chapter 9. As an experienced telephone user, you probably have a number of perceptions about what is involved when a telephone call is made. Probably most of your perceptions are correct. You know that when you touch the buttons on a push-button phone or dial a rotary telephone, a signal is transmitted to the telephone company that causes a connection to be made to the party to whom you wish to talk (assuming that you dialed the number correctly). Normally, you will soon hear a buzzing sound that tells you that the other telephone is ringing. With luck, the person you want to talk to will answer the telephone, and the conversation will begin.

You probably have the perception that no people (telephone operators) are involved at the telephone company in making the connection or otherwise completing the call, and you are correct. Today's telephone switching equipment in the telephone company central office is completely automatic, and the vast majority of calls are completed without human intervention. You probably also feel that the telephone system works fine most of the time, except maybe when the weather is very bad or on Christmas or Mother's Day. Again you are correct, for the vast majority of calls are completed accurately and with high quality. Occasionally, the telephone system gets overloaded, but such occurrences are rare.

The "telephone company" in Figure 1–5 is probably a bit more nebulous. You know that you have seen the telephone company building in your town, telephone poles with wires strung on them, repair trucks, telephone stores, and certainly the monthly bill, but you are probably unclear about how these pieces fit together to provide the telephone service you have come to expect. Suffice it to say that in addition to the parts of the telephone company and its operations that you know about, there are at least as many parts that you probably have never heard about or been exposed to. The details are described in Chapter 4.

Figure 1–6
The telecommunications between a home computer and an Internet access provider.

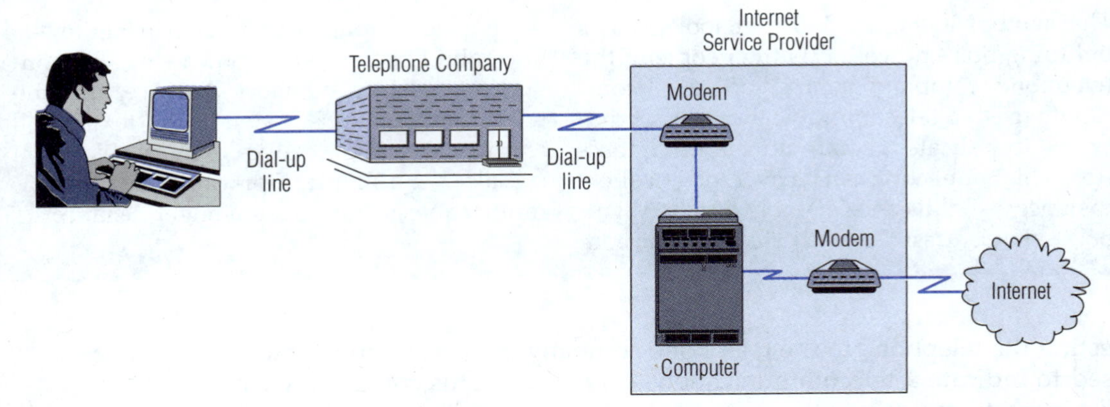

To put this example in terms defined earlier, the calling party in the example is the *source;* the connection to the telephone company, the telephone company itself, and the connection to the called party are the *medium;* and the called party is the *sink.* This is an example of person-to-person communication. The caller and receiver are the direct users of the telecommunications system, which in this case is the telephone system. They operate the terminal (telephone), and that operation is so routine and familiar that they don't think twice about it. Most people learned how to operate this telecommunications system when they were very young.

Using the Internet from Home

Many companies have direct connections to the Internet that allow instant access from any personal computer as easily as accessing software stored on the hard disk of the PC. Accessing the Internet from home typically requires a few more steps. Although there are various options for home connection, a typical one is for the home user to make a dial-up connection from a home PC to an *Internet service provider* (ISP), a company that provides a network connection to the Internet, as shown in Figure 1–6. Instructions are given to the PC's modem to dial the telephone number of the service provider's modem and computer. When the call is answered, the service provider's computer usually performs some logging and accounting operations, so that it can bill the customer, and then it automatically completes the connection to the Internet. Depending on the type of Internet service to be used, the customer may activate a *web browser,* such as Microsoft Internet Explorer or Netscape Navigator, or other software on the home PC to simplify the online activities. When the activity is complete, the user instructs the software to disconnect the call and the modems break the connection.

Internet service provider

web browser

Airline Reservation System

Figures 1–7 and 1–8 illustrate a slightly more complicated use of telecommunications: making an airline reservation. There are several variations on how the reservation can be made; this example illustrates the main points that occur when you call the airline directly. The first part of the figures are the same as Figure 1–5: You make a telephone call through the telephone company to a person—the airline reservation agent. The reservation agent

Figure 1–7
The telecommunications connections between a traveler and an airline reservation computer through a local area network.

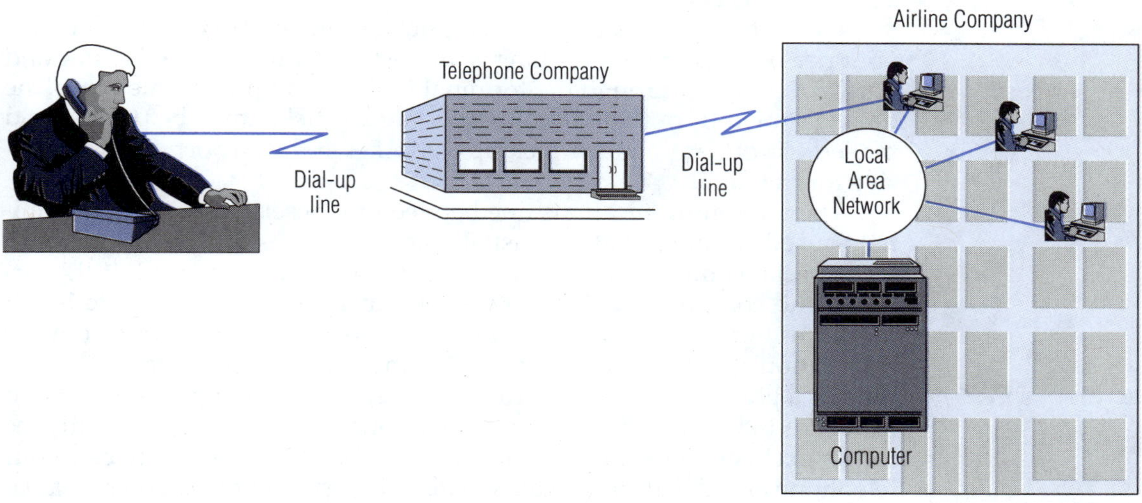

Figure 1–8
The telecommunications connection between a traveler and an airline reservation computer through a leased line.

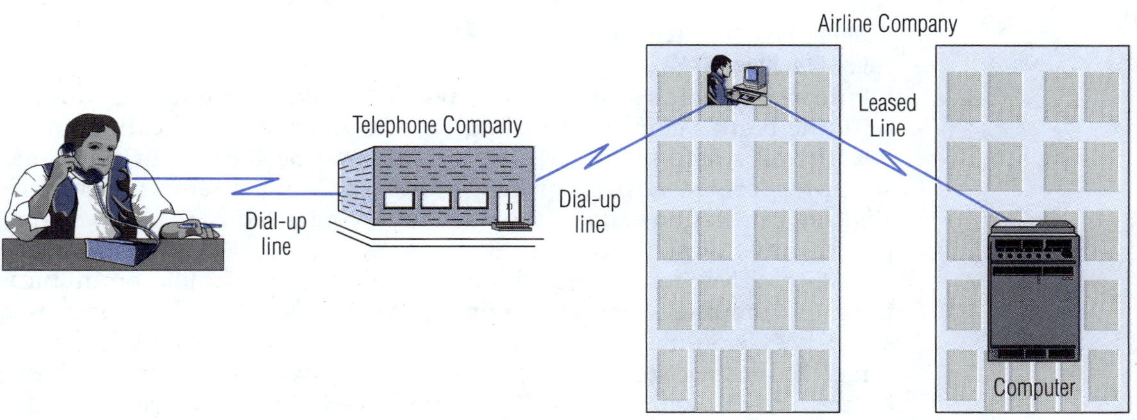

operates a personal computer or *video display terminal (VDT)*, a terminal with a screen that looks like the monitor on a PC and a keyboard. The PC or VDT is connected via a small *local area network* or a telecommunications line to the airline's central computer. You describe the reservation you would like to make, and the agent requests information about flight schedules, alternative connections, and ticket prices from the computer using the terminal. The information displayed on the screen of the PC or terminal is in a highly coded form, which the reservation agent interprets and relays to you on the telephone. Two dialogues are taking place: one between you and the reservation agent and one between the reservation agent and the computer.

Ultimately, you decide on the flight, and the reservation agent enters your personal information, along with the flight number and the time and date of the flight, through the terminal into the computer's memory. The data is copied from there onto disk storage. A ticket may be printed and mailed to you, or you may pick up the ticket at the airport when you arrive for the flight.

The telecommunications line between the reservation agent's terminal is used so much that it is usually advantageous for the airline to install special communications wiring and a local area network if the terminal and computer are in the same building, as shown in Figure 1–7. If the computer is in a separate building or some distance away from the reservation agents, the airline may rent the telecommunications line full-time as a *private* or *leased line* from the telephone company, as illustrated in Figure 1–8. The airline pays the telephone company a flat monthly fee for its exclusive use. By way of contrast, the connection between your telephone and the airline is called a *dial-up* or *switched line.* You pay a basic charge to make telephone calls, plus a usage charge based on the number, distance, and duration of the calls you make. Dial-up lines are discussed in more detail in Chapter 4.

leased line

Banking with an Automatic Teller Machine (ATM)

Figure 1–9 illustrates the modern way of banking: interacting directly with the bank's computer through a computer terminal called an *automatic teller machine (ATM).* The ATM may be located at the bank, shopping center, airport, grocery store—in fact, just about anywhere. Telecommunications allows the ATM to be connected to the bank's computer many miles away.

With ATMs, consumers with little knowledge about telecommunications or computers operate computer terminals. The ATM contains a small television-like screen similar to the airline agent's VDT. On the screen are instructions or questions, such as "Insert your card," "Please enter your password," and "Would you like to make a deposit, a withdrawal, or pay a bill?" The machine "walks users through" the process of

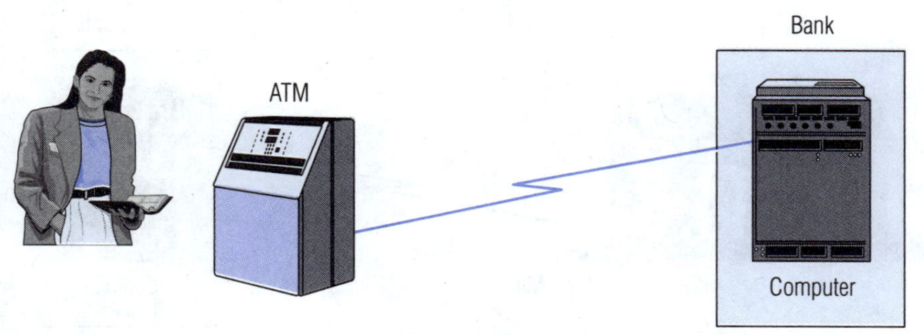

Figure 1–9
An ATM connected to a computer by a telecommunications line.

performing banking transactions. The ATM interacts with customers and with the computer, getting information about the transaction the customer wants to perform and relaying the information to the computer. For withdrawals, the ATM verifies that the customer has enough money in the account by requesting that the computer check the balance.

ATMs may contain a small computer that can be programmed to provide the user with instructions. A programmable ATM is an example of an *intelligent terminal.* The intelligent ATM handles all interactions with the user and only communicates with a central computer to check account balances or to relay the results of the ATM's processing. Alternately, the ATM may receive all of its capability from a computer to which it is connected via a telecommunications line. In that case, the ATM is considered to be a *dumb terminal.* The instructions to the user come from the computer and all input from the keyboard of the ATM is passed to the computer for processing.

Initially, many people are somewhat afraid to use ATMs. Some people never become comfortable using an ATM and prefer the human contact that a live teller provides. The bank prefers to have customers use ATMs because it reduces the number of human tellers, which in turn reduces the bank's costs. ATMs can also improve the bank's service by allowing customers to bank 24 hours a day, 7 days a week.

Automatic Remote Water Meter Reading

Figure 1–10 illustrates another example of the use of telecommunications: water meters with telecommunications capability in residences and commercial buildings. In one city, a computer at the water company office dials the telephone line connected to the water meter in the residence. An encoder on the meter is activated by an interrogation signal. The encoder senses the meter reading and sends back meter data to start the billing process.

The cost advantage to the water company is having no meter readers who walk to all of the houses and buildings in the city to read the water

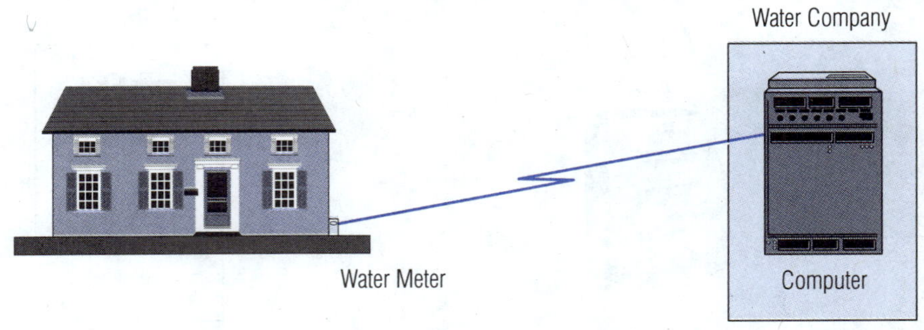

Figure 1–10
Remote reading of a water meter using telecommunications.

meters every month. Although the initial cost to install these automatic, communicating water meters is high, the payback comes rather quickly when fewer people are needed to read meters. In addition, the automatically generated meter readings are more accurate than those read manually.

In some cases, there are practical alternatives to the telecommunications technologies that are described and used as examples in this book. For example, a water company may be able to substantially increase the accuracy of meter readings by equipping its human meter readers with electronic data recorders. Although the meter reader still walks to all of the locations on the route, the time it takes to record the meter reading and the data entry cost are significantly reduced. The key to finding the best solution for any business problem is first to define the problem and then to explore several alternative solutions before selecting one to implement.

REQUIREMENTS FOR TELECOMMUNICATIONS SYSTEMS

Users of telecommunications systems have certain expectations about the capabilities the system will provide and the system operations. In this section, you will examine typical user requirements for voice and data communications systems.

Requirements for Telephone Systems

Put yourself in the position of defining requirements to the telephone company for your telephone service. You might want the system to be

- available when you need it;
- trouble-free and reliable;
- easy to use and easy to learn;
- a universal service so that you can call to and from any location;
- fast (doesn't take a long time to get a call completed);
- inexpensive.

Some people might have special requirements, such as

- amplifiers on the telephone handset if they are hard of hearing;
- easily accessible public phones if they travel;
- telephones with built-in directories and the capability to dial calls automatically if they use the telephone frequently;
- a second line so that they can connect to the Internet without tying up their main telephone line.

If you look at the list of "typical" requirements shown, you would probably conclude that the telephone system in the United States has done a pretty good job of meeting your needs. In fact, this is the general opinion of the American public. In many respects, the telephone companies have been sensitive to user requirements and have provided new services and capabilities as needed.

In a similar way, the telecommunications department in a company must be sensitive to the requirements of the telecommunications users in the organization. The requirements for telephone service in a company are, in general, similar to those for public telephone service. However, there are usually some special requirements, such as

- multiple-line telephones so that secretaries can answer their bosses' calls;
- hold buttons so that one call can be held while a conversation is conducted with a second party;
- call-transferring ability to move a call to someone else in the organization.

There may also be some other more specialized requirements, such as an automatic call distribution (ACD) service as described in the airline reservation example in Chapter 3.

Some of these capabilities have been available for a long time. Others are just becoming available and/or economical because of advances in electronic technology. The important thing, however, is to understand what is required by the users of the telecommunications system.

Requirements for Data Communications Systems

From a user's perspective, many of the characteristics that are desired from the telephone system are also desired from a data communications system:

- availability—the system is ready and operating when it is needed;
- reliability—the system is trouble-free and does not introduce errors into the communication process;
- online and realtime—users are able to operate the system through interactive terminals;

- responsive—the system is quick enough so that it helps the user do the job and does not hinder him by imposing delays on the communication;
- ease of use—it is easy to accomplish the needed communication and dialogues allow the user to interact with the computer;
- ergonomics—the users' workstations and terminals must provide for long periods of comfortable use;
- flexibility—the system must be easy to change.

As in the case of voice systems, some data communications users may have special requirements, such as

- the ability to get hard copy output easily and conveniently;
- multiple terminals or personal computers (e.g., for scientists and stockbrokers);
- terminals that are also high-powered computer workstations;
- large monitors or display screens.

Let's now examine each of these requirements in detail.

Availability *Availability* is having the system or service operating when the user wants or needs to use it. Take, for example, the telephone system. We expect telephone service to be available anytime, 24 hours a day, 7 days a week, 365 days a year. What would it be like if the telephones did not operate during certain hours, say from 10 P.M. to 7 A.M., or during the lunch hour, or on holidays? In many cases, we could get used to these reduced hours of operation. We would complain, and we would certainly have to adjust some of our habits, but in most cases the reduced hours of operation would not be critical.

There are some situations, however, when not having the telephone system available could be disastrous. What if we needed to call the fire department or the police? What if somebody desperately needed to reach us? For these cases, other communication methods would need to be developed.

variable requirements

The real requirement for availability varies by application. Many data applications in business only need to be available during business hours. For example, the order entry application discussed in Chapter 4 may only need to be available during business hours because customers won't be at work to place orders at other times. On the other hand, if we advertise on television at all times of the day or night and our advertisement says "Call 1-800-555-XXXX. Operators are standing by to take your order," our order entry application may need to be available around the clock.

If our company does business nationwide, the hours of availability will undoubtedly have to be longer than from 8 A.M. to 5 P.M. local time.

Figure 1–11
The business days in many major cities of the world have little overlap with one another. Telecommunications systems that serve international locations must have extended operating hours in order to be available during the business day in foreign cities.

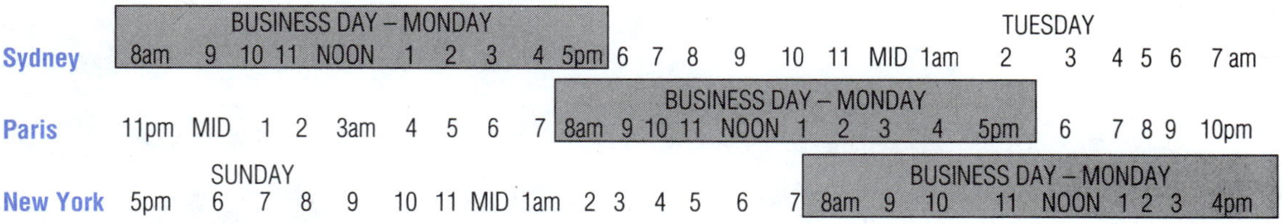

BUSINESS DAY – MONDAY (Sydney) — TUESDAY

Sydney 8am 9 10 11 NOON 1 2 3 4 5pm 6 7 8 9 10 11 MID 1am 2 3 4 5 6 7 am

BUSINESS DAY – MONDAY (Paris)

Paris 11pm MID 1 2 3am 4 5 6 7 8am 9 10 11 NOON 1 2 3 4 5pm 6 7 8 9 10pm

SUNDAY — BUSINESS DAY – MONDAY (New York)

New York 5pm 6 7 8 9 10 11 MID 1am 2 3 4 5 6 7 8am 9 10 11 NOON 1 2 3 4pm

If we are located on the East Coast, we will probably want to keep our systems available until 8 P.M., which is 5 P.M., the close of the business day, on the West Coast. Conversely, if we are located on the West Coast, we may need to start our system operating at 5 A.M. because that is 8 A.M. in the east, and our customers there are ready to do business with us.

If the communication network serves an international business, the window of availability will be longer. Figure 1–11 illustrates the situation. Allowing for an hour or two variation caused by daylight saving time, when it is 8 A.M. in Paris, it is 2 A.M. on the East Coast of the United States. Therefore, the telecommunications system may have to be available from 2 A.M. until 8 P.M. eastern standard time (if it is also serving the West Coast of the United States). Again, allowing for 2 or 3 hours' variation due to daylight saving time, Japan and Australia are approximately 15 hours ahead of the U.S. East Coast. That means when it is 8 A.M. Monday in Sydney, it is 5 P.M. Sunday in New York. When the Australians go home at the end of their business day at 5 P.M. Monday, it is 2 A.M. Monday in the U.S. eastern time zone. If a single network served the United States, Europe, and Asia, it would have to be available nearly 24 hours a day, 7 days a week.

Holidays are another consideration that must be studied when determining the availability requirements of a network. Even within the United States, we celebrate certain regional holidays in some parts of the country and not in others. Different customs for holidays and lunch hours also prevail. For an international network, the situation gets even more complicated. For example, Thanksgiving is celebrated in Canada but on a different day from the United States, and whereas Americans close businesses on July 4, no other country celebrates America's Independence Day.

Determining the real requirement for network availability is key. Whereas the public telephone system and some businesses, such as hospitals, are required to be operational 24 hours a day, 7 days a week, 365 days a year, most other business organizations do not have to operate on that schedule.

The use of cellular telephones has grown rapidly all over the world in the last several years. (Courtesy of Will & Deni McIntyre/Photo Researchers, Inc.)

Reliability *Reliability* in telecommunications is trouble-free operation. When someone uses the system, it must work. Just as we don't want our car to break down when we are on a trip, we don't want our telephone connection to break in the middle of a call. Similarly, we don't want the terminal and computer to go down when we are interacting with it.

One of the most frustrating situations for users of communication and computer systems is unpredictability. Users generally understand that systems occasionally fail, no matter how well they are designed. Once a system fails, users would generally rather have it stay out of service until it is fixed than have it come up but fail again within a short period of time.

MTBF and MTTR

A classic measure of reliability on a system is *mean time between failures (MTBF)*. The MTBF is the average time between the failures of a system. A related measure is the *mean time to repair (MTTR)*. MTTR is a measure of how long, on average, it takes to fix the problem and get the system back up after a failure has occurred. Reliability is often measured

Component	Reliability
Computer	.98
Circuit	.97
Terminal	.99

System Reliability = .98 × .97 × .99 = .941 = 94.1%

Figure 1–12
The overall reliability of a three-component, serial telecommunications system.

9 hour day = 540 minutes

At a reliability of	The system would be down
.999	32 seconds
.995	2.7 minutes
.990	5.4 minutes
.98	10.8 minutes
.97	16.2 minutes
.96	21.6 minutes
.95	27.0 minutes
.90	54.0 minutes

Figure 1–13
The maximum number of minutes a system can be down in a day and still achieve a given level of reliability.

in terms of probability. If a system is 98 percent reliable, that means it is working 98 percent of the time and out of service 2 percent of the time.

Most telecommunications systems are made up of a number of components—such as the terminal, line, and computer—connected in series. This is known as a *serial system.* Each component has a certain MTBF and MTTR. To get the overall reliability of a serial system, the reliability of each of the components is multiplied together. Figure 1–12 shows an example of a three-component telecommunications system in which each component has a certain reliability. The overall resultant reliability of the system is of course *lower* than any of the components individually. You can see from the example that in order to achieve a reliability of even 95 percent, which is a low-typical requirement of a telecommunications system, each of the components must be considerably more reliable than .95.

serial system

The fact that the overall reliability is less than any of its components is an important concept of combinatorial probability. It is particularly relevant, since most communication systems are serial systems and have many components connected in series. To put it in other terms, if a telecommunications system is scheduled to be operational from 8 A.M. to 5 P.M. each day (9 hours), the chart in Figure 1–13 shows how many minutes the system would be down, on average, each day at different levels of system reliability. For many business applications, 20 or 30 minutes of outage each day is simply not good enough. For those applications, reliability must be greater than 95 or 96 percent.

Because the public telephone system is expected to be operational 24 hours a day, 7 days a week, with a very high reliability, the central office telephone equipment is designed with many redundant components. When a component failure occurs, the backup component is automatically switched into operation. With this type of fail-safe design, the expected failure rate of an entire central office is approximately once in 40 years!

Most business systems don't need that kind of reliability. But again, the important thing is for the business to determine the real reliability requirements for each of its applications or systems and to design its systems to meet these requirements. High reliability can be achieved by designing redundancy into any system. Redundant telecommunications lines, computers, or terminals can be put in a telecommunications system to make it more fail-safe. The costs of the redundant equipment must be assessed, however, and an economic analysis must be performed to determine whether the benefits of the increased reliability equal or outweigh the costs.

Online and Realtime For our purposes, *online* simply means "connected to the computer." Most computers are designed for online operation through terminals. With microcomputers, the computer is built into the terminal, and with most microcomputers today, there is no capability to attach additional terminals. In any case, the microcomputer is designed to be used by one person sitting at its VDT working interactively.

If the computer can support multiple terminals, they may be directly cabled to the computer, in which case they do not use telecommunications facilities at all. Alternately, the terminals may be connected via telecommunications lines.

Realtime is a rate of response or operation fast enough to affect a course of action or a decision. The response usually is measured from the time the terminal operator presses the ENTER key, or its equivalent, on the terminal to signal the computer to perform some processing to the time the computer delivers the first part of the output back through the network to the user's terminal. We will discuss more about response time later in the chapter.

Real Enough Time The definition of realtime is "a rate of response or operation fast enough. . . ." The question is, "What is fast enough?" The answer depends on the needs of the particular application. We can therefore think about a concept of *real enough time.* This notion suggests that the response time that is good enough for one application may not be good enough for another. For example, traditional wisdom says that a 2-second response time is good enough in most applications. It isn't good enough, however, when you pick up the telephone handset on your telephone and expect to hear a dial tone by the time you get the handset to your ear. You get the telephone to your ear in less than 2 seconds, and if you don't hear a dial tone, you are annoyed and immediately begin to wonder what is wrong. Two-second response time also is not good enough for the flight controller at Cape Canaveral who is trying to destroy a rocket that is off course and headed for a populated area. The controller wants to give the command to the computer and have the rocket blown up within milliseconds to avoid a disaster. Similarly, 2-second response time is not good enough in many industrial applications in which computers are controlling machine tools or chemical processes. In those applications, real enough time usually means something less than 1 second.

On the other hand, after you complete the dialing of your telephone call, you do not expect (nor do you probably require) instantaneous completion of the call. In that situation, real enough time is more like 10 or 15 seconds. Similarly, in the airline reservation or customer order entry application, multisecond response time is normally acceptable at the completion of a reservation or order. While the computer is busy updating files and completing the transaction, the operator has time to put papers back in a file folder, take a sip of coffee, and get ready to handle the next call.

One must look at the real needs of each application to determine what is real enough time. Indeed, one must look within the application at the various transactions or interactions that occur, since some of them may require a faster response than others.

Response Time *Response time* is traditionally defined as the time between pressing the ENTER key on the terminal signaling the computer that processing is needed until the first character of output is received at the terminal. Many people argue, however, that since the operator can do little when the first character is received, the time ought to be extended until the last character is received at the terminal and the operator is able to begin work again.

The overall response time that the user sees is made up of several components. In most cases, when the operator keys data into a terminal, it is stored in the terminal's memory until the ENTER key is pressed. At that time the data is transmitted over the telecommunications line to the computer. After the computer receives the data, it must process it and formulate a response. Then the response is transmitted back over the telecommunications line to the terminal, where it is displayed or printed. The time it takes to transmit the data on the telecommunications line is a function of the number of characters to be transmitted and the speed of the line.

The transmission time may be extended by delays encountered when a line is shared among several terminals. Sometimes a transaction may have to wait for another transaction to finish using the line. This wait is called *queuing,* and it can have a significant effect on the overall response time. queuing

The processing time on the computer is a direct function of the number of instructions that must be executed to interpret the input message, process it, and formulate a message for transmission back to the terminal. This time often is extended when a computer is dealing with several terminal users concurrently. Because a computer can only process one transaction at a time, arriving transactions may encounter a *queue,* or waiting line, of other transactions waiting to be processed. Thus, if an input message from terminal A arrives while a message from terminal B is being processed, it will be placed in a queue and delayed until the processing for terminal B's transaction is complete or interrupted.

processimg time

Processing time at the computer is most often calculated on an average and probabilistic basis. The usual way of stating processing time is in the form, "computer processing takes *X* seconds *Y* percent of the time." In addition to the average processing time, one is also interested in the variability. It is one thing to know that processing is completed for 95 percent of the transactions in 1 second, but what about the other 5 percent? Do those transactions take 5 seconds to process? Or 10 seconds? Or 90 seconds? Determining the averages, variances, and probabilities for a given computer system is a complicated task. It depends on a knowledge of the mathematics involved and also a knowledge of the characteristics of the workload on the computer.

Figure 1–14 shows a typical but simplified response time calculation. No queuing has been considered. It is evident that the telecommunications network plays a very significant role in determining the overall response time that the user sees. The people who configure the computer and those who design the telecommunications network must work together to ensure that the response time requirements of the user can be met.

IBM response time study

Two studies conducted in different parts of the IBM corporation have attempted to quantify the value and economic benefit of rapid response

Figure 1–14
A simplified response time calculation. Queuing time is not considered.

Action	**Seconds**	**Cumulative Seconds**
Operator types transaction—presses ENTER key		
100-character transaction transmitted to the computer	.10	.10
Computer receives transaction—processes it	.40	.50
1000-character response transmitted to the terminal and displayed	1.04	1.54 total response time

Telecommunication Time = 1.14 seconds = 74% of total response time

time to users doing different kinds of work with the computer. Walter Doherty, who worked at the IBM research laboratories in Yorktown Heights, New York, said that if the response time is fast enough, the computer becomes an extension of the human brain. In reality, the person at the terminal is usually thinking several steps ahead of the work she is doing at any point in time and remembering those steps in the short-term memory of the brain. If response time is slow, however, the short-term memory contents are replaced as the mind wanders. When the computer responds, the person must refocus attention on the work being done with the computer.

Another type of response time is *user response time.* User response time, also called *think time,* is the time that it takes the user to see what the computer displayed, interpret it, type the next transaction, and press the ENTER key. User response time is a significant part of the overall productivity of the human–machine system. Doherty says that the faster the machine responds, the faster the person will respond with the next transaction. His studies showed that the overall productivity kept climbing as the computer response time decreased to less than .5 seconds, which was the fastest computer response time that could be obtained in that particular situation.

think time

The telecommunications network designer must look at the needs of the particular application to determine what is adequate response time or real enough response time for each application. In practice, the response time is a function of the network design and cost. With a good design, and by spending enough money, the response can be reduced to a fraction of a second if that is what is needed, however without a proper design, the response time objectives will never be achieved no matter how much money is spent.

Usable Dialogues As the use of terminals becomes widespread, many people who have had no previous computer experience are becoming telecommunications and computer users. The need to make the interaction with the computer easy is greater than ever before. The interaction or series of interactions between the user at a terminal and the computer is called a *dialogue.* A typical requirement of the user is that the dialogue with the computer be *user friendly.* User friendliness is an attribute of computer interactions that is difficult to describe and in many cases is strictly relative. A dialogue that may be easy for one person to use may not appear to be easy, or friendly, to another person.

dialogue

It helps to break the concept of user friendliness into two subconcepts: "easy to learn" and "easy to use." Easy-to-learn interactions enable a person with little instruction or guidance to figure out how to operate the terminal or system and get the desired results. Easy-to-use interactions are ones that may take some training to learn but, once the education has been completed, are simple to perform in the desired way. The two attributes are not mutually exclusive or always mutually desired.

For example, if the dialogue between an airline reservation agent and the computer is being designed, the major concern should be for ease of use because the same set of transactions will be completed thousands of times as reservations are made. Shortcuts and flexibility are very important so that the reservation agent can jump around within the reservation process when necessary. Usually the input data is highly coded so that a minimal number of characters needs to be typed. Ease of learning the system is of secondary importance, since the operators receive some training and usually work in an environment where other, more experienced operators can provide assistance when necessary.

By contrast, the design of the dialogue for use with an automatic teller machine needs to be easy to learn, since many of the users are completely inexperienced with terminals and may use the ATM infrequently. Furthermore, there is no teacher or coach standing by ready to assist, particularly in off hours when the bank is closed. Ease of use is a secondary concern. This implies that the transactions through an ATM may be somewhat rigid in sequence, content, and format, with little variation allowed. There should be an option to abort the transaction or go back to the beginning, but beyond that the user should be taken through a straightforward series of inputs and actions to accomplish the desired results.

Ergonomics Ergonomics is another user requirement that the telecommunications designer must consider and understand. As with other requirements, the goal is to ensure that the network and all of its components meet user requirements. *Ergonomics* is, according to Webster, "the study of the problems of people in adjusting to their environment, especially the science that seeks to adapt work or working conditions to suit the worker." In recent years, as the use of computer terminals has become more widespread, ergonomic issues have received considerable attention.

The telecommunications managers or designers need to understand the ergonomic issues and deal with them, but they do not have total responsibility for resolving them. The design of the individual office or workspace and the selection of furniture is not usually within the telecommunications manager's responsibility. Often this is done by office designers or consultants who lay out the office and select the furniture to go in it. Hardware manufacturers determine the physical characteristics of their terminals, and the telecommunications department has little direct influence over the decisions made. However, equipment manufacturers have typically been sensitive to the ergonomic issues and have designed their equipment with the flexibility to meet personal preferences or legislative requirements.

Flexibility and Growth One thing is certain about telecommunications systems and networks: They change and grow. It is important when you plan and design a network to strive for flexibility and growth possibilities. As companies grow, the network must handle increasing traffic volumes by adding capacity. As companies reorganize, the network may have to be reconfigured to handle new traffic patterns. As technology changes, the user community will demand the newest terminals and capabilities.

Users will expect that changes can be made to the telecommunications system and will have little empathy with technical arguments as to why changes are difficult to make. However, users will not directly ask for telecommunications flexibility, so the network designer must ask probing questions to draw the users into thinking about the future. Although not all changes can be foreseen, the network designer should work with and anticipate as many of the users' needs as possible.

HISTORY OF TELECOMMUNICATIONS

What do you think of first when you think of telecommunications history? Alexander Graham Bell? Samuel F. B. Morse? Telegraphers sitting with telegraph keys to send messages across the continent? The old-style, telephone your grandmother used to have? All of these images are certainly a part of telecommunications history. The timetable in Figure 1–15 lists many of the significant events of recent telecommunications history (since communication was first performed using wire as the medium).

Let's go back further in time. Long distance or *tele* communications was used in ancient times, when people used fires to communicate simple messages over long distances. Similarly, drums, smoke signals, and the printing press were used by cultures long before electricity or magnetism was known. Humans have always needed to communicate over long distances and have found ways to do so without sophisticated tools.

Invention of the Telegraph

The history of modern telecommunications as we think of it really begins with Samuel F. B. Morse, who invented the telegraph and first demonstrated it on September 2, 1837. In 1845, Morse formed a company with private money to exploit the telegraph, and his idea caught on. By 1851, there were 50 telegraph companies in the United States, and the invention was beginning to be used by railroads, newspapers, and the government. In 1856, the Western Union Telegraph Company was formed. By 1866, it was the largest communication company in the United States and had absorbed all of the other telegraph companies.

Invention of the Telephone

On March 7, 1876, a patent entitled "Improvements in Telegraphy" was issued to Alexander Graham Bell. This patent, which did not mention the word *telephone,* discussed only a method for the electrical transmission of

1837	Samuel F. B. Morse invents the telegraph.
1838	Telegraph demonstrated to government. Government declines to use.
1845	Morse forms a company with private money to exploit the telegraph.
1851	Fifty telegraph companies in operation.
1856	Western Union Telegraph Company formed.
1866	Western Union Telegraph Company was the largest communications company in the United States.
1876	Patent issued to Alexander Graham Bell for telephone.
1876	Bell offers to sell telephone patents to Western Union for $100,000. Western Union declines.
1877	Bell Telephone Company formed.
1878	First telephone exchange with operator installed.
	Western Union Telegraph Company sets up its own phone company, sued by Bell for patent infringement, gets out of phone business, and sells network to Bell.
1885	American Telephone and Telegraph Company (AT&T) formed to build and operate long distance lines interconnecting regional telephone companies.
1893–94	Original Bell patents expire; independent telephone companies enter market.
1911	Bell Telephone franchise companies reorganize into larger organizations known as the Bell Associated Companies. Beginning of the Bell System.
1913	Invention of the vacuum tube.
1941	First marriage of computer and communication technology.
1943	Development of submersible amplifier/repeaters.
1947	Invention of the transistor.
1948	Hush-a-Phone case.
1956	First trans-Atlantic telephone cable installed.
1957	First satellite launched.
1968	Carterfone decision.
1971	Computer Inquiry I.
1981	Computer Inquiry II.
1982	Modified Final Judgment.
1984	Divestiture.
1986	Computer Inquiry III.
1996	Telecommunications Act of 1996.

Figure 1–15
Significant events in telecommunications history.

"vocal or other sounds." At the time Bell's patent was issued, he did not have a working model of the telephone—only plans and drawings—but within a week of the patent's being issued, he and his assistant, Thomas Watson, got the telephone to work in their laboratory. In July of 1877, one of Bell's financial backers, Gardinar Hubbard, created the Bell Telephone Company. By the fall of that year, there were approximately 600 telephone subscribers.

first telephone company

This early telephone "system" was a little different from what we are used to today. Telephone switching equipment, which could connect any telephone to any other telephone, had not yet been invented. Telephone subscribers in 1877 had one pair of wires coming into their home or business for each telephone they wanted to connect to! Since there were 600 subscribers, it is possible, though not likely, that one individual could

A re-creation of Alexander Graham Bell's original laboratory. (Property of AT&T Archives. Reprinted with permission of AT&T)

have had 600 pairs of wires coming into the home and then would have to find the right wires and connect them to the telephone before making the call! There were also no ringers or bells on the telephone. If the other party didn't just happen to pick up the telephone when the caller wanted to talk, there was no conversation!

The technology advanced quickly. By January of 1878, the first telephone exchange with an operator was in place. With that innovation, it was possible to have just one pair of wires connecting a telephone to the central switchboard. The operator, with a series of plugs and jacks, could make the connection from one telephone to any other telephone that was connected to that switchboard.

Later in 1878, Western Union Telegraph Company set up its own telephone company and took advantage of its network of telegraph wires, which was beginning to blanket the country. Bell sued Western Union for patent infringement. After studying the situation, the Western Union attorney became convinced that Bell would win the suit. Western Union settled out of court, got out of the telephone business, and sold its network to the Bell Telephone Company.

In 1885, American Telephone and Telegraph Company (AT&T) was formed to build and operate long distance telephone lines. These lines

The first successful telephone call in 1876. The first complete sentence to be transmitted electrically was, "Mr. Watson, come here, I want to see you!" (Property of AT&T Archives. Reprinted with permission of AT&T)

interconnected the regional telephone companies that had established franchises with Bell to provide telephone service in various parts of the country.

competition begins

In 1893 and 1894, the original Bell patents for the telephone expired. Many independent telephone companies entered the market and started providing telephone service. For the first time there was substantial competition in the telephone business as these independent telephone companies competed with the regional telephone companies that were franchised by Bell.

Bell System

In 1911, the regional companies with Bell franchises were reorganized into larger organizations, which became known as the Bell associated companies. This marked the beginning of the *Bell System* as the collection of companies, headed by AT&T, came to be known.

computers, communications, cables, and satellites

Since the structure of the telecommunications industry and its basic capabilities were established in the early 1900s, technological advances have allowed new capability, new services, and reduced cost almost continually. The marriage of computers and communications in the early 1940s was a major milestone that had synergistic effects on both technologies as they developed. The development of the submersible amplifier/repeater made undersea telephone cables possible and greatly expanded long distance calling capabilities. The launch of the first satellite in 1957 opened up a totally new type of communication capability.

The invention of the transistor in 1947, and subsequently the development of large-scale integrated circuits and microprocessors, have undoubtedly had the most profound impact of all of the technological advances to date. These devices made it possible to develop miniaturized devices with low power requirements, such as amplifiers and microprocessors, without which the networked world we know today would not exist. We would long ago have reached the limits of physical size, required power, and reliability which are absolutely essential to the network capability we have available today and have come to rely on.

transistors, integrated circuits, and microprocessors

Regulatory actions have been another major area of activity in the communications industry during this century. The regulatory posture was first oriented to protecting the fledgling telecommunications industry and allowing a nationwide compatible network to get on its feet. Recently, the movement has been toward deregulation to encourage competition, innovation, and lowering of costs.

Telecommunications and the Computer

It is interesting to note that the connection between telecommunications and computers first occurred in 1941, before computers had even emerged from development laboratories. In that year, a message recorded in telegraph code on punched paper tape was converted to a code used to represent the message data on punched cards to be read into a computer. Although it was certainly unsophisticated, this process demonstrated a way that these two technologies could work together.

THE CHALLENGE OF STAYING CURRENT

One of the things that make telecommunications such an interesting field is that change is occurring rapidly. The rapid technological change is similar to the type of change that has occurred in the computer field. The basic building blocks, the electronic chips and circuits, are very similar. However, in the telecommunications field, we also have experienced the advent of satellites and fiber-optic technology, both of which present new alternatives for connecting pieces of telecommunications equipment to one another.

Another dimension of change affecting telecommunications is the legislative and regulatory process. The movement from a monopolistic to a competitive structure has had a profound impact on the companies within the industry.

The third dimension that continues to change rapidly is the business environment. Some strong competitors in the telecommunications industry didn't even exist five years ago. Some of the older companies are not the powerhouses they once were. Everyday you can read about startups, mergers, acquisitions and dissolutions of telecommunications companies. It's hard to keep up with who owns what!

While all of the change can be frustrating at times, it also makes it possible, practical, and economical to use telecommunications in new and innovative ways. The good news is that this keeps work interesting and exciting for people in the field. The bad news is that it is very difficult to keep current with all that is happening and to understand the significance or applicability for your organization or your personal life.

Serious telecommunications students and professionals must constantly educate and reeducate themselves about products, technology, and trends that are appropriate and relevant for their companies. Fortunately, there is no limit to the number of opportunities to do so. Seminars are taught frequently in major cities, numerous telecommunications trade magazines exist, and specialized books on a wide variety of telecommunications topics are available.

This book distinguishes between the basic telecommunications principles and concepts that are relatively constant and stable, and current products or implementations that change rapidly. Understand, however, that if you are going to stay current in the telecommunications field, you must be prepared to continue your study.

SUMMARY

The focus of this book is telecommunications in a business environment. Telecommunications is important to study because it is used widely and is an important part of our lives at work and in the home. The technologies on which telecommunications is based are changing rapidly. Advances in microelectronics and transmission media, such as fiber optics and satellite communication, exemplify this change. Telecommunications is changing in another dimension—the regulatory one. For many years the movement in most countries of the world has been toward deregulating the telecommunications industry. Today the United States has a mixed environment with part of the telecommunications industry being regulated and part being unregulated. The business environment is in constant flux too, as companies enter and leave the market. Like any discipline, telecommunications has its own terminology to be learned. You have begun building your telecommunications vocabulary in this chapter, and will continue to do so throughout the book.

CASE STUDY

Telecommunications at Work in the Home

Virtually everyone, even those who don't work in telecommunications is aware of the lightning-speed pace by which the industry is changing. This progress is not only limited to the corporate world; perhaps, even more remarkable is the impact that telecommunications advancements have made in the home. For some, it has simply made keeping in touch with far-away family and friends easier, while for others it has dramatically altered day-to-day life.

Lori and John Andrews live in Connecticut, are in their mid-thirties and are the parents of a two-year-old. They are a good example of how advancements in telecommunications have affected the home user. "We 'surf' the net, send electronic mail to friends around the world and pay our bills on-line," said Lori. Until I started talking with the Andrews, they hadn't really thought about their use of telecommunications or the role it plays in their lives. In addition to a standard phone line, they have a second line, which is shared with the fax machine and their personal computer. They each have a cellular phone, and John has a pager for work.

When asked how their lives have changed because of developments in home telecommunications, John was quick to respond. "Life is so much easier, especially when it comes to banking. We hardly ever go to the bank anymore. If we need a statement we go on-line. If we want to transfer money from one account to another, we can do so on-line. It's remarkably convenient. I log on to PC Banking and within seconds I'm looking at all the activity in our accounts, paying bills or e-mailing customer service with a question."

Most banks now offer free PC banking, but just 2 years ago that wasn't the case. The concept of free on-line banking is becoming widely available, and this makes good business sense for financial institutions. Every transaction conducted with an actual teller costs a bank approximately \$1–\$2; every transaction processed through an automated teller machine costs around 40 cents, but an on-line transaction costs an institution only a fraction of a penny. In addition to PC banking from traditional brick and mortar banks, there are now virtual Internet banks as well as on-line bill paying services that e-mail you when a bill is received and with one click of your authorization, the bill is paid.

Another telecommunications innovation, the cellular phone, has made the Andrews' lives less stressful. Lori was the first to get a cell phone, primarily for safety reasons. At one point, she traveled an 80-mile round-trip route twice a week, not arriving home those evenings until 11:00 P.M. "I just felt safer knowing I wouldn't be stranded on Interstate 95 with a flat tire or a dead engine. The cell phone was my safety net." Lori continued, "But now with cell rates becoming more and more competitive, I find myself using the cell phone for other reasons." John added, "I use my cell phone as a business tool. I commute 2 hours a day on the train, so I can get caught up with work and listen to my voice mail. It saves a fair amount of time and probably even lets me leave work earlier than I could have before the advent of the cell phone."

Although Lori and John have had home access to the Internet for more than 6 years, I asked them if they still think about the changes it has brought to their day-to-day lives. "Definitely!" said Lori immediately. "Being a stay-at-home mom has brought me a more appreciative view of the net.

I probably do 60 percent of my shopping on-line—baby items, books, gifts for others, etc. My son Alec goes down for a nap, I log on and within 30 minutes, I've accomplished what it would have taken me 3 hours to do in the car." Lori laughed, "I even find myself not buying from stores that aren't on-line shopping-ready yet. I'll find another store with the same item and buy it from there instead. But in all seriousness, the whole business to customer aspect of the Internet is life-changing and for the better, I believe."

Lori told how she was amazed at the number of friends who did not bank or shop on-line. "They have personal computers, but for some reason are not taking advantage of it. They all e-mail and do research, but that's it." A friend once referred to Lori as an "Internet maniac." Lori laughed. "What I do on the net is a mere fraction of what's available to me, yet these people think I'm at the height of computer savvy. I'm not sure why they aren't taking advantage of the net and its uses. Maybe it's their age; after all, those of us in our mid to late thirties didn't grow up with computers in the classroom. We typed college papers on electric typewriters and used Whiteout. It's not that these people are anti-computer; that's not it at all. It's more like it's overwhelming." John laughed, "And here we are considering buying a second computer, and I can easily see that evolving into a network of computers in our home within a few years."

John added another Internet story. "A few months ago we were concerned that Lori had contracted Lyme disease. We used the search engine Yahoo!, typed in Lyme disease and within seconds we had located a list of the symptoms, what to be aware of, plus a color picture of what to look for on the skin. Because of the information we had found on the Internet, we were able to immediately rule out Lyme disease." He concluded, "Not only was it a big time-saver, but it put our minds at ease in a very short period of time."

When I asked about their phone service, I learned that although the Andrews primarily rely on electronic mail to keep in touch with their overseas friends, they still make a number of international calls every month. "After our first few bills from AT&T, I knew something had to be done," said Lori. She went on to explain that she had been bombarded with phone calls and mailings from MCI, Sprint and other long distance companies, all claiming to offer better rates than AT&T. I always ignored them, but after realizing our high phone bills were becoming a problem, I began to pay attention to their offers." Lori received an offer from MCI for calls to Japan at a lower rate than what she was currently paying. "I liked AT&T's service and really didn't want to get into the phone company wars, but I did phone Japan a lot, so I decided to call AT&T and see what they could do." Lori explained the situation to the customer representative at AT&T and within a short time the representative called Lori back and offered her a rate lower than the MCI offer. "I realize we probably make more international calls than the average residential phone customer, but I was still impressed that AT&T was willing to negotiate a deal, so to speak."

In finishing our interview, I asked the Andrews if they felt they were a techno-savvy family; in other words, were they up to date with the latest in home telecommunications offerings. Lori said, "If you would have asked me that question 3 years ago, I wouldn't have hesitated to answer 'yes, definitely.' But now, I have to admit that not only are there internet services available that I don't understand, but I don't think we've changed much in how we use telecommunications in our home over the past 3 years. Yes, we shop more on-line or send more e-mail, but those are both things that were available 3 years ago. The reason we shop more is because there are more businesses on-line. The reason we e-mail more is simple—more people have Internet access."

John went on, "Broadband access to the Internet is becoming available in our area, yet we haven't taken advantage of that." Lori added, "It's something that I want to understand more. It's probably naive, but I have a problem with being connected to the net 24 hours a day, even if my computer is turned off. I'm uncomfortable with that."

"MP-3 is something we haven't taken advantage of," Lori said. "I know it's a way to download music from the net, but that's about it. I definitely feel out of it on that one. Technology is speeding by us," added Lori. "Wireless Internet is another one," said John. "I have a Palm Pilot, but I know people who use their Palm Pilots for wireless Internet access."

In closing the Andrews said, "The bottom line is that telecommunications advancements, for us, are convenient and time saving which has made life noticeably less stressful."

QUESTIONS

1. How has your life changed because of the advancement of telecommunications? Think of the telecommunication devices you use regularly. Is your life easier or more complicated?
2. What advancements in telecommunications do you see in the future? How will they benefit the home?
3. The high demand for home telecommunication devices has brought about the need for people with a skill set particular to this industry. Explain how this has affected the economy.

CASE STUDY

Dow Corning Corporation—Background

This case study is intended to describe how a company is using telecommunications. The Dow Corning case will continue throughout the book, with a different aspect of the company's telecommunications network and management being discussed each time. It is hoped that the student will see how many of the ideas and concepts discussed in the text apply in a real life situation.

INTRODUCTION TO THE COMPANY

Dow Corning Corporation was founded in 1943 as a 50-50 joint venture of The Dow Chemical Company and Corning, Inc. The company's business is to develop, manufacture, and market silicones and related specialty materials. Dow Corning's corporate headquarters is in Midland, Michigan, located about 120 miles north of Detroit. Midland is a town of approximately 38,000 people and is also the corporate headquarters for The Dow Chemical Company. From Midland, Dow Corning oversees a worldwide operation with 1999 annual sales of about $2.6 billion. The company has sales offices in major cities throughout the world and manufacturing plants in many industrialized countries.

Since silicone products can take many forms, Dow Corning's product line is extensive. In various forms, including fluids, rubbers, and resins, silicone products function as additives to other products, as ingredients in consumer products, as processing aids, as maintenance materials, and as final products.

Dow Corning Corporation's corporate headquarters in Midland, Michigan. (Courtesy of Dow Corning Corporation)

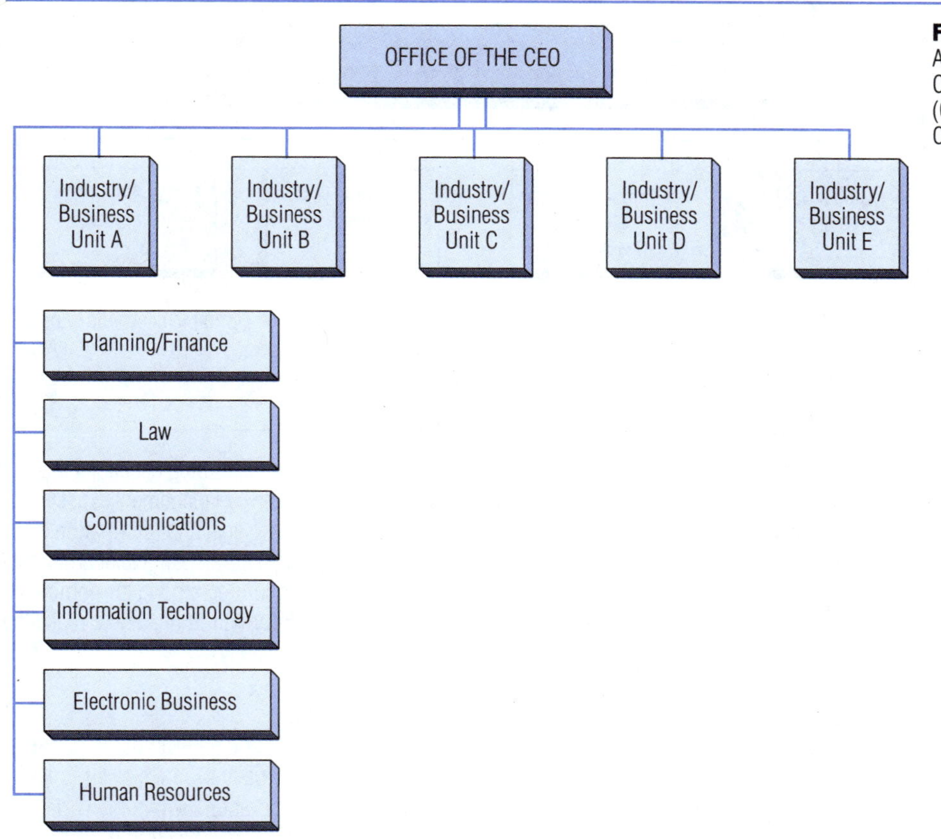

Figure 1–16
A diagram of Dow Corning's organization. (Courtesy of Dow Corning Corporation)

Dow Corning's manufacturing activities are highly integrated. Products produced by one plant may be sold to customers directly or used as chemical intermediates in other manufacturing processes. For this reason, there must be close coordination and communication between marketing and manufacturing to determine which products will be sold and which will be shipped to other plants for further processing. Furthermore, the plants must coordinate their activities to ensure that they have a steady supply of materials from one another.

Dow Corning's organization is divided into five major product groups called Industry Business Units (IBUs) as shown in Figure 1–16. IBU general managers are responsible for setting strategy for the products for which their groups are responsible, and for the worldwide profitability of those products. The industry managers who report to IBU general managers are responsible for the worldwide sales of Dow Corning products to the industry for which they are responsible. Dow Corning also loosely divides the world into geographic units called regions. People located in the regions focus on cultural, marketing or product differences that are required in the countries they serve. The focus of operation for North and South America is in Midland, for Europe in Brussels, and for Asia in Tokyo.

Historically, Dow Corning's management style and methods have been quite centralized. Most of the major decisions about company operations have been made at the Midland

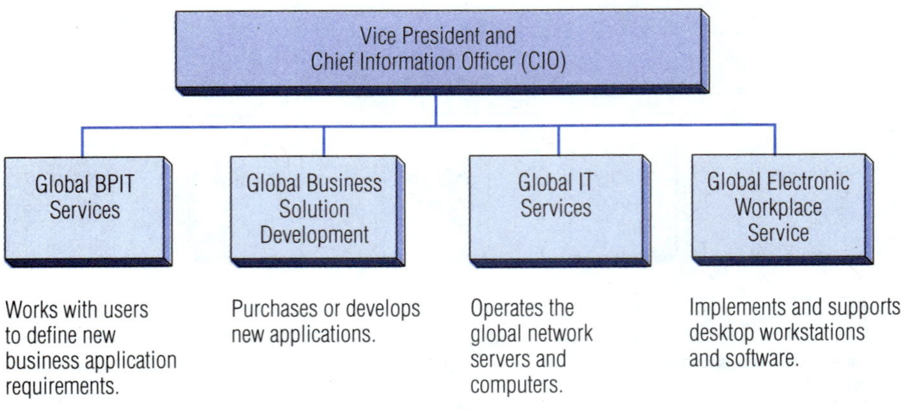

Figure 1–17
Dow Corning's Global IT Organization

headquarters, with some freedom given to the foreign regions to make operating decisions that are appropriate for their countries. At the same time, the company's executive management expects that the strategic direction for finance, human resources, communications, legal and information technology will continue to be centralized. There is a strong feeling that integrated financial and information systems are essential to maintaining the close coordination required among the company's operating units. There is also a belief that these systems provide information needed to make the appropriate decisions that enable the company to maintain its profitability.

TELECOMMUNICATIONS AT DOW CORNING

The responsibility for telecommunications in Dow Corning lies within the corporate Information Technology (IT) department. The Vice President in charge of IT is called the Chief Information Officer (CIO), and reports to the Executive Vice President of the corporation. Within the IT department, the directors of Global Information Technology Services, Global Electronic Workplace Services, Global Business Solutions Delivery, and Global Business Process/IT Services report to the Vice President and CIO, as shown in Figure 1–17. Telecommunications responsibility falls within the Global Information Technology Services group.

The telecommunications staff has reported to different parts of the organization at various stages in its evolution. Before 1982, data communication was managed by the IT department, but voice communication reported to a different part of the company. In 1982, the data and voice responsibilities were integrated in the IT organization. In 1985, a separate telecommunications department was established within IT, and in 1994, telecommunications was incorporated into the Global IT Services organization. These changes reflect differing needs and emphases placed on telecommunications over the years.

Beginning in 1991, a much stronger emphasis was placed on ensuring that the telecommunications staff in the IT department and the people in the manufacturing function who had telecommunication expertise and requirements worked more closely together. It was recognized that the two groups were gradually drifting apart in philosophy and technical implementations of networks, and there was strong recognition of the need to ensure the ongoing maintenance and further development of the integrated data network that Dow Corning had always enjoyed.

As in the rest of the company, the staff size of the telecommunications staff is kept lean. There are 15 people, not including the people who work on the help desk, most of whom are contractors. The department develops and operates a worldwide data communications network that connects all major Dow Corning locations with one another. The staff is also responsible for the company's voice network. There are more than 11,000 personal computers on the data network, about 5,800 of them in the United States. One goal of the data network is to provide very rapid response time for most transactions. Although this objective is being met in many cases, constant monitoring is required to keep the performance optimized and to try to anticipate impending bottlenecks before they occur.

QUESTIONS

1. What are the pros and cons of the telecommunications organization being a separate department versus reporting to another department?
2. What are the important attributes the senior executive should possess to successfully oversee the systems and telecommunications departments?
3. Why do you suppose the telecommunications and manufacturing departments in Dow Corning began to drift apart in philosophy and technical details of network implementations?
4. Why would a network such as Dow Corning's experience almost constant change?

REVIEW QUESTIONS

1. Define telecommunications. What are the advantages of using a telecommunications system?
2. Define data communications.
3. Distinguish among communication, telecommunications, and data communications.
4. Why is it important to know something about telecommunications?
5. Why was the invention of the transistor important to the progress of telecommunications technology?
6. Explain the terms:

source	*private line*	*ATM*
medium	*switched line*	
sink	*VDT*	

7. Describe the human protocol of making a telephone call.
8. Discuss reasons why telecommunications is becoming increasingly important to business.
9. In what ways can telecommunications education be obtained?
10. List some of the careers that are available in the telecommunications industry. Which ones do you think might be of interest to you? Why?
11. What are the factors that determine the hours during which a telecommunications network must be available?
12. Compare and contrast the terms *reliability* and *availability* as they apply to a telecommunications network.
13. Explain how the reliability of a serial system is calculated.
14. Explain the difference between an *online* system and a *realtime* system.
15. Explain the concept of *real enough time.*
16. How is *response time* measured?
17. What are the factors that determine what a system's response time will be?

18. Why is *queuing* a factor in calculating response time?

19. Why does fast response time help the productivity of a terminal user?

20. Why is response time normally calculated on a probabilistic basis?

21. What is *think time?*

22. Compare and contrast the concepts *easy to use* and *easy to learn.*

23. Why does the telecommunications manager need to understand ergonomic issues?

24. Why is it important for a telecommunications network to be flexible?

25. Explain why it is important for a telecommunications department to be proactive and forward thinking.

26. Explain why senior management in a company is interested in cost-effective telecommunications.

27. Briefly describe the history of the telephone industry from its inception through the early 1900s.

28. What company passed up the opportunity to own the basic patents on the telephone?

29. In what situations is it necessary to stay current with developments in telecommunications? Why is it difficult to stay current?

PROBLEMS AND PROJECTS

1. Data communications is one way of making information available at the right place at the right time. Identify other ways that information can be transported rapidly without using data communications.

2. List the basic business transactions that are fundamental to the operation of a retail store. Which ones are candidates for data communications?

3. If an ATM is 98 percent reliable, the telecommunications line to which it is connected is 96 percent reliable, and the computer to which they are attached is 99 percent reliable, what is the overall reliability of the three-component system?

4. If you were designing an "ideal" telephone system for the United States, what characteristics would it have that the present system lacks?

5. Make a chart that shows the time differences between Chicago, Brussels, Hong Kong, and Tokyo at different times of the year. (You may have to do some research to investigate the impact of daylight saving time in the various countries.)

6. Calculate the average reliability that each component of a three-component communication system would need for the reliability of the total system to be 99 percent.

7. You have just been named the manager of a full-service department store, one of several in a statewide chain. The company will soon be installing its first point-of-sale terminals, which will have hand-held scanners to read merchandise tickets. You have heard that the terminals in your store will be connected to the central computer at company headquarters, but you have no other details. Next week two analysts from the corporate telecommunications department will be coming to talk to you about your requirements for the new system. In preparation for their visit, make a list of the attributes and operating characteristics that you hope the new terminals and communication network will have, and the questions you will want to ask the analysts.

8. The text gives several examples of how telecommunications is shrinking the world. List several examples of the way you use data communications today that were not possible or would have been considered extravagant 15 years ago.

9. Describe how airline reservations were made before the advent of computers.

10. Do you feel that the Internet and CD-ROM-based encyclopedias will eliminate the need for printed reference books and libraries' reference sections? Why or why not?

Vocabulary

networked society
the Internet
communication
telecommunications
data communications
data
information
source
medium
sink
protocol
basic business transactions
Internet service provider (ISP)
web browser
video display terminal (VDT)
private line
leased line
dial-up line
switched line
automatic teller machine (ATM)
intelligent terminal
dumb terminal
availability
reliability
mean time between failures (MTBF)
mean time to repair (MTTR)
serial system
online
realtime
real enough time
response time
queuing
queue
user response time
think time
dialogue
user friendly
ergonomics
Bell System

References

American National Standards Institute. *Dictionary for Information Systems.* X3. 172–1990.

Doherty, W. J., and R. P. Kelisky. "Managing VM/CMS Systems for User Effectiveness." *IBM Systems Journal* 18, no. 1 (1979).

"The Economic Value of Rapid Response Time." IBM brochure, no. GE20-0752-0 (November 1982).

Levy, Steven. *Hackers: Heroes of the Computer Revolution.* New York: Anchor Press/Doubleday, 1984.

Martin, James. *Design of Man-Computer Dialogues.* Englewood Cliffs, NJ: Prentice-Hall, 1973.

Ramo, Joshua Cooper. "Welcome to the Wired World." *Time* (February 3, 1997): 36.

Stallings, William. *Data and Computer Communications,* 5th ed. Upper Saddle River, NJ: Prentice-Hall, 1997.

CHAPTER

2

Data Terminals and Personal Computers

OBJECTIVES

After you complete your study of this chapter, you should be able to

- classify terminals in several different ways;
- explain the capabilities and characteristics of several types of terminals;
- describe uses for several specialized types of terminals;
- distinguish among intelligent terminals, smart terminals, and dumb terminals and describe the characteristics of each;
- explain the criteria used when terminals are selected for a particular application;
- explain the concept of the "Total Cost of Ownership."

INTRODUCTION

This chapter begins your look at the details of data communications systems by studying the parts with which you are most likely to be familiar—the data terminal and personal computer. The study of data communications in this book takes an outside-in approach. The discussion begins at the terminal and works its way into the computer to which the terminal is attached. For most students, this approach will take them from familiar territory—the terminal or personal computer—through the unfamiliar and more technical aspects of data communications, and then back to more familiar ground at the computer.

This chapter relates to layer 6 of the ISO-OSI model, the presentation layer. Terminals, especially those with intelligence such as personal computers, have a great deal of control over the way that data is formatted to users, so hence the connection with layer 6.

Although you may have studied the material about terminals in a data processing class, the information in this chapter will serve as a quick review of the different types of terminals in common use. The chapter also highlights the telecommunications implications of the various types of terminals. It may also serve to fill in the gaps in your knowledge of data communications terminals and how they work.

DEFINITIONS

A *terminal* is an input/output device that may be attached to a computer via direct cable connection or via a communications line. The terminal may be dependent on the computer for computational power and/or for data. If the terminal is directly connected to the computer by a cable, telecommunications may not be involved. Such terminals are said to be *hardwired*, and they may use signaling methods other than those commonly used in telecommunications.

A VDT or other device does not need to be connected to the computer full time to qualify as a terminal. A personal computer is an example of a device that has its own intelligence and may operate independently of a host computer a good deal of the time. At other times, however, a connection may be made to allow the personal computer to be operated as a terminal attached to a host computer.

data terminal equipment

data circuit-terminating equipment

In communications terminology, both the terminal and the computer to which it is attached are properly known as *data terminal equipment (DTE)*. Data terminal equipment operates internally in digital format. Its output signal is a series of digital pulses. *Data circuit-terminating equipment (DCE)*, provides the interface between data terminal equipment and the communications line. As shown in Figure 2–1, when analog lines are used, DCE provides the translation between the digital format of the DTE and the analog format of the transmission line. Even when digital communications lines are used, DCE is required between the DTE and the line.

TERMINAL CLASSIFICATION

Data terminals can be classified into categories, but the classification scheme may not be definitive because the categories have wide overlap. Because of the overlap, any classification of terminals is questionable. Nonetheless, there are several categories that will serve us well for descriptive and discussion purposes. They are:

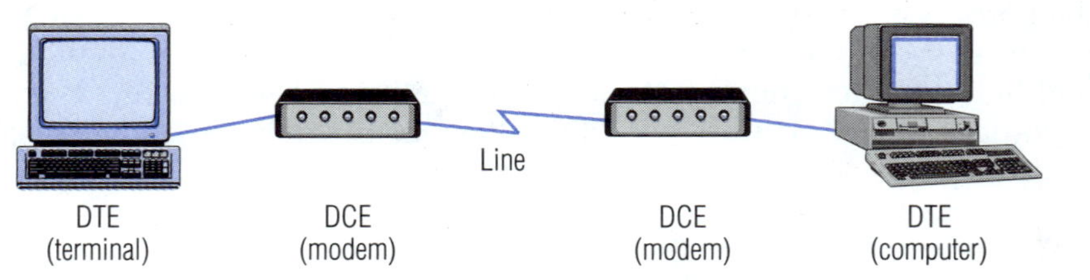

Figure 2–1
The location of data terminal equipment (DTE) and data circuit-terminating equipment (DCE) in a communications system.

- teletypewriters;
- video display terminals (VDTs);
- industry-oriented transaction terminals;
- intelligent terminals;
- remote job entry terminals;
- specialized terminals.

You can see the overlap already. Personal computers are intelligent devices, but they certainly use video display terminal technology; video display terminals are used in many transaction-oriented terminals such as bank ATMs.

Teletypewriter Terminal

The teletypewriter was the primary terminal in use before 1970. The simplest way to think of a teletypewriter terminal is as a typewriter with additional electronics and other features added for communications purposes. Indeed, some early terminals were just that—a typewriter equipped for communication. Most teletypewriter terminals in use today were originally designed for communications and will not operate as ordinary typewriters.

The teletypewriter is equipped with a keyboard and a mechanism for continuous feeding of paper. The keyboard is similar to that of a typewriter, although the keys are usually laid out a bit differently. The printing mechanism varies in how it forms the characters on the paper. Most use a matrix of wires that push the ribbon against the paper and form characters by a series of closely spaced dots, known as a *dot matrix* printing mechanism. Others employ heat as well as a matrix of wires to cause a chemical reaction in specially treated paper to form characters. This type of printing mechanism does not require a ribbon.

dot matrix

Teletypewriters and other terminals operate in one of two ways: *unbuffered* or *buffered*. In an unbuffered terminal, a character is transmitted to the computer as soon as a key on the keyboard is pressed. In a buffered terminal the keyed characters are stored in internal memory, called a *buffer,* until a special key such as the RETURN or ENTER key is pressed. Then all of the characters stored in the buffer are transmitted to the computer in one operation. At a buffered terminal users can correct typing mistakes before data is sent to the computer. Buffered terminals are the most common type today. Buffering is not unique to teletypewriters; it is found in most other types of terminals as well.

buffer

Some other characteristics of teletypewriter terminals are:

- slow speed—seldom more than 15 characters per second;
- very mechanical—therefore not as reliable as all-electronic devices;
- may be appropriate where hard copy is required;
- often connected to a computer only by dialing up.

Video Display Terminal (VDT)

The names *video display terminal (VDT), video display unit (VDU), cathode ray tube terminal (CRT),* and, on a PC, *monitor* are often used interchangeably. Not all video display terminals use cathode ray tube technology, however, so *video display terminal* is more general and appropriate. Other technologies used for VDTs are liquid crystal displays (LCDs), light emitting diodes (LEDs), gas plasma, and electroluminescent displays. These technologies yield a display that is much flatter and takes up less space on a desk, hence the generic name, *flat panel displays.*

flat panel displays

Other characteristics of VDTs are:

- all electronic—highly reliable;
- buffered (usually)—data is stored until the user presses the ENTER key;
- capable of very high-speed display of data;
- various types range in capability from simple, unintelligent "glass teletypewriter" to very intelligent, programmable ones.

The Screen The VDT frequently contains a cathode ray tube on which an electron beam causes phosphors to glow, forming the desired letters, numbers, special characters, or other patterns. Three electron beams and different types of phosphorus are used to create a color image in the same way that a color television picture is formed. The most common size of VDT screens is 15 inches, measured diagonally like television screens. However, 17-inch screens are becoming increasingly popular, and 19-, 20-, and 21-inch screens are available, though quite a bit more expensive. In applications that require high resolution, have detailed graphics, or require many windows to be open simultaneously, the larger screen sizes are definitely a good investment and easier on the eyes.

In a VDT that uses a cathode ray tube, characters are formed when an electron beam energizes selected dots of phosphorus within a matrix. Typical matrix sizes are 5×7, 7×9, and 8×10 dots. The characters are formed so that there is at least one unused row of dots around them to provide spacing between the characters. This concept is illustrated in Figure 2–2.

Screens may be either alphanumeric, which allow screen positions to be addressed at the character level, or *all-points-addressable (APA),* which allow individual dots on the screen to be controlled. These dots are called *picture elements,* commonly known as *pixels* or *pels,* and they can be turned on or off or set to a specific color under a program's control. APA displays are the norm for new video displays today; they are required for windows, graphics, and pictures to be displayed.

pixels

VDTs that use liquid crystal display (LCD) technology have two sheets of polarizing material with a liquid crystal solution between them. An electric current passed through the liquid causes the crystals to align

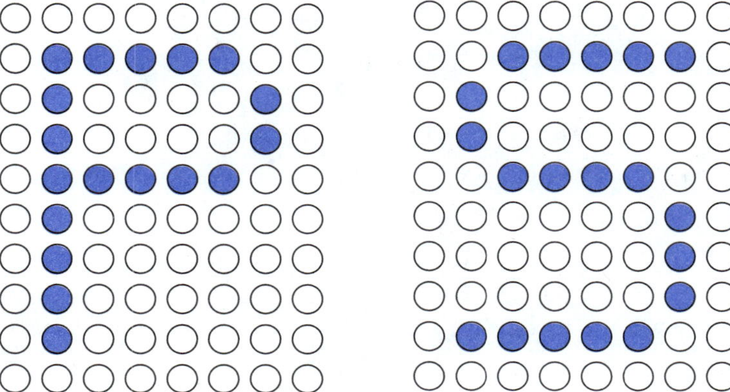

Figure 2–2
Characters formed by a dot matrix.

so that light cannot pass through them. Each crystal, therefore, is like a shutter, either allowing light to pass through or blocking the light. Both monochrome and color LCD screens are available but color screens are more widely used. LCD-based devices have a very slim profile, and a bright distortion-free image on a flat panel, making them especially attractive where space is limited. The problem has been that they were very expensive; however, the cost is coming down, so we can expect to see more of these devices in our offices and homes in coming years.

The screen of a VDT also displays a special place-marking character called a *cursor,* which indicates where the next character from the computer or keyboard will be displayed. In some cases, the cursor can be made to blink or display at a higher intensity than other characters on the screen so it can be seen easily. The keyboard of a VDT has special keys, called *cursor control keys,* for moving the cursor. These are often designated by arrows that point up, down, left, and right and that move the cursor in the indicated direction. Moving the cursor with the cursor control keys is not the same as moving it with the SPACE BAR or BACKSPACE key. The SPACE BAR inserts a space character, which will be transmitted to the computer, in the data stream. The BACKSPACE key removes a character; using a cursor control key has no effect on the data stream.

VDTs have several methods of highlighting characters for easy identification by the user. One technique is called *intensifying,* in which a character (or any collection of dots) on the screen is made brighter than the other characters around it. Some VDTs have several brightness levels. Another technique is to cause a character to *blink* by varying the intensity at which it is displayed several times each second. A third technique is called *reverse video,* which reverses the character and background colors. If, for example, the normal display shows green characters on a black

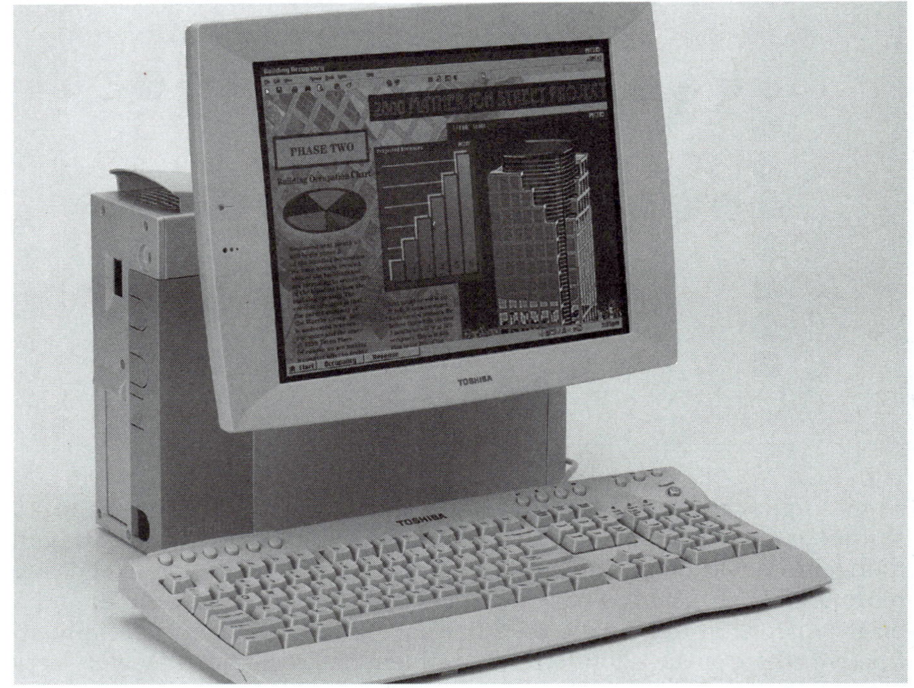

This Toshiba personal computer is typical of many found in the market today and is designed for multimedia use. (Courtesy of Toshiba America Information Systems, Inc.)

background, a reverse video character would be black on a green background. A fourth technique for highlighting characters is with the use of *color,* for example, displaying most of the characters in green and certain characters, such as error messages, in red.

When teletypewriter terminals receive output from a computer, they print it one line at a time. There is no inherent concept of a page, except as a collection of lines. This is known as *line-by-line mode.* VDTs can operate in a similar way, receiving and displaying one or a few lines at a time. When a VDT operates in line-by-line mode, the new lines normally appear at the bottom of the screen. All other lines are moved up, and the top line disappears off the top of the screen. This is much like what the user sees as printed teletypewriter output moves up and eventually disappears over the back of the terminal.

VDTs normally operate in *page* or *formatted mode.* There are several ways this is implemented. It is simplest to think of the screen of the VDT as a "page," consisting of a specific number of lines, each with a set number of characters. Programmatically, output can be placed anywhere on the screen, and if the communications lines are fast enough, the entire screen is displayed to the user at the same time. Page mode allows the screen to be laid out like a paper form with headings, field identifiers, and fields to be filled in as shown in Figure 2–3. The operator may be required

Quality Assurance System
Lot Number Test Results — **10/11/01** **10:57**

Lot Number: FA128639

Item ID	Lot Number	QA Status	Status Date	Sample Type	Test Results
1959042	FA128639	Approved	20SEP94	1A	1:56.2 2: OK 3:7.1cm 4:HIGH AVERAGE
2876691	BQ212598	Approved	29SEP94	2	1:41.0 2:OK 3:4.5cm 4:OKAY
1464552	RM213356	Rejected	30SEP94	1A	1:55.1 2:LOW 3:1.1cm 4:HIGH

Figure 2–3
Page mode allows the VDT to be laid out like a paper form.

This keyboard for an IBM personal computer has a numeric keypad at the right side. Twelve program function keys are at the top. (Courtesy of IBM Corporation)

to fill in certain fields, whereas others are optional. After the operator types certain information on the form, for example, a material's lot number, the computer may respond by filling in other fields, such as the product's name and status.

The Keyboard VDT and personal computer keyboards, like teletypewriter keyboards, are similar to standard typewriter keyboards. The extra keys for cursor control already have been mentioned. In addition, there are usually special *function keys,* sometimes called *program function keys,* that direct the computer to perform actions predetermined by the software being run. Some keyboards have a *numeric keypad,* which is like a 10-key calculator keyboard. The numeric keypad is useful if a lot of numerical data must be entered, and its keys are in addition to the regular numerical keys on the keyboard.

Two other useful keys on a typical VDT keyboard are the INSERT and DELETE keys that the operator uses to insert or delete characters. When the cursor is moved under a character and DELETE is pressed, the character disappears from the screen, and all characters to the right of it on the line are shifted one position to the left to fill the gap. The INSERT key works just the opposite; it allows characters to be inserted on a line with all following characters shifted to the right.

Some terminals have specialized keyboards that usually are designed to help the operator perform his or her job more quickly and efficiently. The terminals in McDonald's restaurants are one example. They have keys for the clerk to press to indicate the item the customer is ordering and the quantity. The keys are actually labeled "Hamburger," "Cheeseburger," "Large Fries," "Shake," and so on. Other specialized keyboards are used on terminals in laboratories, plants, banks, and so on.

Another type of specialized keyboard is one used in countries that use alphabets made up of characters other than Roman letters. In Japan, China, Korea, and the Arab countries, for example, the alphabets and characters are much different from the ones we use in Western countries, and keyboards must be designed to handle those characters. Minor modifications are required in almost every country so that the keyboard has keys for national characters, such as those with an umlaut in German-speaking countries and accented characters where French and Spanish are spoken.

Other Input Mechanisms In addition to keyboards there are other ways to control the movement of the cursor. The most common of these is the *mouse* with which every user of an Apple Macintosh or Windows-based computer is familiar. Similar mechanisms are the *trackball,* often found on laptop computers, and the *joystick,* most commonly used with computer games.

The screens of some VDTs are *touch sensitive.* If the computer displays a question on the screen with a list of possible answers, the user can indicate a choice by touching an appropriate place on the screen. Touch screens have been successful in applications where people unfamiliar with computers must use the terminal because the screens are easy to use and require no training. One example is a VDT at an information booth at a fair or exposition. The general public may use the VDT to obtain information about the location of exhibits or other facilities. Obviously there is no opportunity to train the users, many of whom may never have used a computer terminal before.

VDT Selection Criteria When you select a VDT, consider the following factors:

- Does the face of the screen have a nonglare surface to prevent reflection from nearby light?
- Can the screen be tilted or swiveled to a comfortable viewing position?

- On a monochrome VDT, is the character display in one of the two standard colors (green on a black background or amber on a black background)?
- On a color VDT, can the default background and character colors be selected by the user?
- Is the screen image flickerfree? (Flickering screen images cause eyestrain.)
- Is the size of the screen appropriate for the application?
- Is the resolution of the characters fine enough to minimize eyestrain?
- Is the VDT programmable?
- Does it have graphics capability?

Personal Computers Used as Terminals

Personal computers (PCs), sometimes called *microcomputers,* are now the "norm" when one thinks of terminals on a communications network. In most applications, personal computers are the terminal of choice because of their ability to participate in a distributed processing or client-server system. Software that is commonly found in the personal computer environment, such as word processing and spreadsheet programs, may be used to manipulate data before it is sent to a server or mainframe for further processing, or data from the mainframe may be sent to the personal computer for analysis or formatting before it is presented to the user.

microcomputers

The wide adoption of Microsoft's Windows, by personal computer users, following the lead of the Apple Macintosh computers, has raised the use of personal computers to new levels of sophistication. The *graphical user interface (GUI)* that these operating systems provide is easier to use and more intuitive than previous, command-driven operating systems and is preferred by most people. Of course, users who are very familiar with the commands of DOS must make some adjustment to the GUI because it makes extensive use of the mouse and less use of the keyboard.

graphical user interface

These operating systems simulate or provide a true *multitasking* capability that allows multiple programs to be, or appear to be, operating at the same time. Thus, a user can be communicating with a host computer in one window of his VDT screen, while performing word processing, spreadsheet, or other processing in another window—and of course the number of windows is not limited to two.

Personal computers may be connected to networks and mainframe computers at several levels of sophistication. Sometimes they are connected so that they act like dumb terminals because this is the simplest, least expensive type of connection that can be made. In this case, they emulate a terminal that the host computer recognizes. Terminal emulation is accomplished by special hardware in the personal computer and a program called a *terminal emulation program.* The host thinks it is working with a standard terminal because the hardware or software in the PC

terminal emulation program

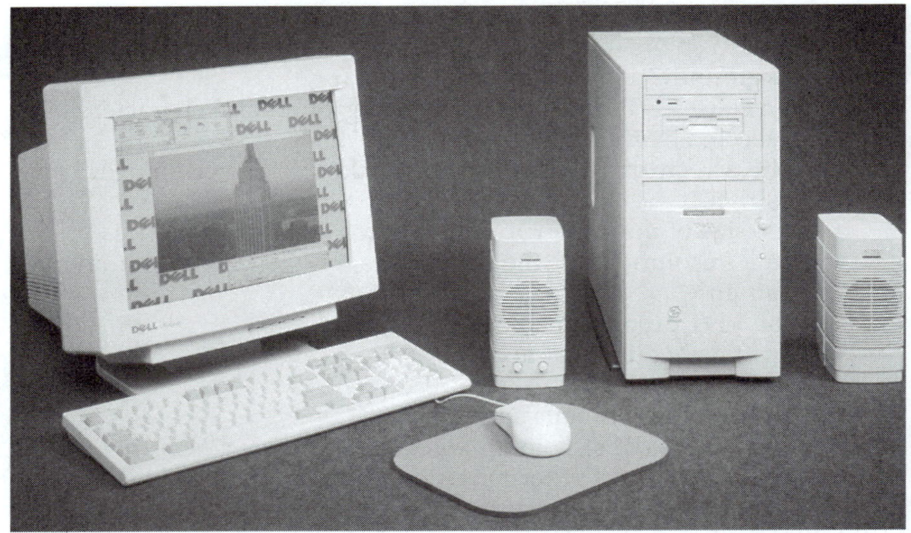

This personal computer, manufactured by Dell, has a CD-ROM player, sound card, and speakers, and is designed for multimedia use. (Courtesy of Dell Computer Corporation.)

responds just as the terminal would. The most common emulated terminals are the Digital Equipment Corporation (DEC) VT-100 and VT-220, and the IBM 3270.

uploading and downloading

Terminal emulation is a simple, inexpensive way to use a personal computer to communicate; however, when a personal computer emulates a dumb terminal, the power of the personal computer is not used to its best advantage. The host doesn't know it is communicating with another computer so it cannot tap the intelligence that resides in the PC. More sophisticated programming is required to allow the two computers to communicate in a distributed processing fashion or as peers. One simple enhancement is to add software that allows the personal computer and the mainframe to transfer files back and forth. Either computer can create a file using its own software, and then the operator can have it sent to the other computer using the SEND or RECEIVE command of the file transfer software. This type of file transfer is called *uploading* if the file is sent from the personal computer to the mainframe or other computer, and *downloading* if the file is sent from the mainframe to the personal computer. In a TCP/IP-based network the *file transfer protocol (FTP)* is most commonly used to accomplish these transfers.

network computer

One special type of computer is the so-called *network computer.* Network computers are designed to allow full connection to the Internet and other networks, but do not have all of the features of a traditional PC. For example, the size of the disk drive may be limited, or they may be required to download software from the network. The primary motivation for producing these machines is to reduce the cost of the computer required to attach to networks, especially the Internet, so that more people will be able to afford to connect.

More sophisticated software for distributed processing allows the host and personal computers to interact through a communications network in a more realtime fashion. Called *client-server computing,* such software allows a user or program on the personal computer, called the *client,* to request information or service from the host computer, called the *server.* Similarly, a user of a personal computer (client) might store or view data on another computer (server) as a simple extension of the disk capacity of the PC. This level of sophistication requires considerably more elaborate software and more powerful computers than are required for terminal emulation.

client

server

When personal computers are connected to a network or other computers, users must be concerned and vigilant about protecting the machines from *computer viruses.* Viruses may be inadvertently downloaded with a file or program, and can cause severe disruption and data destruction if not detected and eliminated. Fortunately virus detection and correction software is available, and it does a good job if it is regularly used.

viruses

Portable, laptop, or notebook computers are often used by sales representatives or other travelers in two modes. They use the machines as stand-alone computers during the day to perform processing independent of the host. At night, when the representative returns to the hotel room, the machines are used as terminals, connected via ordinary telephone lines to a host computer at the company or division headquarters. The results of the day's activities are transmitted to the host, and messages or electronic mail are received from it.

Sometimes the terms *personal computer* (or microcomputer) and *workstation* are used interchangeably, and their use can be confusing because there is little consistency in the industry about the use of these terms. However, generally speaking, when the term *personal computer* is used, people generally think of the hardware, operating system, and perhaps some basic applications, such as word processing, spreadsheets, or business graphics packages. When the term *workstation* is used, people think either of

workstation

- more powerful hardware and operating system software and a more complete, more specialized set of applications, such as would be used by a stockbroker or an engineer doing computer-aided design work; or
- the place where a person sits or stands to do work.

You can see why confusion exists! In this book, the term *workstation* is used both ways, but it will be clear to you which meaning is intended.

This mouse can be moved around on the desk top to control the location of the cursor on the screen of a VDT. This mouse is especially designed for children. (Courtesy of Logitech, Inc.)

Engineering Workstations

computer-aided design (CAD)

Engineering workstations are large, all-points-addressable VDTs with very high resolution. Engineering graphics VDTs are used for engineering design and drafting, the application being called *computer-aided design* or *computer-assisted drafting (CAD)*. The terminals usually contain their own microcomputers to perform specialized calculations to enlarge or reduce a drawing or to rotate the viewpoint of a drawing. Telecommunications for this type of terminal is used for downloading a drawing from the host computer to the terminal and uploading it back to the computer for storage after it has been modified.

Engineering workstations frequently place a heavy load on a communications line. The APA characteristic of the terminals coupled with the large screen size and the complexity of the drawings dictate that many bits or characters must be exchanged with a host computer. The amount of communication is inversely related to the amount of intelligence in the terminal. If the terminal is intelligent, it may only need to communicate with the host to retrieve and store drawings. All other work can be carried out on the terminal. If the terminal is unintelligent, it relies on the host to assist with every change made to the drawing, and the communication is very frequent and lengthy. Most CAD terminals fall somewhere

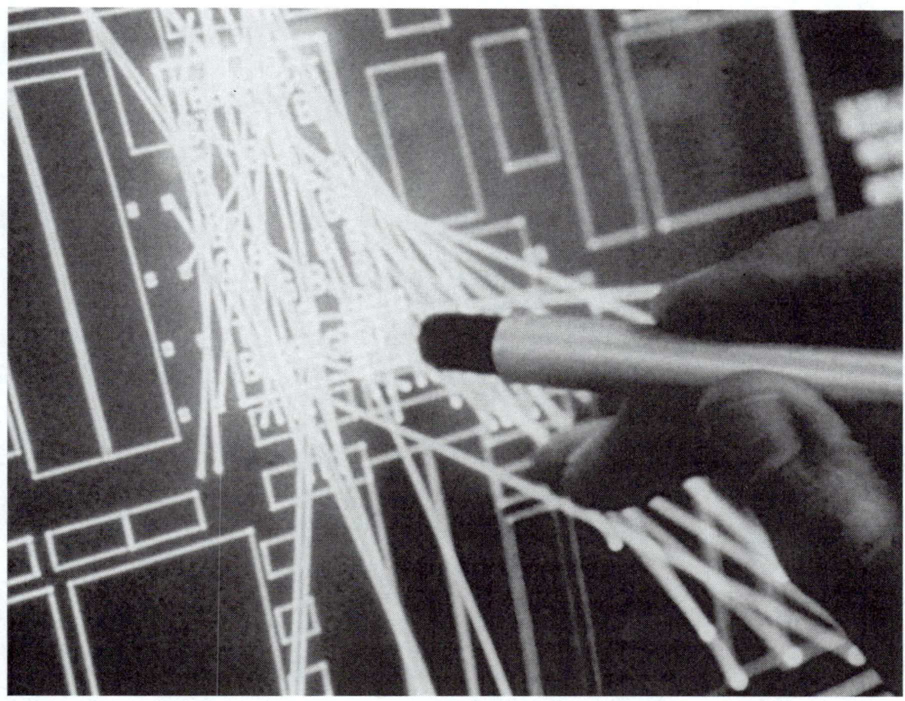

This user is holding a light pen, which is used for selecting items displayed on the screen of the VDT. (Courtesy of International Business Machines Corporation. Unauthorized use not permitted.)

between the two extremes, but the direction is clearly toward more intelligence in the terminal.

Industry-Oriented Transaction Terminals

Industry-oriented transaction terminals are specifically designed for the efficient processing of online transactions in a certain industry. Common examples of these types of terminals are the automatic teller machines and supermarket checkout terminals mentioned in previous chapters. Others include the terminals used by bank tellers. Many of these have special printers for recording changes in passbooks. Point of sale terminals read the data on merchandise tags in retail stores. Badge readers are used for time and attendance reporting in factories. These terminals are all designed around the requirements of a particular type of business transaction. They are designed to be easy to use, even by untrained operators or laypeople. Since the market for these specialized terminals usually is relatively small, the price is often higher than that for a more general terminal with the same electronic components and similar packaging.

Remote Job Entry (RJE) Terminals

Remote job entry (RJE) terminals, as the name implies, were originally used for the remote submission of batch programs or jobs to run on a host

This high-powered workstation looks similar to a standard personal computer but is designed for calculation-intensive engineering applications. (Courtesy of Digital Equipment Corporation)

computer and for receiving and printing the output of those jobs. The classic RJE terminal consisted of a reader for decks of punched cards containing the control statements or programs to be run on the computer and a medium- to high-speed printer for printing the results of the jobs' execution. To the host computer, the job appears to have been submitted from a card reader directly attached to the computer in the computer room, and the output appears to be printed on a computer room printer. The fact that telecommunications is involved is masked from the computer and from much of its operating system software.

With the obsolescence and decline in the use of punched cards and the widespread availability of interactive VDTs, work for the computer is submitted online with a few commands. As a result, the classic RJE terminal is seldom seen, although the high-speed remote printer is still in wide use. Printers of 100 to 1,000 lines per minute are most common.

Facsimile Machines

Facsimile (fax) machines used as specialized computer terminals have some of the same characteristics as OCR machines, which will be discussed in

The New York Stock Exchange is a large user of telecommunications. (Courtesy of New York Convention and Visitor's Bureau)

the next section. Instead of recording and coding individual characters, however, facsimile machines read and code patterns of light and dark areas on a sheet of paper, as will be discussed in Chapter 3.

Facsimile machines are divided into four groups according to their technology and speed, as shown in Figure 2–4. Group I and II machines are internally analog in operation and the transmission of an 8 1/2 × 11 document takes several minutes. Group III and IV machines are internally digital and transmit documents in less than a minute. The speed with which Group IV machines can transmit documents is primarily limited by the speed of the communications line to which they are attached. On a digital line that transmits data at 56,000 or 64,000 bits per second, a Group IV facsimile machine can send an 8 1/2 × 11 inch document in under ten seconds.

Figure 2–4
Facsimile machines are grouped according to their technology and transmission speed.

Group I	Internally analog Transmits a page in about 6 minutes Rarely sold anymore
Group II	Usually internally analog Transmits a page in about 3 minutes Still sold because it is relatively inexpensive
Group III	Internally digital Fully automated operation Transmits an 8 1/2 × 11 page in under 30 seconds Transmits a 9,600 bps Much better copy quality than Group I or II
Group III Enhanced	Same as Group III but transmits at 14,400 bps with better error correction Most popular today
Super Group III	Same as Group III but transmits at 33,600 bsp with enhanced compression
Group IV	Internally digital Designed for digital phone lines Transmits a page in under 10 seconds Letter quality copy Expensive

The digital facsimile machines code a spot on the document (a pixel) as either a 1 or 0 depending on the amount of light that is reflected from it. The receiving machine produces a corresponding black or white pixel on the output document. The resolution or quality of the output depends on how many lines per inch are scanned by the transmitter—in other words, how many samples are taken. Standard Group III machines take 203 samples per inch horizontally across a page and 98 samples per inch vertically, though some models have "fine" or "superfine" modes that take 196 or 391 vertical samples for higher resolution. Most Group III machines are "smart" in that they only transmit what's on a page—they don't transmit white space as earlier machines did. Most facsimile machines apply algorithms to compress the 1s and 0s and reduce the number of bits that must be transmitted.

Group IV machines take 400 samples per an inch, both vertically and horizontally, so the resolution is much improved. Naturally the number of bits is higher too, but Group IV machines use a more sophisticated compression algorithm than Group III machines.

The digitized signal from a facsimile machine can be read into a computer and stored, since it is made up of bits. Conversely, a digitized image can be sent from a computer to a facsimile machine to produce hard copy output. Hardware boards, fax modems, and fax software for personal computers are widely available to provide this capability. The amount of storage required in the computer's memory or on its disk depends on the density of the image that is to be stored, but it ranges from

This Panasonic KX-FL501 facsimile machine with a handset has the ability to store frequently called numbers. It is designed to handle the needs of a small workgroup. (Courtesy of Panasonic Communications & Systems Co.)

25 to 120 kilobytes. You can imagine how quickly the hard disk on a personal computer can be filled if many facsimile images are stored!

If an appropriate all-points-addressable VDT is available, the facsimile image can be displayed. Facsimiles are to OCR terminals as all-points-addressable VDTs are to alphanumeric VDTs. In both cases, one is designed to handle only alphanumeric data, and the other is designed to handle images.

All analog Group III and Group IIIE machines pose a security risk. Anyone can attach a normal audio cassette recorder to a telephone line, record the incoming or outgoing fax tones, and play them back to another fax machine at a later time. A perfect reproduction of the fax will be obtained! There are encryption devices that will make the transmission unintelligible except to a fax machine that has an appropriate decryption unit.

Facsimile machines used as terminals find application where documents must be read into a computer and stored and/or transmitted to another location. They place a significant load on a communications line, however, but the key to reducing the load is sophisticated compression processing that reduces the number of bits to be transmitted without reducing the quality of the image as perceived by the recipient.

Specialized Terminals

Specialized terminals are not designed for a specific application or industry. Their use is more limited than that of a standard VDT or teletypewriter, but for certain applications they are extremely useful or even indispensable.

Telephone One important type of terminal in this category is the standard 12-key push-button telephone, which can be used to send digits and 2 "special" characters to a computer. The telephone is used in banking and other applications where the input is all numerical. A common use is for entering an account number, customer number, or product number used as the key to some information stored on a computer's disk. The computer looks up and reports particular information regarding the item identified by that key.

voice response unit

When the telephone provides the input, the companion output unit is often provided by an *audio response unit,* or *voice response unit,* on the computer that can form sounds from digital data stored on disk and "speak" the response back to the user. Audio response units produced in recent years can speak at varying rates of speed and with a pitch and inflection that is appropriate to the words being spoken. The use of an audio response is an example of the marriage of voice and data communications technology.

Several companies are using telephones and audio response units to allow their employees to select employee benefits in what is called a cafeteria-style benefits program. Employees can choose from several levels of medical insurance coverage, life insurance, contributions to savings plans, and so on. After dialing the special telephone number and providing a password through a Touchtone telephone, the employee hears the audio response unit giving the choices available for each of the benefit options. The employee makes his selection by pressing the appropriate digit on the telephone, and the selection is confirmed by a voice message. When all of the selections have been made, the audio response unit summarizes the choices for the caller before ending the telephone call. The computer application frequently confirms the choices in printed form a day or two later.

As will be discussed in Chapter 4, the increasing popularity of cell phones is causing manufacturers to develop capabilities to use them as terminals, especially for accessing the Internet. In certain countries, especially Japan and in Scandinavia, cell phones are becoming the terminal of choice for sending e-mail, accessing stock reports, and viewing web sites that have been specially programmed to accommodate the cell phone's small screen.

Optical Recognition Another type of device is the *optical recognition* terminal, which can detect individual data items or characters and convert them into a code for transmission to a computer. This type of terminal uses a photo cell to sense areas of light or dark on paper or other media.

bar code readers

There are several types of optical recognition terminals. *Bar code readers* scan bars printed on merchandise or tags. The bars on grocery products are one example, but the use of bar coding is spreading to many industries. *Optical character recognition (OCR)* terminals detect and read individual characters of data. One type reads the characters on a typewritten page; another type can read handwritten data if it is clearly written. A simpler OCR device detects only marks on a page and is used to read survey forms, answer sheets from examinations, and medical questionnaires.

optical character recognition

Other Terminals Many other types of terminals are used for simple tasks, such as counting, weighing, measuring, and reporting results to the computer. On an assembly line, for example, a simple photoelectric cell may detect the passage of each item manufactured and report the event via communications lines to a computer. In a chemical plant, a device may measure the flow rate of a liquid through a pipe (or its temperature or pressure) and report this information to a computer. With advances in microprocessor technology, many devices that previously were unable to communicate are being given communications capability.

CLUSTER CONTROL UNITS

Cluster control units (CCU), sometimes called *terminal control units,* are used with some types of terminals as a way of sharing some of the expensive electronic components needed to support the advanced features of the terminals and the advanced communications software of today's multilayered networks. The IBM 3270 family of terminals is typical: Up to 64 VDTs may be attached to one CCU, and the control unit is attached to the communications line. This is illustrated in Figure 2–5.

CCUs are normally programmable devices, although frequently the programming is provided on diskettes by the manufacturer and cannot be changed by the user. CCUs may contain buffers for the terminals that can be shared. They may also perform code conversion and do error checking to ensure that data is received from the communications line correctly. Another use for the cluster control unit is to allow one or more printers to be shared among the terminals attached to it. A special key on the keyboard of each of the attached VDTs allows the image on the screen of the VDT to be printed immediately on a printer connected to the control unit without sending any data to or from the host computer.

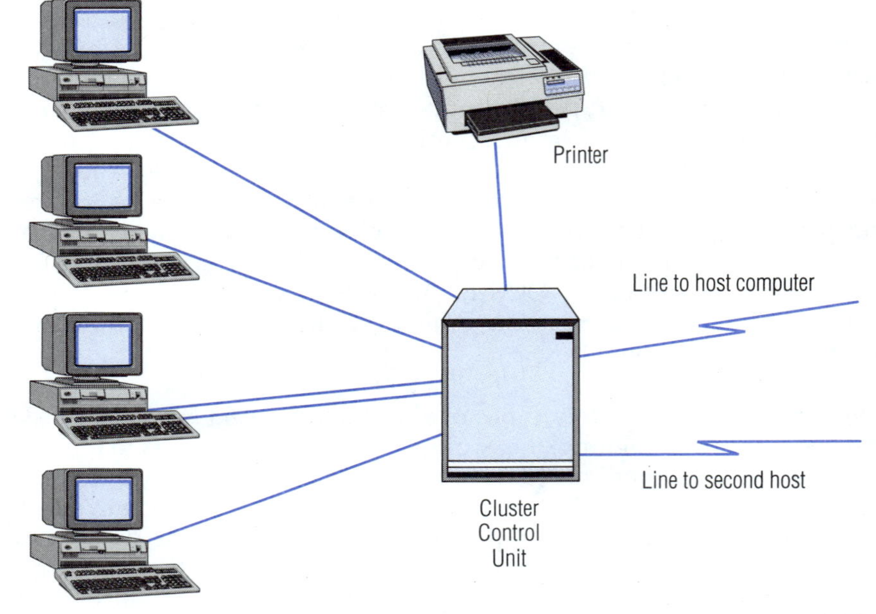

Figure 2–5
A cluster control unit with attached terminals.

Some CCUs can be attached to more than one communications line, allowing a terminal to access more than one computer. This is valuable to users who access multiple computers. Some CCUs allow the user to be logged on to more than one computer simultaneously. The VDT screen displays the information from one computer, but the user can switch to view information from the other computer using a key (or combination of keys) that is frequently called the *hot key*. Some CCUs allow a user to have multiple connections to one computer. Using this capability, the user can be logged on to more than one program on a single host computer and can switch back and forth between applications using the hot key. This capability is called *multiple sessions*.

multiple sessions

Cluster control units can have different degrees of intelligence ranging from simple buffering and translation facilities to being fully programmable controllers. One common use is for the CCU to provide the logic that allows the dumb terminals attached to it to participate in a network with a multilayer architecture. Another example is the cluster controller that manages point-of-sale terminals in a retail store.

With the decline in the use of dumb terminals, cluster control units are not used as frequently as they were before PCs were so widely used. Hence, while there are many older units still installed and connected to networks, few new units are sold.

These two photos show bar code wands in use in typical manufacturing environments where they improve the accuracy of data input compared to inputting the data with a keyboard. (Top: Courtesy of McKesson Corporation. Bottom: Courtesy of PSC Inc.)

TERMINAL INTELLIGENCE LEVELS

With the reduction in the cost of integrated circuit chips, the desktop personal computer of today has as much power as a large mainframe computer had 20 years ago. If we were to classify all terminals on an intelligence scale, we would find that there is a range or continuum from fully

The IBM 3174 cluster control unit can attach up to 16 terminals or printers. Other models can attach up to 32 devices. The cluster control unit connects via a leased communication line to a host computer. (Courtesy of International Business Machines Corporation. Unauthorized use not permitted.)

intelligent, general-purpose computers used as terminals to completely unintelligent ("dumb") terminals. Some people classify terminals into three categories: *intelligent terminals, smart terminals,* and *dumb terminals.* However they are classified, today's terminals offer a wide range of capabilities.

Intelligent Terminals

The more intelligent a terminal is, the more able it is to participate in today's layered networks and in processing data. A fully intelligent terminal is in itself a general-purpose computer such as a personal computer. If a terminal can be programmed, some of the processing tasks can be performed locally on the terminal, in client-server mode, giving a degree of independence from the host. For many reasons, distributed processing is widely used in businesses. Computing tasks can be performed on the computer most suitable for the task. Screen formatting and data editing can be done by the intelligent terminal. However, where access to large databases or extensive computation is required, the power of the host processor can be brought into play. Using several computers also minimizes the risk of a massive computer failure, since users are not dependent on a single mainframe to do their processing.

When properly programmed, the intelligent terminal may be able to operate for long periods of time when there are failures in the data communications system or host computer. The terminal continues to operate without accessing the host and saves the results of its work. When the host computer becomes available, the terminal transmits the results of the processing it has performed.

Terminal intelligence is often present in less obvious ways. For example, a considerable amount of built-in intelligence is required for a supermarket terminal to read and interpret the bar code on a peanut butter jar passed through a laser beam at practically any angle or speed. Considerable intelligence also is required by bank or credit card terminals to read and interpret the magnetic stripe on a bank card, even though the stripe might have been damaged by abrasion from being carried in a person's wallet. The movement toward intelligent terminals is inevitable, depending primarily on their cost-effectiveness.

Smart Terminals

Smart terminals are not programmable, but they have memory that can be loaded with information. Their memory may be loaded by a transmission from a host computer, by keying data from an attached keyboard, or by reading it through some other attached device, such as a diskette reader.

One use for the smart terminal's memory is to store constant data, such as formats, that the operator uses repetitively. An order entry operator's terminal might be loaded with the format of the order form. This would save continually transmitting it from the host to the terminal each time the operator wanted to use the form. The operator would call up the blank format from the memory of the terminal to the display screen. The blanks in the format would be filled in with the data for the order. When the operator had checked the data, he or she would press the ENTER key. Usually only the data the operator entered, but not the order format, would be transmitted to the host, another saving of transmission time.

The smart terminal has a certain amount of independence from the host. The operator works with a format, completing information and making corrections until he or she is satisfied that the form is complete and correct. Only when the operator presses ENTER is there an interaction with the computer. Unlike the intelligent terminal, the smart terminal usually does not have the capability to save the data from an order if the communications line or host computer is down.

When a smart terminal is connected to a cluster control unit, some of its "intelligence" may be provided by the CCU. For example, the CCU might provide the storage for the formats either in its memory or on a disk.

Dumb Terminals

The advantages of unintelligent or "dumb" terminals are simplicity and low cost, but with today's sophisticated networks intelligence must be provided somewhere to allow dumb terminals to connect. Dumb terminals are typically totally dependent on a host computer for all processing capability and have either no storage or only limited, special-purpose storage for buffering and terminal control functions. Because of their low cost, however, dumb terminals are supported in most networks.

Because personal computers have become so ubiquitous and so inexpensive, there is little call for smart and dumb terminals anymore. Like cluster control units, there are still many in use, but few are manufactured or sold. To paraphrase an old song, anything a dumb or smart terminal can do, a PC can do better—and nearly as inexpensively.

WORKSTATION ERGONOMICS

In recent years, with the increased use of terminals in the workplace, a greater emphasis has been placed on workstation ergonomics, and much has been published about the total workstation environment for terminals. One meaning of the word *workstation* is the place where a person sits or stands to do work. It contains the working surface, terminal, chair, and any other equipment or supplies the person needs to do a job. It is the place where the computer meets the user. Having information about workstation design is useful for telecommunications people because they are often called on to advise others in the company about terminal use and environment. A drawing and some information about an ergonomically designed workstation are shown in Figure 2–6.

Figure 2–6
Ergonomically designed furniture allows for natural movement and allows workers to change position to prevent fatigue and stiffness.

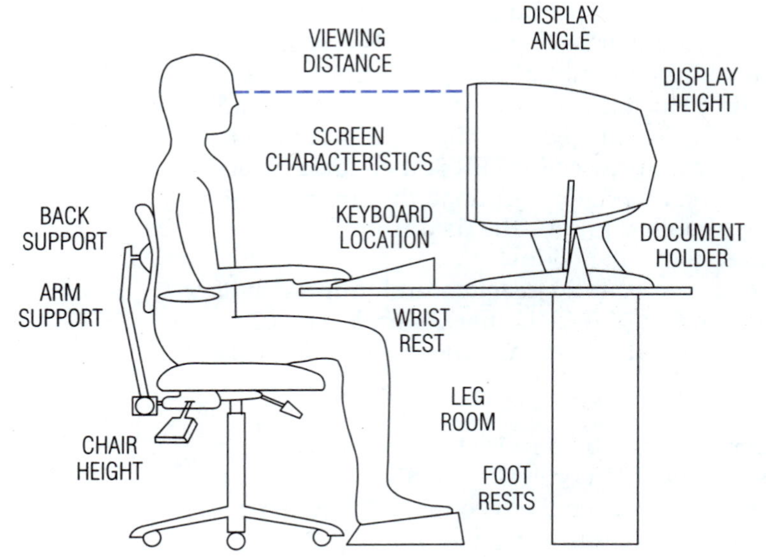

Considerations for Ergonomically Designed Workstations

1. The VDT screen should have a nonglare screen that can be tilted back 10 to 20 degrees.
2. The screen of the terminal should be about 18 inches from the operator's eyes.
3. The top of the screen should be no higher than eye level.
4. The chair should have a seat that adjusts up and down and a backrest that adjusts separately. When seated, the operator's feet should rest flat on the floor or on a footrest.
5. The keyboard should be attached to the rest of the terminal by a cable so it can be moved on the work surface. The keyboard should be positioned so that the operator's lower arms are parallel to the floor and the upper arms are perpendicular to it.
6. Nearby blinds should be closed and other sources of glare eliminated. Small adjustable task lights are usually preferable to overhead lights.

No matter how perfectly the workstation is set up, it is important to take a periodic break from concentrating on the VDT. There is a real incidence of headaches, fatigue, muscle aches, and temporary eyestrain resulting from prolonged use of VDTs under poor conditions. None of these problems are permanent, and they are minimized when VDT workstations, environments, and job structures are properly designed.

WORKSTATIONS FOR THE DISABLED

Telecommunications and computing are fields that disabled persons can actively participate in and contribute to with great success. Sometimes special adaptation must be made in order for a disabled person to access a workstation or other telecommunications device. Some people can't operate keyboards but can use a mouse. Displaying the letters and numbers of a keyboard on the screen and having the person select characters with the mouse is one solution that, while slow, may allow the disabled person to enter data. Voice entry, through voice recognition software, is another option that is applicable in some situations.

The key to finding a solution for a disabled person is ingenuity, creativity, and some assistance from others who have gone before. One source that provides a wealth of useful information is sponsored by the Assistive Technology Industry Association (ATIA) and is located on the Internet at www.atia.org. Searching the Internet and talking with occupational therapists and agencies that provide assistance to disabled people will locate many good ideas and other sources of information. People with small or large disabilities can clearly be productive users of telecommunications and computers.

THE VDT AND HEALTH CONCERNS

Much has been written about potential health hazards stemming from working with VDTs over long periods. The traditional questions are:

- Is there any radiation hazard in working with the VDT?
- Will it affect my eyesight?
- What is the most comfortable method of working with the VDT?
- How can I relieve the stress associated with constant use of a VDT?

Many health-related concerns about working with VDTs involve the radiation emitted from the display tube. Numerous studies by universities and government agencies worldwide have shown that the amount of radiation emitted from the terminal is well below established safety standards and, in most cases, is nearly undetectable. Other studies have shown no significant association between VDT use and vision defects or eye abnormalities.

This workstation is ergonomically designed to provide the operator with comfort, proper lighting, and functionality. (Courtesy of Steelcase)

TERMINAL SELECTION

When you select a terminal, it is important to identify the requirements of the applications for which the terminal will be used. The following questions can help you determine users' needs:

- Is a special application-oriented terminal required, or can a general-purpose terminal be used?
- Is hard copy required, or can a video display terminal be used?
- What types of operators will use the terminal? Will they be highly trained or novices who use the terminal only occasionally?
- Are the proposed terminals compatible with the existing computer?
- How much intelligence is required in the terminal?
- Is a personal computer required, or can a less intelligent, less expensive terminal be used?

Once these questions have been answered and the requirements determined, the next step is to compare alternative terminals from several vendors, looking at required and optional capabilities, vendor service and support, and cost. When all this information has been gathered, a selection can be made.

On a pragmatic basis, the type of terminal selected may be essentially predetermined by the type of computer to which it will be attached or by other terminals that the company has on hand. In many cases, a simple approach may be to assume that the terminal is going to be a standard PC, unless it is shown why some other type of terminal is required. PCs represent a good mix of capability and reliability. They are effective in most applications and are available today at a very low cost.

TERMINAL STANDARDIZATION AND TOTAL COST OF OWNERSHIP

The growth in the capability and complexity of personal computers has created a difficult situation for many corporations and other organizations. They find themselves with a variety of workstations that use different levels of technology, or even different technologies, and with users demanding to have the latest upgrades and features. Organizations can find themselves "chasing technology," trying to install every software release, and implementing every PC hardware advance in an effort to satisfy users.

Several research organizations, most notably the Gartner Group, have conducted research for many years on the *total cost of ownership* of personal computers in organizations. Their research tries to identify all of the costs associated with PC acquisition and usage during its lifetime. The most frequently published numbers from their studies show that a PC costs a company from $6,400 to over $13,000 during its lifetime. The actual hardware and software cost is only about 20 percent of the total. User operational costs, including learning to use the workstation, and training are about 46 percent, technical support costs are about 21 percent, and administrative costs about 13 percent. While these numbers are averages, and do not take into account the benefit that the organization receives because they have the workstations, the general conclusion is that these costs are too high.

total cost of ownership

The most significant opportunities to reduce the costs are in the areas of administration and support, including training. One way to reduce these costs is to have a workstation strategy, typically centralizing the management of the workstations and standardizing them. Companies that have developed aggressive workstation management programs have frequently standardized the hardware and software configurations of the workstations and established a policy to only upgrade or replace them periodically, typically every 3 or 4 years. For example, a company might move from a collection of workstations from a variety of vendors, which run various versions of software, to a standard configuration of two to four PC models, all from the same vendor and all running the same version of control software, such as Windows 98. Furthermore, these PCs would typically all have standard application software, such as the Microsoft Office suite of programs. Centralizing the decision making and standardizing the hardware and software results in less choice, but the organization benefits by being able to negotiate discounted bulk pricing for both the hardware and software. Users do not have to relearn software as often because software upgrades are installed infrequently. In these ways, the total cost of ownership of personal computers is significantly reduced.

Organizations that have adopted such programs are, in general, very satisfied with the results, and the users, after some initial complaining about losing the freedom to choose any hardware or software they want, usually agree that the standardization allows them to more easily exchange e-mail, data files, and other information with their coworkers, and is beneficial.

TYPICAL TERMINAL SCENARIO

This discussion is intended to give a practical example of how terminals are connected to networks, servers, and mainframe computers in typical businesses throughout the world. Although hundreds of options are available, certain configurations are more widespread than others.

The top part of Figure 2–7 shows personal computers connected to a local area network (LAN). LANs operate at very high transmission speeds, but for limited distances. Also connected to the LAN is a server that has a printer attached and which may be shared by all of the PCs when they need to print. The server may have a large disk to provide mass storage capacity for large, shared files. A mainframe computer may also be attached to the LAN to provide additional processing or storage capacity.

The bottom part of Figure 2–7 shows dumb terminals and PCs emulating dumb terminals connected to a mainframe through a cluster control unit. The IBM 3270 series of computers is normally connected this way. The IBM 3270 series is still in use because approximately 80 percent of the mainframe computers in use are made by IBM or are IBM compatible. The IBM 3270 series contains alphanumeric and APA graphics terminals, which can display data in monochrome or color. The terminals are attached to the cluster control unit by cable and the CCU is typically connected to the mainframe computer with a communications line. The CCU also has a printer attached, which, like the printer connected to the server in the first example, may be shared by all of the terminal users.

SUMMARY

A wide variety of terminals are available today with a range of capabilities and prices. For the standard office environment, personal computers are by far the most dominant because they have the capability to do processing on their own, as well as to share processing with a server or mainframe computer. Special purpose terminals are optimized for a particular application, and their special features provide productivity benefits to their users, typically in the form of faster, more efficient data entry. Ultimately, the selection of terminals needs to fit the needs of the application and users.

Figure 2–7
Typical ways that personal computers and terminals are connected in a business setting.

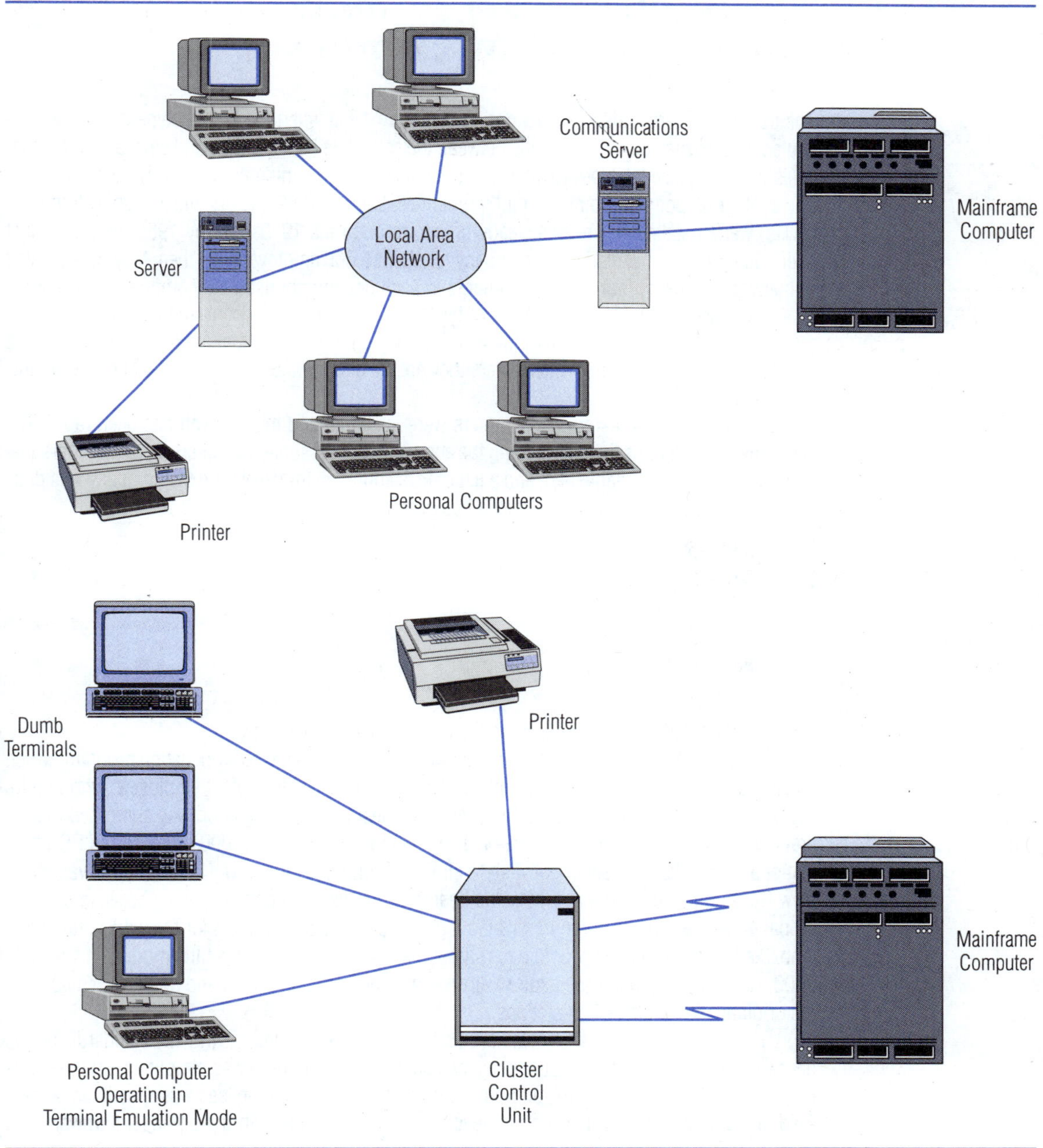

CASE STUDY

Evolution of Data Terminal Purchases at Dow Corning

The use of data terminals in Dow Corning started in 1953 when the first teletypewriters were installed for message communications between the corporate headquarters and several of the larger sales offices. These teletypewriters were not connected to a computer but simply connected with one another on point-to-point and multipoint lines. Early in 1969, the first video display terminals (VDTs) were installed. There was steady growth through the 1970s, but by 1980 there were just over 200 terminals installed in the company for about 5,000 employees. By then, they were located in many departments, but only a few people in each department used the computer applications. By 1989, there were over 3,000 VDTs, but by 1993 the number had decreased to around 2,000 as the number of personal computers increased. Today the only VDTs that are still in use are in the telecommunications control center, where they are used to monitor the status of certain communication circuits.

In 1983, the first personal computers were installed, and their growth has been rapid. The company began aggressively managing the acquisition of personal computers in 1984. A personal computer policy was established, and a list of PCs approved for use within the company was published. The growth in the number of PCs has been rapid.

1983—50
1987—800
1989—2,000
1993—4,600
1996—6,000
2000—11,000

Essentially all of them are connected to the telecommunications network.

In 1997, the last of the dumb terminals were replaced by a global workstation program, which placed standardized personal computers and software on the desks of all employees who require them for their jobs—virtually all employees. A request for price quotation was submitted to several PC vendors asking them to quote on a contract to supply nearly 8,000 standardized PC workstations with a standard set of software to all Dow Corning locations worldwide. After evaluation, Dow Corning determined that IBM could best meet the requirements, primarily because of IBM's global presence. Dow Corning negotiated a global 3-year lease contract for the workstations and embarked on an ambitious program to roll out the new workstations in a little more than 1 year. In 2000, when the original lease expired, up-to-date personal computers and software replaced all the original 1997 vintage workstations.

The company gained significant productivity benefits and cost savings by standardizing the hardware and software tools that employees use. Employee training was simplified, and the ability to share documents, graphs, and other information among employees was greatly enhanced. Also, the company found that it could leverage its negotiations with the potential hardware and

Dow Corning's torn tape message switching system was controlled from this location. Telex machines can be seen at the right. (Courtesy of Dow Corning Corporation)

A terminal user at Dow Corning is scheduling a meeting using one of the personal computers. (Courtesy of Dow Corning Corporation)

The personal computer is used in many Dow Corning departments for spreadsheets, word processing, and project management. (Courtesy of Dow Corning Corporation)

software suppliers because of the large quantity of hardware and software it acquired at one time, so there was a distinct financial advantage to the company as well.

A few other types of workstations are used in the manufacturing and research functions of the company, especially where they are connected to laboratory instruments or plant automation equipment. Dow Corning uses Compaq (formerly DEC), Sun, and IBM computers in its plants and laboratories. Interconnection of plant computers and communications equipment occurred as manufacturing and laboratory systems were integrated with traditional business applications in the early 1990s.

The use of facsimile (fax) machines is also quite extensive. Decisions about the acquisition of fax machines are made at the local departmental level; there is no central management. There are over 150 stand-alone facsimile machines used in the United States and more in the foreign locations. A few people also have fax modems in their personal computer, but the exact number is unknown. Users have found fax machines invaluable for rapidly exchanging printed documents that are not stored in a computer. Another large fax application has been the direct output of faxes from computer applications. One example is Material Safety Data Sheets, which contain safety information about Dow Corning's products. These sheets are distributed to anyone who requests them, and several thousand pages are automatically sent by fax each month. Another example is purchase orders to Midland-area vendors, which are sent directly by fax from the relevant business applications.

QUESTIONS

1. Dow Corning's global workstation program replaced all of the existing personal computers with new standard machines and software. How do you suppose employees, who in the past had been able to choose their own PC, reacted to this program?
2. Dow Corning has over 11,000 PCs for 9,000 employees. What are some situations where a Dow Corning employee might have more than one personal computer for use at work?
3. Identify some of the situations where non-standard PC workstations would still be appropriate.
4. Can you think of situations where Dow Corning might still need or want to retain some dumb terminals? What would be the benefits in doing so?

REVIEW QUESTIONS

1. Distinguish between data terminal equipment and data circuit-terminating equipment.
2. What are some desirable attributes of a terminal that will be used by the general public on an occasional basis?
3. How may the higher cost of an intelligent terminal be justified compared to a standard VDT?
4. What ergonomic factors must be considered when you select a terminal?
5. What are the advantages and disadvantages of a buffered terminal compared to one that is unbuffered?
6. Under what circumstances would an APA terminal be used?
7. Describe several methods of highlighting information displayed on a VDT.
8. What is the purpose of a function key on a terminal's keyboard?
9. Describe the factors to consider when you select a VDT.
10. For what applications is a mouse most useful?
11. How is remote job entry usually performed today?
12. Describe three levels of communication sophistication that may be employed when connecting a personal computer to a host computer.
13. Distinguish between the capabilities of facsimile machines classified as Group III and those classified as Group IV.
14. If a facsimile modem is to be installed in a personal computer, what other capabilities must the PC have to effectively use the facsimile capability?
15. If a typical facsimile requires 100 kilobytes on a hard disk, how many facsimile images can theoretically be stored on a 200 MB hard disk drive? Of course, in practice, the hard drive is not completely available for the user's data because much of the space is used to hold system and application software. On the personal computer you use, how many facsimile images could practically be stored?
16. In order to display an image that has been read into a computer from a facsimile machine, a(n) ______ VDT is needed.
17. List the primary purposes of the cluster control unit.
18. Distinguish among intelligent, smart, and dumb terminals.
19. What is client-server processing? What are its benefits?
20. What is a computer virus? How are they detected and corrected?
21. What are the advantages and disadvantages of VDTs that use LCD technology?
22. What is a network computer?
23. Explain the purpose of the file transfer protocol.
24. What is the difference between uploading and downloading?

25. Why are companies concerned about the total cost of ownership of their terminals, and especially their personal computers?

26. Identify several ways an organization can reduce the total cost of ownership of its PC workstations.

PROBLEMS AND PROJECTS

1. Visit a company that has a large number of terminals installed. Find out what portion of the terminals are "dumb," "smart," and "intelligent." Does the company make a strong distinction in usage between the different intelligence of its terminals? Do programmers design computer applications to take advantage of the capabilities of intelligent terminals? Does the company forecast that the number of intelligent terminals will grow in the future? If so, how fast? Will intelligent terminals ever totally replace dumb and smart terminals in the company?

2. Do you expect the use of terminals in most businesses to grow to the point where there is one terminal for every employee? What are some examples where this might not be the case? Can you think of a situation where there might be more than one terminal for every employee?

3. Vendors of color terminals claim that color improves the operator's productivity. How can a terminal improve productivity? What effect does color have? If color does, in fact, improve productivity, think of some applications where it would be especially useful.

4. Think of some applications that require a user to have a terminal that prints all of the interactions with a computer.

5. Visit a stockbroker and use one of the special "application-oriented" terminals to display current stock prices. How does the special design of the terminal make it easier to get the information? How much more difficult would it be to get stock prices if a general-purpose VDT were used instead? Talk to the broker and find out what other special capabilities the terminals have.

6. Do some research on the latest findings about the potential health hazards of radiation from VDTs.

Vocabulary

terminal
hardwired
data terminal equipment (DTE)
data circuit-terminating equipment (DCE)
dot matrix
unbuffered
buffered
buffer
video display terminal (VDT)
video display unit (VDU)
monitor
cathode ray tube terminal (CRT)
flat panel display
all-points-addressable (APA)
picture element (pixel, pel)
cursor
cursor control keys
intensifying
blink
reverse video
color
line-by-line mode
page mode
formatted mode
function keys
numeric keypad
mouse
trackball
joystick
touch sensitive
microcomputers
graphical user interface (GUI)
multitasking
terminal emulation program

uploading
downloading
file transfer protocol (FTP)
network computer
client-server computing
client
server
computer virus
workstation
computer-aided design (CAD)
computer-assisted drafting (CAD)
remote job entry (RJE)
facsimile (fax) machine
audio response unit
voice response unit
optical recognition
bar code reader
optical character recognition (OCR)
cluster control unit (CCU)
terminal control unit
hot key
multiple sessions
intelligent terminal
smart terminal
dumb terminal
total cost of ownership

References

Arar, Yardena. "Is an LCD Monitor in Your Future? Prices Are Shrinking, Screens Growing." *PC World* (March 1997): 72–74.

Brown, Bob. "Group IV Fax Grows Slowly but Steadily." *Network World* (August 7, 1989).

Chandler, Clay. "Japanese Bypass the PC On Their Way to the Web." *International Herald Tribune* (February 9, 2000).

Corson, Richard G. "VDTs—New Evidence Indicates Helpfulness over Harmfulness." *Data Management* (December 1986): 24.

Deixler, Lyle. "FAX Forges Ahead." *Teleconnect* (November 1996): 52–58.

Martin, James. *Design of Man-Computer Dialogues.* Englewood Cliffs, NJ: Prentice-Hall, 1973.

Sexton, Don. "Microsoft, Intel Boost Breed of 'Dumber' PCs." *The Japan Times* (March 14, 1997).

CHAPTER

3

Data Communications Applications

OBJECTIVES

After you complete your study of this chapter, you should be able to

- categorize telecommunications applications in several ways;
- describe in nontechnical terms how a telephone call is completed;
- explain how data applications evolved from early message switching applications;
- compare and contrast electronic mail to older messaging systems;
- describe several telecommunications applications, such as an airline reservation system and a supermarket checkout system;
- describe the fundamental operation of the Internet;
- discuss the special factors to consider when telecommunications applications are planned;
- explain the importance of planning for telecommunications system outages.

INTRODUCTION

This chapter looks at some practical uses (applications) of telecommunications in the business environment. The purposes of this chapter are

1. to give you a better feeling for the importance of telecommunications to business;
2. to give you some specific knowledge of telecommunications applications for reference as you learn the technical details later in the book;
3. to introduce some additional words and concepts and further build your telecommunications vocabulary;
4. to lay a practical foundation for the technical material in later chapters.

The applications described in this chapter and the next are all representative of layer 7, the application layer of the OSI model.

CATEGORIES OF APPLICATIONS

Human-Machine Interaction

Telecommunications applications can be categorized in many ways, as shown in Figure 3–1. One way is according to how people and machines

Figure 3–1
Several ways to categorize data communications applications.

Category	Example
Human-Machine Interaction	
Person-to-Person	Telephone call
	Electronic mail
Person-to-Machine	Database inquiry
	Transaction processing system
Machine-to-Person	Automated distribution of information from a computer system
Machine-to-Machine	Process monitoring and control systems
	Automated purchasing application to automated selling application
	File transfer between servers
Type of Information	
Voice	Telephone call
	Voice mail
Structured Data	Transaction processing system
Unstructured Data	Word processing
	Text manipulation and retrieval
Image	Video conferencing
	Security monitoring
	Distribution of files containing pictures or movies
Timeliness	
Online, Realtime	Transaction processing system
	Interactive messaging system
Store-and-Forward	Voice mail
	Some e-mail systems
	Some fax systems

person-to-person

interact with each other in the process of communicating. A "person-to-person" communication or application occurs when one person communicates directly with another. Machines may be used in the middle of the conversation, but their presence is transparent to the people. This type of communication is typified by the standard telephone conversation or e-mail. The machine in this example is the telephone company's central office computer or the computer that manages the e-mail system. Its role is transparent to the two people conversing.

person-to-machine
machine-to-person

Person-to-machine and machine-to-person applications usually go hand in hand. They are typified by the user of a data terminal who carries on a dialogue with a computer. First the person, through the terminal, sends a message or command to the computer. Then the computer sends a response to the user. This interchange normally continues until the user gets the result. Examples of this application are the airline reservation agent checking seat inventory on the computer, an ATM terminal user making a deposit or withdrawal, and a warehouse employee determining the location of certain merchandise in the warehouse.

machine-to-machine

A third type of communication, the machine-to-machine interaction, occurs when one machine automatically communicates with another, without human intervention. It is typified by the automated instrumentation found in a modern chemical or manufacturing plant. Intelligent, microprocessor-based instruments gather data about manufacturing processes and relay the data via a telecommunications line to a control computer. Here the data is analyzed, and any appropriate action is taken. No person is directly involved in the communication between the instrument and the control computer, although results of data collected over time or from several instruments may be analyzed and displayed for operator interpretation. Companies such as Monsanto and Ford have thousands of these communicating instruments installed in their plants around the world.

Another type of machine-to-machine application occurs when an automated purchasing application running on one company's server communicates, typically through the Internet, to an automated selling application running on another company's server. The purchasing application might search on the Internet for a product the company wants to buy, checking several sources, looking for information about specifications, quality, and of course price. In a fully automated scenario, the purchasing application would have the authority to select the product and initiate the buying process without human intervention. A less sophisticated application, but one that is more typical of the applications that exist today, would require human intervention before the purchase and sale are consummated. You can envision the day in the not too distant future, however, when the purchase of certain products will occur totally under computer control without human intervention.

One other type of machine-to-machine application is the file transfer process that takes place frequently between computers connected to a network. The file may contain information, a picture, or a computer program that will be useful to the recipient. File transfer is a very common application on the Internet.

Type of Information

Another way to categorize telecommunications applications is by the type of information carried. The telephone call is the simplest example of a "voice" application. "Data" applications are often grouped according to whether the data is "structured" into records and fields in typical data processing fashion or "unstructured" text such as is found in word processing or text manipulation. Applications that transmit "images" can be divided into those that transmit static images, such as facsimile and freeze-frame television, or dynamic images, such as normal, full-motion television.

Timeliness

A third way to categorize telecommunications applications is by the timeliness of the transmission and reception. *Online, realtime* applications, such as interactive messaging or inquiry-response, require that the data

online, realtime

or information be delivered virtually instantaneously. Airline reservation systems certainly fit in this category.

store-and-forward

In *store-and-forward* applications the input is transmitted, usually to a computer, where it is stored, and then later delivered to the recipient. Voice mail applications work this way, as do many electronic mail applications. There are also some fax services that work on a store-and-forward basis. Faxes are sent to a computer, which stores them until the evening or nighttime hours when telephone rates drop. Then the faxes are sent, taking advantage of the lower rates for the call. Of course this approach eliminates the realtime element of fax transmission, but for many types of faxes, such as those being sent overseas, the store-and-forward approach is perfectly acceptable and more cost effective.

batch

Batch applications are usually thought of as computer applications that don't require telecommunications. In some cases this is true, but in many batch applications, the data is collected via a telecommunications system before it is processed by the batch computer programs. One method of collecting the data is to have it entered through VDTs or other workstations, one record at a time. Another method is to have the data collected into a batch and then transmitted to the computer as a unit. This method is called *remote batch* or *remote job entry (RJE)*. The name comes from the fact that frequently the data is prefaced by control statements that instruct the computer to execute a certain program or job as soon as the data is received. In this type of application, the results of the computer processing are frequently returned to the terminal that submitted the data. When the terminal is located off-site from the computer, it is probably connected to the computer by a communication line. Hence, even batch applications may use telecommunications.

With virtually any method of categorization, there is overlap. Most applications have elements from several of the categories. For example, the airline reservation system discussed in Chapter 1 has an element of person-to-person communication between the person wanting to travel and the airline reservation agent. There is also an element of person-to-machine application between the reservation agent and the computer. Both of those elements occur in realtime. Since the data terminal is connected to the computer, it is *online*. If the reservation agent instructs the computer to print a ticket for the traveler at the airport on the day of departure, the computer *stores* the data until the day of departure, when it is *forwarded* to the airport and printed on a ticket form.

DATA APPLICATION EVOLUTION

Before we take a more detailed look at typical data applications that use telecommunications, let's look at how these applications have evolved. The earliest type of telecommunications equipment (other than smoke signals and drums) that did not use voice was the telegraph. Telegraphs sent a message from one person, group, or location to another. Business use of the telegraph evolved quickly. Many companies required rapid communication between their staff at widely separated locations. Originally, companies employed telegraph operators to send the messages using Morse code. Then *teletypewriters* came into widespread use. Remembering the definition of *tele* as distant, we can think of the teletypewriter as a device on which a person types a message; it prints on a similar machine at a distant location.

teletypewriter

Of course, teletypewriters were connected to each other with telecommunications lines, and this application became known as *message switching*. It was one of the first applications of data communications, and conceptually it is still widely used today, though it is now usually called electronic mail.

Message Switching

Figure 3–2 shows the way a company might have set up its telecommunications network for message switching during the 1950s. The company headquarters are in Chicago, and branch offices are in Detroit, New York, and Washington. A telecommunications line connects each of the outlying locations with company headquarters. This type of connection is called a *point-to-point line*. The line runs from one point to another. In the Chicago office, there would be three teletypewriter machines—one connected to each of the three lines. If a person in the Chicago office wanted

point-to-point line

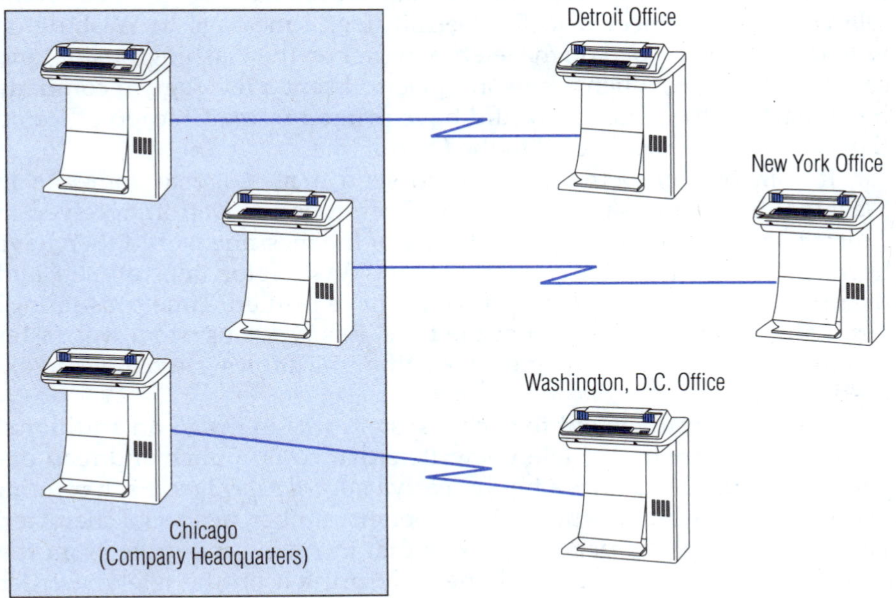

Figure 3–2
A simple network with point-to-point lines connecting offices in Detroit, New York, and Washington, D.C., with company headquarters in Chicago.

An older style teletypewriter. The paper tape punching mechanism is at the center of the machine inside the glass door. The paper tape reader is on the flat surface at the left side of the machine below the two black buttons. (Courtesy of Post Street Archives, The Dow Chemical Company)

to send a message to Detroit, the message would have been typed on the teletypewriter connected to the Detroit line, a message to Washington would have been typed on the teletypewriter on the Washington line, and so on. Conversely, when a person in Detroit sent a message to company headquarters, the message would have printed in the Chicago office on the teletypewriter connected to the Detroit line.

If someone in Detroit wanted to send a message to someone in Washington, the message would have been typed in Detroit, received in Chicago, and printed. The printed copy of the message would then have been taken to the machine connected to the Washington line, retyped, and then sent to Washington where it would have printed. Time consuming? Yes. Labor intensive? Yes, yet at the time, this type of system was faster and more effective than any message communication system that had existed before.

punched paper tape

The first improvement to such a system was to install an additional piece of hardware on the teletypewriters that could punch and read paper tape. Figure 3–3 shows a typical early *punched paper tape.* Each column of holes across the tape represents one letter, number, or special character. The advantage of the paper tape was that incoming messages from the outlying offices could be simultaneously printed on the teletypewriter and punched into the paper tape. If the message was to be forwarded to

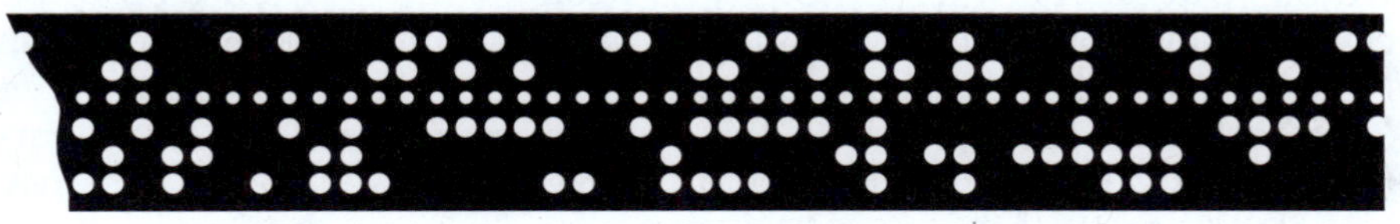

Figure 3–3
Five-level, Baudot coded paper tape from a teletypewriter.

Figure 3–4
The message switching network with offices in New York and Boston sharing a multipoint line.

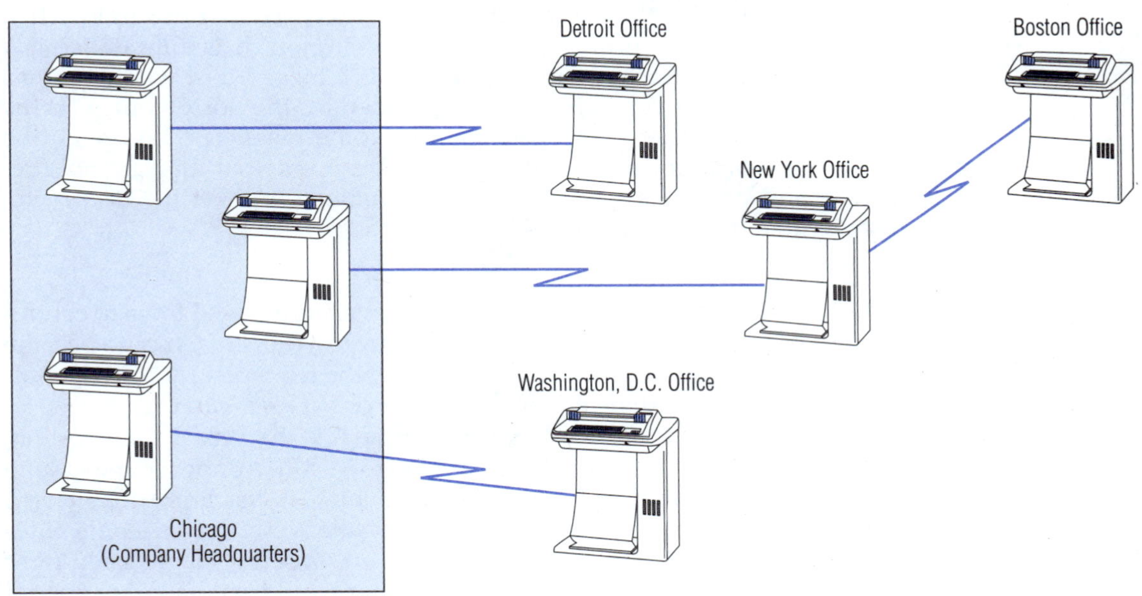

another location, the paper tape could be torn off one machine and read into another machine to be sent to the destination. This eliminated the need to retype the message. This type of operation became known as a *torn tape message system.* In large companies, the *message center* became a large noisy room filled with dozens of machines and many people. Racks were often needed to hold the tapes containing incoming messages that had not yet been forwarded to their destinations. The whole system took on a store-and-forward connotation. Although outmoded by today's standards, torn tape message switching systems vastly improved the efficiency of the message center by eliminating the need to retype all of the messages that were to be relayed.

Getting back to our example, Figure 3–4 shows that the company has grown and opened a new office in Boston. If the network were to expand as it had in the past, an additional point-to-point telecommunications line would be added between Chicago and Boston. However, since Boston is close to New York, it is reasonable to consider running a new line from New York to Boston and having the two locations share the line between New York and Chicago. Indeed, this was the economical thing to do, particularly if the line between Chicago and New York was not always busy and could handle the additional messages to and from the Boston office. This new type of line, which is shared between several terminals, is called a *multipoint line.*

multipoint line

Complications arise, however, when multipoint lines are used. On a point-to-point line using teletypewriters, when a message is typed at one end, it is printed at the other end as it is being typed. For example, when a message is typed on a machine in Washington, it is simultaneously printed and/or punched on the machine in Chicago. But what happens when a message is typed in Chicago destined for the Boston office? Is the message also printed in New York? For some messages, this might be okay, but clearly for many messages it is desirable that they are only received and printed at the intended destination. To meet the need, teletypewriters had to have additional sophistication.

Polling Additional components in teletypewriters allowed them to control the use of the line. In our example, the teletypewriters in Chicago became the *control* or *master station* on each line, and the teletypewriters in the outlying offices assumed the role of *subordinate* or *slave stations.* Chicago's teletypewriter sent out special characters on the line that asked the question, "New York, do you have a message to send to me?" If a punched paper tape was in the transmitter of the New York machine, it was immediately sent on the line to Chicago. If no tape was ready, the New York machine automatically responded with a special character that said, "No, nothing right now." In that case, the Chicago teletypewriter would send another special character sequence that said, "Boston, do you have a message to send to me?" If Boston had a message to send, it would send it; if not, it would respond with the special character saying, "No, nothing right now."

polling

This technique, in which a control terminal asks each slave terminal if it has a message to send, is called *polling*. Having a control terminal poll terminals on the line ensures that two terminals do not try to transmit a message at the same time. This occurrence, which some types of telecommunications systems allow, is called a *collision.* It invariably causes both messages to be garbled and unintelligible at the receiving end. When a collision or garbling is detected, the message must be retransmitted. Detecting a garbled message is usually not too difficult when textual messages are sent between two people. The person looking at a garbled message can usually figure out what a garbled message like this one says:

> I'm cxming tw Lrs Anceles on Moy 17sh. Arriving Nztqwest, flijt 762. P-eabe pick me up ut thx azrport.

An early message switching center in a large industrial company. Short sections of punched paper tape can be seen in the rack in the foreground. Storage bins of punched tape are on the back wall. (Courtesy of Post Street Archives, The Dow Chemical Company)

Obviously, the problem is more difficult when the message contains numerical data. One hopes that the digits in the date and flight number in the above message were received correctly, but asking the sender to retransmit the message would be prudent.

The primary disadvantage of a system that uses polling is the additional number of characters that have to be transmitted (the polling characters) on the line. Another disadvantage is that the slave terminals must wait until they are polled before they send data. If there are a large number of terminals on the line, the delay can be long.

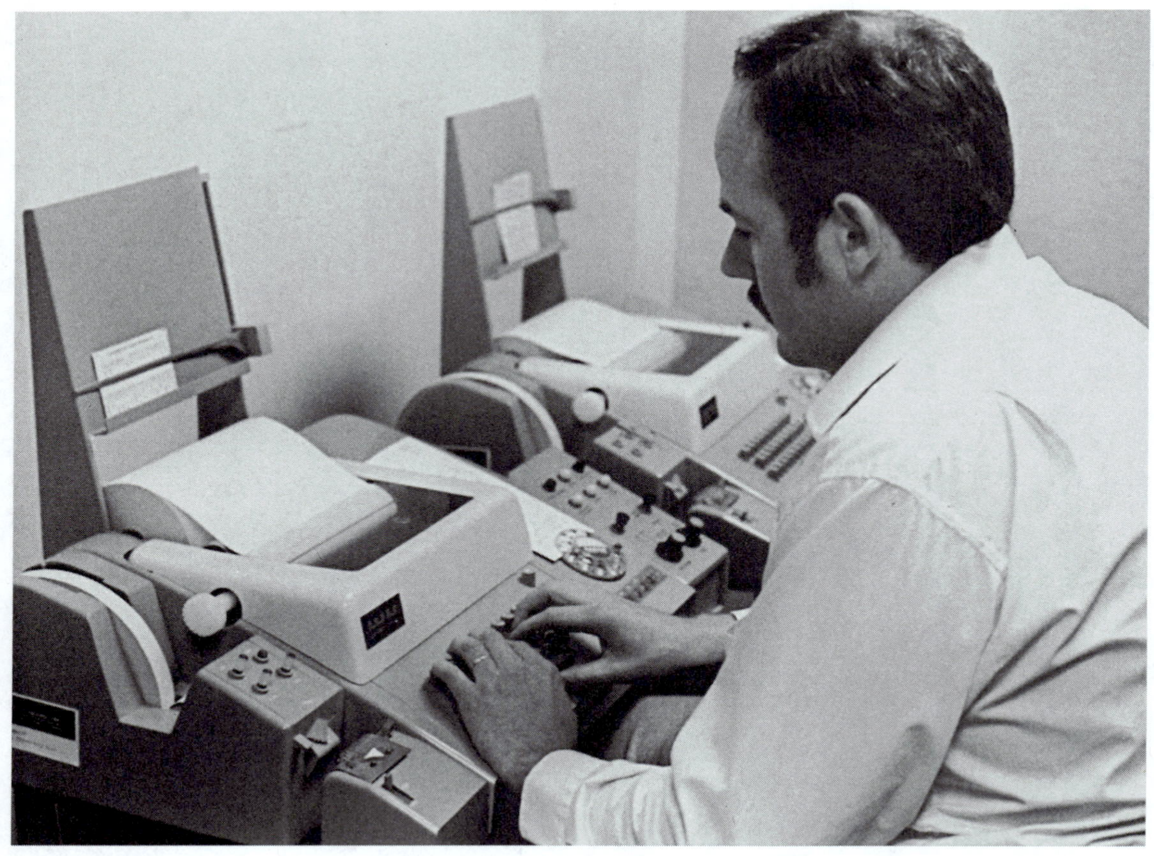

These telex machines are a particular type of teletypewriter, and are connected to the public telex network for the exchange of typed messages. The telex network is being rapidly replaced by more up-to-date electronic mail systems in most countries. (Courtesy of Dow Corning Corporation)

addressing

Addressing A complementary line control technique that evolved at the same time as polling is called *addressing*. When the control terminal has a message to send to one of the subordinate terminals, it first sends special control characters, called *addressing characters*, on the line. The addressing characters are recognized only by the terminal that has the specified address. To that terminal, the addressing characters say in effect, "Slave terminal, I have a message for you. Are you ready to receive it?" The addressing characters also tell all other terminals on the line that the following message is not for them and that they should not print it. If the slave terminal is ready, it responds with a character that says, "Ready to receive," and the control terminal immediately sends the message. After the message is sent, the control terminal either addresses another terminal (if it has more messages to send) or resumes polling the slave terminals to solicit messages from them.

Addressing has the added benefit of preventing the transmission of messages to a terminal that is not turned on, is out of paper, or is otherwise not ready. If a message is sent to a terminal that is not ready to receive, the message usually is lost. Assuming there is a way of detecting when messages have been lost and that the originals have been saved by the sending terminal, they would have to be retransmitted later. If the slave terminal is not ready when it is addressed, it simply does not respond, and the control terminal knows not to send the message.

> The control station *polls* the *subordinate* stations, asking them if they have messages to *send.*
> The control station *addresses* a *subordinate* station, asking if it is ready to *receive* a message.

The complementary techniques of polling and addressing are a simple form of line *protocol,* rules under which the line operates. Most telecommunications systems today use some sort of protocol to control the lines.

protocol

The Evolution to Computers

Soon after businesses started using computers, hardware was developed that allowed telecommunications lines to be connected to the computer. With special programming, data could be read from the line or sent out on the line. It became obvious that message switching was an ideal application for the computer. It could perform all of the functions of the control terminal and, because of its speed, could handle many lines simultaneously. All that was needed was to connect the telecommunications lines to the computer, as illustrated in Figure 3–5.

With proper programming, the computer could read a message from one line and send it out on another line without human intervention. In addition, as computer programming grew in sophistication, computer-controlled message switching systems provided added features, such as adding the time and date to each message, collecting statistics about the number of messages sent and received, logging all messages, and storing messages for later retrieval or retransmission.

Inquiry-Response

Soon there came the realization that a message could be sent to the computer itself (or, more specifically, to a program running in the computer). A very simple example is a coded message sent to the computer asking it to send back the current time. A more useful example is a coded message asking the computer program to look for certain data in a computer file, format it, and send it back to the requestor. This was the beginning of computerized inquiry systems. Figures 3–6 and 3–7 show two examples of simple inquiries to the computer and the responses the computer might generate.

Figure 3–5
The control terminals on each line of the message switching network have been replaced by a computer.

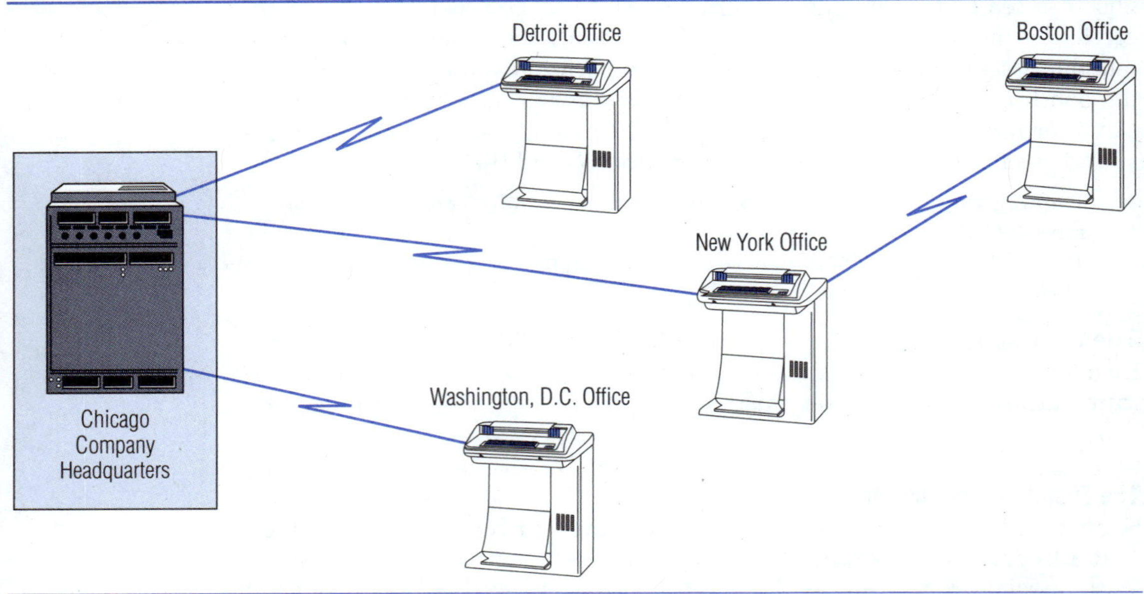

Figure 3–6
An example of a simple inquiry to a computer system and the response from the computer.

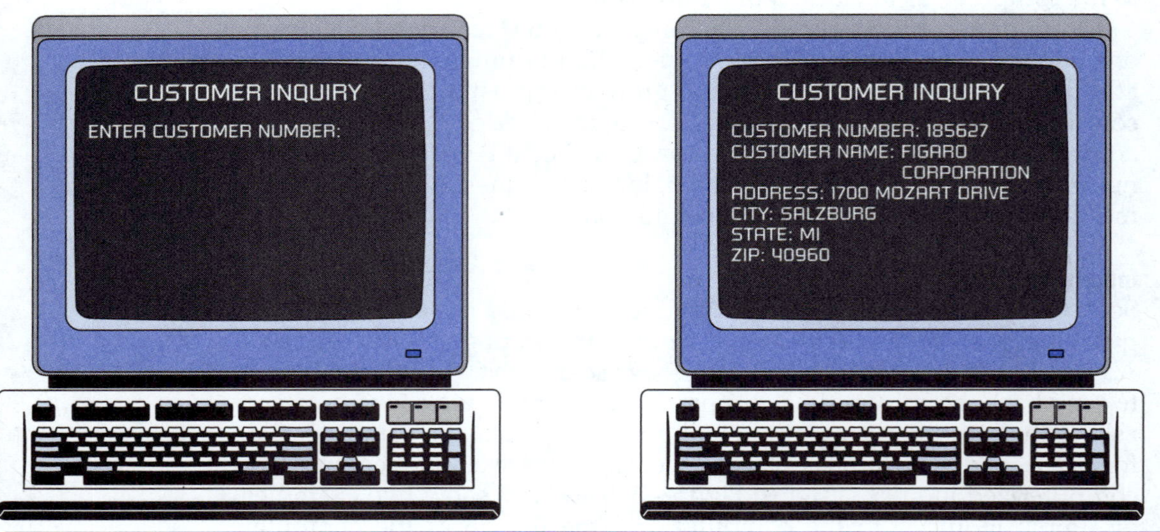

File Updating

From simple inquiries and responses, it is easy to imagine the evolution to more elaborate computer programming in which data is sent to the computer and checked, and ultimately a computer file is updated. Finally, combining a series of inquiries, responses, and file updates gives us the foundation for many modern online computer-based processing systems, such as airline reservation, customer order entry, and inventory applications. Applications of this type, marrying telecommunications and computer technology, were first developed in the late 1950s but did not really come into widespread use until the late 1960s. Today they are common in almost every industry.

Timesharing

Parallel to the development of online applications for business transaction processing, such as those mentioned here, computer software (control programs) was developed to control teletypewriter terminals used for relatively unstructured activities, such as writing programs, executing existing programs, or playing games. This was handled by a process commonly called *timesharing* that first came into its own in colleges and universities for educational purposes, where there were large computers that could handle multiple applications for multiple uses. One student might

Figure 3–7
Another simple inquiry and the computer's response.

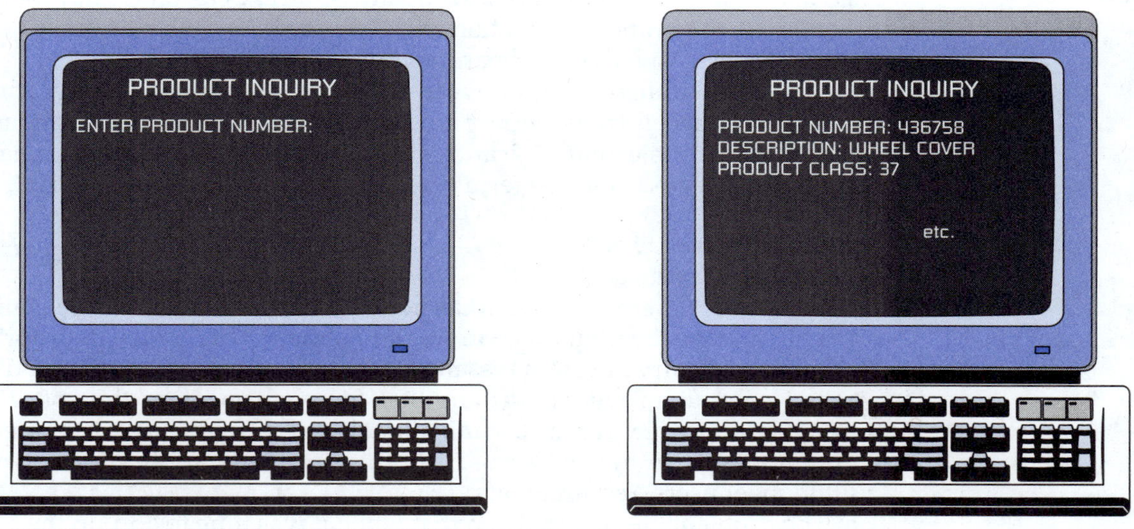

run a program for an economics class while another student wrote a program for a FORTRAN class while a third student wrote a program to solve a mathematics problem.

Transaction Processing Systems

By way of contrast, *transaction processing systems* are generally characterized as those in which the users use prewritten programs to perform business transactions, generally of a somewhat repetitive nature. Typical examples are the airline reservation process, an order entry application, or an online inventory application.

similarities between processing systems

In point of fact, timesharing and transaction processing systems had more similarities than differences. Both share the time of a computer among many users. Furthermore, it is entirely possible that a university system designed primarily for student use might also be used by administrative staff to update student grade records or tuition payments—that is, for transaction processing as well. Similarly, the computer in a business that primarily handles the company's accounting, inventory, and other business transactions might also be used by the scientists in the research department or programmers in the data processing department for data analysis or programming—typical timesharing tasks.

From the standpoint of the computer and telecommunications requirements, the two types of systems had many similar elements and a number of different requirements as well. The workload on a timesharing system was relatively less structured, less defined, and less predictable than the workload on a commercial business transaction processing system. Generally, the workload on transaction processing systems is somehow related to the business volume of the company. As airline customers buy more tickets, more reservation transactions are generated. As bank customers use ATMs more extensively, more financial transactions are generated.

Whereas the distinction between the types of workloads led to the distinction between transaction processing and timesharing systems in the early days of telecommunications and computing, the distinction has largely disappeared, and the term *timesharing* is not often used today.

Distributed Processing and Client-Server Computing

For many years there has been a desire to be able to have multiple computers in an organization that can work together as one when appropriate. For some companies, it makes more sense to have departmental or divisional computers with programs that focus on meeting the specific needs of the people in that organizational unit. Minicomputers gained wide popularity in the 1970s to satisfy this need, and applications were built to meet users' requirements.

The problem has always been that when it was time to add up the total results of the company and get a composite picture of sales, financial,

A bank customer uses an ATM. Some ATMs are designed to be installed inside a building, while others are relatively weatherproof and can be installed outside in a less protected environment. (Courtesy of NCR Corporation)

or production operations, it was very difficult to pull the data together because the applications running on the minicomputers were usually designed and programmed differently, and the computers themselves may have even been incompatible. Trying to link the computers with telecommunications was difficult and, even if they were linked, adding up the data was sometimes even harder or impossible.

distributed processing

In the late 1970s and early 1980s, the concept of *distributed processing* was introduced. The idea was that applications would be designed as an integrated whole, but in such a way that they could execute on multiple computers, which could of course be located in different parts of the company. Vendors introduced new minicomputers that were designed to be connected with a host computer and to share the workload with it. It was much easier to connect the computers and get them to communicate. The problem was that the software capabilities of the day just didn't measure up to the complexity of the work.

Designing applications that execute in a coordinated way on multiple computers and share data is a complicated task. There were no guidelines for how it should be done, little experience among the people who were trying to do it, and the software tools with which to implement the distributed systems were weak. Few distributed applications were successful. The problem was not with the concept of distributed processing, but with the lack of experience of the applications designers, the lack of adequate software tools, and sometimes the lack of adequate computer power on the remote (distributed) computers. It may have been a good idea, but its time had just not arrived.

In the 1980s, technology kept marching ahead: Computer hardware got faster, personal computers became widely used, software tools improved, communications capabilities became easier to implement and use, and applications and software designers became more sophisticated.

client-server computing

In the early 1990s, a new term began to be heard in the computer-communications industry—*client-server computing*. The concept of client-server is that some computers, typically personal computers, are programmed to meet the exact needs of their users, whereas other computers are programmed primarily to store data and perform general functions for a wide group of people. The specialized computers and their users are the *clients*. The generalized, database computers are the *servers*. The two are linked together with telecommunications in a way that makes telecommunications essentially invisible.

client server

As a very simple example, imagine your personal computer being online to a larger computer that is a larger PC, a server, or a mainframe—you don't really care, and you may not even know. You need two years of sales history to prepare a special sales analysis for your boss. You have a statistics software package on your PC that can do the analysis, but the sales data is on the larger computer. With appropriate client-server software, you would simply write your analysis program—using the statistics package—and give a command that in effect says, "Use the last 2 years of sales history. I don't know where it is stored. Please find it." The client-server software would consult tables and directories, and locate the data, which in this case happens to be on the server computer to which you are attached. It gives your analysis program access to the data as though it were on the hard disk of your personal computer.

That's a simple example of how client-server computing works. Obviously it requires very sophisticated database management software, including a directory telling where data is located, and telecommunications software that is transparent to the user (client). Much more complex uses are in use today. Suppose the data is stored on several computers and

Figure 3–8
A small local area network (LAN).

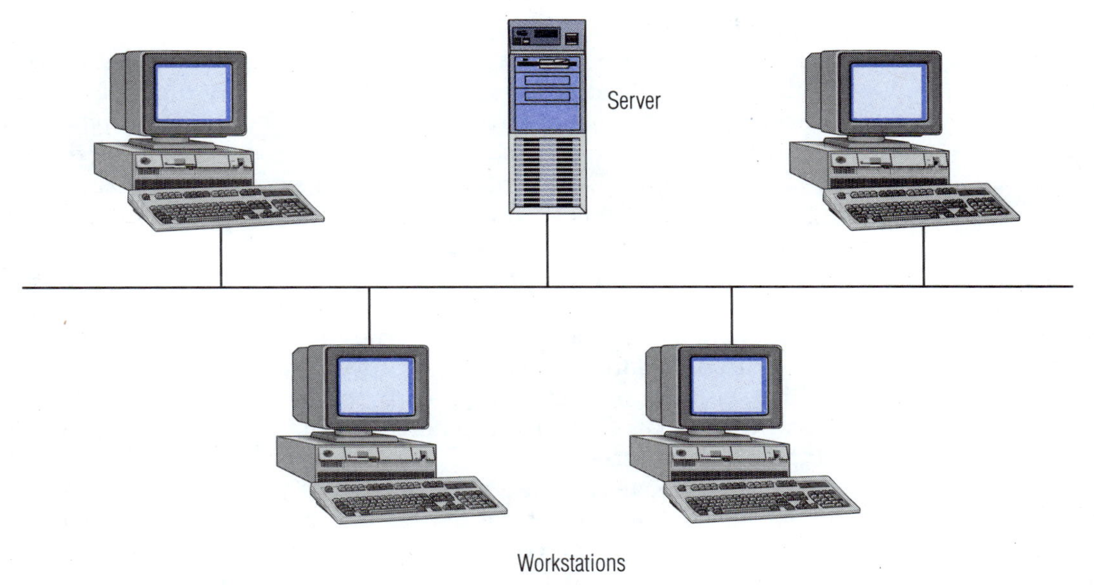

has to be brought together; suppose there are thousands of clients accessing the data on hundreds of servers, all at the same time; suppose the data includes sound and video as well as traditional structured data.

Today client-server systems are most commonly found in companies that have several PC workstations connected together on a *local area network (LAN)*. A LAN frequently has one or more servers that handle the majority of the processing and database access. LANs use cable or a wireless technology to connect the workstations and servers, but all of them must be within a relatively small area, usually no more than 1,000 feet apart. That distance, however, is sufficient for most offices, laboratories and other workplaces, so LANs are very widely used and popular. Figure 3–8 is an illustration of a small LAN with a single server.

LAN

Client-server software is in widespread use today and software vendors and individual companies have built many client-server applications. The technology continues to evolve in several directions. Tools are becoming available to let client-server applications support multimedia applications that incorporate audio and video images. Also, the development tools used to write client-server programs and test them have become very sophisticated, allowing programmers to develop applications more quickly and with fewer bugs. As the applications become more sophisticated, and especially if they include audio or video components, they need increasingly high-speed telecommunications lines to provide adequate response time.

Types of Computers

Several types of computers have been mentioned so far, and it is appropriate to clarify the distinctions between them. You are probably most familiar with *personal computers (PCs)* sometimes called *microcomputers*. PCs normally have between one and four microprocessors, including the main processor, such as an Intel Pentium chip, and several specialized processors to handle functions such as graphics processing. *Minicomputers* are higher-end computers that have dozens of processors to manage larger databases and more intense processing than a PC could accommodate. An example of a minicomputer is IBM's AS-400. A *mainframe computer* is a very high-end, expensive machine that typically has hundreds of processors. They are used by large companies or government agencies that have a very high volume of transactions or other work to process. IBM and Compaq, through its Digital Equipment Corporation (DEC) division make this type of computer.

scalability

Any of the above computers can be used as a server depending on the volume of work the computer is expected to process. Frequently organizations will install a small computer as a server and then upgrade it to a larger size as the workload grows. The term *scalability* is used to describe the attribute of being able to upgrade in a compatible way without having to change software or reorganize data. Organizations want to ensure that whatever server they install is scalable and can be easily upgraded when necessary.

TYPICAL APPLICATIONS OF DATA COMMUNICATIONS

Now that you've seen the differences between processing methods and read a bit of history about how telecommunications and computer processing have merged, it's time to explore several applications that make extensive use of data communications. The applications are grouped according to the primary type of information they process.

Structured Data Applications

automatic call distribution

Airline Reservation System With your new knowledge of the way in which data applications have evolved, look again at the airline reservation and ATM applications that were presented in Chapter 1. Figure 3–9 shows an expanded view of the airline reservation application. Multiple travelers can call multiple reservation agents, each using a terminal connected to the central computer. Between the callers and reservation agents is a new piece of hardware, an *automatic call distribution (ACD) unit*. The ACD unit

Figure 3–9
The telecommunications of an airline reservation system.

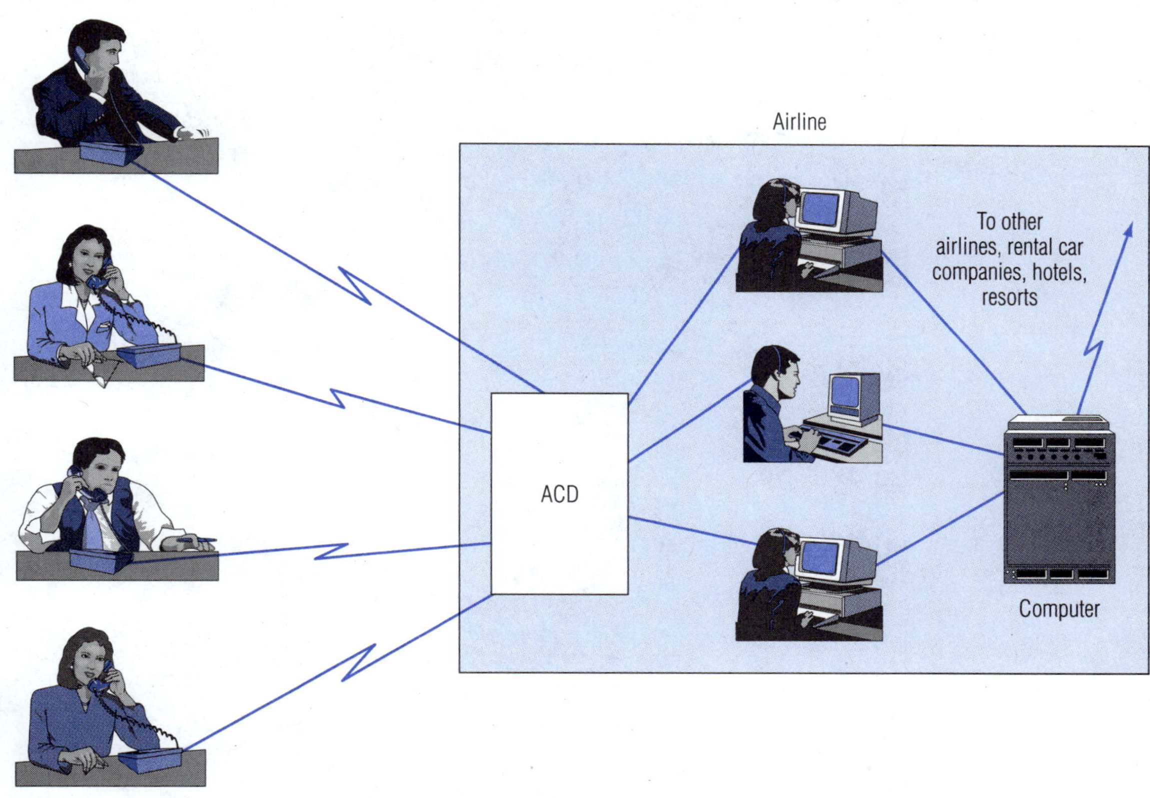

is an adjunct to the telephone system in the airline office. Its purpose is to route the next incoming call to the next available reservation agent based on various criteria, such as the longest wait time, location of caller, or, in slack times, to the agent who has been idle the longest. If all reservation agents are busy, the ACD unit can play a voice recording to the caller stating that the next available reservation agent will serve him or her as quickly as possible. Most of us have encountered ACD units and their "all agents are busy" messages when we have called reservation lines, mail order companies, or software technical support desks!

ACD units work well in any situation where multiple callers must be routed to multiple employees who handle the calls sequentially. Examples include other types of reservation systems, such as rental car companies; customer service lines at utility or manufacturing companies; and companies that have a large number of customers calling to place orders for merchandise, such as catalog sales or toll-free order centers.

These airline reservation agents are using a wide array of telecommunications and computer equipment to service their customers. (Courtesy of American Airlines.)

The data portion of this application has multiple terminals connected to the central computer of the airline. Also, the airline's computer is connected via a telecommunications line to the computers of other airlines. In this way, reservation agents from United Airlines can make reservations on the flights of American Airlines or any other airline whose computer is connected to the network. All of the airlines in the world, except the very smallest, have interconnected their telecommunications net-

A TWA 747 passenger plane. (Courtesy of AP/Wide World Photos.)

works and computers so that travelers can call one airline and make all of the reservations for a trip, even though several airlines may provide the transportation. Furthermore, the computers of the rental car companies and many hotels and resorts also are connected to the same network so that all of the reservations for an entire trip can be made with one telephone call.

American Airlines's Sabre system and United Airlines's Apollo reservation system have been significantly enhanced with additional computer programming. Both airlines have actively sold the right to access the systems to travel agencies and large corporations whose employees travel extensively. The services these systems offer are extensive and go far beyond making airline reservations. Hotel accommodations and theater tickets can be ordered in addition to transportation. The revenue generated by the reservation systems has become a substantial part of the total income of the airlines, sometimes exceeding the amount of revenue generated by the airplane flights themselves.

An airline reservation system is a high-volume transaction processing system that must provide fast response time to the reservation agents. Reservation systems are critical to airline operations, and the airlines spend a great deal of money to ensure that their computer system will always be available by having backup computers ready to take over instantly if a primary computer fails.

In 1985, Delta Airlines had over 4,000 voice communication lines and 18 reservation centers throughout the United States. Delta had 66 data communications lines and handled 340 to 350 transactions per second at peak times. Over 23,000 terminals were connected to the Delta data network—many of these located at the 2,800 travel agencies that were online to Delta. The response time goal was 3 seconds or less 95 percent of the time. While this is an old example, it is still valid for illustrating the high volumes that an active online system needs to be prepared to deal with. And imagine what the transaction volumes must be today, if Delta airlines was experiencing these volumes 15 years ago!

Cathay Pacific Airlines, the flagship carrier of Hong Kong, made a decision to centralize all of its reservation agents in Australia. After looking at all of the factors, the airline concluded that it could provide better customer service at a lower cost by handling reservations from one location, and Australia won the competition. The traditional airline approach of having potential passengers dial a local telephone number regardless of where they are located is complicated by the huge geography of Asia. Long distance telephone lines from each country in Asia tie to the hub in Australia—and the distances are very long! Another complication was language, since customers expected to be able to make their reservations in their native language, and Asia has at least eight to ten major languages. The consolidation of their reservation system was an ambitious undertaking for Cathay Pacific, but one that had significant benefits to the company.

In addition to reservation systems, airlines also operate other online systems for sending administrative messages, tracing baggage, scheduling airplane crews, and scheduling airplane maintenance. A typical 747 flight may involve more than 29,000 transactions, of which 27,000 concern passengers. With such systems, airlines are some of the most advanced, sophisticated users of voice and data telecommunications.

Automatic Teller Machine Figure 3–10 shows an ATM network in which multiple ATMs are connected to computers and several computers are connected together. Networks interconnecting the ATM systems of several banks are common throughout the world. Typically, each branch of a bank has at least one ATM, but in addition, banks may place ATMs in local shopping centers, train stations, or even large business establishments. Banks that have historically been competitors in a local area or region are now cooperating with one another, at least to the extent of interconnecting their ATM networks.

Figure 3–10 shows that any ATM can make a transaction with any bank on the network. It is possible to walk up to a single ATM and withdraw money from an account at one bank and then put the cash back in the machine for deposit in an account at another bank.

Since ATM networks are expensive to operate, service charges are often levied for certain types of transactions to help defray the costs of the

Figure 3–10
A network of ATMs from several banks.

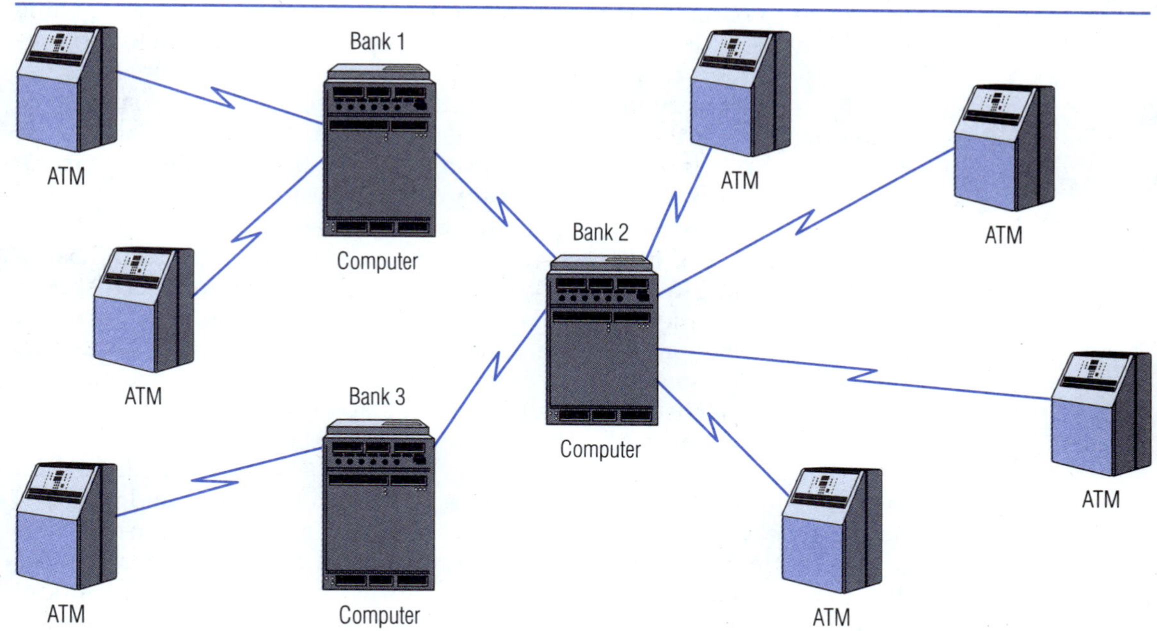

network. Customers whose transactions require access to another bank's computer or network are especially likely to be charged. In Japan, service charges also are assessed for transactions that occur outside of the bank's normal operating hours. That is, ATM transactions are free to the customer if they occur while the bank branches are open. After the branches close, the customer pays a fee for each transaction. It would seem that market competition might change this situation within a few years.

Security in the ATM application is obviously very important. One concern is the physical security of the machine, since it contains hundreds of dollars in cash and checks. This problem is generally solved by keeping the money in a small vault within the machine and having the machine itself mounted in the wall of a building.

Another aspect of security is the identification of the user. Bank customers are identified by issuing each user a plastic card much like a credit card. The back of the card contains a magnetic stripe on which the user's name and account number are coded. When the card is inserted in the ATM, the machine reads the characters on the magnetic stripe. If the account number is valid, the machine asks the person for his or her unique *personal identification number (PIN)*. A computer compares the PIN the user enters with the PIN for that account, which is stored on the computer's disk. If the two PINs match, the user is permitted to proceed with the banking transaction.

personal identification number (PIN)

ATM applications are realtime transaction processing systems that handle a high volume of transactions. Although ATM operation is not yet as critical to banking as the airline reservation system is to airlines, it is obviously in the bank's best interest to keep the ATMs and network operating with high reliability, especially after hours when users can't get assistance with banking elsewhere. In addition, banks save staff costs when people use the ATM rather than a human teller. One nationwide network of ATMs experiences uptime that is better than 97 percent. *Uptime* is defined as the probability that the system is being "up" and available for use whenever someone wants to use it.

The number of different transactions that ATMs can perform has increased dramatically. Originally, the machines did little more than dispense cash. Now, consumers can make deposits, check their balances, get credit advances, pay bills, and transfer funds between accounts; and it is expected that many of these systems will be expanded to new tasks, such as customer orders for checks or inquiries about loan or investment services.

Internationally, bank networks are connected by the SWIFT network. SWIFT, an acronym that stands for Society for Worldwide Interbank Financial Telecommunications, connects most major banks and financial institutions worldwide. Most of the traffic sent on the SWIFT network is interbank financial transactions or confirming messages for verification. The network experienced a 12 percent growth in the message traffic it handled for many years and had to make a complete technical overhaul of its network to cope with the message volumes in the early 1990s.

Both the airline reservation and ATM applications have revolutionized the way business is done in their respective industries. In both cases, the application requires the marriage of telecommunications and computing technology. In addition, communication and cooperation between competing companies must occur. Furthermore, all of the companies must subscribe to the same standards for how transactions are processed. In addition, standards are required to allow computers in different banks, which may be from different computer vendors, to be interconnected with telecommunications. Without telecommunications, these applications would not be possible. These examples clearly illustrate how telecommunications is changing the way business is done and the structure of business itself.

Sales Order Entry Look at another application of telecommunications in the business environment, particularly one found in a manufacturing company. Some of the products the company makes are produced and stored in a warehouse in anticipation of customer demand. Other products are produced only to fill a specific customer order.

Figure 3–11 shows a conceptual view of a sales order entry system that a manufacturing company might have. Order entry operators sitting at terminals may receive orders by mail or telephone (this example as-

Figure 3–11
The telecommunications in an industrial sales order entry system.

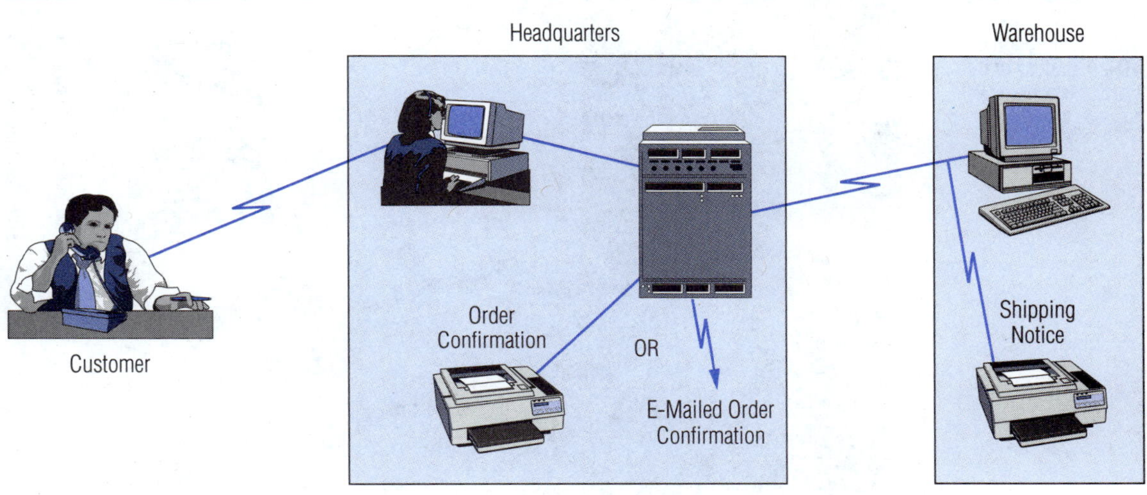

sumes a telephone order). The customer call may be handled as in the airline reservation system with an automatic call distributor routing the call to the next available order entry operator. The order entry operator keys the data required for the order into the computer. When all of the data has been entered, the operator tells the computer to process the order. The computer subtracts the quantity ordered from inventory, and either prints a confirmation notice to be mailed or sends an electronic mail message directly to the customer. The system would also send a notice to the warehouse to ship the order immediately if appropriate.

Notice that in this example there are several uses of telecommunications. The operator uses a terminal connected to the computer via a telecommunications line. The computer is also connected to a local printer that prints the order confirmation notice and a remote printer in the warehouse that prints the shipping document. Electronic mail may be used to contact the customer. There is also a terminal in the warehouse that shares the telecommunications line with the printer in a multipoint configuration. The warehouse employee uses the terminal to notify the computer when the order has been shipped. Obviously, with additional programming, the equipment used primarily for the order entry application could also send messages between the order entry clerk and the warehouse (or vice versa). The warehouse employee could also use it to request the computer balances for any inventory item.

Now imagine adding an Internet-based front end to the application. In that case, the customer might search an online product catalog, select the merchandise to be ordered, fill out the order form, supply shipping

A sales order entry clerk takes an order from a customer and enters the information into the computer through the VDT. (Courtesy of Dow Corning Corporation)

and payment information, and confirm that the order is correct. An application designed in this way would eliminate, or at least significantly change, the nature of the order entry operators. They would now become customer/product consultants, standing by to assist customers who have questions or have trouble using the Internet-based order entry process. The hope would be, of course, that, for a high percentage of the orders, customers could complete order entry transactions themselves.

Point of Sale Systems in a Retail Store or Supermarket *Point of sale (POS) terminals* are used widely in large retail stores and supermarket chains. Although the technology of the terminals used in retail stores differs from that used in supermarkets, the use of telecommunications and the basic application are quite similar.

Many years ago, the grocery industry standardized the Universal Product Code, a bar code that can be used to identify virtually every item stocked in a supermarket. This bar code is quickly and accurately read by a laser scanner built into the supermarket checkout counter. Good design enables the products to be read when they are passed through the laser beam at virtually any angle or speed. The supermarket checkout clerk ensures that the bar code on the item is facing in the general direction of the laser and passes the product through the beam. The laser reads the bar code and sends the product number to the store computer, which looks up the product description and price in a database. The computer trans-

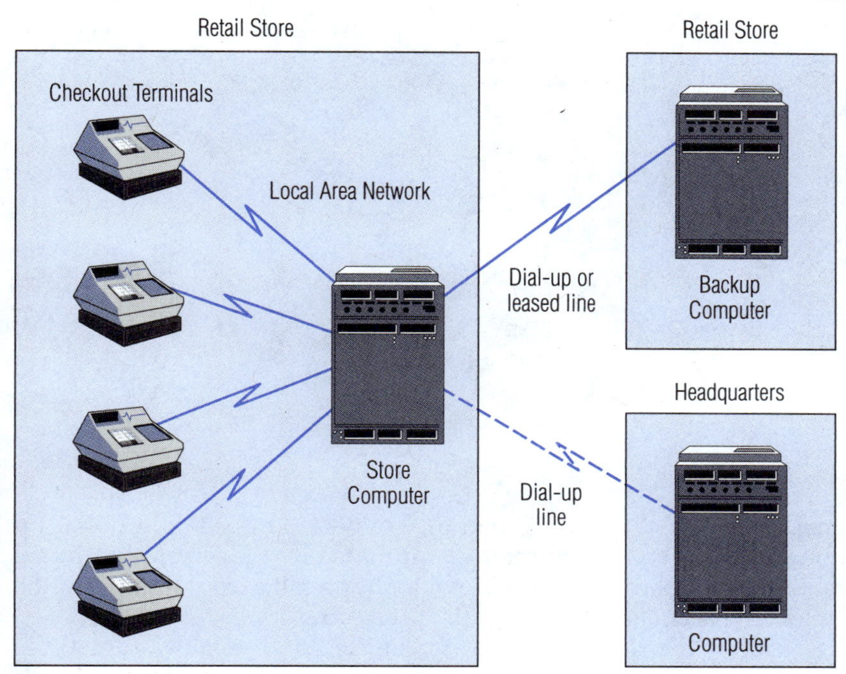

Figure 3–12
The telecommunications of a retail checkout system.

mits that information back to the terminal, which then prints the cash register tape. Occasionally, a product cannot be read or does not have a bar code. In that case, the checkout clerk can key the price into the terminal. It is printed on the tape and added to the running total.

The retail store has a similar type of system. Unfortunately, products in retail stores are not universally coded in machine-readable form. Some stores have merchandise tags with a magnetic stripe or punched holes that can be read by the retail terminal, but in most cases the clerk must manually enter the information.

The most frequent design of supermarket and retail store systems is for the store's computer to contain product and price information, which is completely self-sufficient for normal operations during store hours. Often a telecommunications link is provided to a nearby store for backup purposes. If the store's primary computer fails, the checkout terminals can continue to operate off the backup computer. These telecommunications links are illustrated in Figure 3–12.

At night a central computer at the company headquarters dials the computer at each store to collect data about the day's sales and to check inventory levels. Since the connection between the headquarters computer and the store computer is only needed for a few minutes, it would not be cost effective to have a full-time leased line connecting the two

An automated checkout terminal scans the bar code on a can of raspberries. (Courtesy of NCR Corporation)

machines. In this case, the computers are connected by a standard dial-up telephone line. The call is automatically initiated by the central computer. This call is exactly like a normal voice telephone call except that when the connection is made, data, not voice, is transmitted.

When all of the data has been transmitted and acknowledged, the connection is broken by electronically hanging up. In this way, only the time actually used for transmitting data must be paid for. After the central computer collects the data from one store, it immediately dials the next store in the chain and collects similar data and so on until all stores have been contacted. Once all of the data has been collected on the central computer, it can be processed to generate daily sales reports of various types. Also, since inventory levels were checked at each store, the computer can generate automatic restocking information.

For the customer, scanners reduce the wait in the checkout line by 25 percent, reduce cashier errors, and produce receipts showing an exact description of the products as well as the prices. Although they were largely introduced as labor-saving devices, store scanners have changed the way business is done by revolutionizing inventory control. Indeed, retailing is turning into more of a science than an art because stores can see patterns of sales that were invisible a few years ago. Grocers and customers alike recognize the value and benefits that scanning has brought to the grocery business.

Obviously, the role of telecommunications and the computer is critical in point of sale retail store systems. If a telecommunications line or the computer is not operating, customers cannot buy merchandise. Since competition is heavy in this industry and there are many supermarkets and retail stores in a given area, a failure of the computer or telecommunications system usually means that customers go elsewhere and business is lost.

A retail point of sale (POS) terminal that could be used in many different types of stores. (Courtesy of NCR Corporation)

Unstructured Data Applications

Electronic Mail *Electronic mail* applications, or *e-mail* as they are often called, are some of the most heavily used applications in distributed systems. In 1996, for the first time, more e-mail messages were sent in the U.S. than letters! E-mail is similar to the message switching application described earlier, but is designed so that the user can create, format, and send the message from a computer or terminal. By way of contrast, in older systems the message sender usually wrote the message by hand, gave it to a secretary who typed it, and then delivered it to the communications room where it was rekeyed onto a communications terminal for transmission. Clearly the newer systems are more productive because they eliminate a lot of duplicate work.

As shown in Figure 3–13, an e-mail application requires a terminal or personal computer from which the user can access the e-mail system software. Although e-mail is conceptually a simple application, the software is quite sophisticated. The software provides a directory and translation function so that people can address each other by name, nickname, or at least a mnemonic code. These must then be translated to an address for the user that the network can understand if the destination is on another computer, or simply a mailbox address if the recipient uses the same computer as the sender.

Figure 3–13
A simple electronic mail configuration with users on two computers.

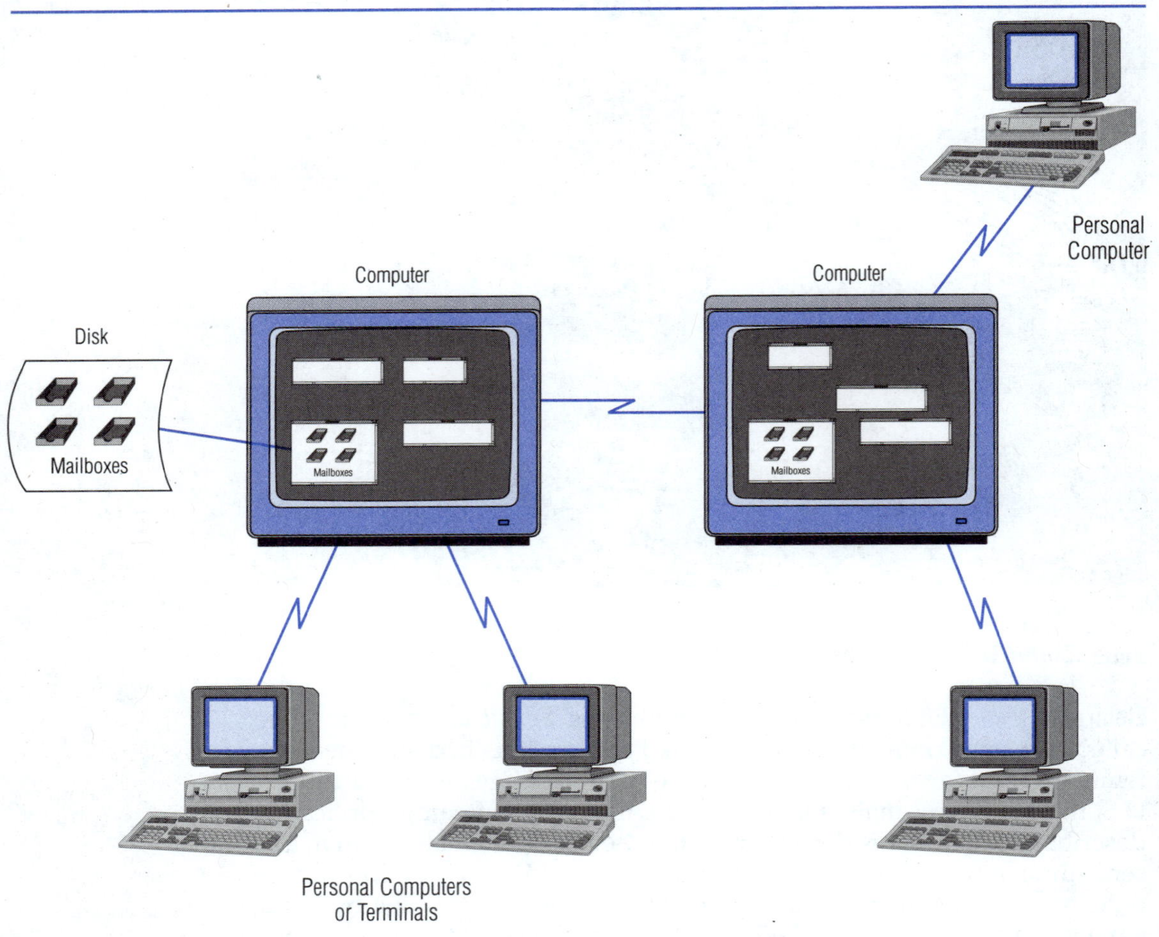

electronic mailbox

The host computer must have adequate disk storage to store incoming messages. Users are each assigned a space on the disk known as the *electronic mailbox*. Messages are stored in the electronic mailbox until the user deletes them, preferably after he or she has read them! Although most users may check their mailboxes and delete messages they have read on a daily (or more frequent) basis, others may leave messages on the system for days or weeks, so the disk capacity must be large enough to accommodate these differences.

The e-mail system provides the user with exclusive access to his or her stored messages. But in a company setting the question is whether the messages are really private. Court rulings have held that if your computer belongs to the company, so does its content. The law lets the company

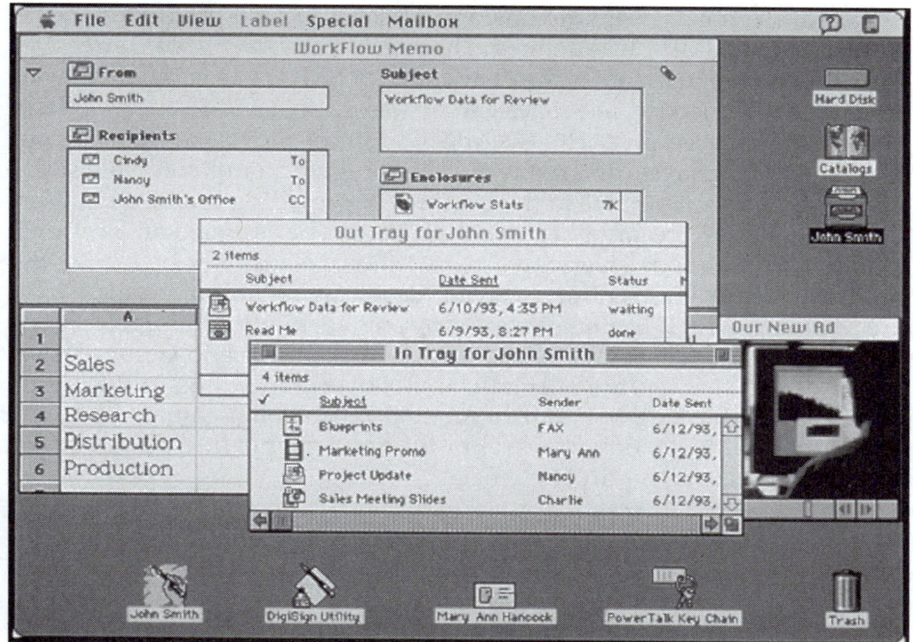

A screen from an electronic mail system. (Courtesy of Apple Computer, Inc.)

read what you put on the computer, and because of the large memory capacities of today's machines, there's little that can't be recalled, even if the user thinks it has been deleted. You shouldn't be fooled into thinking a message or file is really gone just because you have deleted it. Many e-mail systems routinely store copies of all mail that passes through them.

Some TCP/IP-based e-mail systems use the *simple mail transfer protocol (SMTP)*, one of several application layer protocols, to provide a way to transfer messages between computers. Messages are created by a program and passed to SMTP for transmission. Although SMTP is generally not concerned with the format or content of the messages, there is normally a header that tells the address of the recipient and a body containing the message to be sent. The SMTP software on the sending computer takes the message and transmits it, using SMTP transactions, over a TCP connection to the destination computer. SMTP software on the receiving computer accepts the message and either places it in a user's mailbox, or puts it in an outgoing queue if forwarding is required.

SMTP has some limitations that are important in today's environment:

- it cannot transmit text that contains characters from foreign character sets, such as German characters with an umlaut;
- it cannot transmit executable files, such as programs, which a user might want to attach to a message;
- it cannot handle mail over a certain size.

To overcome these limitations, a more sophisticated protocol, which is an extension of SMPT, was defined. The *multipurpose Internet mail extensions (MIME)* protocol eliminates the restrictions of SMTP in a compatible way, so that SMPT encoded messages can be passed to a MIME-based system and will be handled properly. The MIME protocol allows messages to contain foreign languages, binary files, and essentially an unlimited file size.

Several companies are in the business of providing public e-mail services. For a small fee, anyone can subscribe and be assigned an electronic mailbox. Subsequent charges vary, but they are usually based on the number of messages sent or received. Leading vendors of public e-mail are MCI and AT&T. E-mail service is also available from online services and Internet access providers such as America Online and CompuServe. Public e-mail services are normally accessible through one of the public networks, via the Internet, or through toll-free telephone numbers.

Almost all types of businesses or business people find public e-mail services very attractive and beneficial:

- independent business people who need to communicate with their vendors and customers who may be located anywhere in the country;
- small companies that cannot afford their own private e-mail service;
- large companies, which may have their own private e-mail system, may also subscribe to a public service in order to communicate with customers, vendors, or employees;
- salespeople and other travelers, who are frequently away from their office, find public e-mail an ideal way to keep in touch with the home office and to conduct business almost as though they were at their desk.

E-mail systems such as Microsoft's Outlook can also be installed on a company's servers for its private use. Companies that install their own private e-mail system may use their regular data communication network and simply treat e-mail as another application. Usually the private systems have a link to the Internet so that employees can send e-mail outside of the company as well as to other employees.

Unified Messaging System

Some e-mail software allows e-mail, voice mail, and fax messages to be brought together into a *unified messaging* system. These services will let you send voice mail, e-mail, and faxes to a single digital phone number or mailbox. End users need only tap into one mailbox to access all of their messages, greatly simplifying communications and boosting convenience for consumers by reducing the need to carry multiple devices such as pagers, cell phones, and palmtop computers. They can choose between a computer or telephone to receive their messages, because the system will "read" textual e-mail messages to them on the telephone, access voice messages from the PC, or even have e-mail messages faxed. Automatic media conversion provides universal access to messages—e-mail, voice, or fax—no matter where the user is or what type of device is available.

SIDEBAR 3–1

MESSAGE CENTER

Home Is Where the Hub Is

Today's always-on economy means we're always on call, even far beyond power centers of the network economy. The communications devices strewn around a typical American household generate an average of 115 unique outgoing and incoming messages each week. Our daily dose of interruption, er, connection, comes via telephone, postal service, e-mail, voice mail, cell phone, pager, and fax, according to a household messaging study by Pitney Bowes. Of those communications, more than 40 percent are for work-related matters. Are we approaching the saturation point? Not likely. The number of continuous Net connections (DSL lines and cable modems) in US homes is expected to top 25 million by 2003. Add to that a total of nearly 200 million cell phones in the US by year-end—up 100 million from 1999—and it becomes clear that the only way to escape the all-encompassing datasphere is to . . . please hold.

Weekly communications sent/received	Average household	High-volume household
Phone	54	102
Mail	35	50
Email	16	59
Voicemail	4	12
Cell phone	3	8
Pager	2	7
Fax	1	2
Total	**115**	**240**

Reprinted with permission from *Wired Magazine*

Clearly this is the type of mail system that people will be using in the near future since the software is already available.

Image Applications

Facsimile A *facsimile (fax) machine* scans a sheet of paper electronically and converts the light and dark areas to electrical signals, which can then be transmitted over telephone lines. At the other end, a similar machine reverses the process and produces the original image on a sheet of paper. Individual characters are not sent as such; only as contrast between light and dark. As a result, the facsimile is ideal for sending preprinted business documents or forms, as well as letters, contracts, and even photographs. Each facsimile machine, therefore, has two parts: a reader-transmitter and a receiver-printer.

The Sharp FO-6600 facsimile uses plain paper and can send a page in six seconds. (Reproduced with the permission of Sharp Electronics Corporation)

Since the machine deals with light and dark areas (not letters, words, or numbers), any image, photograph, drawing, or graph can be transmitted. The facsimile machine scans back and forth across the original document in a series of scan lines. The most sophisticated facsimile machines can detect several shades of light or dark. The more shades detected, the more faithful the reproduction is at the receiving end. The speed to transmit and print an 8 1/2- × 11-inch document varies from 6 minutes to approximately 2 seconds, depending on the techniques used for transmitting.

Facsimile transmission has several advantages over other data communication methods in certain applications:

- if a document is already printed, it does not need to be rekeyed in order to be transmitted;
- operation of facsimile machines is very simple and requires little training;
- since the recipient receives an exact duplicate of the original image, graphs, charts, and handwritten notes can be sent as easily as typed documents.

An industrial security guard works at his VDT. The television monitors in the background are connected to cameras at various locations throughout the plant and allow the guard to watch many locations simultaneously. Other equipment monitors the use of badge readers at entrance doors. (Courtesy of Dow Corning Corporation)

In business, facsimile is used to transmit any document that must arrive quickly. Examples include contracts going to a law firm or a prospective client, shipping documents sent from the corporate headquarters to a warehouse, and simple engineering drawings going to a contractor or outside engineering firm. Radio stations are now accepting requests by facsimile, and some individuals have facsimile machines at home. In Japan, where addresses are complicated and streets usually are not named, facsimile is regularly used to send a map explaining how to get to one's office or home.

Television Television is used in business in several ways. Among them are

- to monitor doors, parking lots, or other facilities;
- to provide information to employees;
- for video conferencing—conducting a meeting where the participants are in different locations but can see each other on television.

Security Monitoring In the security monitoring application, the television camera can be on top of a building, in a doorway or corridor, or in the corner of a room viewing the room or area being monitored. The camera is unattended, and its video signal is fed to a central monitoring point such as a security desk. A video tape recorder may be connected so that any unusual activity can be recorded and then later replayed for analysis.

A video conference in progress. Cameras are mounted just above the television sets to take pictures of the participants and send them to the other end. (©1997, PictureTel Corporation. All rights reserved.)

For security monitoring, black-and-white television pictures are most often used, and in many cases the picture is updated only every 30 to 90 seconds. This periodic refreshing of the picture is referred to as *freeze-frame television.* It requires a much slower, less expensive telecommunications line than one that must transmit *full-motion television* pictures. Full-motion pictures are like those seen on commercial television stations; to achieve the motion, 30 frames are sent every second.

Providing Information to Employees Providing information to employees is another use for television in business. The information may be textual information that announces promotions, job changes, or upcoming events. An announcement might be displayed on the screen for 15 or 20 seconds and then automatically replaced with the next one. Information could also be conveyed through regular full-motion, full-color television broadcasts. The programming might include interviews with company officers, company news broadcasts, or training films.

Whether textual or full-motion, in-house television is most successful if television sets to receive the broadcasts are located in convenient locations around the office or plant. Having the sets in coffee break areas, the cafeteria, and other gathering places helps ensure that the messages are conveyed to the maximum number of people.

Video Conferencing A third use of television in business is *video conferencing.* In this application, meetings are conducted in rooms equipped with television cameras and receivers. The participants in one room can view those in the other rooms via the screen. The television signals are transmitted between the rooms on telecommunications lines.

There are actually two types of video conferencing: one-way and two-way. In one-way conferencing, a company broadcasts a program from a central location, which is received simultaneously at numerous receiving stations equipped with relatively inexpensive receivers. Some audio audience interaction is possible using telephone lines, but the picture communication is one-way. This is in contrast to two-way teleconferencing, which is more like a conventional meeting and requires cameras and transmission equipment at each end of the connection.

Another way to categorize video conferencing is whether it is full-motion or freeze-frame. In this application, the trend has been toward simple operation using freeze-frame television. In most meetings, full-motion pictures are not necessary. Once participants are in the room and seated, a picture can be transmitted to the other locations so that the participants can see who they are talking to. After that, having an updated picture every 30 to 60 seconds is usually adequate. The use of freeze-frame television greatly reduces the amount of information that has to be transmitted and keeps equipment and transmission costs down.

Television equipment costs and complexity vary widely. Factors that affect them are

- black-and-white versus color;
- full-motion versus freeze-frame;
- lighting sensitivity;
- special equipment for graphics or text transmission.

The more the video conferencing capability becomes like commercial television, the more elaborate and costly the equipment. Sending 30 frames per second obviously requires a much higher transmission speed than sending 1 frame every 30 seconds. Studios and control rooms with editing equipment are sometimes found in the corporate environment, but in most cases they are unnecessary and difficult to justify. They are used where the television broadcast has the elements of a television production.

Most video conferencing today is done from a conference room setting, not in a studio. One camera is usually focused on the meeting participants, and a second camera is used to transmit pictures of transparencies, slides, or drawings that illustrate points during the meeting. Ideally, the video conferencing equipment is simple enough to be operated by the meeting participants.

public video conferencing centers

Several companies have set up public centers in major cities for video conferencing. The centers have fully equipped video conferencing rooms that are rented by the hour. The rental fee includes the use of the room, any technicians required to operate the equipment, and transmission of the video conference by satellite to another, similarly equipped room. Using public centers is ideal for a company that occasionally needs to use video conferencing but cannot justify installing its own equipment. In addition to using the rooms for conducting meetings, some companies regularly use them to announce new products, conduct sales meetings, or communicate with customers. The conference might feature the vice president of marketing in a room in New York City and salespeople gathered in rooms in other major cities. A new product could be announced to the entire sales force simultaneously, and the two-way nature of the media would allow the salespeople to ask questions and interact with the vice president.

A number of companies have established video conferencing networks. Ford Motor Company established its network in 1985 and has since expanded it to plants, district offices, and other facilities in North America. General Motors has a network that links its worldwide facilities as do General Electric and IBM. These links enable management to reach people they were unable or unwilling to reach by traveling. IBM has used one-way video conferencing for several years for employee and customer education. The instructor works in a studio with complete graphic aids available. Students sit in classrooms at IBM facilities throughout the country and watch the instructor on large screen televisions. They can ask questions and respond to the instructor using audio communication.

New video conferencing units are smaller and don't require dedicated facilities. Several companies are now making adapter cards for personal computers that allow the PC, with a small camera mounted on top, to be used for a small video conference between two people or a very small group of people at each end.

Compression technology continues to improve so that pictures can be sent over slower telecommunications lines than in the past and with acceptable quality. Simultaneously, the cost of higher speed lines is dropping so the purchaser of a video conferencing system has more choices, tradeoffs, and possibilities for using this technology than a few years ago.

Delay and Loss Sensitivity It is important to point out that some kinds of telecommunications transmission are more sensitive to delay than others. On the one hand, if your voice is delayed when you are talking on the telephone, it is very noticeable and irritating. Similarly, you may have noticed times when the voice and picture on a television are not synchronized so that the words you hear from the speaker don't match the picture on the screen. This can be caused by several technical problems, but one of them is that either the voice or picture is delayed in transmission relative to the other. The term we apply to this attribute of voice and television transmissions is that they are *time* or *delay sensitive.* On the other hand, if we are sending an e-mail message to a friend, we are normally not concerned whether the message arrives in 1 second, 1 minute, or sometimes even 1 hour. However, we don't want the message to be unreadable as it could be if some of the characters in the message were garbled or lost during the

delay sensitive

transmission. We say that such a signal, a data signal, is highly *loss sensitive,* but not time sensitive.

loss sensitive

Returning to the first example, if a voice or television signal suffers some loss of data during the transmission, you might hear a missing syllable or see white specks on the TV picture, but it would not normally cause you to miss the message or impair your understanding of what was being said or shown. So voice and television signals are not highly loss sensitive, unless of course the loss is carried to an extreme.

The Internet

The Internet has become so widely used in the past several years that special coverage may not be necessary. Nonetheless, while extensive coverage of the multifaceted capabilities of the Internet is beyond the scope of this book, a few words are in order to put the Internet into context with the rest of the material in this book. The Internet and its uses are a microcosm (or maybe a macrocosm!) of all of the applications discussed so far. Whatever application one can imagine seems to be in use on the Internet. Structured, unstructured, voice, data, text, image, video, interactive, batch—they're all there!

The Internet and *World Wide Web* are so widely used that I assume students reading this book have some experience using them. In the mid-1990s the arcane letters *http://www.royal.gov.uk* wouldn't have meant anything to anyone, but now many people know that they're used by the Queen of England to identify the royal family's site on "the web." Similar letters appear routinely in virtually every newspaper, magazine, and advertisement, and on news shows to direct people to sites on the Internet that may be of interest. I did most of the research for this edition of this book using worldwide resources available on the WWW while sitting at my personal computer in my home. Information that was previously hard to come by is now easily and quickly available. The rapid rise in the use of the Internet is a phenomenon unparalleled in history.

World Wide Web

Some recent statistics serve to illustrate how pervasive the WWW has become. It is estimated that there are over 130 million users of the Internet, and in a given month, over 82 million people actually use it. One survey showed that those users are online from home an average of almost 10 hours per month, and for those who use it at work, about 22 hours. Another survey showed that the average overall use was approximately 12 hours per week, far more than is spent reading magazines.

The Internet is a huge interconnected network of networks using telecommunication lines running under the TCP/IP architecture/protocol. Originating in 1969 with the ARPANET, which was sponsored by the U.S. Department of Defense, the connections spread, first to universities and research institutions, then to other government agencies, to private corporations, and finally to individuals. Several studies have been performed attempting to address the subject of who is using the Internet today and what they are doing with it. A summary of many of the studies can be found, on the Internet of course, at *www.cyberatlas.com*. Some typical uses are:

- communication (e-mail);
- downloading software;
- interactive discussions;
- using another computer;
- realtime audio and video;
- looking up information/research.

Access to the Internet occurs in various ways. Some companies and institutions have full-time leased lines operating at very high speed, such as 1.54 million bits per second. This option is on the expensive side, however if the cost is spread over a large number of users who are making productive use of the Internet, it may actually be very economical on a per-user basis.

Access to the Internet through cable television systems is spreading rapidly as more cable companies upgrade their equipment to make Internet access possible. Cable connections are extremely fast, and have the added advantage that the user is always connected to the Internet—there is no logon process. If the computer workstation is on, Internet access is enabled. The downside, however, is that the permanent connection leaves the user more exposed to certain security issues.

ISP

The majority of home users still have a dial-in connection from the modem on their PC to an online service such as America Online or to an Internet service provider (ISP). These connections typically operate at 28.8 or 33.6 thousand bits per second. This option comes at an affordable cost, typically much less than what one would pay for a cable television service on a monthly basis. There are several types of ISPs to which one might subscribe.

- Tier 1 ISP—An organization that has its own, typically national, network that supports very high speeds (45 Mbps) at its core. These ISPs often sell wholesale services to local telephone companies and local ISPs.
- Tier 2 ISP—Organizations that do not have their own network but lease capacity from other service providers. Tier 2 ISPs also typically support more than 100 thousand customers. America Online (AOL) is an example of a company in this category.
- Tier 3 ISP—These ISPs only support regional or local customers through a limited local network. There are currently about 4,000 Tier 3 ISPs in the United States.

At first, the Internet was used primarily for e-mail. Soon after, *user groups*, groups of people who get together on the Internet to exchange ideas or discuss a particular topic, began to develop. File transfer was another early application that is still widely used today. Files contain anything from pictures, to programs, or information on a topic of interest. When people started to discover that there was a lot of potentially interesting information "out there" on the Internet, they needed ways to locate information of interest. The University of Minnesota was one of the early organizations to respond with a program appropriately called *Gopher* (later, a new version was called Gopher+), which searches for information based on parameters specified by the user. Other programs in the same genre are Archie and Wide Area Information Server (WAIS).

By far the most common, and probably easiest, way to use the Internet, however, is by using a *browser program* to access the World Wide Web (WWW). A browser is a program designed to read the information stored on WWW sites and to handle the hypertext that these sites contain. The two most popular commercially available browser programs are Netscape's Navigator and Microsoft's Internet Explorer. The WWW contains textual and non-textual information stored in the form of *hypertext.* Hypertext allows the user to click on a word, which then connects to related information. For example, one might enter the web searching for information about Colorado. Reading a description of the state there would likely be a reference to skiing. Clicking on the hypertext word "skiing" with the mouse would take you to information about skiing, which could lead you off to read about skis, ski equipment, ski resorts, etc. browser

Two concepts that are important to understand about the way the WWW works are *universal resource locators (URL)* and *hypertext transfer protocol (HTTP).* URLs are essentially the addresses of objects located anywhere on the Internet and today there are over five million registered names. The URL consists of the name of the access method for the object, followed by a colon, and then by an identifier of a resource. The major access methods are: URL

- http (hypertext transfer protocol);
- ftp (file transfer protocol);
- gopher (the Gopher protocol);
- telnet (reference to interactive sessions);
- mailto (electronic mail address);
- wais (wide area information servers);
- news (USENET news).

The http URL scheme designates Internet resources that use the hypertext transfer protocol. In particular, these are sites on the WWW. Other Internet resources are accessed using the other protocols shown. An http URL is of the form: http://(host):(port)/path, however, the port normally defaults to a value of 80, and the path is optional, so a typical http URL looks like this: http://www.netscape.com. The URL www.netscape.com

is the name of the host, and since no path was specified, this URL points to the home page of that WWW *site.* A WWW site is a computer (server) containing a collection of information stored in http format and connected to the Internet. Organizations of all types and many individuals have WWW sites providing information on every imaginable topic. Furthermore, many of these same organizations are using the same networking and software technologies to set up private, internal versions of the WWW for their employees. These internal "webs" are called *intranets.*

intranet

The Internet is changing the way that applications are designed as companies look to the web as the entry point for electronic commerce. Internet access provides customers an additional way to find product information and to place orders for products of interest. If customers or prospects prefer to talk in person with a sales representative, that option is of course still available, but if customers prefer to research product options themselves, having an online catalog, product data sheets, brochures, material safety data sheets, and other information available through the Internet is convenient for customers and provides a new channel to the market for the seller.

The Internet and the WWW can serve as an excellent reference point for you as you study the rest of the material in this book. Most of the principals and concepts that will be discussed in later chapters can be illustrated with Internet-based examples.

SPECIAL CONSIDERATIONS OF DATA COMMUNICATIONS APPLICATIONS

Most data communications applications involve people. True machine-to-machine communication with no human involvement is less common. Since people are involved in the majority of data communications applications, a number of human factor elements must be considered in the planning or design of a data communications application or network.

Response Time

Matching the response time of a telecommunications system or network to the user's expectations, or vice versa, is an important human factor consideration. Of equal importance is response time consistency so that the user has the feeling that the system is always performing in the same way. We looked into this issue in detail in Chapter 1.

Security

System security is another important consideration in telecommunications systems, particularly where computer data is involved. Businesses are becoming extremely sensitive about the protection of their data and are insisting that ever more stringent security measures be put in place to protect it. When a telecommunications system is being designed, security must be carefully evaluated, and security techniques appropriate for the application must be implemented.

Planning for Failures

A third consideration of terminal-based systems is the special procedures required when the computer or network fails. Companies using telecommunications networks tend to become extremely dependent on the network to conduct normal business operations, yet network or computer failure does occur. The telecommunications system designer must plan for how the business will operate when the computer or network is down. Telecommunications adds an element of complexity to computer applications, particularly if long distance lines are involved, since they are subject to problems caused by severe weather, electrical interference, and misguided bulldozers or backhoes.

Therefore, it can be safely assumed that someday when a user picks up the telephone or sits down at the terminal, it won't work. The outage may or may not be a problem. Some telephone calls are more important than others; some can wait or were optional in the first place. The same is true of computer applications. In the sales order entry system described earlier in this chapter, the company may not need to enter a customer order or a material today if the product is not to be shipped for several weeks or months. In contrast, if the supermarket checkout system is not operating, customers will go elsewhere to buy their groceries.

failures will occur

The key is planning and having thought through what will happen when (not "if") the computer or network fails. Several options are available, including

- wait and do nothing except try to determine the reason for the failure and the likely amount of downtime;
- fall back to manual procedures, the types that were used before a computer and telecommunications network were in place;
- manually switch to a backup computer or telecommunications line;
- have a standby computer or telecommunications line in place ready to take over automatically in case of failure. This is called a *hot standby* system.

hot standby

Each of these alternatives must be evaluated in light of the business situation. In all but the most critical applications, the usual approach is to try to bring the system back up. At the other extreme, the airlines with their reservation systems have standby computers and duplicated networks to make sure that when a failure occurs, redundant facilities are available to take over immediately without missing a reservation. Few companies would actually wait and literally "do nothing" when the computer or communication system is down.

The problem with falling back to manual procedures is that once staff becomes used to automated systems, almost nobody remembers how to do things manually. Most companies find that manual procedures are not a very acceptable backup alternative. In addition, the volume of transactions often cannot be handled manually.

The difference between having backup computers and lines and a hot standby system is that the backup computers and lines usually are used for other types of work until they are needed. When a failure of the critical computer or network occurs, work is switched off the backup computer and the application is restarted on it. Careful planning will ensure that the time required to switch to the backup computer is not excessive. With a hot standby system, the switchover takes place rapidly and automatically. Again, the speed required is dependent on the application. Hot standby systems are expensive, and the benefits must be weighed against the costs.

planning is key

The key to handling failures is the planning itself. System outages need not be catastrophic if someone has thought through the implications of an outage and actions to be taken when the outage occurs. Many companies conclude that although it would not be convenient, the best alternative for many of their applications is to simply try to bring the system back up as quickly as possible and then catch up on the processing by having people work extra hours. Of course, in some applications, this is just not possible. More elaborate procedures are needed.

Disaster Recovery Planning Disaster recovery planning is an extension of the discussion about planning for normal system outages. For our purposes, a *disaster* is defined as a long-term outage that cannot be quickly remedied. A fire, flood, or earthquake may be the cause, for example. No immediate repair is possible, and the computer facility and equipment are unusable. Figure 3–14 shows a checklist for disaster recovery planning.

Again, planning is the key. Having a computer in an alternate site and the ability to switch the telecommunications lines to the alternate computer is a viable alternative in many situations. In lieu of that, quickly obtaining a new computer from the vendor may be possible. Most vendors state that they will "take the next computer off the manufacturing line" to replace a computer damaged in a disaster. Given the thousands of servers that are produced each day, this sounds like it should guarantee quick delivery of a replacement machine. However, in practice, getting a server with the right configuration, memory size, disk capacity, and other needed features sometimes takes weeks rather than days. One small Internet access company recently lost its e-mail service and a lot of customers when it was unable to get a replacement e-mail server from the

Considerations for Disaster Recovery Planning

1. What level of service should be maintained during a disaster?
2. How will the organization communicate internally?
3. Where will help desks and command centers be located?
4. Are policies and procedures in place to handle customer and other incoming calls in a professional manner and to provide timely information?
5. Are computers and their data sufficiently backed up?
6. What happens in the event of an evacuation?
7. What is the sequence for recovery? Which departments must be put back in operation first, second, etc.?
8. Are procedures in place for regular testing of the disaster recovery plan?

Figure 3–14
A checklist for disaster recovery planning.

manufacturer for over 4 weeks. The customers were without e-mail service for all that time, and the fact that they weren't billed was not enough to keep them from moving to other access providers who could give reliable service.

Even if a replacement computer can be obtained, it is of no use if a suitable facility cannot be found to house it. Of equal importance is the ability to switch the telecommunications network to the new computer site, again something that may be relatively easy if it has been planned for ahead of time. Telephone companies have developed techniques and facilities to allow networks to be switched to alternate sites, a capability that is demanded by companies that are putting disaster recovery plans in place.

mutual aid pact

Sometimes it is possible to work out a mutual aid pact with another company. Both organizations agree to back each other up in case of a disaster. They may agree to provide computer time on the second or third shift in case of a disaster, even if it means not running some of the low-priority processing. Computer centers are easier to back up with mutual aid pacts than are telecommunications networks. With proper planning, however, extra lines could be installed between the companies providing at least some backup transmission capability. If the two companies are in close physical proximity, they must be concerned about a disaster that would hit both of them simultaneously. An earthquake or tornado could easily hit companies in a several-mile radius and effectively neutralize any backup plans.

Several companies exist for the sole purpose of providing disaster backup recovery facilities. These companies, such as Comdisco Continuity Services (www.Comdisco.com), have one or more large computer centers filled with hardware ready for use in an emergency. In order to use the facilities, a business must subscribe to the service by paying a membership fee and annual dues. Then, if the use of the emergency facility is necessary, a one-time activation fee must be paid as well as usage charges for the actual time the disaster site is occupied. Subscribing to one of these services is much like buying a form of insurance.

Whatever plan is developed for disaster recovery, it must be specific for different kinds of disasters. Corning Incorporated, located in Corning, New York, had a disaster plan detailing how the company would recover from a fire. In 1972, however, the town of Corning was hit by a massive flood, which literally put the Corning computer center under water. Although some of the procedures previously developed for a fire were appropriate, many were totally useless or inappropriate for problems caused by water damage.

testing is very important

Disaster recovery plans must be tested. Rarely will all of the problems of a real disaster be covered when a plan is written, and although testing does not recreate a real disaster, it does identify weaknesses in the plan. If a contract has been signed with a disaster recovery firm, that firm will assist in testing the disaster plan. The contract normally provides for a specified number of hours of test time at the disaster recovery site. Companies use this time to ensure that they can transfer their software from their mainframe computers to the backup computer and to test the telecommunications links that connect the disaster site to parts of the company not affected by the disaster.

Tests of the disaster plan can be conducted in other ways. One company's data processing manager worked with the computer vendor to develop a disaster test. Late one night, the vendor's service manager removed a critical but obscure part of the mainframe computer. When the computer operations staff could not bring the computer up the next morning, they called the vendor for service. The vendor's technicians tried for several hours but were unable to precisely diagnose the problem; therefore, they called for help from the national support center. In the meantime, the prolonged computer outage had caused the company to activate its disaster recovery plan and because only the data processing manager, the company president, and the vendor service manager knew the real nature of the outage, the "test" was extremely realistic. It was allowed to run for over 24 hours before it was revealed to be a test. Although there was some grumbling, there was also general consensus among the computer users and management that much valuable information had been gained.

As a company becomes increasingly reliant on telecommunications and computer networks, it must constantly reassess how long it can afford to be without the systems. Getting the users involved in assessing the impact of an extended outage caused by a disaster is one way to build a case for management to support spending time and money on developing and maintaining disaster recovery procedures.

SUMMARY

This chapter has looked at a number of business applications that involve the use of telecommunications and the computer. Telecommunications and computing go hand in hand in providing modern business systems that help companies to be more effective and efficient. Simple uses of telecommunications for message switching and online data collection have given way to sophisticated, interactive applications that enable a company to do business in new ways. The rise in the availability and usage of the Internet and the World Wide Web have introduced a new set of data communication–based applications for business and the general public's use.

The integration of these applications into the business brings with it new responsibilities. Provisions must be made for appropriate security to ensure that company data is not lost or misappropriated. Contingency planning must be done to determine how the company will operate when short or long outages occur. By now, you should have a good understanding of the many ways in which companies use telecommunications and the breadth and depth at which it can penetrate an organization's activities.

CASE STUDY

Telecommunications at Work in a Small Business

F/S Associates is a small computer software development firm located in Hermosa Beach, California. The company specializes in the development of software for telephone companies to aid in the formatting and printing of telephone directories, especially the Yellow Pages. Chet Floyd, president of F/S Associates, incorporated the company and is also the chief software developer. He uses two IBM personal computers for the software development work.

Several years ago, Chet established a business relationship with another company, Strategic Management Systems (SMS), a software development firm located in New Jersey. At the present time, F/S Associates is under contract to Strategic Management Systems to develop and test software for several large customers.

F/S Associates is using telecommunications in its business activities in four different ways. Chet has a small, relatively standard telephone system for his office, which he purchased at a local discount store and installed himself. It provides an intercom capability for easy communication with his administrative assistant, and allows him to use either of the two telephone lines in his office to make telephone calls. Normally, he uses one of the lines for voice calls and the other for data calls from his personal computers. In his business, it is of course very useful for him to be able to talk on the telephone to a client while simultaneously accessing information or sharing data from his personal computer on the other line. A headset is used in these situations to allow full use of the hands to call up support material from the local computers. He says that the capability is extremely useful when he is debugging programs. It allows him to test complex programs as if he were at the customer's site. He adds, "And my availability to a project is increased while costs and lead times are reduced."

Strategic Management Systems uses other software developers besides F/S Associates, and sometimes it is necessary for several of the developers to talk with each other simultaneously. When necessary, the companies establish a conference call through the AT&T audio conferencing service. Because these calls sometimes last more than an hour, Chet bought a high quality speakerphone as a part of his telephone system. Using it saves him from having to hold the telephone handset up to his ear during the calls. "The speakerphone is essential when more than one party is at the local site. Frequently, the other programmer is required in these conferences, and occasionally we might also have a vendor or a contractor on site as well," Chet says. "Sometimes five or six of us will be on a teleconference at the same time. It's amazing how fast we can exchange information and decide who is going to work on what part of a program or solve a problem. Of course we all have to remember not to get too excited and speak at the same time. Common courtesy is a necessary part of the calls to help make them productive."

Because F/S Associates is located on the west coast and Strategic Management Systems on the east coast, electronic mail is the third frequently used communications technique. Both companies use the Internet to exchange e-mail. Chet says, "Years ago we had to write our own software just to automate the dialing process, but now, with Windows 98, I can connect to my Internet service provider effortlessly using Windows 98's built-in dialing capability. It takes just a few seconds and I'm online ready to send e-mail or look up other information I may need." When Chet has long or complicated documents to send on e-mail, he prepares them offline using the Microsoft Word word processing program. "Word gives me great power to create and edit messages or complicated documents," he says, "and I'm not tying up the phone or paying to be online while I'm preparing the document. When I'm ready to send the document, I prepare a simple e-mail and attach the document to it using the e-mail program's 'Attach' command."

The fourth way F/S Associates uses telecommunications is for remote testing and support of software. Chet bought a package called ControlIT, and with it running in an F/S Associates customer's computer and one of Chet's machines, he makes a standard dial-up telephone connection between the two computers. As the developer, Chet can then run or test his program remotely on the customer's computer. This is a big help for demonstrating the program's capabilities or in finding and correcting bugs. Chet says that the ControlIT software also has an excellent file transfer program he uses to send new copies of the program or other data files to his customers over the telephone. The capability is also useful for exchanging updated versions of programs with Strategic Management Systems.

"Without telecommunications capability, it would be impossible for me to conduct business the way I am doing it," Chet says. "We're doing business in a way that lets us get the job done but still be located where we want to live. There would be no practical way to codevelop software with a company across the country if we couldn't send programs, data files, and messages to each other electronically. Nor could we support our customers who are widely distributed, geographically. Internet access is very important as well. We use an economical Internet provider to maintain a customer support site that is linked in from SMS. This provides first level support for frequently asked questions, posting of software updates downloadable by authorized customers, and it has an e-mail submission capability for more detailed inquiries. In addition, we have our own web site for the solicitation of new business not connected with SMS. The Internet service provider hosts all inquiries, so we don't require a dedicated line nor a 24 × 7 server (or staff!) to support it."

QUESTIONS

1. Could F/S Associates survive as a business if it only had telephone capability but not e-mail or the ability to exchange programs and data files?
2. Do you think it would be economically advantageous for a small firm like F/S Associates to consider renting office space in an e-business office park where the costs of the telecommunications capabilities and other office facilities, such as copy machines, fax machines, and secretarial support are shared between all of the small business owners? What would be the downside of such an arrangement?

CASE STUDY

Dow Corning's Applications That Use Telecommunications

Dow Corning is dependent on its telecommunications network to do business. Like most companies, it relies on an effective, cost-efficient voice network, but the real payoff for Dow Corning comes in the way it uses data communications. For a number of years, the company's philosophy was to minimize the number of mainframe computers it used for business applications processing and concentrate on a few large computer centers that were accessible by users through a telecommunications network. Experience showed that by having a few large computer centers the overall unit cost of computing was lower, even though the telecommunications expense was a higher percent of the total expense.

In 1995, the company began moving from the use of mainframe computers to a LAN-based computer-processing network using multiple application servers. Dow Corning acquired the SAP enterprise management software and began the long, expensive transition from applications developed by its own analysts and programmers to the use of the purchased SAP software. Since SAP operates in client-server mode, the computer processing and telecommunications networks needed to be completely overhauled, a process that took about 3 years. Two of Dow Corning's mainframe computers were removed by the end of 1999, and the third mainframe will be removed at the end of 2001.

The situation is different within Dow Corning's manufacturing plants, where computers (typically DEC VAXs) are installed because of unique requirements for sharing information stored on process controllers. However, the major business applications, including plant management applications, for Dow Corning are handled globally on server computers in Midland, Michigan. The major business applications that are processed on these servers include:

- customer order processing;
- inventory management and control;
- manufacturing planning and scheduling;
- finance and accounting;
- personnel and human resource management;
- planning and budgeting.

Users around the world sign on to these applications through the telecommunications network and process transactions in realtime, updating databases, generating routine reports, and finding answers to unique questions.

In most of the plants, local area networks connect sensors and other automation equipment to process computers, which are in turn connected to plant computers. These computers do some plant-specific processing and also pass much of the data on to corporate applications and databases. A data network is also used to connect to customers and suppliers for electronic document interchange (EDI). Routine business transactions are sent from one company to another, saving the delay of mail, and in most cases, eliminating paperwork. Some customers have specifically requested that Dow Corning send documents via EDI instead of in paper form.

The company is making its first forays into the world of electronic business through its Internet web site, www.dowcorning.com. Customers and prospects are able to obtain information about many of the company's products, request additional information through e-mail, and, with appropriate passwords, order some of the company's products in certain countries. This web-based capability will continue to expand, and Dow Corning believes that it must be on the forefront of electronic business in order to remain competitive. The company has also found that there are savings associated with doing business electronically, which help its profitability.

In 1983, an internal study concluded that Dow Corning should provide a comprehensive electronic mail and office automation application on the mainframe. A mainframe-based solution from IBM was selected, and it was used by virtually all employees in the company until it was replaced in 1999 by a significantly upgraded product, Microsoft's Outlook. Having a single e-mail and office system has been a very successful application of communications and computing technology for the company. Over 9,000 employees, contractors, and employees of other companies that Dow Corning works with use the system. The only Dow Corning employees who do not use the e-mail system are certain manufacturing people who have little need to communicate with others outside of their immediate work group.

The company also makes extensive use of voice mail (which will be discussed in Chapter 4) in the United States and other locations around the world. The company has over 4,000 voice mailboxes that employees use to exchange voice messages and leave voice reminders and other information for each other.

Another use of telecommunications is audio and video conferencing. Virtually all locations have audio conferencing capability in many of their conference rooms, which use high quality speakerphones. Video conference centers have been established in Midland, Brussels, Wales, Tokyo, Sydney, Hong Kong, Singapore, Seoul, and at several plants in the U.S. Employees and management routinely "meet on television" to discuss their progress on projects and a wide variety of other topics. Although they have not proliferated widely, a few PC-based video conferencing units are also used at small locations.

From the above examples, you can see that Dow Corning is truly dependent on its voice and data communications systems to conduct its business and to be competitive.

QUESTIONS

1. Suppose that Dow Corning had decided to manage and operate its computer systems and data networks in a less centralized way and to allow each Industry Business Unit (IBU) to implement its own systems and networks. What would be the impact on the company's telecommunications network? Which approach do you think is more cost effective?

2. Given the rapid growth in the power of personal computers, do you think Dow Corning would follow the same centralized philosophy if it were starting over today?

3. Do you think the centralized approach to systems and networks will be an appropriate model for the future, considering the rapid growth of client-server computing?

4. How does Dow Corning's centralized approach to communications and computing heighten the need for good disaster recovery planning of its network and computer centers?

REVIEW QUESTIONS

1. Discuss the three ways in which telecommunications applications can be categorized.
2. Explain the following terms:

   central office
   multipoint line
   polling
   transaction processing system
   freeze-frame
   store-and-forward
   master or control station
   collision
   video conferencing
   World Wide Web

3. Why are airline reservation systems so vital to airlines?
4. Describe how a supermarket checkout system works.
5. Describe some situations where e-mail is inadequate for communicating a message and a facsimile is required.
6. What types of businesses are not candidates to use public e-mail systems?
7. Would you rent an apartment or buy a home based on a picture you had seen on the WWW? What other information would you require so that you could make a decision without visiting the house or apartment?
8. Identify and explain three different uses for television in business.
9. Explain the advantages and disadvantages of using video teleconferencing to conduct a business meeting.
10. Discuss the reasons why a company should have a disaster recovery plan for its telecommunications and computer systems.
11. Identify five types of "disaster" that could disable a computer-communications network.
12. Categorize the applications shown on the left into one or more of the categories shown on the right.

    car rental reservation system
    data collection for machines at a paper mill
    computer-aided drafting
    telemetry from a spacecraft
    a facsimile transmission

    voice
    realtime
    store-and-forward
    structured data
    unstructured data
    person-to-person
    person-to-machine
    machine-to-machine
    image

13. What is the function of a browser program?
14. Describe the purpose of the http protocol.
15. Identify ten types of information you might find on the Internet that would be useful to you in your everyday life.
16. What is a unified mail system?
17. Describe the purpose of the following Internet tools: FTP, Gopher, Archie.
18. What is the World Wide Web? What tool do you need to use it?
19. Identify some ways that the Internet can be used for business.
20. Compare and contrast the terms personal computer, minicomputer, and server.
21. Explain the meaning of delay sensitivity and loss sensitivity and their implications if you were sending a file to a friend over the Internet.

PROBLEMS AND PROJECTS

1. In order to install a video conferencing system, a company must invest money in cameras, monitors, and other equipment. What costs, if any, will be offset by the video conferencing? Is video conferencing an alternative to some other type of communication?
2. As the dean of your school, you have been asked by the president to develop a disaster recovery plan for the school's computers. Describe such a plan, focusing on the recovery procedures in case of fire. If classroom space could be found so that classes could continue,

how would the computing for the students, faculty, and administration be handled?

3. Visit a supermarket that has an automatic checkout system with scanners. Observe several of the checkers for 5 minutes each and keep a count of the number of items whose bar code cannot be read and for which the data must be entered through the keyboard. What is the "read failure" rate? Do you notice any significant difference between the checkers?

4. Visit a travel agency that is connected to one of the airline reservation systems and find out how they conduct business when their computer terminal is down. How often do they experience downtime? What has happened to their telephone use since they installed the reservation terminals?

5. For your school or your organization (if you are working), conceptualize a new multimedia application that will take advantage of new technologies that were not available two to five years ago. For this exercise, don't worry about the cost justification, just be creative and use your imagination to invent a new way to use computers and communications to improve the productivity or quality of life for students, faculty, administrators, employees, or managers.

6. Talk to someone who works in a business that uses e-mail and find out:
   a. to what extent e-mail messages have replaced formal written correspondence for communication within the company and for communication outside the company with vendors and customers;
   b. to what extent correspondence is being faxed instead of being sent through the mail;
   c. to what extent they are using the Internet in their work.

7. Use the Internet to find information about your school or a nearby university.

Vocabulary

online realtime
store-and-forward
batch
remote batch
remote job entry (RJE)
teletypewriter
message switching
point-to-point line
punched paper tape
torn tape message system
message center
multipoint line
control station
master station
subordinate station
slave station
polling
collision
addressing
addressing characters
protocol
timesharing
transaction processing system
distributed processing
client-server computing
client
server
local area network (LAN)
personal computer
microcomputer
minicomputer
mainframe computer
scalability
delay sensitivity
time sensitivity
loss sensitivity
automatic call distribution (ACD) unit
personal identification number (PIN)
uptime
point of sale (POS) terminal
electronic mail (e-mail)
electronic mailbox
simple mail transfer protocol (SMTP)
multipurpose Internet mail extensions (MIME)
unified messaging
facsimile (fax) machine
freeze-frame television
full-motion television
video conferencing
World Wide Web (WWW)
user groups
file transfer
browser program
hypertext
Uniform Resource Locator (URL)
hypertext transfer protocol (HTTP)
site
intranet
hot standby
disaster

References

Behar, Richard. "Who's Reading Your E-Mail?" *Fortune* (February 3, 1997): 57–70.

Boccadoro, Diane. "It's The Next Best Thing To Being There." *Teleconnect* (December 1999): 68–78.

Case, Carol. "Do You Have a Disaster Recovery Plan?" *Teleconnect* (March 1997): 156.

Cortese, Amy. "A Way Out of the Web Maze." *Business Week* (February 24, 1997): 40–45.

Fowler, Thomas B. "Internet Access and Pricing: Sorting Out the Options." *Telecommunications* (February 1997): 41–70.

Hoffman, Dona L., William D. Kalsbeek, and Thomas P. Novak. "Internet and Web Use in the U.S." *Communications of the ACM* (December 1996): 36–46.

Jainschigg, John. "Video for Everyone." *Teleconnect* (September 1995): 126–135.

Jerome, Marty, Jason Toates, and Ron White. "25 Top Technologies That Will Transform Your Business." *SMARTBUSINESSMAG.COM* (May 2000): 98–135.

Levine, John R., and Carol Baroudi. *The Internet for Dummies.* San Mateo, CA: IDG Books Worldwide, 1993.

Mueller, Milton. "Emerging Internet Infrastructures Worldwide." *Communications of the ACM* (June 1999): 29–36.

Nanneman, Don. "Unified Messaging: A Progress Report." *Telecommunications* (March 1997): 41–42.

O'Brien, Ross. "Telecom: Building a Better Asian Network." *Asia, Inc.* (December 1993): 26–32.

Ramo, Joshua Cooper. "Welcome to the Wired World." *Time* (February 3, 1997): 36–48.

Robinson, Teri. "The Revolution Is Here." *Information Week* (November 18, 1996): 106–108.

Rosenbush, Steve. "Telecom Market Prepares for Unified Messaging." *USA Today* (December 7, 1998).

Wallace, G. David. "The Electronic Tutor Is In." *Business Week* (January 20, 1997): 8.

———. "How the Internet Works: All You Need to Know." *Business Week* (July 20, 1998): 58–60.

CHAPTER

4

Voice Communications

OBJECTIVES

After you complete your study of this chapter, you should be able to

- describe the purpose and functions of the various parts of the telephone system;
- describe the evolution of telephone switching equipment;
- differentiate between public and private telephone switching equipment;
- describe the characteristics of analog signals;
- describe several types of telephone lines;
- explain several ways to acquire telephone service at a discount;
- describe several types of special telephone service;
- describe the way wireless voice communications systems work.

INTRODUCTION

Perhaps you think it is a bit strange to be studying voice communications in a book that is primarily devoted to data communications. Fifteen or 20 years ago it would have been strange! But since that time, there has been a merger of the computer and communications industries that has markedly changed both and brought them closer together until, today, they operate as one.

By the time you finish this chapter, you will understand that a study of data communications today wouldn't be complete without understanding voice communications. Furthermore, if you are working, or planning to work, in an organization that uses data communications, you'll find that voice communications is an important part of their total telecommunications picture. Eighty percent of business telecommunications expense in most companies is for voice and only 20 percent is for data, and because it is so large, revenue from voice communications is extremely important to telecommunications carriers. Most probably, in your company, voice and data operations have come together. Perhaps they share the same telecommunications lines. Or perhaps both are managed by the same person. Hence, it is important for you to learn about voice communications and telephone systems. Your knowledge of telecommunications would not be complete without a good understanding of voice communications concepts, capabilities, and products.

This chapter describes and discusses the four basic elements of voice communication systems:

- the telephone handset;
- telephone company switching equipment;
- telephone lines;
- telephone signals.

Through your study of this chapter, you will gain a detailed understanding of the way these four components work together to provide the reliable telephone service that is ubiquitous through most of the world and which we have come to expect. You'll also see how voice signals are sent on telephone lines, which is a basic step in understanding how data is sent. Finally we'll look at other aspects of telephone communications, such as the special capabilities and services provided by the telephone companies.

Telephone communications is one very significant application of telecommunications. It is an application we are familiar with because we use it every day. As such, it serves as an excellent jumping-off point and provides a solid foundation for your study of data communications in the rest of this book. The majority of data transmissions in the world today occur on lines and networks that were originally designed to carry voice. In those cases, the data transmissions are adjusted to fit the parameters of the voice network.

THE TELEPHONE SET

customer premise equipment

The telephone is a primary example of a class of equipment known as *customer premise equipment (CPE)*. CPE includes any communications equipment that is located on the customer's premises and includes telephones, personal computers, fax machines, and telephone key systems, and PBXs (both of which you'll study later in this chapter). The term CPE is used frequently in the communications industry and is one with which you need to be familiar.

Primary Functions

The primary functions of the telephone set are to

- convert voice sound to electrical signals for transmission;
- convert electrical signals to sound (reception);
- provide a means to signal the telephone company that a call is to be made or a call is complete (off-hook and on-hook);
- provide a means to tell the telephone company the number the caller wants to call;
- provide a means for the telephone company to indicate that a call is coming in (ringing).

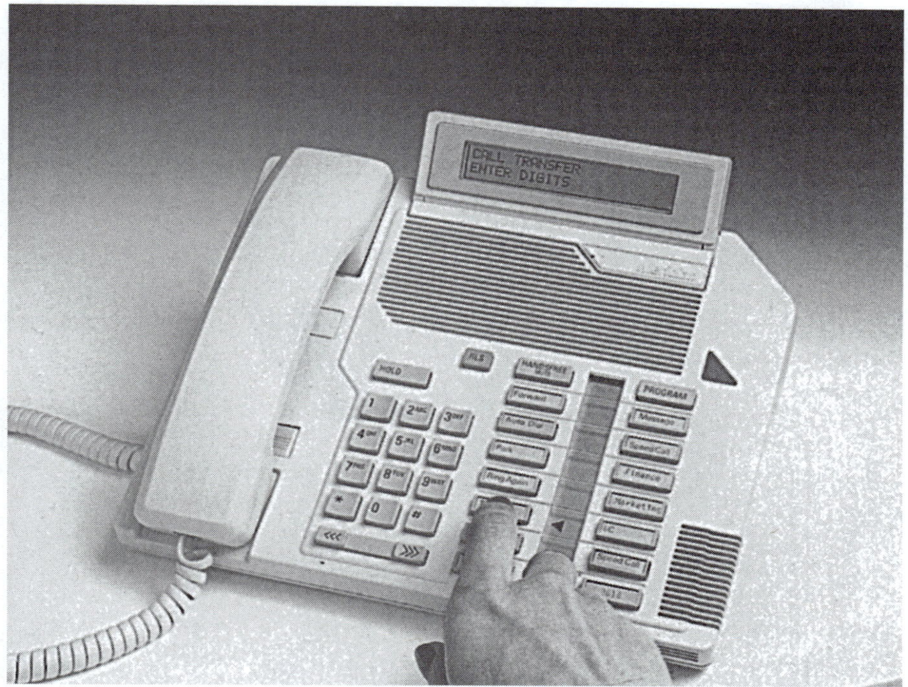

This modern telephone handset has several extra buttons that can be preprogrammed to automatically dial frequently called numbers, or to activate special features of the telephone system such as call transfer. (Courtesy of Northern Telecom, Inc.)

Telephone sets come in many sizes, shapes, styles, and colors. Years ago, there was just one type—the traditional black desk phone—and it was available only from the telephone company. Now phones to fit any decor or color scheme are available from a variety of vendors.

Telephones may be equipped with amplifiers to make the incoming voice signal louder for the hard of hearing. They may have loud bells or lights to indicate ringing in noisy areas. Explosion-proof telephones are available for use in chemical plants or other places where a spark might set off an explosion. Also, telephones with clocks, calendars, and elapsed timers are available.

Telephone Transmitter

Built into the handset of the telephone is the transmitter. It converts sound waves into electrical signals that can be transmitted on telephone lines. When you speak, your voice generates sound waves or vibrations that move the air in ever-widening circles, as shown in Figure 4–1. Some of these sound waves (which are really variations in air pressure) flow into the telephone mouthpiece, causing a thin diaphragm in the microphone to move back and forth. The vibrations put alternately more and less pressure on carbon granules in the microphone. As more pressure is applied, the granules are packed more tightly against one another and conduct

Figure 4–1
In the telephone transmitter, the sound waves of the voice cause the diaphragm to vibrate. The vibration puts varying amounts of pressure on the carbon granules, causing more and less electrical current to flow.

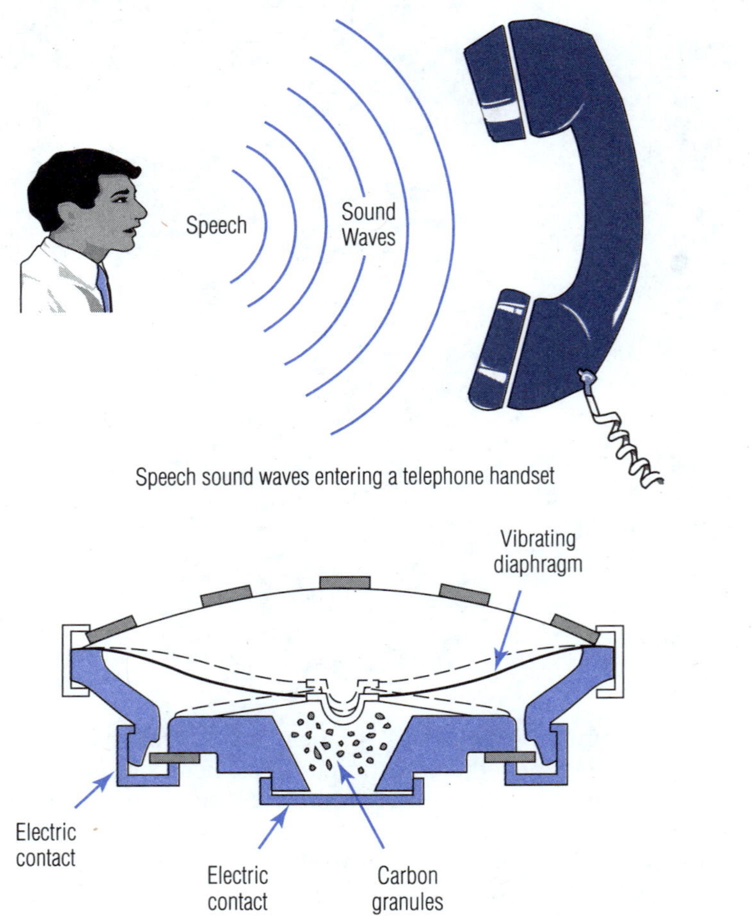

electricity better. Conversely, between the pressure waves, the granules move apart and do not conduct electricity as well. With voltage applied across the electrical contacts, this varying resistance of the carbon granules in the microphone causes a varying amount of current to flow. The varying current is an electrical representation of the sound waves generated by our voice.

analog signal

Since the electrical signal is analogous to the sound waves, we call it an *analog signal.* If we graphed a typical voice signal or watched it on an oscilloscope, it would look like the wave shown in Figure 4–2. To be more complete, an analog signal is one that is in the form of a continuously variable physical quantity, such as voltage.

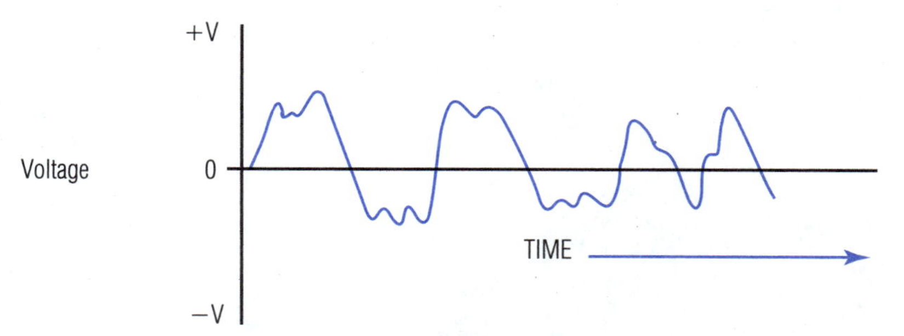

Figure 4–2
Wave of a typical voice signal.

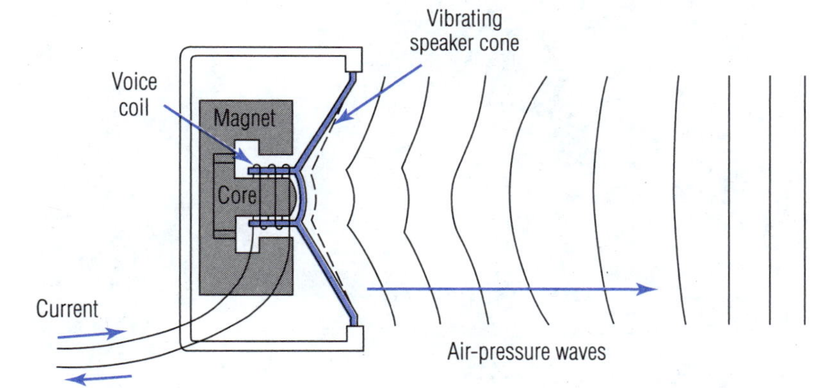

Figure 4–3
In the telephone receiver, the electrical current activates the voice coil, causing the speaker cone to move. The vibrating speaker cone creates air pressure waves that are heard as sound by the ear.

Telephone Receiver

At the other end of the telephone handset, the receiver's job is just the opposite. The receiver converts incoming electrical signals to sound waves that can be heard by the listener. Figure 4–3 is a diagram of this process. The incoming electrical signal flows through the voice coil in the receiver, and the interaction of the current in the voice coil with the magnet causes the coil to move. The coil is attached to a large diaphragm called the *speaker cone,* which vibrates back and forth causing sound waves that flow outward from it and into the ear of the person listening.

An important aspect of the telephone and its handset is that when you talk into the transmitter, some of the electrical current generated by the microphone in the transmitter is fed into your own receiver so that you hear yourself talk. This small amount of signal is called *sidetone.* Although sidetone is not technically required for the telephone to operate properly, it is generated for human factors purposes. Without sidetone, the telephone seems dead, and people tend to talk too loudly. With too much sidetone, people talk too softly. Sidetone is a form of feedback to the

sidetone

The Merlin cordless telephone can connect to up to five lines through a key system. (Property of AT&T Archives. Reprinted with permission of AT&T)

person who is speaking and gives the person a reference point for determining whether he or she is speaking too loudly or too softly.

Telephone Switchhook

The telephone *switchhook* derives its name from old-style telephones that had a hook on the side on which the handset was hung. In many telephones, the switchhook consists of the buttons that are depressed when the handset is placed in the cradle of the telephone. These buttons might better be called just "the switch."

When a user lifts the handset, the switch is closed, and electrical current flows to the telephone company's central office. This current signals the central office that a call is about to be made. This condition is called *off-hook.* The central office equipment responds with a *dial tone,* which lets the caller know that the central office is ready to accept the call. At this point, the line is said to be *seized.*

off-hook

At the end of a call, replacing the handset in its cradle depresses the switchhook buttons, opens the circuit, and signals the central office that the call is complete. This condition is called *on-hook.* When the caller hangs up the phone, the on-hook signal causes the creation of a data record in the central office computer that is used for billing the customer at the end of the month.

on-hook

MAKING A TELEPHONE CALL

Now we will look at the actions that take place when we make a telephone call. Some are obvious and visible to the caller, but many occur behind the scenes in the telephone company central offices.

"Dialing" a Number

Many years ago, when someone lifted the handset on a telephone, the response from the telephone company central office was not a dial tone but instead the voice of a human operator asking "Number, please?" In those days, the caller spoke the number he or she wished to call and the operator made the connection manually. As the volume of telephone calls grew, telephone company forecasts showed that many additional operators would be required. In fact, the forecasts showed that all young women leaving high school would need to be employed as operators just to handle the projected volume of telephone calls! It was evident that the process of completing the call had to be automated.

automating call connections

Rotary dials were added to telephones, which transferred the manual aspect of making the call to the caller. In more recent years, rotary dials have largely been replaced by numerical pads also known as dual-tone-multifrequency tone generators. Both the *dial pulsing* and dual-tone-multifrequency methods of signaling the central office the number of the telephone to be called will be discussed.

Dial Pulsing The *rotary dial* shown in Figure 4–4 generates pulses on the telephone line by opening and closing an electrical circuit when the dial is turned and released. The number of pulses is determined by how far the dial is turned. When the dial is released, the pulses are generated as a spring rotates the dial back to the resting position. The pulses are generated at the rate of 10 pulses per second. Each pulse is 1/20 of a second long, with a 1/20 of a second pause between pulses. This process is called *out-pulsing.*

out-pulsing

The rotary dial mechanism has largely been replaced by an integrated electronic circuit. This allows the telephone to have a push-button keypad, but the signaling is still done by electrical pulses that are generated

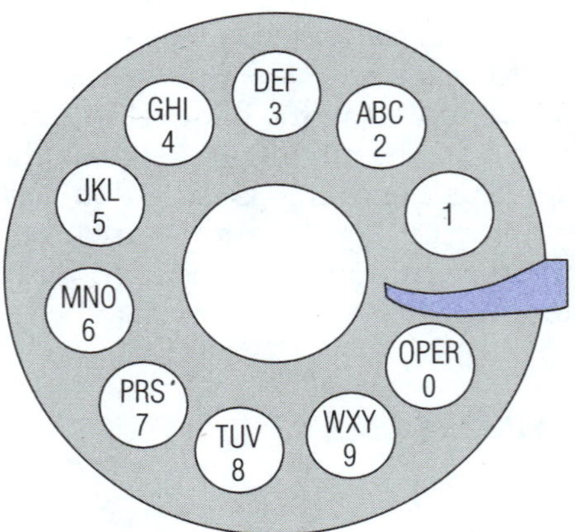

Figure 4–4
A diagram of a telephone's rotary dial.

by the electronic circuitry. Since people can push the buttons faster than the pulses can be sent on the telephone lines, this type of telephone must be equipped with an electronic buffer to store digits that have been keyed but not yet out-pulsed.

Worldwide, many telephones still use the rotary dial and dial pulse technique for signaling the desired number, but it has largely been replaced in the United States and many other countries by the dual-tone-multifrequency method.

Dual-Tone-Multifrequency (DTMF) The newer technique for signaling the desired number to be called is called *dual-tone-multifrequency (DTMF).* It is accomplished by sending tones on the telephone line. In its most common implementation, the telephone is equipped with a 12-button keypad. When a button is pressed, electrical contacts are closed that cause two oscillators to generate two tones at specified frequencies, much like pressing two keys on a piano at the same time. The combined tones are the signal for one of the digits. Figure 4–5 shows the combinations of tones generated for each key on the telephone keypad. The frequencies were carefully selected to be different from other tones or signals on the telephone line. To be accepted by the central office, the dial tones must have a duration of at least 50 milliseconds.

Tone dialing is considerably faster than pulse dialing. For example, dialing the number zero with tones takes 50 milliseconds for the tones plus 50 milliseconds between tones for a total of 100 milliseconds or 1/10 of a second. Using the dial pulse technique at 10 pulses per second, it takes 1 second to dial the digit zero. The digit 1 takes the same length of time for either pulse or tone dialing. The average telephone number can be dialed 10 to 15 times faster with tone dialing than with rotary pulses. Tone dialing is replacing pulse dialing because it is faster and because it

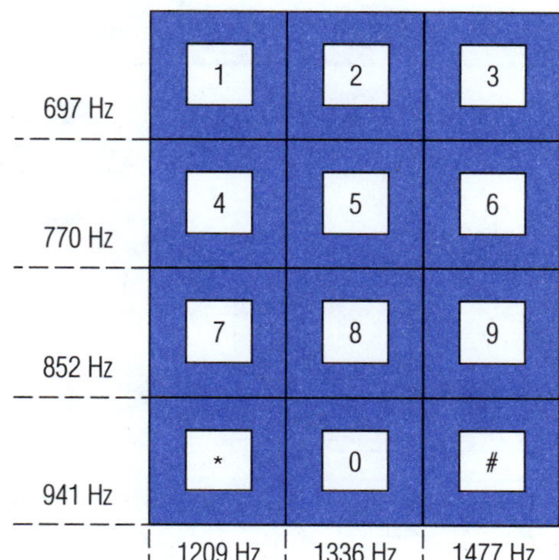

Figure 4–5
DTMF (Touchtone) pad. When the digit 6 is pressed, for example, tones of frequencies 770 Hz and 1477 Hz are sent on the telephone line.

is generated electronically rather than mechanically and is therefore more reliable. The tradename for DTMF dialing is *Touchtone.*

Making the Connection

Figure 4–6 shows the equipment and the facilities involved when a call is made. The connection between the telephone in a residence or business and the local telephone company's central office is called the *local loop.* The building that houses the telephone equipment for a specific geographical area is called the *central office.* When a caller lifts the telephone handset from the cradle, an electrical signal is sent to the central office, signaling it that the person is placing a call. The central office responds by sending the dial tone back on the local loop to the telephone. Assuming things are working normally, the person hears the tone by the time the telephone handset reaches his or her ear.

When the caller dials the number, the number is stored in the telephone switching equipment in the central office. The switching equipment is usually a computer, but in older offices it might still be an electromechanical device. In either case, it is called the *central office switch.* The first three digits of the telephone number determine whether the call is local or long distance. If it is local, the switch determines whether it can complete the call by itself or it needs to forward the call to another nearby central office that handles that telephone number. If the switch can complete the call (because the number being called is also handled through the same central office), it does so, as described below.

If the caller's central office determines from the first three digits of the number that this is a long distance call, it passes the call on to a communication line called a toll trunk to another central office called the toll

Figure 4–6
Diagram of the components of a telephone call.

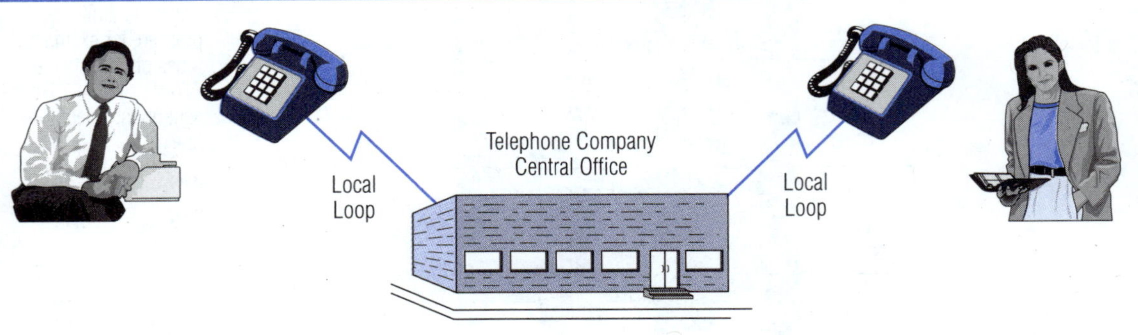

office, as shown in Figure 4–7. From the toll office the call may be passed directly to the central office that handles the receiving telephone or to another toll office. Ultimately a toll office passes the call to the central office that handles the receiving telephone. It is impressive to realize that all of these steps take place in a matter of seconds.

Ringing

When a call has been dialed and a connection through the central office of a telephone network has been made, the telephone company's central office that handles the receiver's telephone indicates the incoming call to the receiving telephone by sending a ringing signal (voltage) to it. This voltage may activate a bell, an electronic ringer, a light, or other device. In the United States and Europe, the ringing signal is sent for 2 seconds with a 4-second pause between rings. Other countries have different timings.

At the same time the ringing signal is being sent to the called telephone, an audio ringing signal is sent to the calling telephone. This signal lets the caller know that the telephone company has completed the call connection process and that the called telephone is ringing. The two ringing signals are generated independently, however, and occasionally the called telephone will be answered before the ringing signal back to the caller has been generated. You may have been surprised by this situation yourself when someone you were calling seemingly answered the call "before it rang."

When the called party picks up the telephone (goes off-hook), a signal is sent to the central office that tells it to stop sending the ringing signal to both the caller and receiver.

tracking call costs

In most cases, it also signals the telephone company to begin charging for the call, although some carriers use other methods to determine when the call begins. Among the long distance carriers, AT&T uses this signal to time all of the long distance calls it handles. By doing so, it mea-

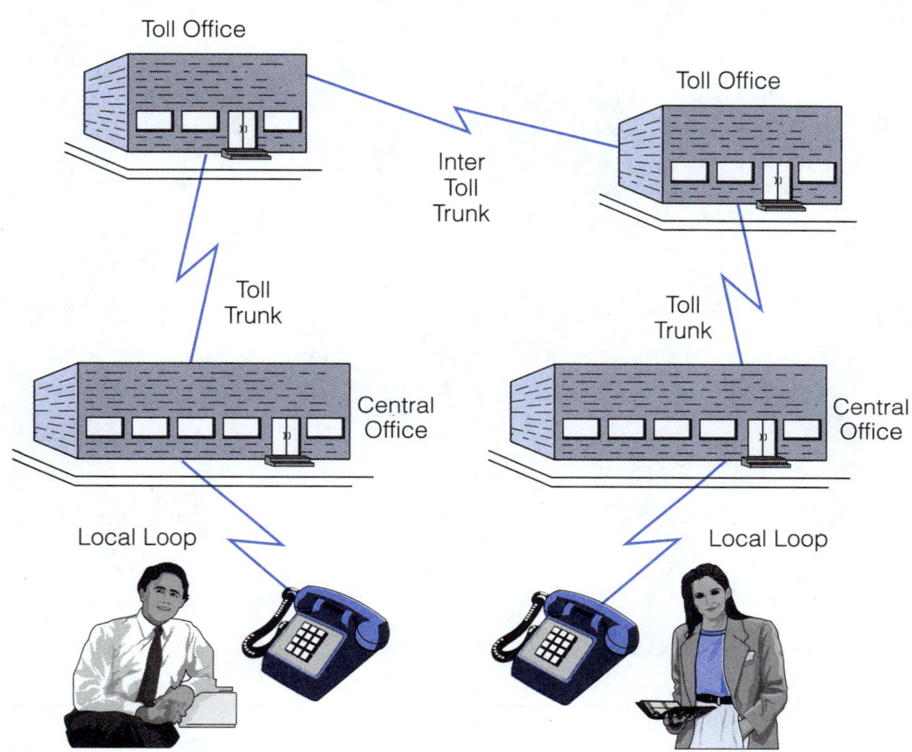

Figure 4–7
Diagram of a telephone call involving toll trunks and toll offices.

sures and charges only for the duration of the conversation. Some of the other carriers include the time to connect the call, which is called *call setup time,* in their charges. Still other carriers subtract a predetermined number of seconds to compensate for an average call setup time, and others measure noise on the line and begin charging for the call when talking begins.

call setup time

■ CENTRAL OFFICE EQUIPMENT

For a short time in the early days of telephones, there was no central office or switching equipment. As described earlier, all telephones had to be connected directly to each other or they could not communicate. Clearly this situation was cumbersome and neither economical nor manageable. Switching (connecting) equipment quickly evolved. The concept is quite simple: All telephones are connected to a central office switch, and the central office switches are connected with one another as illustrated in Figure 4–8.

The early manual telephone switchboard was installed in New York City in 1888. (Property of AT&T Archives. Reprinted with permission of AT&T)

Figure 4–8
It is more efficient to connect telephones to a central office switch and then connect the central office switches together than to connect all telephones to each other.

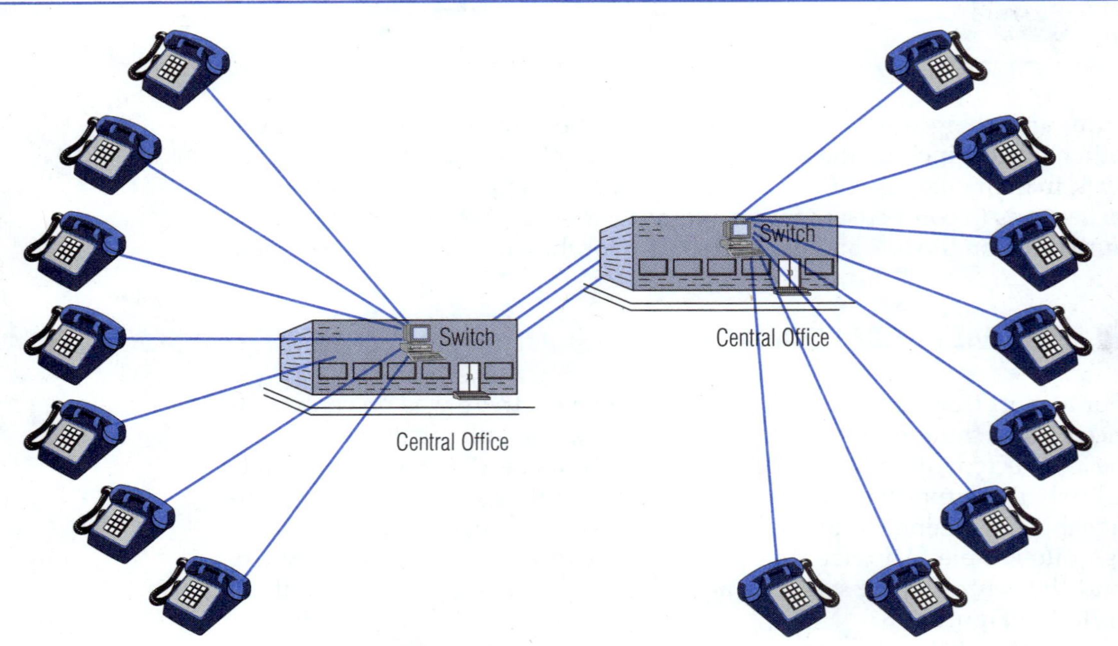

Manual Switching

The earliest type of switching equipment had a central console where all telephone lines terminated in jacks similar to the headphone jack on a stereo receiver. When a caller went off-hook, a light on the console lit, and the operator plugged her headset into the jack and talked to the caller. She got the number to be called and plugged a *patch cord*, a cable with plugs on both ends, into the caller's and receiver's jacks to connect the two. Special jacks were available so that the operator could connect her switchboard to other operator's switchboards and to special lines that went to other cities for long distance calls.

patch cord

Automatic Switching

From the 1920s (when telephones with dials began to replace older style telephones) until today, the connection of telephones at the central office has been increasingly automated. The equipment used has progressed through a series of technologies from *step-by-step switches* (also known as *Strowger switches* after their inventor, Almon B. Strowger), to *crossbar switches* and *reed relays*. Each of these switches was electromechanical and, therefore, more prone to failure than today's electronic switching equipment.

Electronic Switching

With the development of the transistor and the evolution of the integrated circuit, telephone switching equipment has moved rapidly from the electromechanical to the electronic age. Modern central office switches are entirely electronic, and the connection of calls is completed much more rapidly than before. Since the switches are electronic, they are much less prone to hardware failure than their electromechanical predecessors. However, since they are really programmable computers, they are susceptible to program bugs. Central office switches are designed to be highly redundant so that the failure of any portion of the equipment can be circumvented. The most sophisticated central offices are designed to have no more than one total failure in 40 years.

rare central office failures

Electronic central office switches handle thousands of lines. Compared to switches implemented with older technologies, such as step-by-step switches, they are physically much smaller by thousands of square feet. They are also significantly quieter because there are no relay contacts opening and closing or crossbars moving in frames.

As central offices have evolved to electronic switches, the staffing requirement in the central office has dropped dramatically. The main reason is that the newer equipment is more reliable, and fewer maintenance people are required to keep it operating. Another reason is that much of the electronic equipment can be tested remotely and spare equipment switched into the system if necessary. At the same time, the education and skill levels of the central office work force have increased because the newer equipment is more sophisticated. Diagnosing the problems that do

staff costs reduced

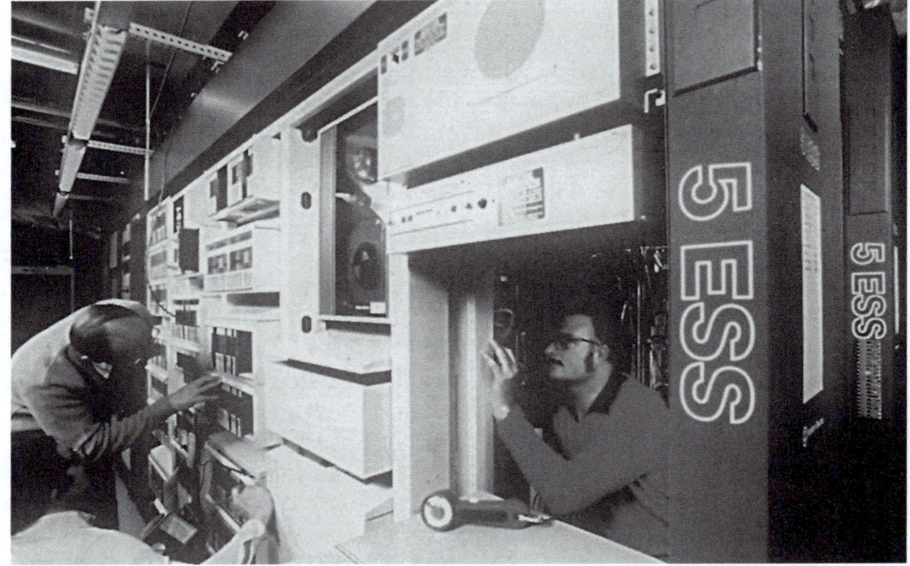

A modern electronic central office switch is a specialized digital computer and is considerably more compact and reliable than earlier mechanical switches. (Property of AT&T Archives. Reprinted with permission of AT&T)

occur requires sensitive electronic test equipment and a knowledge of how to use it to isolate the failure.

Design Considerations

Blocking When telephone facilities are designed to provide good service, designers must make a trade-off between the amount and cost of central office switching equipment and the level of service it provides. It is not necessary to include enough equipment or lines to handle simultaneous calls from every telephone connected to a central office. In normal circumstances, only a small percentage of the telephones are in use at any one time. Therefore, the central office can be designed to handle a fraction of the maximum theoretical number of simultaneous calls. If, however, all of the central office equipment is in use and one more person tries to make a call, that call is said to be blocked because there are no central office facilities available to handle it. The call cannot be completed even though the called number's telephone is not in use. *Blocking* can also occur when all of the lines connecting the central offices are in use. In that case, the central office handling the caller's telephone may be able to handle the call, but it is unable to make a connection to the central office handling the receiver's telephone. Locations where blocking can occur are shown in Figure 4–9.

blocking

In the U.S. telephone system, blocking is rare. When it does occur, the condition is signaled to the caller by either a fast busy signal or a voice recording. The most common occurrences of blocking are when all lines are busy on major holidays, such as Thanksgiving or Mother's Day.

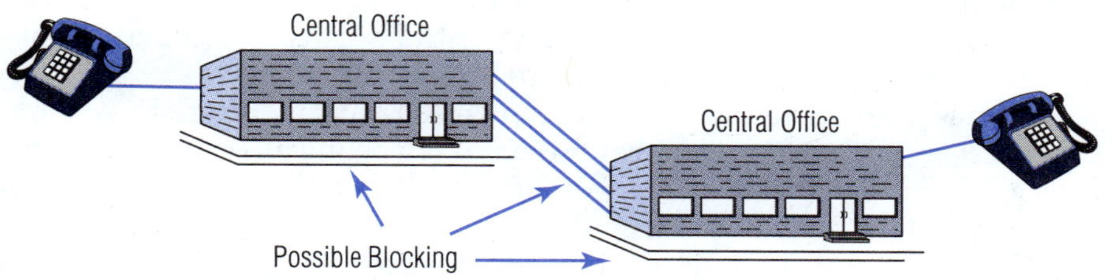

Figure 4–9
Blocking can occur at any central office or on the lines connecting them.

Busy Hour When deciding how much equipment and how many lines to install, the usual procedure is to study or forecast how many calls will occur during the busiest hour of the day. In businesses in the United States, the *busy hour* usually occurs between 10 and 11 A.M., and sometimes another peak occurs between 2 and 3 P.M. By way of contrast, in Japan, the busy hour is between 9 and 10 A.M. Most offices in Japan open at 9 A.M., and Japanese people typically get on the phone as soon as they come to work. Obviously, if enough equipment and lines are installed so that all calls can be handled during the busy hour, there are sufficient facilities available to handle calls made during other hours of the day.

A study of the number of calls to be handled during the busy hour must also take into account their durations. Clearly, eight 3-minute calls tie up more equipment and lines than do eight 1-minute calls. Three 8-minute calls tie up a different mix of equipment than either of the other situations.

For cost reasons, the equipment and lines in a telephone system frequently are designed to handle less traffic than occurs during the busiest hour. When a detailed analysis is performed, the results often show that there is a significant savings in equipment costs by designing the facilities to handle 99, 98, or even 95 percent of the busy hour traffic. This means that 1, 2, or 5 percent of the calls will be blocked, and the caller will have to try again. For most telephone systems, some level of blockage is tolerable.

The study of telephone traffic patterns involves probability and statistics and has grown to be a very rigorous mathematical discipline, although many of the critical calculations have been reduced to tables. The *grade of service* is the proportion of blocked calls to attempted calls expressed as a percentage. If 5 calls of 100 are blocked, the grade of service would be 5/100 or 5 percent. This is designated as a P.05 grade of service. Most public telephone facilities are designed to provide at least a P.01 grade of service, meaning that only 1 call out of 100 would be blocked.

grade of service

■ CENTRAL OFFICE ORGANIZATION

Each central office serves all of the telephones within a specific geographical area. The size of the area served depends on the density of the telephones. In rural areas, the central office might serve many square miles, whereas in New York City many central offices are needed to handle all of the office buildings and residences.

In the United States, there are about 25,000 central offices. The central office acts as the hub for the wires and cable connecting all of the telephones it serves. Wiring comes together in a rack called a *main distribution frame* in the central office from which it connects to the switching equipment.

Central offices are optimized to perform specific functions. Some are primarily designed to switch local telephone calls from and to businesses and residences. This type of central office is commonly known as an *end office.* The central office to which a specific telephone is connected is known as that telephone's *serving central office.*

toll offices

Other central offices, called *toll offices* or *switching offices,* are designed primarily for forwarding long distance calls to other parts of the country. Offices are connected in a weblike pattern that provides a high level of redundancy and alternate routing, as shown in Figure 4–10. Any central office may be connected to any other central office by direct lines, but a major consideration as to whether to connect two offices is the amount of traffic (number of telephone calls) that flows between them. In some cases, several lines are needed to carry the traffic between offices; in other cases, a direct connection is not necessary, and traffic is routed in a less direct fashion.

A call is handled at the lowest level office that can complete it or provide the required service. If a call cannot be handled by the serving central office that first received it, the call is forwarded to the most appropriate central office. The routing is determined by tables stored in the memory of the central office switch. For example, a call from a business in Dallas going to New York City might be routed from the serving central office in Dallas to a toll center serving part of Dallas. The toll center's tables might tell it that calls for New York should be routed to a certain toll office in Atlanta or, if Atlanta is busy, to Saint Louis. The objective of the network is to route the calls to the destination central office in the shortest, fastest way possible.

THE PUBLIC TELEPHONE NETWORK

The *public telephone network,* sometimes called the *public switched telephone network (PSTN),* consists of many distinct pieces. Telephones in a home or business are most commonly connected to their serving central office by

local loop

a pair of copper wires called the *local loop.* In telephone company jargon, these two wires are often referred to as *tip and ring.* In a residential neighborhood, the wire coming from the house, called the *drop wire,* runs to a pole (or underground equivalent) where it joins other similar wires to form a *distribution cable.* Eventually, several distribution cables join to-

Figure 4–10
The connection of the central offices in the nationwide telephone network.

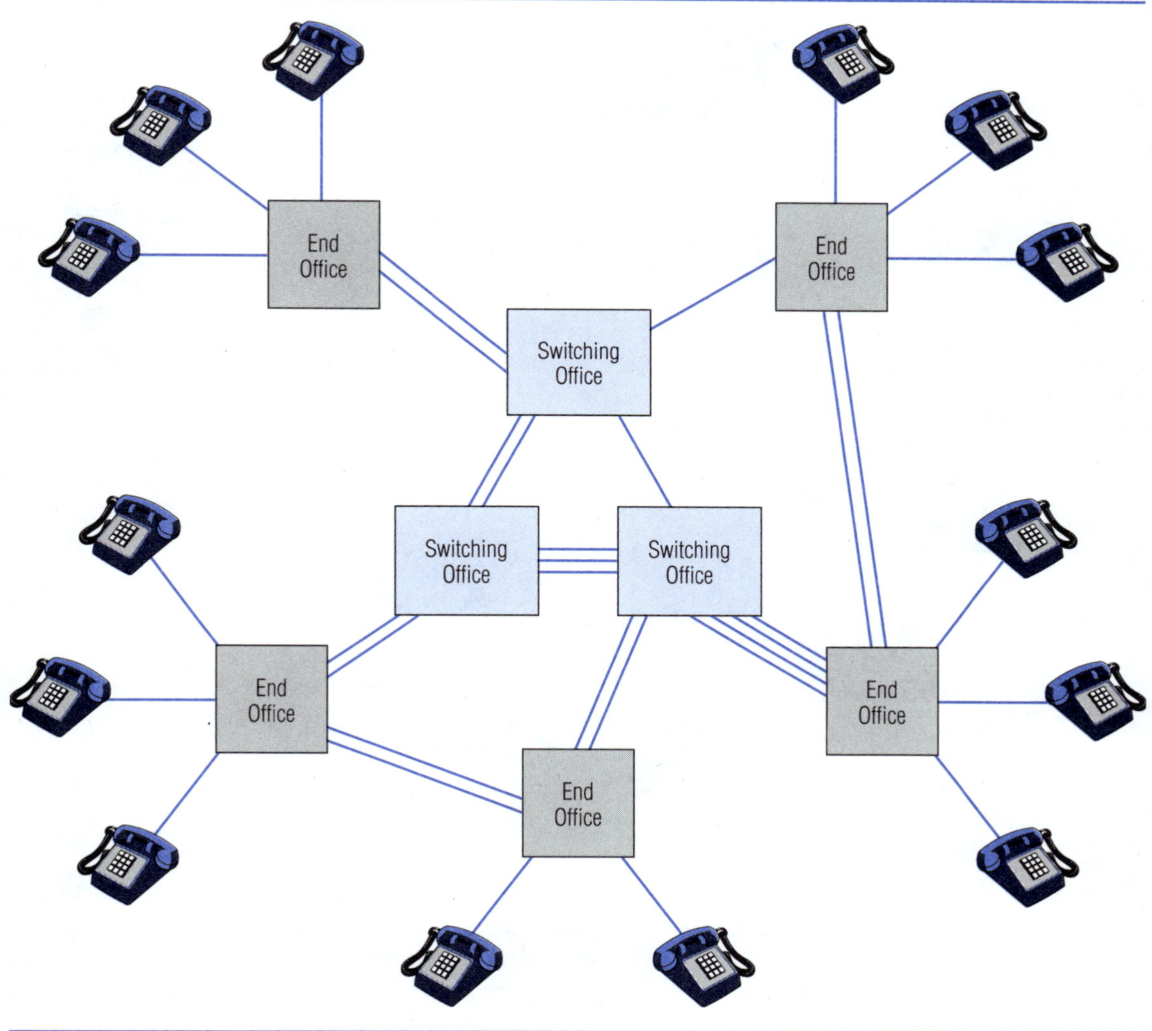

gether to form a *feeder cable* that terminates at the central office, as shown in Figure 4–11. Clearly, the cable gets physically larger the closer it gets to the central office. Cables may run above ground on poles or underground, but most new installations being made today are underground where they are better protected and out of sight.

Central offices are connected to each other with multiple lines called *trunks*. A trunk is defined as a circuit connecting telephone switches or

trunk

Figure 4–11
Residential telephone cabling.

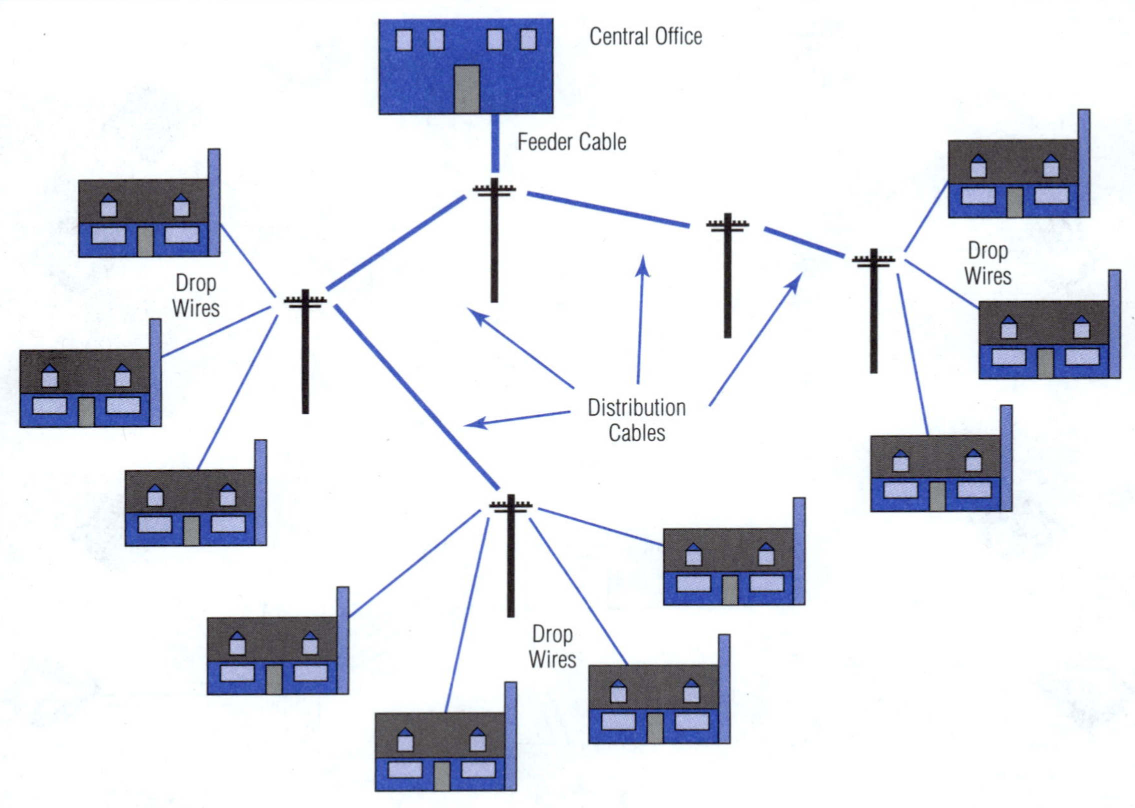

switching locations. (The term *circuit* is defined in Chapter 9, but in the meantime, think of a circuit and a line as being synonymous.) Functionally, a trunk and a line do the same thing—carry communications—but a trunk connects switching equipment, whereas a line connects to a telephone, computer terminal, or other device. Trunks may be implemented with regular copper wire but are more often implemented with coaxial cable, microwave radio, or fiber-optic cable.

The PSTN, with its millions of miles of lines, handles virtually all of the voice and data communications in the world. It is diverse and highly redundant; therefore, it is impervious to massive outages. It is resilient when failures do occur. Most countries consider their public communications network to be a national asset and take steps, including regulation, to protect it.

In the United States, the PSTN is facing a new challenge. Local telephone networks have been engineered under the assumption that the average telephone call lasts about 3 minutes. When users of the Internet or other online services dial up from their computers, they stay on the line an average of 20 minutes, and sometimes for hours. With those local lines tied up, the network and switching equipment can become congested, making it impossible for other people to make calls. Telephone companies and others are studying alternative solutions to this problem, including charging data users on a per-minute basis. One way or another, the problem will be solved, and over time the solution is likely to cost the data user more money.

ANALOG SIGNALS

When voice is converted to an electrical signal through a microphone, it provides a continuously varying electrical wave like the one shown in Figure 4–2. This electrical wave matches the pressure pattern of the sound that created it. The wave is called an *analog signal* because it is analogous to the continually varying sound waves created when sound is generated by speech or other means. (Another type of signal frequently used to transmit voice or data signals is a digital signal.) In order to understand the characteristics of the telephone network, you need to understand something about the characteristics of analog signals.

Signal Frequency

The sound waves we generate when we speak and the electrical waves that result after the sound has been converted for transmission have many common characteristics. One attribute is their *frequency,* which for sound waves is the number of vibrations per second that cause the particular sound. If you strike the A key above middle C on a piano keyboard, you generate a very pure tone that is created by the A string on the piano vibrating back and forth 440 times per second. If you held your telephone up to the piano and struck the A key, the microphone in the telephone handset would convert the 440 vibrations per second to an electrical signal on the telephone line that also changes 440 times per second. This signal is commonly diagrammed as a *sine wave,* as shown in Figure 4–12. Each complete wave is called a *cycle,* and the frequency of the signal is the number of cycles that occur in 1 second. The unit of measure for frequency is the *Hertz,* abbreviated *Hz.* We say that the A key we struck on the piano generated a tone with a frequency of 440 Hz. The corresponding (analogous) electrical signal also has a frequency of 440 Hz. By way of comparison, a higher tone on the piano has a higher frequency. The A key that is an octave above A 440 has a frequency of 880 Hz. The lowest note on the normal piano keyboard has a frequency of 27.5 Hz, and the highest note has a frequency of 4,186 Hz.

sine wave

Figure 4–12
Sine waves of differing frequencies.

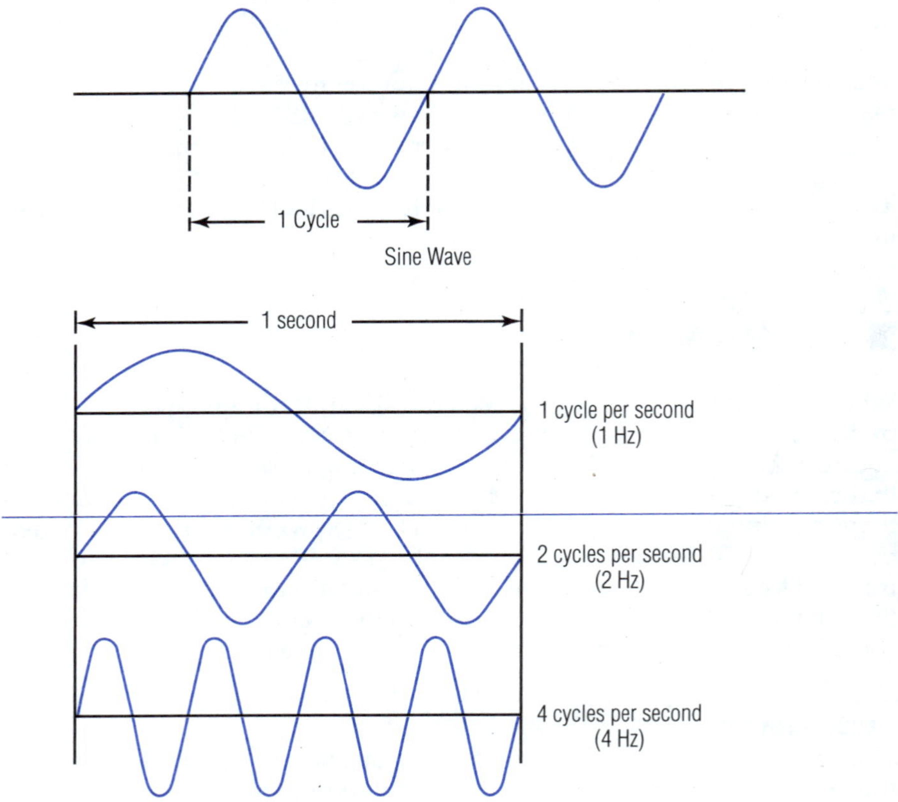

The human ear can hear sound with a range of frequencies from about 20 Hz to approximately 15,000 Hz. Between 15,000 and 20,000 Hz, most people can sense the sound but not actually hear it. Good stereo systems reproduce sounds up to approximately 20,000 Hz and have better fidelity (sound better) than systems that do not reproduce frequencies that high. Figure 4–13 illustrates some of these frequency ranges.

Sound waves, electrical waves traveling in a wire, and electromagnetic waves traveling through space, such as radio waves, have essentially the same characteristics. All are represented as sine waves whose frequency is measured in Hertz. Figures 4–14 and 4–15 show the frequency spectrum, the full range of frequencies from zero Hertz to several hundred thousand million Hertz. When referring to very high frequencies, we commonly use the designations *kilohertz (kHz), megahertz (MHz),* and *gigahertz (gHz)* to more easily describe the frequencies. Figure 4–16 shows the full range of abbreviations used for very large and small units of measure in the scientific world.

Figure 4–13
The frequency ranges of some common sounds.

Maximum acoustical (hearing) range (mostly youngsters) 20 kHz
Typical acoustical range for adults 15 kHz
Voice range 10 kHz
Transmitted voice range 3 kHz
Hz
0
20
30
100
300
3300
10,000
15,000
20,000

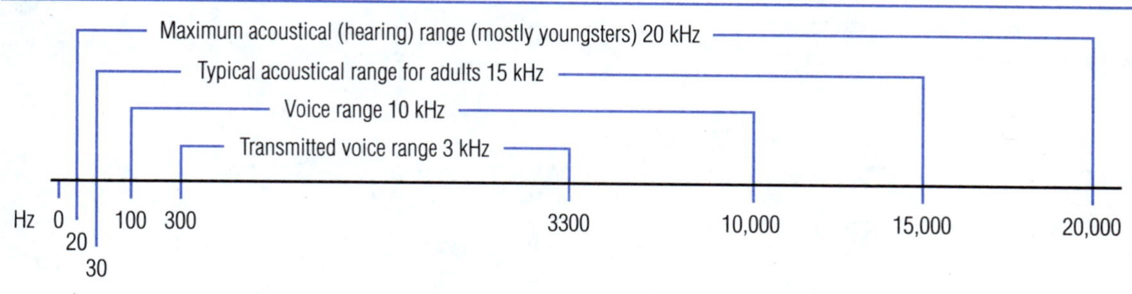

Figure 4–14
The frequency spectrum showing the common names applied to certain frequency ranges.

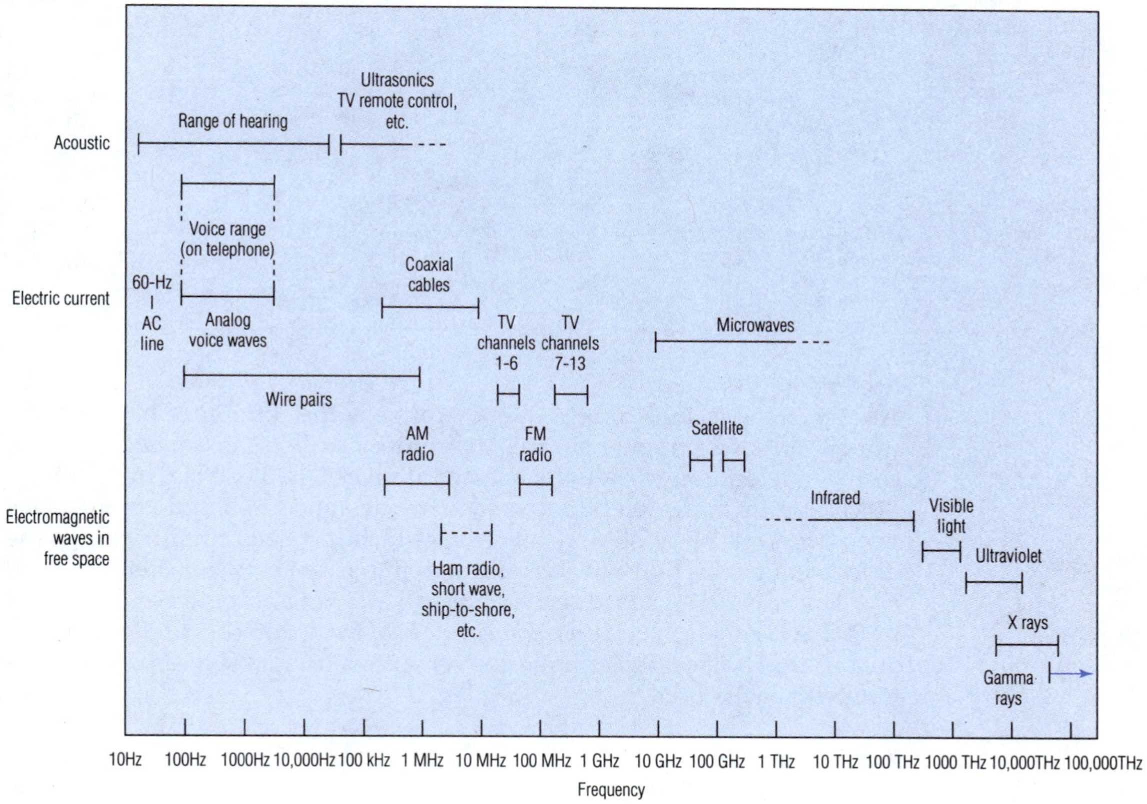

Acoustic
Range of hearing
Ultrasonics TV remote control, etc.
Voice range (on telephone)
Electric current
60-Hz AC line
Analog voice waves
Coaxial cables
Wire pairs
TV channels 1-6
TV channels 7-13
Microwaves
Satellite
AM radio
FM radio
Electromagnetic waves in free space
Ham radio, short wave, ship-to-shore, etc.
Infrared
Visible light
Ultraviolet
X rays
Gamma rays
10Hz
100Hz
1000Hz
10,000Hz
100 kHz
1 MHz
10 MHz
100 MHz
1 GHz
10 GHz
100 GHz
1 THz
10 THz
100 THz
1000 THz
10,000THz
100,000THz
Frequency

Figure 4–15
A more detailed view of the frequency spectrum relevant to telecommunications.

AM radio	.535–1.7 MHz
Shortwave	1.7–30 MHz
Cordless phones	43–49 MHz
TV channels 2–4	54–72 MHz
FM radio	88–108 MHz
Police, weather	150.8–174 MHz
TV channels 7–13	174–216 MHz
Military, space	225–400 MHz
TV channels 14–69	470–824 MHz
Cellular phones	824–849 MHz
Cellular phone towers	869–894 MHz
Airplane phones	894–896 MHz
Pagers	928–932 MHz
Radio astronomy	1,400–1,427 MHz

Figure 4–16
Common abbreviations for very large and very small quantities.

pico	trillionth	.000000000001	1×10^{-12}
nano	billionth	.000000001	1×10^{-9}
micro	millionth	.000001	1×10^{-6}
milli	thousandth	.001	1×10^{-3}
centi	hundredth	.01	1×10^{-2}
deci	tenth	.1	1×10^{-1}
deca	ten	10	1×10^{1}
centa	hundred	100	1×10^{2}
kilo	thousand	1000	1×10^{3}
mega	million	1000000	1×10^{6}
giga	billion	1000000000	1×10^{9}
tera	trillion	1000000000000	1×10^{12}

Bandwidth

Another way to look at a frequency range is the difference between the upper and lower frequency. This difference is called the *bandwidth.* In the case of a telephone signal, the bandwidth is 300 to 3,000 Hz, or 2,700 Hz. Voice circuits in the telephone system are designed to handle frequencies from 0 to 4,000 Hz as shown in Figure 4–17, but special circuitry limits the voice frequencies that can pass through it to those between 300 and 3,000 Hz. The additional space between 0 and 300 Hz and between 3,000 and 4,000 Hz is called the *guard channel* or *guard band,* and it provides a buffer area so that adjacent telephone conversations or data signals don't interfere with each other.

guard band

Signal Amplitude

Another characteristic of analog signals is their loudness, or *amplitude.* As you speak more loudly or softly into the telephone, the sound waves cre-

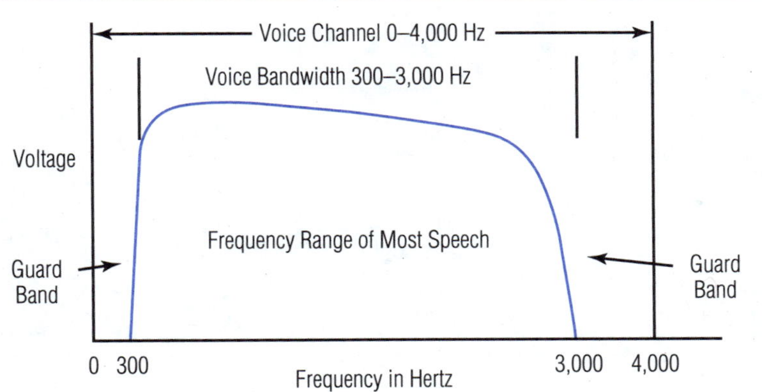

Figure 4–17 Bandwidth of a voice channel.

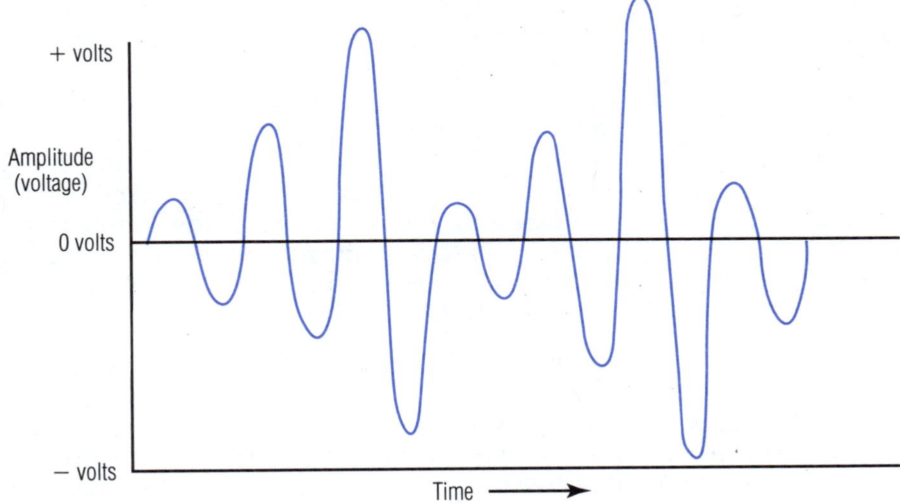

Figure 4–18 Analog wave with constant frequency and varying amplitude.

ate larger and smaller electrical waves that are represented by higher peaks and valleys of the signal's voltage (shown in Figure 4–18). The amplitude of the signal is also called its *level,* and whereas with sound the amplitude relates to loudness, in an electrical signal the amplitude is the difference between its most negative voltage (the lowest point in the sine wave) and its most positive voltage (the highest point in the sine wave).

decibels

Analog signal level is measured in *decibels (dB),* which is a logarithmic ratio of signal input and output power. Because the dB is a logarithmic measure, doubling the strength of a signal increases its level by 3 dB.

Figure 4–19
The relative power of a signal measured in decibels.

Decibels	Relative Power
+30 dB	1000
+20	100
+10	10
+3	2
0 dB	1
−3 dB	1/2
−10	1/10
−20	1/100
−30	1/1000

This is true regardless of the signal's original strength. If we say that a signal increased by 3 dB, we mean it doubled in strength, without knowing what the original or new signal strengths are. In the same way, increasing its strength by a factor of 10 raises its level by 10 dB, by a factor of 100, 20 decibels, and so on. Working in the other direction, we find that reducing the signal to 1/2 of its former level causes the strength to be measured as −3 dB; 1/10 of the power is −10 dB; 1/100 of the power is −20 dB, and so on. Figure 4–19 shows these values.

For electrical telecommunications signals, 0 dB is defined as 1 milliwatt of power. An increase of the power to 2 milliwatts is a doubling of the power, and the signal would therefore have a relative strength of +3 dB. Doubling the power again to 4 milliwatts would yield a signal with a strength of +6 dB. The mathematical formula for the relationship between power and signal strength is

$$dB = 10\log(\text{Power out}/\text{Power in})$$

The quotient of power out to power in is a mathematical way to show the number of times the power was increased. If the power out is 30 watts and the power in was 10 watts, then the power was increased three times and the multiplier used in the formula would be 3. So the formula may be expressed in words as: The decibels = ten times the logarithm of the power increase. By the way, the formula works if the power is decreased too. If the power is reduced from 5 milliwatts to 2 milliwatts, then the multiplier used in the formula would be .4. The reason we need to use logarithms in this equation is that signals traveling through a medium weaken *exponentially* fast. Logarithms relate to exponents and therefore accurately reflect the signal's behavior through a transmission medium.

Decibels and the strength of a signal are of considerable interest in telecommunications. If too much power is put on a line, a particular type of interference called *crosstalk* (which is discussed in Chapter 9) can occur. The loss of signal strength is also of interest because if a signal does not

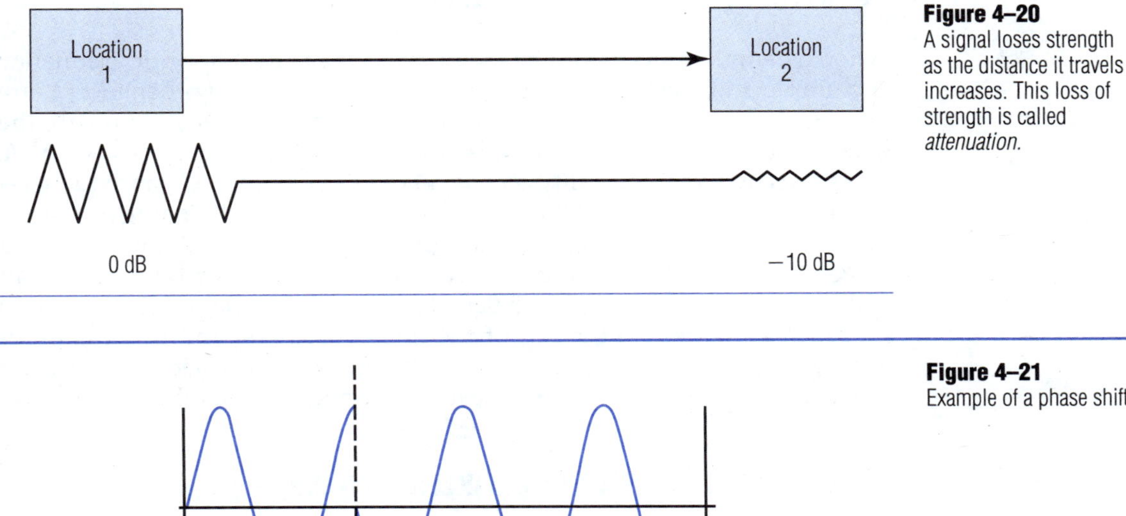

Figure 4–20
A signal loses strength as the distance it travels increases. This loss of strength is called *attenuation.*

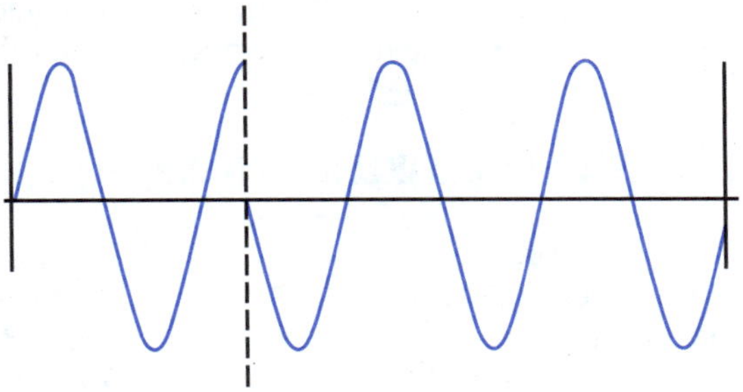

Figure 4–21
Example of a phase shift.

have enough strength at the receiving end of a communication path, it will be unusable. This loss, which is called *attenuation,* is measured between two points on a line as shown in Figure 4–20. At the point where the signal is injected on the line, it has a certain strength. As the signal moves away, its strength is reduced due to the attenuation of the line. The reduction is measured in decibels.

attenuation

Signal Phase

A third attribute of an analog signal is called its *phase.* In contrast to frequency and amplitude, phase is harder to relate to the physical world and, therefore, is somewhat harder to understand. Sine waves can be measured in degrees, where 360° is one complete cycle of the wave. A signal's phase is the relative position of the sine wave measured in degrees. Figure 4–21 shows a sine wave that appears to break and start again, skipping a portion of the wave. This is a phase shift. Since 1/4 of the wave has been skipped, it is called a 90° phase shift. Phase shifts are created and detected by electronic circuitry.

While amplitude and frequency changes can be detected by the human ear, phase changes cannot, and they therefore are of little importance in voice transmission. They are very important in data transmission, however.

ATTRIBUTES OF A VOICE SIGNAL

Whereas single tones produce clean sine waves of a specific frequency and amplitude, the human voice, music, noise, and most other sounds are made up of a large range of frequencies and amplitudes. As a result, the wave pattern is far more complex than the simple sine waves we have looked at thus far. Normal speech is made up of sounds with frequencies in the range of 100 to 6,000 Hz, but most of the speech "energy" falls in the 300 to 3,000 Hz range. Although some people with high-pitched voices emit occasional sounds above 6,000 Hz, the majority of the sound still falls in the range of 300 to 3,000 Hz. That is why the public telephone system is designed so that all of the lines, handsets, and other components will pass voice frequencies in that range. Frequencies outside that range are filtered out by electronic circuitry and are not allowed to pass.

FREQUENCY DIVISION MULTIPLEXING (FDM)

While the individual telephone circuit has a bandwidth of 4,000 Hz, the pair of wires or other media carrying it has a much higher bandwidth capacity. Twisted-pair wires have a bandwidth of approximately 1 million Hz. Dividing 4,000 Hz into 1 million Hz shows us that, at least theoretically, a standard pair of telephone wires should be able to carry approximately 250 telephone conversations. This is a very theoretical number; in practice 12 or 24 voice signals normally are carried. Naturally, the telephone company would like to take advantage of the ability to carry multiple conversations on one line, especially on trunk lines between central offices in which hundreds of telephone calls are handled simultaneously.

The technique of packing several analog signals (phone calls in this case) onto a single wire (or other media) is called *frequency division multiplexing (FDM).* It is accomplished by translating each voice channel to a different part of the frequency spectrum that the media can carry. Using the telephone wire pair as an example, if a second voice signal could be relocated from its natural frequency of 0 to 4,000 Hz to, say, 4,000 to 8,000 Hz, and a third voice signal relocated to 8,000 to 12,000 Hz (as shown in Figure 4–22), many telephone conversations could be packed on one pair of wires.

MODULATION

carrier wave

Frequency division multiplexing is accomplished by transmitting a sine wave signal in the new frequency range in which the original signal is to be relocated. The new sine wave is called a *carrier wave,* not to be confused with a *common carrier.* The carrier wave in itself contains no information, but its attributes are changed corresponding to the information in the

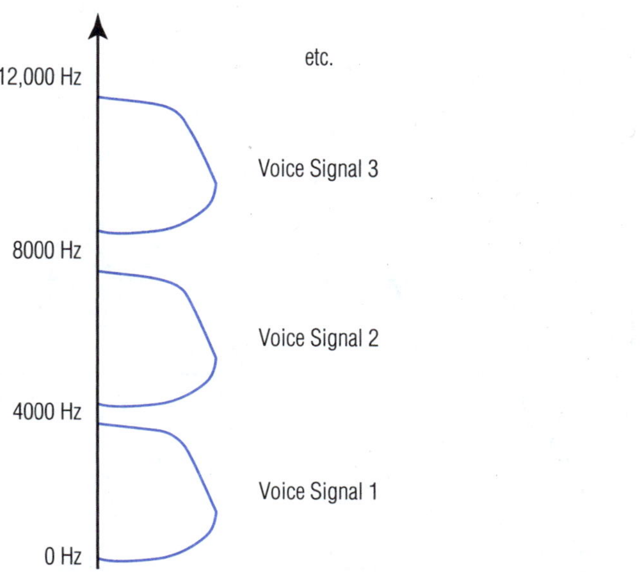

Figure 4–22
Frequency multiplexed voice signals.

original signal. This change to the carrier wave is called *modulation.* Modulation converts a communication signal from one form to another, more appropriate form for transmission over a particular medium between two locations.

AM, FM, and PM

You have learned that there are three attributes of the sine waves that can be changed. If the amplitude is changed, it is called *amplitude modulation (AM);* changing the frequency is called *frequency modulation (FM);* and changing the phase is called *phase modulation (PM).* Amplitude and frequency modulation are shown in Figure 4–23. Combinations of these modulation techniques are also possible, for example, phase amplitude modulation (PAM).

Shifting the frequency of a signal to a different frequency range is one important use of modulation, and the result is that the original signal is relocated to a different set of frequencies. At the receiving end, an electronic circuit called a *detector* must be able to unscramble the modulated signal and relocate it back to the original frequencies—a process called *demodulation.* In the telephone example, the modulation of the original 0 to 4,000 Hz voice signal occurs at the central office serving the person who is speaking, and the demodulation occurs at the serving central office near the listener.

multiplexers

Multiplexing equipment (multiplexers) at the central office pack groups of twelve 4 kHz voice signals into 48 kHz signals called *base groups, channel groups,* or just *groups.* Other multiplexers then pack five 48 kHz groups into *supergroups,* which have a bandwidth of 240 kHz and contain 60 voice

Figure 4–23
Amplitude and frequency modulation.

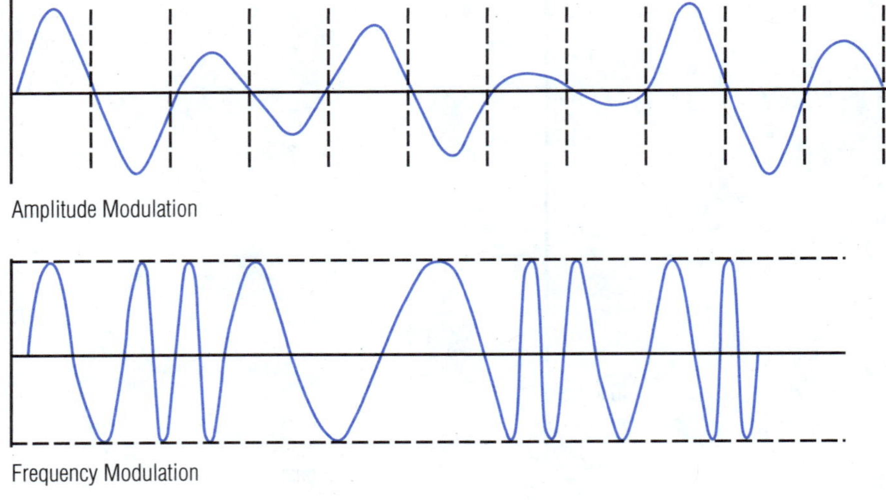

Figure 4–24
The hierarchy of voice channels as they are multiplexed together.

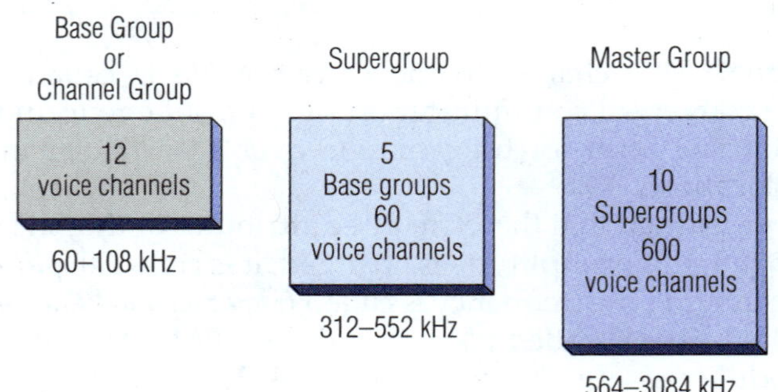

signals. Ten supergroups are multiplexed into *master groups,* or even larger *jumbo groups* for long distance transmission. You can see from Figure 4–24 that as it travels from transmitter to receiver, the individual 4 kHz voice signal is modulated to different frequencies several times by the FDM equipment of the telephone company. As a result, lines and trunks are used efficiently between telephone company offices where traffic volume is high.

Although the above discussion shows how the telephone companies can achieve efficiency through FDM techniques, it must be pointed out that they have changed virtually all of their high-speed trunks and interoffice communications to digital transmission, which yields even higher efficiencies. Digital techniques are of course applicable to data transmission as well. Suffice it to say for now that when a voice signal is digitized, it becomes a stream of bits that is indistinguishable from digitized data. As a result, digital voice and data signals can be multiplexed together on the same line, and the efficiencies are higher than with the analog techniques that have been discussed so far.

TASI VOICE TRANSMISSION

A technique that has long been used on undersea cables is called *time assignment speech interpolation (TASI).* TASI is another way of packing multiple voice conversations onto a single telephone line. TASI takes advantage of the fact that there are pauses in speech and that approximately 10 percent of the time in a normal voice conversation, no one is speaking. TASI equipment detects when a person starts speaking and, within a few milliseconds, assigns a communication circuit to the speaker. Although a very small amount of the first syllable may be lost, it is almost undetectable by the listener. When the person stops talking, the communications circuit is taken away and assigned to another speaker. When the person starts talking again, a new circuit is assigned.

Using TASI, 100 talkers require only about 45 circuits to carry their conversations. Therefore, when the volume of calls is high, TASI provides a way to economize on the number of circuits required.

INTEROFFICE SIGNALING

Direct Current (DC) Signaling

In addition to carrying voice signals, the telephone lines must also carry various other kinds of signals used to set up a telephone call and indicate its status. One type of signaling occurs simply by opening or closing the electrical circuit between the telephone handset and the central office. This is called *direct current (DC) signaling*. DC signaling is used primarily between the serving central office and the customer. It is analogous to turning on a light switch that allows electrical current to flow to a light bulb. The electrical current required for DC signaling is generated by a power supply at the serving central office.

As used on the local loop, DC signaling works as follows. When the telephone handset is on-hook, the circuit is open, and no current can flow. When the handset is lifted, the circuit is closed, current flows to the central office, and it sends a dial tone (a tone signal) to the handset.

Another type of DC signaling is pulse dialing. When a digit is pulsed, the flow of current is interrupted by the pulsing mechanism (a rotary dial or its electronic equivalent), which opens and closes the circuit a certain number of times depending on which digit is being dialed.

Tone Signaling

Another type of signaling used in the telephone system is *tone signaling*. When you lift the handset, you hear a *dial tone* (assuming everything is working) that is a combination of a 350 Hz tone and a 440 Hz tone. On telephones with DTMF dialing, each button pressed creates a tone also made up of a combination of two frequencies. As the call is set up, you either hear a *ringing signal* that is a combination of 440 Hz and 480 Hz tones, a *busy signal* that is a combination of 480 Hz and 620 Hz tones, or a congestion signal, which means that toll trunks between central offices are busy. This is sometimes called the *fast busy* and is made up of tones with a frequency of 480 plus 620 Hz that are sent more rapidly than a normal busy signal. If you leave your telephone off-hook, you get an *off-hook* signal that combines tones at 1,400 Hz, 2,060 Hz, 2,450 Hz, and 2,600 Hz. This signal is much louder than the others in order to get your attention. All of these tone signals are collectively called *progress tones* because they indicate the progress of your call.

fast busy

Other signal tones are used between central offices. For example, the DC signal generated by a pulse dial telephone cannot be transmitted between central offices, so it is converted to tone signals at the originating central office. This conversion is an example of *E&M signaling*—a special type of signaling that takes place between switching equipment.

Notice that all of the tones mentioned so far fall in the 300 to 3,000 Hz frequency range allowed for the voice signal. These are called *in-band signals*. Most of the tones that the central offices use for signaling each other also use in-band signals, but frequencies between the 3,000 Hz cutoff for the voice signal and the 4,000 Hz boundary of the telephone circuit are sometimes used. These are called *out-of-band signals*, and the most commonly used frequency is 3,700 Hz.

in-band signals

out-of-band signals

Common Channel Signaling

The most important signaling between central offices occurs on a special network of lines that are reserved exclusively for signaling information. This network, called the *common channel interoffice signaling* (CCIS) system, uses a set of signals called *Signaling System No. 7* or *SS7*. SS7 was first proposed by the ITU-T in 1980 and updated in 1984 and 1987, and the implementation is essentially complete in the United States and in most other countries.

SS7

SS7 uses separate lines to set up telephone calls from those used for the actual voice or data transmission. The advantage of using a separate signaling system is that you don't have to tie up a regular telephone line until the call is actually established. Since up to 40 percent of calls that are attempted result in busy signals or no answer, SS7 saves a great deal of time on the actual voice lines.

SS7 is optimized for use in digital telecommunications networks in conjunction with intelligent, computerized switches in the central offices.

It allows for database access as a part of the call setup, and that allows the telephone companies to provide certain enhanced telephone services, such as automatic callback and calling number identification. Implementing SS7 has been a big job for the telephone companies in the last few years, but the benefits to the companies and telephone users far outweigh the costs.

TELEPHONE NUMBERING

Under the guidance of the international standards group, the ITU-T, a reasonably consistent numbering plan exists for telephones around the world. This ensures that every telephone number, in its fully expanded form, is unique. According to the ITU-T plan, the world is divided into 9 geographic zones:

1. North America;
2. Africa;
3. Europe (part);
4. Europe (part);
5. South and Central America;
6. South Pacific;
7. Russia and Eastern Europe;
8. Far East;
9. Middle East and Southeast Asia.

Countries within each zone are assigned country codes beginning with the zone's digit. The countries that have, or are projected to have, the most telephones are assigned one-digit country codes; countries with the fewest number of phones are assigned three-digit country codes. In general, the form of a telephone number is as shown in Figure 4–25. The area code is sometimes shortened to one or two digits. In some countries it is called a *routing code* or *city code*, but the results are the same.

The North American Numbering Plan (NANP) (www.nanpa.com) covers the United States, Canada, and some Caribbean countries. This territory has been divided into areas, each with a unique three-digit area code. Areas in close geographical proximity to one another have area codes that are quite different to avoid confusion and accidental misdialing. Approximately 800 area codes are available for assignment.

The first three digits of a seven-digit telephone number are called the *exchange code*. Within each area code, the exchange codes are unique. Most central offices handle more than one exchange code, although some of the smaller offices only handle one. For example, a central office might handle exchange codes beginning with 631, 839, and 832.

exchange code

Figure 4–25
The general form of a telephone number and sample country and area/city codes of several countries.

Country Code		Area/City Code		Exchange Code		Subscriber Code
XXX	-	NXX	-	NXX	-	XXXX

where X = 0 – 9 (any digit)
N = 2 – 9
0/1 = 0 or 1

Sample Countries and Area/City Codes

Country	Country Code	Area/City Code	Area
United States	1	212	New York City
		616	Western Michigan
Australia	61	2	Sydney
Brazil	55	11	Sao Paulo
Ireland	353	1	Dublin
		91	Galway
Japan	81	3	Tokyo
United Kingdom	44	1	London
		222	Cardiff
Germany	49	069	Frankfurt
		89	Munich

LOCAL CALLING

Local calling is defined as telephone service within a designated *local service area.* The local service area includes telephones served by the central office and usually several other central offices nearby. Calls within a local service area are *local calls.* Local calls are charged in one of two ways. *Flat rate service* gives the user a specified and sometimes unlimited number of local calls for a flat monthly rate. *Measured rate service* bases the charges for local calls on the number of calls, their duration, or the distance.

Local service areas frequently overlap as shown in Figure 4–26. Mayville's local service area includes Middleburg, Freeland, and Wanigas. Bayport's is Hopedale, Freeland, and Wanigas. Freeland's local service area includes all of the communities shown.

LONG DISTANCE CALLING

There are two types of *long distance calls.* Both are sometimes referred to as *direct distance dialing (DDD). Toll calls* are calls outside of the local service area but within the LATA. Toll calls are handled by the local exchange carrier (telephone company), which also does the billing. The other type

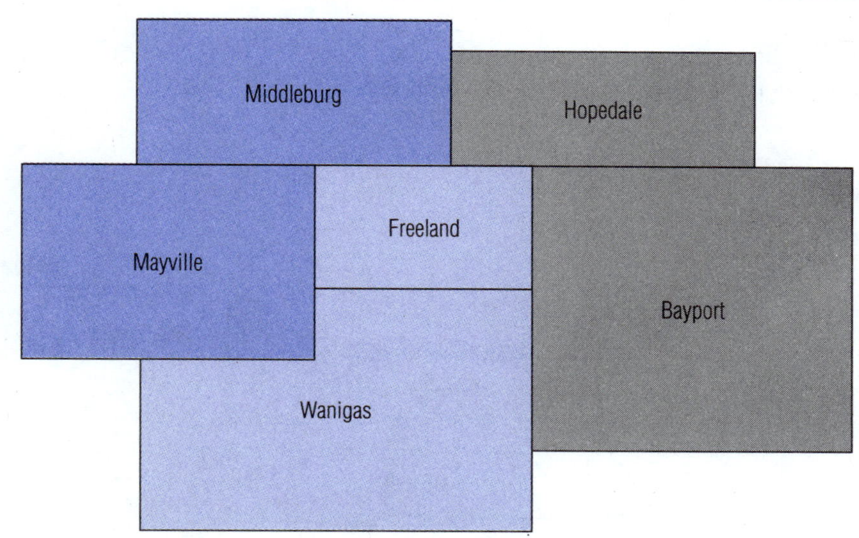

Figure 4–26
A local service area usually includes the territory covered by several central offices.

of long distance call is one that crosses LATA boundaries and must be handled by an interexchange carrier (IXC).

Recall that LECs provide telephone service within a service area consisting of one or more LATAs. Until the advent of the Telecommunications Act of 1996, LECs could not provide service across LATA boundaries; that type of service was classified as long distance and had to be provided by the long distance carriers (IXCs). Looking at Figure 4–27, you can see that because the caller and receiver are in different LATAs, Ameritech had to pass a call between Lansing and Detroit to one of the IXCs, even though Ameritech serves both cities. Because the call crossed LATA boundaries it was a long distance call. Now that restriction is lifted, and Ameritech is allowed to carry the call.

When someone calls out of a LATA, a long distance carrier's facilities are accessed by appending an access code to the front of the telephone number. Each long distance carrier has its own three-digit code. To reach a long distance carrier, the access code 10 must first be dialed, to let the central office know that a carrier's code—and not a telephone number—follows. The total sequence is

Access Code	**Carrier's Code**	**Area Code**	**Telephone Number**
10	XXX	NXX	NXX-XXXX

To reduce the number of digits that have to be dialed, each telephone customer designates one long distance carrier as its primary carrier, and

Figure 4–27
An inter-LATA call from Lansing to Detroit is considered to be a long distance call even though Ameritech serves both cities.

that company can be reached with the single-digit access code 1. The shortened form of the long distance number is

Prefix	**Area Code**	**Telephone Number**
1	NXX	NXX-XXXX

To reach a carrier other than the designated primary carrier, the caller must dial that company's prefix plus the carrier's normal three-digit code.

international direct distance dialing

operator service

Telephone calls to most foreign countries can be completed automatically by dialing an international access code, which is 011 in the United States, then the country code, the city/area code, and the foreign telephone number. Some foreign telephone numbers are seven digits long, as in the United States, and some are eight digits, as in Japan or Australia. Dialing an international telephone is called *international direct distance dialing.*

Although the vast majority of long distance calls are self-dialed by the caller, operator services still exist. When a telephone operator places a call, a premium is paid for the operator assistance, but the per-minute rates for the call are the same as for self-dialed calls. Certain types of calls, such as collect calls, calls billed to a third number, and person-to-person calls, must be set up by an operator. However, calling card calls are rapidly being automated. The burden is placed back on the caller to enter the calling card number through a DTMF telephone.

As an additional way of automating the process of placing calls, many of the telephone companies have implemented speech recognition systems. Callers are instructed to "touch or say" a digit or series of digits to obtain the service they need. Callers with rotary dial telephones may speak the digit to select the service they want. Of course, callers with a DTMF telephone may either touch the digit on the telephone's keypad or speak the digit to obtain the service.

SPECIAL TYPES OF TELEPHONE SERVICES

Everything that has been discussed in this chapter so far can loosely be called *plain old telephone service (POTS)*, and while the term is somewhat humorous, in fact it is used industry wide and is well understood among telecommunications professions. POTS is basic telephone service with no extra features or frills.

plain old telephone service

Many people and businesses have special situations, however. They may make a large number of calls, need to have the telephone answered when they aren't at home, want to know who is calling before they answer, or have any number of other special requirements. To meet these needs, telephone companies offer a number of special calling services, including extra service features available on residential and business phones, and discounted prices for high-volume telephone use. Many of these services are specially oriented to the customer who has particular calling patterns, such as a large number of calls from a certain part of the country or the desire for the receiver to pay for the call instead of the calling party. Plans that are aimed at long distance calling are offered by the interexchange carriers (IXCs), while those aimed at residential or business telephone use are offered by the local exchange carriers (LECs).

Telephone Service Features

LECs offer a number of enhanced features that can simplify or improve telephone service beyond what is available with POTS. The specific services each company offers will vary, and customers must evaluate each service on its own merits to determine whether it provides useful value.

Caller identification provides the number of the calling party to the called party as the telephone is ringing. The number is displayed on the telephone, if it has the ability, or on a small box that sits alongside the telephone. Telephone subscribers can specify that they don't want their number displayed when they make a call.

Call forwarding automatically transfers incoming calls to a different number. This feature is often useful to people who have a home office. When they are away, they can still receive calls, and the caller may not be any the wiser that the person they are calling is not "in the office."

The call waiting feature automatically sounds a tone that alerts you of another incoming call. You can put one call on hold to accept another by pressing the receiver button and continue to switch back and forth between calls if necessary.

Three-way conference calling allows you to speak to two other people at the same time. It can often eliminate a lot of back-and-forth calling.

Discounted Calling

Customers who make a large number of long distance calls are eligible for discounts from the normal charges. One category of discounting is based on call volume, measured by the amount of money spent for long distance calls each month. For example, if an individual or business has more than $100 per month in long distance calls, it may receive a 10 percent discount. If the call volume is greater than $500 per month, a discount of 20 percent may apply. Call volumes over $3,000 per month might receive a 35 percent discount, and so on. Each long distance carrier has its own plan, but all are similar.

Very large customers, those spending more than $10,000 per month, qualify for even higher discounts of 45 or 50 percent. Usually, however, they are required to have a direct connection to the long distance carrier's nearest point of presence (POP). This full-time line is capable of carrying at least 20 or 25 simultaneous voice calls. Long distance calls are routed through the dedicated line to the POP and from the POP on the public telephone network. For these very large customers, the cost of the special access line is usually well justified because they can obtain the larger discounts.

Regardless of the size of the customer and whether it is residential or business, the telephone companies have a wide variety of discount plans that may save money. The plans change quickly so it is worth inquiring and then staying in touch with the telephone companies. This is not to suggest that it makes sense to switch residential services every time one of the telephone companies calls, but rather that if you or your company has established calling patterns or specific calling needs, a discussion with a telephone company representative about your requirements may yield cost savings.

800 Service

The *800 service* provides numbers that allow toll-free calls; the cost of the call is paid by the sponsor of the 800 service. There is a widespread perception that 800 calls are "free," but indeed they are not! Telephone numbers that are part of an 800 service plan begin with the familiar 800 or the newer 888, 877, 866, or 855 area codes. Companies provide 800 numbers so that their customers or prospective customers can call for information, to place an order, or for technical service.

Each of the long distance carriers offers a variety of 800 service plans based on the coverage needed, the number of hours a month the service will be used, and in some plans, the distance of the calls.

All 800 numbers are stored in a nationwide database. When an 800 number is dialed, the LEC queries the database, using SS7, to find out which IXC provides service for that number, and passes the call to that company. Because of the central database many special features are available to 800 service users. Incoming calls may be routed to different locations depending on the time of day, the day of the week, or the location from which the call originated. The caller may be prompted to enter a digit to indicate which of several parties he or she wishes to speak to. Incoming calls can be automatically rerouted in case of an emergency or a temporary shutdown of a call center, for example, for training.

Outbound 800 service provides discounted calling with the cost depending on the duration, distance, and volume of the calls. Companies use this service when employees must make many calls to various parts of the country. The price would be less, for example, if all of the calls were to adjoining states rather than spread throughout the country.

Many countries offer toll-free plans similar to 800 service. There is also a coordinated global service called *Universal International Freephone Numbering (UIFN)*, which, for countries that choose to participate, allows the same toll-free number to be used globally. Billing for UIFN calls goes back to the sponsor of the toll-free number, regardless of where the call originates.

The 800 service offerings are very profitable for the telephone companies because, in most cases, no special equipment is required and standard telephone lines are used. The main difference in the service is the way the calls are billed. As a result, the 800 service offerings tend to be quite dynamic because the telephone companies can essentially offer a new service by changing the computerized billing program.

900 Service

The *900 service* is a sponsored service for businesses that have a message they wish to convey to the public. The message may be prerecorded, such as an advertisement, or live, such as listening to the astronauts on the space shuttle. The message (recorded or live) is controlled by the sponsor and can be changed as often as needed.

Normally the caller pays for the call, although the sponsor may elect to pay. The charges for the call vary, but after a certain volume of calls or call-minutes is reached, the sponsor begins earning income on each additional call-minute. There are other charges to the sponsor that depend on the number of calls made to the 900 number.

Another use for 900 service is for taking public opinion surveys. A question may be asked of the public in newspapers, on television, or through other mass media. Callers call one 900 number to express a positive vote and another 900 number for a negative vote.

Because of controversy surrounding the costs of 900 calls—which can be quite high—and the messages that some of the sponsors play, the telephone companies offer a service to block outgoing 900 calls. Any telephone subscriber can tell the telephone company not to allow 900 calls to be made from his or her telephone, and any attempted calls will be stopped (blocked) in the telephone company office.

Software Defined Network

The *software defined network (SDN)* is another bulk pricing offering designed for large companies. A business accesses SDN on either dedicated or dial lines, after which the calls are carried on the carrier's normal long distance network. In addition to a discounted price, SDN provides some additional services, such as seven-digit dialing to all company locations that are connected to the network and special billing. Additionally, the network can be defined so that special authorization codes are required by individuals to make certain types of calls.

Foreign Exchange (FX) Lines

If a telephone customer makes or receives many telephone calls from a particular city, a *foreign exchange (FX) line* can be installed. An FX line provides access to a remote telephone company central office so that it appears as though the subscriber has a telephone in that city. If a company in Dallas had a foreign exchange line to Houston, employees in Dallas could make Houston telephone calls at local Houston rates. Also, the company would have a Houston telephone number that, when called, would ring at the company switchboard in Dallas. Companies located outside a major city often have FX lines to the heart of the city if they make many telephone calls or want to provide a local telephone number for their customers who are located downtown.

An FX line can handle calls in either direction but, of course, only one call at a time. The subscriber pays a flat monthly rate for the line, plus a per-call charge from the local carrier.

In order to decide which of the many discount pricing plans is best for a given company, a network analyst needs a knowledge of the number and duration of the telephone calls that will use the service, calling patterns by location and time of day, and information about the carrier's discount pricing plans. The carriers will help the customer analyze a firm's requirements for these services by performing a traffic study of telephone call frequency, length, and distribution patterns, hoping, of course, to influence the customer to buy more services.

Integrated Services Digital Network (ISDN)

The *Integrated Services Digital Network (ISDN)* is an offering of the telephone companies that is applicable in some businesses and homes. ISDN service, which will be discussed in detail in Chapter 9, provides a high-speed line that may be used for one voice circuit and one 64 kbps data circuit, or one 128 kbps data circuit. For homes or small businesses that need simultaneous voice and dial-up data capability (for example, to access the Internet), ISDN may be a good fit. In the United States the ISDN offerings of the telephone companies all vary slightly, and have been notoriously hard to install and make operational. However, progress has been made, and the service is becoming more widely used. In other countries, such as Japan and Australia, ISDN has been standardized at a national level and is widely available and is used frequently by businesses and residential customers.

Telephone Calls on the Internet

Making telephone calls on the Internet uses a technology called *voice over IP (VoIP)*. Internet telephone calls are only a subset of the uses of this technology because IP is primarily a data communications protocol that is used much more widely than on the Internet. But anywhere the VoIP technology is employed, voice calls can be made. The IP protocol will be discussed, but suffice it to say here that to use VoIP, telephone calls must be converted to digital signals and divided into small pieces called *packets*, which are sent through the network independently. Each packet may travel by a different route to its destination, and each packet risks the possibility of being delayed. The result of these conversions, path differences, and timing issues is that it is possible for voice calls that travel on the Internet (or any other IP-based network) to be of variable and sometimes poor quality compared to what we expect from the normal voice network. Nonetheless, the technical problems are being worked out, and there is an intense amount of interest in developing the VoIP technology to the point where the quality of the calls is at least as good as what we are used to on the public switched network today.

voice over IP

The reason that is usually stated for wanting to place telephone calls on the Internet is that the calls are free. While this may be true in the short term, if the number of telephone calls grows, the capacity of the Internet will have to be expanded, and that cost will eventually get passed back to the users. So while users might not pay for Internet telephone calls directly, they may find that the cost of Internet access goes up faster than it would if the Internet wasn't used for telephone calls. While this is difficult to measure, except in a macroeconomic sense, one must rely on the basic principle that nothing is free, not even the Internet.

So the real reasons that companies are so interested in developing VoIP capabilities are that it allows voice signals to be transmitted using the latest digital technologies, and to avoid the constraints of the current voice network, which was originally designed for analog transmission and then later converted to be able to carry digital signals. Using VoIP, voice transmission can be sent using much less bandwidth than is required on the PSTN, yielding more efficient use of wire circuits, fiber optic cables, and the other components that make up a digital network.

PRIVATE TELEPHONE SYSTEMS

When a business requires more than two or three telephones, it usually acquires some type of private telephone system to provide special services and help manage the telephone traffic. As a company grows, a large number of the telephone calls that are made are intraoffice calls from one department to another or one building to another. Without a private telephone system, each telephone would require a local loop connection to the central office, and each call would have to go through the public telephone network—even if it were destined for an office just down the hall. With a private telephone system connected as shown in Figure 4–28, the intraoffice calls can be handled internally, and only external calls must be sent to the telephone company's central office.

Earlier in the chapter, a *trunk* was defined as a circuit connecting telephone switches or switching locations. Our previous use of the word has been in the context of trunk lines connecting telephone company central office switches. A private telephone system is another type of telephone switch. Therefore, the lines connecting it with the switch in the telephone company central office are also trunks. Since a high percentage of the calls

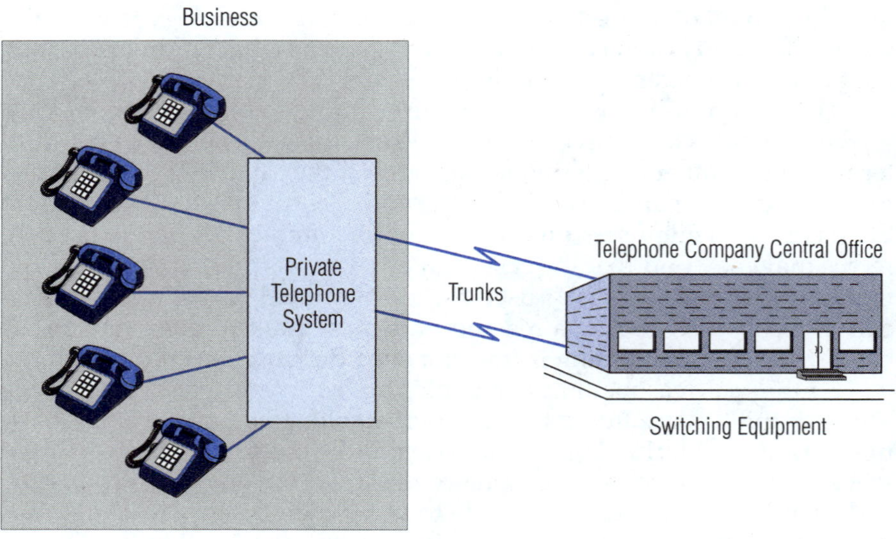

Figure 4–28
The private telephone system could be a key system or a PBX.

in a business are internal, the number of trunks connecting the private telephone system to the central office can be substantially less than the number of telephones in the office.

Key Systems

Small private telephone systems are called *key systems.* This name is a holdover from earlier days when a telephone connected to this type of system had push buttons or keys that allowed a line to be selected. In a typical key system, each telephone can access two or more lines, and lamps on the telephone indicate whether each line is busy. The caller selects a line by pushing a button on the telephone to seize the line, then dials the call. The telephone usually also has a hold button so that a call on one line can be held while a second call is made or answered.

Key systems typically handle from 3 to 50 telephones. This segment of the telephone equipment market is the largest and fastest growing because of the thousands of small businesses that can use this size phone system. In the past, key systems were available only from telephone companies, and the capabilities they offered were closely tied to the capabilities of the central office to which they were connected. Since the Carterfone decision and particularly since deregulation in the early 1980s, many vendors of key systems have entered the market, and the equipment has become significantly more sophisticated and better able to provide capabilities independent of the telephone company's central office equipment.

Key systems are available with a wide range of capabilities. The price of the system is partly related to the number of features that the system offers. The types of features available are similar to those found on PBXs.

Private Branch Exchange/ Private Automatic Branch Exchange/ Computer Branch Exchange

Private branch exchange (PBX), private automatic branch exchange (PABX), and *computer branch exchange (CBX)* are terms often used interchangeably to describe private telephone switching systems that are larger and usually more sophisticated than key systems. In this book, the term *PBX* is used to refer to any of these telephone systems.

A PBX is a private telephone system designed to handle the needs of a large organization. It is the next step up from a key system in capacity and the number of special features it supports. Private branch exchanges (PBXs) are typically designed to handle from 50 to more than 10,000 telephones. Each telephone on a PBX (or key system) is called a *station* or an *extension.* Larger sizes of PBXs are similar in capacity and capability to the switching equipment used in telephone company central offices. Since PBXs are designed for the exclusive use of one company, however, they are located on the company's premises.

These two PBX systems can handle different numbers of lines and handsets depending on the size and needs of the customer. (Courtesy of Northern Telecom)

PBXs, like the switching equipment in central offices, are computers especially designed for handling and switching voice telephone calls. Older PBXs, like older central office switches, had mainly mechanical components, and although some of these older PBXs still exist, the new units are all electronic and programmable. That is, they require an environment suited to computers—clean and air conditioned; they can be upgraded to add more capacity; they are physically smaller than their predecessors; and they require software to operate. PBXs, like key systems, are available from telephone companies and many other firms.

purchasing a PBX

The decision to acquire a PBX is not one to be taken lightly. The prospective purchaser needs to be sure he or she understands the firm's needs as well as the types of maintenance, training, and other support required by the firm as opposed to support provided by the PBX vendor. The level of support the vendor will provide is usually somewhat flexible. Support, along with price, are two of the major points of negotiation between the PBX vendor and a prospective customer.

A PBX gives its owner more control over its telephone system and usage than telephone systems provided by the telephone company. In addition, the PBX may provide features to improve the capability and efficiency

Station Features	System Features
Automatic redial	Automatic call distribution (ACD)
Automatic reminder	Class of service
Call forwarding	Data communication
Call park	Direct inward dialing
Call transfer	Hunt group
Call waiting	Least cost routing
Camp on	Paging
Conference calls	Pickup group
Distinctive ringing	Ring-down station
Do not disturb	Station message detail recording/Call detail recording (SMDR/CDR)
Speed dialing	Voice messaging

Figure 4–29
Features of a PBX. Many of these same features are also found in key systems.

of the telephone service that are otherwise not available. Features are usually divided into two categories: system features and station features. System features are capabilities that operate for all users of the PBX and that are in many cases transparent or unnoticeable to the user. Station features are customized to each user or telephone to provide the separate capabilities most useful to the individual. A list of system and station features is shown in Figure 4–29. The most common features are described next.

System Features

PBX *system features* are available to all users. In reality, all of the features may not be activated for all users because some are designed for particular needs and may be applicable only in certain departments or parts of the company. We will look at some of these features in more detail.

Data Communications Most PBXs have the capability to handle data communications as a standard part of their hardware. With this feature, a user with a computer terminal who needs to access several computers can use the PBX as a switch. First, the user dials one computer and connects the terminal to it through the PBX, and then, when the communication to it is finished, the user can dial the number of another computer and repeat the process. The data communications feature can be used to connect the terminals or personal computers in a company to other computers within the company, or through outside telephone lines the PBX can make the connection to computers in outside service bureaus or other organizations.

Direct Inward Dialing (DID) This feature gives outside callers the ability to call directly to an extension number so calls don't pass through an operator. Outside callers dial the normal seven-digit telephone number, and the call passes from the telephone company central office through the PBX and directly to an individual's telephone. Without the DID feature, all incoming calls pass through an operator who makes the connection to the desired extension.

Hunt Group The hunt group is another method of distributing calls to one of several individuals in a predetermined sequence. Hunt groups are often set up for departments in which several individuals can handle incoming calls but where there is a definite preferred sequence. When a call comes in, it is passed to the first extension in the hunt group. If that extension is busy or is not answered, the call is passed to the second extension and so on throughout the entire group.

Least Cost Routing The least cost routing feature attempts to place outgoing long distance calls on the line over which the call can be completed at the least cost. For example, if a PBX had foreign exchange lines and 800 service lines connected to it, the least cost routing feature would use a table stored in the memory of the PBX to determine which line should be used to place a particular call. If the preferred type of line is not available, the second choice is used and so on. When all alternatives have been tried, the call is sent out on the standard long distance facilities as a regular DDD call (the most expensive alternative). The least cost routing facility usually provides statistics showing the number of calls that went out on each type of line as well as the number of calls that had to overflow to a more expensive alternative. Using these statistics, the network analyst can determine whether more lines of a particular type are required.

Pickup Groups Pickup groups allow any member of the group to answer an incoming call. For example, in a group of marketing people that are connected on a pickup group, if a ringing telephone is not answered, any member of the group may pick up his own phone, key in the pickup code (usually an asterisk), and have the call transferred to his telephone so that it can be answered. The idea is that incoming calls will be answered by someone who does a similar kind of work and who can potentially help the caller.

Station Message Detail Recording (SMDR) Station message detail recording (SMDR), sometimes called call detail recording (CDR), is the feature of the PBX that records statistics about all calls placed through the system. The data recorded includes at least the calling and called extension numbers, the time of the call, and its duration. It may also include other statistics, such as the user's class of service or the line numbers used. The statistics usually are accumulated on a magnetic tape or disk attached to the PBX. Once the data is captured, it can be used for recording and billing purposes. Usually the data is taken off the PBX and transferred to another computer that performs the reporting and billing functions. Some PBXs can transmit the call detail data over a communications line to another location for processing.

The SMDR capability is very important to network management and analysts. In addition to providing the source data for telephone billing, the SMDR data can:

- show the busy hour thereby providing data as input to network staffing decisions,
- provide input for analysts monitoring for telephone abuse or toll fraud,
- be used to analyze whether the mix of toll free lines and other discount calling services is correct,
- show the cost of every call,
- show the effectiveness of an advertising campaign,
- be used to analyze the effectiveness of operators in a call center, and identify training needs,
- show business trends over time when they are related to call volume or duration.

In most organizations, SMDR data is regularly analyzed as a way of ensuring that telephone service is optimized for cost and capability.

Station Features

Station features are activated by a PBX system user. Whereas the features may be made available to individuals or groups of people, it takes some action by the individual to use the feature.

Automatic Reminder The automatic reminder feature lets a user tell the PBX to call back at a specified time. Its most common use is in a hotel for wake-up calls. You tell the hotel operator when you want to be called, and the operator instructs the PBX to ring your telephone at the specified time. Often the PBX can play a prerecorded message when it makes the automatic reminder call, such as "Good morning, it is 7:00 A.M."

Call Forwarding Call forwarding lets calls for one extension ring at another extension. If a person is going to be out of the office, she can activate call forwarding to have all of the calls ring at the secretary's desk or at whatever extension she will be. Call forwarding can also be set to forward the call if the extension is busy. A person might have calls forwarded to different extensions depending on which condition (such as a ring with no answer or a busy signal) occurs.

Call Transfer The call transfer feature allows calls to be transferred to another extension. In the blind transfer, a transfer code and the extension

This model of Northern Telecom's Meridian 1 is very compact. Line cards and additional cabinets of various sizes can be added or removed for smaller or larger configurations. (Courtesy of Northern Telecom)

number are keyed in. When the person who was originally called hangs up the telephone, the call is transferred. In the consultation transfer, keying in the transfer code places the caller on hold. The new extension is dialed, and when it is answered the person originally called and the person to whom the call is being transferred can converse. When the original answerer hangs up, the transfer is completed.

Call Waiting The call waiting feature indicates an incoming call while a call is in progress. The second call is indicated by a tone or lamp, and the parties in conversation can decide whether to take the second call.

Camp On When you place a call and the number you called is busy, the camp on feature lets you tell the system to call you back when the number is free. The PBX tests the extension that was called and, when it is free, calls you back. If you answer your telephone, it automatically redials your call for you. This keeps you from having to continually redial a busy number yourself.

Distinctive Ringing With the distinctive ringing feature, a telephone may have different ringing signals for calls from within the company and outside calls. Other distinctive rings may be available for emergency calls or trouble calls.

Do Not Disturb The do not disturb feature may be implemented in several ways. In its simplest form, it gives the caller a busy signal even though the extension called is not in use. Another implementation causes the caller to receive a distinctive busy signal that indicates the person being called has his or her telephone in do-not-disturb mode. A third implementation signals the PBX to automatically forward calls to another extension, such as to a voice mail system.

Speed Dialing Speed dialing allows frequently called numbers to be stored in the PBX's memory and then accessed with a shorter set of digits. For example, a PBX may allow every user to store 100 ten-digit telephone numbers. Each one can then be accessed by dialing a speed dialing code followed by a two-digit number, 00–99. A common use for speed dialing is to store the numbers of other company locations or frequently called customers or suppliers.

Several of the features just described are becoming available on the public telephone system. These features become available when the serving central office is upgraded to an electronic switch, which is a big brother of the PBX. Call waiting, call forwarding, and conference calling are available from most telephone companies today. Since there is an extra charge for these features, you must notify your telephone company if you wish to have them activated for your telephone. In addition, automatic redial is a feature available on many home telephones today.

PBX Security

During the 1980s, businesses became aware of *hackers* on telephone and computer networks and the millions of dollars in damages and expenses they can cause. Until several years ago, telephone fraud was mostly limited to employees placing long or expensive personal calls during business hours.

With the increased sophistication of PBXs and the granting of external access to the PBX by legitimate users, telephone hackers have found a lucrative niche by breaking into organizations' telephone systems and placing or selling long distance calls. Phone hackers use computers with auto-dialing modems to break security passwords and gain access to telephone systems. Once inside, they use or sell long distance calls, leaving the PBX owner holding the bill.

toll fraud

AT&T reports that toll fraud cost U.S. businesses more than $2 billion in 1993. Companies should take preventive measures including blocking outgoing international calls during off-hours, blocking remote access features of PBXs, and changing access codes and passwords frequently.

HYBRID SYSTEMS AND COMMUNICATIONS SERVERS

hybrid systems

It used to be that the distinction between key systems and PBXs were quite clear. Then more manufacturers declared their products to be *hybrid systems,* which have characteristics of both a key system and a PBX, such as the ability to be programmed to act like a key system (select the line you wish to use to make a call) or like a PBX (pick up a handset and the PBX selects an outbound trunk for you when you dial "9"). Whereas key systems typically use digital or analog phones, hybrid systems can use both.

communications servers

Key systems and PBXs are increasingly using personal computers as their main hardware platform. With appropriate software, they are sometimes categorized as *communications servers.* The term is very loosely defined, so the capabilities and features that a communications server from one vendor provides may be somewhat different from the offerings from another vendor. Typically communications servers are connected to both the outgoing telephone lines and a company's local area data network or LAN. The server acts as the office's phone system and has many of the standard features of a PBX, but may add other capabilities such as the ability to dial the telephone from the PC screen or from a program. The server can also answer incoming calls, handle incoming faxes and e-mails, page you if you're not at your desk, or transfer the caller to voicemail. You can expect to hear a lot more about communications servers in the very near future as their capabilities evolve and they become more widely used.

CENTREX SERVICE

Centrex service, which some telephone companies call by a different name for marketing purposes, provides a telephone service much like that of a PBX, but the telephone companies use equipment located at their central office, not at the customer site. The central office equipment may be dedicated to the customer, but more likely it is the same equipment used to provide normal public telephone switching functions. It is important to understand that Centrex service is not precisely defined or standardized even though the name is used nationwide. Since each telephone company can offer Centrex service and several different types of central office equipment are used, the Centrex offering is a combination of the technical capabilities of the central office equipment and the features that the telephone company decides to make available to its customers. Centrex service is regulated by the state public utilities commission; a PBX is a private system that is unregulated.

Centrex capabilities have advanced rapidly in the past few years. The switches used in telephone company central offices are very powerful computers that allow many unique features to be programmed. Some

PBX	Centrex
Ultimate control	Control shared with telephone company
Not regulated	Regulated by state PUC
Total ability to manage	Management shared with telephone company
Total responsibility to manage	Telephone company is primarily responsible
Requires capital to buy the system	No capital required
User/vendor must provide service	Telephone company provides all service
Usually less redundancy is built in	More redundant hardware may mean higher reliability
Growth capability depends on the inherent design of the PBX	Essentially unlimited growth capability

Figure 4–30
Factors to be considered in selecting a PBX versus a Centrex system.

people feel that Centrex features and technical capabilities are now better than what is offered by PBXs.

You might wonder why a business would consider acquiring a PBX if telephone company-provided Centrex would give the same or better service. There are definitely pros and cons to both types of systems, as shown in Figure 4–30. On the one hand, a PBX gives the company ultimate control of its telephone system and the total ability to manage it. On the other hand, it requires the company to make the capital investment in the PBX equipment and to provide space, power, and air conditioning, as well as skilled technical people to operate it. By way of contrast, when a Centrex system is used, the telephone company manages and services the equipment, and the customer pays the telephone company a service fee.

PRIVATE VOICE NETWORKS

When a company has several locations, each with its own PBX or key system, it is often desirable to tie the locations together with telephone lines. By renting lines to connect the PBXs or key systems, a private network can be built that saves money compared to the cost of making standard long distance calls. In addition, it simplifies the dialing and, in many cases, can appear to the telephone user as a single, integrated private telephone system.

Tie Lines

Leased lines that connect the private PBXs or key systems are called *tie lines* or, more properly (because they connect switching equipment), *tie trunks*. They are acquired from the common carrier or can be installed privately if the locations are in close proximity. If leased from the telephone company, a fixed price is paid for full-time, 7-day, 24-hour use.

tie lines
tie trunks

An audio teleconference in progress. The flat microphone on the table is omnidirectional and can easily pick up voices from anywhere in the room. (Courtesy of Dow Corning Corporation)

With tie trunks in place, a telephone user at one location dials an access code to access the trunk and PBX at the other end. Usually, a second dial tone is heard from the remote PBX, and then the extension number of the called party is dialed. If a speed dialing feature is installed, this process may be simplified.

Private Networks for Large Organizations

When an organization has a very large volume of calls it may be economical to build a private network. In past years companies leased a variety of full-time lines from the telephone companies to build such networks; however, today most of the networks that are built are virtual. That is, they use standard telephone company facilities rather than dedicated lines. *Virtual networks* and discounted telephone calling go hand-in-hand, and a company must work with telephone company sales representatives and engineers to define the best solution. Service offerings from the telephone companies change frequently, and new capabilities become available regularly because of the onward march of technology.

AUDIO TELECONFERENCING

Another type of telephone service that some businesses find useful is audio teleconferencing. Usually used in a conference room, an audio teleconferencing setup has an omnidirectional microphone in the center of

The Octel 200 voice messaging system includes many advanced features. It is modular and can be expanded to support several thousand users. (Courtesy of Lucent Technologies Octel Messaging Division)

the table and a speaker, both of which are connected to the telephone. Participants sit around the table, and one participant makes a standard telephone call to an individual or to another similarly equipped conference room. All the people in the room can hear what is said at the other end of the connection on the speaker, and the microphone picks up everything that is said and transmits it over the telephone lines. In some audio teleconferencing systems, multiple rooms can be connected so that several groups of people can converse. About the only special requirement—in addition to the microphones and speakers—is the human factor consideration of taking turns and being polite.

Businesses have found audio teleconferencing useful for allowing a group of people to converse with a specialist or expert at a remote location, for having status meetings between groups of people at diverse locations, and for holding meetings when the participants are in many locations. In some cases, it can be a substitute for travel. In one recent audio teleconference, a company conducted a sales meeting. Eleven locations, each with approximately 20 participants, were connected in a large audio teleconference.

VOICE MAIL

Voice mail provides an electronic voice mailbox where callers can leave messages for other people. Voice mail is the voice equivalent of the e-mail systems discussed in Chapter 3. Voice mail systems may be a system feature built into a PBX or provided as a separate piece of hardware. Some companies make voice mail units that may be attached to a wide variety of PBXs or that work with Centrex systems.

Whether it is a feature on a PBX or a stand-alone system, the voice mail system can be used by callers inside a company or those calling in from the outside. In addition to simply providing a voice mailbox capability, a voice mail system provides other functions as well. It allows voice messages to be sent to several people at the same time. For example, a manager could communicate to everyone in a department and be sure that they all heard the same message said the same way. Comments may be added to voice messages, and the original message with the comments can be forwarded to another party. Voice messages may be put in the system with instructions to place them in voice mailboxes at a later time.

Using this capability, a department manager could, before leaving on a trip on Tuesday afternoon, put a voice message in the system for all of the department's employees, announcing a job change or new product. The manager could tell the system not to put the message in the employees' mailboxes until Thursday morning if it were important that the announcement not be made until a certain time.

A voice mail system is not just a simple tape recorder. It converts an analog voice signal to a digital signal and stores it on a magnetic disk for later recall. When a person retrieves the calls in a mailbox, the digital signal is converted back to an analog signal, and the voice message is spoken to the recipient.

Voice mail capability is useful in a variety of situations. Research has shown that up to 83 percent of all business telephone calls do not reach the called party on the first attempt. An important advantage of voice mail is that the calling and called parties do not need to be present at the same time. Voice mail allows the caller to easily leave a detailed message. If the caller can go into detail and ask a question or explain a situation, it is possible to avoid the need for a callback in 50 percent of the cases. For these situations, telephone tag can be minimized or avoided altogether. Some people expect that electronic conversing, where the two people never actually talk to one another, will become an accepted form of intracompany communication.

Another use for voice mail is in minimizing the problems caused by time zone differences. Callers on the east coast can leave messages for business associates on the west coast before they get to work. Conversely, west coast callers can leave messages after east coast workers have gone home for the day.

Voice mail is also useful for salespeople and marketing people who do a lot of traveling. They can call into the voice mail system from any tone-dialing telephone and have the system play back all of the messages stored for them. Then they can respond to the messages by sending a reply, forwarding the message to another person for handling, or sending new messages.

While special hardware is required to set up a voice mail system, technology has shrunk the circuitry so that small systems may now be established by installing a few special-purpose circuit cards in a personal computer. A key attribute to be considered is the size of the computer's hard disk, because digitized voice messages take a lot of disk space and rapidly fill a personal computer's hard disk.

Automated Voice Response

The automated processing of incoming calls has made rapid advances in recent years. There are three concepts to understand, and they are often confused: *automated attendant, audiotex,* and *interactive voice response.* They can be implemented separately but are frequently used in combination. All require the use of a Touchtone telephone by the caller.

Automated Attendant

The automated attendant capability is at work when you call a telephone number and an automated voice asks you for some information in order to route your call to a person. Substitute the word *operator* for *attendant,* and it is easy to imagine how an operator might answer you, ask you a few questions, and then pass on your phone call to an individual who could serve you. The automated attendant brings the power of the computer to bear by eliminating the person who routes the call. You provide information to the computer by pressing keys on your telephone rather than by speaking to a person.

Audiotex

Audiotex is the service that provides fixed information when you call a certain telephone number. The information is fixed in the sense that the caller cannot select information. Of course the information itself can be changed as often as necessary. If you call a number to get the current time or the weather report, you are being served by an audiotex system.

Interactive Voice Processing

When you call a telephone number and are answered by an automated voice that asks you for information, and then you are routed to another part of the automated system, you are using interactive voice response. Visualize the information as being stored in a tree structure. Depending on the response you give to the question—using your Touchtone telephone—you proceed down a branch of the tree, perhaps answering more questions as you go. Finally you get to the information you need, and the system reads it to you using the automated voice. Note that the fixed information itself is a form of audiotex.

Of course, one option in the tree structure may be to route your call to a person if the system does not have the information you want prestored. In that case, the system is behaving like an automated attendant system.

It is important to point out that the features of automated voice response systems must be carefully designed and programmed to avoid setting up tedious and time-consuming messages, loops, or other situations that may frustrate the caller. If prospective customers get caught in the tangle of a poorly programmed automated voice response system they may well take their business elsewhere—to a company where a real person answers the phone! Automated voice response systems should not be viewed as a cheap substitute for people!

WIRELESS COMMUNICATIONS

One of the fastest-growing segments of voice communications is *wireless communications*. First we'll look at two applications of voice wireless technology that you are probably already familiar with, cordless and cellular telephones. Then we'll explore the rapidly expanding world of wireless beyond these two.

Cordless Telephones

Cordless telephones represent a subset of wireless technology that has become very familiar to most of us. The base of the telephone, which is connected to a normal telephone line, contains a small radio transmitter and receiver that broadcast a signal to the handset. The handset, operated by rechargeable batteries, also contains a small transmitter and receiver for communicating with the base. The normal radius for clear, static-free operation of a cordless handset is 50 to 800 feet from the base.

Cordless telephones are usually designed so that they operate in standby mode, conserving battery power but able to detect incoming calls and signal the user with a buzz whenever the base unit sends a ringing signal. When users want to answer or place a call, they switch the transmitter on and then continue with the call. Most units are designed so that the handset will recharge its batteries when placed in a cradle on the base unit.

broadcast

An important word in the above description is *broadcast*, for indeed the base and the handset broadcast their signal like a small radio station.

That means that anyone listening on the right frequency and located fairly close can pick up the telephone conversation and listen in. Telephone conversations conducted using cordless telephones or any other wireless technique are not private! In the United States, a federal law makes eavesdropping a crime, but it is virtually impossible to enforce.

Digital cordless phones are also available, and they address the security issue and some other problems that users often experience. Specifically, digital cordless phones offer improved transmission quality (less noise), greater range, and security against eavesdroppers. Rather than transmit the phone conversation on a single channel, most of the new digital cordless phones use a sophisticated technique called *spread spectrum.* Although there are several different spread spectrum techniques, it is easiest to visualize how it works by thinking of the transmission jumping between several frequencies. With the digitized signal dispersed among multiple frequencies, the chances of successful eavesdropping are significantly reduced.

spread spectrum

Most vendors claim that digital cordless phones have an operating range two to four times greater than conventional analog cordless phones, allowing the users greater freedom to move around while talking.

Cellular Telephone Service

Cellular telephone service was originally designed to provide mobile telephone service as the caller moves around within a relatively small geographic area—typically a city. In the past, cities had a single powerful radio transmitter and receiver for mobile telephone service. Each telephone call required a separate frequency, and although a city like Chicago had approximately 2,000 frequencies available, there was a large demand for more.

The problem of insufficient frequencies became so acute in large cities that the whole concept of mobile telephone service was reworked in the early 1980s to take advantage of modern computer technology. Cities were divided into cells (shown in Figure 4–31), and low-powered radio equipment controlled by a central computer was installed in each cell. Because the transmitters use low power, the same frequencies can be reused in nearby cells without interference. Thus if a city has 10 cells, 5 to 8 times as many channels are available for telephone conversations as were available in the previous system.

This type of system is called a *cellular telephone system;* its basic technology was developed at the Bell Laboratories in the early 1960s. Access to the system is made from a telephone that also contains a radio transmitter and receiver. When a call is initiated from a cellular phone it is picked up by the nearest cellular antenna and forwarded, usually on wire, to a *mobile telephone switching office (MTSO),* the equivalent of a central office in the regular telephone system. MTSOs are connected to the regular telephone network so that calls from cell phones can be made to other cell phones or to regular phones, and vice versa as shown in Figure 4–32.

mobile telephone switching office

Figure 4–31
The layout of a cellular telephone system.

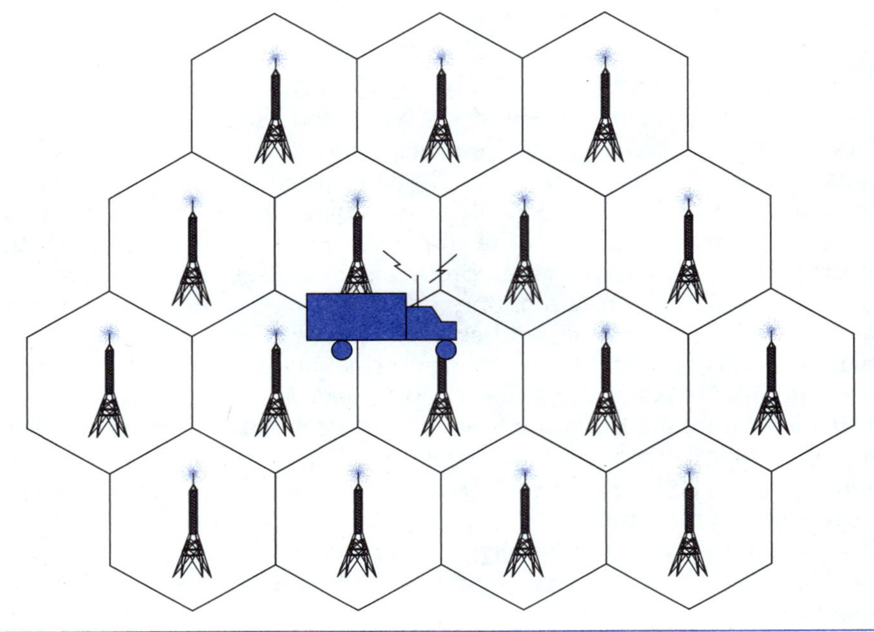

Figure 4–32
Cellular telephone users can make calls to other cellular users or to telephones on the public (wire based) switched network.

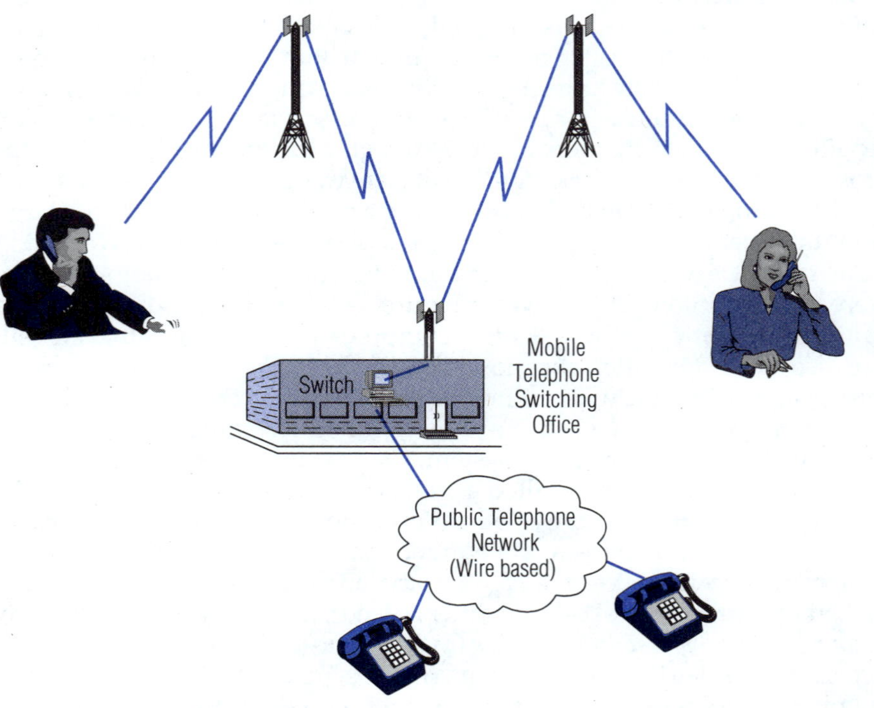

Cellular telephones can be useful in cases of emergencies as well as for normal business or personal conversations. (Courtesy of AirTouch Cellular)

Cellular telephone calls are monitored every few seconds by a central computer in the MTSO. When the signal from the cell phone starts getting weak, the computer determines which cell to switch the call to and instantaneously switches it to the new cell's radio equipment. The switch occurs so fast that it is unnoticeable by the individuals who are conversing. (It can present problems if data is being transmitted on the cellular connection, however.) One of the key attributes of cellular telephone systems is that they operate completely automatically. No operator is required to set up, monitor, or switch calls from one cell to another.

A growing number of people are using cellular telephone service for facsimile and data transmissions. Data transmission can be nearly

This Motorola cellular telephone is extremely small and compact, yet contains a full set of features for cellular operation. (Courtesy of Motorola, Inc.)

100 percent reliable if the proper error-checking circuitry is built into the equipment. One ambulance company is using a cellular telephone system to transmit data about patients to the hospital while the ambulance is en route. Contractors are sending facsimiles of drawings from the office to the job site by cellular phone. And the American Chemistry Council maintains a database of information about hazardous chemicals that can be transmitted via a cellular telephone system to the site of a chemical spill.

An interesting sidelight to cellular phone usage: A study conducted by the *New England Journal of Medicine* showed that motorists are four times as likely to have an accident when they are using cellular phones. Inattention to their driving rather than dexterity in using the phone is the major reason why, the study showed. Among other findings:

- Phones that allowed the driver's hands to be free did not appear to be safer than hand-held phones.
- Younger drivers were at a somewhat higher risk.
- More drivers tended to get in a crash during the work week than during the weekend. Wednesdays were the worst day; Saturdays the best.

Since cellular telephones also transmit calls by radio, there has been some concern about eavesdropping. Cellular calls can be picked up by some radio scanners as far as 5 to 10 miles away from the transmitter. Users need to be aware that calls on cellular telephones are not as secure as calls placed on conventional telephones.

Cellular telephone service has been a big commercial success. Although cellular service is more expensive than a regular telephone line, it can be a boon to any company that makes its living from customer service. It also is widely used for business and pleasure by people who spend large amounts of time commuting or tied up in traffic.

Today's cellular systems are so-called second-generation systems and they are not all globally compatible with one another. People who use a cellular phone system that uses one technology cannot communicate with people on a system that uses a different technology. Currently there are three ways that digital cell phones transmit their signals: TDMA, GSM, and CDMA.

Time division multiple access (TDMA) is the oldest technology. TDMA divides radio frequencies into separate channels, assigns a specific channel to your call, and then broadcasts the call with precision timing. Since its capacity is not high, TDMA technology is not well suited for applications such as e-mail or web browsing, and call quality is often not very good. Nonetheless, TDMA is the most frequently used technology for cellular phone calls in the United States.

Global system for mobile communications (GSM) is based on TDMA technology but has a higher capacity and therefore better call quality. It supports both voice and data transmission and has become the standard for cellular phone service in Europe and Asia. GSM service is available in the United States but only in limited areas.

Code division multiple access (CDMA) is the newest of the technologies and broadcasts calls within the same channel. Conversations are distinguished from one another by special codes that are assigned to them. A CDMA phone actually receives all the calls being transmitted, but only those with your call's special code are assembled back into voice for you to hear. Like GSM, CDMA supports both voice and data transmissions, and the quality of the voice is the best of the three technologies.

So today, a European traveler can use a GSM cell phone in Europe and Australia, but is likely to need a different phone and a subscription to a U.S. cell phone plan when traveling in the U.S. This problem is gradually getting resolved with newer cell phones that can operate on any of the technologies, but it is still a major inconvenience.

Third generation cellular systems are scheduled for operational startup in Japan and Europe in 2001–2002. The hope for these systems, which are generically called 3G (third generation), is to create a universal system that will be used worldwide. It is planned for 3G phones to be able to transmit data at a very high rate, especially compared to today's cell phones.

Formerly equated only with cellular phone technology, wireless now includes mobile access to the Internet and other kinds of data networks as well. People are constantly on the go, and there are times when they want to be able to initiate communications of various types—to check the stock market on the Internet, to make a dinner reservation while traveling home on the train or in a car, or to exchange e-mail when they aren't connected to their company's network. Convenience seems to always be high on people's list of priorities as it relates to their ability to communicate.

As most Europeans and Japanese know, the Internet is entering a new phase in its short but dramatic existence. Engineers of every major computer, telecommunications, and software company in the world are working hard to give customers anywhere, anytime access to the Internet. Millions of Japanese and Europeans (especially Scandinavians) can exchange e-mail and surf certain web sites from their mobile phones, though they use proprietary standards that are interim to 3G. The basic Japanese system is called i-mode and is offered by NTT's cellular services division, DoCoMo. Over seven million Japanese surf the Internet and exchange e-mail on wireless devices. Today's phones have a tiny screen, but despite its small size, i-mode users see a menu of choices such as news, games, chat, and search. Roughly 10,000 web sites have been specially formatted so that pages will download quickly to i-mode phone screens.

Europe is further behind but is investing heavily in the *wireless application protocol (WAP)* technology, which downsizes fat, graphics-rich web pages so that they are usable on small cell phone displays. In the U.S., only a small number of cell phone and Palm Pilot customers can access such services because they are not widely available. Basically, the rest of the world has bypassed the United States in cell phone technology, and the U.S. is playing catch-up.

In addition to the new WAP and 3G standards for wireless communications, a third standard called *Bluetooth* is emerging. Bluetooth is a standard for wireless connectivity within a 33-foot radius. It allows wireless communication between mobile phones, laptop computers, personal digital assistants, and other portable devices. Being a radio-based link, Bluetooth doesn't require a line-of-sight connection in order to establish communication. A person could, for example, wear a wireless headset that communicates to a cell phone being carried in an attaché case, as long as all three devices are in range of each other. Likewise, a PDA could communicate with a laptop computer, automatically exchanging data when the two are within range of each other.

You can see that the cellular and wireless technologies are merging, and will give us many useful capabilities in the coming years. However, since the concept is relatively new, there are still several questions that vendors are struggling to answer, such as the following:

- What kinds of services do customers really want?
- How much are customers willing to pay for such services?
- What is the likely mix of consumers and business customers?
- Will this be a profitable market?

We can expect major evolution in the coming few years.

SIDEBAR 4–1

WHAT IS I-MODE?

Think of i-mode as a mini-version of Internet sites delivered to 1.5-inch phone screens.

DoCoMo, like Yahoo, runs a megasite that offers everything from news to airline tickets to weather reports. When i-mode is clicked on, users see a menu. By pushing buttons on the phone, they navigate through DoCoMo's site, which links to 500 content providers. An additional 15,000 Net sites are i-mode compatible, but users have to enter the sites' addresses.

In a matter of seconds, and for less than 25 cents per item, i-mode users can do such things as bank via phone, check airline schedules, check the weather, send e-mail, read the news, play simple video games and even make phone calls.

I-mode transmits data at 9.6 kilobits per second, much slower than most dial-up modems in U.S. homes. But most graphics and banners are eliminated so text flows faster.

DoCoMo already sends a monthly bill to its customers for their cellular phone use. It tacks on $1 to $3 for subscriptions to some i-mode sites, such as Nikkei news. DoCoMo kicks back 91% of the revenue to Nikkei and keeps 9% for itself.

DoCoMo also makes money when users send e-mail or flip through Internet pages. Fees run about 4 cents for a 250-character e-mail or about 3 cents per page view.

Marine and Aeronautical Telephone Services

Yet another variation of mobile telephone service are calls made from ships or airplanes. These are called *marine telephone service* and *aeronautical telephone service.* In both marine and aeronautical telephone services, radio communication is established between a transceiver on a boat or airplane and a land-based transmitter and receiver that are connected to the public telephone system. The land-based equipment is usually voice-activated so that it switches automatically from transmit to receive as the parties at either end talk. In most cases, an operator must initially establish the call and monitor its progress to ensure that the radio transmitter and receiver are working properly.

Aeronautical telephone service has the special problem that because the airplane is moving so fast, it quickly leaves the range of the transmitter. Unless a means exists to pass a call from one transmitter to another as the plane moves, the call is terminated as the plane goes out of range. A small system of coordinated ground-based equipment has been established along some major air corridors. The transmitters and receivers are close enough together so that if a plane goes out of range of one, it is within range of another, and the call can be passed with no interruption.

Many commercial airlines offer telephone service on their flights. In the most common implementation, telephones are built into the backs of one or more seats in each row. A passenger inserts a credit card, which allows the handset to be removed from the back of the seat. The telephone number is dialed, and the call is broadcast from the airplane to the nearest ground receiver. When the connection is made, the call progresses like any other telephone call. Upon completion of the call, the passenger returns the handset to the telephone and retrieves the credit card. Billing is done through the credit card. There is a basic flat rate for the call plus a per-minute charge.

THE VOICE NETWORK USED FOR DATA TRANSMISSION

Much of the ubiquitous nationwide public telephone network that we take for granted is, to all appearances, an analog network that was originally designed and optimized to handle analog voice communications. Advances in technology and computer circuitry have made digital transmission possible, and, as you will see in succeeding chapters, there are certain advantages to digital transmission that make it preferable. Because of these advantages, the telephone network has for the most part been changed so that today most of it operates in digital mode.

Furthermore, of the over 300 million telephone calls that take place in a day, several million are connections between terminals and computers or between two computers, sending data that originated in digital form. These transmissions have certain unique attributes and different requirements than analog voice data, but the data transmissions are usually adapted to fit the parameters of the analog telephone network. You will see how this is done in the following chapters.

SUMMARY

This chapter presented the various components of the voice telephone system. It looked at the telephone instrument itself, the switching equipment located in the central office, and the hierarchy of central offices that compose the public telephone network. You have also studied how voice signals are converted to electrical signals, the characteristics of those signals, and the way in which they are modified (modulated) for transmission on the telephone network. In addition, you studied private telephone systems and their features, systems like those found in most businesses today. Finally, you were introduced to a number of the services offered by telephone companies.

Many of the concepts and facilities presented in this chapter will come up in later chapters that discuss data communications. By understanding the vocabulary and subject material presented in this chapter, you will have a good foundation for the chapters that follow.

CASE STUDY

Telecommunications at Work in a Brokerage Office

John Duncan, a vice president of a major brokerage firm, says that he couldn't do his job without the telecommunications and personal computer technology in his office. John manages a team of five people who handle the investment needs and manage the portfolios of over two hundred clients. The brokerage firm that they work for provides a mainframe and personal computer-based information system with workstations on each desk and linked via a wide area network to the firm's mainframe computers at headquarters. This system provides the basic capability that allows John and his staff to buy and sell securities for their clients. Also provided is an AT&T telephone system, which includes call forwarding and voice mail, and is vital to maintaining contact with clients.

What makes John's team unique, however, is the private PC-based system that he has installed to supplement the system provided by his employer. Each member of John's team has a second PC on his or her desk that runs the Goldmine contact management software. "With Goldmine we can keep a complete set of information about each of our clients and the many other people with whom we deal," John says. "Of course we keep basic demographic data, such as names, addresses, and phone numbers, but also information about their securities portfolio, trades, financial goals and the progress they are making toward their goals. We mail a unique birthday greeting to each client on their birthday showing them what happened in history on the day they were born. We use a program called Special Days, and clients love the fact that we remember their birthdays."

Regardless of where he works, John uses the contact management software to help schedule his day. "We preschedule monthly and quarterly phone calls with clients, and record daily meetings and appointments. At the beginning of each day, my secretary prints the schedule for the day, which shows me what I have to do and also indicates the priority of contacts," John says. On a typical day he calls 15 to 25 people in addition to holding meetings with clients, his staff, and associates at his firm.

Perhaps the most distinguishing feature of the operation, however, is that John has connected the telephone and computer systems in his office to a two-line telephone and a PC at his vacation home in another state, which allows him to do his job as effectively there as in the office. For example, when the phone rings in the office, John's secretary can just as easily transfer the call to his vacation home as to his office. When John answers the call, the client doesn't even know that he may be relaxing by the pool or consulting his computerized database from his computer at his vacation home. John says, "I can be just as effective for my clients at our second home as I can in the office. Through the use of telecommunications I have access to all of the same data, and my staff can support me in the same way as when I'm in my office." And John's firm agrees, for they fully support his operation from his second home.

"The biggest improvement in technology in the last three years," John says, "is the full implementation of the Palm Pilot into our daily lives. We now have virtually all of the Goldmine data on our Palm Pilots. We are currently using model Vx, which has 8 megabytes of memory and fits in my shirt pocket. All of the financial data as well as the last five history comments about each client is contained in the Pilot. Naturally we have our calendar and phone numbers for each client as well. We use the Pilot for world news and financial information when we travel. A quick update to

Avantgo.com by a modem that we connect to the Pilot keeps us up to date. Frequently when we travel, we get an update from an airport lounge by dialing a toll-free number, and in a matter of 2 to 3 minutes the update is complete. We also have a list of stocks that gets updated along with the news stories for each company. The publications we download are the *Wall Street Journal, Bloomberg, Financial Times, USA Today,* and Hollywood.com. The last one tells us what movies are playing and the times for each movie theater in our particular zip code. Map Quest is also on the Pilot and we can input a request for directions and it shows us a map with driving instructions, just like on the computer. I also have The Weather Channel with Manhattan programmed in so that when I travel to New York each quarter, I get an accurate forecast, so I know what to pack. On the Palm, we also have Vindigo, a restaurant, nightlife, and movie guide for several cities. I input my exact location and I choose what type of food I would like to eat, and it gives me a *Zagat* review as well as the address, phone number, and walking instructions and distance from where I am. I can sort the results by distance, price, or review. When traveling to a different city it has proved invaluable. A modem connection is not needed to get the results. A periodic update through the regular synching process is all that is needed. We synchronize the Palm with our desktop computer daily when we are in the office. It is a 5-minute process. In addition to synching with Goldmine, it goes to the Internet and updates all of the aforementioned services and deletes the outdated information. Any changes we make in the Pilot, say an address change, gets changed in Goldmine when we synch. When we are out of the office, we synch with the Internet only for our daily information. We could synch with Goldmine over the telephone line, but it isn't something we have needed to do. I read my Pilot sometimes when I am at lunch or even at home to keep updated. I have canceled most of my paper subscriptions."

"Contained within the Pilot is a clock that keeps track of different time zones and has an excellent alarm feature. Recently I stayed in a very upscale New York City hotel and asked for a 6:00 A.M. wakeup call. I never did get the call, but I had programmed the Pilot to wake me at 6:15 A.M., which it did."

"We use a program to store all of our passwords, logons, and scripts for the many electronic gatekeepers we need to pass through. The data is securely encrypted on the Palm for security.

"Recently while in a business meeting, I took out the Palm and the pocket keyboard for note taking. The keyboard opens to full size. The Pilot sits atop on a connector. I have replaced the laptop as a tool I take to meetings with the Pilot and the keyboard. Both the Pilot and keyboard fit in my pocket. The power in the Palm lasts me about 2 to 3 weeks before it needs to recharge. When the Pilot sits in the cradle near my desktop for synching, it also recharges so the need for a full charge is only needed when I return from a business trip."

"While on the road, I send and receive all of my e-mail using the Pilot and the modem. My cell phone can also receive short e-mails, so that if I am traveling and cannot receive phone coverage, I can see the e-mail when I get back into range and can take appropriate action."

"Three years ago, I said that what I was looking for in the future was a portable device that would give me most of the PC capabilities while I'm on the move and not at either my office or second home. Everything I asked for then is available to me in my Palm Pilot now! So what do I want going forward from here? The integration of the telephone, the Palm Pilot, and the computer communicating wirelessly from anyplace on the globe is technically possible. I envision information being pushed to me in an intelligent manner that learns my preferences. Home, office, and handheld devices will communicate easily and effectively. Technology such as Bluetooth is paving the way. Voice recognition, I believe, is still several years away from being practical. Technology is leveraging my time both personally and business-wise."

QUESTIONS

1. Is it unusual today for a company to allow employees to work from a second home the way John does? How does the firm measure and monitor an employee's productivity and effectiveness when he or she isn't working in the office?

2. Is it unusual for an employee to supplement the employer's information and communications system with a private system as John has done with his team? What factors would influence or motivate an employee to invest his or her money in this way?

CASE STUDY

Dow Corning's Telephone System

Dow Corning's main telephone system in Midland is a digital Centrex system provided by Ameritech. In actuality, because of the way its locations are spread in relation to the telephone company central offices, there are three different Centrex systems that are loosely connected together. These three systems between them have over 5,000 lines connected. The systems have direct inward dialing (DID) and provide four-digit dialing between stations on the same Centrex, but seven-digit dialing is required between systems. The DID feature allows the company to provide good telephone service with only two central telephone operators on duty at one time, and two others trained as backups. These operators also serve as receptionists for the Dow Corning Center headquarters complex.

In the past, each department in the company paid for the local and long distance calls of its employees. The company produced an internal telephone bill each month from magnetic data tapes provided by Ameritech and AT&T and some internal tables of information that Dow Corning maintained. However, in 1999 a decision was made by the finance department to eliminate all charge backs within the company, so now the telephone costs are all kept in the IT department.

Users in the Midland area make long distance telephone calls by dialing the standard ten-digit telephone number (three-digit area code plus seven-digit telephone number). Calls are routed through one of the Centrex systems and out through AT&T's software defined network (SDN), which was installed in 1992. The result is that Dow Corning receives a very low per-minute rate for long distance calls—much lower than it would if the SDN arrangement had not been implemented.

Voice calls to one plant are not routed through SDN. The plant is in Hemlock, a town fairly near Midland, and Dow Corning has leased lines to the plant location so voice calls are routed on the leased line. Users dial a three-digit access code and then the four-digit extension number of the person they are calling at the plant. Of course, if a caller who forgets about the special line and access code may dial the Hemlock plant directly, which costs the company more money; but the manager of voice communications says that this has not been a big problem.

Dow Corning's plants and sales offices in the United States have a variety of equipment suited to their unique requirements. Some of the plants have small PBXs and others have key systems. Many of the sales offices are quite small, so key systems serve their needs adequately. If a plant needs an 800 line or other special service, the requirement is rolled into the overall voice network arrangement with AT&T and managed by Dow Corning's telecommunications staff.

The company's central customer service department, which enters and processes all orders for Dow Corning products from customers throughout the United States and Canada, has its own PBX. It was installed to handle the special needs of that department, including handling a high volume of incoming 800 calls from customers and distributors of Dow Corning's products and the need for special telephone usage reporting. The department has its own 800-service network for customer calls. Calls pass through an ACD system that allows customers to enter a customer service representative's extension number, if it is known, and directs callers who want to order product literature to another department. Callers are then transferred to a customer service operator who screens out a few other calls that have been misdialed and then routes the call to the appropriate customer service representative. The customer service PBX is connected to one of the Midland

Dow Corning's telephone operators also serve as receptionists for the corporate headquarters. (Courtesy of Dow Corning Corporation)

A Dow Corning customer service representative takes an order. She is using a headset connected to her Rolm telephone and a flat panel video display terminal that allows her to log on to four different applications simultaneously. (Courtesy of Dow Corning Corporation)

area Centrex systems and all of the telephones on the PBX have four-digit telephone numbers that can be accessed by Centrex users the same way they access any other telephone.

Connected to the main Centrex system is a voice mail system provided by Lucent Technologies. Voice mail was first investigated in 1982 and seemed to have applicability, particularly for sales people who travel a great deal. In 1983, Dow Corning began using voice mail on a public service bureau system and then installed its own voice mail computer in 1984. Today the Lucent system has more than 4,000 mailboxes for voice mail users throughout the company. Like the overall telephone costs, the costs of the voice mail system are borne by the IT department. The Lucent system has proven to be very reliable, and the users are extremely happy with the capability it provides.

The staff that manages the system has noticed that some people prefer to use voice messaging and others prefer to use e-mail when communicating with other employees. In general, people from marketing, sales, and the corporate communications departments are the biggest voice mail users, perhaps because much of their job content involves verbal communication. Research and IT people tend to prefer e-mail. Of course people in all of these departments have access to and use both the e-mail and voice mail systems, but the relative preferences are an interesting observation.

QUESTIONS

1. The use of a Centrex telephone system is a good example of "outsourcing." What benefits would Dow Corning have accrued by using a Centrex system compared to having its own large, in-house, PBX-based telephone system? What benefits or trade-offs would the company realize if it replaced the Centrex system with a PBX?
2. Assuming it is true that a PBX requires more in-house staff to manage than a Centrex system, do you suppose there could be a conflict between lower-level managers who want to expand their staff to increase their influence, and senior managers who want to reduce staff size?
3. Because standards exist, is tight control needed to build a company-wide voice communications network, or are products and services standardized enough so that each location in the company can be given autonomy, knowing that the voice network can be tied together after the local units decide what voice communication equipment they are going to buy?
4. Employees at Dow Corning and most large companies have a variety of ways to communicate with each other. e-mail, voice mail, fax, and the standard telephone connections are just some of the examples. How does an employee decide which is the most effective method for a particular communication?

REVIEW QUESTIONS

1. List the five functions of the telephone set.
2. Compare and contrast dial pulsing with the DTMF technique for dialing a telephone number.
3. If the telephone system is designed for a P.03 grade of service, how many calls would you expect to be blocked for every 500 calls placed?
4. Distinguish between a telephone line and a trunk.
5. In normal speech, some sounds above 3,000 Hz are generated. What happens to these frequencies when they are sent through the public telephone network?
6. Explain the term *modulation*. For what is it used?

7. Is the electrical representation of the voice signal that is transmitted between the home and the telephone company central office modulated? Explain your answer.
8. What are the three attributes of a sine wave?
9. Explain what a foreign exchange line does.
10. Compare and contrast key systems and PBXs.
11. Distinguish among drop wires, local loops, distribution cables, and feeder cables.
12. What is the bandwidth of the AM radio broadcasting band of frequencies in the United States? The FM radio band? (If necessary, do some research at the library.)
13. An analog signal is fed into one end of a twisted pair of wires. At the other end, the relative strength of the signal is measured as −10 dB. How much has the power of the signal dropped as it traveled through the wire?
14. List an example of an electrical wave with a frequency of 60 Hz, a radio wave with a frequency of 640 kHz, a radio wave with a frequency of 102 mHz, and a sound wave with a frequency of 880 Hz.
15. What are the attributes of a tone used for tone signaling in the telephone system?
16. What is the importance of Signaling System 7?
17. Explain the difference between LATAs and area codes. Can an LEC carry a telephone call between two telephones whose telephone numbers have different area codes? If so, under what conditions?
18. Explain 800 service.
19. What factors must the network analyst consider when selecting the type of long distance service that is best for his or her company? How can he or she get help in analyzing the data and making the decision?
20. Compare and contrast a voice mail system with an ordinary telephone answering machine.
21. Explain how a cellular telephone system works.
22. Explain toll fraud and some of the steps that can be taken to prevent it.
23. What are the security concerns surrounding cordless and cellular telephones?
24. Why do dial-up circuits have more errors than leased circuits?
25. Why is the world's telephone system being changed to digital circuits?
26. Describe how TASI works.
27. Describe some situations in which a business might want to have 800 service for its employees to use.
28. Why are voice signals multiplexed?
29. What are the trade-offs between a Centrex telephone system and a PBX?
30. Compare and contrast cordless phones and cellular systems.
31. What is the difference between e-mail and voice mail?
32. What are the reasons companies might like to use the Universal International Freephone Numbering service?
33. Why do some telephone customers not want to use the automatic number identification feature that is available on most public telephone systems? Why wouldn't they want to use the call waiting feature?
34. Why is the United States behind in cellular telephone technology? What capabilities do other countries have with their cell phones that are not available in the U.S.?

PROBLEMS AND PROJECTS

1. A company with 300 employees in Texas wants to acquire a private telephone system. Would you suggest a key system or a PBX? Why?
2. Visit a local hotel/motel and find out what type of telephone system it uses. Does the system have the automatic reminder feature for wake-up calls? If not, how are wake-up calls handled? Are there any special

features on the hotel's telephone system that weren't described in the text? If so, what do they do?

3. Visit a local small business that has a key system installed. How many telephones and outside lines will the system handle? How much expansion capability does it have? Did the company purchase the system, or is the firm leasing/renting it? What features does the key system have? (Use the features described for PBXs as a checklist.)

4. Pick one of the following services to investigate: cellular telephone system; voice mail system; audio teleconferencing system. Find a company in your area or do research at the library, and write a two-page report describing the capabilities, features, and shortcomings of the system you have chosen.

5. Investigate the current status of Internet telephone service and report to your instructor or class.

Vocabulary

customer premise equipment (CPE)
analog signal
speaker cone
sidetone
switchhook
off-hook
dial tone
on-hook
dial pulsing
rotary dial
out-pulsing
dual-tone-multifrequency (DTMF)
Touchtone
central office
central office switch
call setup time
patch cord
step-by-step switch
Strowger switch
crossbar switch
reed relay
blocking
busy hour
grade of service
main distribution frame
end office
serving central office
toll office
switching office
public telephone network
public switched telephone network (PSTN)
local loop
tip and ring
drop wire
distribution cable
feeder cable
trunk
frequency
sine wave
cycle
Hertz (Hz)
kilohertz (kHz)
megahertz (MHz)
gigahertz (gHz)
bandwidth
guard channel
guard band
amplitude
level
decibel (dB)
attenuation
phase
frequency division multiplexing (FDM)
carrier wave
common carrier
modulation
amplitude modulation (AM)
frequency modulation (FM)
phase modulation (PM)
detector
demodulation
multiplexer
base group
channel group
group
supergroup
master group
jumbo group
time assignment speech interpolation (TASI)
direct current (DC) signaling
tone signaling
fast busy
E&M signaling
in-band signals
out-of-band signals
common channel interoffice signaling (CCIS)
Signaling System No. 7 (SS7)
routing code
city code
exchange code
local calling
local service area
local calls
flat rate service
measured rate service
long distance calls
direct distance dialing (DDD)
toll calls
international direct distance dialing (IDDD)

plain old telephone service (POTS)
800 service
Universal International Freephone Numbering (UIFN)
900 service
software defined network (SDN)
foreign exchange (FX) line
Integrated Services Digital Network (ISDN)
voice over IP (VoIP)
key system
private branch exchange (PBX)
private automatic branch exchange (PABX)
computer branch exchange (CBX)
station
extension
system features
station message detail recording (SMDR)
call detail recording (CDR)
station features
hacker
hybrid systems
communications servers
Centrex
tie line
tie trunk
virtual network
voice mail
automated attendant
audiotex
interactive voice response
wireless communications
cordless telephones
spread spectrum
cellular telephone service
cellular telephone system
mobile telephone switching office (MTSO)
time division multiple access (TDMA)
global system for mobile communications (GSM)
code division multiple access (CDMA)
wireless application protocol (WAP)
Bluetooth
marine telephone service
aeronautical telephone service

References

Arnst, Catherine. "Uncle Sam Please Pick a Cell-Phone Standard." *Business Week* (February 24, 1997): 34.

Baker, Stephen, Neil Gross, Irene M. Kunii, and Roger O. Crockett. "The Wireless Internet." *Business Week* (May 29, 2000): 136–144.

Barrett, Amy. "Before We Get a Worldwide Busy Signal." *Business Week* (December 16, 1996): 72.

Barrett, Amy, Peter Elstrom, and Catherine Arnst. "Vaulting the Walls with Wireless." *Business Week* (January 20, 1997): 45–46.

Bass, Steve. "Nightmare on ISDN Street." *PC World* (January 1997): 236.

Castaneda, Carol J. "Drivers on Phone Proven 4 Times More Likely to Crash." *USA Today* (February 13, 1997).

Creswell, Julie. "The Battle to Control Your Cell Phone." *Fortune* (March 29, 2000): 170–174.

Maney, Kevin. "Megahertz Remains a Mega-Mystery to Most." *USA Today* (February 13, 1997).

Mitchell, Dan. "Waiting for Wireless." *PC Computing* (January 2000): 72–77.

Ousey, Alison. "Simplify Your Life—Centrex Gives You Easier Access to Phone Features." *Teleconnect* (November 1996): 68–71.

Pollack, Andrew. "Cheaper Mobile Phones Capture Japan's Ear." *International Herald Tribune* (January 21, 1997).

Shannon, Victoria. "The Wireless Way: Are We Obsessed?" *International Herald Tribune* (February 24, 2000).

Stripp, David. "The Idol of the Geeks." *Fortune* (March 3, 1997): 40.

Varshney, Upkar, and Ron Vetter. "Emerging Mobile and Wireless Networks." *Communications of the ACM* (June 2000): 73–81.

CHAPTER

5

Connecting the Dots—Transporting Information across the Superhighway

Objectives

After reading this chapter, you should be able to

- Describe the local telephone network infrastructure
- Describe the long distance telephone network infrastructure
- Describe the type of circuits used to connect switches
- Describe the data network infrastructure
- Define new telephone terms

Outline

INTRODUCTION

One of the best ways to learn how information travels across the telecommunications network is to visualize our system of roads. The multitude of interstates, state highways, and rural one-lane roads can be compared with the multitude of transport media found in the telecommunications network—the local loop, the local switch-to-switch connection, and long distance connections. Interstates are able to accommodate large numbers of vehicles while the local one-lane roads usually only carry local traffic. The same holds true in telecommunications. The fiber optic systems—the superhighways—connect switching centers, large office complexes, and other high-volume areas. The local loop services one customer and provides an ample amount of bandwidth in the same way the local road carries residential traffic without too much congestion.

Telecommunications also mimics the railroad network, with its hubs or switching centers where trains come in, drop off railroad cars, pick up other railroad cars, and continue on to their destinations. The telecommunications network also has switching centers where traffic is dropped off or added to the information stream. We don't need separate telephone lines to talk to Aunt Sally in California and Uncle Art in Florida, and the phone company doesn't need separate telephone networks. The switching center distributes the information instantaneously.

The goal of this chapter is to "connect the dots" of the network. We will demonstrate how the local network connects to other switches within the local area, how the local network connects with the long distance network, and how the long distance network connects to the international network. We will then discuss specific pieces of the network and the types of circuit media used to carry the zillions of bits of information. The chapter will conclude with a simple highlevel explanation of the Internet.

5.1 THE LOCAL TELEPHONE NETWORK

5.1.1 Connecting Local Telephone Company Switches

We will now trace a call as it leaves the serving central office and travels to a central office that serves a different area across town.

serving CO
The central office that provides telephone service to the subscribers within the CSA.

Andy decides to make dinner reservations at Alfonso's. He picks up the phone, listens for dial tone, and dials Alfonso's number. The digits travel down the wire into the Wilmount Street central office (the *serving CO*). (All central offices are referred to by a street or location name.) The switch receives the digits 232-5522 and determines that the number belongs to a switch located elsewhere

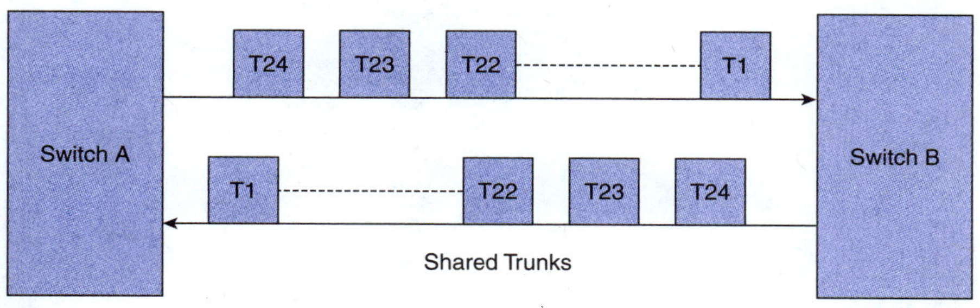

Figure 5–1 Shared trunks between two switches, which pass calls via the shared trunks.

in the local network. In other words, Alfonso's restaurant is not physically connected to the Wilmount Street switch.

The Wilmount Street switch, through the magic of the SS-7 *signaling network* (to be discussed later) determines that the number 232-5522 resides in the Maple Street central office. The Wilmount Street switch routes Andy's call onto a trunking circuit that connects the two central offices. Figure 5–1 illustrates how the two switches connect using shared trunking circuits.

What would happen if the Maple Street CO and the Wilmount Street CO were not connected directly? An intermediary, or tandem, switch is directly connected to both the Wilmount CO and the Maple Street CO. The tandem switch would route the incoming call from the Wilmount CO onto a *trunk* riding on a circuit to the Maple Street CO. Figure 5–2 illustrates how the call would travel through the tandem switch. Both scenarios—direct connection between the two *end-office* switches and connection through a tandem—are possible. Both are very common in the local telephone network.

The Maple Street CO happens to be the serving central office for Alfonso's restaurant, that is, Alfonso's telephone line is connected to the Maple Street CO switch. Therefore, when Andy dials Alfonso's telephone number, the call travels into Andy's serving central office switch, where it is routed onto shared trunks that terminate at Alfonso's serving central office switch located on Maple Street.

The Maple Street CO examines the number, knows that it belongs to Alfonso's business, and routes the call onto the switching line card attached to Alfonso's telephone.

The term *trunk* is used to define the channel connection between two central office switches. Andy's call to Alfonso's traveled on Andy's line into the Wilmount CO switch, then onto a trunk that connected the Wilmount CO to the Maple Street CO, and finally onto Alfonso's line from the Maple Street switch. In telephony, that is referred to as a line/trunk/line call.

It is also an intraoffice trunk connection, which brings us to a discussion of IntraLATA and InterLATA. The telephone network is divided into 161 *LATAs* for local access transport area. LATAs represent geographical regions as defined by the Modified Final Judgement in 1982, and every area within the United States resides within a specific LATA.

SS-7 network
Signaling system 7—The out-of-band signaling network used to set up calls.

trunk
Circuit shared by multiple users that connects two switches together. A trunk carries calls between switches, such as a long distance switch and a local switch. Once the call is complete, the trunk becomes available for a different call.

end office
The serving central office providing dial tone to the end subscriber.

LATA
Local access and transport area. Geographic areas defined after the Modified Final Judgement of 1982.

Figure 5–2
ILEC local network with two end offices connecting into a tandem switch office. Traffic passes from end office switch A to the tandem, and from the tandem to end office switch B. Shared trunks are used to pass traffic between the end office switch and the tandem.

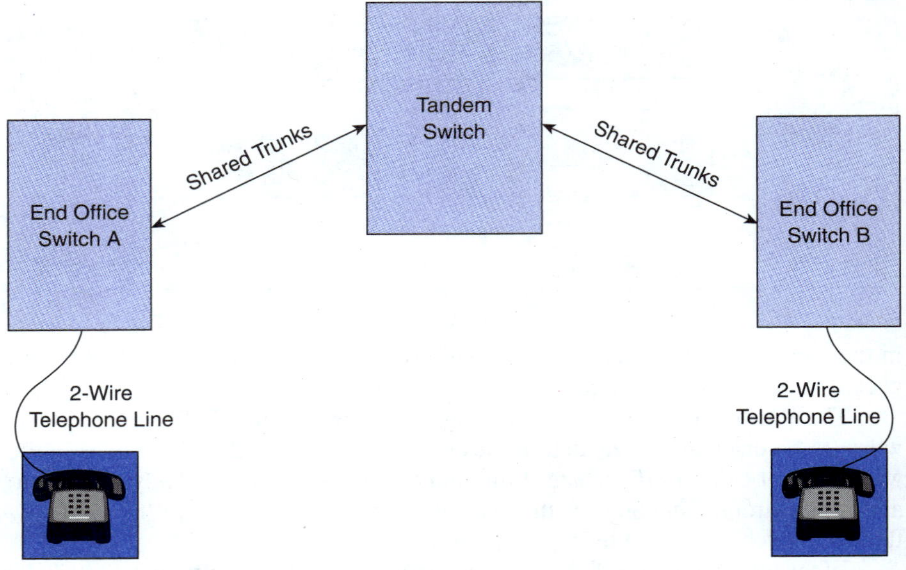

Calls traveling within a LATA are charged differently than calls traveling across LATAs. InterLATA calls travel between LATAs and are carried by long distance telephone carriers. Calls traveling within a LATA are IntraLATA calls, which may have long distance charges.

5.1.2 Connecting Two Local Telephone Companies' Switches

CLEC
Competitive local exchange carrier.

ILEC
Incumbent local exchange carrier.

The second type of call we'll trace is one that travels between two different local telephone companies, or service providers. This is an Intercompany/IntraLATA call. Thanks to the 1996 Telecommunications Act, Intercompany/IntraLATA calls are very common. New competitive local exchange carriers (*CLECs*) are offering telephone services in local areas. The incumbent local exchange carrier (*ILECs*) must allow CLECs to connect to their end office switches or to their access tandem, therefore trunking circuits must be established between the ILEC's tandem and the CLEC's local switch.

If Alfonso's dial tone was provided by one of the many new CLECs, the call would be routed as shown in Figure 5–3. The digits Andy dialed would travel into the Wilmount CO switch as before. The switch would then determine that the call should go to the access tandem to be routed to the destination switch. The call would then travel onto trunking circuits connected to the local ILEC's tandem. The access tandem would examine the incoming number and determine that it belonged to CLEC SpiderCom. The access tandem would switch the call onto a trunk on a circuit traveling to SpiderCom's class 5 switch located in their State Street regional switch center. The call would arrive at SpiderCom's switch, which would route it to Alfonso's telephone line.

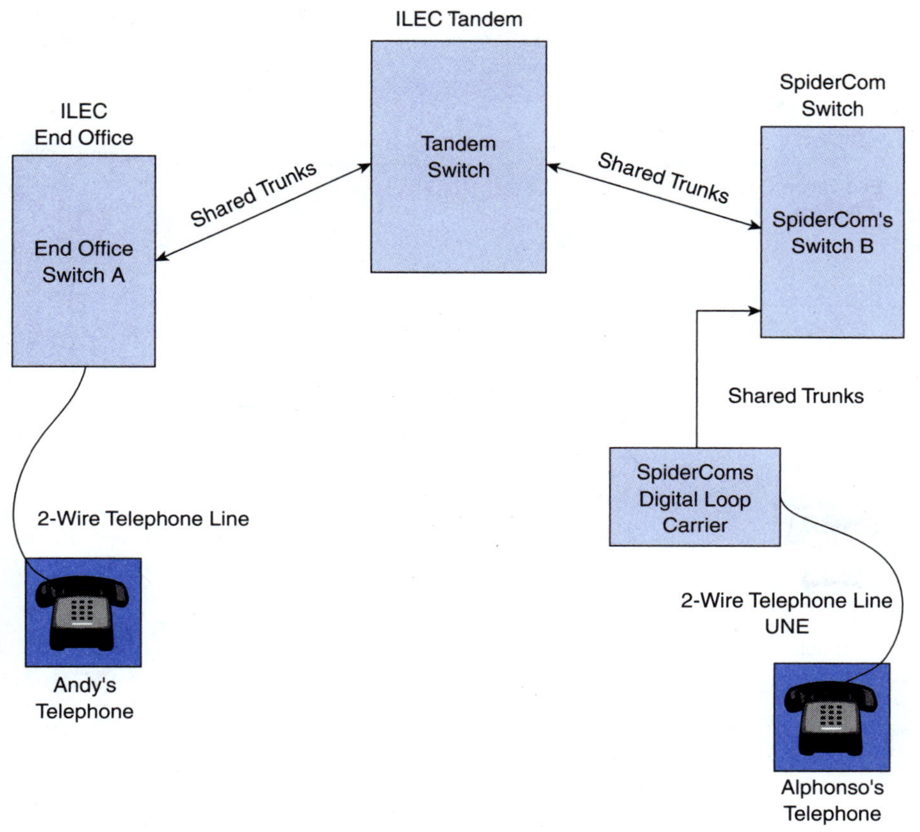

Figure 5–3
An ILEC local network connecting into a SpiderCom (CLEC) local network via shared trunks at the tandem switch office. Traffic passes from end office switch A to the tandem, from the tandem to SpiderCom's office switch B and then to a digital loop carrier located at the ILEC end office serving Alfonso's restaurant. Shared trunks are used to pass traffic between the two companies' networks. The end connection between the SpiderCom's switch and Alfonso's telephone requires a special piece of equipment called a UNE for unbundled network element, which is located in a cage in the ILECs central office. The cable pair serving Alfonso's home is owned by the ILEC and leased to SpiderCom.

Connecting the SpiderCom switch directly to the ILEC's end-office switch that serves Andy's telephone is a second option often used in the local network. The call would travel from Andy's CO switch to the CLEC's CO switch, completely avoiding the ILEC's tandem switch, as shown in Figure 5–4.

5.1.3 Connecting the Local Telephone Switch to a Tandem/Toll Switch

A *toll switch* owned by the local telephone company switches calls between the local telephone network and the long distance network. A toll tandem switch interfaces with long distance switches. All 1+ calls are routed to the toll tandem switch that connects to long distance companies. The toll *tandem switch* contains routing software that looks at the digits to determine which trunk group to send the call out on. The toll/tandem switch is the gateway between the local telephone network and the long distance telephone network. The toll/tandem is concerned with the first three digits (area code) for long

toll switch
A switch that is capable of switching long distance traffic. The local class 5 switches may function as a toll switch if long distance software has been installed. Therefore, a toll switch is a switch that has the ability to switch long distance calls.

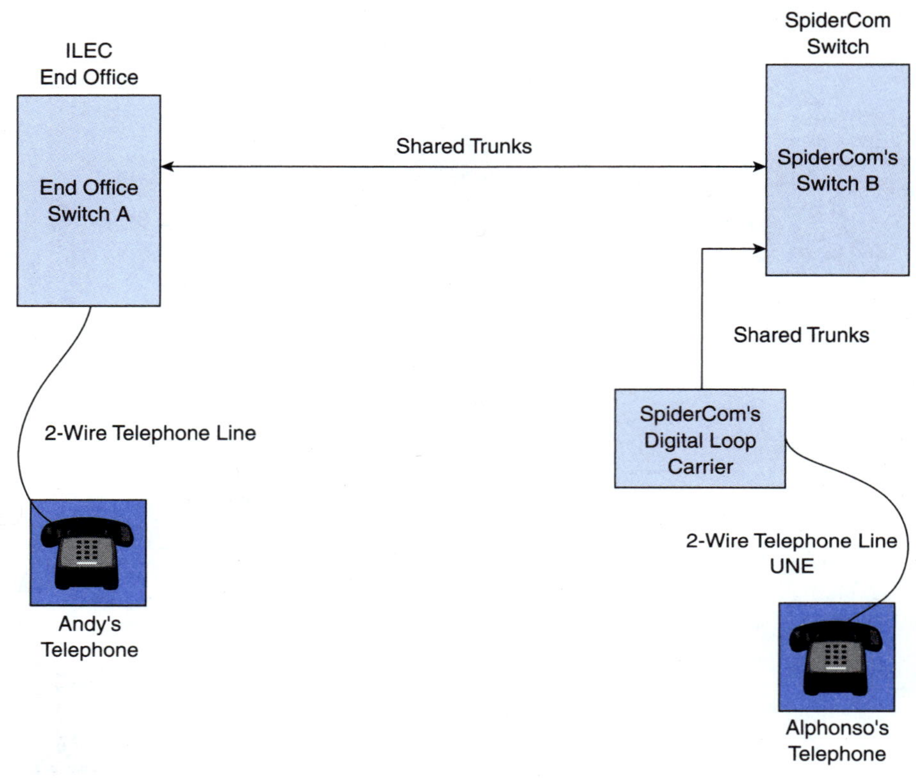

Figure 5–4
An ILEC local network connecting into the SpiderCom (CLEC) local network via shared trunks between the ILEC end office serving Andy's home and the SpiderCom switch. Traffic passes from end-office switch A to SpiderCom's class 5 switch, then from SpiderCom's office switch B to a digital loop carrier located at the ILEC end office serving Alfonso's restaurant. Shared trunks are used to carry traffic between the two companies' networks. The end connection between SpiderCom's switch and Alfonso's telephone requires a special piece of equipment called a UNE or unbundled network element, which is located in a cage in the ILECs central office. The cable pair serving Alfonso's home is owned by the ILEC and leased to SpiderCom.

tandem switch
Switch that has connections to other switches—end office, toll, cellular and others. A tandem switch is used to switch traffic between switches. Today, access tandems are used to interconnect ILEC networks to CLECs and other providers.

distance calls and the exchange code (second set of three digits) for local switch calls. The toll/tandem routes calls between trunks, not between lines.

5.2 THE LONG DISTANCE NETWORK

Since divestiture in 1982, local telephone networks have had to connect with more than one long distance telephone company. Initially, to connect two networks, callers had to input special access codes in order to directly dial any of the many long distance carriers. Thanks to equal access, which will be discussed in detail in chapter 7, we now just dial 1 before the 10-digit number. The local switch knows which long distance carrier the call should be routed to. The only stipulation is that the long distance company must have a point of presence within the LATA, where it connects with the local phone company or other CLECs offering local telephone service.

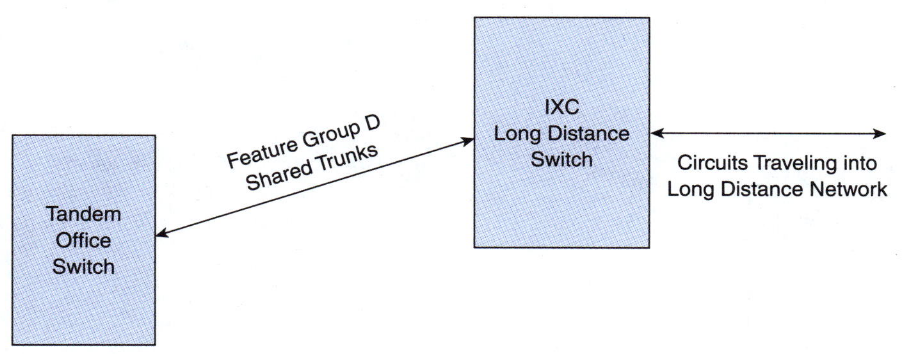

Figure 5–5
Long distance switches connect to local telephone switches via Feature Group D trunks, which provide special signaling options that allow the switches to communicate and carry traffic correctly.

How does the local network connect to the many long distance networks? The answer is fairly simple, having just discussed intraswitch trunking. The difference is the way the trunks are defined. The type of trunks used to connect long distance telephone companies to local telephone companies are called Feature Group trunks. The FCC's National Exchange Carrier Association defined the Feature Groups used to connect the many long distance carriers with the local telephone companies.

The purpose of the standard is to ensure that all long distance carriers are treated equally by local telephone companies. For instance, if you chose MCI as your long distance company in 1985, you had to dial 10322 1 + the number to place a long distance call. The FCC was concerned that consumers would hesitate to leave AT&T if they had to dial additional numbers every time they wished to make a long distance call.

equal access
All carriers have equal access to the local telephone network. Allows any long distance provider to terminate trunks into the local telephone network tandem switch or end-office switch.

The solution was *equal access*. Equal access trunks are Feature Group D trunks. A switch's database holds the customer record that shows which long distance carrier (primary interexchange carrier [PIC]) the customer has chosen and in turn eliminates the need for the customer to dial the special access code. If you could climb into the switch, you would actually see the special access code in front of the number the customer dials. Today, the most common type of trunk used to connect a long distance company switch to a local switch—tandem or end office—is the Feature Group D trunk. Figure 5–5 shows Feature Group D trunks connecting a local tandem switch to a long distance carrier's switch. Figure 5–6 shows Feature Group D trunks connecting a local end-office switch to a long distance carrier's switch.

We'll finish connecting the dots between the local and long distance network by walking through a long distance call scenario. The call will travel from Andy's home in Portland, Maine, to his friend Sam's home in Philadelphia, Pennsylvania. Andy picks up his telephone and dials Sam's number—1-818-555-7788. The Wilmount Street CO receives the digits and

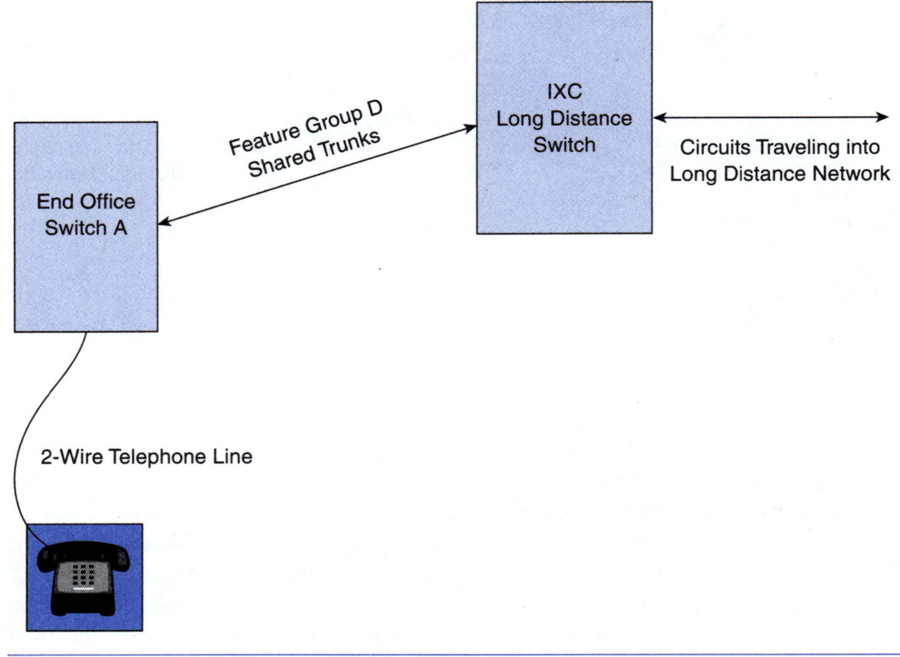

Figure 5–6
Long distance switches connect to local telephone switches via Feature Group D trunks and provide special signaling options that allow the switches to communicate and carry traffic correctly.

looks up Andy's profile in the customer information record in the switch's database to determine which long distance telephone company Andy has chosen. It shows that Andy has chosen ABC Long Distance Company. The switch attaches the access code—343—to the beginning of 818-555-7788 and ships the number out on an intraoffice trunk that connects Andy's switch to the local toll/tandem switch.

POP
Long distance company point of presence in a region. The long distance provider must have a presence in an area in order to route calls onto their network.

The tandem receives digits from the Wilmount Street switch, then examines the access code and sends the call to ABC's point of presence (*POP*). Each long distance carrier must establish a point of presence in each LATA they wish to terminate/originate long distance traffic in. A POP may consist of one relay rack holding transmission equipment to a full blown switch site with a long distance switch. The POP must have trunks connecting it to the local telephone company in order to pass the traffic to the local network. Many POPs also have connections to other long distance providers, ISPs, and CLECs in the area. The call is switched onto the trunk that connects the local telephone company's tandem to ABC's long distance switch. ABC's switch may be in the same city as the local toll/tandem switch or it may be miles away in another city. If they are in the same city, the trunks that connect the two switches travel a few blocks, much like the local end-office switches. If ABC's switch is not

Figure 5–7
Long distance connection between two ILECs through ABC's long distance network.

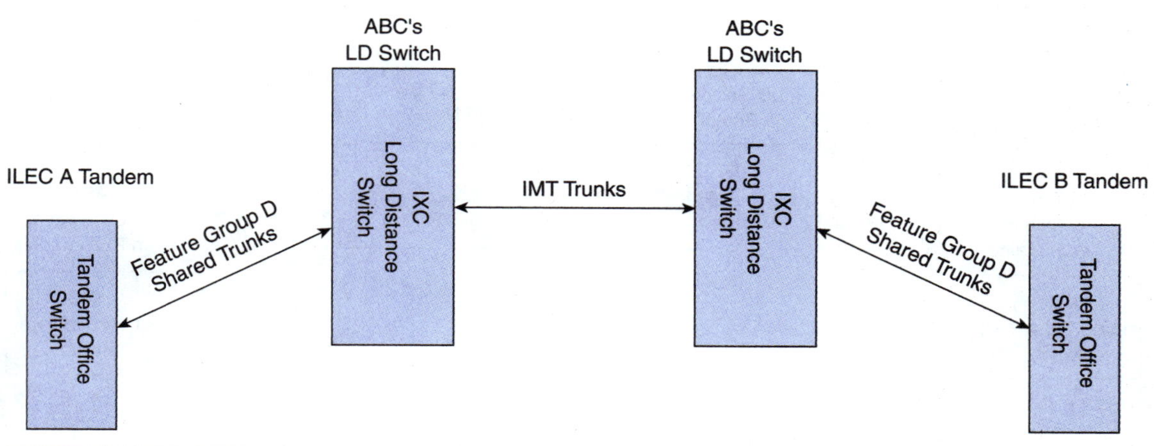

located in the same city, long-haul circuits are used to connect the two switches. The trunks connect the local tandem switch into ABC's long distance switch. Figure 5–7 illustrates the connection between ABC's long distance switch and the local telephone company's toll/tandem switch.

The route that the call takes from ABC's long distance switch in Portland to ABC's Philadelphia long distance switch may vary. In one scenario, shown in Figure 5–8, the call travels entirely on ABC's long distance network. In the other scenario, illustrated in Figure 5–9, the call travels on ABC's network from Portland to New York City and then on a wholesale long distance carrier's network from New York City to Philadelphia.

In the first scenario, the call leaves the ABC long distance POP in Portland on a trunk that connects directly into ABC's Philadelphia long distance switch. The trunks connecting the two long distance switches are intermachine trunks (IMT). These are similar to Feature Group D trunks and will be discussed in detail in Chapter 7.

From ABC's long distance switch in Philadelphia, the call is routed onto a trunk that connects the local telephone network's tandem to ABC's long distance switch, probably via a Feature Group D trunk. The local tandem, as before, directs the call to the correct end office serving Sam's telephone line. The serving CO points the call to the line pair connecting to Sam's telephone and sends a ringing voltage. Sam's telephone rings, he picks up the handset, and the call is connected all the way through the network.

The other route the call could take is to travel onto ABC's long distance network, then onto a wholesale long distance carrier's network that ABC has

Figure 5–8
Long distance connection between two ILECs through ABC's long distance network. ABC has switches in Portland, Boston, New York City, and Philadelphia.

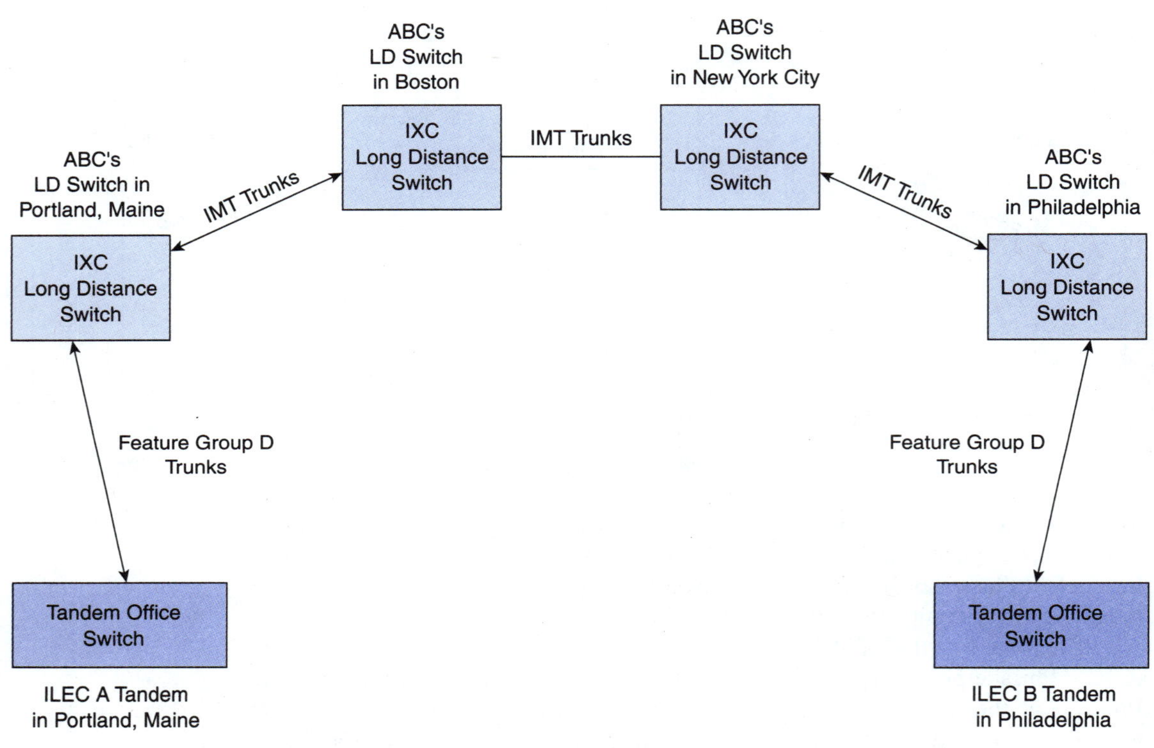

leased, and then into the ABC's long distance telephone switch in Philadelphia. The difference between the two scenarios is the additional trunks that connect from the ABC long distance switch in Portland to XYZ's wholesale carriers network. Figure 5–10 shows how ABC's long distance networks and XYZ's network connects. This is a very common method of transporting calls. Many smaller long distance carriers do not have end-to-end networks across the country and therefore must use third-party networks to complete connections.

A third scenario, and the most complicated, is one in which ABC long distance company does not have a switch in either Philadelphia or Portland. Instead,

Figure 5–9
Connection between two ILECs through ABC's long distance network. The long distance portion of the network contains two LD carriers' networks. ABC leases the network between New York City and Philadelphia from a wholesale LD carrier. Most LD calls travel across multiple networks, but customers are not usually aware of this.

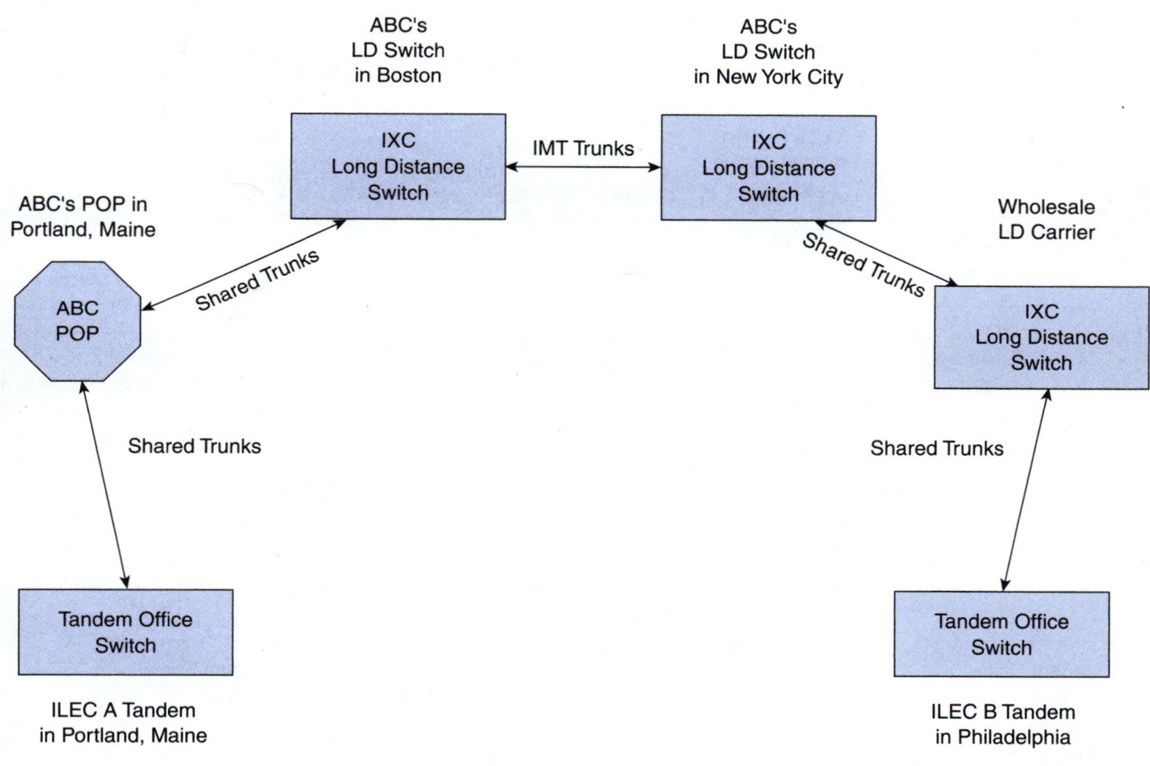

the closest switch to Portland is Boston, and the closest switch to Philadelphia is New York City. Figure 5–11 shows the path of the call as it travels from the local tandem in Portland to ABC's POP in Portland and from there on circuits that connect into ABC's long distance switch in Boston. From the switch in Boston, the call travels on IMT trunks that connect into ABC's long distance switch in New York City, and from there on Feature Group D trunks that connect into the local tandem switch in Philadelphia. Again, the tandem routes the call to the local end office that serves Sam's home.

Even though the call hops off ABC's network and travels across a third party wholesale network, the telephone still rings within 1000ths of a second once the

Figure 5–10
Two ILEC networks are connected through ABC's long distance network. The long distance portion of the network contains two LD carriers' networks. ABC does not own the network from Portland to Philadelphia, but leases it from XYZ who transports all of ABC's traffic across the country through special shared trunks between the switches. Most LD calls travel across multiple networks, but customers are not usually aware of this.

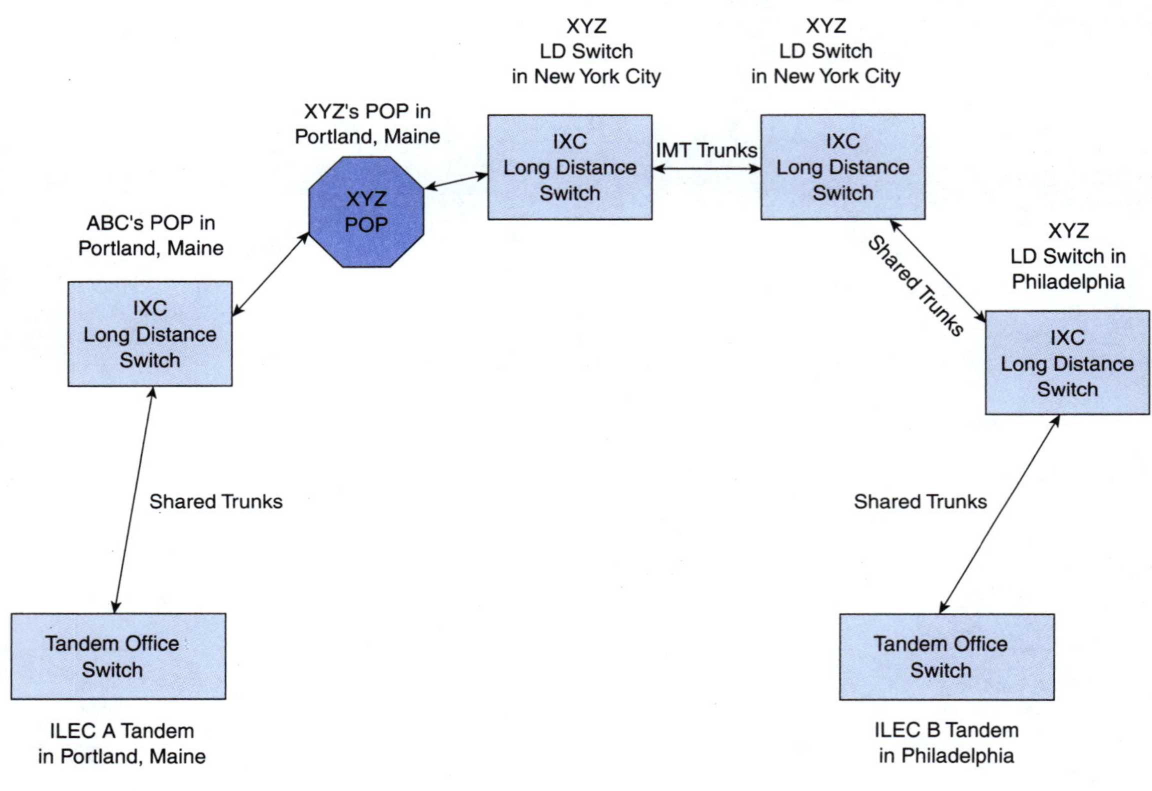

digits are dialed. The digital switching network using special SS-7 signaling links is responsible for the instantaneous switch times.

5.3 THE INTERNATIONAL NETWORK

Andy now decides to call his good friend Shawn who lives in Ireland. Andy looks up Shawn's number and dials the digits—011-353-555-229292.The numbering plan for international calls requires a country code, a city code, and the subscriber's number. In addition, the 011 is needed in the same way a 1+ is required for a long

Figure 5–11
Long distance connection between two ILECs through ABC's long distance network. ABC has switches in New York City and Boston. Portland, Maine, and Philadelphia are POP sites. POP sites are not capable of switching calls; instead they transport traffic to a switch site where calls are routed to the correct destinations. The diagram represents an architecture commonly used by long distance companies.

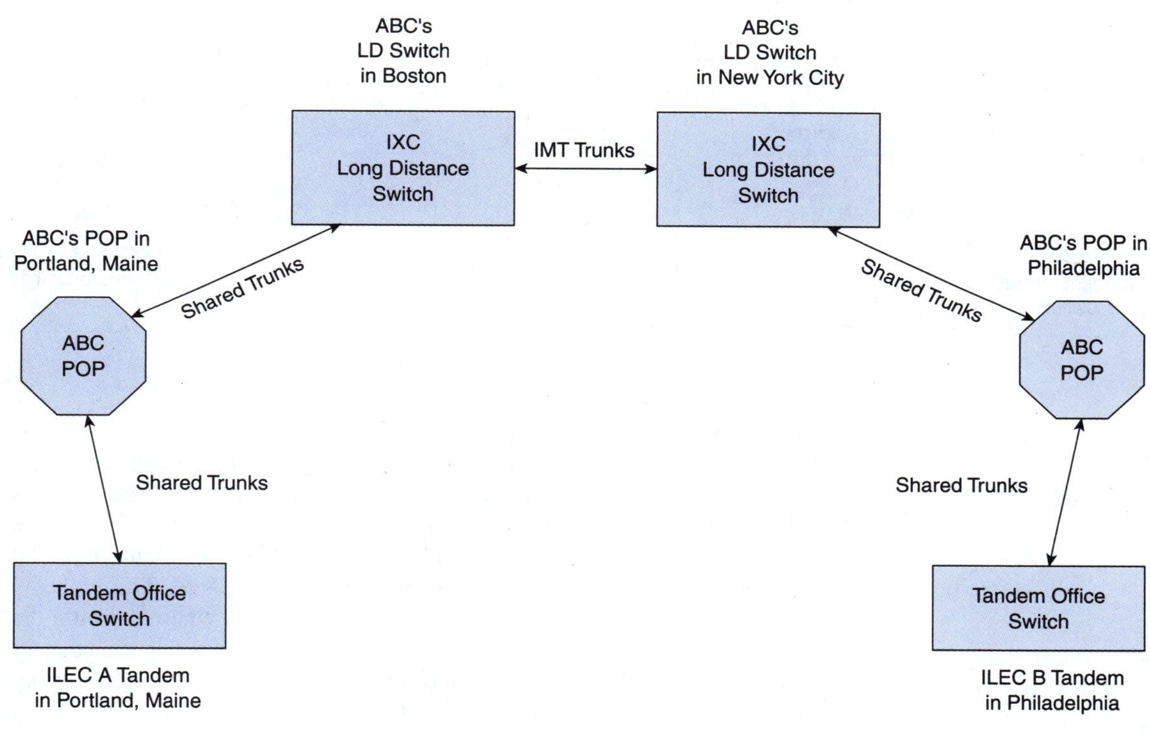

distance call. Therefore, an international call to Ireland from the United States always starts with the 011 *international code*, and is followed by the 353 country code, a city code, and the subscriber number.

international code The 011 prefix used to tell the switch that an international call is being placed.

The method used to route a call from the United States to Ireland is very similar to that of routing a long distance call. The international number Andy dials is accepted by his local serving switch on Wilmount Street. The switch looks in the customer profile record to see which long distance carrier Andy uses and routes the call to that carrier. The difference occurs when the call arrives at the ABC long distance switch. The switch sees the 011 prefix and realizes that the call must be routed

Figure 5–12
For calls between countries, a long distance network connects to an international gateway switch that performs two critical functions. It converts T1 to E1 format or it converts signaling information.

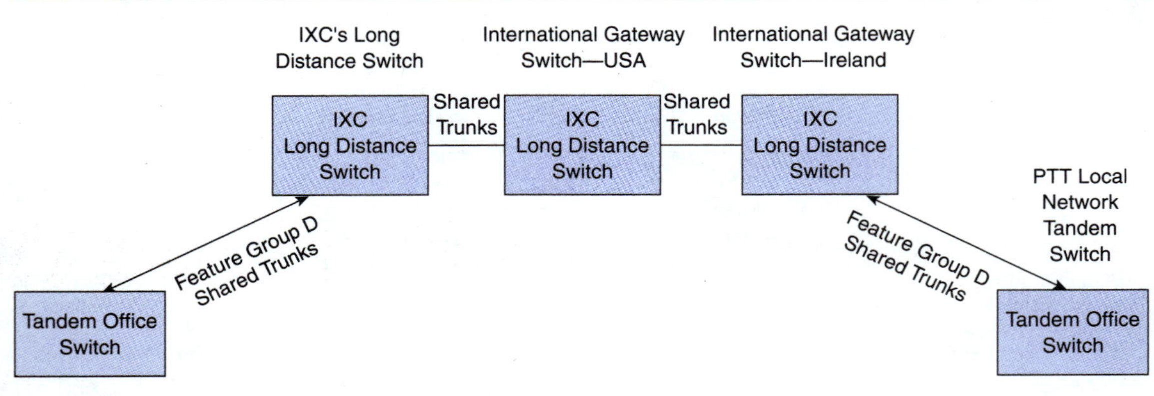

gateway switch Telephone switch capable of switching international calls and converting the SS-7 signaling protocol into protocols used elsewhere in the world such as C7—the European Standard.

bypass agreement Agreement established between a country and a carrier allowing the carrier to legally terminate international calls from its network into the country's network.

to an international *gateway switch*. A gateway switch is one that interfaces with the far-end international gateway switches located at the international gateway POP.

ABC has a gateway switch in New York City. The call travels from ABC's Portland, Maine long distance switch to the long distance switch in New York City. The long distance switch in New York City has IMT trunks that connect it to ABC's international gateway switch located at the same site. The gateway switch strips off the international 011 prefix and determines where to route the call by analyzing the 353 country code. The gateway switch sees that the country is Ireland and that all calls going to Ireland must be routed onto the trunk group that connects to a gateway switch located in Dublin.

The gateway switch in New York directs the call onto the IMT trunk riding on a circuit that connects into the Dublin gateway switch. The call arrives in Dublin where the gateway switch directs the call to a long distance switch that then directs the call to a local switch that finally directs the call to the telephone sitting in Shawn's kitchen. Figure 5–12 provides a comprehensive description of how the call travels between countries. There are several scenarios that are actually more common than directly connecting into a country gateway switch. In fact, a small long distance company such as ABC would not be allowed to connect directly into Ireland's telephone network. Due to regulatory restrictions, special *bypass agreements* are required for a long distance carrier to directly connect into a country's phone network. Today, many European countries have opened their networks, just like the United States divested the long distance and local telephone companies' networks. Initially, the European Postal, Telephone, and Telegraph (PTT) networks were controlled exclusively by the individual governments. Unlike the United States, whose network was privately owned and operated by AT&T, the rest of the world depended on governments to operate the phone network—much like our post office. Third-world countries are just

Figure 5–13
A long distance network that does not have direct connections to a country connects to an international gateway switch owned by another carrier.

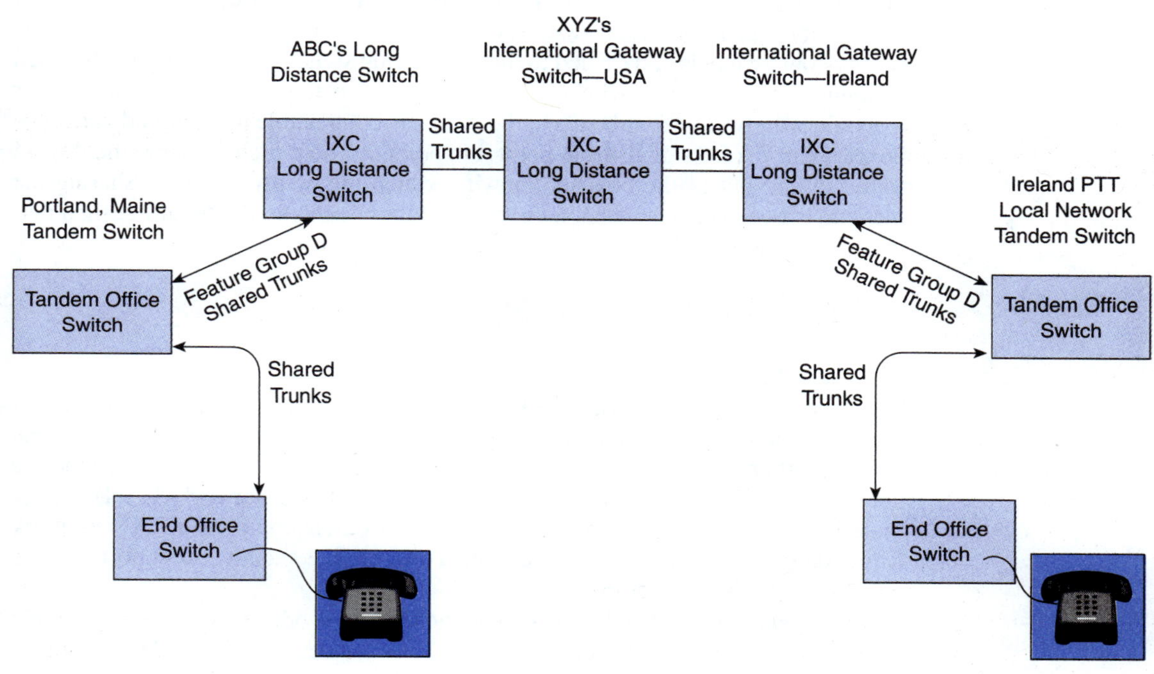

beginning to open up their telephone networks to competition, thereby allowing long distance companies to directly interconnect.

Therefore, a company like ABC long distance would connect their gateway switch with a large older carrier such as AT&T or MCI for international calls. Figure 5–13 shows a common method of connecting a long distance company to a bypass carrier going into a country's PTT.

5.4 THE DIGITAL NETWORK CIRCUIT

A digital *network* is a type of circuit used to connect two switches. The circuits may transport Intraswitch trunking, Interswitch trunking, and even international IDDD trunking. In the United States, telephone networks use T1 circuits.

The medium used to connect the two switches may be copper, radio (microwave), or fiber optic cable. The information traveling on the medium behaves the same, looks the same, and sounds the same whether it moves on fiber, copper, or air. The connection between the two switches is shared by all of the residents terminating on that switch. The physical medium is like a highway built to

dial-up data
Establishing data communications using the public switched telephone network. Dial-up data requires a modem to establish the call.
LAN
Local area network—Multiple computing devices such as PCs, servers, and printers are connected to a LAN. Each device on the LAN is able to exchange information.
modem
Modulator/demodulator. Device that converts the digital signal coming from the PC into an analog signal that can be transported onto a voice grade POTS line.
dedicated data circuit
Point-to-point circuit established for data communications only. Dedicated data circuits carry information between two locations, such as between a bank and its branches. The network is closed to anyone other than the bank.

carry ones and zeros, with the makeup of the medium determining how fast the ones and zeros are able to travel.

Andy's call shares the same medium as it travels between his serving central office on Wilmount Street and Alfonso's on Maple Street. A T1 circuit carrying trunk has twenty-four information channels. Andy's voice signal is placed in one of the twenty-four channels and carried to the terminating switch. T1 circuits are also used to connect long distance switches. The circuits connecting the switches are similar to a train with twenty-four boxcars; the switch is comparable to a railroad yard. The boxcars carry voice signals from point *A* to point *B*. The switch manages the flow of traffic in and out of the boxcars knowing which are empty and full. Sharing the medium between switches enables communication carriers to better utilize their network and consequently reduce prices to the end subscriber.

5.5 DEFINING THE DATA NETWORK

5.5.1 Dial-Up Data Network

The *dial-up data* circuit was one of the first methods used to transport data information across the telephone network, and it can still be used to connect one PC to another PC. A simple example is using a dial-up connection to connect a home PC to a file server, that is connected to a local area network (LAN) at a remote business site. Many people today dial into their company's LAN network from home. To establish this connection, a dial-up line and an access port into the company's LAN are required.

Andy remembers that he has to respond to some work-related e-mail. He turns on his PC and clicks on the local dial-up icon on his desktop. The PC's modem dials out the telephone number of the LAN at Andy's place of business. The switch receives the digits in the same way it would receive and handle the digits for a normal telephone call. It sees that the number 234-1000 is a local number and that it resides in the Elm Street CO. The switch directs the call onto a trunk group connected to the Elm Street CO. The Elm Street switch sends the call onto the line attached to Boxes, Incorporated and rings the end station. In this case the end device is a *modem* pool attached to a router. The router is a piece of communication equipment that routes data packets using the source and destination addresses of the devices on the network such as the LAN. Once the call travels through the modem pool and into the LAN, Andy is able to access his e-mail just as he would if he were attached to the LAN at work. The dial-up connection has established a point-to-point connection that will last as long as the PC and end station remain off-hook. Once Andy logs off the LAN and disconnects his modem from the line, the point-to-point connection is dropped and the telephone line becomes idle waiting for an off-hook condition.

5.5.2 Dedicated Data Circuits

A *dedicated data circuit* is one that is permanently open. A good example is the connection between an ATM bank machine and the bank's main office. Andy suddenly realizes he is low on cash. He rushes down to the corner ATM machine, and slides in his ATM card. As Andy punches his personal identification number (PIN) into the machine, the bank receives the digits and determines if Andy is allowed to access the account defined on his ATM card. The information packet travels between the ATM machine and the main hub on the data communication circuit. The ATM machine transfers Andy's request for $200.00 to the main frame where his account information is stored. The mainframe responds to the request from the ATM by replying with a "yes, approved" transaction. The ATM machine discharges $200 dollars and a receipt detailing the transaction. Andy picks up his money, asks for his card back, and leaves. The communication circuit between the ATM machine and the bank's mainframe is a dedicated data connection used only by the two end devices. The circuit, unlike a dial-up line, is always up. The ATM or the mainframe initiates sessions by sending special wake-up characters to the receiving device. During idle times, a keep-alive signal is transmitted to ensure the two ends remain synchronized. The purpose of a dedicated data line is twofold. One is to ensure the security of the information, the second is to improve the speed of the transmission.

When Andy punches in his PIN, the circuit sends the digits out on the copper line that is connected to the Wilmount CO. The difference between this circuit and Andy's telephone line is that the bank/ATM circuit does not go through the switch. Instead it travels into special service equipment connecting it to the Walnut Street CO, which serves the bank. The copper line travels from one point at the ATM to the Wilmount Street CO, then to the Walnut Street CO and finally to the bank office. Dedicated point-to-point lines are very common in telecommunications.

5.5.3 Packet Networks—The Internet

The last network we will discuss is the *packet network*. Andy wants to order some flowers for Daisy. He decides to order the flowers by logging onto the Internet and visiting a flower shop, which will require the use of a dial-up modem to establish a connection through the network.

packet network Statistically multiplexed network that carries information in the form of variable-length packets. The information is typically all data and is used to help increase the amount of information that can be transferred between multiple locations using the same links.

Andy double clicks on the Internet icon on his desktop and waits as the modem dials the internet service provider's (ISP's) telephone number. Again, the digits are received by the Wilmount Street switch and routed to the tandem switch which directs the call to a trunk connecting into his ISP, Surf the NET. Surf the NET's modem pool synchronizes with Andy's modem and establishes a connection. Andy types in the flower shop's web address and waits for a response. Surf the NET's modem is connected to a gateway router that sends the web address out across Surf the Net's Internet backbone. The Internet backbone is connected to several peering points that continue to route the request through the World Wide Web to the destination web site. The response from the flower shop web site travels back across the network to Andy's PC, where it "paints" its web page across his screen.

The information traveling between Andy's PC and the Flower Shop's web site is in packets, something like envelopes, containing information. The shop's web site graphics traversed the phone lines as bits of data (ones and zeros). These packets don't have to travel in sequence on the same link. The first packet of information may travel down one path, and the second down a completely separate path. The local loop between the serving central office, Andy's home, and the flower shop are the only dedicated portions of the network. The information travels through the network across multiple routes depending on traffic load and circuit availability. The address attached to each of the packets directs it through the network.

5.6 NEW TELEPHONY TERMS

The telecommunications industry has gone through dramatic changes during the past 100 years. A change in lingo accompanied the technological changes. Following are some of the terms used to describe the new telecommunications players and where they fit in the industry.

- ILEC—Incumbent Local Exchange Carrier—An ILEC is a local telephone company that served an area before the 1996 Telecom Act. For example, Southwestern Bell was the ILEC for Dallas Texas, Bell Atlantic (now Verizon) for Pittsburgh, and Frontier for Rochester, New York.
- CLEC—Competitive Local Exchange Carrier—CLECs evolved as a result of the 1996 Telecom Act. They compete with ILECs as local exchange services, building switches and offering dial tone but using ILEC's wire facilities to provide services to subscribers served by the ILECs' CO. A facilities-based CLEC places their own equipment in the ILEC's CO and only relies on the ILEC for the last mile of copper. A non-facilities-based CLEC buys a port on the ILEC switch but does not place equipment in the ILEC's CO. It simply resells dial tone using the ILECs equipment and facilities.
- DLEC—Data Local Exchange Carrier—DLECs are similar to CLECs except that they offer only data services in the local telephone network. They collocate in the ILECs COs and offer data services, such as DSL, to subscribers fed out of that office.
- BLEC—Building Local Exchange Carrier—A BLEC also provides services in the local area but does so by placing equipment in the basement of high-rise buildings or in strip malls. The BLEC offers local services to building tenants and bypasses the ILECs network.
- ICP—Interexchange Communications Provider—An ICP, though the term has not caught on, is a company that offers data in the local market, voice, data services such as web hosting, and long distance.
- ASP—Application Service Provider—An ASP offers application services such as web hosting and storage units to hold content. They are popping up all around the country and are normally strategically placed to service entire regions.
- IXC—Interexchange Carrier—An IXC is a long distance provider such as MCI, Sprint, Global Crossing, Quest, and AT&T.
- CAP—Competitive Access Provider—A CAP offers access in local markets. For example, an IXC or a CLEC might lease facilities from a CAP to gain access to the local telephone network. The CAP provides an alternative to the ILEC's local network, helping to reduce the cost to the CLEC and IXC.

SUMMARY

Chapter 5 provided an overview of the telephone network. Calls were traced through the local network, and the long distance network. T1 circuits were introduced as the backbone of the network used to carry voice and data traffic. The chapter concluded with a discussion of the data network and how information is transported between two PCs.

REVIEW QUESTIONS

1. Make a sketch of how a local telephone network interfaces with a long distance telephone network.
2. Make a sketch of how a long distance telephone network interfaces to an international telephone network.
3. Explain what is meant by *interoffice trunk connection.*
4. I've decided to call my friend Jane who lives next door. Jane's telephone line and my telephone line are both served out of the Oak Street CO. Draw the call path between Jane's telephone and my telephone.
5. I now need to call my friend Ernie who lives on the other side of town and is served out of the Monroe Street CO. Draw the call path between Ernie's telephone and my telephone.
6. I decide that I need to call my friend José who lives two states away. Trace the call path between my telephone set hanging off the Oak Street CO in Burlington, Vermont, and José's telephone set hanging off the Clinton Street CO in Muncie, Indiana.
7. After talking with José I realize I haven't talked with my friend Karl, who lives in Denmark for some time and decide to call him. Trace the call path between my telephone hanging off the Oak Street CO in Burlington, Vermont, U.S.A. and Karl's telephone hanging off the Boulevard Street CO in Copenhagen, Denmark.
8. Connections are built between switches, whether the switches are used to switch local calls or long distance calls. The circuits connecting the switches are of different types of media. List the three common types of media used to connect two switches together.
9. What is a T1 circuit used for?
10. Define the term *LATA*.
11. Define the term *IntraLATA*.
12. Define the term *InterLATA*.
13. List the three types of data networks described in this chapter.
14. Draw a dial-up data connection.
15. What is the difference between an ILEC and a CLEC?
16. What is the difference between a BLEC and a DLEC?
17. What is the difference between a CAP and an IXC?
18. What is the difference between an ASP and an ISP?
19. What is an ICP?

KEY TERMS

serving CO (214)
SS-7 network (215)
trunk (215)
end office (215)
LATA (215)
CLEC (216)
ILEC (216)
toll switch (217)
tandem switch (218)
equal access (219)
POP (220)
international code (225)
gateway switch (226)
bypass agreement (226)
dial-up data (228)
LAN (228)
modem (228)
dedicated data circuit (228)
packet network (229)

CHAPTER

6

Manipulating Information for Transmission

Objectives

After reading this chapter, you should be able to

- Describe analog to digital conversion
- Define Multiplexing
- Define Modulation

Outline

INTRODUCTION

Chapter 6 focuses on the various ways information is transformed, packaged, and readied for transport. Analog-to-digital and digital-to-analog conversion is detailed, as is the method used to format digital-to-digitals signal for transport. Multiplexing methods, including frequency division multiplexing, time division multiplexing, statistical multiplexing, and wave division multiplexing are also covered. The concepts presented in this chapter lay the groundwork for information presented in the rest of the book.

6.1 DEFINING ANALOG-TO-DIGITAL CONVERSION

6.1.1 Digital Signals Defined

digital signal
Signal that has limited, discrete number of values such as 0 and 1.

The analog voice or data signal must be manipulated into a digital one and zero bit stream before transporting the information onto a digital circuit. In communications, the term digital refers to information being transmitted using a one state or a zero state. Voltage being turned on is a one and no voltage is a zero. Figure 6–1 illustrates a typical digital waveform showing a 110010011 word.

unipolar
All pulses are of the same polarity. Every state change produces a pulse of the same polarity such as +,+,+.

Similar to the analog waveform, digital waveforms can be defined by the way the bit pattern is outpulsed onto the transmission medium. The three common digital patterns are *unipolar*, *bipolar nonreturn to zero* (BPNRZ), and *bipolar return to zero* (BPRZ), as illustrated in Figure 6–2. A unipolar digital signal consists of positive *pulses* moving in one (uni) direction. A unipolar waveform is never transmitted further than a few feet. Signals traveling between circuit packs inside the equipment often use unipolar digital waveforms. Unipolar signals are difficult to synchronize and hard to monitor with error-checking schemes because there are no opposite polarity pulses to count.

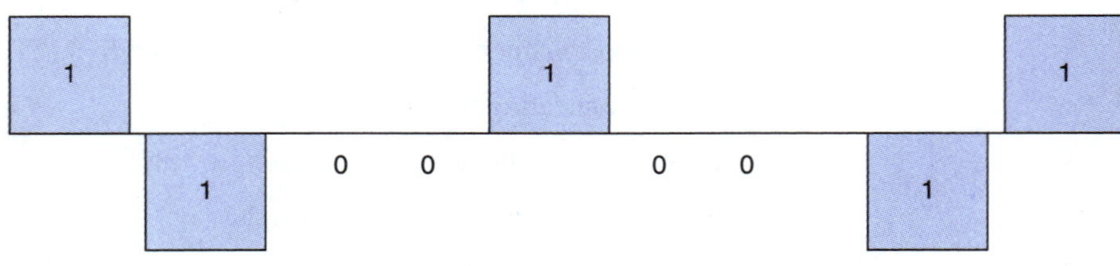

Figure 6–1
Digital waveform showing 110010011 bipolar return to zero format.

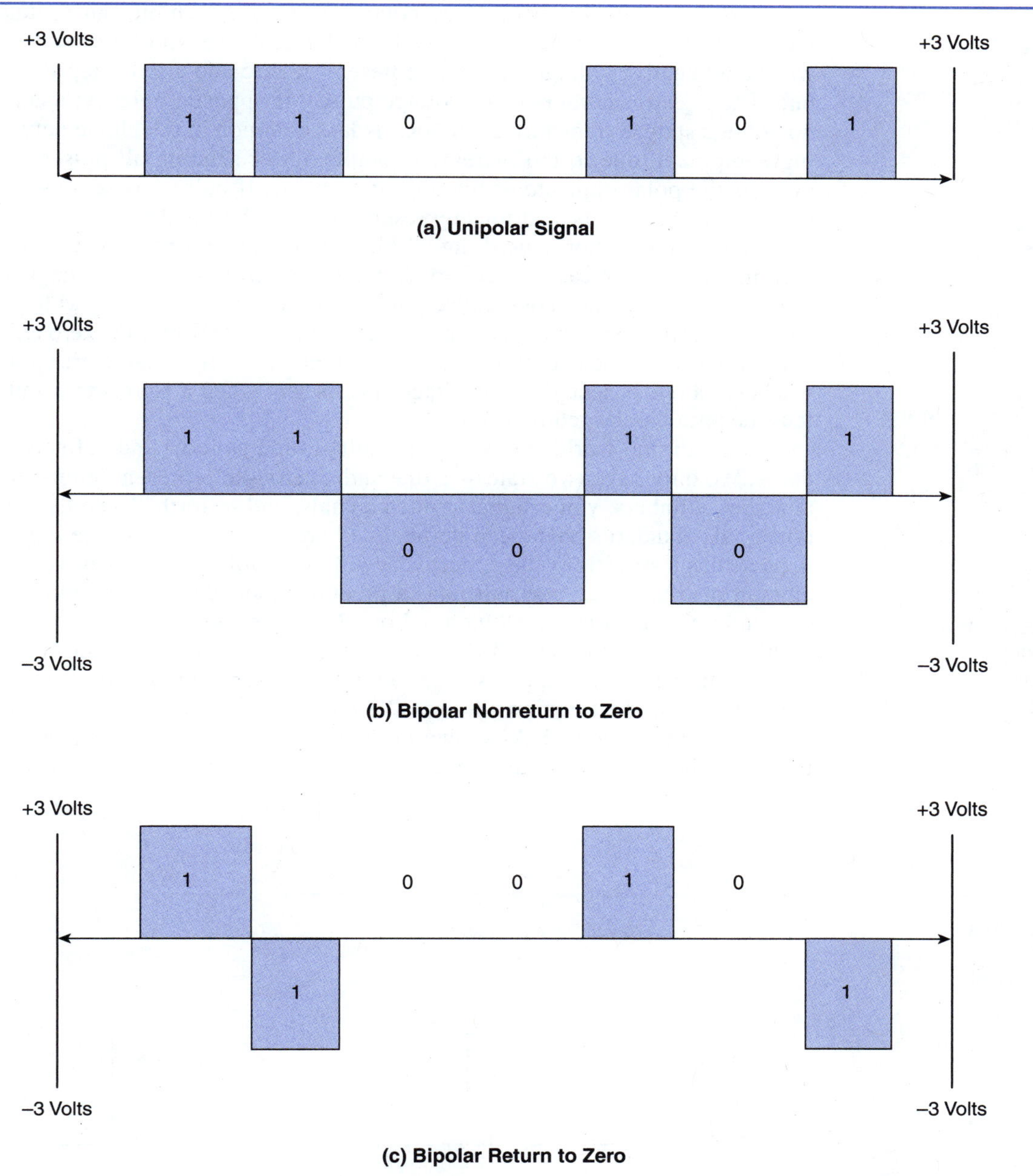

Figure 6–2
(a) A state equaling a pulse at +3 volts and a state equaling 0 voltage. (b) A state equaling a pulse at +3 volts and a 0 state equaling a pulse at –3 volts. (c) A pulse equaling a 1 state alternating between a +3 volt pulse and a –3 volt pulse. 0 is represented by no voltage.

BPNRZ
Bipolar nonreturn to zero—Pulse states do not return to zero but do reverse polarity for each state change.

BPRZ
Bipolar return to zero—Zero pulse is represented by the zero state and the state reverses polarity for each state change.

pulses
Electrical occurrences of a defined length and amplitude. The pulse created to represent a one state is defined by the amplitude and the length of time it lasts.

A *BPNRZ* signal uses opposite polarity states for each bit transmitted. If the first state is transmitted as a positive voltage, the second bit or state sent will be a negative voltage. A pulse represents a zero and a pulse represents a one. The signal is comprised of voltage pulses of opposite polarity; a zero or no voltage state is transmitted. BPNRZ is less common in telephone networking equipment, due to the increased complexity of sending all pulses. Each pulse is the polar opposite of the preceding pulse. If pulse 1 is sent as a +3, pulse 2 will be sent as a –3 thus representing a bipolar bit stream.

The most commonly used digital bit pattern and the one most commonly used in the communications network is the *BPRZ* waveform. Again, the bipolar pattern means that each consecutive pulse is of the opposite polarity as the previous one, forming a + voltage state and a – voltage state. Return to zero tells us that a zero is represented by a zero state. Simply, a voltage state is transmitted whenever a one is sent. A zero voltage state is sent when a zero is transmitted, thus the term bipolar return to zero.

In the digital world, everything is built around patterns and defined standards. We only have two states—a one and a zero—to represent letters of the alphabet, numbers, voice signals, video signals, and so forth. To do this, digital signals standards have been defined and are followed within the industry. A pulse has a specific voltage, normally +3 or –3 volts, and it lasts a specific amount of time. Each one pulse has a predefined standard height and width. The end equipment is expecting a +3 or –3 *voltage state* and a specific pulse width, as shown in Figure 6–3. The zero state must conform to a standard pulse length. The term *pulse mask* is used to represent the standard pulse shape for that bit stream. Test equipment uses the pulse mask to determine whether a digital word is corrupted. As shown in Figure 6–4, it is a little like a template that is placed against the pulse to see if it fits within its border. When the pulse

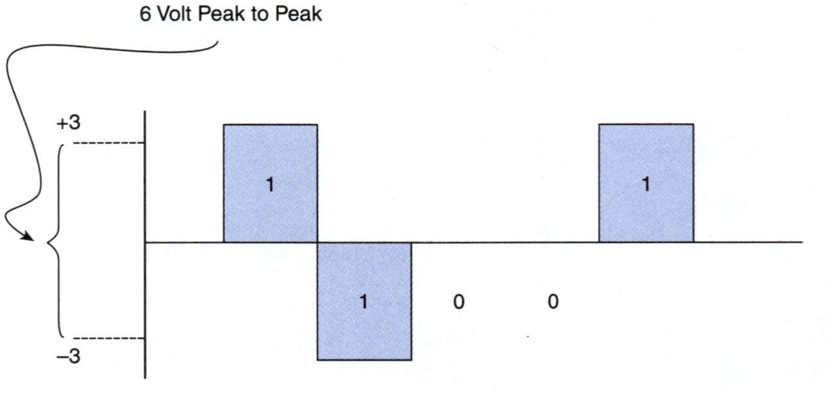

Figure 6–3
6 volt peak-to-peak digital waveform.

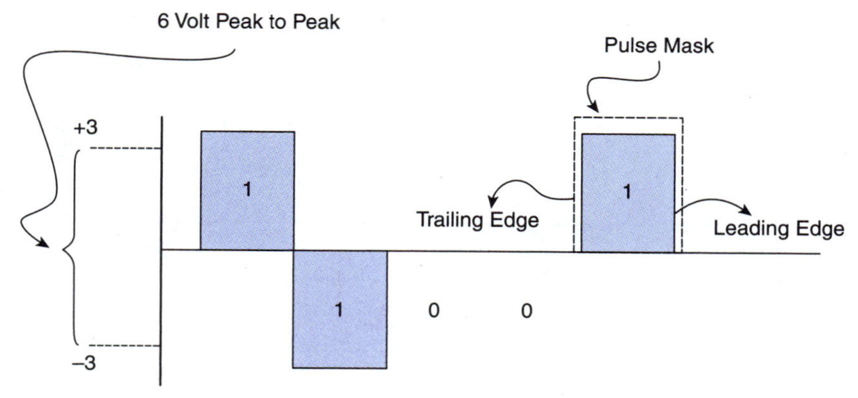

Figure 6–4 Pulse mask placed around a one pulse. The pulse mask represents the correct size of a pulse. When the pulse falls outside the mask or does not fill the mask, the end equipment has difficulty distinguishing where the pulse starts, where it stops, and whether it exists at all. Both the leading and the trailing edge of the pulse must meet the pulse mask parameters.

width and height varies beyond pulse mask borders, it means that errors are occurring and that the information is viewed as corrupted. The end equipment defines the pulse shape and pulse width. For instance, some computer equipment transmits a +6/–6 voltage state to represent a one pulse, however the common standard for pulse height is a +3/–3 pulse for transmitting a one state.

Bipolar return to zero provides the best method for transmitting digital signals longer distances. It also allows for an error-checking scheme in which bits are counted based on their *polarity*. The number is then tallied to determine whether a bipolar error occurred, that is, two consecutive pulses of the same polarity. The BPRZ bit stream is less cumbersome to deploy than the nonreturn to zero, and thus provides the best method for transmitting information across a digital signal. The pulse shape is also used to determine whether the signal is clean or corrupted.

Beyond pulse shape and voltage states, the FCC has mandated specific rules regarding the transmission of multiple zeros. Digital equipment uses synchronized clocks to align the bits being received. If too many zeros are sent, the receiving equipment becomes confused and doesn't know what portion of the bit stream it is looking at. The equipment depends on the opposite polarity pulse states to synchronize the incoming bit stream and determine the demarcation point for each channel. The rule states that there can be no more than fifteen consecutive zeros, or 12.5% of the pulses can be zeros. Two methods have been devised to solve the all zeros problem–*B8ZS* and *AMI*.

To discuss analog to digital conversion you must first understand circuit direction. There are three modes of transmission—*simplex*, *half duplex*, and *full duplex*, as illustrated in Figure 6–5. An example of a simplex circuit is a loudspeaker in a school. The principal speaks into the intercom, which projects his voice out to a classroom. The signal travels in one direction—from principal to student. The circuit is not capable of carrying the student's response back to the

voltage state
The voltage level of the pulse.

pulse mask
Shape the pulse should fall within in order to be considered a pulse. Similar to a standard outline the pulse should match.

polarity
Positive and negative values represent the polarity of the signal.

B8ZS
Zero suppression code used to replace 8 consecutive 0s in order to meet the one's density rule defined by the FCC.

AMI
Alternate mark inversion—Line code. Each alternate pulse is the opposite polarity.

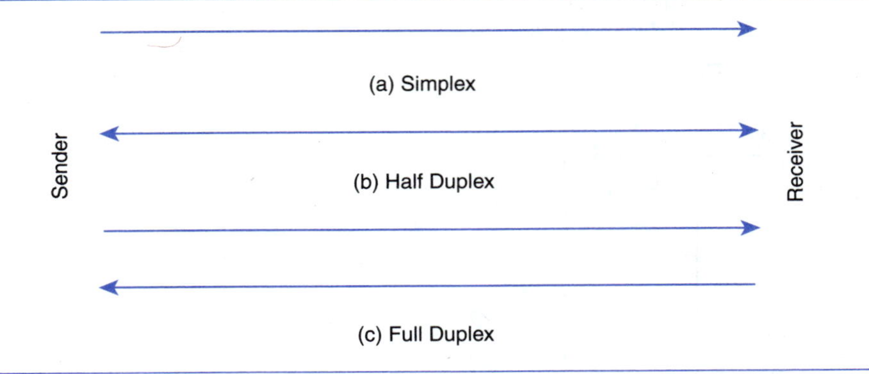

Figure 6–5
(a) Simplex transmission mode allows information to travel in only one direction—from sender to receiver. (b) Half duplex mode allows information to travel between sender and receiver in both directions but in only one direction at a time. (c) Full duplex mode allows simultaneous transmission between sender and receiver.

simplex Communication occurs in one direction only—source to receiver.

half duplex Communication can occur in both directions, but in only one direction at a time.

full duplex Communications occur in both directions at the same time.

principal. Because the circuit carries information in only one direction, it is a one-way transmission circuit.

A half-duplex circuit can carry information in both directions, but not simultaneously. A good example would be a two-way radio. You can talk to your friend by pressing the transmit button, but your friend can't talk to you until you release the button. The circuit carries information in only one direction at a time.

The full-duplex circuit can carry information in both directions simultaneously. Most digital circuits are full-duplex circuits. Telephone lines are technically full duplex but are used as if they are half duplex because it is difficult to carry on a simultaneous conversation.

6.1.2 Building the PCM Word

Analog-to-Digital Conversion Converting an analog waveform into a digital waveform was first accomplished in the 1960s when the advent of microprocessors and digital electronics spilled over into the world of telecommunications. Scientists and engineers were quick to recognize the simplicity of sending a signal composed of ones and zeros, compared to an analog signal with multiple frequencies. Analog signals required much more time to turn up and maintain due to the complex nature of dealing with many frequencies. For example, every time the weather changed, the analog carrier circuits had to be tuned to line up the equipment on both ends and the amplifiers located along the circuit path between them. When temperature increases, so does the resistance on a link. When the equipment on one end of the circuit varied because of the increased resistance, the receiving equipment was unable to decipher the content of the message.

In addition, the analog signal was limited in the range or number of frequencies allowed over distances, thus reducing the total bandwidth of the circuit. The digital signal bandwidth far exceeds that of the analog signal because the transmission of one and zero states is much less complicated. Analog signals have multiple frequencies to deal with, increased noise on the line, greater signal degradation (especially on the higher frequencies), and complex waveforms. Converting the analog telephone network into a digital network produced an

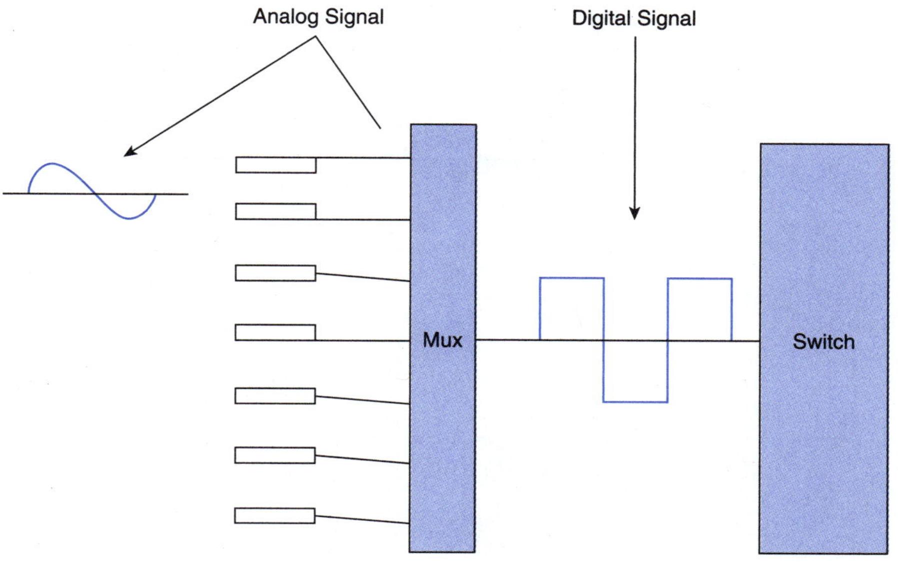

Figure 6–6
Analog data signals terminate into a modem pool. The modems connect to a TDM multiplexer that converts the analog signal into a digital signal, which then feeds into a telephone switch that routes the calls accordingly.

extremely reliable network capable of carrying huge amounts of information, thus making way for the "information superhighway."

Converting signals from analog to a digital is one of the fundamental processes of telecommunications networks. The only analog portion of the network left today is that found between the serving central office and the subscriber's residence. Large businesses use digital circuits for their voice and data networks. When a signal enters the switch, or arrives at the ISP's modem pools or a company's PBX, the signal is converted into a digital signal, multiplexed, and transported digitally to its destination, as illustrated in Figure 6–6. Pundits often speak of the new digital society. As you can see, it is an accurate description.

Moving to the analog-to-digital process, we will revisit Andy and Daisy's conversation as it travels across the telephone circuit and enters the class 5 switch. Andy's voice signal, "Hi Daisy, how ya doing?" enters the line card in the switch. The line card converts the analog signal into a digital signal and, conversely, the digital signal into an analog signal. A coder/decoder (Codec) that is located on the line card does the analog-to-digital and digital-to-analog conversion. In this example, the codec looks at the analog waveform created by Andy's voice frequencies saying "Hi,"as depicted in Figure 6–7. A three-stage process occurs during the analog-to-digital conversion; sampling, quantizing, and encoding.

The codec samples the analog waveform 8000 times every second. Think of the codec as a photographer who takes 8000 pictures of an erratic waveform speeding past every second. The samples taken are *pulse amplitude modulated* (PAM) samples. They move through the microprocessor chip where they are converted into binary ones and zeros to make a digital waveform. This is called *quantizing*. During the quantizing process, the sample is placed against a 255-level quantizing

PAM
Pulse amplitude modulation—part of the analog-to-digital conversion process.

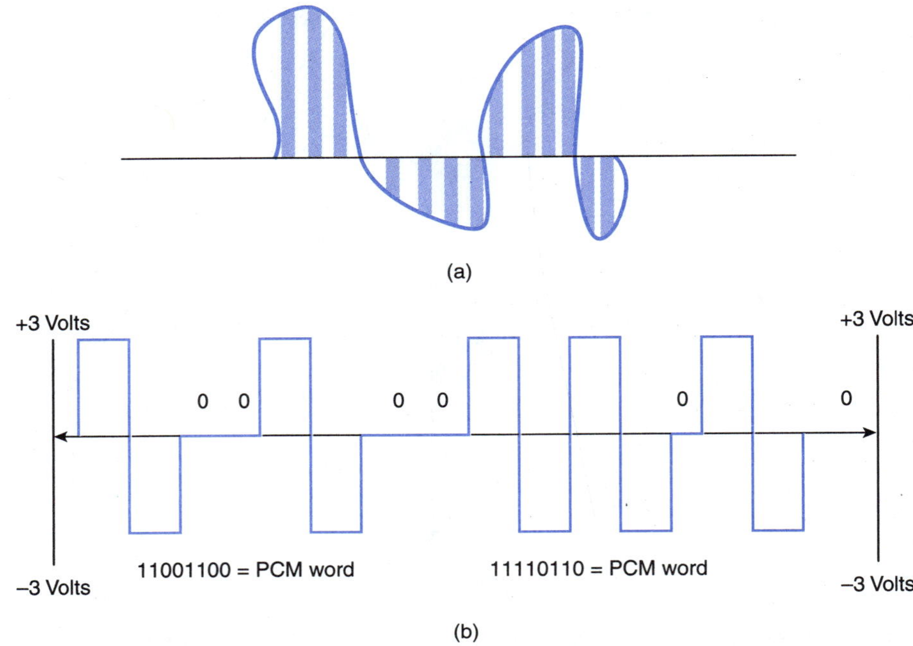

Figure 6–7 Comparison of an analog voice waveform and its digital equivalent. The analog waveform goes through an analog-to-digital conversion that produces multiple 8 bit words consisting of, ones and zeros, or voltage pulses and no voltage pulses. a) Analog waveform showing pulse amplitude modulated samples from the first step of the digital-to-analog conversion. b) Two 8-bit PCM words representing the analog frequencies shown in (a).

quantizing Step that converts a voltage value of the analog waveform to a digital word in analog-to-digital conversion.

PCM Pulse code modulation digital word.

encoding Step in which digital words are encoded for transport in analog-to-digital conversion.

scale—similar to a yardstick. Each of the 255 levels has an eight-bit one and zero word associated with it as shown in Figure 6–8. The sample, which is simply a voltage level, is matched to one of the 255 levels. The eight-bit word associated with that level is the *pulse code modulation* (PCM) word. Technicians often refer to the bit pulses they view on their test equipment as PCM words. Each PCM word refers to one sample of the analog waveform. Early scientists determined that 255 eight-bit words sufficiently represented all of the levels of human speech.

The final step in the process is *encoding*. Encoding formats the PCM words and ships them out onto the physical transmission medium, whether it is a copper wire or a fiber-optic strand.

Figure 6–9 shows a PCM word as it would appear on an oscilloscope screen. Notice the bipolar structure of the bit stream and the similarity in the height and width of each pulse. Bit format does not vary. It might be viewed as an army of similarly clad soldiers marching at the same pace in the same direction, following the same order and routine, but the entire process happens within millionths of a second. In fact, it takes only 125 microseconds to take a sample from the analog waveform, quantize it. and encode it onto the line.

Now that we understand how analog-to-digital conversion works, we can discuss how the reverse—digital-to-analog conversion—is performed. The eight-bit PCM word is received by the receiving end codec. Using the quantizing scale, it translates the eight-bit one and zero word back into one sample or voltage level. The word "Hi" becomes multiple voltage samples, as shown in

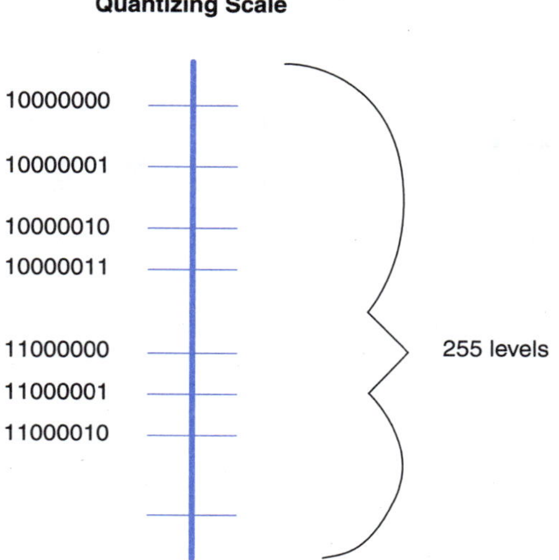

Figure 6–8
The 255 levels that are used to define 8-bit words from voltage samples.

Figure 6–10. The samples are then connected to form the original analog waveform. Figure 6–11 illustrates the decoding process of the digital signal. The eventual analog waveform is not an exact mirror image of the original "Hi Daisy, how ya doing?" because the waveform is a compilation of the samples of the original. However it is so close that the ear can't tell the difference.

The Nyquist Theorem was used when determining the sampling rate for PCM words. The Theorem states that a waveform should be sampled at two times

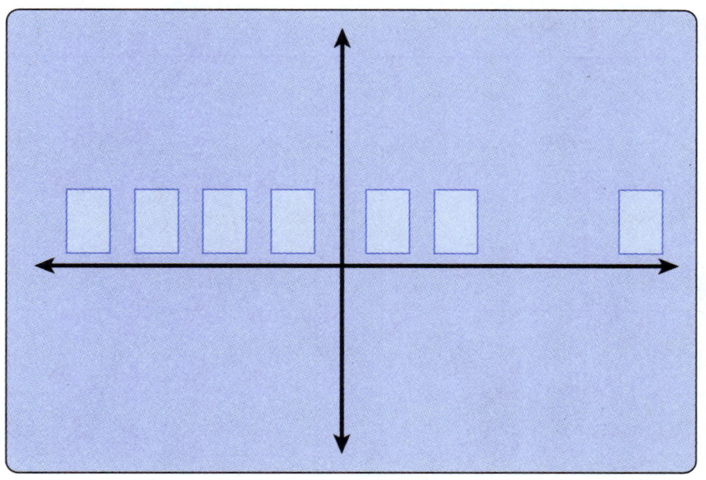

Figure 6–9
A digital signal can be fed into a piece of test equipment called an oscilloscope, which can be slowed down to show the actual one and zero pulses of the signal.

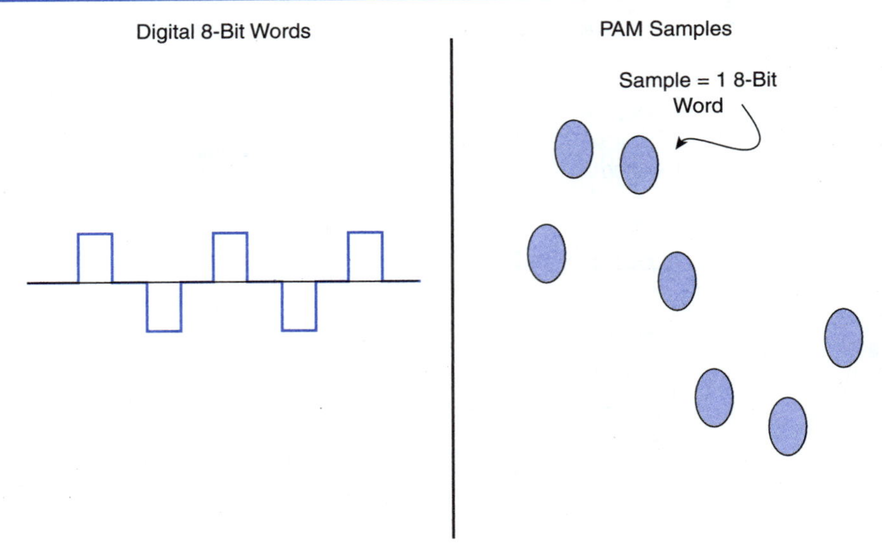

Figure 6–10 In digital-to-analog conversion, the digital word is converted into voltage samples. Each of the samples is shown as a circle representing one 8-bit word.

its highest frequency in order to obtain a toll quality signal. Because the frequency range for a voice signal is 300 Hz to 4000 Hz, the sample must be 2 × 4000, or 8000 samples every second to create a digital waveform that will adequately represent the source voice waveform. Consequently, a toll quality voice signal requires 64 kbps of bandwidth, as shown below.

toll quality Voice signal meeting specs provided by standards organizations.

8 bit PCM word × 8000 samples per second = 64,000 bits per second or 64 kbps.

The term *toll quality* refers to a voice signal that meets the toll voice specifications, referred to as Mean Opinion Scores (MOS), by standards organizations such as the ITU and ANSI.

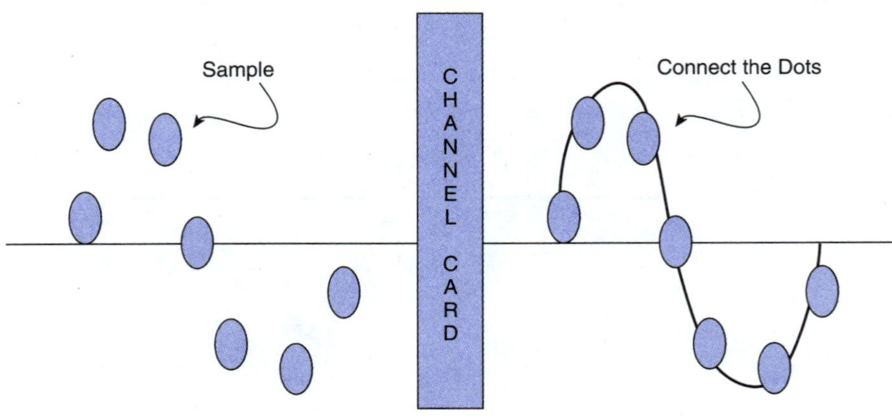

Figure 6–11 An abstract view of how the PAM samples are converted back into an analog waveform.

With the advent of the transistor in the 1960s, Alec Reeves from ITT patented a PCM word process based on the Nyquist Theorem. The transistor allowed for the fast processing required for analog-to-digital conversion.

Microprocessor speed and buffering capability (temporary information storage), has made it possible to decrease the number of samples needed in order to transmit toll-quality voice. Today, sampling rates have been halved, thus reducing the amount of bandwidth required to ship an analog signal. For example, when an analog signal is sampled 4000 times every second instead of 8000 times, a 32 kbps word is formed instead of a 64 kbps word. Adaptive Pulse Code Modulation (*ADPCM*) refers to a process that uses 2 000 samples per second to form the PCM word. Other more involved techniques such as LD-CELP have also been created to compress the voice signal and reduce the number of ones and zeros needed for each PCM word. The bandwidth required per voice channel has been reduced to levels as low as 16 kbps and even 8 kbps while still providing toll-quality voice.

ADPCM Adaptive pulse code modulation—Compressed digital word.

Once analog-to-digital conversion is complete, the signal leaves the switch line card and is routed to the correct trunk port, or trunk group. Normally, the trunk group interfaces with the outside world via a T1 circuit. The multiple 64 kbps words are multiplexed onto the T1 circuit and carried to the terminating end.

T1 circuits form the backbone of our communications network. A T1 circuit has 24 time slots capable of carrying twenty-four digital signals or twenty-four customers' signals on a transmit-and-receive pair. The method used by the switch is to sample each line in sequence starting with the first customer circuit and working down to the twenty-fourth, as shown in Figure 6–12. For example, when Andy's voice is sampled, the sample becomes a PCM word that is placed in the first channel (time slot) of the T1. The second sample is taken from the second subscriber's line and is converted into an eight-bit PCM word that is placed in the second channel of the T1. The same is done with the third customer's line and the process continues until the twenty-fourth customer's analog waveform is sampled, converted into an eight-bit PCM word, and placed in the twenty-fourth channel. When that channel is filled, the process starts again with the next frame. To better understand this concept, review Figures 6–3 through 6–12. Figure 6–13 illustrates the entire process.

Digital-to-Digital Conversion The source of the analog waveform may be a voice, a data call placed through a modem, or a video signal. The T1 circuit may also carry digital data traffic that does not require an analog-to-digital or digital-to-analog conversion. Remember that the type of signal leaving your PC is a binary one or zero signal. The modem interfacing your PC to the telephone line converts the one and zero signals into an analog waveform using the same frequencies produced by the human voice.

Though regular analog POTS lines feed most homes, some have digital lines that connect to a digital telephone and/or a PC. When a digital line interfaces with our PC, the signal doesn't have to go through analog-to-digital conversion. Instead, special interface equipment formats the digital signal leaving the PC and prepares the signal for transport across the communication link. The one and zero

Figure 6–12
To multiplex individual signals into channels on a digital circuit, a sample is taken from signal 1, an analog-to-digital conversion is performed, and the resulting 8-bit word is placed in the first channel. The process is repeated on the second signal where the resulting 8-bit word is also placed in channel 1. The process continues through the 24th signal and then begins again. The process continues until all signals have been converted.

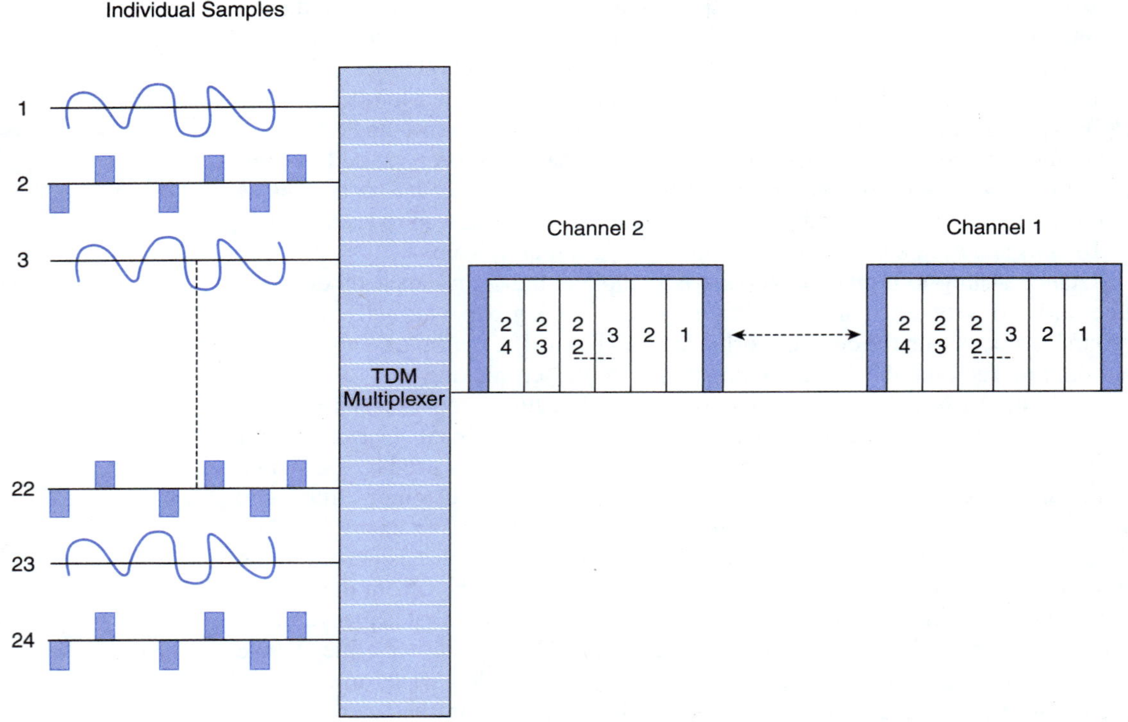

bits coming from the PC are normally in a unipolar bit format and need to be converted into a bipolar return to zero format. Devices placed between the PCs and the outside telephone circuit perform the conversion process and prepare the signal in much the same way as the encoding process discussed earlier. The ones and zeros are pushed into the predefined channels and then sent out across the network. If you could somehow open a signal midstream, you would not be able to decipher which of the ones and zeros belonged to an analog signal and which to a digital signal from a PC. The end pieces of equipment are able to count the bits and determine the borders of each channel and frame. From this segmentation of the bit stream, the end equipment is able to send the correct eight-bit words to the appropriate *channel* cards. There are cases in which a T1 circuit or ISDN circuit will carry digital data traffic and in order to accept the digital data traffic the data stream must be formatted to fit into the 64 kbps channels. Formatting digital signals directly onto a digital circuit is simpler than formatting a voice. The information is segmented into

channel
Term used to define the individual signal riding within the multiplexed signal.

Figure 6–13
a) Analog signal converted into a digital signal. The signal is sampled at a rate of 8000 times every second, then compared to a predefined scale called quantizing, converted into one and zero 8-bit words, and encoded into the digital bit stream. b) Digital signal converted into an analog signal. The digital 8 bit PCM words are decoded into PAM samples, connecting the dots to form the analog signal.

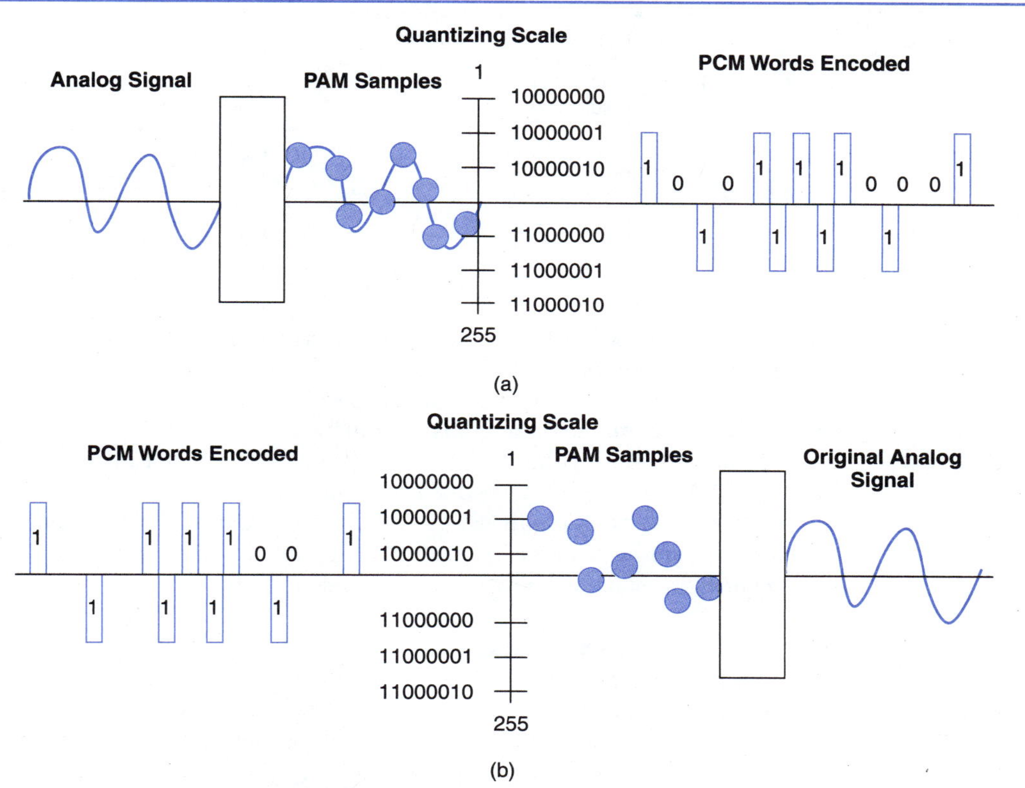

groups of eight ones and zeros. The ones and zeros are pushed into the time slot (or channel) of the circuit. If the signal does not have enough bits to fill the channel, stuffing bits are added to fill up the space. The stuffing bits are then stripped out at the termination end. The digital-to-digital conversion is more formatting of information than converting it. The interface equipment formats the digital signal into a BPRZ signal before transmitting it out onto the network.

6.2 MULTIPLEXING

The dilemma facing engineers since the first communications network began was the cost of handling hundreds of calls between two points. The options for the early engineers were to increase the number of wires between two points or have customers vie for space on the shared facilities. Today, engineers have multiple

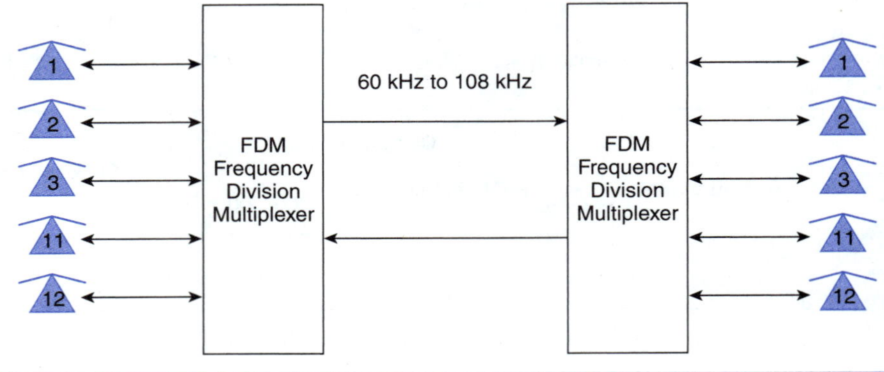

Figure 6–14
Frequency Division Multiplexing aggregates multiple channels onto one transmission circuit.

options for transporting large amounts of information between two points. The introduction of *multiplexing* technology helped eliminate the need to add new facilities or force customers to compete for space every time a customer was added. A multiplexer combines numerous information signals onto one transmission pipe. It may combine as few as 24 channels onto one T1 transmission link or as many as 129,024 channels onto one fiber optic strand.

multiplexing
Process of combining multiple signals into one larger signal.

The four most commonly used multiplexing methods in telecommunications networks are *frequency division multiplexing*, *time division multiplexing*, *statistical multiplexing*, and *wave division multiplexing*.

6.2.1 Frequency Division Multiplexing

FDM
Frequency division multiplex—Method that multiplexes different frequencies together into one signal.

In the early 1900s, frequency division multiplexing (*FDM*) was added to the telephone network. The purpose of the first FDM systems was to reduce the number of copper wires needed to transport voice calls across the long distance network. Once FDM proved to be a practical means to connect two sites, the technology was introduced into the local telephone network as central offices were connected to one another using FDM systems. The calls that traveled between switch sites were fed into an FDM multiplexer that combined the signals into one signal that was then pushed out onto the copper link. At the far end, the incoming signal was fed into a second multiplexer that pulled out the individual signals and fed them into the switch. These multiplexed links were called *shared trunks* and were similar to the trunking connections used to connect switchboards.

FDM works by dividing the frequency spectrum into subchannels, or frequency chunks, and transporting individual voice signals across each channel. For example, a 12 channel FDM system using the 60 kHz to 108 kHz frequency spectrum divides the bandwidth into 3 kHz chunks, plus guard bands placed before and after each subchannel. As the signals arrive, they are multiplexed into one of the 12 subchannels illustrated in Figure 6–14. For example, signal 1 is multiplexed into the 60 kHz band and signal 12 is multiplexed into 108 kHz band. The example shown illustrates 12 voice lines feeding into the FDM multiplexer, which places the channels into the correct frequency subchannel, then transports the frequencies out onto a four-wire

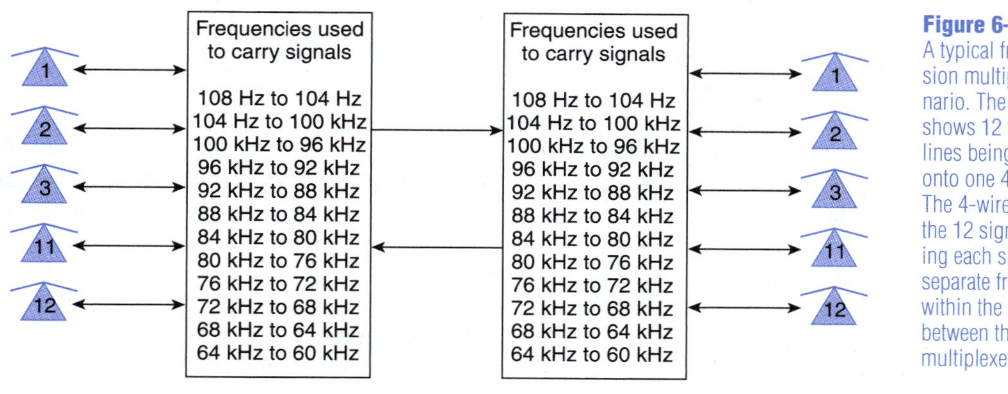

Figure 6–15 A typical frequency division multiplexing scenario. The example shows 12 telephone lines being multiplexed onto one 4-wire pair. The 4-wire pair carries the 12 signals by shoving each signal into a separate frequency within the range shown between the multiplexers.

copper circuit. The multiplexer is also capable of demultiplexing the incoming frequencies back to the original 3 kHz signal and sending them out onto the copper line interfacing the multiplexer and the customer's site as shown in Figure 6–15.

Obviously, FDM reduces the number of copper wires needed in the network. Early systems carried twelve signals (voice calls) on two pairs of wires. Running two wire pairs instead of twelve wire pairs produced an immediate financial incentive to place multiplexers in every central office and long distance switch site. When FDM was invented it solved many problems and reduced costs for outside plant facilities for telephone companies. Today, FDM is seldom used because of several technical and logistical problems associated with it. The three major ones are the power required to energize the circuits, the increased noise in the line, and the task of tuning the circuits.

In every FDM system, the signal must be amplified at regular intervals. Each time the signal passes through an amplifier, both the signal and the line noise is amplified. After the signal has passed through multiple amplifiers, the noise on the line becomes so loud that the information signal is drowned out and rendered useless. Because of the noise on the line, the distance between multiplexers was limited. The engineers constantly measured and calculated when they designed trunking FDM circuits between sites. If the signal passed through too many amplifiers, the end equipment found it hard to distinguish between the noise and the good signal. Therefore, the distance a signal could travel on an FDM circuit was limited and the engineer had to invest in either additional multiplexers or more copper.

A second problem with FDM amplified systems was the need to tune the systems whenever seasonal temperature change occurred. Analog signals must arrive at a certain signal level and continue to mimic the original signal. When the weather changes in the spring and fall, the physical characteristics of the in-line amplifiers and the resistance value of the copper cable changes. The higher the temperature, the higher the resistance values. The change in the resistance of the circuit causes the signal to change as it travels down the wire. Because the signal is a representation of the original, any change is unacceptable. If changes do occur, deciphering the signal at the terminating end becomes impossible. To alleviate this problem, technicians must tune the circuit between each amplifier. The procedure requires two technicians—one at each amplifier—adjusting the levels of the circuit to maintain signal quality.

The third problem with FDM systems was the need to line power the circuit. Because the amplifiers placed in the circuit required power, the only solution was to place power on the line at the central office. The amount of power required was much higher than for a POTS line and the longer circuits needed more power to energize the amplifiers. Therefore, power requirements also limited the distance an FDM system could send a signal.

FDM systems are beginning to be used again today. New DSL line codes that were accepted as standard in 1998 use an FDM scheme called DMT. DMT divides the 10 MHz frequency spectrum that is available on a copper twisted pair line into 256 4000-Hz segments. Information is multiplexed into these 4 kHz bands. FDM is still a viable multiplexing method for certain applications such as DSL, which is used for short distances between central offices and subscribers' locations. Also, newer microprocessors are able to automatically align the signal levels, relieving the technicians from manually adjusting the line cards.

6.2.2 Time Division Multiplexing

TDM
Time division multiplexing. Method that multiplexes digital words into time slots together in one signal.

Time division multiplexing (*TDM*) is the most common method of multiplexing used today. TDM was first introduced into the network in the late 1970s when the first T1 circuit was turned up. TDM, like FDM, combines multiple signals onto one pipe. TDM rides on all types of media—copper, radio frequencies, and fiber. TDM is the most widely used transport protocol in the world-wide communications network. ILECs, CLECs, IXCs, enterprise customers, global communication providers, and ICPs all have built networks using the TDM protocol. The two most significant differences between the FDM and TDM multiplexing technologies is that TDM uses time slots to carry signals instead of frequencies and multiplexes digital signals into the time slots, not analog signals, as with FDM. TDM time slot technique requires that the signals are clocked at a defined rate and that the bits are interleaved serially onto the link. The bits are fed into the time slots, also referred to as channels, according to the framing structure of the circuit. For example, the time required to encode and place one 8 bit PCM word into a channel is 125 microseconds. The two ends of the circuit are able to synchronize because both use the same time calculations.

conversion
First step in TDM process. Analog-to-digital words.

multiplexing
Second step in TDM process. Digital words are multiplexed into time slots.

There are two distinct steps in the TDM process, *conversion* and *multiplexing*. The conversion process involves either an analog-to-digital conversion or formatting the digital words. The next step in the process is to multiplex the digital words into the time slots (channels). The number of channels is dependent on the type of multiplexer and the medium being used. TDM systems vary in size from as small as two 64 kbps channels multiplexed onto one copper line, as in an ISDN BRI circuit, or as large as an OC-192 signal that carries 129,024 channels

Figure 6–16
Signals entering the channel bank may be either analog or digital. Analog signals go through an analog-to-digital conversion, which requires a Codec chip. A digital signal must be encoded and buffered or stuffed, if necessary.

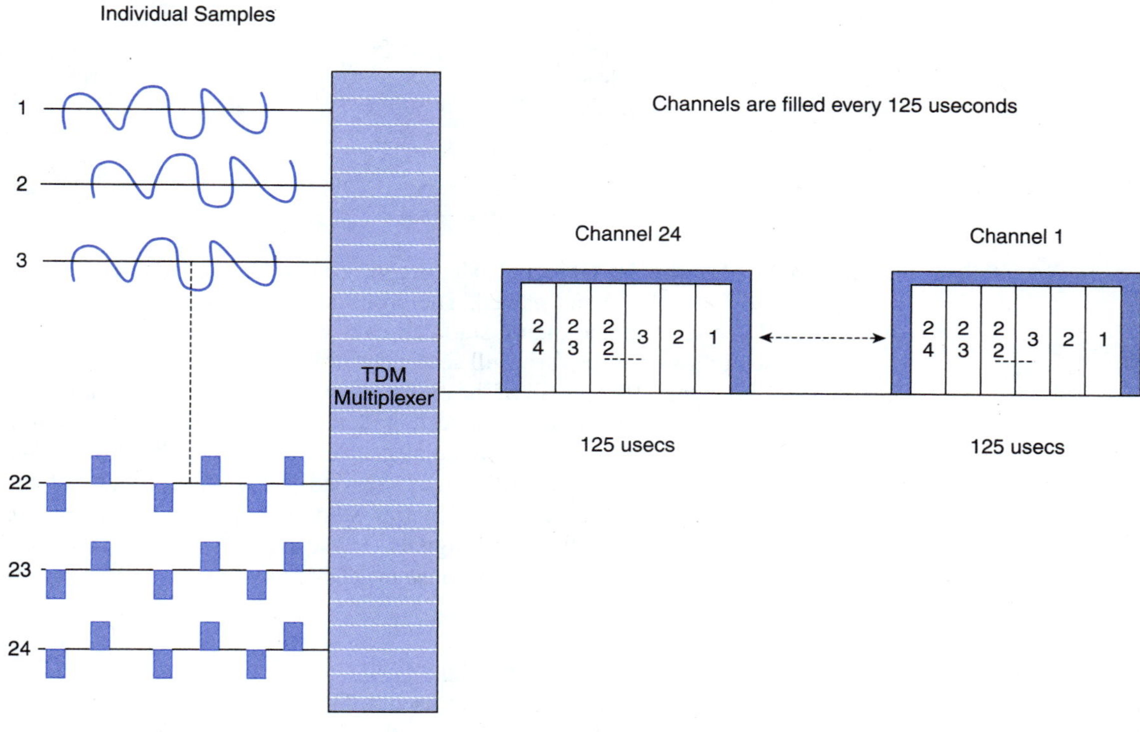

on one single fiber strand. The method, however, remains constant. The signal is first converted into digital binary words and then multiplexed into individual time slots on the circuit, using the rules defined by the TDM protocol standard.

A standard T1 multiplexer accepts information signals on a per-port basis. For a voice signal, the multiplexer runs the signal through a codec chip where it is converted from analog to digital. Newly converted ones and zeros are packaged into eight-bit words and placed in specific channels on the T1 bit stream. If the signal is already in digital format, the signal is packaged into eight-bit words and is then also placed into specific channels in the T1 bit stream. The multiplexer we are discussing has twenty-four input ports that are receiving twelve voice signals and twelve data signals. The multiplexer uses a round robin approach when determining which signal to grab and convert. The first input channel is selected, as shown in Figure 6–16. The channel card in the multiplexer converts the analog signal into an eight-bit digital word, then places the word into

Table 6–1 Digital signal levels as defined by the North American Digital Hierarchy.

Digital Signal Level	Bit Per Second Rate	No. of DS0s	No. of DS1s	No. of DS3s
DS-0	6.4 bps	1	NA	NA
DS-1	1.544 Mbps	24	1	NA
DS-2	6.44 Mbps	96	4	NA
DS-3	45 Mbps	672	28	1
DS-4	274 Mbps	4032	336	6
560 Systems	560 Mbps	8064	336	12

the first channel of the digital signal. The second channel is then selected and an eight-bit word is produced and placed. The process is repeated until the twenty-fourth signal is complete and then it starts all over with channel 1.

Multiple eight-bit words form full sentences or full streams of data, depending on the input signal. Piecing all of the eight-bit words together in a round robin fashion produces smooth coherent speech and uncorrupted data because the process happens so fast that there is no delay between words. Each sample takes 125 microseconds (usecs)—one millionth of a second. We learned earlier that one fiber optic strand can carry as many as 129,024 signals or channels and that one microwave link can carry multiple T1 signals. These systems are able to handle such large quantities of information because of TDM.

6.2.3 North American Digital Hierarchy and SONET

SONET Synchronous optical network—Optical standard that defines specific bit-per-second rates.

DS-3 Digital signal level 3—45 Mbps.

DS-1 Digital signal level 1—1.544 Mbps.

DS-0 Digital signal level 0—64 kbps.

There are two standard digital hierarchies used in North America. The older of the two is the North American Digital Hierarchy, the newer is the synchronous optical network (*SONET*) standard. The North American Digital Hierarchy has been around since the beginning of digital circuits in the late 1970s. The hierarchy defines the circuit bit-per-second rate. For instance, twenty-four 64 kbps DS-0 channels represent a T1 circuit. A digital signal 0 (DS-0) is a channel that can hold 64 kbps. In other words, one time slot can carry 64,000 ones and zeros each second. The T1 can carry twenty-four 64 kbps time slots and, therefore, has a bit per second rate of 1.544 Mbps or 1,544,000 bits per second. The hierarchy's purpose is to allow equipment vendors to produce standard equipment interfaces. If an equipment vendor produced a multiplexer with a T1 card that allocated 30 time slots instead of 24, the circuit would not work with other vendors' equipment. The North American Digital Hierarchy is shown in Table 6–1. The most common rates are the *DS-3*, also called T3; the *DS-1* also called T1; and the *DS-0*. Even within the SONET structure, the DS-3, DS-1, and DS-0 are used to define the subnetwork.

TDM is used to multiplex lower-rate signals into higher-rate signals. Figure 6–17 illustrates how a TDM system can aggregate thousands of lower-speed channels into one high-speed pipe. As shown in the diagram, twenty-four 64 kbps DS0 signals are time division multiplexed into one 1.544 Mbps T1 signal. The second step illustrates how twenty-eight 1.544 Mbps signals are time division multiplexed

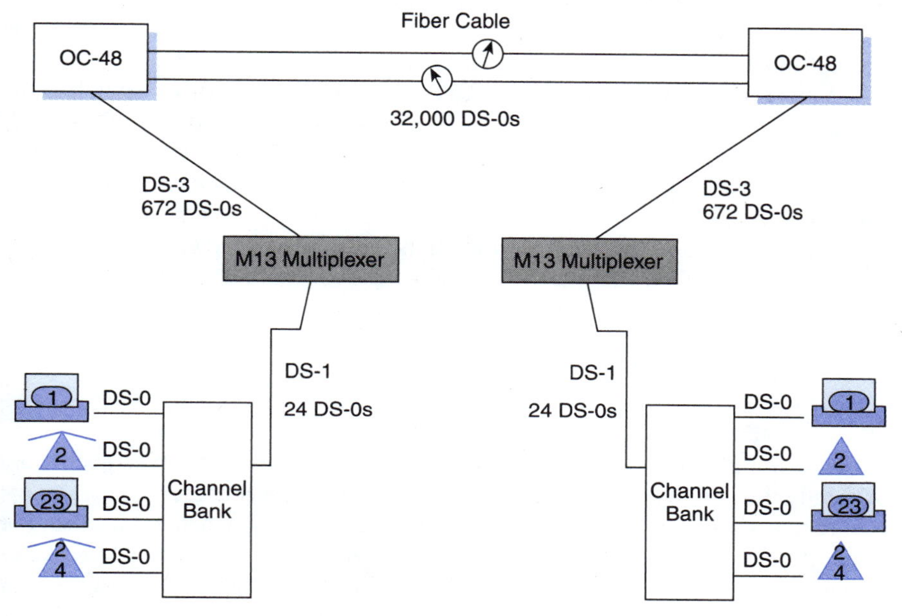

Figure 6–17 Multiplexing lower rate signals into higher rate signals. Individual DS-0 signals are multiplexed into a T1 circuit in the Channel Bank. 28 DS-1 signals are multiplexed in an M13 multiplexer into a DS-3 signal. The DS-3 signal is multiplexed into an OC-48 in the Optical SONET multiplexer.

into one 45 Mbps DS-3 signal. The third step shows how forty-eight 45 Mbps DS-3 signals are time division multiplexed into one OC-48 (2.5 Gbps) signal.

6.2.4 Connecting the Dots

The following is an example of using the North American Hierarchy and SONET in an end-to-end network scenario. Top Spot telephone company requires trunks between two of the towns they serve—Crystal Falls and Olive Grove. The transmission engineer decides to use an existing microwave link between the two towns. The microwave site in Crystal Falls sits on top of Crystal Mountain. Olive Grove's microwave antenna sits on top of a 3000 foot tower in the middle of farmer Dempsey's cow pasture. In order for the residents in the two towns to call each other, one T1 circuit is needed to carry the shared trunks between the two towns' central office switches.

First a link must be established between the central office in Olive Grove and the microwave site in the cow pasture. Fortunately, a fiber optic cable with spare capacity exists between the switch site and the tower in the pasture. The Olive Grove central office switch multiplexes twenty-four DS-0s into one T1 bit stream. It is then fed into a DS-3 multiplexer where the 1.544 Mbps T1 signal is multiplexed into a 45 Mbps DS-3 signal. The DS-3 signal from the DS-3 multiplexer is fed into the existing fiber-optic multiplexer. It is then multiplexed into a high-speed OC-12 signal that rides across the fiber optic strand to the microwave tower site in farmer Dempsey's field. Once at the microwave tower site, the OC-12 signal is demultiplexed into twelve DS-3 signals, one of which is carrying the new T1 circuit from the central office switch. One of the

DS-3s is then fed up the microwave waveguide and transmitted out across the airways toward the Crystal Mountain microwave antenna. The T1 carrying the shared trunks is in the fifth time slot of the DS-3.

A copper T1 circuit connects the Crystal Springs central office switch to the Crystal Springs microwave tower. Once at the tower, the T1 is fed into a DS-3 multiplexer where it is multiplexed into channel 5 on the 45 Mbps DS-3 signal. The T1 is multiplexed together with twenty-seven other T1 circuits into a DS-3 signal. The DS-3 signal that travels between the two microwave towers carries twenty-eight T1 circuits that can carry information between the two towns. The Top Spot engineer has used the fifth time slot to carry the T1 signal for shared trunks.

From this example, we can see that different digital signal rates can be multiplexed together, demultiplexed and multiplexed again. Figure 6–18 documents the example.

6.2.5 Statistical (Fast Packet) Multiplexing

fast packet
Method using packets, cells, or frames to statistically transmit information. IP, frame relay, and ATM are common fast packets.

Fast-packet multiplexing is a method used to transmit information. It is much more efficiently than TDM or FDM. Statistical multiplexing does not reserve time slots or frequencies. Instead, it dynamically allocates bandwidth only when it is needed. For instance, information being transported using TDM requires an assigned time slot or channel, similar to box cars on a train. FDM reserves specific frequencies per user channel. The consequence is that bandwidth is unused when the user is not transmitting information. For example, if the subscribers in Olive Grove and Crystal Falls decided never to call one another again, the twenty-four trunks connecting the two towns would never be used. The circuit would sit idle. Statistical (fast-packet) multiplexing is similar to the post office. The route a letter will take through the postal system depends on many factors. It might take a certain route depending on the day, the time, and the letter's priority. It's very possible that two letters going to the same address would take completely different routes. Many packet protocols handle packet transmission in a similar way. Packets are statistically multiplexed and routed according to the availability, time, and number of hops along the route.

In packet multiplexing, the pipe is similar to free space. A user's information is shipped out and vies for available bandwidth—similar to buying concert tickets without assigned seating. If the stadium holds 10,000 people, the promoter may sell 15,000 tickets, expecting that a percentage of the ticket holders won't show up. The promoter may prioritize tickets, guaranteeing high-priority ticket holders a seat and only allowing others if there are unfilled seats. When the stadium is full, those outside are turned away. Statistical multiplexing handles information in the same way. Circuits may be oversubscribed in the same way that the stadium seats are oversold. Being able to oversell capacity makes fast packet multiplexing a much more efficient way to use expensive transmission pipes. The engineer can oversubscribe the bandwidth because every user will not be on line at the same time. Statistical calculations are made when designing networks to determine the number of users per pipe. A concentration (oversubscription) rate is then determined.

Packet multiplexing has been used since the late 1960s as a means of transmitting data information. The difference between early packet networks and

Figure 6–18
Connection between the Olive Grove local switch and the Crystal Mountain local switch. A DS-3 connects the two towns via a microwave transmission link. Local switches are connected via land line. T1s connect the Crystal Mountain microwave tower to the local switch, while the Olive Grove microwave tower is connected to the local switch with fiber optic cable.

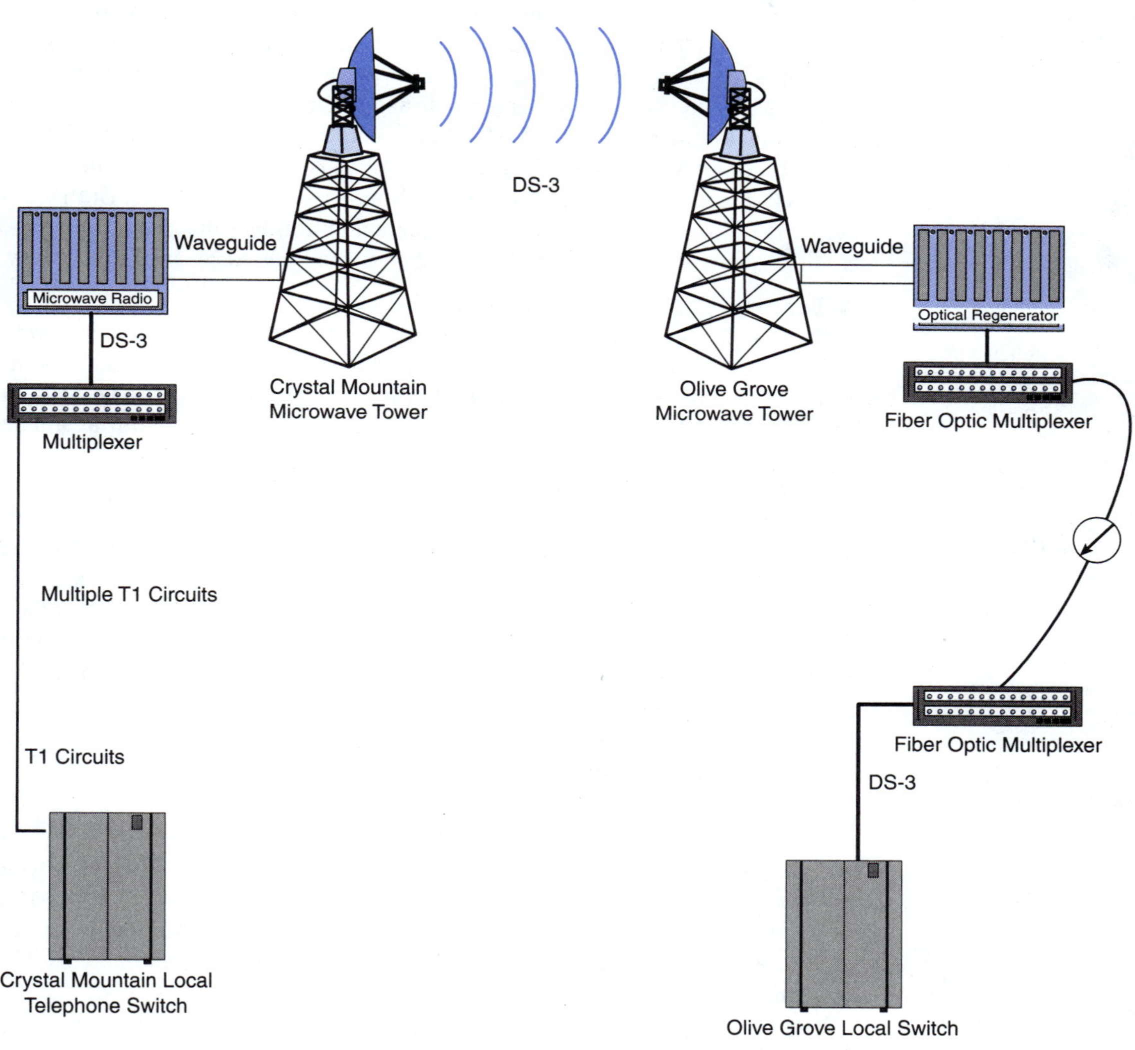

today's fast-packet networks is the increased transmission rate and the ability to ship time-sensitive information such as voice and video. Early *X.25* networks were able to transmit only 2.4 kbps. Today's ATM networks transmit 155 Mbps and more. Digital transmission facilities and fiber optic pipes have increased transmission rates while reducing transmission errors encountered in the facility.

X.25
Early packet transmission protocol used to transmit slower-speed data rates.

ATM Asynchronous transfer mode—Fast packet transmission protocol that statistically multiplexes fixed-length cells.

IP Internet protocol—transmission protocol that statistically multiplexes variable length packets.

FR Frame relay—Fast packet transmission protocol that statistically multiplexes variable-length frames.

DWDM Dense wave division multiplexing. The newest multiplexing technology in the communications networks.

In order to send time-sensitive information, such as voice and video, fast packet uses very fast DSPs (digital processors) to prioritize time-sensitive information by stamping a high-priority bit on the frame. By using cell-based *ATM* networks, voice, video, and data can all share the same statistically multiplexed network without producing choppy and delayed voice or video streams. Even Internet protocol (*IP*) networks are now able to carry voice and video signals.

Fast-packet multiplexing is quickly becoming the multiplexing method of choice. ATM, frame relay (*FR*), and IP all use fast-packet multiplexing and are quickly replacing the standard TDM scheme while still using the SONET fiber network. Technically, ATM and frame are not always called packet technologies, because ATM is a cell-based technology and frame relay ships frames. Both technologies do, however, depend on statistical multiplexing methodologies. Figure 6–19 shows the statistical multiplexing protocols—IP, ATM, and Frame Relay.

6.2.6 Dense Wave Division Multiplexing

DWDM is the newest multiplexing technology in the communications network. DWDM systems multiplex different colors of light onto fiber strands, thus increasing the bandwidth available on fiber optic systems. The rapid development of DWDM systems has helped to increase the amount of bandwidth available throughout the world.

To understand these concepts, imagine three flashlights emitting different colors of light; red, blue, and purple; each shining into a fiber strand. Space is left between each light beam to ensure that the colors do not mix together. The red beam carries a signal from an OC-48 multiplexer, the blue beam carries a signal from an OC-192 multiplexer, and the purple beam carries a signal from an OC-12 multiplexer. The fiber strand carrying the three colors (wavelengths) of light is transporting 169,344 DS-0s of traffic, as shown in the summation below.

OC-48 = 48 × 672 = 32,256 DS-0s
OC-192 = 192 × 672 = 129,024 DS-0s
OC-12 = 12 × 672 = 8,064 DS-0s
169,344 DS-0s or
169,344 DS-0s × 64 kbps = 10,838,016,000 bits per second

Systems deployed today carry 80 to 120 wavelengths (colors) of light on one strand of fiber, and each of these wavelengths could carry an OC-48 or OC-192 signal. The amount of bits per second being transported over one strand of fiber the size of a human hair is phenomenal. Lab trials have proven as many as 700 wavelengths carried by one strand of fiber.

Wavelengths used in DWDM systems vary, depending on a manufacturer's lasers. The ITU has defined wavelength standards and segmented the spectrum into 6 windows, as shown below.

Window 1 = 850 nm wavelength
Window 2 = 1300 nm wavelength = S Band
Window 3 = 1550 nm wavelength = C Band
Window 4 = 1600 nm wavelength = L Band
Window 5 = 1350 nm to 1530 nm wavelength
Window 6 = 1260 nm to 1650 nm wavelength

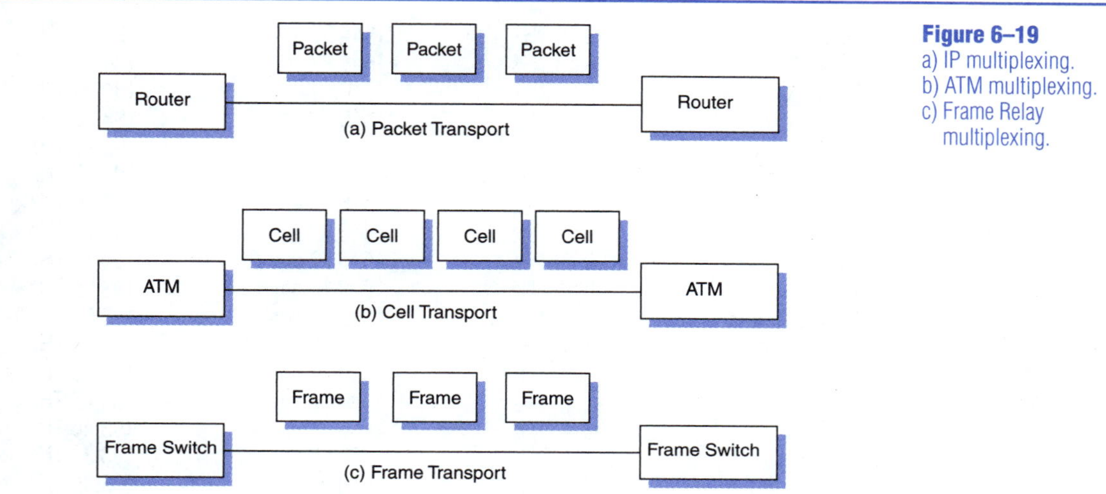

Figure 6–19
a) IP multiplexing.
b) ATM multiplexing.
c) Frame Relay multiplexing.

The ITU has designated specific wavelengths within each of the windows by segmenting the spectrum into grids. The most common grid deployed today is the C-band as shown in Table 6–2. Wavelengths are often referred to as channels or lambdas, the Greek word for wavelength, and are capable of carrying a high-speed signal such as an OC-48. Figure 6–21 shows a typical DWDM system using the 1550 nm C band grid.

Figure 6–20
A 9-wavelength DWDM multiplexing system. 9 OC-48s are fed into a DWDM, where they are multiplexed onto different wavelengths before being transported out onto the fiber. Two strands of fiber, one for transmit and one for receive, carry all 9 OC-48 signals.

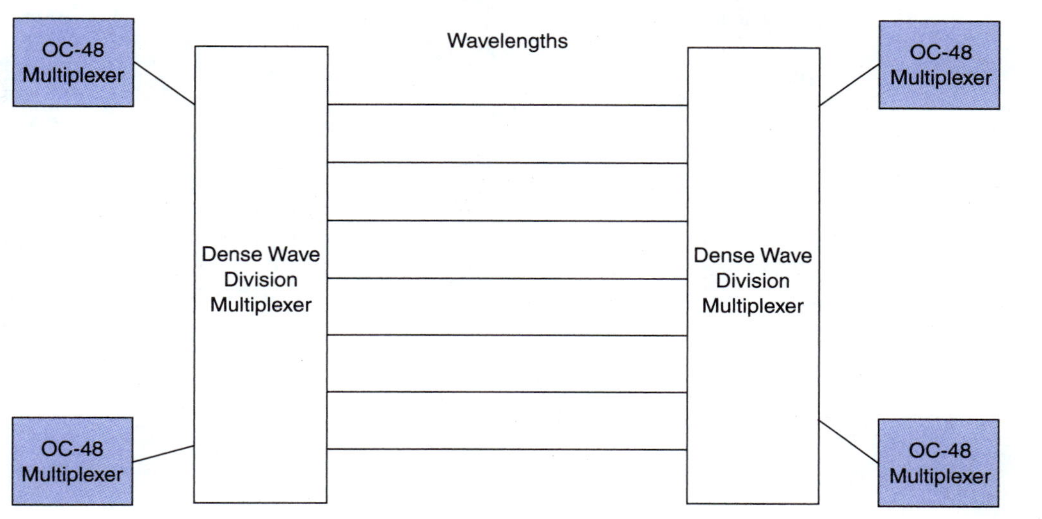

Table 6–2
ITU Wavelength Grid.
C Band.

Wavelength	Frequency	Wavelength	Frequency
1528.77 nm	196.10 THz	1544.53 nm	194.10 THz
1529.16 nm	196.05 THz	1544.92 nm	194.05 THz
1529.55 nm	196.00 THz	1545.32 nm	194.00 THz
1529.94 nm	195.95 THz	1545.72 nm	193.95 THz
1530.33 nm	195.90 THz	1546.12 nm	193.90 THz
1530.72 nm	195.85 THz	1546.52 nm	193.85 THz
1531.12 nm	195.80 THz	1546.92 nm	193.80 THz
1531.51 nm	195.75 THz	1546.32 nm	193.75 THz
1531.90 nm	195.70 THz	1547.72 nm	193.70 THz
1532.29 nm	195.65 THz	1548.11 nm	193.65 THz
1532.68 nm	195.60 THz	1548.51 nm	193.60 THz
1533.07 nm	195.55 THz	1548.91 nm	193.55 THz
1533.47 nm	195.50 THz	1549.32 nm	193.50 THz
1533.86 nm	195.45 THz	1549.72 nm	193.45 THz
1534.25 nm	195.40 THz	1550.12 nm	193.40 THz
1534.64 nm	195.35 THz	1550.52 nm	193.35 THz
1535.04 nm	195.30 THz	1550.92 nm	193.30 THz
1535.43 nm	195.25 THz	1551.32 nm	193.25 THz
1535.82 nm	195.20 THz	1551.72 nm	193.20 THz
1536.22 nm	195.15 THz	1552.12 nm	193.15 THz
1536.61 nm	195.10 THz	1552.52 nm	193.10 THz
1537.00 nm	195.05 THz	1552.93 nm	193.05 THz
1537.40 nm	195.00 THz	1553.33 nm	193.00 THz
1537.79 nm	194.95 THz	1553.73 nm	192.95 THz
1538.19 nm	194.90 THz	1554.13 nm	192.90 THz
1538.58 nm	194.85 THz	1554.54 nm	192.85 THz
1538.98 nm	194.80 THz	1554.94 nm	192.80 THz
1539.37 nm	194.75 THz	1555.34 nm	192.75 THz
1539.77 nm	194.70 THz	1555.75 nm	192.70 THz
1540.16 nm	194.65 THz	1556.15 nm	192.65 THz
1540.56 nm	194.60 THz	1556.55 nm	192.60 THz
1540.95 nm	194.55 THz	1556.96 nm	192.55 THz
1541.35 nm	194.50 THz	1557.36 nm	192.45 THz
1541.75 nm	194.45 THz	1557.77 nm	192.40 THz
1542.14 nm	194.40 THz	1558.17 nm	192.35 THz
1542.54 nm	194.35 THz	1558.98 nm	192.30 THz
1542.94 nm	194.30 THz	1559.39 nm	192.25 THz
1543.33 nm	194.25 THz	1559.79 nm	192.20 THz
1543.73 nm	194.20 THz	1560.20 nm	192.15 THz
1544.13 nm	194.15 THz	1560.61 nm	192.10 THz

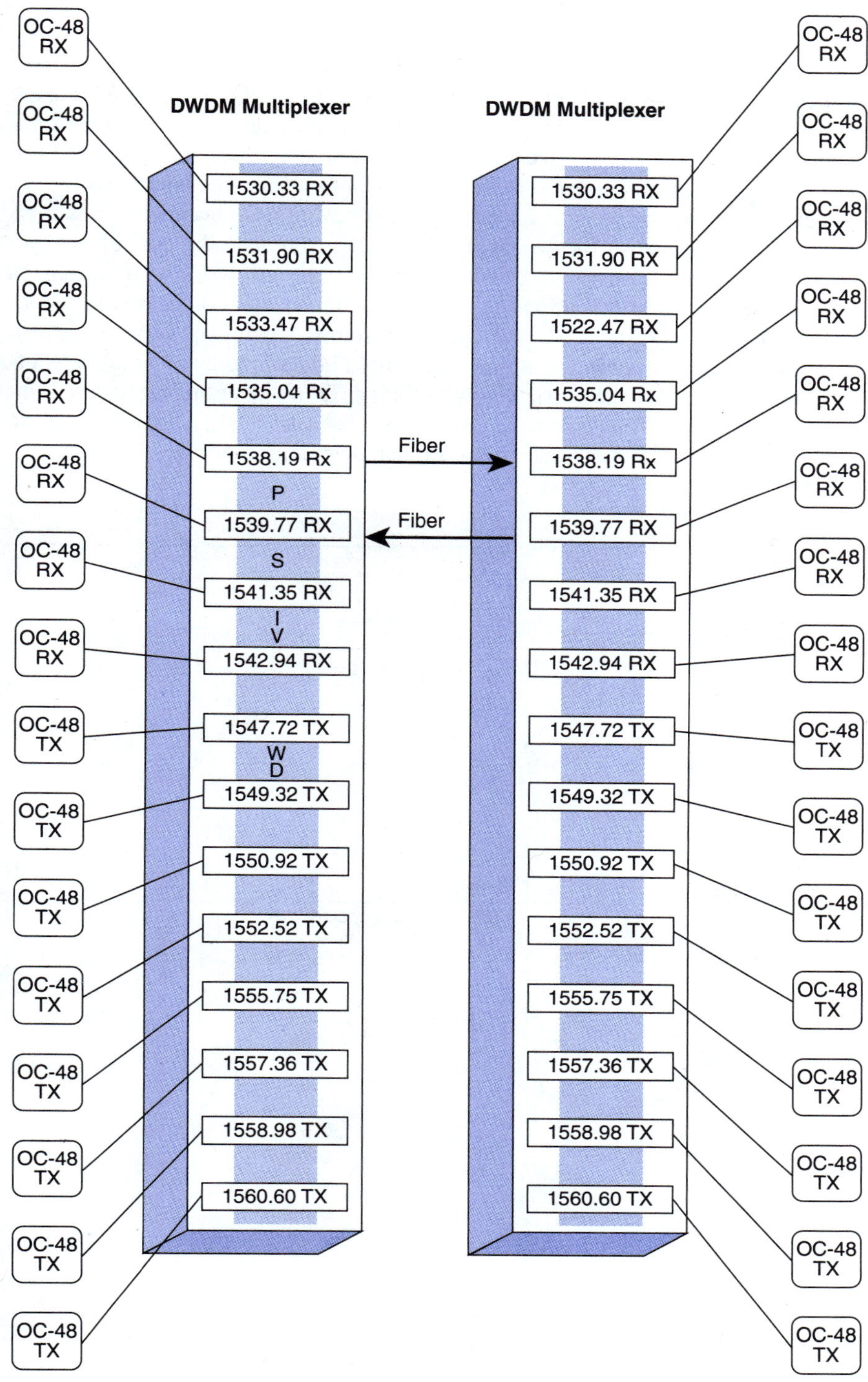

Figure 6–21
A DWDM system using the ITU-C band grid. Each wavelength may be viewed as a channel that carries a signal. The system shown is carrying 16 wavelengths.

CWDM
Systems with very wide spacing fields between each wavelength.

An additional parameter that determines the number of wavelengths per fiber is the amount of spacing placed between each channel. 50 GHz and 100 GHz are the most commonly used spacing arrangements. If the spacing is too narrow, adjacent channels could cross over and corrupt their neighbor's signal. The term *coarse wavelength division multiplexing (CWDM)* refers to systems with very wide spacing fields between each wavelength that limit the number of channels per system. The purpose for deploying CWDM is to reduce the cost of the system. For example, an 8-lambda or wavelength system will work with large gaps between the channels, thus allowing less precise lasers and consequently reducing the cost of the system. 80 wavelength systems depend on very expensive, finely tuned lasers, to maintain signal credibility and eliminate any cross-over effect (as cross talk). Spacing as small as 25 GHz is being promoted as a way to increase the number of channels per system. The cost, of course, is extremely high. Figure 6–22 shows the difference between narrower and wider spacing methods.

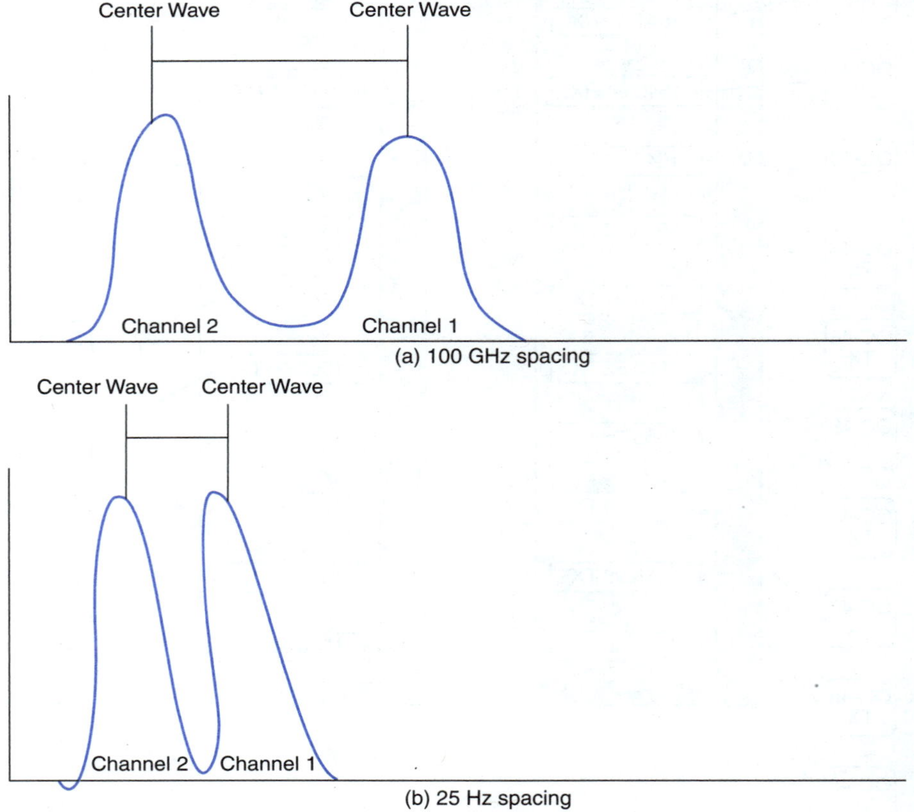

Figure 6–22
a) Wider spaced DWDM system b) Narrower spaced DWDM system.

6.3 MODULATION

Modulation is a key concept in the world of communications. It might even be thought of as the underlying river that flows through all communications links. Modulation, though important, can be difficult to explain.

Information is modulated onto a signal (carrier signal). The carrier signal is produced by the end equipment and is projected out onto the circuit. Think of it as being similar to a river. The information signal rides on the carrier wave, while the information manipulates the carrier wave to match the originating signal. The carrier wave, in essence, becomes the information signal—they have a symbiotic relationship. The information signal depends on the carrier wave to carry it to its destination. Modulation, then, is the process of incorporating an information signal onto a carrier wave.

modulation Process of manipulating a defined carrier wave with an information signal. Information signal is imposed onto a carrier wave, which adjusts to carry the signal across the medium.

SUMMARY

Chapter 6 focuses on the way information is manipulated for transport. Analog-to-digital conversion is discussed in detail. Several methods used to multiplex information onto a line are explored. Frequency division multiplexing, time division multiplexing, statistical multiplexing, and dense wave division multiplexing are detailed. The chapter also explains modulation and why it is needed for sending information.

CASE STUDY

You are now familiar with the types of media used in the network and also with the use of multiplexers to decrease the number of facilities needed in an area. Using the map and the information on population distribution provided in Appendix H, put together a preliminary design showing what areas require multiplexers. Place a star on the map showing where you will place the multiplexers. Determine the break point between the cost of adding cable pair and the cost of placing a multiplexer. Again, this is a preliminary design based on the assumption that you may place multiplexing equipment on the end of the circuit, such as in the hospital or in the factories.

The main purpose of this exercise is for you to become familiar with the number of residents in the area and the number of signals that will be carried on the cable. Break points will be supplied to determine whether or not a multiplexer using fiber optic cable is needed or if copper cable can be used instead. Information on the capacity per location and the cost of each type of multiplexer is given in Appendix H.

Rules:

- All residential customers will be served by copper cable.
- A distance of greater than ten miles may warrant an RF system.

Determine the type of connection that should be made between Green Grass and Grass Hopper. The distance is 35 miles.

REVIEW QUESTIONS

1. Why is it necessary to convert an analog signal into a digital signal?
2. List and explain each of the steps involved in converting an analog signal to a digital signal.
3. List and explain each of the steps involved in converting a digital signal to an analog signal.
4. When a voice signal is converted into a digital signal, do the ones and zeros of the digital signal represent letters?
5. Explain what is meant by *PAM*.
6. Explain what is meant by *PCM*.
7. Explain why analog waveforms are sampled 8000 times every second.
8. What portion of the telephone network still depends on analog signals?
9. Draw and define the three encoding schemes used to format a digital signal—unipolar, bipolar nonreturn to zero, and bipolar return to zero.
10. Explain the ones density rule defined by the FCC and define the two encoding schemes used to solve the all-zeros dilemma.
11. Draw a +6/–6 volt peak-to-peak digital waveform using a bipolar return to zero format.
12. Why do digital signals require timing sources?
13. What is the purpose of placing a multiplexer at the end of a circuit?
14. Explain how a frequency division multiplexer multiplexes lower rate signals onto one link.
15. Explain how a time division multiplexer multiplexes lower rate signals onto one link.
16. What advantage does a statistical multiplexer have over a TDM multiplexer or an FDM multiplexer?
17. Define *modulation*.
18. Define *carrier wave*.
19. Why is it necessary to modulate a signal onto a carrier wave?

TROUBLESHOOTING

A channel card in a channel bank in the Ontario central office has stopped working. The circuit interfacing the card has gone into alarm. What are the steps you should take to correct the problem?

ABC uses SpiderCom's data network to transport intracompany information between New York City and Los Angeles. Lately, the network manager has noticed that numerous retransmissions are occurring on that link. List five possible reasons why the information has to be retransmitted between the two sites.

KEY TERMS

digital signal (234)
unipolar (234)
BPNRZ (236)
BPRZ (236)
pulses (236)
voltage state (237)
pulse mask (237)
polarity (237)
B8ZS (237)
AMI (237)
simplex (238)
half duplex (238)
full duplex (238)
PAM (239)
quantizing (240)
PCM (240)
encoding (240)
toll quality (242)
ADPCM (243)
channel (244)
multiplexing (246)
FDM (246)
TDM (248)
conversion (248)
multiplexing (248)
SONET (250)
DS-3 (250)
DS-1 (250)
DS-0 (250)
fast packet (252)
X.25 (253)
ATM (254)
IP (254)
FR (254)
DWDM (254)
CWDM (258)
modulation (259)

CHAPTER

7

Time Division Multiplexing Networks

Objectives

After reading this chapter, you should be able to

- Describe the North American Digital Hierarchy
- Define SONET
- Describe TDM networks

Outline

INTRODUCTION

In the late 1970s, the telecommunications infrastructure changed dramatically with the introduction of time division multiplexing (TDM) and fiber optic systems. The terms *transport* and *transmission* are used interchangeably to describe the method used to carry information across a network. The two most common ways to transport information are TDM and statistical multiplexing, using either packet, frame, or cell multiplexing. The usage of TDM as a transport technology is the focus of Chapter 7.

During the 1980s, the TDM network emerged as the dominant transmission network. New long distance companies were able to build reliable, efficient, cost-effective networks using the new digital transport methods. Once fiber-optic systems were introduced, TDM made it possible to carry huge amounts of information (on one strand of fiber) over long distances. By the mid-1980s, long copper and microwave links using TDM were being replaced by fiber cables, but TDM was still used to multiplex the information onto the transmission media. Today, although TDM is being challenged by more efficient packet and cell transmission technologies, it is still the predominant transmission method used throughout the world.

Chapter 7 defines the North American Digital Hierarchy, SONET, and how TDM is used in the network. It looks at the structure of the T1 digital circuit, and concludes with a comparison of TDM and new packet transport techniques.

7.1 THE NORTH AMERICAN DIGITAL HIERARCHY

7.1.1 Definition: The North American Digital Hierarchy

The *North American Digital Hierarchy* is a standard for the amount of information a digital circuit carries. To understand this, we will look at a circuit between St. Louis and Nashville. The equipment in St. Louis must work with the equipment in Nashville. For this to happen, a standard link rate and a standard protocol to define the bit structure is needed. The North American Digital Hierarchy defines the standard transmission rate. Table 7–1 illustrates the standard rates used throughout North America and Japan. Common rates used in the industry are DS-0 = 64 kbps, DS-1 = 1.544 Mbps, DS-2 = 6.31 Mbps, DS-3 = 45 Mbps, 560 Mbps, and 1.2 Gbps.

North American Digital Hierarchy Digital signal standard used in North America to define the bit per second rate.

Table 7–1
Digital signal levels as defined by the North American Digital Hierarchy.

Digital Signal Level	Bit Per Second Rate	Number of DS-0s	Number of DS-1s	Number of DS-3s
DS-0	64 kbps	1	n/a	n/a
DS-1	1.544 Mbps	24	1	n/a
DS-2	6.312 Mbps	96	4	n/a
DS-3	45 Mbps	672	28	1
560 Systems	560 Mbps	8064	336	12

7.1.2 The DS-0 (64 kbps) Channel

digital signal level zero (DS-0)
64 kpbs.

The *Digital Signal 0 (DS-0)* channel is equivalent to one channel of information. When we speak on the telephone, the sound is placed in one DS-0 channel after another to travel across the country. Digital-to-analog conversion, as discussed in Chapter 6, separates words into 8-bit one and zero "words" that are placed in specific time slots on a T1 circuit. The 64 kbps DS-0 is one channel on a T1 circuit. Twenty-four 64 kbps can travel on one DS-1 circuit, and there are 672 DS-0s on one DS-3 45 Mbps circuit.

One data or voice signal is transported inside each DS-0 channel, which has room for 64,000 ones and zeros traveling down a circuit every second. The following example should help explain how a DS-0 carries information from one point to the next.

Rod and Jake are talking to each other in an Internet chat room. Rod types "Did you see the game on Sunday?" and hits the Send button. Following digital conversion we determine that there are 31 characters in the sentence (Remember to count letters, spaces, and all punctuation!). Because each character is represented by eight ones and zeros, there are 248 ones and zeros that need to travel between the two computers. The network between Rod and Jake is one DS-0 channel that allows 64,000 bits to be carried every second. Our sentence composed of 248 ones and zeros easily fits into one 64,000 bps channel, so the sentence, "Did you see the game on Sunday?" will reach Jake within one second. This is a simplified example of how information travels through the network. The key concept is that information travels in the form of ones and zeros, and for all of those ones and zeros to make sense at the opposite end, a standard bit sequence is needed to identify where the information begins and ends.

Increasing the content traveling between the two computers allows us to expand on our example. Imagine that Jake wants to send Rod a data file with a short video clip of his fishing trip. The file contains one million bits of information.

To determine how long it will take to transport the file, we first need to divide the 1,000,000-bit file into 64,000 bit sections. $1{,}000{,}000 \div 64{,}000 = 15.6$. Therefore, it will take sixteen seconds to carry 1,000,000 bits between the two

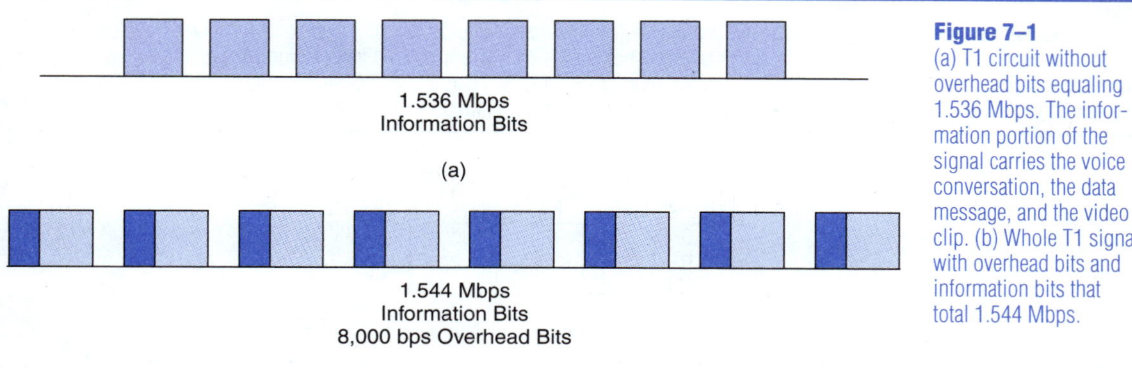

Figure 7–1
(a) T1 circuit without overhead bits equaling 1.536 Mbps. The information portion of the signal carries the voice conversation, the data message, and the video clip. (b) Whole T1 signal with overhead bits and information bits that total 1.544 Mbps.

sites. The DS-0 channel will be filled and will traverse the network 16 times in order to deliver the entire file.

7.1.3 T1 (DS-1) Circuits

The DS-1 (or *T1*) circuit (the names are used interchangeably) is the core of TDM networks. TDM multiplexing techniques (breaking information into chunks and placing it in specific time slots) was first demonstrated by using the 1.544 Mbps T1 circuit. T1 circuits, used by the PSTN and small customers alike, form the backbone of the communications network. Later chapters will discuss T1 applications in detail, but for now we only need to understand the makeup of a T1 circuit, the bandwidth available, and where it fits in the digital hierarchy.

T1
Stands for T1 carrier digital circuit able to carry 1.544 Mbps.

A T1 circuit consists of 24 64 kbps channels. By multiplying 24 channels by 64 kbps, we determine that the bandwidth available on one T1 circuit is 1.536 Mbps. Comparing this value with the value stated in the digital hierarchy shown in Figure 7–1 illustrates a difference of 8000 bps. Those 8000 bits per second are used for overhead, the bits used to format the information, and carry maintenance bits and other *information bits*. The *overhead bits* are used to synchronize the equipment on each end, send alarms when the circuit is in trouble, carry signaling flags, and carry data link information. All overhead bits are reserved for circuit functions and are not used to carry customer traffic. So, while the true information-carrying capacity of a T1 circuit is 1.536 Mbps, the actual number of bits being sent every second is 1.544 Mbps.

information bits
Bits used to represent the information being transported—the data produced by the PC, or a voice signal produced by the speaker.

overhead bits
Bits used to carry information about the signal— such as error rates or signaling.

Zooming in on the structure of the T1, we will discuss the framing patterns, line code, and signaling methods (diagrammed in Figure 7–2) used to transport information across the network. This will help to explain why a T1 circuit must comply with an accepted standard in order to communicate. This will also provide a building block for network analysis. All circuits, whether they are TDM based or they

Figure 7–2
T1 signal format. (a) One 8-bit word from one information source. Information source may be a telephone, computer, or video server. (b) 24 8-bit words fill one 192-bit frame. Each 192-bit frame holds 24 8-bit words from 24 different information sources. The information source may be a voice signal converted into a digital one/zero word, a data information from a computer, or a picture from a video clip. (c) 24 192-bit frames each holding 24 8-bit words. $8000 \times 192 = 1.536$ Mbps.

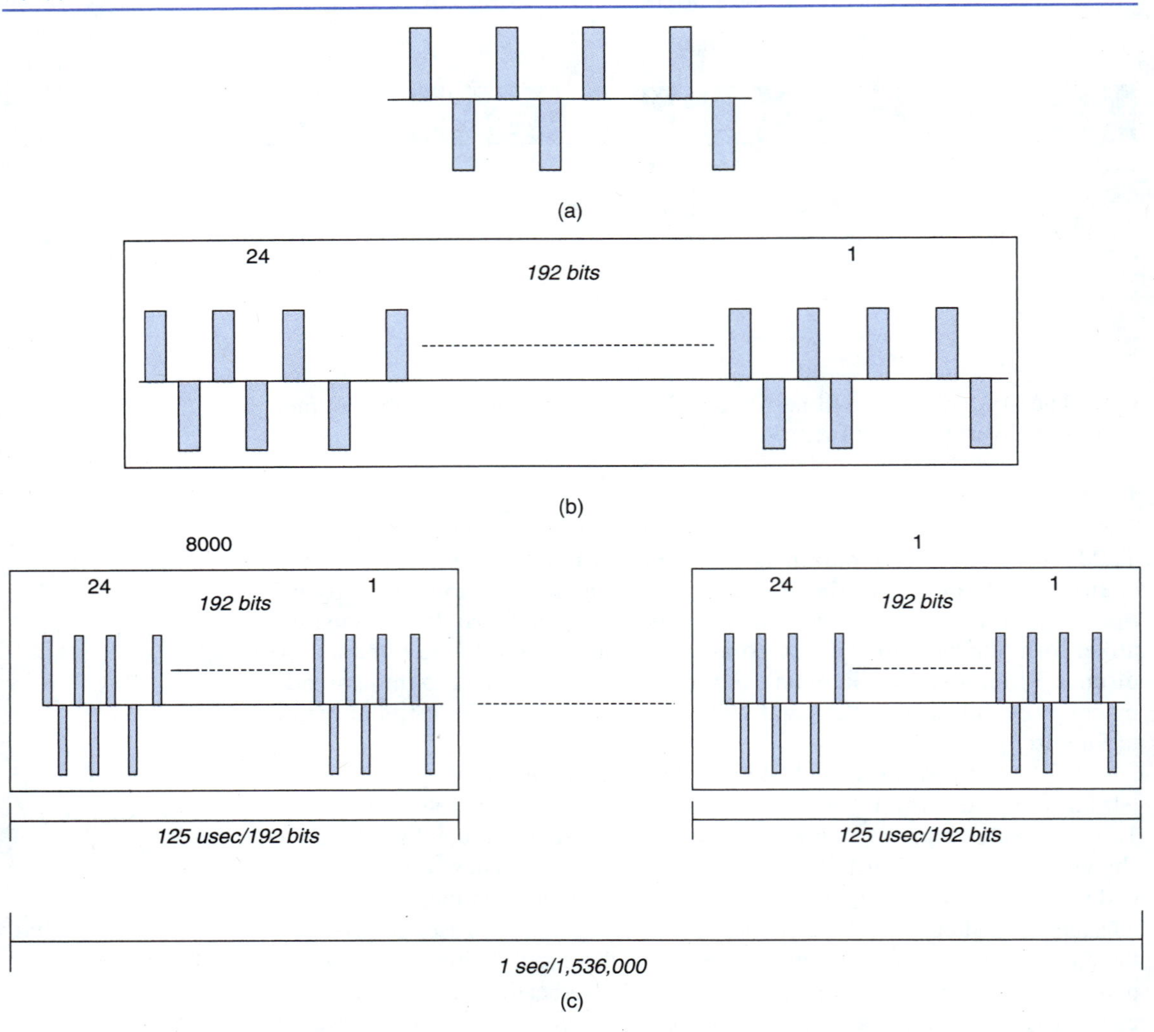

use statistical multiplexing, follow a common structure of information bits, overhead bits, circuit synchronization, and so forth.

The T1 circuit has designated bits that tell the end equipment how to synchronize the incoming bit stream, how to identify signaling states, and whether or not there is a problem on the line. Every T1 circuit provides several options, depending on the application. Three key parameters that define a T1 circuit are the type of framing, the signaling method, and the line code.

Framing is simply partitioning a bit stream into definable patterns. Two common framing methods are used in T1 applications. Continuing with the railroad analogy, *framing bits* tell the end pieces of equipment where the train begins and ends. This is called synchronization, meaning that the two pieces of equipment are in step or timed to the same bit pattern.

framing bits
Bits used to align frames in a signal. Frame bits produce a pattern of ones and zeros that the equipment uses to sync up.

To further explain framing, we again compare the T1 circuit to a train (as shown in Figure 7–3). A frame consists of 24 eight-bit words and one framing bit. The number of bits per frame is calculated as follows:

$$(8\text{-bit word} \times 24 \text{ channels}) + 1 \text{ framing bit} = 193 \text{ bits every frame}$$

One frame is equivalent to a train car with 24 seats and one small cubby hole for the framing bit. Each seat holds one eight-bit PCM word. Because there are 8000 samples taken every second, we can calculate the T1 rate by multiplying the number of bits in a frame by the number of samples taken every second.

$$24 \text{ seats} \times 8\text{-bit word} \times 8000 \text{ samples per second} = 1.536 \text{ Mbps}$$

The seats in the train car are filled with 24 eight-bit words taken from 24 different users (or ports) every 125 microseconds. Whether the source is a voice line, a data line, or a video line; 8000 train cars (frames) are filled every second.

The 24 seats in the train car are filled in the same sequence every time a sample is taken. The first seat is filled with the eight-bit word from the first user; the second seat is filled with an eight-bit word from the second user; and so on. By combining all of the bits from all 8000 cars, we can build our 64 kbps DS-0.

$$8 \text{ bits} \times 8000 \text{ samples per second} = 64 \text{ kbps}$$

To finish our calculation of the T1 bit stream, we need to add one framing bit to our calculation for every 24-seat train car. The total bit per second rate for a T1 is as follows:

$$24 \text{ seats per frame} \times 8\text{-bit word} + 1 \text{ framing bit} = 193 \text{ bits per frame}$$
$$193 \times 8000 \text{ samples per second} = 1.544 \text{ Mbps}$$

superframe
Framing standard used to define framing sequence for T1 circuits.

extended superframe
Framing standard, similar to SF, that improves the reliability of the circuit and extends the number of overhead bits available.

Two framing methods, the *superframe* (SF) and the *extended superframe* (ESF), are used in T1 circuits. The SF is the older of the two formats. ESF was developed to improve the reliability of the circuit and extend the number of overhead bits available. Both are used within the North American TDM network.

8000 frames are sectioned into groups according to the type of framing format selected. The SF scheme combines 12 frames into one master frame. Figure 7–4 shows an SF-formatted T1 signal. Every second, 667 master frames

Figure 7–3
T1 signal format.

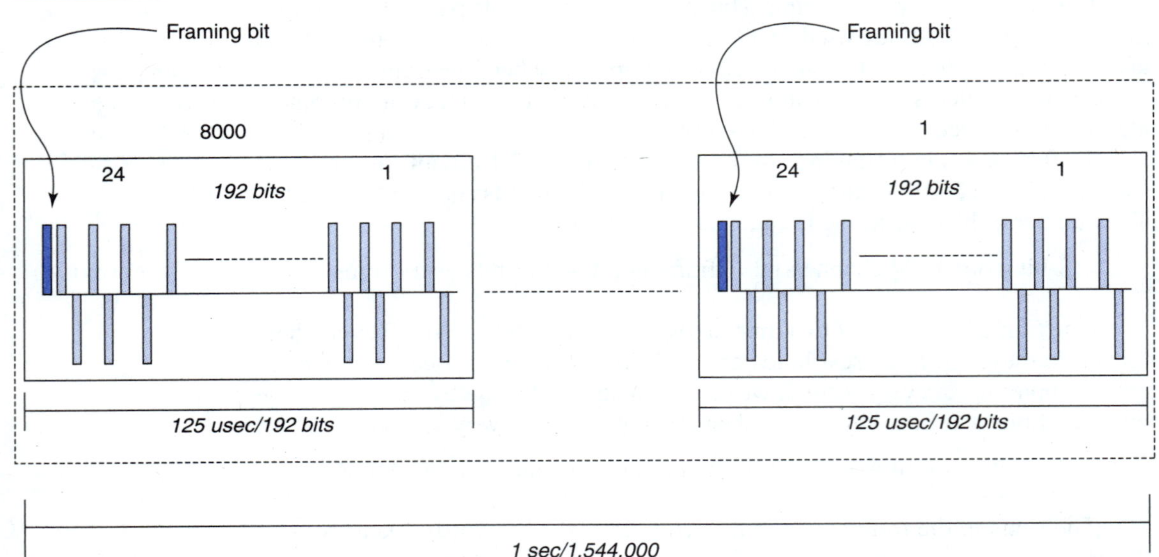

are produced. Framing bits become significant because of the patterns they form. Neither a one nor a zero is significant by itself, but placing the one and the zero together can be significant if a meaning is attached to the pattern. If the pattern 10 always means "Yes" and the pattern 01 always means "No," we could communicate yes and no by using 10 and 01. Framing bits form patterns that are used by network equipment as a means of communication.

Ft
Framing bit used to synchronize the signal. Term used to define the framing bits.

channel associated signaling
Signaling method used by T1 circuits. Robbed bit signaling is used to steal bits from defined frames.

In SF, the twelve framing bits synchronize the equipment and identify channels containing signaling patterns. Framing bits that synchronize the equipment are synchronization flags, also known as the *Ft* bits. The equipment looks for an alternating 10 pattern, 101010, occurring in all odd frames. When the equipment locks onto the pattern, the 24 time slots are identified and the eight-bit words are separated or demultiplexed and pointed toward the correct output ports.

Framing bits also identify which channels are carrying signaling information. Voice circuits require that ringing, off-hook, on-hook, and busy signals be carried by the digital signal. The system devised to identify these states is called *channel associated signaling* (CAS). In the SF T1 circuit, the 6th and 12th frames carry signaling patterns that the end equipment interprets. A 000111 pattern in the even frames tells the end equipment where the 6th and 12th frames reside. When

Figure 7–4
Superframe framing format for a T1 signal. (a) Superframe format has twelve 192-bit frames that equal one master frame. There are 12 framing bits that may be used to synchronize or line up the signal between devices. (b) Framing pattern sequence is used by the end devices to synchronize the bit stream. The end device buffers the 12 frames of data and picks out the framing pattern. Once the equipment reads the frame pattern sequence 101010 it is able to read the ones and zeros coming and translate them into information.
(c) Signaling bits are designated in all even frames and are used to flag the 6th and 12th frames. The end equipment uses the signaling bit pattern to find the 6th and 12th frame.

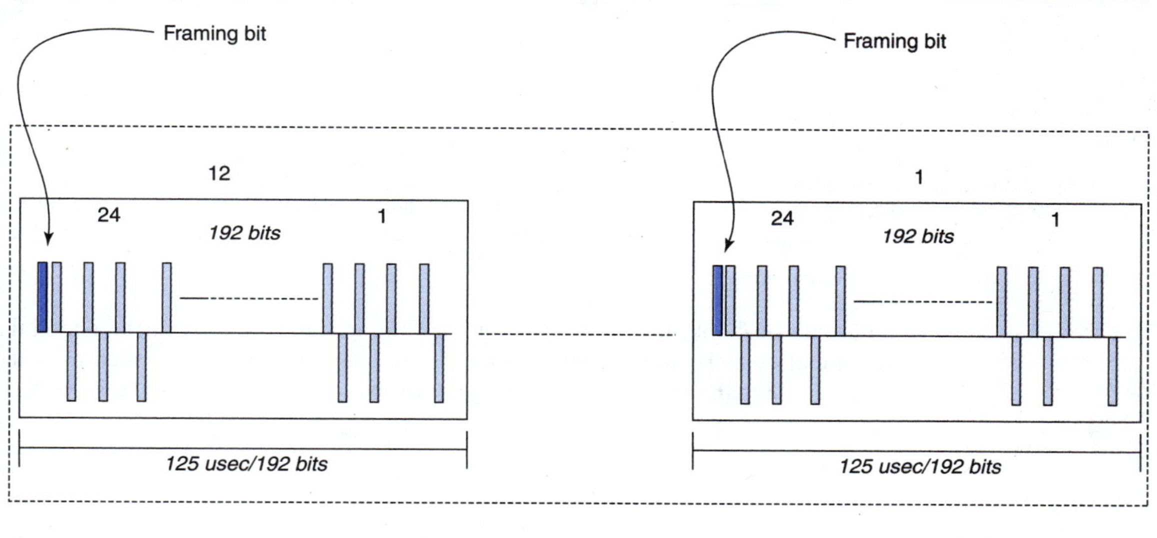

12 Frames = 1 Master Frame

Framing Pattern Sequence for Superframe Format

Fs = 1	Ft = 0	Fs = 1	Ft = 1	Fs = 1	Fs = 0	Fs = 0	Ft = 1	Fs = 0	Ft = 0	Fs = 0	Ft = 1

(b)

Fs = 000111

the end equipment finds these frames within the bit stream, it looks at the bits for a special signaling pattern, as illustrated by Figure 7–5. Frame bits used for signaling are called *Fs* bits. The SF CAS signaling method is A, B signaling. The A signifies the sixth frame and the B signifies the twelfth frame.

Fs
Framing bit used to designate signaling frames.

Signaling patterns require that the least significant bits in the 6th and 12th frames be reserved for communicating signaling status. *Robbed bit signaling* occurs when the least significant bit is robbed and used to form a pattern that

Figure 7–5
In order for ringing, off-hook, or idle channels to be communicated across digital circuits, special patterns are used. The least significant bit of each 8-bit word in the 6th and 12th frame are used to build the pattern.

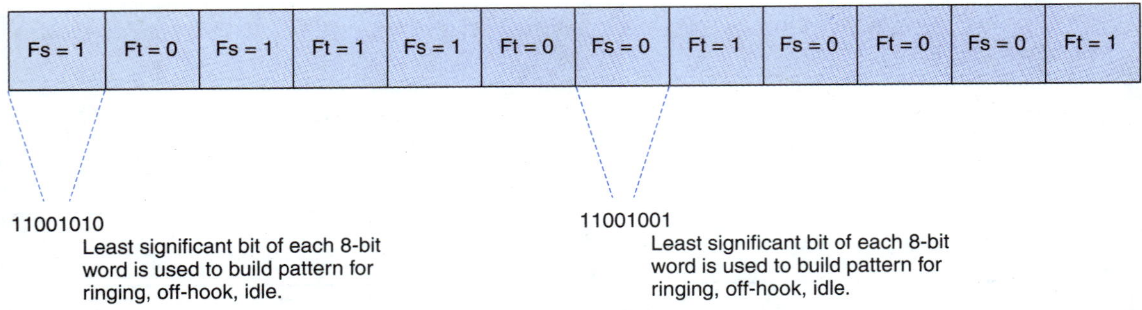

A/B bits
Either A or B designates the bits in the frame that indicate signaling states.

robbed bit signaling
Signaling method used to designate on-hook, off-hook, etc. in digital signals. The sixth and twelfth frames are the designated signaling frames where the least significant bit is stolen as needed.

clear channel signaling
Term used to describe disabling the signaling option in order to eliminate the loss of bits when data is being transported.

represents on-hook, off-hook, ringing, no ringing, busy, and so forth. The end equipment converts the pattern into the normal signaling methods, such as dial tone, busy signal, or ringing. An example of robbed bit signaling is shown here:

6th frame = **1**0101000
12th frame = **0**1110101
Pattern = 10 = On-hook condition
6th frame = **0**11010100
12th frame = **1**01010100
Pattern = 01 = Off-hook condition

Because robbed bit signaling reduces the number of bits per channel in every 6th and 12th frame to seven, we do not have a full 64 kbps worth of information in a 64 kbps channel. Instead, the overall bit rate is 56 kbps, not 64 kbps. The difference in the quality of the sound between a 56 kbps and a 64 kbps voice channel is not noticeable. Data, of course, is a different matter. To eliminate the loss of bits when data is being transported, the robbed bit signaling option is disabled. This is called *clear channel signaling* (CCC). Therefore, there are two options to choose from when configuring a channel on a T1 circuit—robbed bit signaling or clear channel signaling.

SF-formatted T1s cannot carry error checking algorithms, overhead data, or additional signaling information because of the twelve-frame master frame architecture. The older equipment required more bits to synchronize the data stream and this used a longer framing flag. As technology improved, the number of bits needed to synchronize and designate signaling was lessened.

The introduction of extended superframe format improved the frame structure of the T1 signal. The main difference between ESF and SF is the number of frames within the master frame. The master frame in ESF consists of 24 frames, increasing the number of framing bits to 24, as shown in Figure 7–6.

Figure 7–6

Extended superframe framing format for a T1 signal. (a) Extended superframe format has 24 192 bit frames that equal one master frame. There are 24 framing bits that may be used to synchronize the signal between devices; carry maintenance bits; and error checking algorithm. (b) Framing pattern sequence is used by the end devices to synchronize the bit stream. The end device buffers the 24 frames of data and picks out the framing pattern. Once the equipment reads the frame pattern sequence 101010, it is able to read the ones and zeros coming in and translate them into information. (c) Signaling bits may now reside in the 6th, 12th, 18th, and 24th frames. AB signaling happens in the 6th and 12th frames. A, B, C, & D signaling information is found in the 6th, 12th, 18th, and 24th frame. (d) D bits are used to carry link information. 8000 bits are available for link status information such as whether there are errors being received at the far end. (e) C bits are used to carry an error-correction algorithm. The algorithm is referred to as CRC (cyclic redundancy check), which guarantees the health of the circuit to 99.95%.

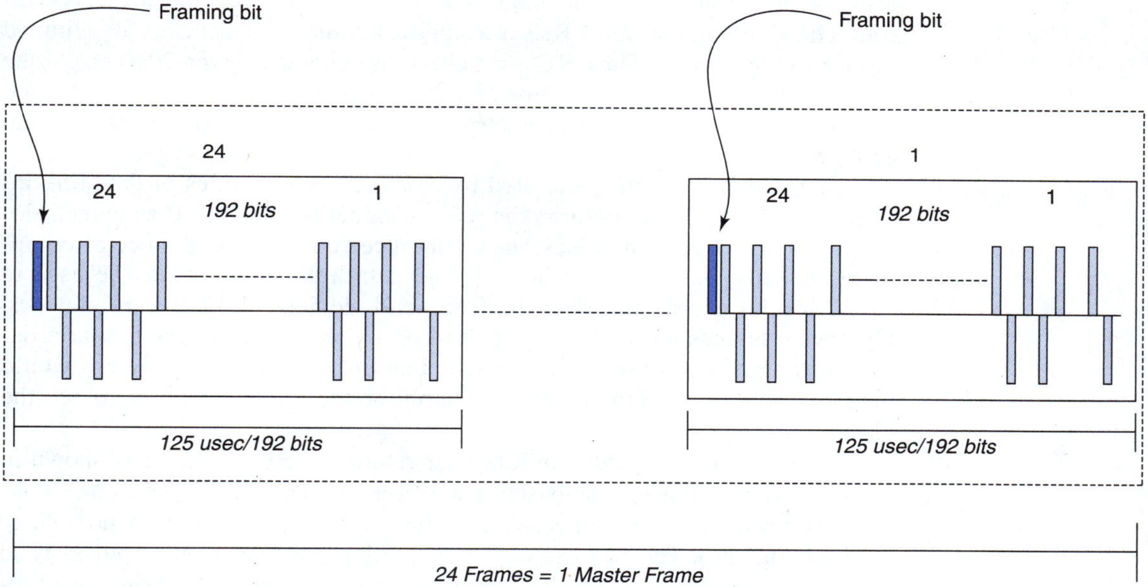

Framing bit

Framing bit

24

1

24

192 bits

1

24

192 bits

1

125 usec/192 bits

125 usec/192 bits

24 Frames = 1 Master Frame

(a)

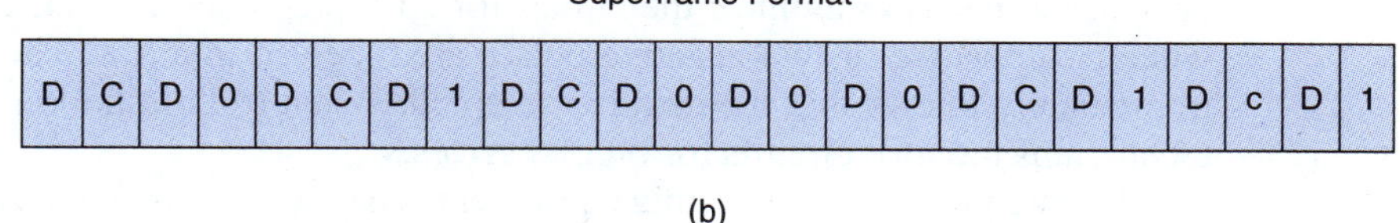

Framing Pattern Sequence for Extended Superframe Format

D	C	D	0	D	C	D	1	D	C	D	0	D	0	D	0	D	C	D	1	D	c	D	1

(b)

This allows additional one/zero patterns to be developed, expanding the overhead information available between the two pieces of terminating equipment.

ESF uses the 24 framing bits as follows:

Ft and Fs = 2000 b/s = 6-bit frame sequence
C = 2000 b/s used for cyclic redundancy check
D = 4000 b/s used for data link channel

Synchronizing the equipment requires fewer bits, so the Ft and Fs frame bits require only a six-bit frame sequence. The use of 24 frames also increases the number of signaling states combinations. The 6th, 12th, 18th, and 24th frames can be used to carry signaling information. CAS signaling in ESF T1 allows for A, B, C, D signaling, although even with ESF framing, A, B robbed bit signaling is the most common method used for voice applications. This section defines how signaling is carried out on a digital signal.

cyclic redundancy check
Error checking scheme used on digital circuits. CRC error checking is one of the most robust error checking algorithms.

Cyclic redundancy check (CRC) is a robust error-checking algorithm that guarantees a 99.999% error-free circuit. When a technician monitors a T1 circuit for CRC errors and finds none, there is a 99.999% chance that the circuit is error free. The ability to monitor CRCs is a significant improvement over SF's limited error-checking ability. The CRC error checking scheme is given 2000 bps of the 8000 bps framing bits. 4000 frame bits are given to the data link, which is used for facility maintenance and telemetry interface (the ability to log onto the end equipment).

Maintenance alarms generated by a device are examples of data link information. Equipment monitors the receive signal of a circuit. If a device is located at a customer's premises, the errors received by the end piece of equipment are only visible to that device. End data link channels may be used to carry special alarm information from end devices to upstream devices. Upstream devices recognize alarms and pass them on as a remote alarm detected. If alarms were not delivered via data link channels, technicians would have to drive to the remote site and monitor the circuit in order to see the alarms.

A bit stream is encoded in a bipolar return to zero structure, as shown in Figure 7–7. The first 1 pulse is sent out as a + voltage, the second as a − voltage. The resulting bit stream is an alternating +/− pulse stream with no voltage representing zero. The purpose of the alternating positive/negative pulses is so that end equipment can decipher the beginning of the pulse by using synchronized clock. If multiple 1 pulses are sent, the start and stop of the pulse (called the leading and trailing edge) becomes blurred. The end equipment then finds it difficult to distinguish one pulse from the other. Bipolar return to zero formatting provides a means to monitor the circuit for corrupted data. Bipolar errors occur when two positive or two negative pulses are received in a row. The equipment immediately knows that the data is corrupted. When troubleshooting problems, technicians monitor circuits for bipolar errors.

Picture pieces of terminating equipment. They receive ones and zeros and try to determine where they belong. If a series of zeros is sent one right after another, meaning no voltage is being sent, two things can happen. The first is that the terminating equipment becomes confused, loses synchronization, and causes disturbance on the line. This outcome is unacceptable. Because of it, the telephone company and the FCC established rules specifying the number of zeros that could be "shipped" in a row on digital circuits. The ruling can be found in Parts 15 and 68 of the FCC's Rules and Regulations docket. Part 15 is the ones density ruling,

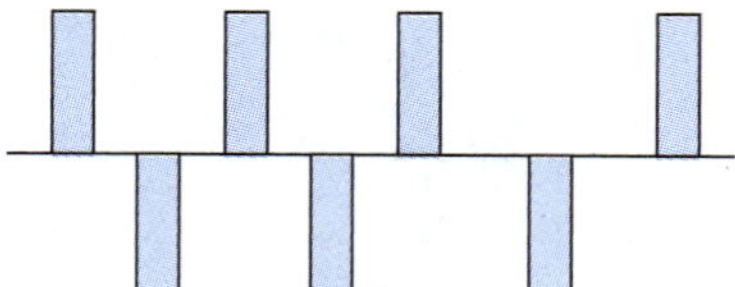

Figure 7–7 Bipolar return to zero digital T1 signal.

which states that no more than fifteen consecutive zeros can be transmitted in a row. Part 68 requires that a keep-alive signal be placed on the circuit when the circuit is not transmitting data. The *keep alive* signal is also called an all ones signal because an all ones pulse is interleaved on the circuit when there is a loss of signal or an idle channel condition. Line code is what ensures that the ones density rule is not violated.

keep alive Signal pattern sent out when no signal is present. Also called all ones, help to keep the end pieces of equipment synchronized. If no signal (no voltage) state exists, the end equipment cannot read any one and zero patterns and could lose synchronization.

Bit7 (also called AMI) refers to the way some signals handle an all zeros transmission. Bit7 line encoding adds ones when more than eight consecutive zeros are sent. Whenever eight zeros are sent, the seventh bit of the eight-bit word is jammed to a ones pulse. The end equipment receives the ones pulse in the seventh bit and converts it back to a zero. Jamming the seventh bit reduces the number of information bits within a channel to seven, so when a circuit is optioned for Bit7, the total number of data bits is 56,000. The Bit7 line code option remained the only method of solving the ones density issue for many years, making it difficult for companies to interface the North American standard T1 circuits to the European E1 standard circuits. In addition, customers complained that they wanted to be able to use all 64 kbps of the DS-0 channel when shipping data. Fortunately, voice transmission is not affected by Bit7 line encoding.

A solution was found in the early 1990s that has become the most common line-coding scheme used today. Bipolar with 8th zero substitution (B8ZS) was devised specifically to allow the full clear channel of 64 kbps DS-0 to be used. The B8ZS option substitutes a four-bit code into the bit stream whenever eight consecutive zeros are transmitted, and has two bits of the same polarity. The end equipment detects the B8ZS code and replaces it with zeros.

ZBTSI, a third line code scheme, was developed in the early 1990s. ZBTSI is not often used in the network, but some private networks use it. Figure 7–8 depicts the T1 overhead bits and line code scheme.

channel bank Multiplexer that muxes DS-0 level signals such as voice or data into DS-1 signals. Channel banks are most often found at customer premises, and terminate T1 circuits.

A T1 circuit is defined as an SF or ESF framed circuit with either Bit7 or B8ZS line coding. If the channel carries voice, robbed bit signaling is enabled. If the channel carries data, robbed bit signaling is disabled and clear channel signaling is selected.

We have described bit stream, framing bits, line code, and how the bandwidth of a DS-0 is calculated. The next step is to pull all these concepts together and explain the end product—multiplexing channels onto a T1 digital circuit. To do so, we will follow the multiplexing, bit-interleaving process from *channel bank* A to channel bank B.

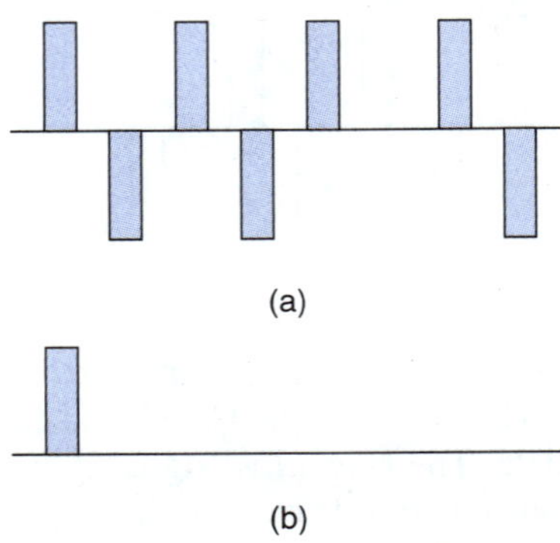

Figure 7–8
(a) The B8ZS code inserted into the all zeros bit stream. (b) Jamming a one bit is the method used in the Bit7 zero suppression scheme.

Amy's phone is connected to port one of channel bank A; Carol's phone is connected to port one of channel bank B. Amy and Carol are talking to one another over the T1 circuit. Amy asks Carol, "Have you studied for your calculus test?" The channel bank line card samples Amy's voice and coverts it into a digital signal. The question is turned into multiple eight-bit words. The channel bank takes the first eight-bit word and places it into the first seat in the first train car (i.e., frame). It then grabs an eight-bit word from the second line connected to the second port on the channel bank. This line belongs to Hank, whose voice signal is converted into an eight-bit word that is put into the second seat in the first train car. The channel bank then grabs an eight-bit word from the third line, which connects to a computer. The eight-bit data word is placed in the third seat of the first frame. The channel bank continues to grab samples from the remaining 11 lines placing each in consecutive seats in the boxcar or frame. When the 24th seat is filled, the channel bank attaches the framing bit to the frame, jumps back up to the first line, and takes a second eight-bit sample from Amy's voice signal. The sample is placed in the first seat of the second frame, while the channel bank continues to multiplex the eight-bit word samples onto the T1 circuit. Figure 7–9 shows back-to-back channel banks.

Channel bank B receives the incoming bit stream from channel bank A. Bank B synchronizes according to the framing bit patterns and begins to demultiplex the incoming bit stream. It takes the first eight-bit word in the first seat of the frame and sends it to the line card that Carol's phone interfaces with. The line card converts the eight-bit word into an analog voltage signal and outputs it on the line connecting to Carol's phone. Channel bank B then takes the second eight-bit word in frame one and points it to the line card attached to Rod's phone. The line card converts the digital one and zero bits into an analog sample and outputs the signal on the line connecting to Rod's phone. The third seat in the frame is pointed toward the line card attached to Hillary's computer. The line card receives the digital eight-bit word and outputs it on the line attached to Hillary's computer. The process continues until all 24 eight-bit

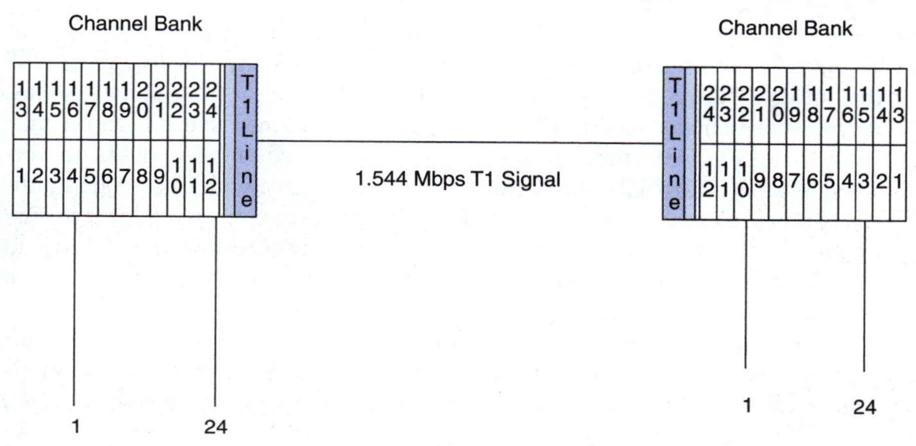

Figure 7–9 Two back-to-back channel banks connected together by a T1 circuit. 24 information sources feed into each channel bank.

samples have been demultiplexed. When channel bank B receives the framing bit, it immediately grabs the eight-bit word in the first seat of the second frame and points it toward the line card attached to Amy's phone. The process then repeats itself.

Signaling is handled as follows. Hillary logs off her computer and decides to call Ralph. She picks up her telephone handset and waits for dial tone. Terminating equipment sends a dial tone to Hillary's receiver. Hillary dials Ralph's number and waits to hear ringing. The terminating equipment changes the eighth bit in the sixth frame to a one and the eighth bit in the twelfth frame to a zero to signify ringing. The end equipment has a special conductor in the sixth and twelfth frame that walks through the boxcar and watches each of the 24 eight-bit samples for signaling information. The frame conductor notes whether the eighth bit in each of the seats is a one or a zero. The head conductor takes the information from the frame conductors to determine if it needs to ring the phone, send dial tone, or do something else. In this case, the head conductor sees that in the third seat in frame six, the eighth bit is a one, and in the third seat in frame twelve, the eighth bit is 0. This tells the head conductor to ring channel one's telephone. The format just described is a *byte-interleaved* multiplexing scheme. Byte-interleaved multiplexing is the process of shipping out one byte (eight-bit word) from each line. If the transmission were *bit interleaved,* the equipment would send out one bit from line one, then move to line two and send out one bit, and so on. The T1 circuit standard is built around a byte-interleaved format.

byte interleaved Multiplexing scheme that interleaves an eight-bit word from one channel into the higher level signal.

bit interleaved Multiplexing scheme that interleaves one bit from one channel, then moves to a second channel and interleaves one bit.

A, B signaling means that the bits in the 6th and 12th frames are being manipulated by signaling states. Most test equipment has LEDs labeled A, B, C, and D, that turn on and off when signaling is occurring on the channel. Technicians monitor signaling LEDs when troubleshooting signaling problems.

7.1.4 T2 (DS-2) Circuits

T2 (or DS-2) circuits are less common than T1 or T3 circuits. T2 circuits combine four T1 1.544 Mbps circuits onto one transmission pipe that carries 6.312 Mbps of data between two points. It was first deployed on fiber-optic systems. The four-wire copper medium is not capable of handling such a high bit rate. (Today, thanks to DSL, the line can carry 6 Mbps although the signal is not formatted as a T2.) Most T2 circuits ride on fiber-optic cable with fiber-optic multiplexers on each end. Because fiber-optic cable can carry Gbps worth of information on one fiber optic strand, carrying 6.312 Mbps of information is similar to using a school bus to carry one passenger. For this reason, T2 circuits have not gained network acceptance.

T2 circuits can often be found embedded in a DS-3 circuit. In fact, the multiplexing method used to combine T1 circuits onto a DS-3 depends on an intermediary step in which four T1 circuits are grouped together and multiplexed into a DS-2 signal. Seven DS-2 signals are multiplexed together to form the DS-3 signal. Unlike the T1 byte-interleaved signal, the DS-2 uses a bit-interleaved structure when multiplexing ones and zeros. It is unlikely that the DS-2 signal will emerge as a popular transmission method, but it will always be found embedded in the DS-3 signal.

C-bit parity
Newer DS-3 framing scheme that provides additional OH bits to the DS-3 signal for management. The C-bit parity mux similar to the M13 multiplexer provides a DS-3 multiplexer using the C-bit parity frame format.

7.1.5 T3 (DS-3) Circuits

DS-3 signals carry 45 Mbps. In most situations, bits are separated into 28 DS-1 circuits. The true information-carrying capacity is less than 45 Mbps because overhead bits are needed to synchronize the equipment and maintain the circuit. In most cases, DS-3s are multiplexed into even larger signals. Commonly, the DS-3 is the terminating signal type at the end location. For instance, most long distance switches connect to one another using a DS-3 signal. Transmission equipment such as M13 multiplexers and SONET multiplexers also terminate DS-3 signals.

The three methods used to define the structure of the DS-3 signal are M23 framing format, *C-bit parity* format, or clear channel. M23 is the most common DS-3 framing format used today. The M23 format starts with 28 byte-interleaved DS-1s that are divided into seven groups of four ($4 \times 7 = 28$). Each

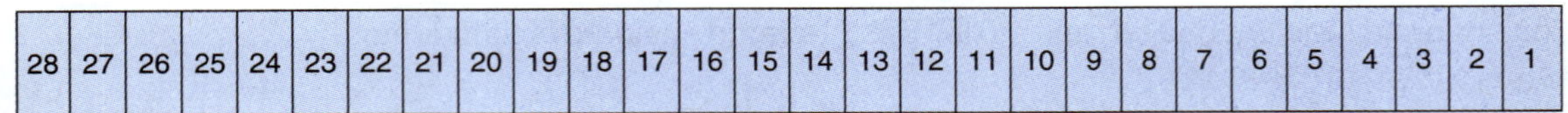

Figure 7–10
28 DS-1 signals ride inside a DS-3 45 Mbps signal.

group forms one DS-2 signal that can add or remove bits in order to keep the 28 T1s synchronized.

Because the DS-2 signal relies on bit stuffing to control the timing of the circuits—making sure the signals arrive and leave on time—the DS-2 signal is called an *asynchronous* signal, meaning there is no timing source. Seven bit-interleaved DS-2s are combined into one DS-3 signal as shown in Table 7–2. The DS-3 signal is also bit-interleaved and considered an asynchronous system.

asynchronous Untimed signal that depends on stop and start bits to identify the information being sent.

Digital signals must have a timing source or a timing method in order to make sure the ones and zeros travel according to the same clock. The best analogy is that of an army platoon marching in step. The drill sergeant controls the speed at which the individual members of the platoon march. If the sergeant suddenly left, the 2000 soldiers obeying his commands would lose their metronome. Chaos would ensue due to the loss of the timing source.

Table 7–2 DS-2 Frame Format.

SubFrame Total bits	Block 1 49 bits	Block 2 49 bits	Block 3 49 bits	Block 4 49 bits	Block 5 49 bits	Block 6 49 bits
1st	M0	C11	F0	C12	C13	F1
2nd	M1	C21	F0	C22	C23	F1
3rd	M1	C31	F0	C32	C33	F1
4th	MX	C41	F0	C42	C43	F1

Description of DS-2 Frame Structure.

Each DS-2 signal has 6 blocks containing 49 bits. 48 of the bits are T1 signal bits. The remaining bits per block are overhead bits. The DS-2 decides whether or not to stuff the T1 signal in order to synchronize the bit streams.

M bits are used to align the multiframes.

M0 = 0
M1 = 1
MX = Either 1 or 0

F bits are used to align the Frame.

F0 =0
F1= 1

C Bits are used to indicate stuffing or no stuffing.

C11, C12, C13 = indicate stuffing for DS-1-1
C21, C22, C23 = indicate stuffing for DS-1-2
C31, C32, C33 = indicate stuffing for DS-1-3
C41, C42, C43 = indicate stuffing for DS-1-4

Table 7–3 DS-3 M13 Frame Format.

Sub Frame Total bits	Block 1 85 Bits	Block 2 85 Bits	Block 3 85 Bits	Block 4 85 Bits	Block 5 85 Bits	Block 6 85 Bits	Block 7 85 Bits	Block 8 85 Bits
1st	X	F1	C11	F0	C12	F0	C13	F1
2nd	X	F1	C21	F0	C22	F0	C23	F1
3rd	P	F1	C31	F0	C32	F0	C33	F1
4th	P	F1	C41	F0	C42	F0	C43	F1
5th	Mo	F1	C51	F0	C52	F0	C53	F1
6th	M1	F1	C61	F0	C62	F0	C63	F1
7th	Mo	F1	C71	F0	C72	F0	C73	F1

Description of DS-3 M13 Frame.

The DS-3 M13 frame has 7 M subframes. Each of the subframes has 85 bits per block. Within each block, 1 bit is used for overhead and the remaining 84 bits are used for information. The overhead bits include X bits, P bits, M bits, F bits, and C bits.

Description of Overhead Bits.

1. F bits are used to align the frames. The code used is 1001.
2. M bits are used for multiframe alignment signal.
3. P bits are used for parity checking.
4. X bits are used for messages.
5. C bits are used as stuffing bits.

In telecommunications, various methods are used to provide a timing source to keep the signals in step. For asynchronous signals, timing is handled within the DS-2 multiplexing step. A DS-3 signal is formed by first multiplexing four DS-1s into one DS-2. One DS-3 contains seven DS-2s each containing four DS-1s. The DS-2 signal examines the incoming DS-1 bit stream to make sure it is arriving at the correct rate. The DS-2 adds bits or takes bits away in order to speed up the signal or slow it down to the 1.544 Mbps rate. Bit stuffing keeps all of the DS-1s moving at the same speed.

Several overhead bits are used to control synchronization, frame boundaries, and maintenance of the circuit. The bits are defined in Table 7–3 and Table 7–4. Similar to DS-1 circuits, DS-3s require a framing structure to ensure correct synchronization between the two-end multiplexing. The end multiplexer is referred to as the terminating mux or terminating equipment.

The second type of framing used by a DS-3 signal is C-bit parity. It is the newer of the two framing formats. C-bit parity added the ability to monitor the performance of the circuit and improved network maintainability. Unlike

Table 7–4 DS-3 C-Bit Parity Frame Format.

Sub Frame	Block 1 85 Bits	Block 2 85 Bits	Block 3 85 Bits	Block 4 85 Bits	Block 5 85 Bits	Block 6 85 Bits	Block 7 85 Bits	Block 8 85 Bits
1st	X	F1	AIC	F0	Na	F0	FEAC	F1
2nd	X	F1	DL	F0	DL	F0	DL	F1
3rd	P	F1	CP	F0	CP	F0	CP	F1
4th	P	F1	FEBE	F0	FEBE	F0	FE BE	F1
5th	Mo	F1	DL	F0	DL	F0	DL	F1
6th	M1	F1	DL	F0	DL	F0	DL	F1
7th	Mo	F1	DL	F0	DL	F0	DL	F1

Description of DS-3 C-bit Parity Frame.

The C-bit parity frame structure differs from the M13 frame format. The main difference between the two frames is found in Blocks 3, 5 and 7. The overhead bits for C-bit parity signals are X bits, P bits, M bits, F bits, ALC bits, DL bits, CP bits, FEBE bits, Na bits, and FEAC bits.

Description of bits unique to C-bit Parity signals.

1. AIC bits are used for Application Identification Channels.
2. N bits are reserved for future uses.
3. FEAC is used for Far-End Alarm and Control Channels.
4. DL is used as a Data Link
5. CP is the C-bit Parity bit
6. FEBE is used for Far-End Block Error.

ESF framing, which was quickly adopted as the favorite T1 framing method, C-bit parity was not universally accepted. One reason was the introduction of the SONET standard. Another was the fact that existing *M13* multiplexers, cross-connects, and other interfaces would need to be replaced in order to implement the C-bit parity frame structure. Consequently, it has not been widely deployed.

Clear channel DS-3 is the third type of framing format used by DS-3 signals. When a DS-3 is optioned for clear channel, there is no framing format attached. The signals travel transparently across the DS-3 pipe, and framing is attached at each terminating end. The many pieces of equipment the DS-3 travels through are optioned as clear channel. Framing passes through along with the data information. To clarify this point, we will "walk through" a company that employs clear channel DS-3.

Imagine we are associated with a large manufacturing company with two major factories, one in Alabama and one in Pennsylvania. Our telecommunications network manager has determined the need for a DS-3 circuit between the two

M13
DS-3 framing scheme that is used to mux 28 DS-1 signals into one DS-3 signal. M13 multiplexer is a term used to describe the DS-3 multiplexer that transport DS-3 signals with the M13 frame format.

clear channel DS-3
No framing is assigned leaving the signal clear for data such as ATM.

InterXchange Carrier Interexchange carrier or long distance provider.

locations. We order a point-to-point DS-3 from our *InterXchange Carrier* (IXC). On the order we request a clear channel DS-3.

The IXC provisions the clear channel DS-3 from Alabama to Pennsylvania. The DS-3 terminates in an M13 multiplexer using the M23 framing format at our sites in Alabama and Pennsylvania. The IXC connects the DS-3 into their fiber-optic multiplexers that carry multiple DS-3s across the country. The IXC's equipment is optioned as a clear channel DS-3. Their multiplexers are passive devices used to transport our DS-3 signal from Alabama to Pennsylvania. The two M13 multiplexers located in the telephone room in each manufacturing plant define the framing format. If the IXC wanted to define the frame type, it could as long as it matched the frame format of the terminating multiplexers.

The 45 Mbps DS-3 signal can travel on almost any medium. The issue is the distance it can travel. A DS-3 signal on coaxial cable travels about 350 feet before the signal diminishes to the point of being indecipherable. Most microwave systems are built to carry DS-3 signals about 35 miles. A DS-3 is often one of many signals carried on one fiber-optic system.

The local telephone companies, both ILECs and CLECs, use DS-3 signals extensively to carry traffic between two points. IXCs, ICPs, and ISPs also use DS-3s, as do large corporations, universities, and governmental agencies, to carry information between two locations.

To see how an end-to-end DS-3 circuit works, we are going to build a DS-3 pipe between two microwave towers. "High Top Mountain" and "Blueberry Mountain" have microwave antennas pointed toward one another. A DS-3 circuit will be turned up between the two towers. The technician at "Blueberry Mountain" connects the M13 multiplexer to the radio transmission equipment. 28 T1 signals feed into the M13 multiplexer where the DS-1 signals are combined to form one DS-3 signal. That signal is fed into the radio equipment that transmits the DS-3 signal from the antenna into the atmosphere. The signal travels 33 miles to get to the receiving microwave antenna at "High Top Mountain." The DS-3 signal enters the antenna and travels down the waveguide into the radio receiver. The radio receiver converts the RF signal into an electrical signal and sends it into an M13 multiplexer that demultiplexes the DS-3 signal into 28 DS-1 signals. Figure 7–11 illustrates the flow of the DS-3 signal between the multiplexers.

7.1.6 The 560 Mbps Fiber System

560 Mbps One of the higher order signals defined in the North American Digital Hierarchy.

The *560 Mbps* system does not have a digital signal level number. However, the systems have been deployed extensively by IXCs, local telephone companies, and large corporate networks. The purpose of the 560 Mbps system is to multiplex more information on one fiber-optic strand. Large point-to-point networks take advantage of the great amount of bandwidth fiber optic cables provide. Until recently, almost every central office in the country had numerous 560 Mbps mul-

Figure 7–11
A DS-3 M23 multiplexer. Within the multiplexer, the T1 signals are multiplexed into DS-2 signals. Each DS-2 signal carries 6.176 Mbps. The DS-3 signal contains 7-bit interleaved DS-2 signals.

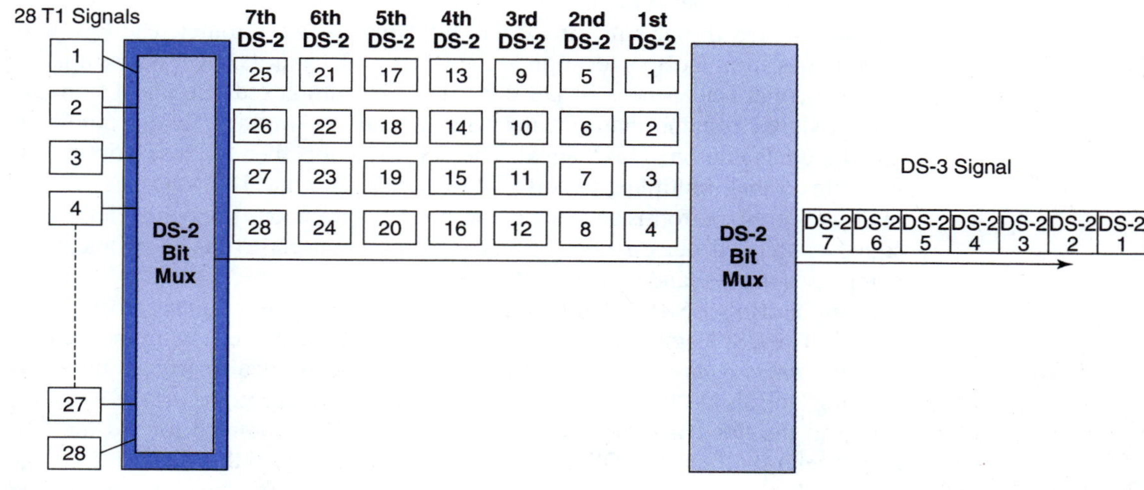

tiplexers. Before the SONET standard was introduced, these asynchronous systems were the primary units deployed to connect central offices in metropolitan areas or long distance POPs and switch sites. The SONET standard has since replaced the point-to-point asynchronous 560 Mbps systems.

The 560 Mbps multiplexer TDMs 12 DS-3 signals onto one fiber-optic strand. The individual DS-3 signals multiplex seven DS-2 signals; DS-2 signals multiplex 4 DS-1 signals; and DS-1 signals multiplex 24 DS-0 signals. The DS-0 signal carries an analog voice signal, an analog data signal, or a digital data signal.

7.1.7 Connecting the Dots

The past few sections have focused on individual systems used to carry information between two points. We can combine that information and build an asynchronous fiber network from end to end.

The example we'll use starts at the local telephone company's central office. Our customer, HoBo Inc., has ordered a point-to-point circuit between their headquarters in Albany, New York and their branch office, also in Albany. They require one full DS-0 of bandwidth and would like to be able to use the entire 64 kbps channel. HoBo Inc. headquarters is served by the local phone company's Black Oak central office and the branch office is served out of the Red Rover central office in Albany. HoBo ordered the circuit from the local phone company, which will need to provision a circuit from HoBo's Plymouth Avenue site to their Forest Street location.

The circuit begins at HoBo Inc.'s headquarters on River Street in Albany where a 64 kbps four-wire line is terminated. HoBo's network manager connects the 64 kbps DS-0 four-wire circuit into the HoBo network router. The four-wire circuit goes from HoBo's location to the Black Oak central office, where it is fed into a channel bank where 24 DS-0 circuits are multiplexed into one T1 circuit. The T1 signal from the channel bank is fed into an M13 multiplexer that combines 28 T1 signals into one DS-3 signal. The DS-3 signal is then fed into a 560 Mbps multiplexer that multiplexes twelve DS-3 signals into one 560 Mbps signal. The multiplexer also performs an electrical-to-optical conversion. The optical 560 Mbps signal is shipped out on fiber-optic cable that connects to the local telephone company's access tandem office. At the access tandem office, the DS-3 channel carrying HoBo's DS-0 is demultiplexed from the 560 Mbps signal into 12 DS-3 signals. The DS-3 signal carrying their DS-0 is fed into a piece of equipment called a *digital cross connect system* (DCS). The DCS electronically grooms the DS-3 carrying HoBo's DS-0 down into 28 DS-1s. The DCS then grooms out the 24 DS-0s riding in the DS-1 and cross connects them to a DS-1 pointed toward the Red Rover central office. The DS-1 is then groomed into a DS-3 that feeds an external fiber multiplexer. The fiber multiplexer receives all traffic heading to the Red Rover central office. The 12 DS-3s are converted into an optical signal then transported on a fiber-optic cable to the Red Rover central office. The twelve DS-3s arrive at Red Rover central office where they are converted into an electrical signal and demultiplexed down into 12 individual DS-3s. The DS-3 carrying HoBo's DS-0 is fed into an M13 multiplexer, which demultiplexes the DS-3 signal into 28 individual T1 signals. The T1 carrying the HoBo's DS-0 is fed into a channel bank. The channel bank demultiplexes the 24 DS-0 channels out of the T1 signal. Each of the DS-0 signals are transported out on individual copper loops to the different businesses in the area. In our case, HoBo's DS-0 is carried on a four-wire link that connects the Red Rover central office to HoBo's branch office. There the four-wire 64 kbps circuit is connected to a router.

digital cross connect system Electronic cross connect used to cross connect circuits without having to physically wire the circuits together at a DSX panel.

7.2 THE SONET STANDARD

7.2.1 Defining SONET

SONET Synchronous optical network.

SONET stands for synchronous optical network. The SONET standard was first defined in the early 1990s. Equipment manufacturers, IXCs, RBOCs, international carriers, and businesses formed a working forum to build a standard fiber-optic protocol. SONET is the resulting standard. It provided several improvements over the North American Digital standard, including the following main advantages:

1. Ensures equipment interoperability.
2. Combines the international standard and the North American standard transmission rates, allowing smooth handoffs between the two networks.

3. Provides a flexible network topology that allows for circuits to be added or dropped at any level.
4. Increases the transmission rate from 1.2 Gbps to 10 Gbps and higher.
5. Introduces the ring architecture to increase the networks survivability.

SONET networks are now deployed throughout the world. The flexibility, interoperability, and the high bit rates have spurred the growth of large multi-ring networks that span North America and the continents.

7.2.2 The SONET Hierarchy

The SONET hierarchy is similar to the North American Digital Hierarchy. Bit rates are defined to provide guidelines to equipment manufacturers, network engineers, and planners. Bit rates begin very low, 1.78 Mbps, and go as high as 10 Gbps on one fiber strand. Ten Gbps is equivalent to ten billion bits or 10,000,000,000 ones and zeros being transported every single second. SONET bit rates grow sequentially with each being a multiple of the previous rate. There are numerous bps rates listed in Table 7–5, but the industry has built equipment and networks around seven common interfaces: VT-1.5, VT-6, OC-1, OC-3, OC-12, OC-48, and OC-192.

As shown in Table 7–5, the signal level equivalent to a T1 is now called a *VT-1.5*. The VT stands for virtual tributary and is used to define the lower rate signals mapped into a SONET STS-1 frame. The SONET STS-1 frame is the building block of the SONET hierarchy. The VT-1.5 is used in North America to map T1 circuits into a SONET frame. The difference between a VT-1.5 and a T1 is that the VT carries 1.78 Mbps compared to the 1.544 Mbps carried by a T1 signal. A

Electrical Interface Name	Optical Interface Name	Bit Per Second Rate	Number of DS-0 Channels
VT-1.5		1.78 Mbps	24
VT-6		6.912 Mbps	96
EC-1 (STS-1)	OC-1	51.84 Mbps	672
	OC-3	155 Mbps	2016
	OC-3c	155 Mbps	
	OC-12	622.08 Mbps	8064
	OC-12c	622.08 Mbps	
	OC-48	2.5 Gbps	32,256
	OC-192	10 Gbps	129,024

Table 7–5 SONET Digital Rate Chart.

VT-1.5 carries 24 DS-0s, the same as a T1 circuit. The additional bits per second found in a VT-1.5 circuit are used as overhead bits to monitor the status of the circuit and carry user data.

After the VT-1.5 comes the *VT-6,* which carries 6.912 Mbps of traffic. Commonly used for video transmission, a VT-6 is also referred to as a VT group. Much like the DS-2, the VT-6 carries four VT-1.5. The difference between the two is that the VT-6 is not used to aggregate DS-1s in order to encapsulate them in the DS-3 signal. All signals in SONET rely on themselves. They are individuals within the bit stream and are often referred to as visible at all times. Simply, the *STS-1* is composed of 28 VT-1.5s. The 1.7 Mbps VT-1s are not multiplexed into an intermediary signal before they are allowed to be encapsulated into the STS-1 frame. A VT-1.5 is always visible within the higher-order signal, unlike the T1 that is hidden within a DS-2 signal before being multiplexed into a DS-3 signal.

OC-1—optical carrier 1
SONET level comparable to an electrical DS-3.

EC-1—electrical carrier 1
SONET level signal comparable to an electrical DS-3.

OC-3—optical carrier 3
SONET level signal that carries 155 Mbps of information—3 DS-3s.

OC-12—optical carrier 12
SONET level signal that carries 622 Mbps of information—12 DS-3s.

LEC
Local exchange carrier.

OC-48—optical carrier 48
SONET level signal that carries 2.5 Gbps of information—48 DS-3s.

The purpose of the SONET hierarchy is to simplify the way lower rate signals are multiplexed into higher rate signals. The developers' goal was to create a standard hierarchy that would combine all world standards into one, and provide a robust method for monitoring and maintaining the circuit and a common frame structure accepted by all vendors. The STS-1 frame was devised to meet this goal. The STS-1, synchronous transport signal frame is the building block used for each of the SONET signals. The STS-1 signal carries 52 Mbps, as does the *OC-1* signal. OC stands for *optical carrier,* so the OC-1 as it sounds, is used when the signal is in its optical form. *EC-1* stands for *electrical carrier* and is used when the signal is in its electrical form. The term STS-1 defines the signal rate riding in the OC signal, but technically EC-1 should be used whenever the STS-1 signal is in its electrical state. Most telecom professionals use STS-1 exclusively. There is a slight difference in the two meanings, but it probably doesn't matter which you use as long as the person you're talking to understands what you mean.

The 52 Mbps signal carries 28 VT-1.5 signals, and a VT-1.5 carries a 1.78 Mbps signal. The STS-1 carries the same amount of information as the 45 Mbps DS-3 signal and uses the additional bps for overhead information. The overhead bits are used to keep the signal synchronized, carry maintenance information, carry user data, and help sectionalize trouble according to the SONET architecture.

The next step up in the SONET hierarchy is the *OC-3* signal, an optical signal that carries 155 Mbps. Three STS-1 signals ride in one OC-3 signal. The term OC-3c, in which the c stands for concatenated, refers to combining all 3 STS-1s into one frame instead of 3 separate frames. OC-3c is used for ATM, video, and packet transmission.

The *OC-12* is the next most common interface after the OC-3. As it sounds, there are 12 STS-1 signals within the OC-12, forming a bit rate of 622 Mbps. OC-12c indicates that the 12 STS-1s are grouped together in one large pipe.

The *OC-48* signal carries 48 STS-1s equaling 2.5 Gbps of total bandwidth. The OC-48 signal is used extensively by IXCs, LECs, and international carriers. One OC-48 signal can carry as many as 32,000 simultaneous voice conversations.

Figure 7–12
Structure of an STS-1 frame of the SONET hierarchy. The frame has two main sections. The transport section includes bytes responsible for the section overhead bytes and line overhead bytes of the network. The path overhead resides in the synchronous payload envelope portion of the frame and contains the overhead bytes for the path portion of the network.

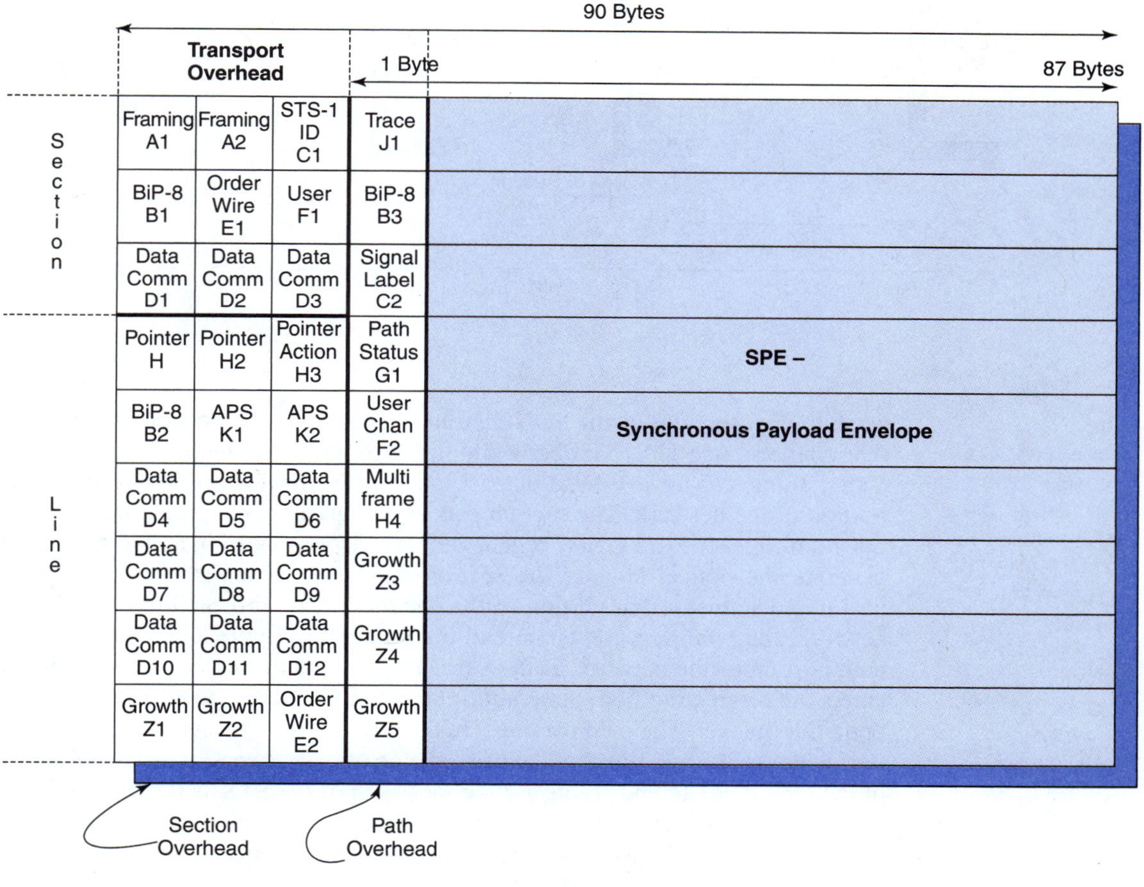

	Transport Overhead			Path Overhead (1 Byte)	SPE – Synchronous Payload Envelope (87 Bytes)
Section	Framing A1	Framing A2	STS-1 ID C1	Trace J1	
Section	BiP-8 B1	Order Wire E1	User F1	BiP-8 B3	
Section	Data Comm D1	Data Comm D2	Data Comm D3	Signal Label C2	
Line	Pointer H	Pointer H2	Pointer Action H3	Path Status G1	
Line	BiP-8 B2	APS K1	APS K2	User Chan F2	
Line	Data Comm D4	Data Comm D5	Data Comm D6	Multi frame H4	
Line	Data Comm D7	Data Comm D8	Data Comm D9	Growth Z3	
Line	Data Comm D10	Data Comm D11	Data Comm D12	Growth Z4	
Line	Growth Z1	Growth Z2	Order Wire E2	Growth Z5	

The final OC rate, shown in Table 7–5, is the *OC-192*. It carries 192 STS-1s equaling a bit rate of 10 Gbps. One hundred twenty-nine thousand simultaneous telephone conversations can travel on one OC-192 pipe.

OC-192—optical carrier 192
SONET level signal that carries 10 Gbps of information—192 DS-3s.

7.2.3 Structure of the STS-1 Frame

Figure 7–12 illustrates an STS-1 frame. As shown in the picture, the frame is divided into 4 areas—line, section, path, and payload. Figure 7–12 illustrates how the STS-1 frame relates to the network. A SONET network is divided into the

Figure 7–13
The three main segments of a SONET network—section, line, and path.

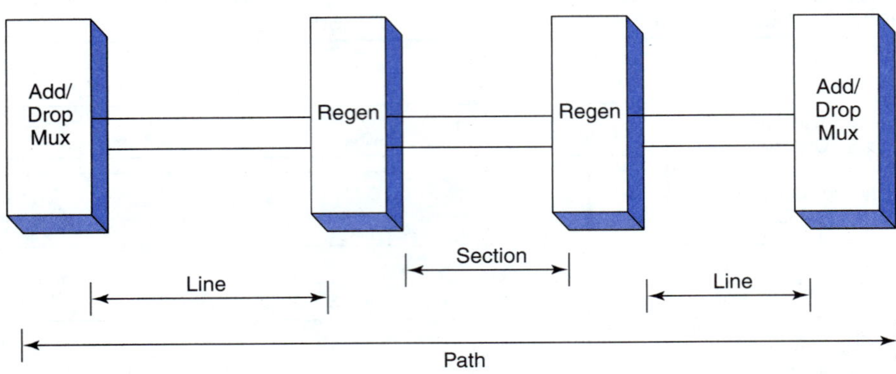

line
Portion of the SONET network—line terminating equipment to line terminating equipment.

section
Portion of the SONET network—regenerator to regenerator.

path
Portion of the SONET network—end to end path.

same logical sections as the SONET frame. The *line* is the portion of the circuit that connects one SONET fiber multiplexer to another. The line section in the STS-1 frame carries overhead bytes relating to the health and status of the line portion of the network. The *section* part of the circuit connects a SONET fiber-optic multiplexer to a SONET regenerator—a device placed in a fiber span to regenerate the optical signal. The section overhead carries information on the health and status of that portion of the network. The third section of a SONET network, the *path,* represents the end-to-end circuit. Figure 7–13 illustrates the path portion of the network. Path overhead monitors the signal from the time it enters the originating fiber optic multiplexer until it leaves the terminating fiber-optic multiplexer. The path overhead in the STS-1 frame is responsible for monitoring the health and status of the path portion of the network, which is the health of the circuit end to end. Table 7–6 defines each of the STS-1 overhead bytes.

Imagine you are a transmission technician responsible for maintaining Spidercom's SONET network. The SONET hierarchy helps you determine where and what the trouble is by using the overhead bytes of the path, the section, and the line. SONET test gear is used to translate the overhead bytes into human terms. As a technician, you can quickly determine that a cable break has occurred between the last regenerator and the terminating multiplexer by sending section errors that relate to that portion of the network. The structure of the SONET frame increases the reliability of the network, while greater amounts of traffic being carried on one fiber requires a robust, easy to troubleshoot, reliable network. The SONET standard provides the foundation required to build such a network.

7.2.4 Timing the Network

An asynchronous DS-3 ensures that the DS-1 signals riding in it derived timing or kept in step. We also discussed the need to multiplex four DS-1s into one DS-2 that

Table 7–6 SONET Frame Overhead Bytes.

Specific Byte Section Overhead	Description of Byte Overhead
A1, A2	Frame Synchronization—The beginning of the STS-1 frame is defined by A1 and A2 bytes.
B1,	Section parity is handled by the B1 bytes. Parity is used to determine whether errors have occurred.
D1, D2, D3	DCC—Data Communications channel is used to carry management information plus to carry information on the health of the transmission.
E1	The E1 byte provides a path for order wire.
F1	Assigned to the user for whatever they wish to use it for.
C1	The C1 byte is used to carry a defined sequence of bits that represent a text message used to trace the signal from end to end often referred to as a Section Trace.
	Line Overhead
H1–H2	The H bytes are used as pointer bytes used to designate where the path OH begins. The H bytes are responsible to keep the frame lined up.
H3	The H3 byte is used for bit stuffing if needed.
B2	BIP-8 is the name used to define the B2 byte. The byte is used for error monitoring of the line portion of the frame.
K1–K2	The K bytes are used for automatic protection switching. The bytes send out and receive orders that a switch has to happen.
D4–D12	Provides a DCC—data communications channel between two line terminals.
S1 (Z1)	The S byte is used to monitor the quality of the clock source.
Z2	Designated for future use.
E2	Line side Order Wire.
	Path Overhead
J1	Path Trace is a text message placed in the J1 byte and is used to identify the end to end path of a signal.
B3	The B3 byte carries a BIP-8 path error scheme to monitor the end to end path.
C2	The C2 byte is called the Signal Label and is used to identify the type of signal in the payload. For example 02 represents Floating VT mode. 04 represents Asynchronous DS-3.
G1	The G1 byte carries information on the status of the path.
F2	The F2 byte (path user channel) is reserved for User specific information.
H4	The H4 byte (multiframe indicator) is used to indicate the VT payload.
Z3–Z5	Designated for future use.

Table 7–7 Timing Standard Hierarchy.

Timing Source	Precision	Number of Frame Slips
Global Positioning System	1×10^{-12}	.2 per year
Loran—C	5×10^{-12}	1.25 per year
Stratum 1	1×10^{-11}	5 per year
Stratum 2	1.6×10^{-8}	11 per day
Stratum 3	4.6×10^{-6}	132 per hour
Stratum 4	3.2×10^{-6}	15.4 per minute

then became the intermediary that made sure all DS-1s arrived at the same time. Asynchronous networks use a bit stuffing/unstuffing timing methodology. Timing in the asynchronous network is called asynchronous timing.

stratum 1 Stratum clock level 1 is the highest clock level provided by GPS or Cesium source.

stratum 2 Stratum clock level 2 is the second clock level below stratum 1.

stratum 3 Stratum clock level 3 is the third clock level below stratum 1.

stratum 4 Stratum clock level 4 is the fourth clock level below stratum 1.

GPS Global positioning satellite provides a Stratum 1 clock source to telecommunications networks.

Synchronous timing depends on an external timing signal to provide a clock for the network equipment. The stratum clock level defines the external clock. For example, as shown in Table 7–7, a *stratum 1* clock source will keep the digital bit streams synchronized for 72 days before a slip or error will occur. A *stratum 2* clock source holds the digital bit stream in sync for 24 days before the signal wanders out of line. *Stratum 3* clocks provide a reliable timing source that will hold the equipment in sync for seventy-two hours and *stratum 4* timing sources provide a twelve-hour hold times. The stratum clock levels have been around since the first digital circuits were deployed. Their hierarchy defines how reliable the timing source is.

Most vendors' transport equipment have stratum 3 clocks built into their circuitry. Networks' equipment will not tolerate timing slips, so networks require a higher-level stratum clock to maintain synchronization. The normal clock distribution is illustrated in Figure 7–14. As shown, a stratum 1 clock source feeds a timing shelf called a building integrated timing source (BITS) in the switch site. The BITS shelf accepts the stratum 1 source and uses it as a reference clock, then distributes a stratum 2 timing source to all the digital equipment in the office from an internal stratum 2 oscillator. The stratum 2 oscillator uses the stratum 1 timing source as a reference and depends on it to synchronize its oscillators. Downstream equipment located at offices that don't have BITS shelves pull their timing from the upstream network equipment that is being fed with a stratum 2 timing source. Timing is fed out into the network as needed, as shown in Figure 7–15.

For years, in telecommunications, the stratum 1 timing source was hidden deep within a cave in Hillsboro, Missouri. AT&T provided circuits to all of their regional switch sites, which in turn provided clock through the network. Most communications companies now pull stratum 1 clock timing from the global positioning satellite *(GPS)* system. Small satellite antennas are placed on the roof

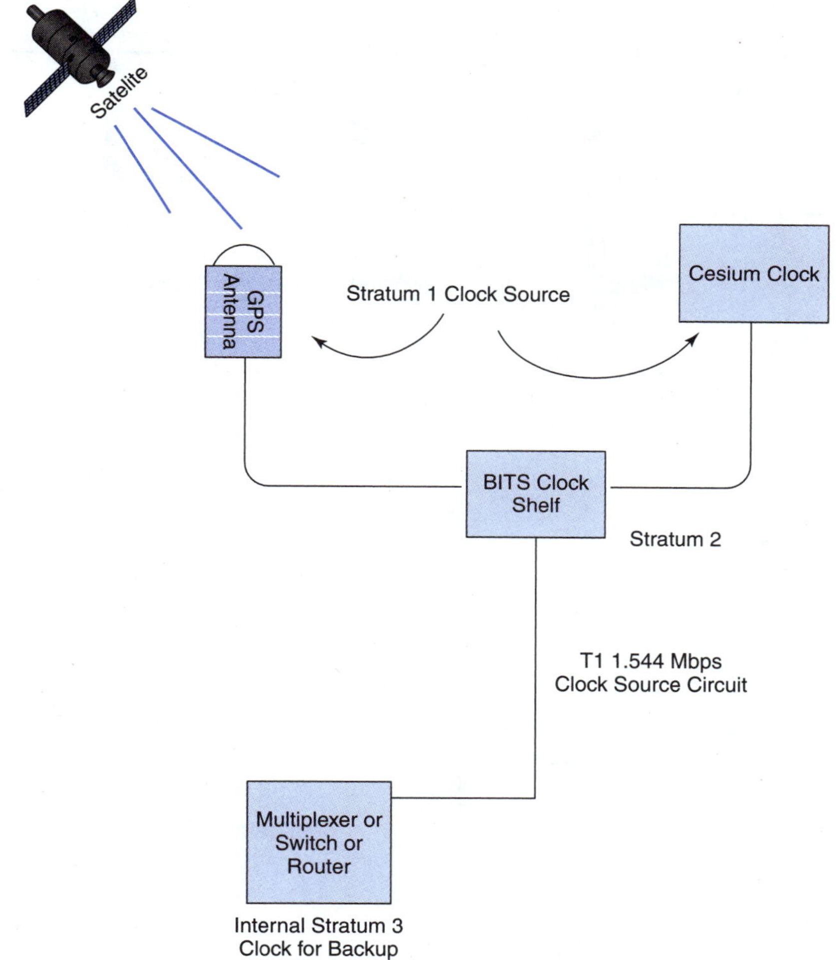

Figure 7–14
Every communications network requires a timing source. Timing is fed through the network from the stratum 1 source to the network equipment.

or a window. The signal is then shipped to a BITS shelf located in the equipment room where coaxial cable connects the antenna to the BITS shelf. GPS is the standard stratum 1 timing source used in the United States. The Hillsboro, Missouri clock was slowly phased out and is no longer being used as a timing source.

7.2.5 SONET Network Topology—Ring Architecture

SONET rings are SONET multiplexers connected together in a ring topology. Figure 7–16 illustrates a typical ring architecture. The purpose of the ring architecture is to improve the reliability of the network and the flexibility of dropping and adding circuits at different nodes, and to use fiber optic strands

Figure 7–15
The path portion of the SONET network refers to the end-to-end circuit path. Path errors received at a test box signify that problems are occurring on the path portion of the network.

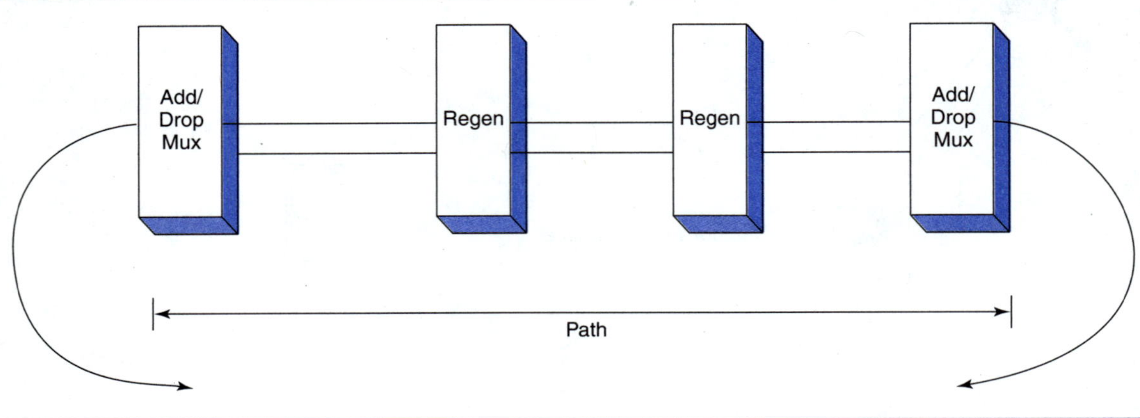

Figure 7–16
SONET ring architecture is one of the most common methods used to connect locations together. The ring architecture provides diverse paths when fiber troubles occur on the network.

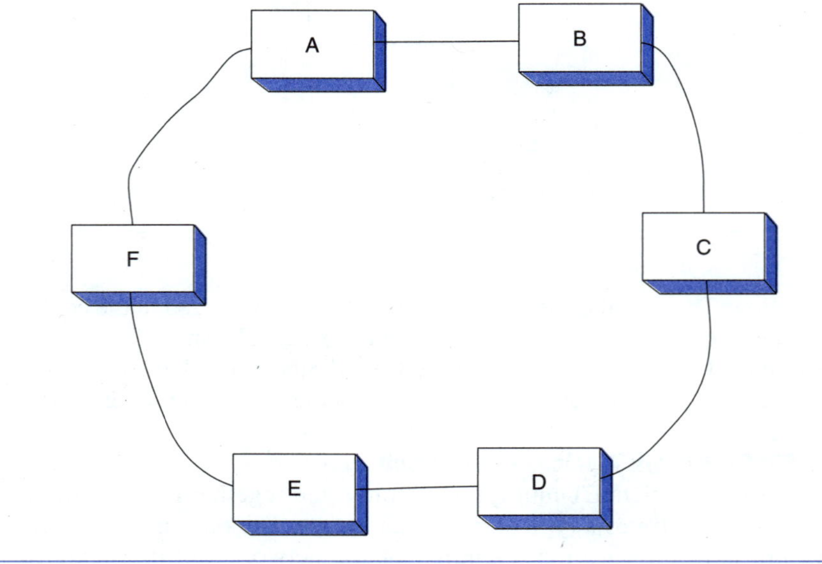

more efficiently. There are two types of ring architectures in SONET: *unidirectional path switched ring* (UPSR) and *bidirectional line switched ring* (BLSR). The difference between the two is the way they switch traffic when a fiber-optic cable cut occurs or a multiplexer fails.

unidirectional path switched ring SONET standard ring type. Protection switching occurs at the path level. One signal travels in a clockwise direction and the protection signal flows in a counterclockwise direction.

bidirectional line switched ring SONET standard ring type. Protection switching occurs at the line level of the network.

The best way to explain a UPSR ring is to provide an example of one. Figure 7–17 shows a 6-node UPSR ring. As you see from the diagram, each node, or multiplexer, on the ring is connected to its adjacent node.

The UPSR takes all incoming traffic and simultaneously routes the signals around the ring in both directions. If the fiber-optic cable was damaged or cut between nodes C and D, as shown in Figure 7–18, the traffic between C and D would automatically reroute D to E, E to A, A to B, B to C. This is possible because there are two distinct paths—one traveling clockwise and one traveling counterclockwise. Assume that node A has two STS-1s mapped between it and node B. Node B receives a primary signal directly from node A. Node B also receives a secondary identical signal that travels from node A to node E, D, C, and B. B normally accepts the primary signal from node A but when a fiber cable is cut, node B immediately realizes that the primary signal from node A is gone and switches to the secondary signal arriving from node C.

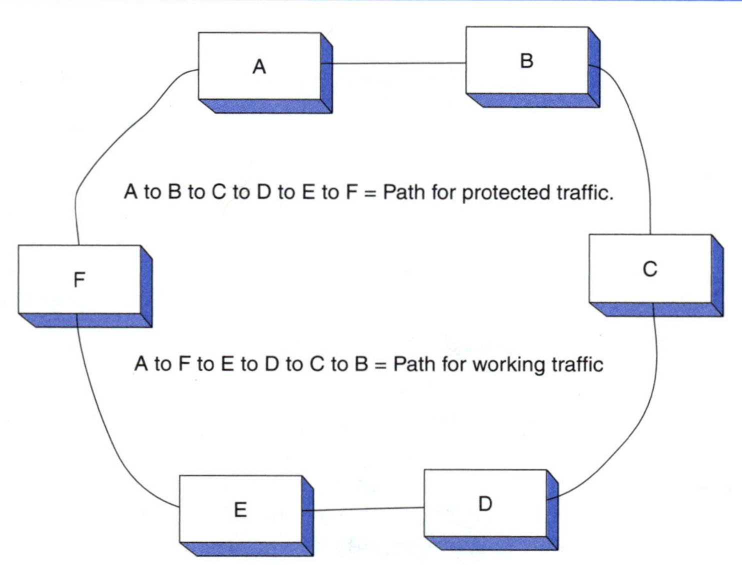

Figure 7–17
The UPSR ring sends all traffic in one direction or the other. All traffic from each node travels either in a clockwise or a counter-clockwise direction.

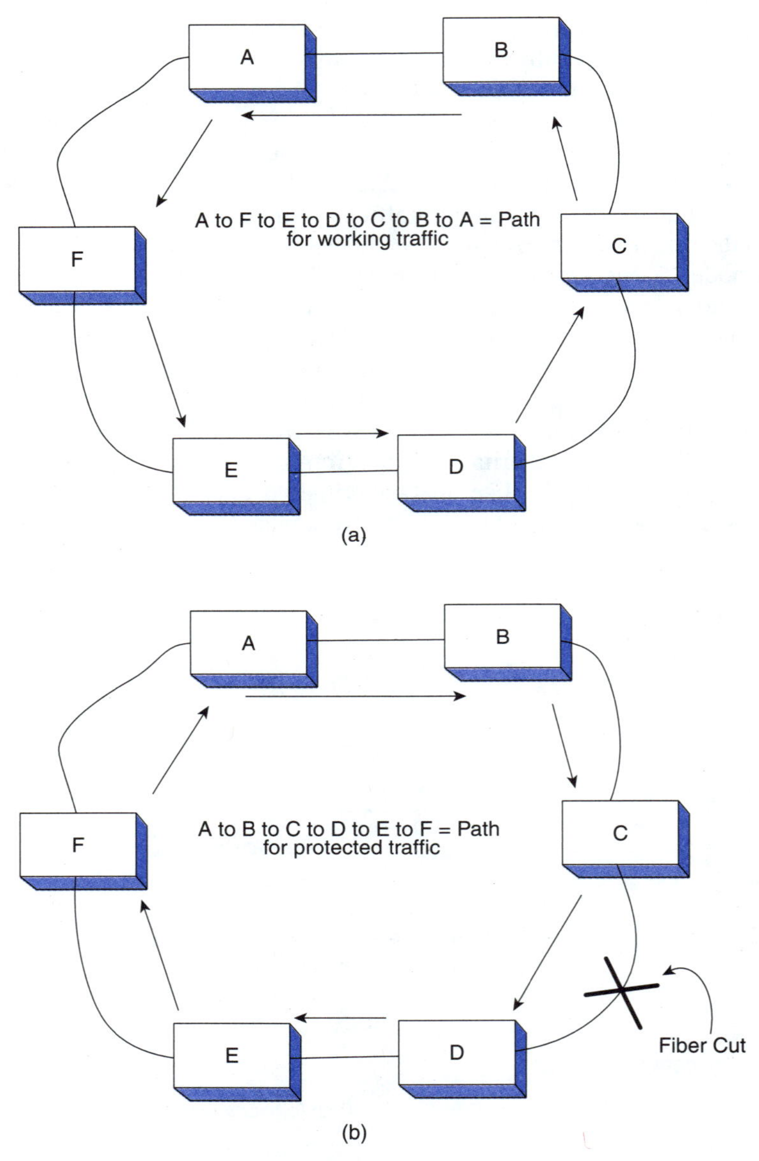

Figure 7–18
(a) Traffic is flowing in a counter-clockwise direction. (b) The fiber cut between C and D causes all traffic traveling in a counter-clockwise direction around the ring to switch and travel around the ring in a clockwise direction.

The second ring architecture used in the SONET world is the bi-directional line switched ring (BLSR). The BLSR is more complicated than the UPSR, but it has the advantage of offering an increased amount of available bandwidth on the total ring. Returning to the UPSR architecture, an OC-12 ring means there are 12 STS-1s worth of bandwidth available for the entire ring. If 12 STS-1s are mapped between node A and node B, all of the STS-1s in the ring are used up. Normally, UPSR rings are not used for signal rates higher than OC-12 due to the bandwidth limitation. The BLSR ring solves this problem by switching at the line level instead of at the path level as the UPSR does. An OC-48 BLSR ring allocates 24 STS-1s in each direction. Channels 25 through 48 are reserved as protection channels. An STS-1 is often referred to as a channel on a ring.

Figure 7–19 illustrates what happens when a fiber cut occurs between nodes C and D. The traffic riding on the 24 channels between the two nodes is immediately looped back at each node and placed on channels 25 through 48, traveling around the ring in the opposite direction. Therefore, we are able to use more than 48 STS-1s in the entire ring. Remember that a BLSR ring provides better bandwidth usage than the UPSR but is more complicated and has a slightly longer switch-to-protect time.

7.2.6 Connecting the Dots

We have only touched the surface of the SONET architecture; entire texts have been devoted to the subject. To review how the total network connects, we will walk through a call traveling from a subscriber's home in Savannah, Georgia, to a subscriber living in Indianapolis, Indiana.

Carmen picks up his phone and dials Paula's number. The local class 5 switch in Carmen's serving central office sees that the call is a 1+ long distance call and therefore has to be routed to Carmen's PIC, SpiderCom Telecommunications. The switch routes the call to the local access tandem by way of a trunk leaving the class 5 switch. The trunk is multiplexed into a T1 signal, then into a DS-3 signal, and then a 560 Mbps signal. The trunk rides on the point-to-point asynchronous optical network to the access tandem at Oak Street. There, the 560 Mbps multiplexer demultiplexes the 560 Mbps pipe into 12 DS-3s, which are fed into M13 multiplexers where the individual 28 T1s are demultiplexed. In this case, the T1 is fed into the access tandem where the trunk carrying Carmen's request for call set up is received. The access tandem knows the call has to travel to Carmen's long distance carrier and knows that SpiderCom is connected to it on T1 number 500. The access tandem routes the trunk onto T1 500, which is multiplexed at the Oak Street central office into a SONET OC-12 signal. Carmen's long distance carrier, SpiderCom connects to the Oak Street access central office using an OC-12 pipe. T1 500 rides on the OC-12 pipe into Spidercom's point of presence, also called POP.

Once in the POP, SpiderCom maps the T1 circuit onto their OC-48 network that carries it to Raleigh, North Carolina, where SpiderCom's regional long distance switch resides. The OC-48 signal breaks out the STS-1 signal carrying Carmen's voice signal and feeds it directly into SpiderCom's long distance toll switch. The toll switch interprets the telephone number Carmen punched in and determines the call has to travel to Indiana. The route the switch takes is on trunk group 100 that rides on SpiderCom's OC-48 network

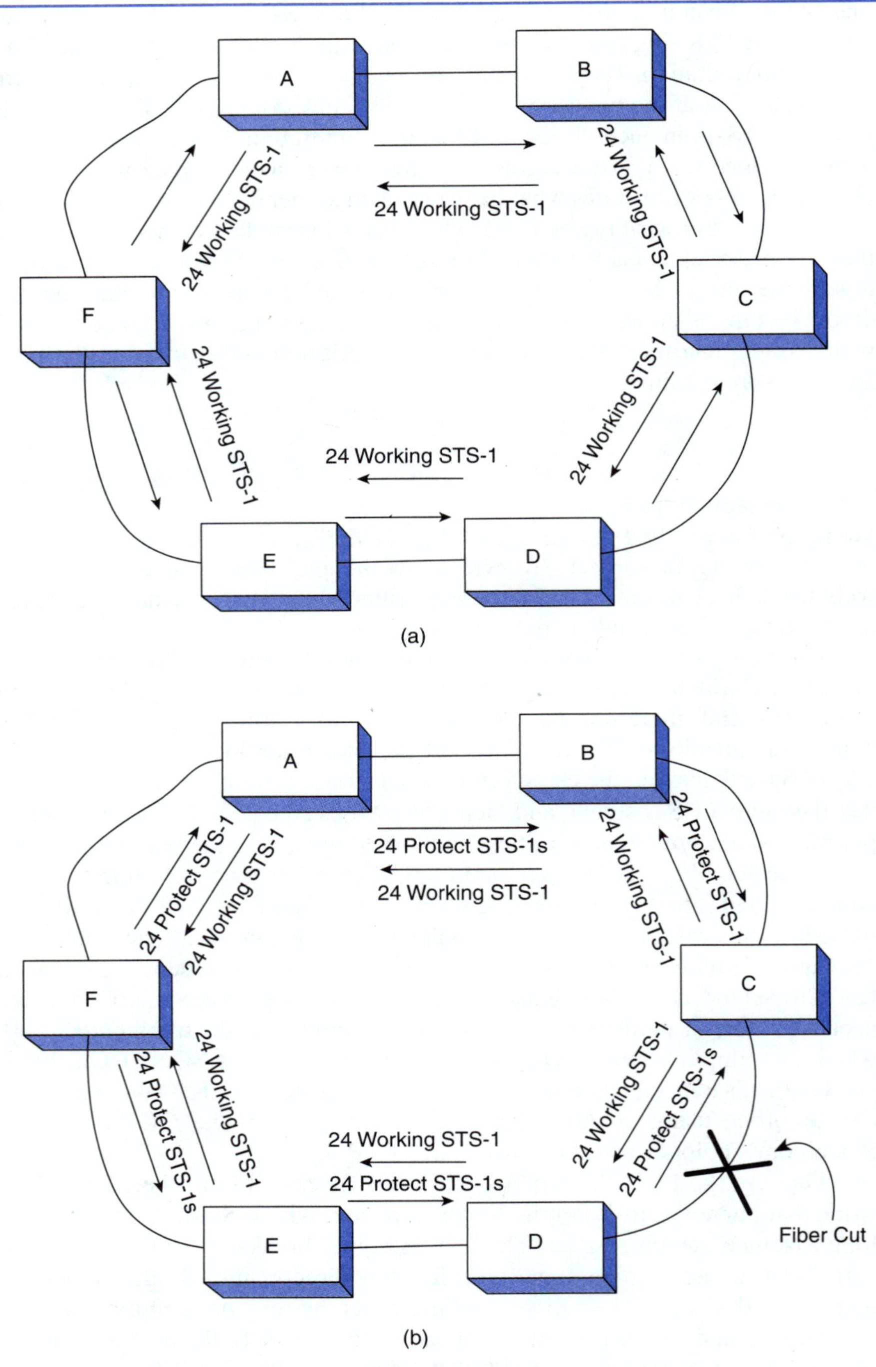

Figure 7–19
(a) The BLSR ring varies from the UPSR in that traffic is carried between each node in both the clockwise and counterclockwise direction. For example A to B in the clockwise direction has 24 STS-1s working and 24 STS-1s for protect. (b) When a fiber cut occurs, the 24 STS-1s traveling between C and D reverse their direction and travel on the protection STS-1 is in the opposite direction.

connecting Raleigh to Indianapolis where SpiderCom's regional long distance switch resides.

Carmen's call leaves the Raleigh regional switch and heads out on the OC-48 ring network that connects Raleigh to Indianapolis. Because it is ring architecture, the signal passes through other cities along the way; there are four nodes between Raleigh and Indianapolis. The call arrives in Indianapolis and is demultiplexed down to T1 signals. The regional long distance switch accepts T1 100 and looks at the information in channel 10 where Carmen's call resides. The switch sees that the call has to travel to the local telephone company's network in order to reach Paula's home. The call is routed out onto T1 300 that connects SpiderCom's long distance switch to the local telephone company's access tandem. (An access tandem is a switch that is used to interface long distance switches into the local telephone network.) The call travels into the local telephone network's access tandem in Indianapolis where it is routed to the Wayne Street central office serving Paula's home. The T1 leaving the access tandem is multiplexed into an OC-48 signal that rides on a local OC-48 SONET network. The T1 is demultiplexed out of the OC-48 multiplexer at the Wayne Street central office and fed into the class 5 end-office switch. The end-office switch looks at the trunk carrying Carmen's call and knows that the call has to be routed to line card 10 where Paula's telephone line terminates. The switch looks to see if Paula's line is idle and when it sees that it is, it places ringing voltage on the line to ring Paula's phone. When Paula picks up the handset of her phone, a circuit connection is completely cut through and Carmen can talk to Paula.

Information travels many different routes as it traverses the world's telecommunications network. Many different types of networks are tied together using a tremendous amount of equipment, signal rates, and switches to carry information in the most efficient and reliable way possible.

SUMMARY

Transport is the portion of the network that connects switch sites, long distance switch sites, large corporate networks, and international links around the world. The telecommunications network depends on this "spider web" of networks that uses fiber optics as a means to transport large quantities of information. Chapter 7 defined the North American Digital Hierarchy and the SONET standard as it relates to the TDM transport network. The concept of time slots was discussed as it relates to the different types of digital circuits. The structure of the T1, T2, T3, 560 Mbps and the SONET STS-1 signal was defined. SONET network ring topology was described, and both the UPSR and the BLSR ring architecture were presented. Timing the digital TDM network was explained and stratum clock levels were given.

CASE STUDY

So far you have decided where you will run fiber-optic cable and where you will run copper cable in Green Grass. You have also determined where you will place a multiplexer in the network. At this point you need to determine the size of the multiplexer at each business site, each school, the hospital, the senior citizen home, the court house, and the central office in Green Grass. The number of employees and their information needs are listed in Appendix H, along with the geographic map showing Green Grass. The cost of the multiplexers is also listed in Appendix H.

Your task now is to choose the correct size multiplexer for each location. This is the first step telecommunications engineers perform when designing a network. The cost of the equipment and the expected capacity are used to build a solution that is cost effective yet reliable.

REVIEW QUESTIONS

1. Explain why the North American Digital Hierarchy was developed.
2. List the four bit per second rates defined by the North American Digital Hierarchy.
3. Define each of the following terms and explain what each is used for.

   DS-0
   DS-1
   DS-3
4. What are the framing bits used for in the T1 signal?
5. Which frames in the T1 frame are used to carry signaling information?
6. Explain the purpose of overhead bits in digital signals.
7. How many DS-0 signals are multiplexed into a T1 signal?
8. Are DS-0 signals byte interleaved into the T1 signal?
9. How many DS-2 signals reside in a DS-3 signal?
10. Explain how a T1 signal is multiplexed into a DS-3 signal. Define the role of the DS-2 signal within the DS-3 signal.
11. Explain the term *time slot* and list other terms used to refer to time slot.
12. Why was the SONET standard developed?
13. List the SONET bit per second rates that compare to a T1 and a T3.
14. Explain the difference between an OC-1 and an STS-1.
15. Draw the SONET STS frame and label each section.
16. Define the terms *line, section,* and *path* as they relate to a SONET network.
17. How many DS-0s ride inside an OC-192 signal?
18. How many DS-3s ride inside an OC-48, an OC-12 and an OC-3 signal?
19. What is meant by the term OC-3c?
20. Explain the difference between an asynchronous fiber-optic network and a SONET fiber-optic network.
21. Draw a typical SONET ring and explain why most carriers prefer the ring architecture.
22. Explain the difference between a UPSR and a BLSR SONET ring.

TROUBLESHOOTING

Problem 1: A T1 circuit connecting the Emory Street CO and Corner Street CO has gone into alarm, showing a loss of frame. You review the design layout record to determine the types of equipment the circuit is traveling through. You note that the T1 travels from a channel bank in Emory Street into an M13 DS-3 multiplexer in Emory Street to a second M13 in Corner Street and then to a second channel bank in Corner Street. You drive your truck to Emory Street first and look at the channel bank to see how the line card is optioned. Following are the options set for each device. Using the information presented, correct the problem and turn up the T1.

- Channel bank #1 = ESF framing, B8ZS line code
- M13 #1 = ESF framing, B8ZS line code
- M13 #2 = SF framing, AMI line code
- Channel bank #2 = SF framing, AMI line code

Note: The customer requires that they have access to all 64 kbps of each DS-0 channel.

Problem 2: The DS-3 carrying the T1 in problem 1 is showing a loss of signal at the Emory Street M13 multiplexer. Using Diagram 7–1 in Appendix C, show how you would initiate a loop back at DSX-3 panel in Corner Street toward the Emory Street M13 and explain what the loop back will prove. The technician sitting in Corner Street sees a yellow alarm. Explain the significance of receiving a yellow alarm and list reasons why it is generated.

Note: The term *yellow alarm* is defined in Appendix I.

KEY TERMS

North American digital hierarchy (263)
digital signal level zero (264)
T1 (265)
information bits (265)
overhead bits (265)
framing bits (267)
superframe (267)
extended superframe (267)
Ft (268)
channel associated signaling (268)
Fs (269)
A/B bits (270)
robbed bit signaling (270)
clear channel signaling (270)
cyclic redundance check (272)
keep alive (273)
channel bank (273)
byte interleaved (275)
bit interleaved (275)
C-bit parity (276)
asynchronous (277)
M13 (279)
clear channel DS-3 (279)
InterXchange Carrier (280)
560 Mbps (280)
digital cross connect (282)
SONET (282)
OC-1 (284)
EC-1 (284)
OC-3 (284)
OC-12 (284)
LEC (284)
OC-48 (284)
OC-192 (285)
line (286)
section (286)
path (286)
stratum 1 (288)
stratum 2 (288)
stratum 3 (288)
stratum 4 (288)
GPS (288)
unidirectional path switched ring (291)
bidirectional line switched ring (291)

CHAPTER

8

Data Communications

Objectives

After reading this chapter, you should be able to

- Define data communications
- Discuss the OSI Model
- Discuss data networking topologies

Outline

INTRODUCTION

How many times have you logged onto the Internet to chat with a friend, send an important e-mail, or transfer a file to a coworker? Have you ever wondered how that information is packaged, shipped, and translated back into human terms? Chapter 8 explains how data communications networks, as extensive and complex as the voice network, have evolved over the past thirty years into a reliable means to transport data information. Exchanging e-mail, documents, photos, and real-time video are common applications that use data communications networks.

The chapter is divided into five general areas. The first section describes the open systems interconnection (OSI) model, which is the model used to transport data across the network. Each of the seven layers and the different applications they serve are described. The second area defines the data communications standards that were created to ship information from point A to point B. The third section outlines network topologies and how they affect the way information is carried across the network. The fourth section includes modes of transmission as it pertains to the method used to structure the bit stream. The chapter concludes with a section on local area networks (LANs) and the different types and configurations used to connect computing devices.

8.1 THE OSI MODEL

8.1.1 Defining Open Systems Interconnection

open systems interconnection Standard that defines how information flows from start to finish.

Open systems interconnection (OSI) defines how networks communicate with networks and how networks communicate with applications. OSI provides rules for equipment vendors, software engineers, and network designers for designing equipment, networks, and applications. The OSI model could be compared to the English language. Rules define each letter of the alphabet, the sounds associated with each vowel and consonant, and the sentence structure necessary to send clear, coherent communications. Every form of communications requires rules. Data communications is no different. The OSI protocol model is used globally when building data communications languages, software applications, networks, and equipment.

The model is comprised of seven layers—applications, presentation, session, transport, network, data link, and physical. The seven layers define how information from the end user is transported to a second end user, and how both are able to understand what the other is saying. Table 8–1 defines each of the layers in technical terms. In addition to the technical explanation, we will tie each layer's function to a real-world application. The purpose of this exercise is to help correlate the abstract concepts of the OSI model to practical applications.

8.1.2 Seventh Layer—Application

To explain the OSI model, we will follow a data communications session from start to end, explaining each step as it pertains to the different layers and how each of the layers depends on the rest in order to function properly. The exercise begins in Katmandu, Nepal, where Henry has just finished a ten-day trek through the Himalaya Mountains. Upon returning to Katmandu, Henry wants to call his mother and tell her about all of his experiences. The hotel clerk explains to Henry that the time difference between Nepal and Watertown, New York, where Henry's mother lives, is twelve hours. Henry looks at his watch and sees that since it is 2 P.M. in Katmandu, it is 2 A.M. in Watertown. The hotel clerk also explains the cost of placing a call from Nepal to the United States. Henry quickly realizes his mother would not appreciate a collect call in the middle of the night. The hotel clerk offers Henry the use of the hotel Internet service. The fee associated is minimal and the message will arrive tonight but not have to be read until tomorrow, thus allowing Henry's mother to sleep, but giving Henry a chance to express his feelings about his trip.

Level	Description
Level 7—Application Layer	Application layer is the top layer of the OSI protocol stack. The Application layer is responsible for the interconnection between the lower layers of the stack and the applications such as e-mail, FTP and other programs. The Application layer helps the information be displayed and formatted for transport to, for example, the workstation.
Level 6—Session Layer	The Session Layer establishes a communications path for data streams between the application layer and the lower layers.
Level 5—Presentation Layer	The Presentation Layer is responsible to format the data in a form that can be presented by the application. For example syntax conversion is handled at the Presentation Layer.
Level 4—Transport Layer	The Transport Layer is responsible for ensuring the information received from the network is error free and ready for transport to the higher three layers. TCP is a layer 4 protocol. Retransmission of corrupted information is initiated at the Transport Layer. The lower layers establish a route through the network and Layer 4 ensures the data being received and transmitted are accurate. The Transport Layer handles end to end transport of information.
Level 3—Network Layer	The Network Layer routes the data to the correct destination. The Network Layer handles all routing, addressing, packet sequence, and switching of packets. IP is an example of a Layer 3 protocol.
Level 2—Data Link Layer	The Data Link Layer establishes a connection between the physical layer and the Network Layer. The Data Link Layer is responsible for error detection and formatting fields. ATM, Frame Relay and Ethernet are Layer 2 protocols.
Level 1—Physical Layer	The physical layer deals with the physical transmission medium such as the copper circuit. The electrical specifications such as the pulse width and height along with the voltage levels are defined in the physical layer.

Table 8–1
Open System Interconnection Protocol Stack Definitions.

Henry turns on the computer and waits as the *operating system* boots up. Every computer has an operating system; common ones are Windows, UNIX, and MAC OS. The operating system is similar to a little factory that resides in the computer and performs tasks at the request of the user. Software programs also perform specific tasks. Word processing, spreadsheets, drawing programs, and e-mail are some of the many common types of software programs loaded onto a typical desktop computer. The software program is built from many lines of programming code that tell it what to do and when. This program is what the user sees. The operating system is in the background, making it all happen.

operating system
Software that runs a computer.

The hotel clerk shows Henry how to access the e-mail application on the computer. Henry is amazed at the similarity between his system at home and the hotel's system in Nepal. The page has a location for the e-mail address of the person he wishes to send the message to, a subject field, and a page delineation where the message is typed. The e-mail application is built specifically to work with the Internet network. A unique address defines the Internet provider and the user.

application layer Seventh layer of the OSI stack.

file transfer program Used to transfer files across a network.

The *application layer* is the highest level in the OSI stack. Its main function is to handle communications between the application process (AP) and the computer. Common application processes are file transfer programs, transaction processing programs, virtual terminals, and message-handling programs. A *file transfer program* (FTP) transfers a file between two locations. It formats the data and readies it for its journey across the data circuit. Every time you swipe your credit card through a machine, a transaction process prepares the data for shipment. The application layer is the first layer to receive the formatted data from the AP. The application layer interprets the information within the AP and readies the information for transmission. The application layer is the closest layer to the actual application.

8.1.3 Sixth Layer—Presentation

presentation layer Sixth layer of the OSI stack.

Once the e-mail is formatted and packaged, it is handed to the *presentation layer,* which is concerned with the actual syntax of the information. The presentation layer ensures that the information is in a format that can be read by both ends. It does this by translating the information on the monitor into a one and zero format to be transmitted out onto a data circuit and then translated back at the far end. The three most common types of format codes are ASCII, EBCDIC, and the newest ASN-1 BER. Henry's e-mail is formatted in ASCII, a common code used by most e-mail applications. He sends a photo along with the text message. The presentation layer formats the photo using a bit map code. The photo is translated into ones and zeros, which allows the content to be transmitted across the network and reassembled at the far end. Just as it sounds, the presentation layer is responsible for the presentation of the information at each end. If the presentation layer is not working, the screen shows gibberish.

8.1.4 Fifth Layer—Session

session layer Fifth layer of the OSI stack.

The *session layer* establishes and maintains the communications connection between the end-user's applications. Information flow rules are negotiated at this layer between the two end users, and special bits are used to synchronize the information and negotiate the session. Besides being responsible for making sure data is exchanged, the session layer also monitors the session, initiates data recovery, and terminates the session. If the application becomes corrupted, the session layer asks the session to be terminated or retransmitted.

8.1.5 Fourth Layer—Transport

The *transport layer* correctly assembles blocks of data. It receives data blocks from the lower layers and makes sure they are in order. Therefore, the upper layers do not have to assemble the bits into a network-friendly format before handing them to the lower layers. In fact, the transport layer can be viewed as the layer sitting between the higher applications and the network communications layers watching for corrupted data. It ensures clean transport between entities.

transport layer Fourth layer of the OSI stack.

The transport layer and the session layer are similar in that they are responsible for making sure information is accurate. The difference is the portion of the network they are responsible for. The session layer is responsible for end-system functioning. For example, if Henry's mother's computer crashed just as the photo was being downloaded, the session layer would ask the file to be retransmitted. If, on the other hand, the telephone line failed, the transport layer would handle the retransmission request and notify the upper layers of the problem.

8.1.6 Third Layer—Network

As it sounds, the *network layer* is responsible for the communications network. As we move further down the stack, the layers become less involved with the applications being used than with the actual network that carries the information created by the applications. The network layer determines the path that the information will travel. In this example, as Henry's e-mail traverses the Internet, the network layer protocols act as navigators, directing information from one point to the next.

network layer Third layer of the OSI stack.

This layer works closely with the two lowest layers and acts as the network communicator. It knows how to handle disruptions, how to talk to the upper layers, and how to route individual packets end to end. The network layer is often the dividing line between end user and network provider. Telephone companies, ISPs, cable TV companies, and cellular companies provide end-to-end connectivity of the network. They are responsible up to layer three. If a user's PC crashes or the operating system fails, the network providers, such as ISPs and telephone companies, are not responsible. If the circuit fails or the packets are misdirected, they are responsible. Though the line *seems* clear, many network problems cause disagreements between the group responsible for the network and the system administrators responsible for the end-users devices. A good understanding of layer three protocols helps reduce the number of disagreements.

8.1.7 Second Layer—Data Link

The *data link layer* watches the point-to-point link and notifies the network layer when trouble occurs. Error detection, framing, error recovery, and flow control are handled by the data link layer of the OSI model. It is similar to the network layer in that both belong to network providers such as telephone companies, ISPs, cable TV companies, cellular companies, and other carriers.

data link layer Second layer of the OSI stack.

The most common network-layer protocol is the Internet protocol (IP), which depends on the network layer of the OSI stack to determine how to route all of the packets assembled for transport to their correct terminating devices. A popular data link protocol is asynchronous transfer mode (ATM), which places all the network layer 3 packets into data link cells. Data link defines the route the cells will travel and handles the data link transport end to end. Today's network is often defined by saying it is a layer 2 cell-based network or a layer 3 packet-based network. The difference between the two is that network layer protocols are used to build the packet network, and layer two protocols are built using the data link layer rules. Layer three is more complex than layer two.

8.1.7 First Layer—Physical

physical layer First layer of the OSI stack.

The final layer of the OSI model is the *physical layer,* which is responsible for the physical attributes of the circuit. The voltage level, the pinouts of the wire interface, the formatting of the binary digits onto the line, the voltage level of each binary pulse, and the transmission characteristics of the line are all defined by the physical layer. When a telephone cable is cut, it is a physical-layer problem. The packets are not being corrupted and shipped to the wrong devices, nor is the flow of the packets being disrupted due to a faulty clock. The problem with the line is strictly due to its being physically severed. The data link layer will report the occurrence to the network layer, and the network layer will notify the upper layers. Whenever data is transferred, a physical circuit is involved, even when printing to your local printer. The circuit may be only two feet long but someone somewhere had to define the number of wires between the devices, which of the wires would transmit from the computer, which would receive at the printer, the voltage level needed, and the distance limitation. The physical side of the network may be seen as the least complicated when it comes to software and applications but the most complicated when configuring and troubleshooting the circuit.

The OSI model is used all over the world whenever new software applications are developed, new transmission protocols are standardized, new devices are designed; and new types of transmission media are introduced. The model is often adjusted to fit particular needs, but the basic structure remains intact. Data communications is as dependent upon the rules defined by the OSI model as it is upon the circuits used to connect the devices.

The next morning, Henry's mother opens the e-mail that arrived from Nepal the night before. She reads Henry's description of his trek, then prints out the photograph. The message from Henry to his mother is possible because of the OSI protocol model data communications standards used throughout the world. Data communications has created a revolution. Only 150 years ago, news traveled by pony express. It took three weeks to notify Washington that Custer had died, and less than three minutes for Henry's e-mail to travel from Katmandu, Nepal, to Watertown, New York.

8.2 STRUCTURE OF DATA COMMUNICATIONS

8.2.1 Defining Data Communications

Data communications, quite simply, is the use of a physical medium to transmit data between two points. The medium can be copper wire, fiber-optic cable, or air. The information may be a batch file carrying the bank balance for everyone from Tin Cup, Indiana, or a full unabridged encyclopedia of the world. Data communications is used by the majority of businesses today from the largest corporations to the smallest establishments. According to analysts, data transmission is growing exponentially and will soon exceed voice traffic on the PSTN.

8.2.2 Binary Information Encoding—ASCII and EBCDIC

Every letter in the alphabet must have an equivalent binary code unique to that letter. For example, when a *C* is typed, a *C* appears on the monitor, but the computer sees 1000011. That is the binary word for *C* in the seven-bit *ASCII* binary code. Every computer must adhere to the same code to know what the transmitting computer is saying. In our example, the seven-bit binary code is from the ASCII standard developed by the American National Standards Institute (ANSI). As shown in Table 8–2, each letter, number, and special character has an equivalent seven bit one and zero number.

ASCII
American Standard Code for Information Interchange.

There are other types of encoding schemes, but ASCII is the most popular for personal computing devices. A second type of ASCII is eight bit ASCII. The additional bit is added to increase the number of characters the code can represent. For example, 128 letters, numbers, and special characters are possible with a seven-bit code. To determine the number of possible combinations of ones and zeros, take 2 to the power of the number of bits. In our example that would be 2 to the power of 7 or 2 multiplied by itself 7 times. The letters in the alphabet must each have a character for lower case and a character for upper case. The numbers from 0 to 9 punctuation, and special numeric symbols must all be represented. Eight-bit ASCII can represent 256 characters, or 2 to the power of 8. The additional characters are used for foreign language letters. If one computer is using 8-Bit ASCII and the second computer is using 7-Bit ASCII, the first 128 characters of both codes are the same. So even if one computer is using seven-bit ASCII and the other is using eight-bit ASCII, the two computers will be able to communicate.

The second most popular code in North America is *extended binary coded decimal interchange code* (EBCDIC). It is an eight-bit code that IBM developed specifically for their machines. If I were using EBCDIC and my neighbor was using either seven or eight-bit ASCII, we would not be able to communicate until a translation between the codes was completed. Converting ASCII to EBCDIC and vice versa is handled by the computer and is fairly simple. Today ASCII is the primary code deployed.

EBCDIC
Extended binary coded decimal interexchange code.

Table 8–2
ASCII Code Values.

Symbol	One Zero Code	Letter	One Zero Code	Letter	One Zero Code
!	1000010	A	1000001	a	1000011
"	0100010	B	0100001	b	0100011
#	1100010	C	1100001	c	1100011
$	0010010	D	0010001	d	0010011
%	1010010	E	1010001	e	1010011
&	0110010	F	0110001	f	0110011
'	1110010	G	1110001	g	1110011
)	0001010	H	0001001	h	0001011
(	1001010	I	1001001	I	1001011
*	0101010	J	0101001	j	0101011
+	0011010	K	1101001	k	1101011
,	0011010	L	0011001	l	0011011
-	1011010	M	1011011	m	1011011
.	0111010	N	0111001	n	0111011
/	1111010	O	1111001	o	1111011
:	0101110	P	0000101	p	0000111
;	1101110	Q	1000101	q	1000111
<	0011110	R	0100101	r	0100111
=	1011110	S	1100101	s	1100111
>	0111110	T	0010101	t	0010111
?	1111110	U	1010101	u	1010111
[	1101101	V	0110101	v	0110111
\	0011101	W	1110101	w	1110111
]	1011101	X	0001101	x	0001111
∧	0111101	Y	1001101	y	1001111
–	1111101	Z	0101101	z	0101111
{	1101111	0	0000110		
|	0011111	1	1000110		
}	1011111	2	0100110		
~	0111111	3	1100110		
@	0000001	4	0010110		
'	0000011	5	1010110		
		6	0110110		
		7	1110110		
		8	0001110		
		9	1001110		

8.2.3 Transmission Modes—Serial and Parallel

Transmission mode refers to the way data bits travel across the physical medium and defines the pulse sequence of the bits as they are transported. In the world of data transmission there are two common types of physical interface modes—*serial* and *parallel*.

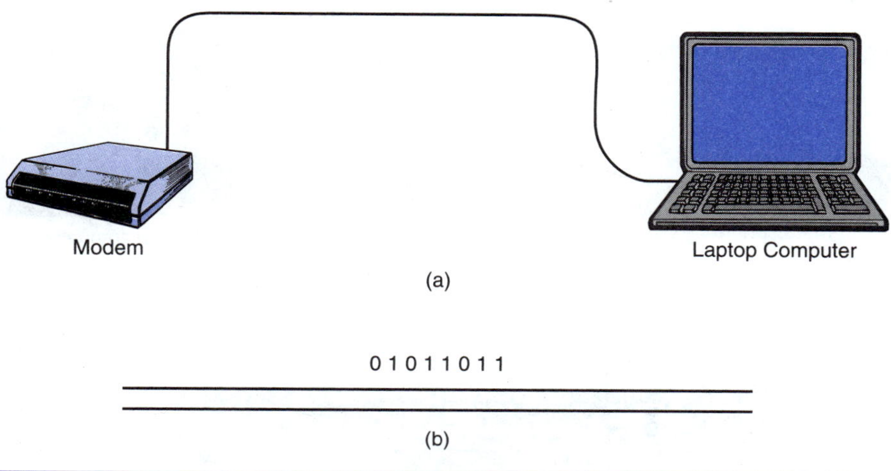

Figure 8–1
(a) Serial interface between the laptop and a modem. The serial interface is a two-wire connection that has data transmitted one bit after the other bit across the wires. (b) Section of a serial interface.

serial
Serial interface carries information one bit after the other.

When information travels across the network in serial fashion, bits are shipped out onto the medium one at a time. When Henry hit the send key on the computer in Katmandu, his message left the computer by way of the modem interface jack connecting to the telephone line on the back of the PC. A serial interface means that each signaling change is sent out one after the other. Multiple changes in the signal cannot be sent simultaneously on the same wire. It seems logical to say that only one bit is transmitted on a serial interface at one time, but because of sophisticated modulation schemes that allow for multiple bits to be transmitted every time a pulse is sent, this is not the case. Rather, serial transmission is able to handle one pulse change at a time because there is only one physical connection between the two devices. Figure 8–1 illustrates two devices connected to one another with a serial interface.

parallel
Parallel interface carries bits across multiple conductors at one time.

The other mode used in data communications is parallel transmission mode. As it sounds, it is a way to send multiple signals over parallel facilities. The best example of a parallel interface is the connection between the printer and the PC. If you were to cut in half the cable that connects the two, you would find eight individual wires. Because the distance between your computer and the printer is relatively short, placing eight individual wires is cost effective. The eight wires each carry information from the PC to the printer. When we hit the print key, the information flows out of the computer onto the wire eight bits at a time. The bits that make up one character are shipped simultaneously. Figure 8–2 illustrates parallel transmission mode between Henry's PC and the printer. Because parallel transmission can carry eight signals at once instead of only one (as in serial mode), you might wonder why the network doesn't use parallel transmission. The answer is that eight lines would be needed between each person's home and the central office, which would not be cost effective.

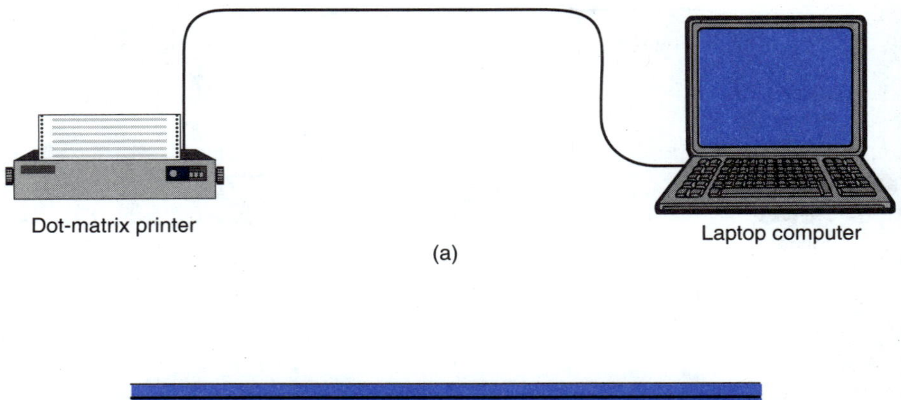

Figure 8–2
(a) Parallel interface between the laptop and the dot-matrix printer.
(b) Section of ribbon cable that provides a parallel interface.

8.2.4 Asynchronous Data Transmission

asynchronous transmission Data transmission using stop and start bits to define frames.

Asynchronous transmission is used to tell receiving equipment which bit is the first, which is the second, and so on when receiving information. It delineates each of the characters that are shipped across the network. For example, like every other character, the character *H,* is preceded by a start bit and followed by a stop bit. The end equipment synchronizes the bit stream according to start and stop bits. In a sense, it is similar to saying "over" during short wave radio conversations to signal the far end that the message is over. In the case of asynchronous transmission, the stop bit serves the same purpose.

The problem associated with using start and stop bits is the amount of bandwidth used every time a character is sent. In fact, the asynchronous transmission format contains 20% overhead due to the use of stop and start bits. The need to synchronize the bit stream between transmitting and receiving devices is essential. Asynchronous transmission is the most common format used for slower speed terminals. The maximum bit per second rate handled by asynchronous transmission is 9.6 kbps. See Figure 8–3a for an illustration of asynchronous transmission.

8.2.5 Synchronous Data Transmission

synchronous transmission Data transmission scheme using clock source to sync up the frames.

Synchronous transmission, like asynchronous transmission, is responsible for synchronizing, transmitting, and receiving equipment to ensure that the information is received in the same order that it is sent. Synchronous transmission does not use stop and start bits to align the bit stream. Instead, synchronous transmis-

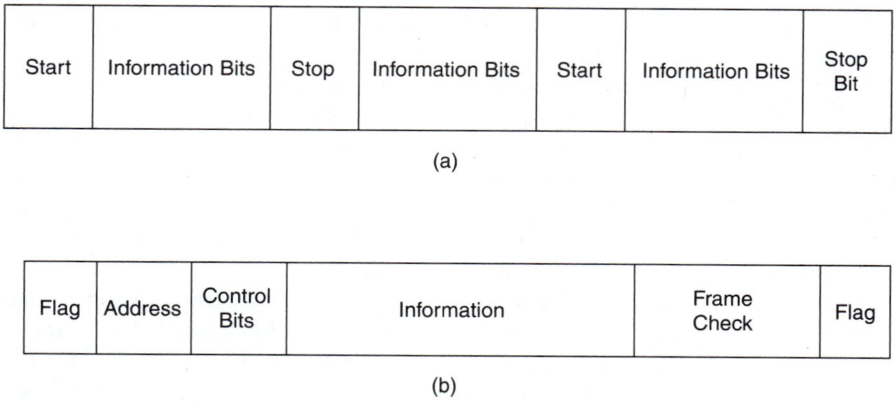

Start	Information Bits	Stop	Information Bits	Start	Information Bits	Stop Bit

(a)

Flag	Address	Control Bits	Information	Frame Check	Flag

(b)

Figure 8–3
(a) Asynchronous transmission requires that an acknowledgement be sent every time information is shipped.
(b) Synchronous transmission allows a variable amount of information to be shipped. The signal uses a clock source to keep the end equipment in sync.

sion uses a clock source as a reference to align the bit stream. The end equipment uses the same clock as a reference. The use of one clock to reference the start and stop of the bit stream allows the equipment to send characters without individual stop and start bits.

Synchronous transmission, as illustrated in Figure 8–3b, formats the bit stream with sync bits and flags placed around blocks of data. The block becomes a frame that is shipped intact ready to be read by the receiving equipment. The receiving equipment opens the frame and reads the information inside using the same clock signal as the transmitting equipment. The clock is either embedded in the data stream or it rides on a separate clock circuit. Digital ones and zeros require a timing source in order to move to the same reference. Synchronous systems require a more advanced timing system than asynchronous data systems.

8.2.6 Error Checking

Asynchronous and synchronous transmission formats ensure that receiving equipment is able to synchronize the incoming bit stream to the bit stream being transmitted. If one of the bits is corrupted during the transmission, for example a one pulse becomes a zero pulse, error checking tells the receiving equipment that the zero should be a one. Error checking is performed continuously on data communications circuits to ensure that the number of ones and zeros being sent is the same as the number being received.

As information flows between two points, the receiving equipment looks at the incoming bit stream, counts the bits, and determines whether the information is correct or corrupted. The equipment receiving the bit stream runs the ones and zeros through an algorithm that calculates the number of odd or even ones in the bit stream. When the bit stream is corrupted, the end equipment sends a no acknowledgment (NAK) to the transmitting equipment telling it the information was corrupted.

Error checking happens at different levels of the OSI stack, including the physical level that watches the digital bit stream, the data link level looking for errorred frames, and higher levels looking for applications errors.

Parity checking is an error-checking scheme that counts the positive and negative pulses to determine whether or not there is a polarity violation. A parity violation is when a positive one pulse follows a positive one pulse or a negative one pulse follows a negative one pulse. Bit streams are formatted as alternate mark inversions (AMIs), meaning that every other pulse is the opposite in polarity. A positive one follows a negative one. Parity checks are looking for polarity violations; when one is found it means that the information being sent is incorrect and must be retransmitted. There are two types of parity checking: *odd parity* and *even parity*. Odd parity wants to see an odd number of either positive or negative one pulses; even parity wants to see an even number of either positive or negative one pulses. The equipment on the ends are optioned for either odd or even parity, but both parity checking schemes perform the same function.

odd parity Error checking method that counts the bits to make sure they equal an odd number. If they don't, the assumption is that an error has occurred.

even parity Error checking method that counts the bits to make sure they equal an even number. If they don't, the assumption is that an error has occurred.

cyclic redundancy check Error checking algorithm used to ensure data transmission.

amplitude modulation (AM) Modulation technique that manipulates the amplitude of the signal.

frequency modulation (FM) Modulation technique that manipulates the frequency of the signal.

Cyclic redundancy check (CRC) is another error-checking scheme used to monitor the data stream. CRC characters are appended to a block of data leaving the transmitting equipment. The receiving equipment reads the block and uses the CRC algorithm to calculate whether or not the information has been corrupted. CRC error checking is a robust method that guarantees the circuit is free of errors. A 99.99% validity score is possible when using CRC error checking. This means that 99.99% of what CRC claims is true. If there are no CRC errors, then you can feel confident there are no errors.

8.2.7 Analog Data Transmission

Analog data transmission occurs every time you log onto the Internet using your PC, your modem, and your telephone line. The information from your PC is converted into an analog signal within the modem, similar to a voice signal, and shipped out onto the telephone line. This section deals with the way the analog signal carries data information. A typical telephone line is designed to carry frequencies between 300 Hz and 4000 Hz. Frequencies of 0 to 300 Hz and 3300 to 4000 Hz are reserved as guardbands. The guardbands ensure that the data transmission will not interfere with other signals. The typical data sent through a modem out onto the PSTN is restricted to the frequency range of 300 Hz to 3300 Hz, so the digital data arriving from the computer must be modulated onto frequencies within this range.

Therefore, the digital signal leaving the computer is converted into an analog signal format before being transmitted out onto the telephone line. The modem converts the digital signal into an analog waveform, and the analog signal carries the one and zero bits across the network. The modem uses various modulation techniques to convert the digital signal into an analog signal. The three most common methods are *amplitude modulation* (AM), *frequency modulation* (FM), and *phase modulation* (PM).

AM is the simplest technique. The amplitude of the waveform is varied to represent either a one or a zero bit. For example, in Figure 8–4 the higher

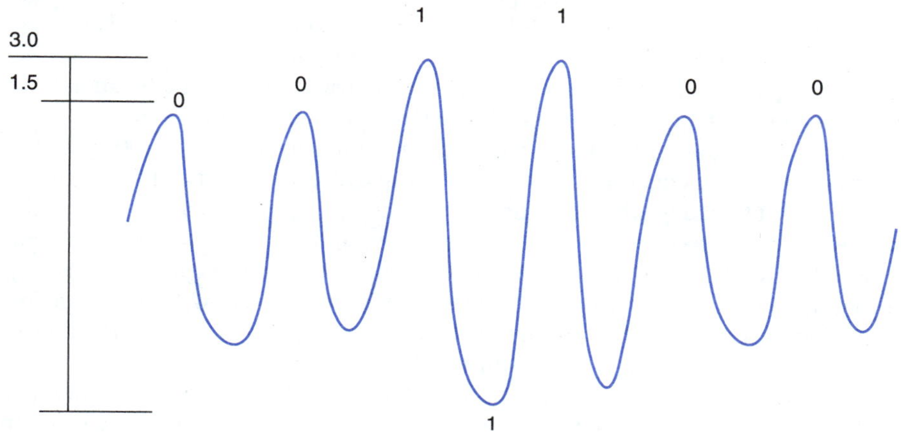

Figure 8–4
Data may be transmitted across an analog signal by manipulating the amplitude of the waveform. This waveform represents a 1 when the amplitude is 3 volts or 0 when the amplitude is 1.5 volts.

amplitude represents a one and the lower amplitude represents a zero. The modem increases the amplitude of the carrier wave to adjust the voltage value when a one is transmitted, and reduces the amplitude of the waveform when a zero is transmitted. This process is called modulation. The amplitude of the waveform is being modulated.

phase modulation Modulation technique that manipulates the phase of the signal.

FM is a second modulation method. In this case, the waveforms' frequencies are modulated when a one or a zero pulse is transmitted. A one pulse is represented by 2400 cycles every second and a zero is represented by 1200 cycles every second. The frequency of the carrier wave is modulated, as illustrated in Figure 8–5. Frequency shift keying is the phrase used to describe FM modulation.

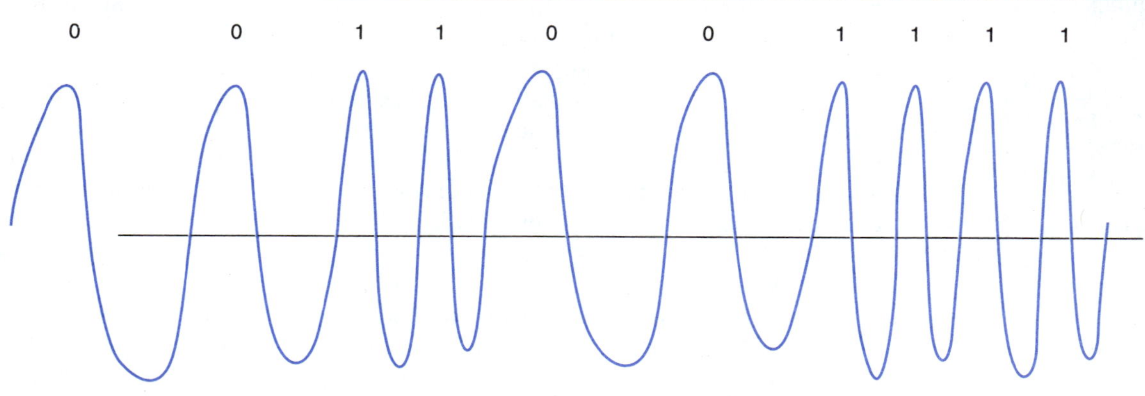

Figure 8–5
Data may be transmitted across an analog signal by manipulating the frequency of the waveform.

Phase modulation (PM) manipulates the phase of the waveform. For example, a one is represented by a 180-degree phase shift in the waveform. The phase of the carrier wave is modulated to represent the digital bit.

To determine the number of bits per second carried by an analog signal, we need to understand the term *baud*. Baud stands for the signaling rate of the circuit. For example, a 2400 baud per second circuit means there are 2400 signaling changes or changes occurring in the waveform every second. The two terms are often used interchangeably, but they are not the same. The type of circuit, the physical limitations of the circuit, and the end equipment determine the baud rate of a link. The bit rate is determined by the modulation technique performed by the equipment. The ability to send multiple bits per baud is how a normal analog line is able to carry a 56 kbps signal. The modem modulates multiple bits per baud rate and in so doing increases the bit per second rate.

The first modems used straight AM, FM, or PM techniques to modulate bits onto a waveform. Each method was limited to no more than a four bits per baud rate every second due to the difficulty encountered when trying to differentiate between the two states. When two modulation techniques are combined, the number of bits per baud increases dramatically. *Quadrature amplitude modulation* (QAM) is an example of combining modulation techniques to increase the number of bits per baud. QAM combines PM and AM to produce a four-bit per baud signal. *Trellis coded modulation* (TCM) allows up to eight-bits per baud. An analog data line is not 2400 bits per second or 56 kbps because the frequency range of the circuit has been increased or changed. Instead, modulation techniques have been perfected to allow multiple bits to be transmitted every baud.

quadrature amplitude modulation
Modulation technique that manipulates the amplitude of a signal to increase the number of bits shipped per signal change.

trellis coded modulation
Modulation technique that manipulates the phase and amplitude of the signal to increase the number of bits shipped per signal change.

The amount of data the analog data circuit is able to carry depends on the type of modem on each end, the length of the circuit from the subscriber to the central office, the cable gauge, and the total impedance of the line. Subscribers often purchase 56 kbps modems and then complain when they are only able to transmit 33 kbps or less. Unfortunately, there is little a telephone company can do to increase the speed of the modem.

Early data communications circuits used specially designed, dedicated, point-to-point analog circuits that, at the time, provided a more reliable, faster means to transmit data. These dedicated data lines are now obsolete, thanks to new digital line technologies. Business customers still use the existing analog data lines, mainly because of the cost to upgrade the end equipment. Unfortunately for the telephone company, the circuits are difficult to maintain.

8.2.8 Digital Data Transmission

We live in a digital age. The telecommunications network has evolved into a digital network, changing the way we all communicate. First, trunking circuits were converted from analog carrier lines into T1 digital circuits. Next, analog switches were converted into digital switches while the size and price of the digital computer reduced, allowing for mass distribution of data to business and residential customers. Following a voice call or data call

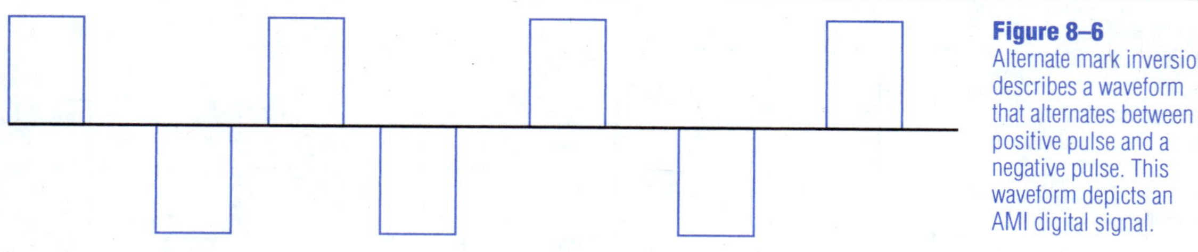

Figure 8–6
Alternate mark inversion describes a waveform that alternates between a positive pulse and a negative pulse. This waveform depicts an AMI digital signal.

through the network, we quickly see that for most residential customers, the local loop is the only portion of the network that continues to use an analog signal. To understand why the local loop has not been converted to carry a digital signal, we need to find out how a digital data signal is transmitted across the network.

digital dataphone service
An AT&T copywrited term to define a digital data service.

The first digital circuit was deployed by AT&T in the early 1980s. The *digital dataphone service* (DDS) was designed to replace the dedicated analog circuits used by business customers to transmit data from one office to another. It provided a link that could handle speeds from 2.3 kbps up to 56 kbps. Because older analog circuits were only capable of carrying up to 19.2 kbps under the best conditions, the trend was established. Business owners soon asked for even faster speeds, and T1 circuits were deployed to help satisfy the desire for bandwidth. Finally, ISDN was introduced as a POTS line replacement. ISDN was the first digital-switched service.

Digital data transmission, whether it is an ISDN line or a DDS, requires special terminating equipment to format the bit stream before it is transmitted out onto the line. In place of a modem, the dedicated digital line requires a CSU/DSU and the ISDN line requires an NT-1. A dedicated DDS digital circuit's CSU accepts the one and zero bit stream from the computing device. The signal is converted from a unipolar signal, in which all of the pulses are of the same polarity, to an alternate mark inversion (AMI) format, as shown in Figure 8–6. The alternating one and zero signal is transmitted out onto the network at the speed set by the end equipment. For instance, if a PC is set to transmit 56 kbps, the DSU receives the signal and outpulses it onto the copper pair. If the PC ships a 9.6 kbps signal, the CSU receives the signal and outpulses the bits onto the digital circuit.

NT-1
ISDN termination device.

An ISDN circuit is similar to a DDS circuit. The significant differences are that an ISDN circuit is able to carry two 64 kbps signals and a 16 kbps signal and interface into the class 5 switch. The unit used to interface an ISDN line is called an *NT-1*. The NT-1, like the CSU, is responsible for the bit stream format as it is transmitted onto the physical circuit. ISDN was built upon a *2B1Q* line-code format that allows two bits to be transmitted for each pulse shape, thereby producing the ability to send more bits every second. The 2B1Q line format carries two bits per signal change compared with the AMI line code that carries one bit per

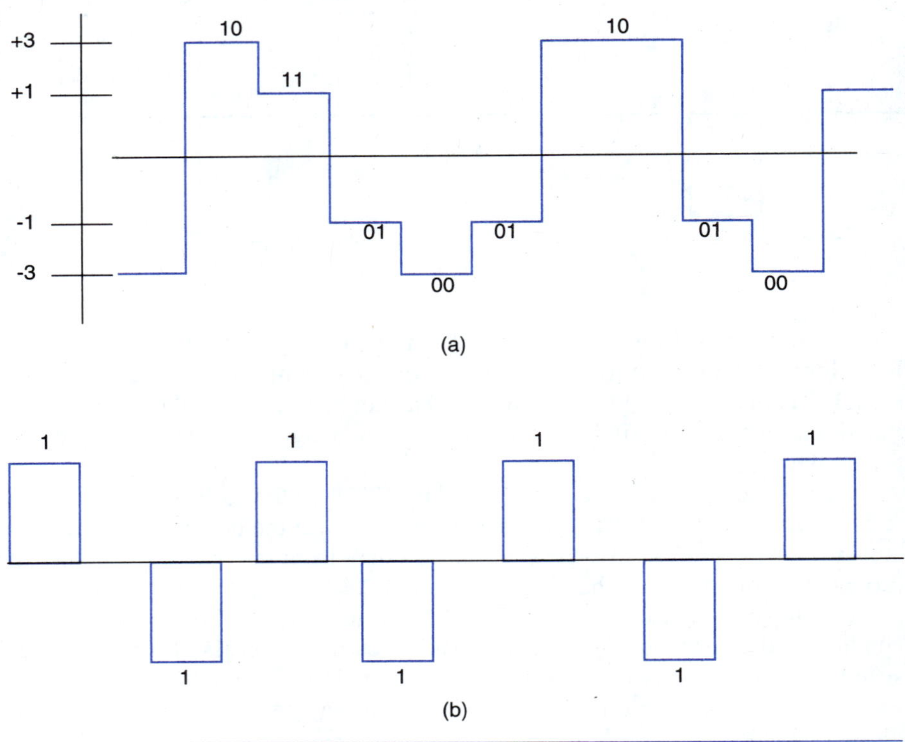

Figure 8–7
(a) The ISDN BRI signal is a quarternary signal that increases the number of bits per pulse to two showing the 2B1Q line code. (b) Illustrates one pulse per signal change and each alternate pulse occurs at the opposite polarity.

2B1Q
Line code used to encode ISDN circuits and DSL circuits.

signal change. The difference between the two line coding schemes is shown in Figure 8–7.

To review, an analog data circuit carries an analog signal. The modem is responsible for modulating the signal onto the circuit and determining the bit per second rate. The digital data circuit carries a digital data signal that has been formatted by the end device. The two most common types of devices are the CSU, used for dedicated circuits, and the NT-1, used for switched ISDN circuits. Both the analog data circuit and the digital data circuit are able to carry more than one bit per signal change. The bit per second rate for both types of transmission circuits is ultimately dependent on the quality of the physical link.

8.3 DATA NETWORK TOPOLOGIES

8.3.1 Defining Data Network Topology

The term *topology* is used in data communications to explain how a network is laid out, such as in a ring, mesh, star, or bus topology. Network engineers take many factors into consideration when designing a data network, including the size of the network, the number of locations, the distance between the locations, the amount of traffic between each of the locations, the transport costs for link, and the types of data circuits available at that location. Different types of data applications lend themselves to specific types of data topologies. For example, the Internet is built on a mesh network topology, in which multiple locations are connected together forming a spider web-like network. A bank's network is often built with multipoint circuits allowing connectivity from one central database to multiple ATMs or branch offices. This portion of the chapter looks at the different architectures that are used to build a data network and the reasons they are used for specific applications.

8.3.2 Point-to-Point Network Topology

The *point-to-point* topology is the simplest network design, consisting of one link connecting two end locations, such as two corporate LANs. For example, IGE pharmaceuticals has a research campus in Burlington, Vermont, and a factory in Huntsville, Alabama that exchange large amounts of data every day. The information being exchanged is highly sensitive and must travel on secure pipes. The network engineer knows that a dial-up circuit will not provide the needed bandwidth and is much less secure than a dedicated pipe. An ISDN line does not provide the bandwidth needed and the cost-per-minute charges would exceed the cost of a dedicated pipe. The IGE engineer decides to connect the two locations with a T1 1.544 Mbps circuit, thus creating a point-to-point network topology that provides both the needed bandwidth and the required security. Point-to-point networks are very common in this type of situation and are a viable solution when the amount of data exchanged between the two locations warrants a dedicated pipe.

point-to-point circuit
Circuit that carries information only between two points.

8.3.3 Multipoint Network Topology

A *multipoint topology* is, as it sounds, a network tied together at multiple points, as depicted in Figure 8–8. A common example of a multipoint network is that of ATMs feeding into a central bank. The machines must talk to the bank's main database in order to exchange customer balance information. Often, dedicated 56 kbps digital data circuits are used to connect the geographically dispersed ATMs into the bank's central database. The machines do not need to talk to each other, just to the central database. The central bank, on the other hand, must be able to communicate with each of the ATMs and therefore must have a connection to each device.

multipoint circuit
Circuit that carries information between one hub and multiple locations.

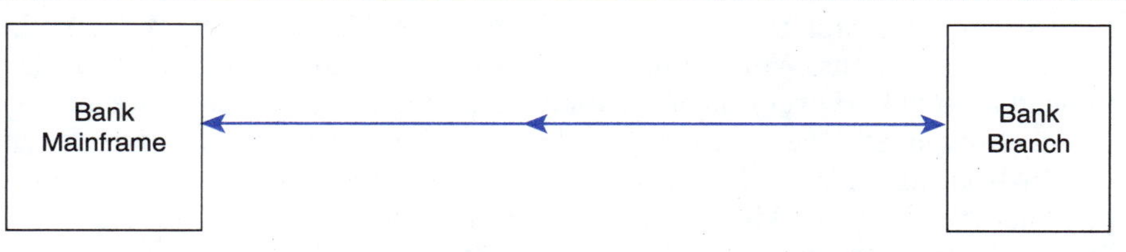

Figure 8–8
Point-to-point data circuit. The circuit speed may vary depending on the bandwidth needs. The circuit architecture is commonly used by banks in order to keep the network secure.

Figure 8–9
Multipoint data circuit with three remote ATM locations feeding into a front end processor (FEP). From the front end processor, the transaction is routed to the main frame. The mainframe polls each of the sites and asks for information. The remote sites are not able to talk with each other, only to the mainframe at the main office.

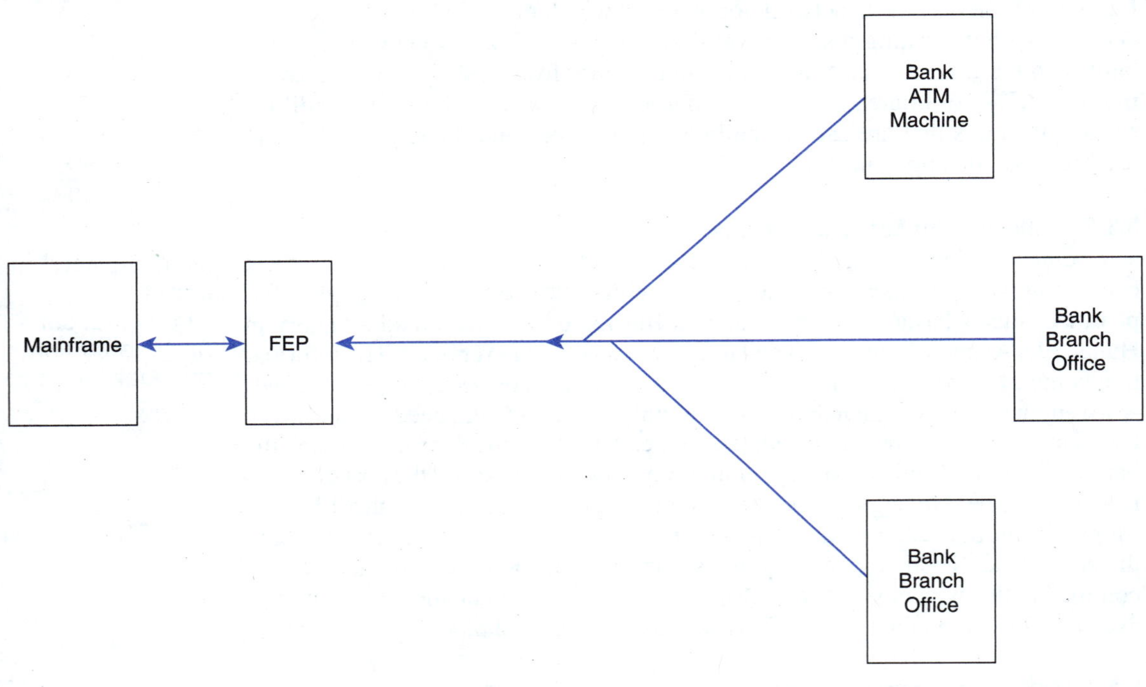

The multipoint topology fits this application perfectly. Each of the machines has dedicated circuits that feed back to a central hub, usually located in the telephone company's serving central office. One circuit is placed between the hub location, as shown in Figure 8–9, and the main branch of the bank where the database resides. The dedicated 56 kbps circuit provides a secure pipe and substantial bandwidth for the transactions being made. The front-end processor in front of the database polls each of the branch locations asking whether they have data to send. If a branch site does have data to send, it sends it at that time. The database continuously queries each of the branch sites using a round-robin polling scheme to ensure that each site is given a chance to exchange information.

A multipoint architecture is fairly common and has been used for years in data communications. With the Internet, networks normally expect every device to be able to talk to every other, making the multipoint and point-to-point networks obsolete. Still there are many applications, such as the one mentioned, that benefit from the older architectures. Like the point-to-point topology, a multipoint network is justified if the amount of traffic to be exchanged is great enough to warrant dedicated circuits and if the application requires secure links.

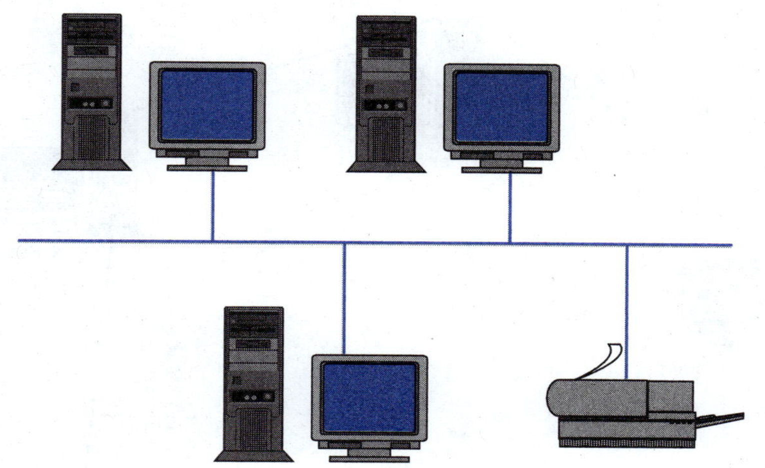

Figure 8–10
The bus network topology. The network consists of elements tied together along a shared route. Traffic from each device flows through the adjacent device as it travels down the line.

8.3.4 Bus Topology

The *bus topology* is very common in the world of local area networks (LANs). A LAN is a network that connects multiple computing devices with one another in a local area. A common architecture used to connect the devices is the bus topology. In fact, bus topology is rarely used for anything except LANs. It is similar to a local bus run in which a bus travels around the city and stops at each bus stop, picking up some passengers and letting others off. Multiple PCs are attached to the LAN. The data leaving the PC jumps onto the link and travels to the desired location on the LAN, such as another PC, a file server, or a printer. The data may need to travel from my PC to my neighbor's PC or it may only need to travel to my printer. Either way it is riding on the linear circuit that connects all of the devices together. Figure 8–10 illustrates a typical LAN connected by bus topology.

bus topology
Network topology based on a shared bus architecture.

8.3.5 Ring Topology

Ring topology may refer to a LAN's design or to a large SONET network connected with fiber optic cable. Each device on ring architecture is connected to the adjacent device, thereby forming a closed ring, as shown in Figure 8–11. The advantages of the network should be apparent. If the connection between device A and device B is severed, device B is still able to communicate with device A by way of devices F, D, C, and B. The reliability of the ring architecture is the key selling point when determining the type of topology to implement. A second advantage is its ability to send traffic to any node on the ring by simply building a connection to that node. The circuit does not have to be ordered or physically built; the ring is already in place. Instead, the circuit is provisioned through software, which takes less than 2 minutes. Ring

ring topology
Closed network topology based on passing information around the ring.

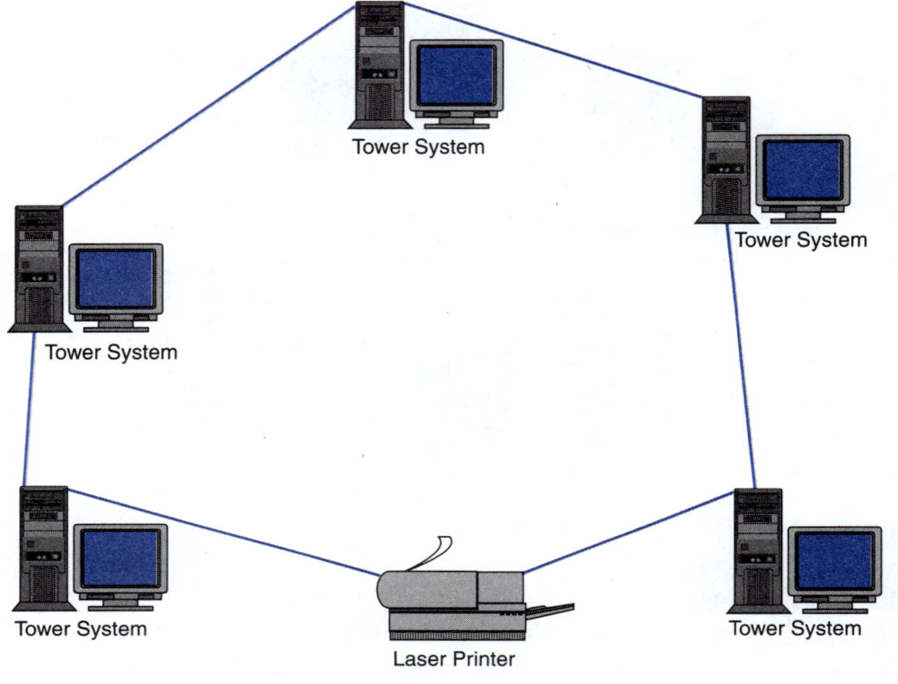

Figure 8–11
A typical ring architecture. Traffic flows around the ring passing through each node along the route.

architecture has become one of the most popular architectures for large fiber-optic networks. A typical fiber-optic network carries anywhere from 32,000 channels to 80 × 32,000 channels and higher on one cable. The need for a fully redundant path is apparent, and ring topology provides redundancy, simple provisioning methods, and a secure network. For years, backbone data networks have been built around a mesh design, but they are now beginning to be designed in ring configurations.

8.3.6 Mesh Topology

mesh topology
Fully connected network topology based on each device connected to two or more devices.

Mesh topology is one of the most common topologies used in data communications. Not only does it provide connections to and from every device on the network, it also provides diverse routes to every device on the network. The Internet is the best example of a mesh network. Web sites are all tied together by way of a large "spider web" of connections.

Figure 8–12 illustrates a typical mesh network in which each device has a way to reach every other device. Unlike the multipoint design discussed earlier, each device in a mesh network is able to talk to every other device. Figure 8–13 also illustrates the diverse routing functionality provided by a fully meshed

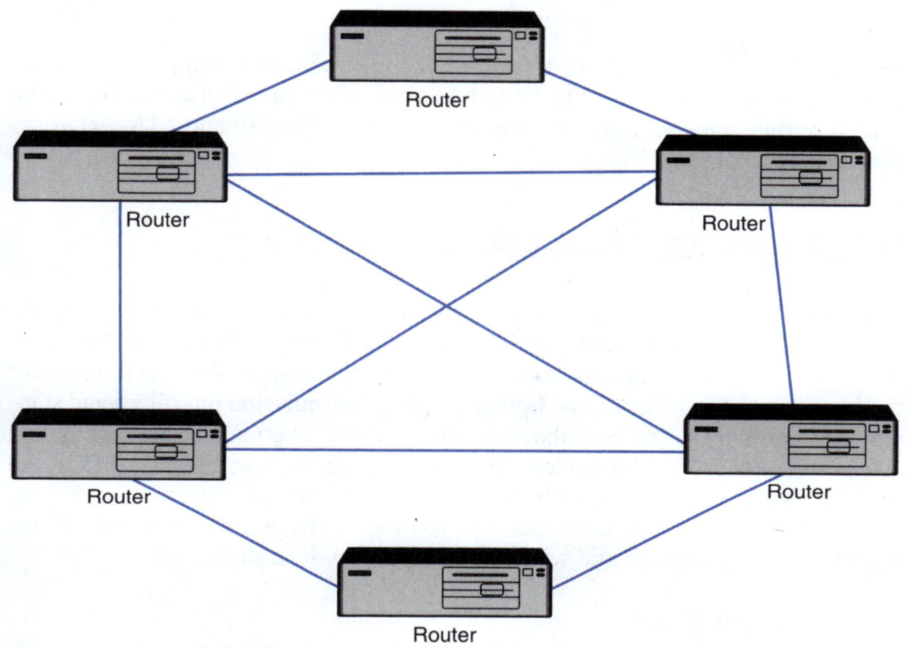

Figure 8–12
This partial mesh network provides connectivity between at least two other nodes. Some networks are fully meshed, meaning that each node is connected to every other node in the network.

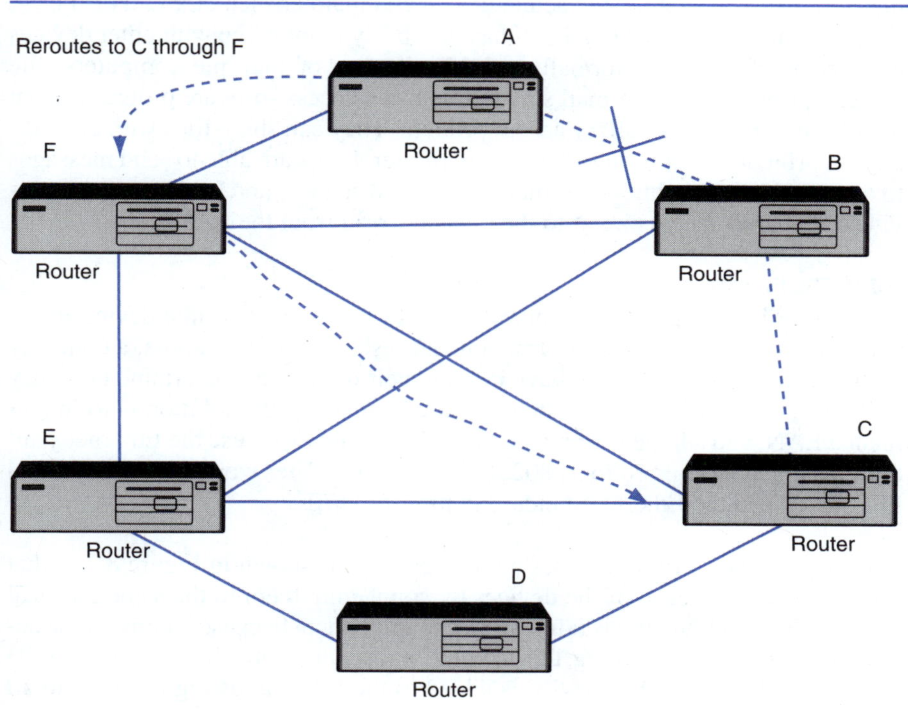

Figure 8–13
Mesh networks provide redundant paths to each device on the network. For example, if the link between A and B fails, the traffic to C is rerouted through F, then to C.

network. If route A to route C is severed, the information is shipped from route A to route F and then to route C. IP and ATM transport protocols were built to be able to reroute packets and cells onto diverse links. Most IP and ATM networks use mesh topologies.

8.4 DATA NETWORKS—LANs

The data communications network has evolved into a highly sophisticated system of protocols and devices. The overall network can be divided into two general areas—the local area network and the wide area network. Similar devices are used to carry traffic on both, and both depend on transmission interfaces and standard protocols to define how the network operates. The main difference is that one is concerned with the devices in the local area, such as the user's PCs, the company's file server, and the printers, while the other is concerned with connecting multiple diverse networks and routing traffic across the connections. Both local area networks and wide area networks will be discussed.

8.4.1 LANs—A Definition

The local area network can be defined as a group of data communications devices that are tied together allowing each to share network resources. Though the explanation is simple, the actual design and maintenance of a LAN is not. A computer that is attached to a LAN has the ability to interface with other devices attached to that LAN. Normally a LAN consists of multiple computers, file servers, printers, and an e-mail server. Users can access software programs from the file server, send e-mail, or access printers. They can share files with coworkers and print documents on a community printer. Users are able to send messages to one another via an internal e-mail system and schools and businesses can provide one shared access circuit to the outside world from the LAN.

8.4.2 The Ethernet

Ethernet LAN
LAN that uses the Ethernet layer 2 protocol to send information out across bus topology.

Ethernet LAN The Ethernet standard provides a way for multiple devices to be connected in order to share information and resources. For example, a company with 1000 employees who all have PCs on their desks must determine how they will interface all 1000 devices onto a shared network. The solution is to implement a LAN, and a large percentage of the LANs deployed use the Ethernet standard, technically referred to as 802.3. Xerox, which later worked with DEC and ITT, developed the Ethernet standard in the late 1970s.

Network Topology Ethernet uses a bus topology, as shown in Figure 8–14, that provides access to each of the devices by connecting them to the same physical medium. The architecture is fairly simple to implement because adding a new device only requires extending the medium and connecting the device onto the medium at that point. The device is added to the LAN, allowing it access to all

Figure 8–14
LANs are composed of devices tied to a shared bus, forming one segment. One segment is defined by the same IP address structure.

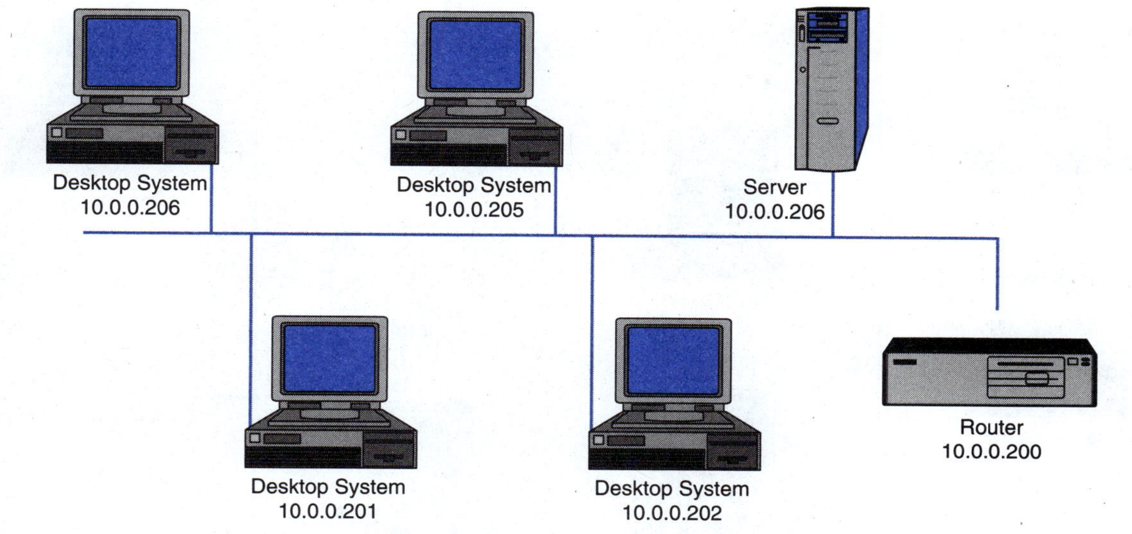

other devices on the LAN, and allowing the other devices access to it. The term *segment* defines a grouping of devices that are attached to a portion of the LAN. Multiple segments are interconnected forming the entire LAN. The purpose is twofold. Adding users is simpler if the total LAN is divided into groups, because adding or deleting the new user affects only those in the segment. Dividing LANs into multiple segments also simplifies troubleshooting and maintenance of the network. The technician is able to pinpoint a problem faster by eliminating segments one at a time instead of eliminating PCs one at a time.

Physical Interface The physical cable used to connect Ethernet LANs varies depending on the structure of the building or buildings, the distance the signal has to travel, the number of devices connecting to the network, and the amount of traffic expected. Three types of cable are used to connect Ethernet LANs: category 5 or 6 twisted pair, thin Ethernet, and thick Ethernet. The most important criteria to use in deciding which type of medium to use is the distance between the devices.

Thin Ethernet, also called 10Base2, allows a signal to travel 185 meters or 500 feet and allows thirty connections per segment as shown in Figure 8–15. Thick Ethernet, also known as 10Base5, allows a signal to travel 500 meters or 1640 feet with a maximum of 3 segments and three regeneration points, as shown in Figure 8–15. The most popular and most practical physical medium is category 5 or 6 twisted pair, also called universal twisted pair (UTP), allows the signal to travel

Figure 8–15
Three Segment Ethernet LAN.

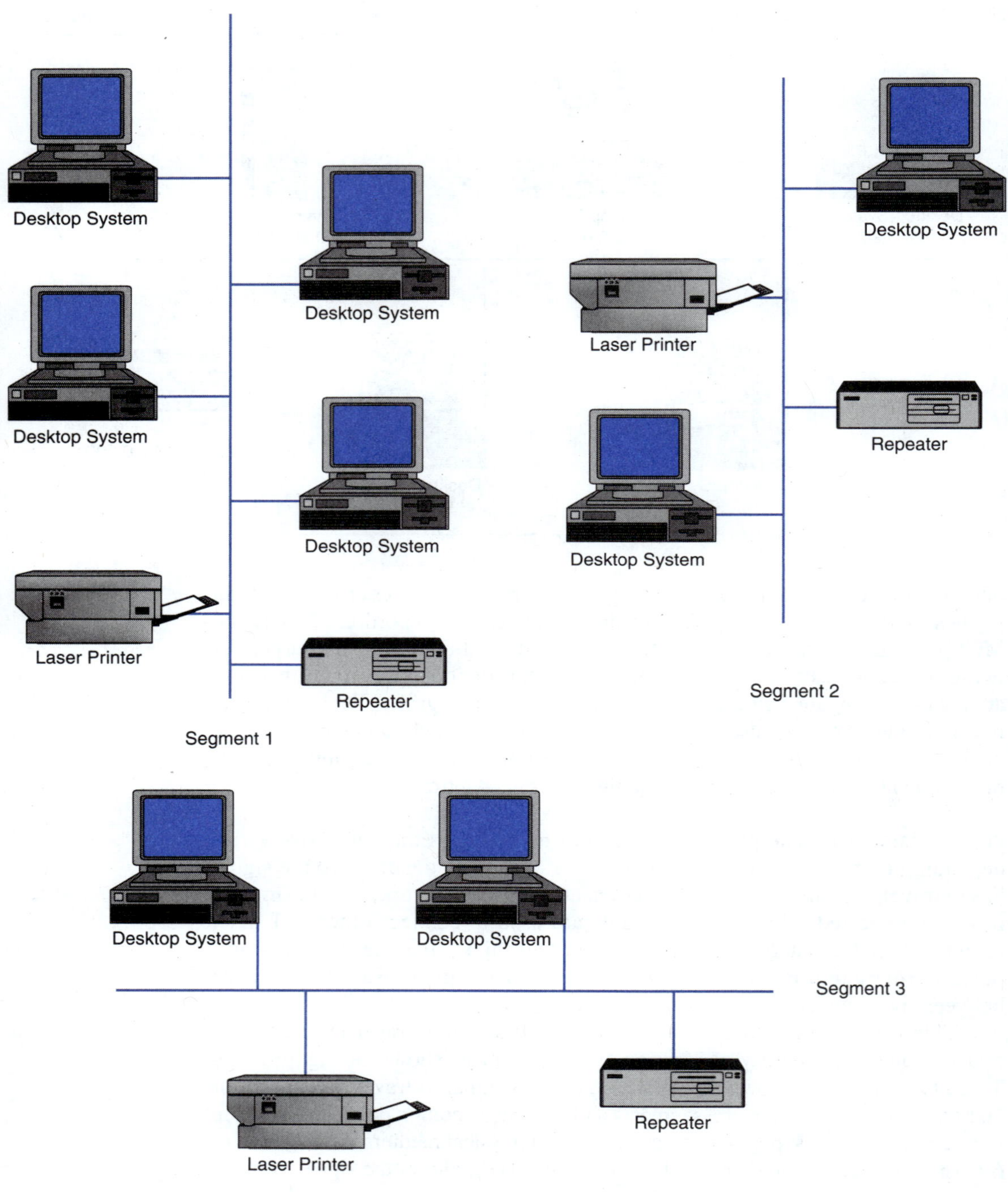

Figure 8–16
LAN connections are made between multiple users devices and a hub using twisted copper pair as the connection medium.

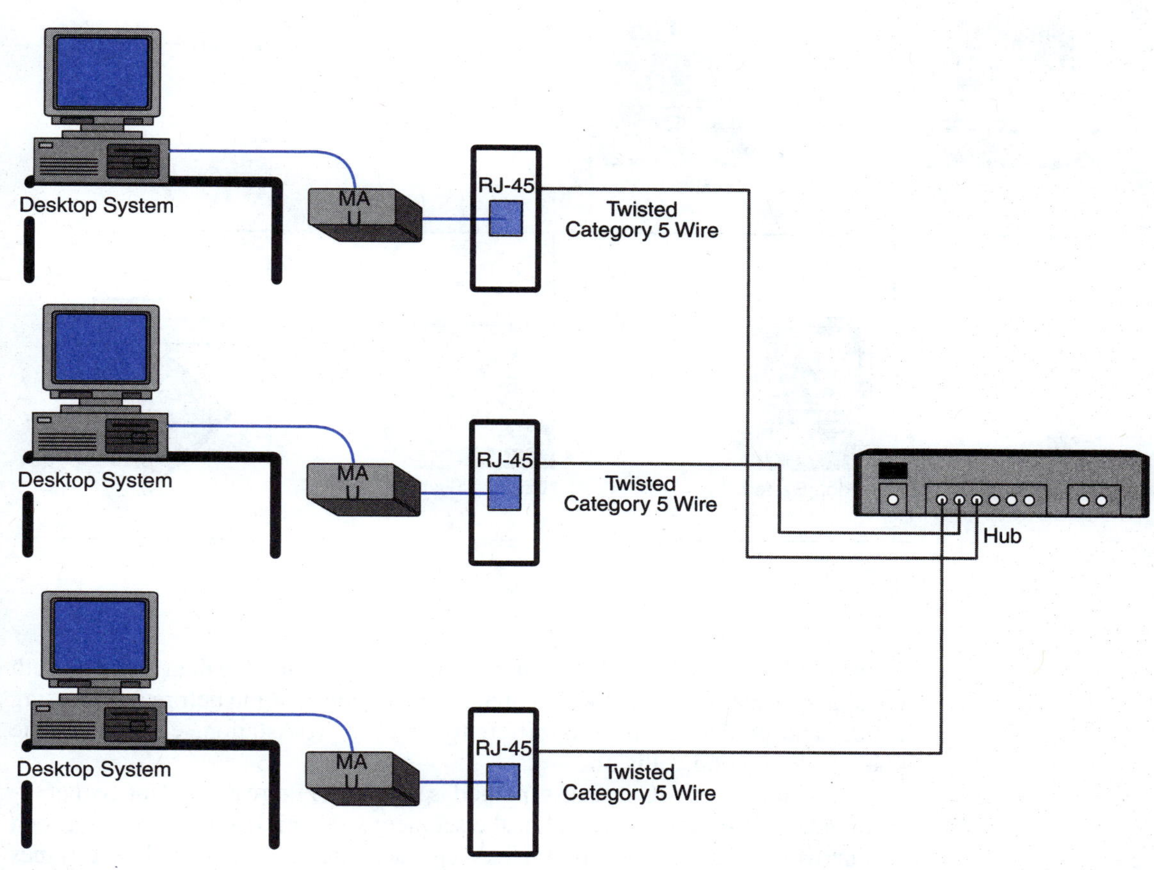

distances as far as 3000 feet while carrying up to 100 MHz. The advantage of using Category 5 cable is that it requires less space in the conduit, is less expensive, is easy to acquire, and is much easier to install and maintain. Figure 8–16 illustrated a typical LAN connected with copper twisted cable.

Access Method The term *access method* refers to the way data is handled by the different devices in the network. Ethernet uses a *CSMA/CD* contention scheme, which stands for carrier sense multiple access with collision detection. Each workstation on the LAN listens to the network to see if the network is being used by another workstation before transmitting its data. Once it determines that the network is clear of other transmissions, it transmits its data out onto the network.

CSMA/CD
Carrier sense multiple access/ carrier detect.

Figure 8–17
Data packets are absorbed at the end of the segment in a CSCD/MA.

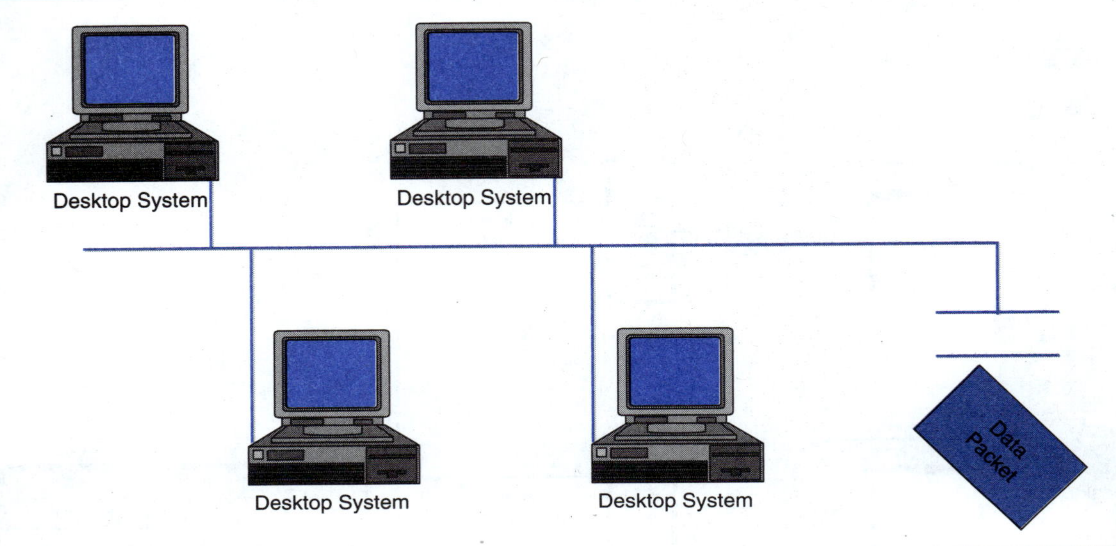

If two workstations do send their data at the same time and the data collides, both terminate transmission and wait a predefined amount of time before transmitting again. The predefined time is different for each workstation, eliminating the chance of a second collision.

A typical CSMA/CD access method is shown in Figure 8–17. Notice that orphan data is absorbed at the end of the segment so that it doesn't repeat through the network. Each workstation picks up each piece of data and determines whether or not the data belongs to it or the data should be passed on to the next entity. CSMA/CD is the most popular access method used by LANs, and it works well with Ethernet's bus topology.

Addressing Each device on the LAN must have a unique address identifier in order to receive data. The data link layer (DLL) handles addressing for the individual physical devices connected to the LAN. The DLL is divided into two sublayers, one called the *media access layer* (MAC) and the other the logical link layer (LLC). Both are shown in Figure 8–18. The MAC layer interfaces the physical layer to the LLC, and the LLC interfaces layer 2 with the upper level layers. They work together when routing information through the network.

media access layer
Interface between the physical layer and the upper portion of the data link layer.

The address given to each device connected to the LAN is a MAC address. It is a unique identifier burned into the ROM of the equipment that specifies the vendor and the serial number. The MAC address is used by routing protocols as

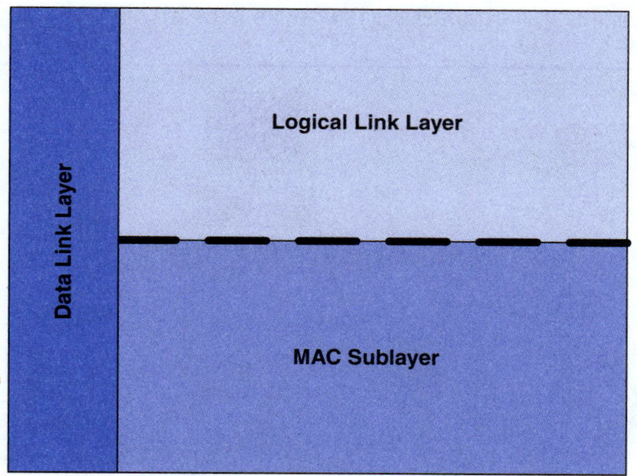

Figure 8–18
The data link layer is divided into two separate functions—the MAC and LLC layers. The MAC layer interfaces the physical hardware letting the LLC interface with layer 3 functions.

a way to direct traffic to the end device. The forty-eight-bit address is divided into two sections—the first twenty-four bits designate the vendor, the second twenty-four bits designate the serial number unique to that equipment. The MAC address is a flat addressing scheme because it is not dependent upon an address hierarchy, as is an IP address.

The MAC address is used by data networking devices to learn what devices are hanging off the network. For instance, a router will send out a message and ask for everyone's MAC address. The equipment will automatically respond (ARP) the MAC address to the router, which will then store the address in memory and use it when routing information to that device.

The MAC address is placed in the data frame of the data packet and is viewed by each device as it works its way around the network. The workstation looks at the MAC address in the frame to see if it matches its own. If it does, it keeps the frame; if it doesn't it passes it on.

8.4.3 Token Ring LAN Architecture

Token Ring Token ring LAN architecture was developed by IBM in the 1970s. It is similar to the IEEE's 802.5 standard and, as with Ethernet 802.3, we will use the two standards synonymously. Token ring is the second most popular LAN technology after Ethernet. It is one of the oldest LAN technologies and, as such, continues to be used in the network.

token ring LAN
LAN architecture invented by IBM. Devices on the ring pass a token to the next device signifying whether anyone is transmitting at that time.

Network Topology Token ring LANs are configured logically as a ring, but physically as a star. Tokens are passed around the ring. Each device on the network depends on the token to notify it when it may send data or receive data, as shown

Figure 8–19
Token ring LANs depend on tokens that are passed between terminals through the network. If one device fails on the network, the entire network fails.

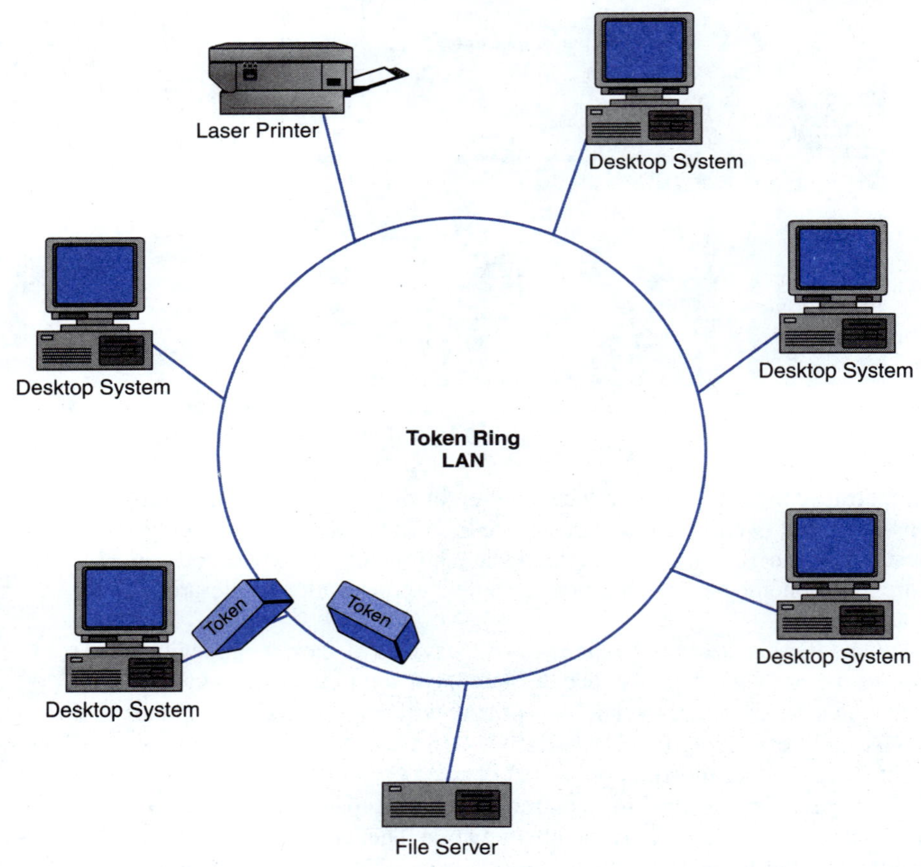

in Figure 8–19. The workstation, which is attached to a central hub called a multistation access unit (MSAU) (shown in Figure 8–20) receive a signal from its nearest active upstream neighbor (NAUN). The device then repeats the signal to its nearest downstream neighbor. Workstations attached to a token ring LAN also act as repeaters, thus increasing the number of devices allowed on one segment.

Each MSAU is able to handle up to eight devices. One disadvantage associated with token ring LANs is that each time a new device is added to the LAN or taken off the LAN, service to all devices on the LAN is disrupted. In addition, only eight devices are allowed per MSAU, fewer than the thirty devices per segment on the Ethernet LAN. These are the two main reasons that token ring LANs have lost popularity.

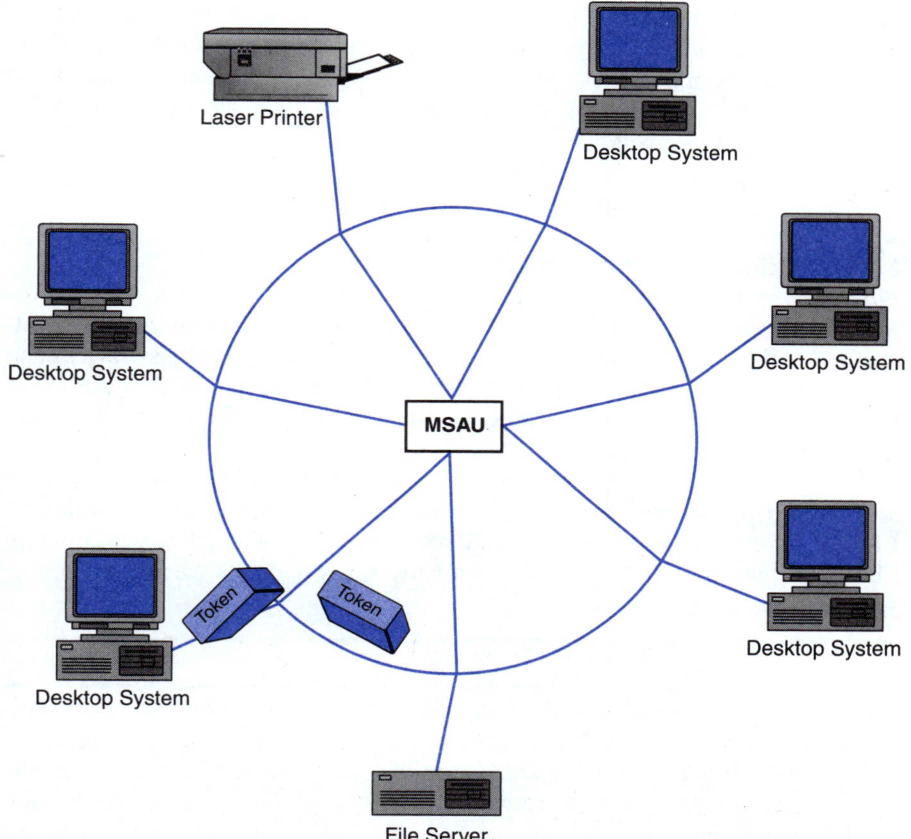

Figure 8–20
Token Ring LANs are logically configured as a ring but physically as a star. Each device attaches to a central aggregation device called a MSAU.

Physical Interfaces The common physical medium used to connect devices on a token ring LAN is twisted copper pair. Initially, IBM required shielded twisted pair (STP) cable be used, allowing a data rate of 16 Mbps. Currently, the cost of STP cable has forced network managers to use UTP cable, which provides a data rate between 4 and 16 Mbps.

Access Method The method used to transmit data around a token ring LAN requires that a three-octet token be passed around the ring stopping at each workstation. The workstation determines whether the priority indicator in the token is marked with a low or high priority bit. If the workstation's data requires high priority, the token is marked as high and the information from the workstation replaces the data already in the packet with its own. The purpose of the token is to ensure that the network is fully utilized while reducing the possibility of contention between workstations.

One workstation is designated the active monitor (AM) and is responsible for overseeing the network. The AM watches for errors and congestion in the network and monitors the ring for any breaks or disruptions. The AM has the power to discard the token if congestion or ring disruption occurs. Each workstation has the capability of serving as the AM. A secondary AM is normally configured to fill in if the primary AM fails.

Addressing The addressing method used is the same as for Ethernet.

8.4.4 Fiber Distributed Data Interface

fiber distributed data interface Fiber LAN architecture.

Fiber distributed data interface (FDDI) uses fiber-optic strands to carry information between devices. It is a ring architecture, and the purpose of implementing an FDDI LAN is to provide large amounts of bandwidth between devices and to extend the distance between the devices and the segments. FDDI LANs may be found on college campuses where large amounts of information must be carried between all of the buildings.

FDDI, similar to token ring, uses tokens to determine when data should be sent or held. The addressing method is the same as the token ring and Ethernet LAN technologies—the MAC layer addressing scheme. Though not as common FDDI still provides a viable solution for networking a local area.

SUMMARY

The need to understand data communications concepts is critical for all telecommunications professionals. No longer can technicians claim they only work on voice circuits, because the convergence of the two types of traffic is inevitable. The chapter started with an explanation of the open standards interconnection (OSI) model as it pertains to communications networks.

The chapter then moved to basic data communications concepts and terms such as *binary, asynchronous,* and *modulation* were discussed. An exploration of the difference between an analog data circuit and a digital data circuit followed, along with a discussion of the network topologies used in data communications.

CASE STUDY

Every telephone company needs an internal LAN network similar to a typical business LAN. Assume that Bob wants every building owned and operated by Green Grass Telephone Company to be on the LAN, including the truck garage, the corporate headquarters, each CO, and the LD POP. Design a simple Ethernet LAN for Green Grass Telephone Company.

Hint: You may build segments such as the bus garage on one LAN, the CO on one LAN and so forth that are connected to form a WAN.

Draw the LAN network for Green Grass Telephone company.

REVIEW QUESTIONS

1. Define each of the seven layers of the OSI model and give an example of a real application that depends on each particular layer.
2. When information is carried across a wide area network, what three layers play a vital role in making sure the traffic arrives safely?
3. The ATM and frame relay protocols are considered layer 2 protocols. True or False? Explain.
4. The IP protocol is considered a layer 3 protocol. True or False? Explain.
5. The framing method used on a T1 circuit is associated with the physical layer of the OSI stack. True or False? Explain.
6. Explain why the letters of the alphabet are converted into a special one/zero code.
7. List the two types of encoding schemes and explain the differences between the two.
8. Define the term *data communications*.
9. Explain the differences between asynchronous and synchronous data transmission.
10. Explain the differences between data that is carried on an analog signal and data that is carried on a digital signal.
11. What is the typical *bit per second* speed of an analog transmission?
12. The connection between a PC and a printer is a parallel connection. The connection between a modem and a PC is a serial connection. Explain the difference between the two connections.
13. Why does a 3600 baud modem have a maximum bit per second rate of 28 kbps?
14. Draw a picture of a point-to-point network showing a main frame connected to an ATM bank machine.
15. Draw a picture of a multipoint network showing a mainframe connected to five ATM bank machines. Place arrows on the ends of the lines to show the direction of traffic flow between the mainframe and the ATMs.
16. Explain the difference between a dedicated digital data service and an ISDN BRI data connection.
17. What are the differences between the Ethernet LAN protocol and the token ring LAN protocol? Which is more popular?
18. Describe *FDDI*.
19. What is the purpose of a LAN?
20. What types of equipment are found on a LAN?

TROUBLESHOOTING

You are the network manager for a software design company on the West Coast. You are receiving numerous complaints that information being sent from New York City takes twice as long to arrive as it did a week ago. You have a new protocol analyzer and can't wait to try it out. You place the analyzer in the network and wait to see the incoming data. On which layer will you focus to see whether information is being retransmitted? Which layer will you look at to determine whether there is a cable problem? Which one will you look at to determine whether there is a routing problem.

KEY TERMS

open systems interconnection (300)
operating system (301)
application layer (302)
file transfer program (302)
presentation layer (302)
session layer (302)
transport layer (303)
network layer (303)
data link layer (303)
physical layer (304)
ASCII (305)
EBCDIC (305)
serial (307)
parallel (307)
asynchronous transmission (308)
synchronous transmission (308)
odd parity (310)
even parity (310)
cyclic redundancy check (310)
amplitude modulation (310)
frequency modulation (310)
phase modulation (311)
quadrature amplitude modulation (312)
trellis coded modulation (312)
digital dataphone service (313)
NT-1 (313)
2B1Q (314)
point-to-point circuit (315)
multipoint circuit (315)
bus topology (317)
ring topology (317)
mesh topology (318)
Ethernet LAN (320)
CSMA/CD (323)
media access layer (324)
token ring LAN (325)
fiber distributed data interface (328)

CHAPTER

9

Communications Circuits

OBJECTIVES

After you complete your study of this chapter, you should be able to

- distinguish among a communications line, circuit, and channel;
- discuss various types of communications circuits and their distinguishing attributes;
- describe the characteristics of the various types of media used to carry circuits;
- describe multiplexing and concentrating and tell when they are most productively used;
- describe the major types of errors that occur on communications circuits;
- describe the primary error prevention and detection techniques for communications circuits.

INTRODUCTION

Previous chapters discussed communications lines or circuits without defining them. In this chapter, circuits are defined more precisely, and the many alternatives for the physical media used in a circuit's construction are examined. Information about the ways in which circuits can be configured and used is also presented.

This chapter continues the discussion and description of the first layer of the ISO-OSI model. Communications circuits provide the physical path on which the communications signals flow. The information in this chapter and the next is at the heart of telecommunications. You must understand the characteristics of circuits to learn how telecommunications can be applied to meet the requirements of a particular application. This chapter describes many types of telecommunications circuits, and it gives examples of how they are being used by companies.

DEFINITIONS

Authorities differ somewhat in the details of the definition of the word *circuit*. The commonly accepted definition of a telecommunications circuit, however, is the path over which two-way communications take place. A circuit may exist on many different types of media, such as wire, coaxial cable, fiber-optic cable, microwave radio, or satellite. The word *line* is often used interchangeably with *circuit,* although line gives a stronger implication of a physical wire connection. In fact, many circuits today do not run on wires at all. The longer the distance, the higher the probability that the circuit runs on at least one medium other than wire.

line
circuit

link

A *link* is a segment of a circuit between two points. For a telephone circuit, one link exists between the residence or business and the local telephone company central office. Other links exist between the central offices. The final link is from the remote central office to the remote residence or business. When the term *data link* is used, it almost always includes the data terminal equipment, modems, and all other equipment necessary to make the complete data connection—software as well as hardware.

channel

Circuits are often subdivided into *channels,* which are one-way paths for communications. Channels may be derived from a circuit by multiplexing, or they may be an independent entity, such as a television channel. A data circuit is sometimes divided into two channels, one of which is high speed for data transmission and the other is low speed for control information. The data channel is called the *forward channel,* and the control channel is the *reverse channel.* As the name implies, the reverse channel carries information in the opposite direction from the data channel. The type of information carried on a reverse channel depends on the rules of communications or protocol used.

node

A *node* is a functional unit that connects to transmission lines. It also can be an end point on a circuit or a junction point of two or more circuits. Typical nodes are telephones, data terminals, front end processors, and computers.

The data flow on a circuit can be in only one direction, called *simplex;* in both directions, but not simultaneously, called *half-duplex;* or in both directions simultaneously, called *full-duplex.* From the standpoint of the telephone company or other circuit provider, the way in which the circuit is actually configured may differ depending on the intended data flow.

■ TYPES OF CIRCUITS

Point-to-Point Circuits

A *point-to-point circuit,* illustrated in Figure 9–1, connects two—and only two—nodes. A typical circuit of this type connects two locations of a company or connects a computer to a terminal or a personal computer to a server. The standard telephone call between two locations is another example of the use of a point-to-point circuit.

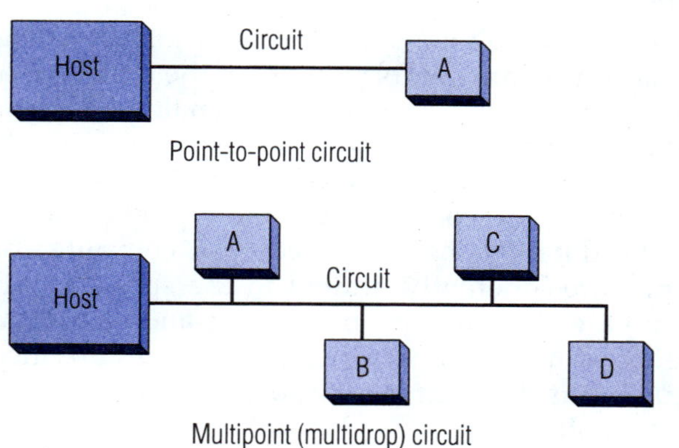

Figure 9–1 Types of circuits with nodes A, B, C, D, and the host computer.

Multipoint Circuits

If there are several nodes connected to the same circuit, as shown in Figure 9–1, it is called a *multipoint* or *multidrop circuit*. With multidrop circuits there is a clear distinction between the circuit and the links. The connections from the host to A, from A to B, and from B to C are links. The overall connection from the host to D is the circuit. In most cases, a multipoint circuit is less expensive than four point-to-point circuits, each connecting the host to one of the terminals (A, B, C, and D). Multipoint circuits are used to connect locations that have a relatively low volume of traffic and can share the line without interfering with one another and still get adequate performance.

Two-Wire and Four-Wire Circuits

Point-to-point and multipoint data circuits are normally implemented with either two wires or four wires connecting the points. Normally, two wires are required to carry a communication in one direction. Therefore, a *two-wire circuit* has traditionally been viewed as being a half-duplex circuit and a *four-wire circuit* as a full-duplex circuit. However, some modems are capable of splitting a circuit into two channels through frequency division multiplexing or other techniques. In that case, it is possible to obtain full-duplex operation on a two-wire circuit. In most cases, however, four-wire circuits are preferable for data communications. With four-wire circuits, two wires provide the forward channel in one direction while the other two wires provide the forward channel in the other direction.

Standard dial-up telephone circuits are two-wire circuits. Four-wire circuits must be ordered from the telephone company and installed on a leased basis. The advantage is that the circuit is then available for full-time use. The disadvantage is that a leased circuit may cost more than a dial-up connection, and it may be uneconomical if relatively little data will be transmitted.

Analog Circuits

Because the public telephone system was originally designed to carry voice transmissions in analog form, most of the circuits that run to individual homes or small businesses today are analog. Using analog circuits to carry data requires using a modem to convert the digital signal from a terminal or other DTE to analog form before it is transmitted, and then using another modem to convert it back to digital form at the receiving end, before the data can be presented to a computer or other DTE. Analog circuits are inherently limited in the speed at which they can carry data, and are also more prone to noise and errors than digital circuits. Hence, communications carriers of all types are installing digital circuits as quickly as they can to take advantage of the benefits that digital transmission offers.

Whereas the modem usually determines the actual speed at which an analog circuit transmits data, the carriers offer analog circuits that are capable of certain speed ranges. Traditionally, these have been known as *low-speed circuits* or *subvoice-grade circuits, voice-grade circuits,* and *wideband circuits.* Subvoice grade circuits are designed for telegraph and teletypewriter usage but may also be used for low-speed signaling applications, such as fire alarms, burglar alarms, door opening indication, or for process monitoring systems where the data rate is low and/or infrequent. These circuits operate at speeds of 45 to 200 bps. They cannot handle voice transmission or data at higher speeds. In fact, subvoice-grade circuits are derived by dividing a voice-grade circuit into 12 or 24 low-speed circuits.

Voice-grade circuits are designed for voice transmission but they can also transmit data at up to 56,000 bps, when sophisticated modems are used. These are the type of circuits that have been most commonly described throughout this book so far. Wideband circuits are high-speed analog circuits designed to carry multiple voice or data signals. They are delivered to customers in a bandwidth of 48,000 Hz, which, with the use of appropriate multiplexing equipment, will carry 12 to 4,000 Hz voice channels. However, these circuits are rarely sold anymore because they have been largely superseded by digital circuits.

Digital Circuits

A *digital circuit* is one that has been designed and engineered expressly to carry digital signals. The direct digital transmission of data is simple and eliminates the signal conversions at each end. Digital transmission capability became available to end-users in the late 1970s, although the common carriers had been using digital transmission techniques and circuits for many years before that. Most new circuits being installed are designed especially for digital transmission.

One of the main advantages of digital transmission is that the distortion of pulses that inevitably occurs along the transmission path is easier

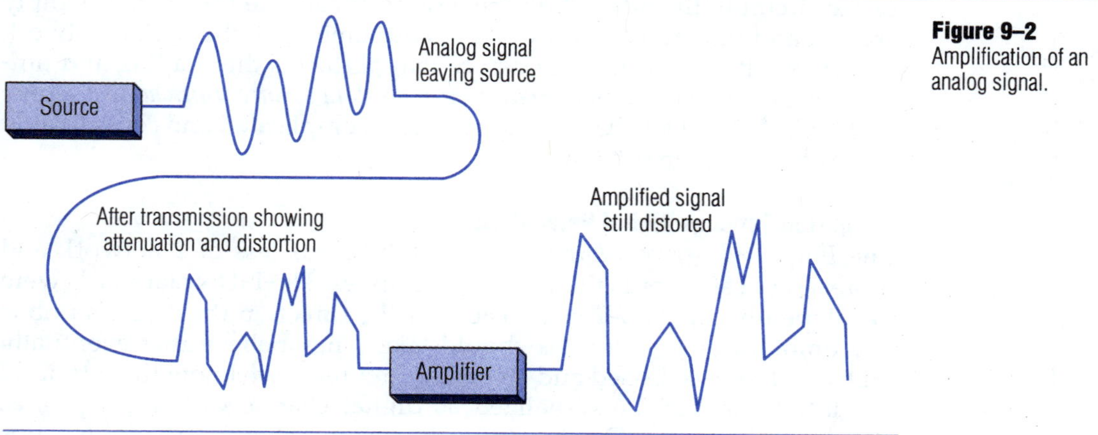

Figure 9–2
Amplification of an analog signal.

Figure 9–3
Regeneration of a digital signal.

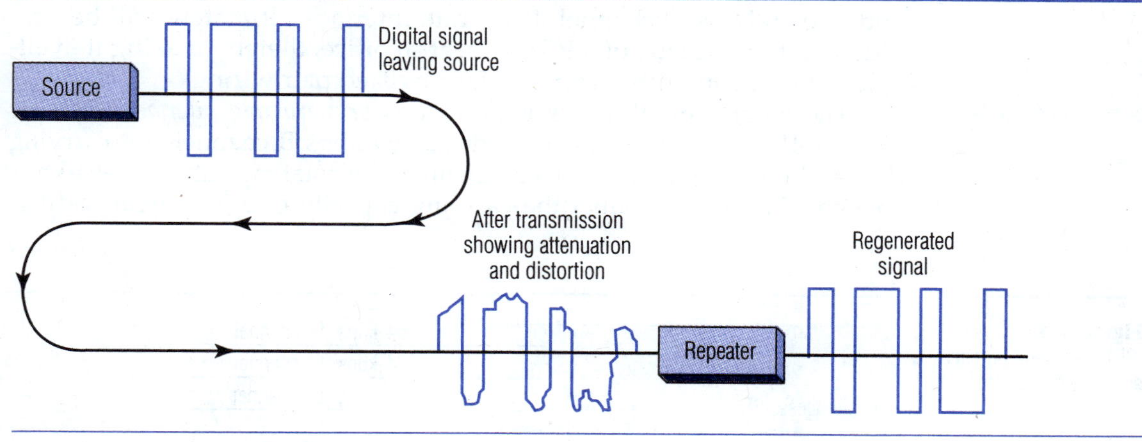

to correct than the distortion of an analog transmission. Analog signals are periodically amplified to increase their signal strength, and the distortions in the wave form are amplified as well as the original signal, as shown in Figure 9–2. Digital signals are made up of simple pulses and are not amplified but regenerated by a *repeater*. The regeneration eliminates any distortion that has occurred, as shown in Figure 9–3. Thus, the signal that arrives at the receiver is cleaner. The result is that digital transmissions have a lower error rate than do their analog counterparts.

repeater

Another advantage of using digital transmission is that no analog-to-digital conversion is required. Assuming digital links exist from one end of the circuit to the other, the digital output from the DTE can be simply shaped and timed to conform to the requirements of the digital network and transmitted directly. The device that performs the shaping and timing is called a *digital transmitter/receiver* or *data service unit/channel service unit (DSU/CSU)*. DSU/CSUs are much less complicated and considerably less expensive than modems.

DSU/CSU

Integrated Services Digital Network (ISDN)

The *Integrated Services Digital Network (ISDN)* is less of a network and more a set of standards than the name implies. The ISDN standards were developed by the ITU-T as a vision for the direction the world's public telecommunications systems should take. They believe that eventually ISDN will replace leased and switched circuits as we know them today.

ISDN can best be visualized as digital channels of two types, as shown in Figure 9–4. One type, the "B" (bearer) channel, carries 64 kbps of digital data. The other type, the "D" (delta) channel, carries 16 kbps of data and is used for signaling. These two types of channels are packaged, according to ISDN standards, into two types of access services. The *basic rate interface (BRI),* also known as 2B+D, provides two 64-kbps B channels and one 16-kbps D channel. Basic rate interface ultimately will be provided on the line side of a PBX or central office, thereby making it available in homes and offices on standard twisted pair wiring.

basic rate interface

primary rate interface

The other type of access is known as *primary rate interface (PRI),* or 23B+D. Primary rate access provides 23 64-kbps B channels for carrying data and 1 64-kbps D channel for signaling. The total capacity of 24–64-kbps channels happens to equal the carrying capacity of a T-1 circuit as it is

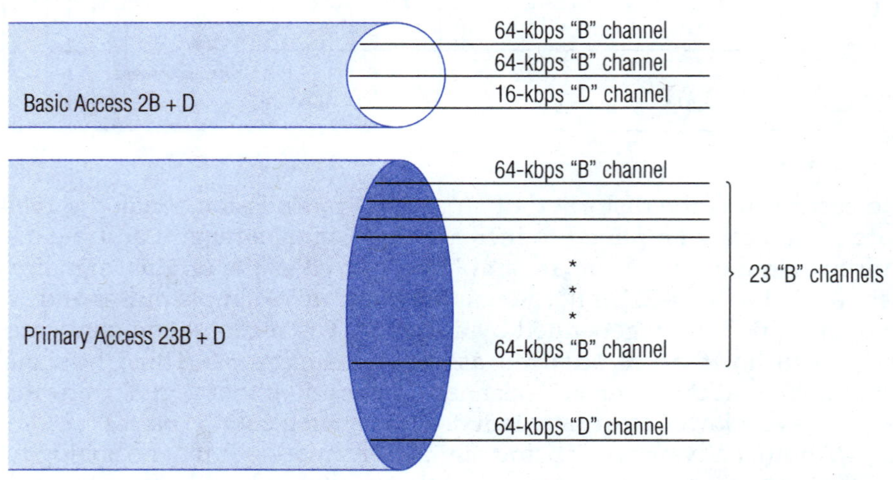

Figure 9–4
ISDN basic and primary access arrangements.

defined in the United States, Canada, and Japan. (T-1 circuits are described later in this chapter.) In Europe, primary access is defined as 30B+D, which matches the capacity of a European T-1 circuit. Figure 9–4 shows the two types of access schematically.

The large bandwidth provided by ISDN circuits can be used for digitized voice and data. With basic access in a home, a person could be having a telephone conversation and simultaneously transmitting data at 64 kbps from a personal computer. A business with a primary ISDN access group could subdivide the bandwidth in any way necessary to meet the needs of its application set. Half of the capacity, or 772 kbps, might be used for a television transmission while the other 772 kbps is further subdivided to support 24 voice conversations at 16 kbps each and 6 64-kbps data channels. At another time, the bandwidth could be configured differently—all under the control of the customer. In fact, these configuration changes could be programmed into a computer so that the ISDN capacity is automatically reconfigured at certain times of the day. There could be a daytime configuration, a nighttime configuration, or any other combination to meet the business needs of the company.

An upgrade to ISDN called *broadband ISDN (B-ISDN)* has been defined but has not yet been widely implemented. Broadband ISDN has three services:

- a full-duplex circuit operating at a speed of 155.52 Mbps;
- a full-duplex circuit operating at 622.08 Mbps;
- an asymmetrical circuit with two simplex channels, one of which operates at 155.52 Mbps and the other at 622.08 Mbps.

The first two options would be used as very high speed data circuits, whereas the third option would typically be used where the flow of data in one direction is much greater than in the other.

B-ISDN circuits are actually transported from one node to another using the asynchronous transfer mode (ATM) for transport. ATM will be discussed in Chapter 11, and at that point, B-ISDN will be mentioned again. Suffice it to say that ATM is transparent, and the user of a B-ISDN circuit is not aware that ATM is operating in the background. Furthermore, B-ISDN is backward compatible, meaning that a standard ISDN BRI or PRI transmission can be handled transparently on a B-ISDN circuit.

The benefits of ISDN are that

- it provides efficient multiplexed access to the public network;
- it has the capability to support integrated voice and data;
- it has a robust signaling channel, which is important for network management;
- it provides an open system interface that is internationally defined. This will go a long way toward making multivendor telecommunications systems a reality.

ISDN service has been implemented more slowly in the United States than in many other countries in the world, partly because the RBOCs and long distance carriers have had difficulty agreeing on precise standards, partly because they have not actively marketed the service, and partly because costs have been high. There have also been frequent problems in getting ISDN service to operate properly when it is first installed. In Japan and Australia, however, ISDN has been used by businesses for data circuits for many years, and now ISDN is being installed in many homes for little more than the cost of a regular analog telephone line.

T-Carrier Systems

A family of high-speed digital transmission systems, known as the *T-carrier systems,* has evolved within the carriers over the past 30 years. T-carrier systems are designated according to their transmission capacity, as shown in the table below.

Designation	Bit Capacity
T-1	1.544 Mbps
T-2	6.312 Mbps
T-3	44.736 Mbps
T-4	274.176 Mbps

The T-2 and T-4 circuits are used primarily by the carriers. T-1 and T-3 circuits are used by both the carriers and their customers.

A T-1 system uses a standard pair of wires for transmission. Repeaters are spaced about every mile to regenerate the signal and transmit it over the next link of the circuit. A T-1 system can carry 24 circuits of 64,000 bps ($24 \times 64{,}000 = 1.536$ Mbps; the extra 8,000 bps are used for signaling). Multiplexing equipment is used to combine signals for transmission over the T-1 system and to separate them at the receiving end. A 64,000 bps channel can carry one or two digitized voice signals, depending on whether Pulse Code Modulation (PCM) or Adaptive Differential Pulse Code Modulation (ADPCM) is used to modulate the signal.

It should be noted that in Europe T-carrier systems are also in use. They are defined slightly differently, however. A European E-1 circuit is made up of 32–64 kbps channels for a total capacity of 2.048 Mbps. Other T circuits are multiples of the E-1 capacity.

Companies acquire T-1 or T-3 facilities when they have a high volume of voice, data, or video transmissions between two locations. One company found it economical to install a T-1 circuit to carry three 56 kbps data circuits and five voice tie lines. Even though the capacity of the T-1 circuit was not fully used, it was less expensive than if the individual voice and data circuits were leased separately. Either the carrier or the customer may provide multiplexing equipment to divide the capacity of the T-1 into usable circuits. Some carriers offer full T-1 packages that include the

This is one example from the family of Ascom Timeplex multiplexers, which comes in various sizes depending on the capacity required. (Courtesy of Ascom Timeplex, Inc.)

equipment at both ends of the circuit, configured to the customer's specifications, while other carriers offer the bare T-1 without the multiplexers. Several companies such as Cisco Systems, Inc., Timeplex, Inc., and General DataComm, Inc. develop and sell multiplexing equipment suitable for T-1 circuits.

The major reasons for using T-1 circuits are that they can save large amounts of money, can give flexibility in reconfiguring the T-1 capacity to meet different needs at different times of the day, and can improve the quality of voice and data transmission because the information being transmitted is digitized.

Fractional T-1 A newer communications offering is called *fractional T-1.* In the past, companies needing digital transmission service had no choice of speed between 56 kbps and T-1's 1.544 Mbps. Fractional T-1 provides companies with other transmission speed choices by subdividing a T-1 circuit into multiples of 64 kbps. Thus, the IXCs now offer leased circuits that operate at any multiple of 64 kbps, although speeds of 64, 128, 256, 512, and 768 kbps are most common. A company can select and pay for only the capacity it needs rather than having to lease a full T-1 circuit. This new capability is particularly interesting to companies with smaller networks that have not been able to justify the cost of a full T-1.

Fractional T-1 is provided by the IXCs, but potential customers must check to see if their local telephone company provides fractional T-1 service. If not, an alternative must be found to connect from the customer's premises to the IXC office.

Switched Multimegabit Data Service (SMDS)

connectionless service

Switched Multimegabit Data Service (SMDS) is a high-speed switched digital service offered by the carriers. Because the user does not have a dedicated line between locations, SMDS is called a *connectionless service.* Data to be transmitted via SMDS is broken down into 53 byte cells. Two SMDS speeds are available, either 1.544 Mbps (T-1 speed) or 44.736 Mbps (T-3 speed). The difference between SMDS and T-1 service is that a user must lease a T-1 circuit from point to point, all the way between two locations, whereas with SMDS the user leases a circuit to the nearest carrier's office at both ends, and the carrier handles the transmission in between using normal, shared communication facilities. For example, if a company wanted to connect each of its eight plants to headquarters at 1.544 Mbps, it could either lease eight T-1 lines, one from each plant to headquarters, or it could lease a 1.544 SMDS line from each plant to the nearest carrier's office, and then perhaps a 44.736 Mbps SMDS line from headquarters to the nearest carrier's office. Although a detailed cost analysis would have to be done for the particular locations involved, in most instances the SMDS configuration would be less expensive.

Digital Subscriber Line (DSL)

In 1987, in anticipation of competition with cable companies in the area of delivering video signals to homes, Bellcore developed a technology called *asymmetric digital subscriber line (ADSL),* which was originally designed to enable telephone companies to deliver digitized signals to subscribers at about 1.5 Mbps over existing twisted pair copper telephone wire. The general name for the service is *digital subscriber line (DSL),* and it has spawned many variants that collectively are also referred to as xDSL. While originally developed as a competitor for cable television, xDSL is turning out to be a boon for home and business users who want higher data communication speeds, especially for accessing the Internet.

xDSL services are dedicated, point-to-point, public network access over twisted pair copper wire on the local loop between a network service provider's central office (typically the telephone company) and the customer site. ADSL technology is asymmetric. It allows more bandwidth downstream from the central office to the customer's site than upstream from the customer to the central office. This asymmetry makes it ideal for Internet surfing, and indeed, ADSL is viewed as more of a consumer- than a business-oriented product offering.

DSL technology in general is very sensitive to distance and is not even available to customers who are located more than 3 or 4 miles from the central office. The speed of the service depends on the distance, but for ADSL is in the range of 16 to 640 Kbps upstream and 1.5 to 9 Mbps downstream, which, even at its slowest, is significantly faster than the typical customer has today. The actual speed that can be obtained de-

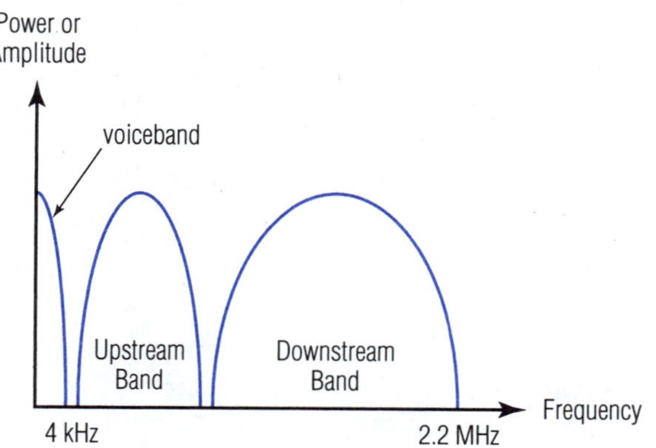

Figure 9–5
An ADSL circuit is divided into several channels and uses a much wider frequency range than a standard telephone circuit.

pends on a number of factors, including the distance from the central office, the wire size that is used, and the quality of the circuit.

ADSL circuits have a modem at each end, which divide the circuit into the high-speed downstream channel, the medium speed upstream channel, and a standard telephone channel as shown in Figure 9–5. Customers can, therefore, obtain their telephone service from the same wires that supply the ADSL service. The DSL provider almost always supplies the modems and includes a rental fee in the total price for the ADSL service. In the future, it may be possible for customers to purchase their own modems off the shelf at retail outlets.

There are three new offerings in DSL technology, G.Lite ADSL, SDSL, and VDSL. G.Lite ADSL is a newer standard ADSL service that offers a maximum speed of 1.5 Mbps downstream and 384 kbps upstream, and some carriers will allow the customer to order lower bandwidths for a lower cost. Because the speed is limited, the specifications for the wire are not as severe, and G.Lite is easier to install and maintain.

Another offering that is just becoming available is *SDSL, symmetric digital subscriber line.* SDSL provides equal speed channels in both directions and may not include a telephone channel. SDSL is capable of speeds up to 768 kbps in each direction and is targeted at business customers. Technically, it is easier for the network service provider to implement SDSL than ADSL because simpler, less expensive equipment is required at both the head end and the customer end of the circuit.

The newest development is *VDSL, very-high-rate digital subscriber line.* VDSL transmits data at top speeds of 51 to 55 Mbps over short twisted pair telephone lines of up to 1,000 feet and low speeds of 13 Mbps at 4,000 feet. Early versions of this technology are asymmetric, like ADSL, and have an upstream channel of 1.6 to 2.3 Mbps.

While DSL is a very interesting capability for many businesses and consumers at home, it is important to remember the distance limitation—the customer must be located within 3 to 4 miles of the central office. That means that DSL service will not be available to at least 30 percent of the potential users in the U.S. Hence, there will still be plenty of need for other high-speed access services, such as cable modems, ISDN, and direct satellites. For more information about the status of DSL development and implementation, check the web site www.2wire.com.

CIRCUIT MEDIA

conducted media

radiated media

This section discusses the various media used for communications circuits. In general, media can be divided into two categories: *Conducted* or *guided media* provide some type of physical path, such as wire, cable, or optical fiber, along which the signal moves from end to end. *Radiated* or *unguided media* employ an antenna and the transmission of waves, such as radio waves, microwaves, or infrared waves, through air, water, or a vacuum. Although there is a wide overlap in their characteristics and capabilities, each medium has found a particular niche in which it is most commonly used.

Twisted Pair Wire

twisted pair

crosstalk

The most common medium used for telecommunications circuits is ordinary wire, usually made of copper. Over the years, the common carriers have laid millions of miles of wire into virtually every home and business in the country, so wire is used for virtually all local loops. Originally, open wire pairs were used. However, they were affected by weather and were very susceptible to electrical noise and other interference. Today, the pairs of wires are almost always insulated with a plastic coating and twisted together. This type of wire is called *twisted pair* or *unshielded twisted pair (UTP);* it is illustrated in Figure 9–6. Wire emits an electromagnetic field when carrying communications signals, but twisting the pair together has the effect of electrically canceling the signals radiating from each wire. To a large extent, it prevents the signals on one pair of wires from interfering with the signals on an adjacent pair. This type of interference is called *crosstalk.* The wire used for inside applications and local loops normally is 26, 24, or 22 gauge. The smaller the gauge number, the larger the wire.

The Electrical Industries Association (EIA) has defined five categories of unshielded twisted pair wire for telephone and data transmission use. These categories, known commonly as *Cat 1* through *Cat 5,* are

Figure 9–6
Twisted pair wires are the most commonly used medium for communications transmission.

defined as follows. With the exception of Category 1, all wire is typically 24 gauge solid copper.

- **Category 1**—Basic twisted pair wire for telephone use. Not recommended for data.
- **Category 2**—Four unshielded, solid twisted pair. Certified for data transmission to 4 Mbps.
- **Category 3**—At least three twists per foot. About the same as normal telephone cable installed in most office buildings. Certified for data transmission to 10 Mbps but with proper design and over limited distances, may work to 16 Mbps. If there is more than one pair in the same jacket, it must not have the same number of twists per foot in order to minimize interpair crosstalk.
- **Category 4**—Similar to Category 3, but more twists per foot, and certified to 16 Mbps.
- **Category 5**—Three to four twists per inch. Data-grade cable certified for data transmission to 100 Mbps.
- **Category 5E (5 extended)**—An extension of the standards for Category 5 cable designed to handle data transmission up to 1 Gbps. Recommended for all new cable installations in office buildings.

Categories 3 and 5 have received the most attention, since Cat 3 wire is the type that is installed in most existing office buildings, and Cat 5 is the type that companies are choosing for new installations. Many companies are finding that if the distance isn't too great, they can successfully use it at speeds greater than the 100 Mbps that is specified.

In addition to the six existing standards for UTP cable, there are two other developing standards that you may hear about. *Category 6 (Cat 6)* is an emerging standard for cable consisting of four twisted pairs separately wrapped in foil insulators and twisted around one another, and intended to support high speed LANs operating at speeds up to 1 Gbps. *Category 7 (Cat 7)* is a developing standard for shielded twisted pair wiring also designed for data rates up to 1 Gbps.

Where wire enters a building, it is connected to a terminating block, sometimes called a *punchdown block,* with lugs or clips. This terminating block marks the demarcation point between the common carrier and the building owner, who is responsible for providing and maintaining all wiring within the building. Before divestiture in 1984, the Local Exchange Carriers (LECs) provided and owned all inside wiring. This wiring represented a substantial asset on the accounting books of the LECs. Over time, this large base of previously installed inside wiring is being sold or given to the owners of the buildings where it is installed.

As wires leave a building, they may be directly buried in the ground or suspended from overhead poles, as shown in Figure 9–7. As they approach the central office, they are grouped together in cables that get

Figure 9–7
Wires leaving a building may be buried or hung from poles above ground.

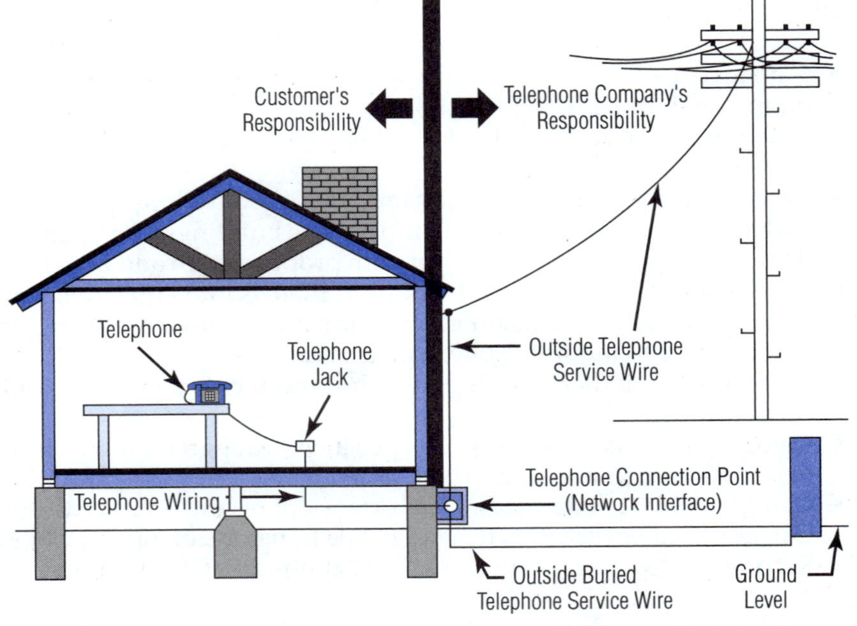

The telephone connection point (network interface) may be located inside or outside the building.

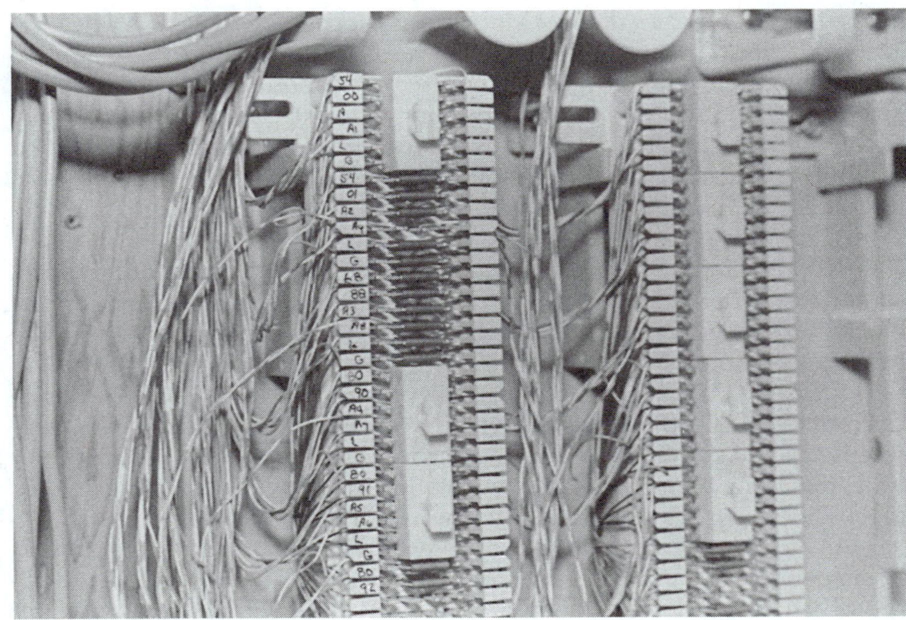

Twisted pair wires are connected together at this punchdown block in the telephone equipment room.

larger the closer they get to the office. Up to several thousand pairs are grouped together into large cables. They are sometimes surrounded by a wire shielding to provide protection from electrical interference or a heavy metal armor for physical protection. On local loops, one pair of wires usually is dedicated to one telephone or data circuit.

Shielded Twisted Pair Wire

A variation of twisted pair wiring is *shielded twisted pair.* Twisted pair wire is placed inside a thin metallic shielding, similar to aluminum foil, and is then enclosed in an outer plastic casing. The shielding provides further electrical isolation of the signal-carrying pair of wires. Shielded twisted pair wires are less susceptible to electrical interference caused by nearby equipment or wires and, in turn, are less likely to cause interference themselves. Because it is electrically "cleaner," shielded twisted pair wire can carry data at a faster speed than unshielded twisted pair wire can. The disadvantage of shielded twisted pair wire is that it is physically larger and more expensive than twisted pair wire, and it is more difficult to connect to a terminating block.

Coaxial Cable

Coaxial cable, as the name implies, is cable made of several layers of material around a central core, as illustrated in Figure 9–8. The central conductor is most often a copper wire, although occasionally aluminum is used. It is surrounded by insulation, most typically made of a type of

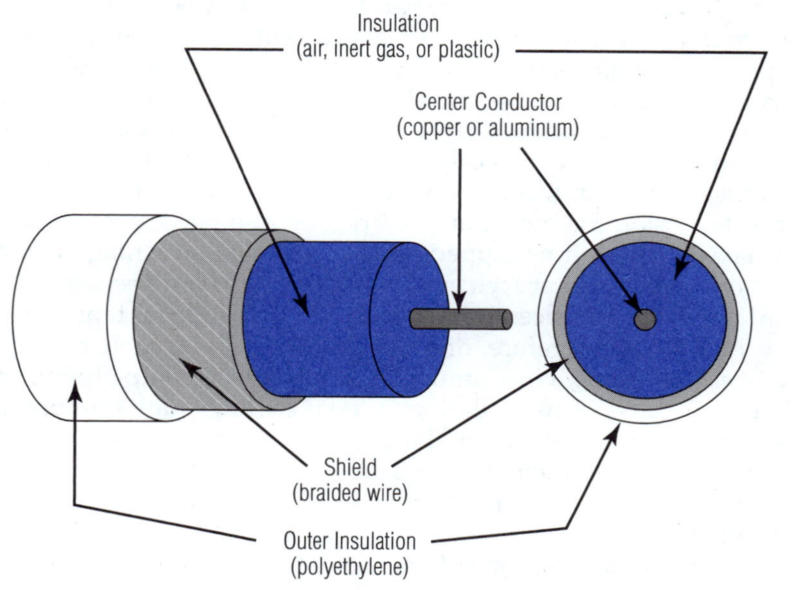

Figure 9–8
Parts of coaxial cable.

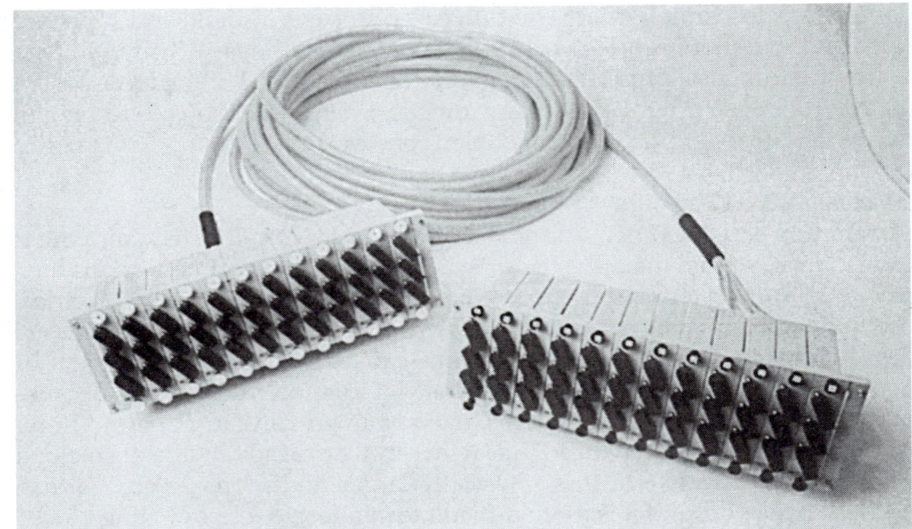

This shielded twisted pair cable is useful in electrically noisy environments or where high data rates must be guaranteed. (Courtesy of International Business Machines Corporation. Unauthorized use not permitted.)

plastic. Sometimes spacers are put in the cable to keep the center conductor separate from the shielding, and in that case, the insulation material is air or an inert gas. Outside of the insulation is the shielding, which is also a conductor, typically fine, braided copper wire. The shielding is surrounded by the outer insulation, which is almost always a form of plastic that also provides physical protection for the cable.

Coaxial cable has a very large bandwidth, commonly 400 to 600 MHz, and therefore a very high data-carrying capacity. The telephone industry uses pairs of coaxial cable in areas where the population density is high. One coaxial cable can carry up to 10,800 voice conversations when amplifiers, spaced about a mile apart, are used to boost the signal. The cable television industry uses coaxial cable extensively for carrying television signals from a central transmitter to individual homes or other subscribers. Over 50 television channels can be carried on a single coaxial cable.

Coaxial cable can be tapped easily. This is an advantage when it is used around an office or factory where many taps are needed but a disadvantage if one is concerned about security and illegal taps. The cable can be bulky and, therefore, difficult to install. Some cable has a rather large bending radius, which must be considered when planning the installation. Because of its shielding, coaxial cable is quite immune to external electrical interference, making it a good candidate for use in electrically noisy environments.

Optical Fiber

Optical fiber technology is one of the most rapidly advancing segments of telecommunications technology. The worldwide use of optical fibers has

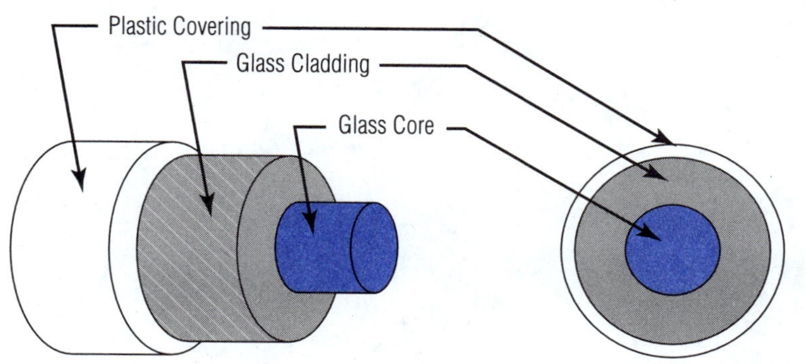

Figure 9–9
Parts of optical fiber cable.

been growing at a compounded growth rate of 20 percent per year since 1998, and the trend is expected to continue or accelerate until at least 2003. One of the byproducts of the rapid installation of optical fiber in the United States is that by 2001, the U.S. telephone infrastructure will have more than 80 times the capacity it had five years before. This fantastic buildup in capacity should be a boon for consumers and businesses alike, and at least one industry executive predicts that in the not-too-distant future, long distance calls may be offered free to consumers who buy a bundle of services including high-speed Internet access and wireless telephony. Every few months one reads of the latest developments, which frequently have to do with the bandwidth or speed that a single fiber can carry and the rapid conversion of networks to be optical fiber based.

The optical fiber itself, illustrated in Figure 9–9, is a very thin glass fiber of high purity. The glass *core* at the center provides the transmission-carrying capability. It looks like a very fine fishing line but is in fact a very pure, clear strand of silica glass. The core is surrounded by another type of glass called *cladding,* which is reflective and acts like a mirror to the core. The cladding is covered by a protective covering, usually of plastic. The total diameter of the fiber is less than that of a human hair. Individual fibers often are bundled together in groups around a central metallic wire that provides strength for pulling the fiber cable through conduit when it is laid.

light source

Data is placed on the cable with a light source, either a *light-emitting diode (LED)* or a *laser.* The laser is more powerful and is used when the distance between the transmitter and receiver is greater than 5 to 10 miles. For shorter runs, the less expensive LED can be used. The light stays in the core because the cladding has a low refractive index. When the light beam hits the edge of the core, it is reflected back toward the center by the cladding's mirrorlike surface. The light output of the LED or laser is modulated to provide the variations in the signal that can be interpreted at the receiving end. Without special techniques, a fiber carries a signal in one direction only, so fibers are normally used in pairs.

Several coaxial cables are often packed together as shown in this photograph. The 4½-inch cable on the left can carry as many as 40,300 telephone conversations. The optical fiber cable on the right is only ½ inch in diameter and can carry more than 43,600 telephone conversations. (Courtesy of AT&T Bell Laboratories)

single mode

Two primary types of fiber are used. One is called *single mode* and uses a fiber with a glass core approximately 5 microns (.005 millimeter) in diameter. With this very small core size, the light beam travels down the center of the core with little reflection from the cladding. Because the core is so small, however, it requires a very concentrated light source to get the signal into the fiber with adequate strength for long distances.

multimode

The other type of fiber is called *multimode.* The usual core size is 62.5 microns (.0625 millimeter) in diameter. With the larger core size, it is easier to get the light into the fiber, but there is more reflection from side to side off the cladding. Some of the light rays travel essentially straight down the center of the fiber, whereas others reflect at various angles. Those that travel straight through the fiber arrive at the destination faster than those that reflect, a phenomenon called *dispersion.* The effect of dispersion is that it causes the square pulses of a digital signal to become rounded and effectively limits the signaling rate that can be achieved. The trade-off, then, is that implementing a multimode fiber system costs less than a comparable system built with single-mode fiber. The cable and light source cost less, but the signal-carrying capacity is also less than in a single-mode fiber system.

One of optical fiber's most notable characteristics is its high bandwidth. A strand of fiber can carry 320 Gbps of data per second, enough to support 5.7 million PCs with 56 kbps modems simultaneously. Stated another way, the total bandwidth of radio is 25 GHz, whereas an optical fiber has a bandwidth of 25,000 GHz. Signals do not travel faster in fiber than copper, but the density or data capacity of fiber is much greater. Light has higher frequencies and hence shorter wavelengths, so more bits of information can be packed in the same space. Furthermore, photons, the base element of light, can occupy the same space. To visualize this concept, think of two flashlight beams that cross each other. The light from one passes through the other, and both are unaffected. Utilizing this principle, and a technique called *wavelength division multiplexing (WDM)*, many light beams of different wavelengths can travel along a single fiber simultaneously without interfering with one another. Each light beam can carry many individually modulated data streams, hence the high data rates that optical fibers can achieve.

wavelength division multiplexing

Optical fiber cables are very difficult to splice, requiring specialized tools and skills. They are best suited for long point-to-point runs in which few or no splices are required. Splices can be detected using a reflectometer, an instrument that sends a light wave down the fiber and measures the reflection that comes back. From a security standpoint, this difficulty in splicing optical fiber cables and the ability to detect unwanted taps is an advantage. In addition, since the transmission is optical rather than electrical, the cables do not radiate signals, as all electrical devices do. Given these attributes, optical fiber cables are excellent in situations that require very high security.

Another advantage of optical fiber cables over wire or coaxial cables is that the fibers are so thin that a optical fiber cable has a very small diameter and is lightweight. This makes the cables easier to install, since they can be pulled through smaller conduits and bent around corners much more easily than coaxial cable. They can even be installed under carpeting or floor tiles, giving additional flexibility in laying out an office.

Costs of optical fiber cable and its related components continue to drop and are expected to continue doing so for the foreseeable future. These cost reductions are the result of improved manufacturing techniques and an ever-expanding market size. In addition, a lower cost optical cable made of plastic instead of glass is available. Although it doesn't have the capacity of glass cable and can't carry data as far without a repeater, it may be an inexpensive alternative for bringing fiber and its high bandwidth to the desktop in some offices.

The first undersea telephone cable between the United States and Europe was installed in 1956 and could handle 36 simultaneous telephone calls. In late 1988, the first optical fiber undersea cable, TAT-8, was completed on approximately the same route and could handle 40,000 simultaneous calls using two pairs of fibers. That capacity was subsequently upgraded with advances in the shore-based electronics. The

SIDEBAR 9–1

THE CABLE UNDER THE SEA

Underwater fiber-optic cables handle most international voice calls and Internet traffic calls (satellites handle most of the broadcast video). Each fiber-optic cable, as thin as a human hair, can carry at least 20,000 simultaneous calls. The C.S. Global Link, one of the ships that lays the cable, has accommodations for 138 crew, technicians, and guests.

How the cable is laid

1. At least a year before the ship goes out to sea, topographical surveys are conducted to plan the cable route, taking into account such factors as underwater earthquake faults, canyons and shipping routes.
2. Over the course of several weeks, thousands of miles of cable are manually coiled into the ship's storage tanks.
3. While the ship is still anchored, the cable is floated out to the shore and connected to the shore cable station. Cable running close to the shoreline or near a continental shelf is buried in a tunnel dug by a plow.
4. Once past the continental shelf, burying the cable isn't necessary. Guided by shipboard computers that communicate with global satellites, the ship begins dropping cable, which rests on the ocean floor, four or five miles deep. Two cable engines, one in the bow and one in the stern, lay out cable at the proper tension.
5. As the cable is lowered into the sea, buoys mark the location.
6. During installation, engineers continually test the cable system, which is powered and operating as it is laid.
7. If cable needs to be repaired, a remote-control robot submarine tethered to the ship dives to the bottom of the ocean and hauls the cable to the surface, where repairs are made.

Inside the cable

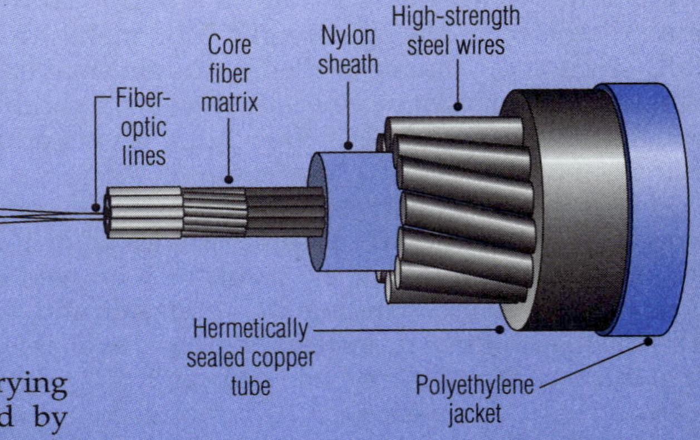

Sources: Tyco Submarine Systems, TeleGeography.

newest trans-Atlantic cable, called "Atlantic Crossing," can handle 2.4 million voice conversations at one time. In 1998, Lucent Technologies unveiled the capability to transmit as many as 10 million calls over a single fiber by dividing the strand into 80 separate wavelengths.

Literally hundreds of optical fiber cables connect the continents. Figure 9–10 shows most of the world's undersea cables, a few of which are the older coaxial cable type, but all of the new ones are optical fiber. As of the end of 1999, there were over 400,000 miles of fiber optic cable on the floors of the world's oceans, enough to circle the globe over sixteen times. These cables are sponsored and funded by the carriers of the countries served, working in cooperation with one another. The network continues to grow as the world's telecommunications users continue to demand new services and seem to have an insatiable demand for bandwidth.

In summary, the characteristics of optical fiber are

- high bandwidth—very high data-carrying capacity;
- little loss of signal strength—depends on the details of the cable construction, but the overall characteristics are excellent;
- immunity to electrical interference—since it operates in the optical part of the spectrum, electrical noise is not an issue;
- excellent isolation between parallel fibers—crosstalk between fibers does not exist;
- small physical size—lightweight;
- very secure—difficult to tap and splice and does not radiate electrical signals.

One large company in New York recently installed several fiber-optic cables to connect several locations in its community. In one case, the fiber cable was run along a railroad track, and in another situation, the fiber was run through some abandoned underground conduit formerly used for electrical wires. The fibers carry voice traffic today to allow a single PBX to serve the company's multiple locations around the city and high-speed data traffic between local area networks.

Synchronous Optical Network (SONET) *Synchronous Optical Network* is a standard for transmitting data on optical fibers that was originally created to allow easier connection between carriers that were using different vendor's products for their optical networks. SONET has become the de facto standard for carrying voice and data traffic over an optical network, and the American National Standards Institute (ANSI) has approved it. SONET provides for transmission at gigabits per a second (Gbps), as shown in Figure 9–11. Europe uses a similar standard, as approved by the ITU-T, but it has different designations for the various circuit speeds.

While SONET was originally developed by the carriers for their own use, it is now available to users who need the capacity it offers. The carriers

Figure 9–10
The world's undersea cable network.

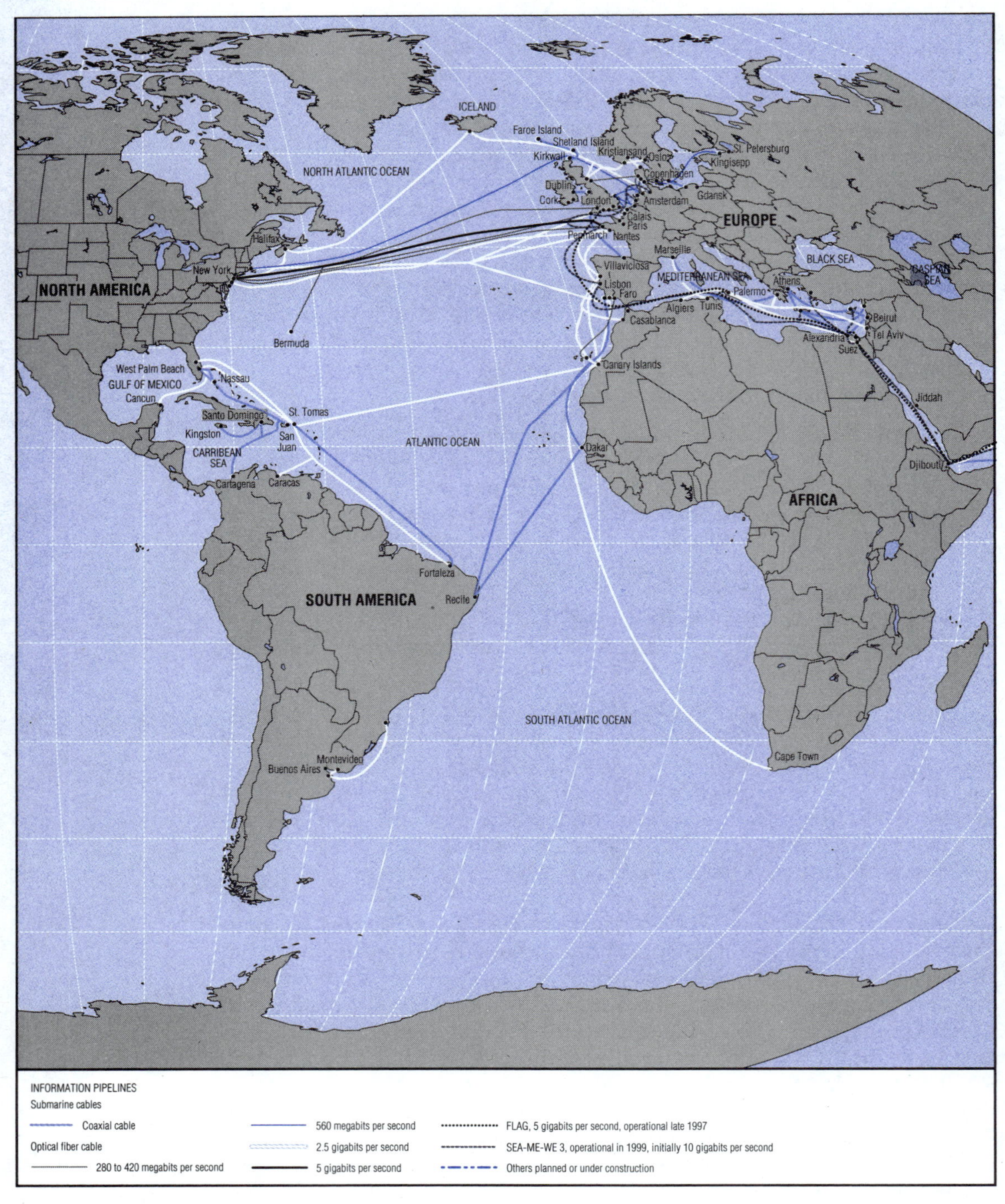

Figure 9–10
Continued

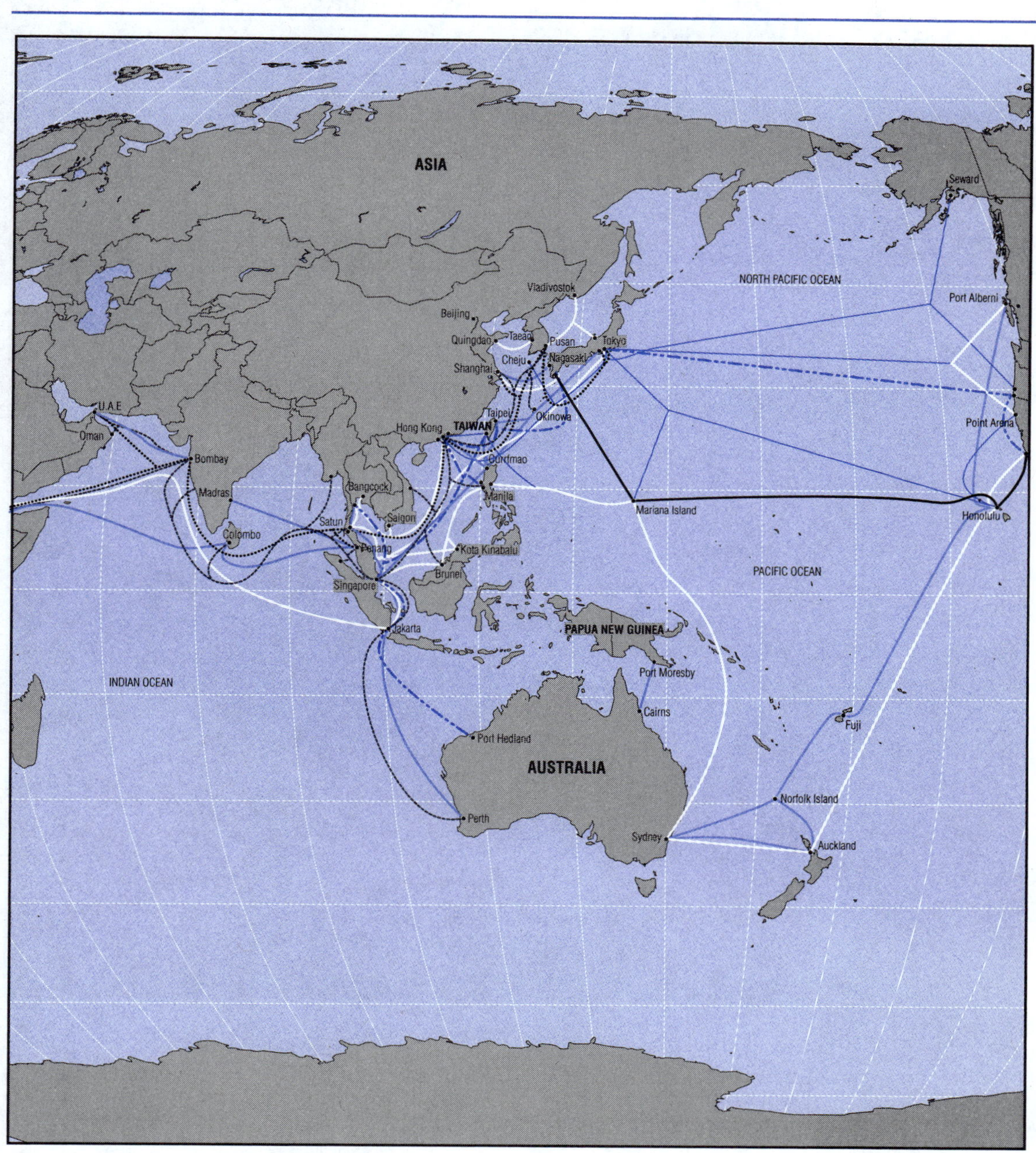

The flexible optical fiber shown in this photograph is approximately the diameter of a human hair but can carry signals for miles without repeaters. (Courtesy of Corning, Inc.)

are still the primary users, however, since they have thousands of miles of optical fiber installed. Notice that the basic OC-1 data rate is slightly faster than the T-3 data rate. Telephone companies and other carriers are replacing their T-3 and T-4 services with SONET, especially between exchange offices.

Synchronous Optical Network (SONET)	ITU-T Designation	Data Rate
OC-1		51.840 Mbps
OC-3	STM-1	155.250 Mbps
OC-9	STM-3	466.560 Mbps
OC-12	STM-4	622.080 Mbps
OC-18	STM-6	933.120 Mbps
OC-24	STM-8	1.244 Gbps
OC-36	STM-12	1.866 Gbps
OC-48	STM-16	2.488 Gbps
OC-192	STM-64	9.953 Gbps
OC-255		13.219 Gbps

Figure 9–11
Comparative data rates for the SONET and ITU-T optical fiber transmission standards.

Microwave Radio

Microwave radio was the medium most used by the common carriers for long distance communications transmission before optical fibers became so prevalent. Microwave radio transmissions occur in the 4 to 28 GHz frequency range. Specific frequency bands are set aside, and channels are allocated within the bands. Up to 6,000 voice circuits are carried in a 30 MHz-wide radio channel.

At the frequency range in which they operate, microwave radio signals travel in a straight line. Therefore, the transmitter and receiver must be in a direct line of sight with each other. Because of the curvature of the earth, microwave antennas are usually placed on high towers or building roofs to extend the line of sight to the greatest distance possible before another antenna is required. Practically speaking, a range of 20 to 30 miles between towers is common if the terrain is not too hilly. Where the distance to be covered is short, microwave antennas can be placed on the side of a building or even in an office window.

Microwave signals may carry data in either analog or digital form, but analog is more common. Voice, data, and television signals are carried, but each is given its own channel. Depending on the frequency used, some microwave signals are subject to interference by heavy rain. When this occurs, the channel is unusable until the rain subsides. Therefore, when a microwave system is designed, provisions must be made for this possibility. Temporarily stopping the transmission, sending it on an alternate path, and transmitting via a different medium are alternatives to be considered.

Microwave is sometimes installed privately by companies to connect locations that are near but not adjacent to one another. A radio license must be obtained from the Federal Communications Commission (FCC), but no right-of-way permits are necessary. Several companies in New York City have private microwave links connecting offices in different

This microwave tower is located in New Jersey. Both parabolic and horn antennas can be seen. (Property of AT&T Archives. Reprinted with permission of AT&T.)

parts of Manhattan. Similar private microwave installations can be found in most major cities.

Microwave systems should be considered when T-1 circuits are not available, when there is a financial advantage or other requirement to have a privately owned transmission system, or when alternative routing is required for certain critical communications links. Sales engineers from the microwave equipment vendors help to obtain the required transmission license, as well as configuring the equipment for the specific terrain, transmission speed, and reliability requirements. Major vendors of microwave equipment are Digital Microwave Corporation, Motorola, Inc., and Rockwell Communication Systems.

Satellite

Transmission using an earth satellite is a particular type of microwave radio transmission. In a typical satellite system, a microwave radio signal is transmitted from an antenna on the ground to a satellite in an orbit 22,300 miles above around the earth. At that distance, the circular speed of the satellite exactly matches the speed of rotation of the earth, and the satellite appears to be stationary overhead. This is called a *geosynchronous orbit.* An antenna on the earth can be aimed at the satellite, and because the satellite appears stationary, the aim doesn't have to be changed. Although the distance is great, the antennas are definitely in sight of each other. The microwave radio signal is beamed to the satellite on a specific frequency called the *uplink,* where it is received, amplified, and then rebroadcast on a different frequency, called the *downlink.* This is illustrated in Figure 9–12.

geosynchronous orbit

Because of its distance from the earth, a geosynchronous satellite can see and be seen from approximately one-third of the earth. The signals broadcast from the satellite can, at least theoretically, be picked up by any antenna and receiver in that area. This broadcast attribute is an advantage in some applications and a disadvantage in others. It is advantageous for organizations that want to use satellites to reach a mass market. Home Box Office (HBO) uses the broadcast capability to distribute movies to cable TV companies. Financial companies use satellite transmission to distribute stock market information to brokers all over the country.

For companies that want to use the satellite for point-to-point transmission, the broadcast capability presents a security concern. Anyone with the proper equipment can receive the broadcast as it is transmitted down from the satellite. When this concern is serious, encryption devices can be used to code the data before it is transmitted to the satellite. This makes it difficult to interpret the broadcast on the downlink.

Another characteristic of satellite transmission is that because of the great distance involved—22,300 miles up to the satellite and 22,300 miles back—there is a noticeable delay from the time a signal is sent until it is received. This delay, called *propagation delay,* exists for all communications circuits and radio broadcasts. It is a function of the fact that light signals or radio waves travel at a maximum speed of 186,000 miles per second in a vacuum. A signal traveling 4,000 miles across the United States on a terrestrial circuit will travel somewhat slower than 186,000 miles per second, but an approximation of the propagation delay can be calculated as

propagation delay

Figure 9–12
Satellite transmission.

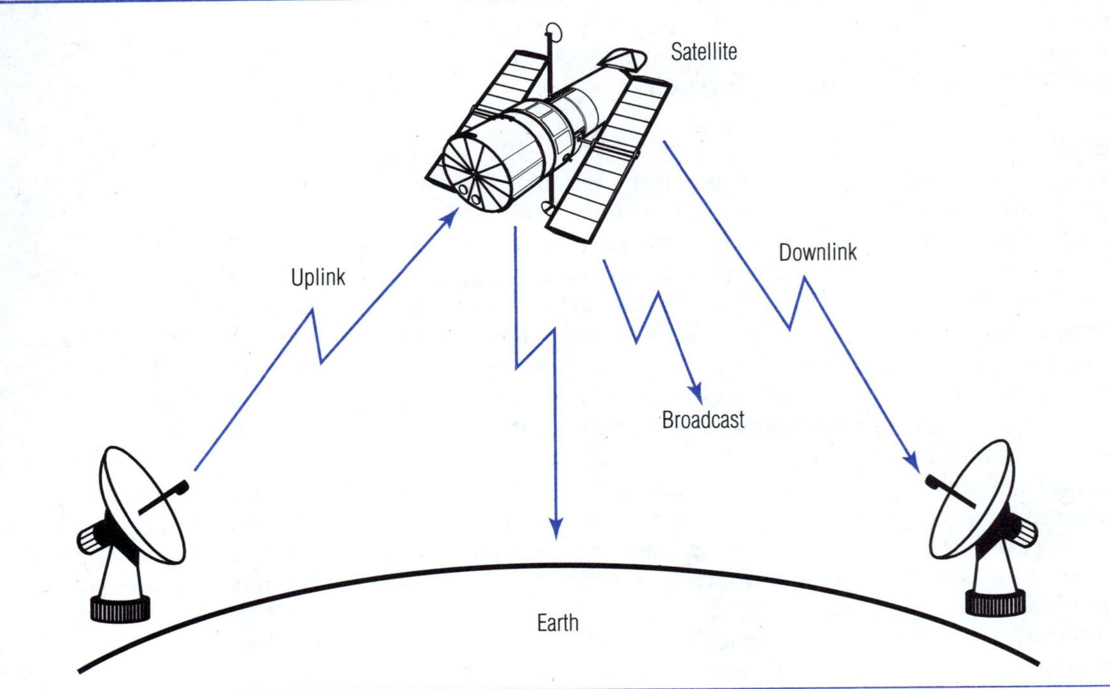

4,000 miles/186,000 miles per second = .0215 second (21.5 milliseconds)

When the signal goes via satellite, the propagation delay is

44,600 miles/186,000 miles per second = .2398 second (239.8 milliseconds)

The satellite signal takes 11 times longer to reach its destination. If a return signal is required, the same amount of delay would be encountered a second time. You may have noticed this satellite delay on some domestic long distance telephone calls a few years ago, and it still can be heard on some international telephone calls today. Most people find the delay annoying, and the common carriers in the United States have switched voice transmissions back to terrestrial media.

The propagation delay when using a satellite can be extremely significant when data is being sent. Since almost a quarter of a second is added to each transmission in either direction, the transmission time becomes a significant portion of the total response time in an interactive application.

This satellite earth station is about 1 meter in diameter. Other dish antennas are as small as 18 inches. (Courtesy of Scientific-Atlanta, Inc.)

Satellites use various frequencies for transmitting and receiving. That's one reason why satellite dish antennas vary greatly in size. The other main reason has to do with the power output of the satellite transmitter; those with higher powered transmitters put out a stronger signal and the receiving antenna on the ground can be smaller. Satellites that transmit in the *Ku band* of microwave frequencies have such a short wavelength that the earth station antennas, called *very small aperture terminals (VSAT)*, can be as small as 18 inches. One use is by news services to communicate between reporters in the field and the main studio. A different application is the *direct broadcast satellite (DBS)* system commonly used to send television programming via satellite directly to homes. DBS antennas are available in the United States for as little as $100 when purchased with one year of programming.

VSAT

DBS

DBS, also sometimes known as *digital satellite service (DSS)*, is also a competitor to cable television and DSL for high speed Internet access. DSS is the most widely available of the three technologies and has been in use by millions of Americans since 1997. As long as you have a clear line of sight toward the sky above the equator, you are a potential DSS customer.

DSS service is receive-only, meaning that the customer must also use a telephone line and modem to send data to the Internet. Also, while the download speeds from the satellite are in the range of 350 kbps, the overall service is much slower. When you click a link to pull up a web page, your signal travels via the phone line to your ISP and then to the Internet. The information you requested is sent 22,300 miles up to the satellite, and back down 22,300 more miles to your DSS dish. There is a noticeable

This satellite dish antenna is used for receiving signals from a direct broadcast satellite. (Courtesy of Stock Boston.)

delay in the response, which is okay for file downloads, but probably not acceptable to most people if they are trying to chat interactively with another person. As usual, the suitability of this technology depends on the application for which it will be used.

In addition to geosynchronous satellites, there are other types of satellite systems in use and on the drawing boards. Medium earth orbit (MEO) satellites tend to circulate at 6,000 miles above the earth, while low earth orbit (LEO) satellites orbit at between 300 and 1,000 miles high. Because of their lower orbits, both of these types of satellites are in motion relative to the rotation of the earth. Nine to twelve MEO satellites or about seventy LEO satellites must be in orbit to ensure that at least one can be seen from anywhere on earth at all times. Users of MEO or LEO satellites need to have omni-directional antennas in order to receive the signal from the satellite as it passes overhead in its orbit.

MEO and LEO satellite systems have potential use for global telephone systems that would allow one handset to be used from any location on earth. However, the costs of such a system are very high, and one company has already failed because it could not get the costs of the telephone calls made through the satellites low enough to compete with terrestrial-based telephone systems.

	Twisted Pair (Cat 5)	Coaxial Cable	Microwave Radio	Satellite	Fiber
Transmission speed	100 Mbps	500 Mbps	275 Mbps	90 Mbps	2 Gbps
Ease of installation	Easy	Moderate	Difficult	Difficult	Difficult
Cost	Least	Moderate	Moderate	Moderate	High
Maintenance difficulty	Low	Moderate	Low	Low	Low
Skill required to install	Low	Moderate	High	High	High
Most common uses	Within buildings	Campus Multidrop	Point-to-Point Short distance	Point-to-Point Long distance	Point-to-point
Advantages	Inexpensive, familiar	Carries more information than twisted pair	Speed	Speed, availability	Speed, secure
Disadvantages	Subject to interference	Bulky	Can be intercepted	Delay, can be intercepted	Difficult to splice, cost
Security	Good	Good	Poor	Poor	Excellent
Notes	Shielded twisted pair allows higher speed	Broadband use is more maintenance intensive	Requires radio license from FCC	Private systems not common	Higher speeds coming

Figure 9–13
Comparison of the attributes of the media most commonly used for business telecommunications transmission.

Infrared

Infrared transmission uses light waves below the visible spectrum. Infrared waves can reflect off a light-colored surface such as the wall of a room, but generally speaking the transmitter and receiver must be in direct line of sight. The signals can also be blocked by fog, smoke, or even heavy rain. Companies sometimes use infrared transmission between nearby buildings. Other applications are to provide wireless communication between personal computers and printers, and between remote control units and television sets.

Summary of Media Characteristics

The chart in Figure 9–13 summarizes the characteristics of the main media used for telecommunications transmission.

CIRCUIT ACQUISITION AND OWNERSHIP

Another way of classifying telecommunications circuits is by ownership and method of acquisition.

Private Circuits

Private circuits are those installed and maintained by a company other than a common carrier. For example, a company may run coaxial cable between its buildings on a manufacturing site and wire within the buildings to form a data communications network. The typical situation where private circuits are installed is within a building or in a campus environment, where all the property is owned. It becomes more complicated if the circuit must cross property owned by others because permission to cross the property must be obtained. It is even more complicated when public roads or highways must be crossed, but it is possible to obtain per-

This photograph of the Advanced Communications Technology Satellite (ACTS) was taken from the space shuttle *Discovery* shortly after the satellite was released. (Courtesy of NASA)

mission to cross or bury cable under them. Permission is obtained from the agency in control of the road; it may be a city, county, state, or the federal government.

In some states, it is possible for private companies to get permission to run wire or cable on public utility poles. Usually, the utility company charges a small fee for the use of the pole. Private circuits also have been installed on the shoulders of public roadways, alongside railroad tracks, and on pipeline routes.

When a company installs a private circuit, it is totally responsible for its design, engineering, installation, operation, and maintenance. But the circuit is available for the company's full-time, exclusive use, and once the circuit is installed, it is usually very inexpensive to operate. One company, which had many locations in a city, received permission to run a private cable on the poles of the local electrical utility company. The rental charge was $6 per year per pole, an amount the company considered very reasonable. Using the cable, the company was able to connect all of its locations in the city into a common data network.

Leased Circuits

Leased circuits are circuits owned by a common carrier but leased from them by another organization for full-time, exclusive use. Leased facilities are attractive when some or all of these conditions are present:

- it is impossible or undesirable to install a private circuit;
- the cost of the leased circuit is less than the cost of a dial-up connection for the amount of time required;
- four-wire service is required (four-wire service cannot be obtained on dial-up connections);
- high-speed transmission is required.

The primary advantage of a leased circuit is that it is engineered by the carrier, installed, and left in place so that the same facilities are always used. This means that once the circuit is adjusted and operating correctly, it will continue to operate the same way for long periods of time. For most business data transmission, this consistency and reliability are significant benefits because they go a long way toward helping ensure that the communications service is reliable and trouble-free.

When a leased circuit does fail, the carrier that provides the circuit performs the diagnostic and maintenance work required to restore it to service. Carriers have special testing equipment located at their central offices with which they can examine all of the parameters of a circuit to determine the cause of failure. Furthermore, the technicians at all of the central offices through which the circuit passes can communicate with each other to determine which link in the circuit is experiencing the problem. In most instances, failures are isolated and corrected and the circuit is returned to normal operation within hours. Often, service is restored in minutes.

The price of leased circuits is based on speed and distance. For voice-grade circuits there is a charge for the local channel from the customer premises to the serving central office. The local channel is acquired from the Local Exchange Carrier (LEC). If the circuit crosses Local Access and Transport Area (LATA) boundaries, it must be carried by an interexchange carrier (IXC). In that case, the local channel and its associated charges extend through the serving Central Office (CO) to the IXC's Point of Presence (POP). Added to the local channel charge is the interoffice channel charge for the circuit connecting the POPs. For point-to-point circuits, the carrier computes the shortest airline mileage between the two POPs and bases the monthly charge on that distance. For multipoint circuits, the carrier computes the shortest airline mileage between all the points on the circuit.

A leased four-wire circuit costs about 10 percent more than a leased two-wire circuit. Since additional throughput can be obtained, most users pay the additional cost for four-wire circuits when they want to use half-duplex or full-duplex transmission.

One final note: Leased circuits often are called "private" circuits in common use. The distinction between the two types that has been made in this book frequently is not made by people in the communications industry. It is common to hear someone talk about "our private line" when they really mean "our leased line." For many purposes, the distinction makes no difference, but if in doubt, it is best to request a clarification.

Bypass In its simplest form, *bypass* involves installing private telecommunications circuits to avoid using (to bypass) those of a carrier. The usual reason for considering bypass is to reduce costs, although in some cases a company may consider bypass in order to obtain a capability the LEC cannot provide.

One application of bypass is to connect a company's facility directly with an IXC, bypassing the LEC. An example where this might be necessary is when the LEC cannot provide fractional T-1 service. A full T-1 circuit or microwave link could carry the voice and data traffic directly from the company's location to the IXC, providing access to the IXC's fractional T-1 service. In another case, bypass circuits might be installed to eliminate the local access charges for circuits that the LEC would normally impose. An economic analysis would have to be performed to determine over what time period the elimination in local access charges would offset the cost of installing the bypass circuit. Another practical consideration may be the company's relationship with the LEC, since the elimination of circuit revenue caused by the bypass will certainly not make the LEC happy.

Switched (Dial-Up) Circuits

Switched or dial-up circuits come from the standard public telephone network, and using them for data is similar to making a normal telephone call. A temporary connection is built between DTEs as though there were direct wires connecting the two. The circuit is set up on demand and discontinued when the transmission is complete. This technique is called *circuit switching*. An obvious advantage of circuit switching is flexibility in network configuration. Transmission speeds of up to 56 kbps can be obtained on normal switched circuits. Charges for switched circuits are based on the duration of the call and the distance, just like a standard telephone call.

circuit switching

One factor that must be dealt with when using switched circuits is that when a dial-up connection is made, the actual carrier facilities used in routing the call depend on the facilities that are available at the moment. For this reason, circuits are variable in quality and may be very good on one connection and marginal on another. We have all experienced this phenomenon on long distance telephone calls. Sometimes it seems as if the person we are talking to is just next door; other times the volume of the person's voice is low; during other conversations, crosstalk can be heard. On a dial-up connection you may find that one time the modems are able to transmit at 33.6 kbps, while the next time, 26.2 kbps is the fastest they will transmit.

When an organization uses switched circuits, it exposes itself to certain security risks. If the organization has a dial-in capability, allowing employees or others to call a computer, it faces the possibility that unauthorized people may dial in and access the computer, either accidentally or maliciously. Of course there are standard security precautions, such as user-IDs and passwords that can be implemented, but a clever hacker can often bypass these measures fairly quickly. One method that has been used is to dial in with a computer that is programmed to try all possible combinations of letters and numbers for the user-ID or password to find a combination that works.

One technique to combat unauthorized dial-ins is to use a *callback* or *dialback unit*. The authorized user dials in and identifies him- or herself to the callback unit. The connection is immediately broken, and the callback unit looks up the user's ID in an internally stored table and calls the user back at the prestored telephone number. Of course this means that the user always has to call in from the same place; the technique does not work well for travelers. Another problem is that the cost of the telephone call now falls on the central location that is being called.

dialback unit

CIRCUIT IDENTIFICATION

Whether a particular facility is a circuit, link, or channel depends to a certain extent on one's point of view. From the user's point of view, a multipoint circuit from Los Angeles to Dallas and Miami has links from Los Angeles to Dallas and from Dallas to Miami. From the carrier's point of view, the user's circuit is a part of a higher-speed facility onto which it is multiplexed. The carrier also sees many more links, in fact, probably thinks of the circuit as being made up of a series of links between each central office through which the circuit passes, plus the links at each end (local loops) connecting the serving central office to the customer premises. As the circuit passes through high-speed, long distance optical fiber or microwave facilities crossing the country, it is likely to be viewed by the carrier as a one-way, two-wire channel within the microwave link. The other channel, running in the other direction, may be on some other fiber or link and running totally independently.

The different viewpoints lead to occasional difficulties when communications customers and carriers talk to each other because the parties may use the same terms to mean different things or different terms to mean the same thing. To partially address this problem, the carrier attaches a circuit number to each circuit for identification purposes. The carrier has blueprints or other documentation that identifies every link making up the circuit and every piece of equipment through which it passes. Customers and carriers use the circuit number when they discuss problems or talk about changes to the circuit.

MULTIPLEXING AND CONCENTRATING

Chapter 4 discussed frequency division multiplexing (FDM). When FDM is used, signals are shifted to different parts of the frequency spectrum so that a single pair of wires can carry more than one transmission. Data signals in analog form are shifted using FDM techniques. With FDM, a channel has use of a limited range of frequencies all of the time. Other channels use the other frequencies.

When transmissions are in digital form, time division multiplexing is normally used. With time division multiplexing, a channel can use the entire frequency range the channel allows, but only for specified periods of time. Other channels use the other time slots. Figure 9–14 illustrates this concept.

Time Division Multiplexing (TDM)

Time division multiplexing (TDM) is a technique that divides a circuit's capacity into time slots. Each time slot is used by a different voice or data signal. If, for example, a circuit is capable of a speed of 9,600 bps, four terminals, each transmitting at 2,400 bps, could simultaneously use its capacity. A TDM takes one character from each terminal and groups the four characters together into a *frame* that is transmitted on the circuit. This process is shown in Figure 9–15. At the receiving end, another TDM breaks the frame apart and presents data to the computer on four separate circuits.

frame

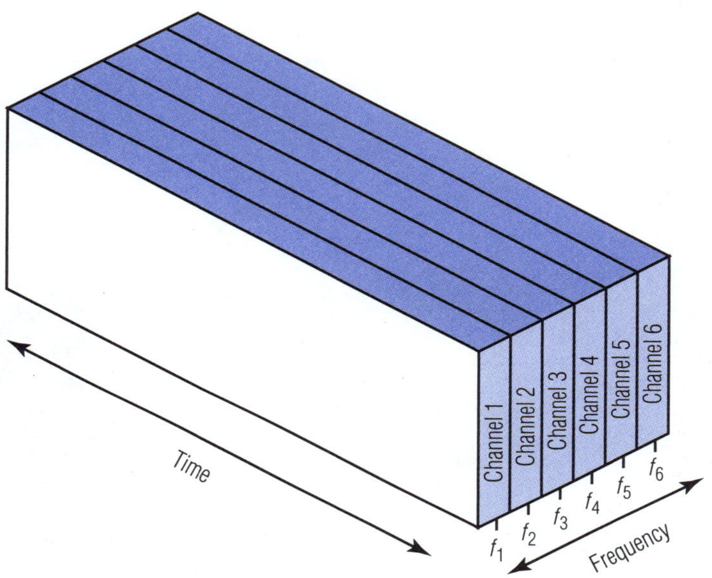

Frequency division multiplexing (FDM)

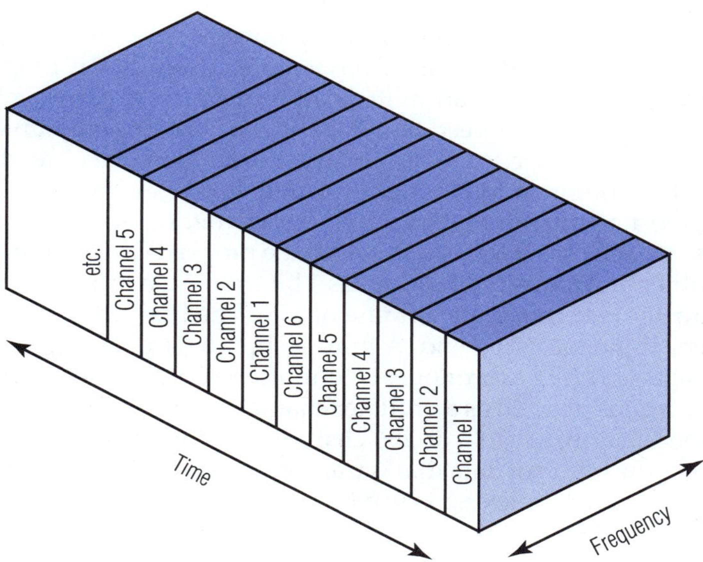

Time division multiplexing (TDM)

Figure 9–14
FDM channels have full time use of a limited range of frequencies. TDM channels can use the full range of frequencies but only during predetermined time slots.

Figure 9–15
Time division multiplexing.

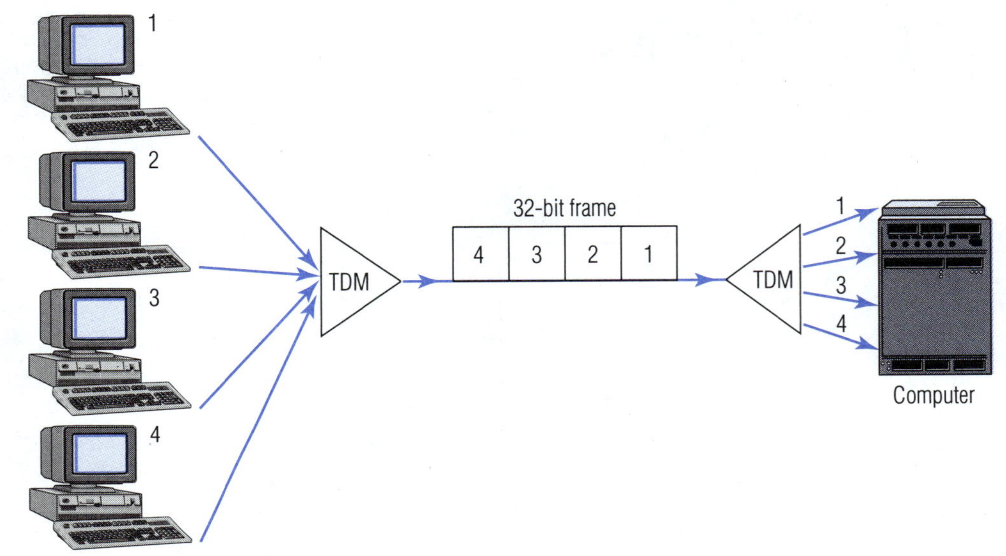

Time division multiplexing is totally transparent to the terminal, the computer, and the user. If a terminal has nothing to send at any point in time, its time slot in the frame is transmitted empty. A typical application for TDM is to have multiple slow-speed terminals at one location communicating to a computer at another location. Although four terminals are shown in Figure 9–15, more than four could be multiplexed (however, multiples of four are most common). Eight terminals transmitting at 1,200 bps would work just as well on a 9,600 bps line with the proper TDM equipment.

Another technique for TDM takes 1 bit from each terminal instead of one character and transmits a frame of bits. The bits are assembled into characters at the receiving end. A third technique, frequently used when the transmission is synchronous, is to multiplex entire messages. In this case, a *message* is defined as a group of characters not exceeding some predetermined length, say 128 or 256 characters. When message multiplexing is used, the frame of data that is transmitted is much longer than when character or bit multiplexing is used.

Statistical Time Division Multiplexing (STDM)

If you think about how terminals are really operated, it is obvious that no terminal with a human operator is transmitting data continuously. In fact, the wait, or "think," time between transmissions may be much longer

Figure 9–16
The STDM tries to avoid having empty slots in a frame, thereby improving the line use. If a terminal has no data to send in a particular time period, the STDM will see if the next terminal has data that can be included in the time slot. When the STDM at the receiving end breaks the frame apart, it uses the terminal address to route the data to the proper device.

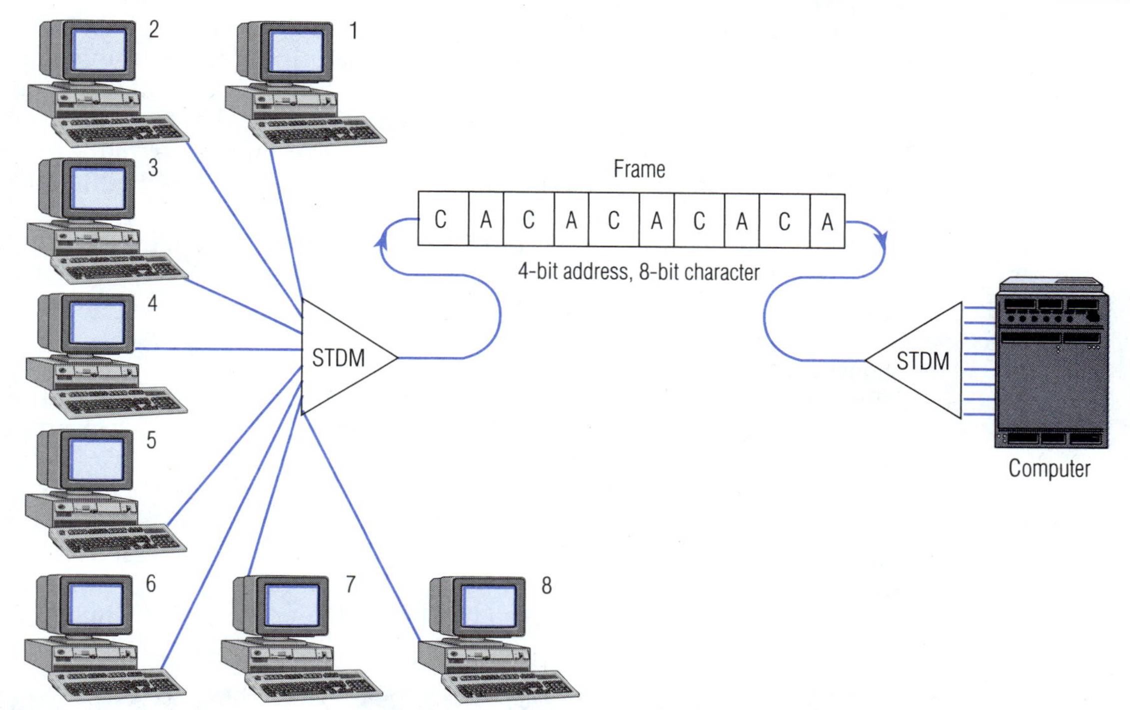

than the actual transmission time. With a time division multiplexer, this means that many of the time slots are transmitted empty and the capacity of the circuit is not fully used.

A *statistical time division multiplexer (STDM)* is a multiplexer that does not assign specific time slots to each terminal. Instead, the STDM transmits the terminal's address along with each character or message of data, as illustrated in Figure 9–16.

If the address field in an STDM frame is 4 bits long, there are 2^4 combinations and 16 terminals can be handled. With a 5-bit address, 32 terminals can be multiplexed. In any case, extra bits are required for the addresses when STDM is used. For most applications, this additional overhead is a good trade-off. Most of the time, the user will not notice any difference in performance or response time, and the line will be better used.

There are times when most or all of the terminals want to send data simultaneously. During these times, the aggregate data rate may be buffer

higher than the circuit can handle. For these situations, the STDM contains a storage area or buffer in which data can be saved until the line can accept it. Buffer sizes of 32,000 characters and larger are common for this purpose. The user may experience a slight delay when buffering occurs.

STDM takes advantage of the fact that individual terminals frequently are idle and allows more terminals to share a line of given capacity. Students who are writing and debugging programs on a university timesharing system normally fit this model nicely. They spend some time typing the program into the computer and a great deal of time interpreting error messages and determining how to correct their program's problems. Using an STDM, 12 terminals running at 1,200 bps could be handled by a 9,600 bps line in most cases.

Leading statistical multiplexer manufacturers are Timeplex, Inc., Cisco Systems, Inc., and Tellabs, Inc. These vendors and others have a variety of products to handle varying numbers of terminals at diverse line speeds.

Concentration

Concentrators combine several low-speed circuits into one higher-speed circuit. A concentrator can be thought of as a circuit multiplexer. For example, six 9,600 bps circuits might be concentrated onto one circuit with a 56 kbps capacity, as shown in Figure 9–17. The intelligence and buffering in the concentrator take care of the fact that 6 × 9,600 bps = 57,600 bps, which is greater than the 56,000 bps capacity of the circuit. A primary reason for performing line concentration is economics. In most cases, it is less expensive to lease a 56 kbps circuit between two points than six 9,600 bps circuits.

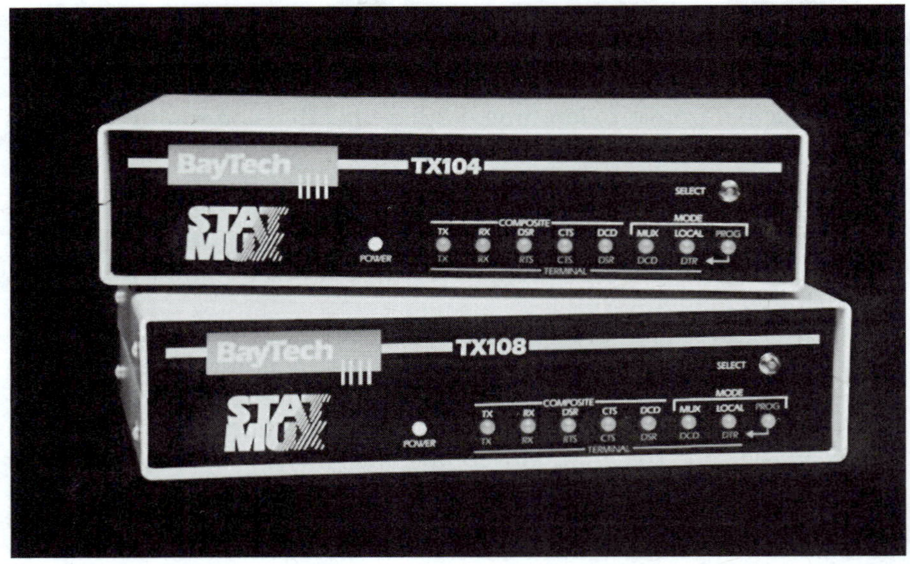

Two models of a statistical multiplexer that look virtually identical but provide different capacities. (Courtesy of Bay Technical Associates, Inc.)

Figure 9–17
Line concentration.

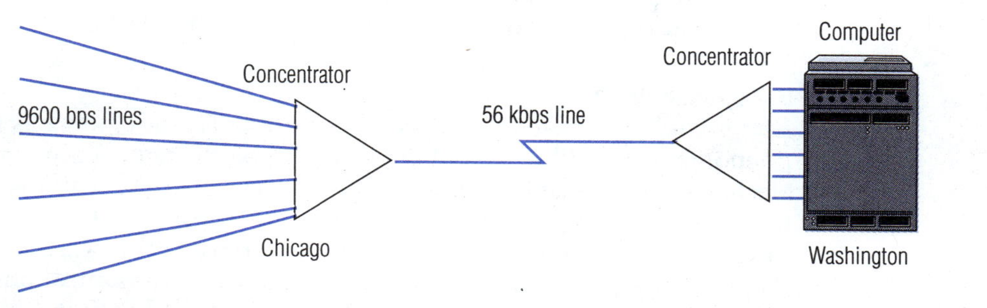

Figure 9–18
Inverse concentration.

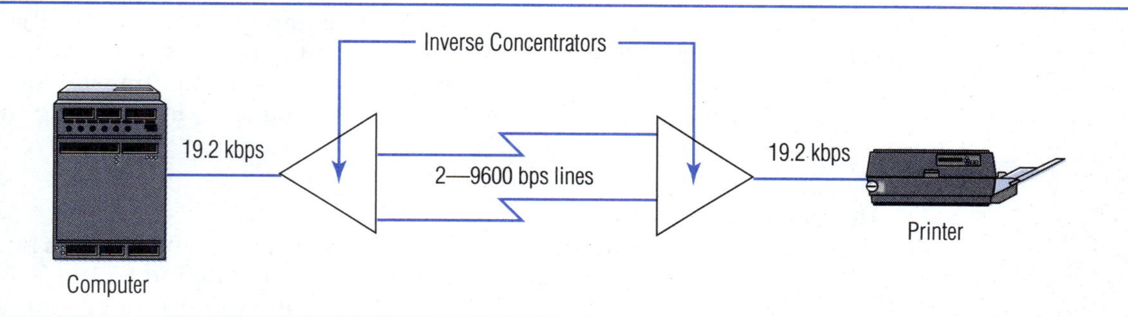

Inverse Concentration

In some cases, high-speed circuits are not available between two points, but it is desirable to provide high-speed service. An example is when there is a need to run a remote high-speed line printer. An *inverse concentrator* takes a high-speed data stream from a computer and breaks it apart for transmission over multiple slower-speed circuits, as shown in Figure 9–18. At the remote end, the slow-speed circuits are brought together again, providing a single high-speed data stream to the remote device.

CIRCUIT ERROR CONDITIONS

Communications circuits are subject to many conditions that cause degradation of the transmitted signal so that the receiving end cannot correctly determine what was sent. Some of these conditions arise because of normal characteristics of signal propagation, others are due to faulty circuit design, and still others are due to natural physical phenomena, such as electrical storms. The following section describes many conditions that can cause errors on a communications line. Of these, the most common are the various forms of noise, distortion, and attenuation.

Background Noise

Background noise, also known as *white noise* or *Gaussian noise,* is a normal phenomenon in all electrical circuitry. It results from the movement of electrons. It is present to some extent on every communications circuit. If the noise is at a high enough level, it can be heard as a hissing sound. It rarely represents a problem for either voice or data transmission because it is a known, predictable phenomenon, and the communications carriers have designed their circuitry and equipment to deal with it.

Impulse Noise

Impulse noise is a sudden spike on the communications circuit when the received amplitude exceeds a certain level. It is caused by transient electrical impulses, such as lightning, switching equipment, or a motor starting. You have probably heard it as annoying static crashes or clicking during a voice conversation. If the noise occurs during a data transmission, the impulse may cause one or more bits to be changed, invalidating the transmission.

Attenuation

Attenuation is the weakening of a signal over a distance, which occurs normally in all communications. Attenuation was illustrated in Figure 5–20. Just as your voice sounds weak at the back of an auditorium or a radio signal fades as you get farther from the transmitter, communications signals traveling through wires fade as the distance increases because of resistance in the medium. When the signal strength gets too low, it is impossible for the receiver to accurately pick out the individual signal changes. Amplifiers or repeaters are inserted in communications circuits often enough so that in normal operation, the signal's strength is boosted before attenuation causes a problem.

Attenuation Distortion

Attenuation distortion occurs because a signal does not attenuate evenly across its frequency range. Without special equipment, some frequencies on a circuit attenuate faster than others. Communications circuits are designed and special equipment is inserted on the circuit so that the signal attenuates evenly across the frequency spectrum. However, attenuation distortion can still occur if equipment is improperly adjusted or there is other maintenance activity.

Envelope Delay Distortion

Envelope delay distortion is an electrical phenomenon that occurs when not all frequencies propagate down a telecommunications circuit at exactly the same speed. The absolute propagation delay is not relevant—only the difference between the delay at different frequencies is relevant. Envelope delay distortion can be made worse when the signal passes through filters that are inserted in the circuit to filter out noise. Noise filters tend to delay certain frequencies more than others.

Phase Jitter

Phase jitter is a change in the phase of the signal induced by the carrier signal. It is especially problematic when phase modulation is used because the sudden shift in the phase of the received signal makes it difficult for the receiving modem to sense the legitimate phase changes that the transmitting modem sent.

Echo

Echo is the reversal of a signal, bouncing it back to the sender. Echo occurs on a communications circuit because of the electrical wave bouncing back from an intermediate point or the distant end of a circuit. Echoes are sometimes heard on a voice circuit when the speaker hears his or her voice coming back a fraction of a second after speaking. On a data circuit, echoes cause bit errors.

echo suppressors

Carriers install *echo suppressors* on switched circuits to eliminate the problems caused by echoes. Echo suppressors permit transmission in only one direction at a time. Since transmission in the reverse direction is prohibited, the echo cannot bounce back to the source. Although echo suppressors are a great help for voice transmission, they are a problem when data is sent because they take approximately 150 milliseconds to reverse and permit transmission in the opposite direction. Many modems turn signals around in 50 milliseconds or less, so if they send data, the first several hundred bits may be lost because the echo suppressors have not reversed.

The solution to this problem is to have the modem disable the echo suppressors at the beginning of a data transmission. When a connection is made, the modems send a tone that disables the echo suppressors. The suppressors stay deactivated as long as the modem sends a carrier signal on the circuit. When the communication ends and the carrier signal is no longer sent, the echo suppressors automatically reactivate. Leased data circuits do not have echo suppressors.

Crosstalk

As mentioned earlier, *crosstalk* is interference that occurs when the signals from one communications channel interfere with those on another channel. In a voice conversation, you may occasionally hear crosstalk as another conversation lower in amplitude than your own. Crosstalk can be caused by one signal overpowering another, by two pairs of wires that are in close proximity and are improperly shielded, or by frequencies of two or more multiplexed channels that are too close together.

Dropouts

Dropouts occur when a circuit suddenly goes dead for a period of time. Dropouts last from a fraction of a second to a few seconds, and then normal operation resumes. They can be caused by brief transmission problems, switching equipment, and other phenomena.

IMPACT OF ERRORS

Many of these errors, especially those caused by noise, occur in short bursts lasting from a few milliseconds to a few seconds. Often a short pause in the transmission or a retransmission of the block of data that is affected will circumvent the problem. An error of a given duration will affect more bits during higher-speed transmission than at lower speeds. One alternative for many types of transmission problems is to reduce the speed at which the data is being transmitted.

The effect of transmission errors is more significant in data transmission than in voice or television. In voice conversations, a crackle of static on the line does not usually cause a big problem. Human speech is very redundant, and the people at both ends of the circuit can interpolate and fill in a missing syllable or word. In television transmission, transmission errors often are seen as white flecks or snow on the screen, but a limited amount does not impair our ability to comprehend or enjoy the picture. In data transmission, on the other hand, an incorrect or missing bit can change the meaning of a message entirely. That is why it is particularly important to identify data transmission errors and take the necessary steps to correct them.

ERROR PREVENTION

Given that errors do occur in data transmissions, it is necessary to take steps to prevent, detect, and correct them. Economics must be considered because many of the error prevention techniques cost money to implement. The manager must judge whether the increased reliability is worth the cost. Certain standard techniques are in common use, however, and they are discussed here.

Line Conditioning

When a leased circuit is acquired from a common carrier, it is possible to request that it be conditioned. A *conditioned line* is one that meets tighter

conditioned line

specifications for amplitude and distortion. Signals traveling on a conditioned circuit are less likely to encounter errors than when the circuit is unconditioned. The higher the level of conditioning, the fewer errors that will occur on the circuit. With fewer errors, faster signaling rates and, therefore, faster transmission speeds can be achieved.

Conditioning is accomplished by testing each link of a circuit to ensure that it meets the tighter parameters that conditioning implies. If necessary, special compensating or amplifying equipment is inserted in the circuit at the carrier's central offices to bring the circuit up to conditioned specifications.

Conditioning in the United States is specified as class C or class D. C conditioning adjusts a line's characteristics so that attenuation distortion and envelope delay distortion lie within certain limits. D conditioning deals with the ratio of signal strength to noise strength, called *signal-to-noise ratio,* and distortion.

With the improved sophistication of many newer modems, circuit conditioning is sometimes not required at all. Some modems have enough signal processing capability that they can tolerate the higher error rate of an unconditioned circuit. Modem manufacturers generally specify the type of conditioning that their modems require. In comparison to the total cost of the line, conditioning is relatively inexpensive. Therefore, it is almost always prudent to request it, especially if it is recommended by the modem manufacturer.

Conditioning cannot be obtained on switched circuits because the physical facilities used to make the connection vary from one call to the next. The variance is wide enough that conditioning facilities cannot be provided realistically or cost effectively.

Shielding

Shielding of a communications circuit is best understood by looking at Figure 9–8, which shows a coaxial cable. A metallic sheath surrounds the center conductor. Frequently, this shielding is electrically grounded at one end. Shielding prevents stray electrical signals from reaching the primary conductor. In certain situations, shielding on critical parts of a communications circuit may reduce noise or crosstalk. Electrically noisy environments, such as in factories or where circuits run near fluorescent light fixtures or elevator motors, are situations in which communications circuits can benefit from shielding.

Improving Connections

One rule of thumb for telecommunications wiring is "always check the cables and connections first." More problems seem to be caused by poor quality cables and loose, dirty, or otherwise poor connections, than anything else. Check to ensure that all cables and connectors are clean and properly seated, with retaining screws, where they exist, tightened. Avoid cable splices if at all possible. Splices in fiber cables can cause echoes, which are a source of interference and slow the throughput.

Electronic versus Mechanical Equipment

Though not entirely a user option, the replacement of mechanical equipment in the common carrier's central office or the company's equipment rooms with modern electronic equipment can lead to improved circuit quality. Not only is mechanical equipment more prone to failure, but it is also electrically noisier and more likely to induce impulse noise on circuits that pass through it. If a central office containing electromechanical switches is upgraded to an all-electronic configuration, it would be natural for the circuits running through that office to be of better quality and more trouble-free.

ERROR DETECTION

Even if circuits are well designed and good preventive measures, such as circuit conditioning, are implemented, errors will still occur. Therefore, it is necessary to have methods in place to detect these errors so that something can be done to correct them and data integrity can be maintained. *Error detection* normally involves some type of transmission redundancy. In the simplest case, all data could be transmitted two or more times and then compared at the receiving end. This would be fairly expensive in terms of the time consumed for the duplicate transmission. With the error rates experienced today, a full duplication of each transmission is not necessary in most situations.

A more sophisticated type of checking is to calculate some kind of a check digit or check character and transmit it with the data. At the receiving end, the calculation is made again and the result compared to the check character that was calculated before transmission. If the two check characters agree, the data has been received correctly.

Echo Checking

One of the simplest ways to check for transmission errors is called *echo checking,* in which each character is echoed from the receiver back to the transmitter. This is done in some timesharing systems in which a terminal operator can verify immediately that what he or she typed is what appears back on the screen as echoed from the computer. Of course, the original data transmission could be correct, and an error might occur on the transmission of the echo message back to the sender. In either case, the operator can rekey the character.

Vertical Redundancy Checking (VRC) or Parity Checking

The next most sophisticated error detection technique is called *vertical redundancy checking (VRC)* or *parity checking.*

Unfortunately, noise on the communications line frequently changes more than 1 bit. If two 0 bits are changed to 1s, the VRC will not detect the error because the number of 1 bits will still be an even number. Therefore, additional checking techniques are employed in most data transmission systems.

Longitudinal Redundancy Checking (LRC)

Horizontal parity checking is called *longitudinal redundancy checking (LRC).* When LRC is employed, a parity character is added to the end of each block of data by the DTE before the block is transmitted. This character, also called a *block check character (BCC),* is made up of parity bits. Bit 1 in the BCC is the parity bit for all the 1 bits in the block, bit 2 is the parity bit for all of the 2 bits, and so on. For example, assuming even parity and the use of the ASCII code, the BCC for the word "parity" is shown below.

block check character

	p	a	r	i	t	y	BCC
Bit 1	1	1	1	1	1	1	0
Bit 2	0	0	0	0	0	0	0
Bit 3	1	0	1	0	1	1	0
Bit 4	0	0	0	1	0	1	0
Bit 5	0	0	0	0	1	0	1
Bit 6	0	0	1	0	0	0	1
Bit 7	0	1	0	1	0	1	1
VRC	0	0	1	1	1	0	1

A VRC check will catch errors in which 1, 3, or 5 bits in a character have been changed, but if 2, 4, or 6 bits are changed, they will go undetected. Thus, VRC by itself will catch about half of the transmission errors that occur. When combined with LRC, the probability of detecting an error is increased. The exact probability depends on the length of the data block for which the block check character is calculated, but even when used together, VRC and LRC will not catch all errors.

Cyclic Redundancy Checking (CRC)

Cyclic redundancy checking (CRC) is a particular implementation of a more general class of error detection techniques called *polynomial error checking.* The polynomial techniques are more sophisticated ways for calculating a BCC than an LRC provides. All of the bits of a block of data are processed by a mathematical algorithm by the DTE at the transmitting end. One or more block check characters are generated and transmitted with the data.

polynomial error checking

At the receiving end, the DTE performs the calculation again, and the check characters are compared. If differences are found, an error has occurred. If the check characters are the same, the probability is very high that the data is error free. With the proper selection of polynomials used in the calculation of the BCC, the number of undetected errors may be as low as 1 in 10^9 characters. To put this in more familiar terms: On a 9,600 bps circuit transmitting 8-bit characters 24 hours per day, one would expect no more than 1 undetected error every 231+ hours, or 9.6 days.

Several standard CRC calculations exist; they are known as CRC-12, CRC-16, and CRC-CCITT. The standard specifies the degree of the generating polynomial and the generating polynomial itself. CRC-12 specifies a polynomial of degree 12, CRC-16 and CRC-CCITT specify a polynomial of degree 16. For example, the polynomial for CRC-CCITT is $x^{16} + x^{12} + x^5 + 1$, where x is the bit being processed. CRC-16 and CRC-CCITT generate a 16-bit block check character that can

- detect all single bit and double bit errors;
- detect all errors in cases where an odd number of bits is incorrect;
- detect two pairs of adjacent errors;
- detect all burst errors of 16 bits or fewer;
- detect over 99.998 percent of all burst errors greater than 16 bits.

Cyclic redundancy checking has become the standard method of error detection for block data transmission because of its high reliability in detecting transmission errors.

ERROR CORRECTION

In most applications, data validity and integrity are of prime importance, so once an error is detected, some technique must be employed to correct the data.

Retransmission

The most frequently used and usually the most economical *error correction system* is the retransmission of the data in error. Although there are many variations, the basic technique used is that when the receiving DTE detects an error, it signals the transmitting DTE to resend the data. This is called an *automatic repeat request (ARQ)* technique, and it is a part of the line protocol. In order for ARQ to work, the transmitting station must hold the data in a buffer until an acknowledgment comes from the receiver that the block of data was received correctly. Another requirement is that there must be a reverse channel for signaling from the receiver to the transmitter.

automatic repeat request (ARQ)

Stop and Wait ARQ In the *stop and wait ARQ* technique, a block of data is sent and the receiver sends either an acknowledgment (ACK) if the data was received correctly or a negative acknowledgment (NAK) if an error was detected. If an ACK is received, the transmitter sends the next block of data. If a NAK is received, the data block that was received in error and is still stored in the transmitter's buffer is retransmitted. No data is transmitted while the receiver decodes the incoming data and checks it for errors. If a reverse channel is not available, the line must be turned around for the transmission of the ACK or NAK and then turned around again for the transmission (or retransmission) of the data block. Stop and wait ARQ is most effective where the data blocks are long, error rates are low, and a reverse channel is available.

Continuous ARQ Using the *continuous ARQ* technique, data blocks are continuously sent over the forward channel while ACKs and NAKs are sent over the reverse channel. When a NAK arrives at the transmitter, the usual strategy is to retransmit beginning with the data block that the receiver indicated was in error. The transmitting station's buffer must be large enough to hold several data blocks. The receiver throws away all data received after the block in error for which the NAK was sent because it will receive that data again.

An alternate strategy is for the transmitter to retransmit only the block in error. In this case, the receiver must be more sophisticated because it must insert the retransmitted data block into the correct sequence among all of the data received. Of the two approaches to continuous ARQ, the first strategy, sometimes called "go back *N* blocks," is more commonly used.

Continuous ARQ is far more efficient than stop and wait ARQ when the propagation times are long, as they are in satellite transmission.

Forward Error Correction (FEC)

VRC, LRC, and CRC checking methods are effective in detecting errors in data transmission. However, they contain no method for automatically correcting the data at the receiving end. By using special transmission codes and adding additional redundant bits, it is possible to include enough redundancy in a transmission to allow the receiving station to automatically correct a large portion of any data received in error, thus avoiding retransmission. This technique is called *forward error correction (FEC).*

Research into FEC techniques has been conducted by organizations such as Bell Laboratories and the military. The military's interest lies in being able to make one-way transmissions to submarines or aircraft, knowing that messages will arrive with a predetermined but very low probability of error. Three well-known error correcting codes are the Bose-Chaudhuri code, the Hagelbarger code, and the Hamming code. The Bose-Chaudhuri code, in its original version, uses 10 check bits for every 21 data bits and is capable of correcting all double bit errors and detecting up to 4 consecutive bit errors. The Hagelbarger code will correct up to 6 consecutive bit errors if the group of bits in error is followed by at least 19 good data bits. The Hamming code, in its 7-bit form, allows single bit errors in each character to be corrected. However, only 16 unique characters are allowed in the character set. Other modifications to the Hamming code allow a larger character set, with a corresponding increase in the number of checking bits.

FEC codes have a high cost in terms of the number of redundant bits required to allow error correcting at the receiving end. In certain applications—particularly where only one-way simplex transmission is allowed or possible—the cost is well justified. Since the FEC techniques are sophisticated, a specially programmed microcomputer in the DTE or DCE normally is used to calculate the FEC codes and perform the error correction.

WIRING AND CABLING

Though not strictly a circuit issue, the subject of wiring and cabling within a building or facility is closely related to circuit installation and operation. Most buildings today contain several pairs of twisted wires, originally installed by the telephone company, running to each office. One pair is for the telephone, and the others are spares. If the office contains a computer terminal, it is, in all likelihood, connected to the server or network via a totally separate wire or cable that was installed by the data processing department. Where private television exists, a third cabling system—perhaps "owned" by the audiovisual department—also may be found.

A commonly stated requirement, which is being implemented in some organizations, is that all of these telecommunications wiring systems need to be merged and consolidated so that a single communications outlet is installed in each office. This outlet would provide jacks for connecting all of the communications equipment in the office. The wire behind the outlet would run to a local wiring distribution center or equipment room on the floor of the office building, as shown in Figure 9–19. The distribution centers would be connected via high-capacity cable, perhaps one of optical fiber, to the wiring center for the building or site. The communications wiring of the future should be similar to the electrical wiring of today, where, for most offices, a single type and size of wire runs to one or more conveniently located standard outlets.

To achieve this ideal standardized communications wiring plan, a long history of nonstandard communications wiring must be overcome. Each vendor of communications equipment traditionally has set individual standards for data communications wiring and for the media that connect terminals to its computers. Of course, these vendors' standards bear little or no relationship to the standards for telephone wiring that the telephone companies have used for years. Even within a single vendor's product line, many standards exist.

Figure 9–19
Simplified wiring diagram of an office building.

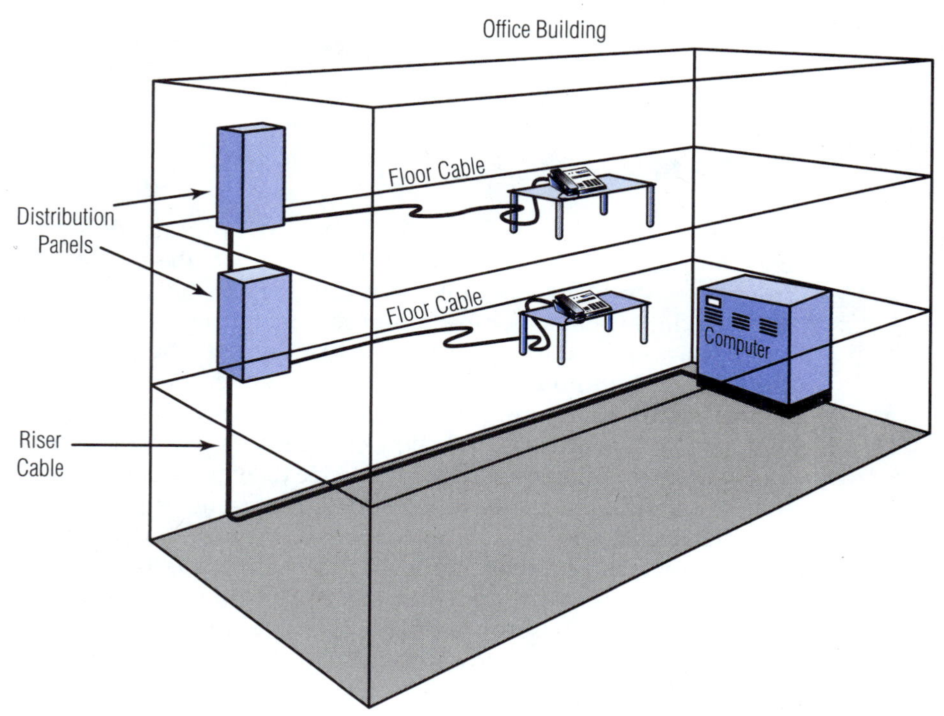

Within the past few years, there has been movement toward using standard Cat 5 twisted pair wire for connecting data terminals to computers and as the media for local area networks. Many companies are choosing Cat 5 for voice too because it gives them the flexibility to use the wiring for data later if circumstances change. Companies are also learning that it makes sense to install spare pairs of wires everywhere. The major cost of wiring is the labor cost to install the cable. Whether the cable contains two pair, four pair, or eight pair of Cat 5 wire makes little difference in the overall cost.

Some general guidelines for managers to follow when involved in a wiring project are:

- Estimate the capacity required and add at least 25 percent.
- Install at least two Cat 5 pair to each desk. Three or four pair is better.
- Consider fiber-optic cable for the backbone between floors and between equipment rooms.
- Choose a wiring contractor carefully, and get test results after the wiring is installed.

The major problem that most companies face is the cost and effort to replace all existing wiring with wire that meets the requirements of the new "standard." In most cases, the only practical, affordable alternative is to convert existing wiring when opportunities such as building renovations arise and to install the new type of wiring in all newly constructed buildings.

THE GROWING DEMAND FOR BANDWIDTH

Any way you view it, companies and people are demanding faster telecommunications circuits—higher bandwidth—at an accelerating pace. The good news is that the technology to provide the bandwidth, such as digital circuits, fiber-optic cables, higher speed modems, cable modems, and the like is progressing rapidly too. The bad news is that the ability of carriers and other companies to deliver the bandwidth to the potential customers is fraught with problems that will take time to solve. If they could, the carriers and their competitors would love to rewire the world and run high-speed digital service to every business and home. But the cost of doing so, at least in a short time frame, is prohibitive.

The rapid rise of Internet usage is unprecedented and has caught most observers and telecommunications suppliers by surprise, but it is providing a new impetus to upgrade the world's telecommunications infrastructure. The base of people who, directly or indirectly, realize the benefits of increased bandwidth is much larger than it was just a year or two ago. That means more potential customers who are willing to pay at least something in order to access the Internet faster.

Overall, research and experience suggest that 5 years from now, a significant percentage of the population of the U.S. will be receiving some or all of its communication, information, entertainment, and educational material by means of broadband Internet. Large numbers of businesses will be using it as well, and significant amounts of commerce will be conducted over the Internet. Users will come to view bandwidth as a *commodity* that they pay for according to how much they use, just like other utilities, but they'll want bandwidth to be available in essentially unlimited quantities, much as electricity is today in most parts of the world.

bandwidth-on-demand

This concept is called *bandwidth-on-demand.* It's not new, but the need for it is recognized more today than ever before. Cable TV operators, DBS broadcasters, telephone companies, and others will all be competing bandwidth suppliers, and applications will be thought of as appliances plugged into the bandwidth outlet. The path to commoditized bandwidth-on-demand will take some restructuring in the telecommunications industry and some years to achieve, but seems to have a very high probability of occurring within 10 if not 5 years.

SIDEBAR 9–2

DOWNLOADING A "TITANIC" FILE

How much of the 3-hour, 14-minute movie 'Titanic' could be downloaded by these modems and data lines in 7 minutes, 23 seconds:

Descriptions

Cable modem—10 Mbps, 100%

This modem uses the cable TV wire, instead of a phone line, for data transmission. The coaxial cable can carry much more data than a copper phone line. It's often faster, as well as less expensive, than most alternatives. But customers in a neighborhood share the trunk lines, which means speed can slow when usage is high.

DSL—4 Mbps, 40%

Digital Subscriber Line technology uses existing phone connections with a DSL modem to provide service at relatively low cost. Speeds vary considerably, and it's often faster to download than to transmit. The variations depend on:

- Quality of the Internet service provider's equipment
- Level of service the customer orders
- Distance from the phone switching facility

T-1 line—1.5 Mbps, 15%

A fast phone technology using a dedicated line to serve several phones. But it's expensive to install, with prices rising the farther the user is from the nearest phone switching facility. Also, the monthly charge is high.

ISDN—128 kbps, 0%

An Integrated Services Digital Network connection can connect several phones. But many say it's not fast enough to be worth the special hardware and, usually, the dedicated phone line it needs. Service is limited to within one mile of the phone-company switching facility.

Phone-line modem—28.8 kbps, 0%

This inexpensive modem—the most common now—connects to an ordinary phone line. It transmits and receives data at one relatively slow rate.

In the meantime, as you have seen, there are many ways that a business or individual consumer can get high bandwidth network access today. Figure 9–20 shows many of the alternatives and the tradeoffs with each one.

Figure 9–20
Types of high speed network access and the tradeoffs between them.

Service	Availability	Typical Speed (downstream/upstream)	Tradeoffs	Typical Uses
Dial-up	Everywhere	56 kbps/33.6 kbps	Inexpensive. Easy to install. Relatively slow.	People who can't obtain or afford other alternatives. Travelers.
ISDN	Widespread	128 kbps/128 kbps	Twice as fast as regular dial-up. Costly. Prone to setup difficulties.	Small office and home users who can't get a faster service.
Satellite (DSS)	Widespread	384 kbps/33.6 kbps	Good downstream speed. Complex installation. Must have clear view of southern sky.	Businesses and home users in rural areas or who can't get other high-speed services.
Cable	Limited	384 kbps–5 Mbps/128 kbps–2.5 Mbps	Least expensive high-speed connection. Always on. Limited availability. Most businesses aren't wired for cable. Can't choose your ISP.	Home office. Telecommuters. Businesses that have cable installed.
DSL	Very limited	144 kbps–8 Mbps/64 kbps–8 Mbps	Uses ordinary telephone line. Always on. Requires technician to install. Expensive.	Businesses that can't justify T-1 service. Home users who can't get cable.
T-1–T-3	Widespread	56 kbps–45 Mbps/56 kbps–45 Mbps	Business oriented. Speed guarantees. Quick repair. Expensive.	Medium size to large businesses that can afford the cost and can't afford service problems.

■ SUMMARY

This chapter looked at the characteristics of telecommunications circuits, various ways of classifying them, and the media with which they can be implemented. The telecommunications network designer is faced with a wide variety of choices for circuits. Only by understanding the characteristics and trade-offs between various circuit types and media can the designer reach a reasonable solution for a given network or application.

More often than not, a company's diverse communications needs indicate that several different circuit types are required. There may be a combination of private, leased, and dial-up circuits. Usually, there is a mixture of transmission speeds to accommodate differing applications and transmission volumes. Different media may be used to satisfy still other needs. All in all, the design of a comprehensive communications network is a complex task requiring both telecommunications and application knowledge.

CASE STUDY

Dow Corning's Data Communications Circuits

One of Dow Corning's philosophies about its data communications system is that it must deliver excellent response time to its users. For that reason, the circuits that make up the system operate at the highest speeds that the company believes it can justify economically.

In 1997, Dow Corning entered into an agreement with WorldCom to provide and manage its international data communications circuits. At the same time, WorldCom proposed converting the network to one based on frame relay technology. This means that between locations, WorldCom provides all of the circuits and backup capability, which are mainly high-speed digital circuits. Dow Corning specifies the capacity it needs and the desired response times, and WorldCom configures the network to meet the requirements. There is, of course, ongoing discussion between Dow Corning and WorldCom about the costs as the service requirements change.

WorldCom digital circuits that operate at 128 kbps or higher connect Midland with the larger U.S. plant locations. Internationally, Dow Corning's data communications circuits tie headquarters in Midland to the following locations:

Brussels, Belgium	512 kbps;
Barry, Wales	512 kbps;
Tokyo, Japan	512 kbps;
Sydney, Australia	512 kbps;
Hong Kong	128 kbps;
Toronto, Canada	128 kbps;
Mexico City, Mexico	128 kbps;
Sao Paulo, Brazil	128 kbps.

To avoid the delays associated with satellite circuits, all of these circuits operate on terrestrial cables. While circuits can be envisioned as a star network fanning out from Midland, in reality it is a mesh subnetwork within the overall WorldCom global network.

Dow Corning uses 30 T-1 circuits in the Midland area and about 60 globally. Three T-1s connect the corporate center with the Midland plant 5 miles away, and others run to nearby plants and other office buildings. A T-1 circuit also runs directly to Ameritech's central office and is used for voice circuits. All of the T-1 circuits are leased from Ameritech, which also did the installation. The circuits are less expensive than the multiple voice and data circuits that would otherwise be required. Timeplex multiplexing equipment is also used by Dow Corning on a limited basis, to divide the T-1 capacity into video, voice, and data circuits, but in most cases Ameritech provides the multiplexing equipment as a part of the T-1 service.

The company has a broadband coaxial cable transmission system in the Midland plant. Midland plant personnel installed it many years ago in response to unique requirements for television and data transmission, and it is operated and maintained entirely by plant people. The broadband cable originally carried data from instruments to process control computers throughout the laboratories and plant, and it was also used for data transmission between the IBM terminals on the site and a concentrator. The concentrator forwarded the data on high-speed circuits to the mainframe computers at the corporate headquarters. A third use of the cable was for a television channel providing news and other information to plant employees. In the early 1990s, the use of the cable for data transmission was phased out, and now it is only used for intraplant television transmissions. The data traffic is carried on LAN circuits, either twisted pair wire or optical fiber cable, either of which are easier to maintain than the broadband cable.

In 1986, Dow Corning installed its first private fiber-optic circuit. The fiber cable connects the corporate headquarters building with a building located 1.1. miles away. The fiber was justified because of the voice and data requirements at the site and because it could provide a stronger security capability than would otherwise have been possible.

GTE won the bid to install the cable and buried it in the ground on Dow Corning property. Installation was fairly simple because all of the property between the two buildings is owned by Dow Corning, and only one road had to be crossed. Permission was obtained from the county to bury cable under the road. The optical fiber cable carries data communications between buildings as well as several television channels. Based on the successful experience, other fiber cables were installed, mainly to connect local area networks with each other.

QUESTIONS

1. Dow Corning's philosophy of providing excellent response time means that some of its data circuits are lightly utilized. Explain why this is so. Do you think the company is wasting money by having low circuit utilization?
2. Is the company missing out on service or cost-saving opportunities by shunning satellite circuits?
3. What difficulties do you imagine arise because the entire global network is configured and specified centrally by the telecommunications staff in Midland? Would there be advantages or disadvantages to having the staffs in the outlying locations configure the network for their areas of responsibility?
4. The line speed, or bandwidth, of Dow Corning's circuits has grown faster than the number of employees. Why would this be so? Do you suppose the growth will continue in the future?
5. What are the tradeoffs of entering into a global network contract such as Dow Corning did with WorldCom?

REVIEW QUESTIONS

1. Explain how a line, a circuit, a link, and a channel differ.
2. Describe a multipoint circuit.
3. Why is a four-wire circuit preferable to a two-wire circuit for data transmission?
4. Compare and contrast the functions of a modem and a DSU/CSU.
5. What is the data-carrying capacity of a T-1 circuit? Can a T-1 circuit be used to carry analog voice signals?
6. What is the normal maximum data transmission speed on an analog voice-grade circuit?
7. Identify five different media used for carrying communications signals and discuss under what circumstances each is most appropriately used.

8. What are the advantages of shielded twisted pair wire compared to ordinary twisted pair?
9. Under what circumstances would it be most appropriate to use a broadband coaxial cable instead of a fiber-optic cable?
10. List the characteristics of optical fiber.
11. What are some potential disadvantages of using microwave radio for data transmission?
12. Explain the term *propagation delay* and why it is important in satellite transmission.
13. Under what circumstances would a company consider installing a private fiber-optic link connecting two of its locations?
14. Under what circumstances would a company consider bypassing its local telephone company?
15. What are the advantages of STDM over traditional TDM?
16. How does dialback improve security on a switched communications line?
17. Discuss the circuit attributes of attenuation, envelope delay distortion, phase jitter, and crosstalk.
18. Why are communications line errors more significant when data is being transmitted than when voice is being transmitted? If voice is transmitted digitally, do line errors become more significant?
19. What is the purpose of communications line conditioning?
20. What is the difference between LRC and CRC checking?
21. Compare and contrast the stop and wait ARQ and continuous ARQ techniques.
22. Why is it desirable for a company to manage its communications wiring?
23. What are the advantages of ISDN circuits?
24. Explain the difference between a private circuit and a leased circuit.
25. What is SMDS?
26. Distinguish among T-1, T-2, T-3, and T-4 circuits.
27. What is Cat 3 wiring? Why is it important?
28. What is Cat 5 wiring? Why is it important?
29. Distinguish between T-1 and E-1 circuits.
30. What is noise on a transmission line? What causes noise?
31. What is a cyclical redundancy check? How does it work?
32. What is the difference between a repeater and an amplifier?
33. Describe several ways to get high-speed access to the Internet. Are all of those methods available today?
34. Distinguish between the capabilities of SDSL and ADSL.
35. What is the major use for SONET in the United States?
36. What is the difference between unguided and conducted media? Give two examples of each.
37. Identify several reasons why a business might and might not select satellite service for high-speed access to the Internet.

PROBLEMS AND PROJECTS

1. Using the VRC and LRC parity checking techniques and the ASCII code, calculate the parity bit and block check character for your last name.
2. A company has a leased satellite circuit between its New York and San Francisco locations. The circuit is routed on a satellite. When 500-character blocks of data are sent from New York to the San Francisco office using a stop and wait ARQ technique, what percentage of the line time is used for actual data transmission and what percentage is spent waiting for acknowledgments and line turnarounds? Assume that
   - line turnaround takes 50 milliseconds;
   - no errors occur during the transmission;
   - line speed is 9,600 bps;
   - an acknowledgment message is 5 characters long.

How does the percentage change if 5,000 character blocks are transmitted?

3. Identify the trade-offs a company would have to consider when deciding whether to implement dial-up data or leased communications circuits. The company has locations throughout the United States. The applications are primarily basic business transactions, such as customer order entry, shipping, purchasing, accounts receivable, and accounts payable.

4. Visit a company that has installed fiber-optic links. Why did they install optical fiber? What difficulties did they have when installing the fiber? What error rate are they experiencing for data transmission on the fiber? How often has it failed? Overall, how has the fiber operated compared to the previous communications technology that was installed?

5. What type of wiring would you suggest for a small service business that just moved into a building recently vacated by a grocery store? The business does no manufacturing, so employees will be sitting in an office environment. The company expects to install a LAN with a data rate of either 10 or 16 Mbps, and will use the telephone company's Centrex system for telephone service.

6. Investigate the status of ISDN service in your community. Is the service available? Try to find someone who has installed ISDN at home. Talk with them about the ease or difficulty of installing it, and how it has been operating since it was installed.

7. Investigate the alternatives for getting high-speed access to the Internet in your home. What services are available today where you live? If you have several alternatives to choose from, which would you select? Why?

Vocabulary

circuit
line
link
data link
channel
forward channel
reverse channel
node
simplex
half-duplex
full-duplex
point-to-point circuit
multipoint circuit
multidrop circuit
two-wire circuit
four-wire circuit
low-speed circuit
subvoice-grade circuit
voice-grade circuit
wideband circuit
digital circuit
repeater
Integrated Services Digital Network (ISDN)
basic access
primary access
broadband ISDN (B-ISDN)
T-carrier system
fractional T-1
connectionless service
asymmetric digital subscriber line (ADSL)
conducted media
guided media
radiated media
unguided media
twisted pair
unshielded twisted pair (UTP)
crosstalk
punchdown block
shielded twisted pair
coaxial cable
optical fiber
core
cladding
light-emitting diode (LED)
laser
single mode
multimode
dispersion
wavelength division multiplexing (WDM)
Synchronous Optical Network (SONET)
microwave radio
geosynchronous orbit
uplink
downlink
propagation delay
Ku band
very small aperture terminals (VSAT)
direct broadcast satellite (DBS)
digital satellite service (DSS)
infrared
private circuit
leased circuit
bypass
circuit switching
callback unit
dialback unit

time division multiplexing (TDM)
frame
message
statistical time division multiplexing (STDM)
concentrator
inverse concentrator
background noise
white noise
Gaussian noise
impulse noise
attenuation distortion
envelope delay distortion
phase jitter
echo
echo suppressor
dropout
conditioned line
signal-to-noise ratio
shielding
error detection
echo checking
vertical redundancy checking (VRC)
parity checking
longitudinal redundancy checking (LRC)
block check character (BCC)
cyclic redundancy checking (CRC)
polynomial error checking
error correction system
automatic repeat request (ARQ)
stop and wait ARQ
continuous ARQ
forward error correction (FEC)
commodity
bandwidth-on-demand

References

Chatterjee, Samir and Suzanne Pawlowski. "All Optical Networks." *Communications of the ACM* (June 1999): 75–83.

Conover, Joel. "Sorting Out Cabling Standards." *Network Computing* (February 21, 2000): 91–93.

Crotty, Cameron. "New Flavor of DSL Brings Faster, Cheaper Web Access to Your Door." *PC World* (September 1999): 62–64.

Fowler, Thomas B. "Internet Access and Pricing: Sorting Out the Options." *Telecommunications* (February 1997): 41–69.

Kaplan, Mark. "Voice over SDSL: Effectively Combining Voice and Data." *Telecommunications* (February 2000): 79–80.

McCracken, Harry. "Bandwidth on Demand." *PC World* (March 1999): 109–118.

Mills, Mike. "A Wealth of Data on Ocean Floors." *International Herald Tribune* (March 10, 1998).

Peterson, Kerstin. "So You Want to Wire a Building." *Teleconnect* (March 1997): 168–173.

Ramo, Joshua Cooper. "Welcome to the Wired World." *Time* (February 3, 1997): 37–48.

Rosenbush, Steve. "Charge of the Light Brigade." *Business Week* (January 31, 2000): 62–66.

Sekar, Richard. "G.lite: Pragmatic, Mass Market High-Density DSL." *Telecommunications* (April 2000): 35–36.

Willis, David, "Staying Sober at the xDSL Party." *Network Computing* (October 18, 1999): 49.

Woods, Darrin. "Shedding Light on SONET." *Network Computing* (March 20, 2000): 47–54.

———. "SONET from Scratch." *Network Computing* (May 15, 2000): 129–146.

———. "Too Much Long Distance." *Fortune* (March 15, 1999): 105–110.

CHAPTER 10

The Network Layer

We learned that the transport layer provides various forms of process-to-process communication by relying on the network layer's host-to-host communication service. We also learned that the transport layer does so without any knowledge about how the network layer actually implements this service. So perhaps you're now wondering, what's under the hood of the host-to-host communication service, what makes it tick?

In this chapter we'll learn exactly how the network layer implements the host-to-host communication service. We'll see that unlike the transport layer, there is a piece of the network layer in each and every host and router in the network. Because of this, network-layer protocols are among the most challenging (and therefore among the most interesting!) in the protocol stack.

The network layer is also one of the most complex layers in the protocol stack, and so we'll have a lot of ground to cover here. We'll begin our study with an overview of the network layer and the services it can provide. We'll then revisit the two broad approaches towards structuring network-layer packet delivery—the datagram and the virtual-circuit model—and see the fundamental role that addressing plays in delivering a packet to its destination host.

In this chapter, we'll make an important distinction between the **forwarding** and **routing** functions of the network layer. Forwarding involves the transfer of a packet from an incoming link to an outgoing link within a *single* router. Routing involves *all* of a network's routers, whose collective interactions via routing protocols determine the paths (or routes) that packets take on their trips from source to destination node. Keeping this distinction in mind as you progress through this chapter will help you place many of the topics covered in an appropriate context.

In order to deepen our understanding of packet forwarding, we'll look "inside" a router—at its hardware architecture and organization. We'll then look at packet forwarding in the Internet, along with the celebrated Internet Protocol (IP). We'll investigate network-layer addressing and the IPv4 datagram format. We'll then explore network address translation (NAT), datagram fragmentation, the Internet Control Message Protocol (ICMP) and IPv6.

We'll then turn our attention to the network layer's routing function. We'll see that the job of a routing algorithm is to determine good paths (equivalently, routes), from senders to receivers. We'll first study the theory of routing algorithms, concentrating on the two most prevalent classes of algorithms: link-state and distance-vector algorithms. Since the complexity of routing algorithms grows considerably as the number of network routers increases, hierarchical routing approaches will are also be of interest. We'll then see how theory is put into practice when we cover the Internet's intra-autonomous system routing protocols (RIP, OSPF, and IS-IS) and its inter-autonomous system routing protocol, BGP. We'll close this chapter with a discussion of broadcast and multicast routing.

In summary, this chapter has three major parts. The first part, Sections 10.1 and 10.2, covers network-layer functions and services. The second part, Sections 10.3 and 10.4, covers forwarding. Finally, the third part, Sections 10.5 through 10.7, covers routing.

10.1 Introduction

Figure 10.1 shows a simple network with two hosts, H1 and H2, and several routers on the path between H1 and H2. Suppose that H1 is sending information to H2, and consider the role of the network layer in these hosts and in the intervening routers. The network layer in H1 takes segments from the transport layer in H1, encapsulates each segment into a datagram (that is, a network-layer packet), and then starts the datagrams on their journey to their destination; that is, it sends the datagrams to its nearby router, R1. At the receiving host, H2, the network layer receives the datagrams from its nearby router R2, extracts the transport-layer segments, and delivers the segments up to the transport layer at H2. The primary role of the routers is to forward datagrams from input links to output links. Note that the routers in Figure 10.1 are shown with a truncated protocol stack, that is, with no upper layers above the network layer, because (except for control purposes) routers do not run application- and transport-layer protocols.

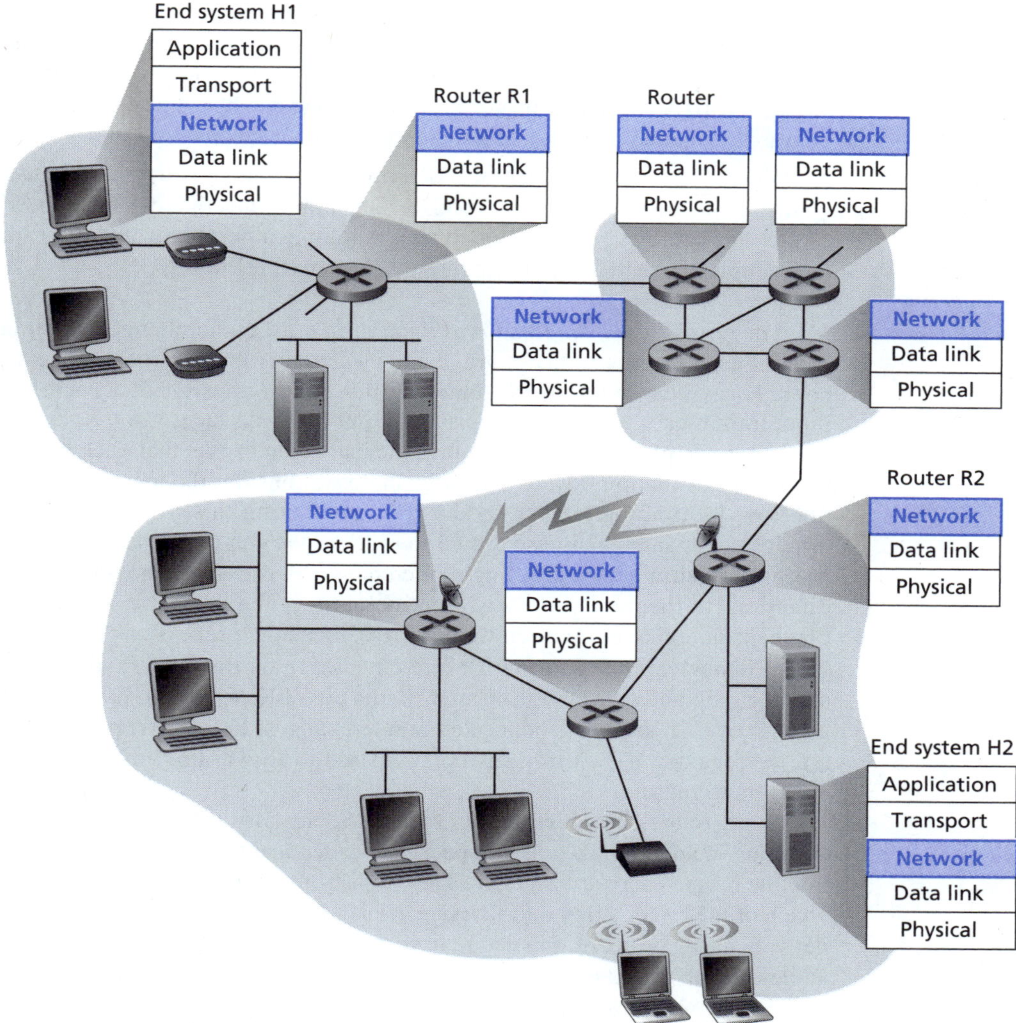

Figure 10.1 ♦ The network layer

10.1.1 Forwarding and Routing

The role of the network layer is thus deceptively simple—to move packets from a sending host to a receiving host. To do so, two important network-layer functions can be identified:

- *Forwarding.* When a packet arrives at a router's input link, the router must move the packet to the appropriate output link. For example, a packet arriving from Host H1 to Router R1 must be forwarded to the next router on a path to H2. In Section 10.3, we'll look inside a router and examine how a packet is actually forwarded from an input link at a router to an output link.
- *Routing.* The network layer must determine the route or path taken by packets as they flow from a sender to a receiver. The algorithms that calculate these paths are referred to as **routing algorithms.** A routing algorithm would determine, for example, the path along which packets flow from H1 to H2.

The terms *forwarding* and *routing* are often used interchangeably by authors discussing the network layer. We'll use these terms much more precisely in this book. *Forwarding* refers to the router-local action of transferring a packet from an input link interface to the appropriate output link interface. *Routing* refers to the network-wide process that determines the end-to-end paths that packets take from source to destination. Using a driving analogy, consider the trip from Pennsylvania from Florida undertaken by our traveler. During this trip, our driver passes through many interchanges en route to Florida. We can think of forwarding as the process of getting through a single interchange: A car enters the interchange, gets directions to the next interchange on its journey, and takes the outgoing road to that next interchange. We can think of routing as the process of planning the trip from Pennsylvania to Florida: Before embarking on the trip, the driver has consulted a map and chosen one of many paths possible, with each path consisting of a series of road segments connected at interchanges. In this first part of this chapter, we focus on network-layer topics related to forwarding; we'll then turn our attention to routing.

Every router has a **forwarding table.** A router forwards a packet by examining the value of a field in the arriving packet's header, and then using this value to index into the router's forwarding table. The result from the forwarding table indicates to which of the router's link interfaces the packet is to be forwarded. Depending on the network-layer protocol, this value in the packet's header could be the destination address of the packet or an indication of the connection to which the packet belongs. Figure 10.2 provides an example. In Figure 10.2, a packet with a header field value of 0111 arrives to a router. The router indexes into its forwarding table and determines that the output link interface for this packet is interface 2. The router then internally forwards the packet to interface 2. In Section 10.3 we'll look inside a router and examine the forwarding function in much greater detail.

You might now be wondering how the forwarding tables in the routers are configured. This is a crucial issue, one that exposes the important interplay between routing and forwarding. As shown in Figure 10.2, the routing algorithm determines the values that are inserted into the routers' forwarding tables. The routing algorithm may be centralized (e.g., with an algorithm executing on a central site and downloading routing information to each of the routers) or decentralized (i.e., with a

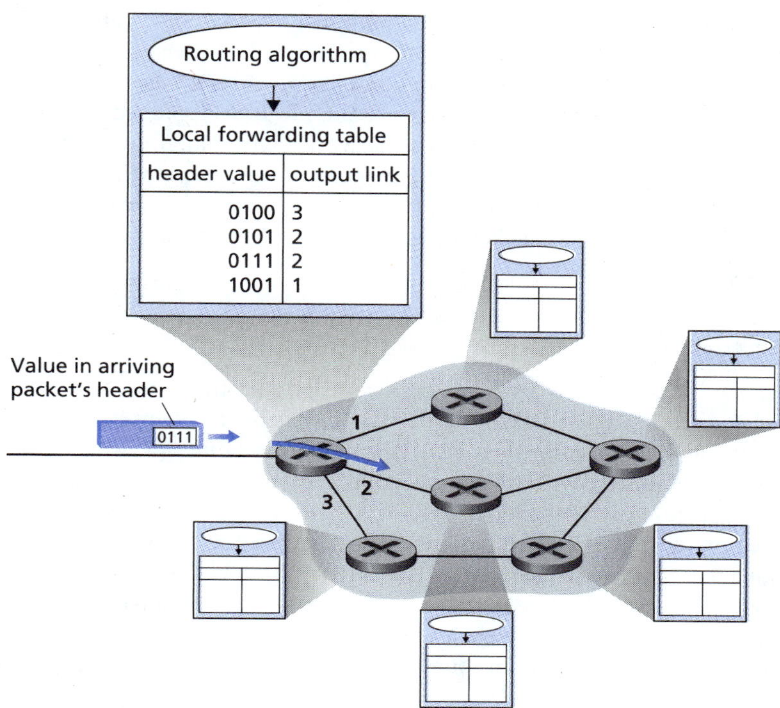

Figure 10.2 ♦ Routing algorithms determine values in forwarding tables

piece of the distributed routing algorithm running in each router). In either case, a router receives routing protocol messages, which are used to configure its forwarding table. The distinct and different purposes of the forwarding and routing functions can be further illustrated by considering the hypothetical (and unrealistic, but technically feasible) case of a network in which all forwarding tables are configured directly by human network operators physically present at the routers. In this case, *no* routing protocols would be required! Of course, the human operators would need to interact with each other to ensure that the forwarding tables were configured in such a way that packets reached their intended destinations. It's also likely that human configuration would be more error-prone and much slower to respond to changes in the network topology than a routing protocol. We're thus fortunate that all networks have both a forwarding *and* a routing function!

While we're on the topic of terminology, it's worth mentioning two other terms that are often used interchangeably, but that we will use more carefully. We'll reserve the term *packet switch* to mean a general packet-switching device that transfers a packet from input link interface to output link interface, according to the value in a field in the header of the packet. Some packet switches, called **link-layer switches** (examined in Chapter 11), base the forwarding decision on the value in the link-layer field. Other packet switches, called **routers,** base their forwarding decision on the value in the network-layer field. (To fully appreciate this important distinction, you might want to review network-layer datagrams and link-layer frames and their relationship.) Since our focus in this chapter is on the network layer, we use the term *router* in place of *packet switch*. We'll even use the term *router* when talking about packet switches in virtual-circuit networks (soon to be discussed).

Connection Setup

We just said that the network layer has two important functions, forwarding and routing. But we'll soon see that in some computer networks there is actually a third important network-layer function, namely, **connection setup.** Recall from our study of TCP that a three-way handshake is required before data can flow from sender to receiver. This allows the sender and receiver to set up the needed state information (for example, sequence number and initial flow-control window size). In an analogous manner, some network-layer architectures—for example, ATM, frame-relay, X.25, but not the Internet—require the routers along the chosen path from source to destination to handshake with each other in order to set up state before network-layer data packets within a given source-to-destination connection can begin to flow. In the network layer, this process is referred to as *connection setup*. We'll examine connection setup in Section 10.2.

10.1.2 Network Service Models

Before delving into the network layer, let's take the broader view and consider the different types of service that might be offered by the network layer. When the transport layer at a sending host transmits a packet into the network (that is, passes it down to the network layer at the sending host), can the transport layer count on the network layer to deliver the packet to the destination? When multiple packets are sent, will they be delivered to the transport layer in the receiving host in the order in which they were sent? Will the amount of time between the sending of two sequential packet transmissions be the same as the amount of time between their reception? Will the network provide any feedback about congestion in the network? What is the abstract view (properties) of the channel connecting the transport layer in the sending and receiving hosts? The answers to these questions and others are determined by the service model provided by the network layer. The **network service model** defines the characteristics of end-to-end transport of data between one edge of the network and the other, that is, between sending and receiving end systems.

Let's now consider some possible services that the network layer could provide. In the sending host, when the transport layer passes a packet to the network layer, specific services that could be provided by the network layer include:

- *Guaranteed delivery*. This service guarantees that the packet will eventually arrive at its destination.
- *Guaranteed delivery with bounded delay*. This service not only guarantees delivery of the packet, but delivery within a specified host-to-host delay bound (for example, within 100 msec).

Furthermore, the following services could be provided to a *flow of packets* between a given source and destination:

- *In-order packet delivery*. This service guarantees that packets arrive at the destination in the order that they were sent.
- *Guaranteed minimal bandwidth*. This network-layer service emulates the behavior of a transmission link of a specified bit rate (for example, 1 Mbps) between sending and receiving hosts (even though the actual end-to-end path may traverse several physical links). As long as the sending host transmits bits (as part of packets) at a rate below the specified bit rate, then no packet is lost and each packet arrives within a prespecified host-to-host delay (for example, within 40 msec).
- *Guaranteed maximum jitter*. This service guarantees that the amount of time between the transmission of two successive packets at the sender is equal to the amount of time between their receipt at the destination (or that this spacing changes by no more than some specified value).

This is only a partial list of services that a network layer could provide—there are countless variations possible.

The Internet's network layer provides a single service, known as **best-effort service.** From Table 10.1, it might appear that *best-effort service* is a euphemism for *no service at all*. With best-effort service, timing between packets is not guaranteed to be preserved, packets are not guaranteed to be received in the order in which they were sent, nor is the eventual delivery of transmitted packets guaranteed. Given this definition, a network that delivered *no* packets to the destination would satisfy the definition of best-effort delivery service. (Indeed, the public Internet might sometimes appear to be an example of a network that does so!) As we'll discuss shortly, however, there are sound reasons for such a minimalist network-layer service model. We'll cover additional, still-evolving, Internet service models in Chapter 13.

Other network architectures have defined and implemented service models that go beyond the Internet's best-effort service. For example, the ATM network architecture [ATM Forum 2004, Black 1995] provides for multiple service models, meaning that different connections can be provided with different classes of service

Network Architecture	Service Model	Bandwidth Guarantee	No-Loss Guarantee	Ordering	Timing	Congestion Indication
Internet	Best Effort	None	None	Any order possible	Not maintained	None
ATM	CBR	Guaranteed constant rate	Yes	In order	Maintained	Congestion will not occur
ATM	ABR	Guaranteed minimum	None	In order	Not maintained	Congestion indication provided

Table 10.1 ♦ Internet, ATM CBR, and ATM ABR service models

within the same network. A discussion of how an ATM network provides such services is well beyond the scope of this book; our aim here is only to note that alternatives do exist to the Internet's best effort model. Two of the more important ATM service models are constant bit rate and available bit rate service:

- ***Constant bit rate (CBR) ATM network service.*** This was the first ATM service model to be standardized, reflecting early interest by the telephone companies in ATM and the suitability of CBR service for carrying real-time, constant bit rate audio and video traffic. The goal of CBR service is conceptually simple—to provide a flow of packets (known as cells in ATM terminology) with a virtual pipe whose properties are the same as if a dedicated fixed-bandwidth transmission link existed between sending and receiving hosts. With CBR service, a flow of ATM cells is carried across the network in such a way that a cell's end-to-end delay, the variability in a cell's end-end delay (that is, the jitter), and the fraction of cells that are lost or delivered late are all guaranteed to be less than specified values. These values are agreed upon by the sending host and the ATM network when the CBR connection is first established.
- ***Available bit rate (ABR) ATM network service.*** With the Internet offering so-called best-effort service, ATM's ABR might best be characterized as being a slightly-better-than-best-effort service. As with the Internet service model, cells may be lost under ABR service. Unlike in the Internet, however, cells cannot be reordered (although they may be lost), and a minimum cell transmission rate (MCR) is guaranteed to a connection using ABR service. If the network has enough free resources at a given time, a sender may also be able to send cells successfully at a higher rate than the MCR. Additionally, ATM ABR service can provide feedback to the sender (in terms of a congestion notification bit, or an explicit rate at which to send) that controls how the sender adjusts its rate between the MCR and an allowable peak cell rate.

10.2 Virtual Circuit and Datagram Networks

Recall that a transport layer can offer applications connectionless service or connection-oriented service. For example, the Internet's transport layer provides each application a choice between two services: UDP, a connectionless service; or TCP, a connection-oriented service. In a similar manner, a network layer can also provide connectionless service or connection service. Network-layer connection and connectionless services in many ways parallel transport-layer connection-oriented and connectionless services. For example, a network-layer connection service begins with handshaking between the source and destination hosts; and a network-layer connectionless service does not have any handshaking preliminaries.

Although the network-layer connection and connectionless services have some parallels with transport-layer connection-oriented and connectionless services, there are crucial differences:

- In the network layer these services are host-to-host services provided by the network layer to the transport layer. In the transport layer these services are process-to-process services provided by the transport layer to the application layer.
- In all major computer network architectures to date (Internet, ATM, frame relay and so on), the network layer provides either a host-to-host connectionless service or a host-to-host connection service, but not both. Computer networks that provide only a connection service at the network layer are called **virtual-circuit (VC) networks;** computer networks that provide only a connectionless service at the network layer are called **datagram networks.**
- The implementations of connection-oriented service in the transport layer and the connection service in the network layer are fundamentally different. We saw in the previous chapter that the transport-layer connection-oriented service is implemented at the edge of the network in the end systems; we'll see shortly that the network-layer connection service is implemented in the routers in the network core as well as in the end systems.

Virtual-circuit and datagram networks are two fundamental classes of computer networks. They use very different information in making their forwarding decisions. Let's now take a closer look at their implementations.

10.2.1 Virtual-Circuit Networks

We've learned that the Internet is a datagram network. However, many alternative network architectures—including those of ATM, frame relay and X.25—are virtual-circuit networks and, therefore, use connections at the network layer. These network-layer connections are called **virtual circuits (VCs).** Let's now consider how a VC service can be implemented in a computer network.

A VC consists of (1) a path (that is, a series of links and routers) between the source and destination hosts, (2) VC numbers, one number for each link along the path, and (3) entries in the forwarding table in each router along the path. A packet belonging to a virtual circuit will carry a VC number in its header. Because a virtual circuit may have a different VC number on each link, each intervening router must replace the VC number of each traversing packet with a new one. The new VC number is obtained from the forwarding table.

To illustrate the concept, consider the network shown in Figure 10.3. The numbers next to the links of R1 in Figure 10.3 are the link interface numbers. Suppose now that Host A requests that the network establish a VC between itself and Host B. Suppose also that the network chooses the path A-R1-R2-B and assigns VC numbers 12, 22, 32 to the three links in this path for this virtual circuit. In this case, when a packet in this VC leaves Host A, the value in the VC number field in the packet header is 12; when it leaves R1, the value is 22; and when it leaves R2, the value is 32.

How does the router determine the replacement VC number for a packet traversing the router? For a VC network, each router's forwarding table includes VC number translation; for example, the forwarding table in R1 might look something like this:

Incoming Interface	Incoming VC #	Outgoing Interface	Outgoing VC #
1	12	2	22
2	63	1	18
3	7	2	17
1	97	3	87
...	...	...	...

Whenever a new VC is established across a router, an entry is added to the forwarding table. Similarly, whenever a VC terminates, the appropriate entries in each table along its path are removed.

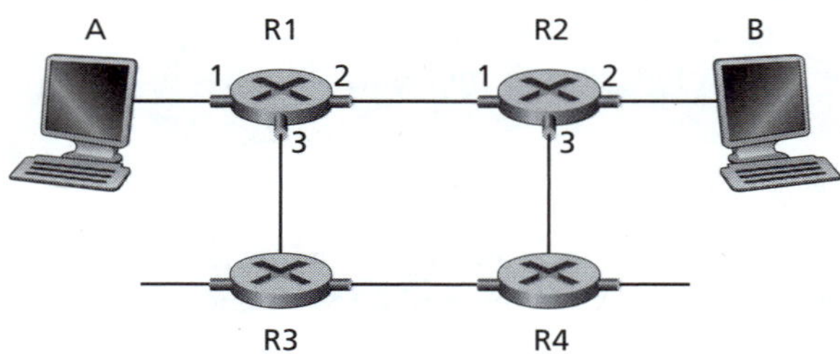

Figure 10.3 ♦ A simple virtual circuit network

You might be wondering why a packet doesn't just keep the same VC number on each of the links along its route. The answer is twofold. First, replacing the number from link to link reduces the length of the VC field in the packet header. Second, and more importantly, VC setup is considerably simplified by permitting a different VC number at each link along the path of the VC. Specifically, with multiple VC numbers, each link in the path can choose a VC number independently of the VC number chosen at other links along the path. If a common VC number were required for all links along the path, the routers would have to exchange and process a substantial number of messages to agree on a common VC number (e.g., one that is not being used by any other existing VC at these routers) to be used for a connection.

In a VC network, the network's routers must maintain **connection state information** for the ongoing connections. Specifically, each time a new connection is established across a router, a new connection entry must be added to the router's forwarding table; and each time a connection is released, an entry must be removed from the table. Note that even if there is no VC-number translation, it is still necessary to maintain connection state information that associates VC numbers with output interface numbers. The issue of whether or not a router maintains connection state information for each ongoing connection is a crucial one—one that we'll return to repeatedly in this book.

There are three identifiable phases in a virtual circuit:

- *VC setup.* During the setup phase, the sending transport layer contacts the network layer, specifies the receiver's address, and waits for the network to set up the VC. The network layer determines the path between sender and receiver, that is, the series of links and routers through which all packets of the VC will travel. The network layer also determines the VC number for each link along the path. Finally, the network layer adds an entry in the forwarding table in each router along the path. During VC setup, the network layer may also reserve resources (for example, bandwidth) along the path of the VC.
- *Data transfer.* As shown in Figure 10.4, once the VC has been established, packets can begin to flow along the VC.
- *VC teardown.* This is initiated when the sender (or receiver) informs the network layer of its desire to terminate the VC. The network layer will then typically inform the end system on the other side of the network of the call termination and update the forwarding tables in each of the packet routers on the path to indicate that the VC no longer exists.

There is a subtle but important distinction between VC setup at the network layer and connection setup at the transport layer. Connection setup at the transport layer involves only the two end systems. During transport-layer connection setup, the two end systems alone determine the parameters (for example, initial sequence number and flow-control window size) of their transport-layer connection. Although the two end systems are aware of the transport-layer connection, the routers within the network are completely oblivious to it. On the other hand, with a VC network layer, *routers along the path between the two end systems are involved in VC setup, and each router is fully aware of all the VCs passing through it.*

The messages that the end systems send into the network to initiate or terminate a VC, and the messages passed between the routers to set up the VC (that is, to modify connection state in router tables) are known as **signaling messages,** and the protocols used to exchange these messages are often referred to as **signaling protocols.** VC setup is shown pictorially in Figure 10.4. We'll not cover VC signaling protocols in this book; see [Black 1997] for a general discussion of signaling in connection-oriented networks and [ITU-T Q.2931 1994] for the specification of ATM's Q.2931 signaling protocol.

10.2.2 Datagram Networks

In a **datagram network,** each time an end system wants to send a packet, it stamps the packet with the address of the destination end system and then pops the packet into the network. As shown in Figure 10.5, this is done without any VC setup. Routers in a datagram network do not maintain any state information about VCs (because there are no VCs!).

As a packet is transmitted from source to destination, it passes through a series of routers. Each of these routers uses the packet's destination address to forward the packet. Specifically, each router has a forwarding table that maps destination addresses to link interfaces; when a packet arrives at the router, the router uses the

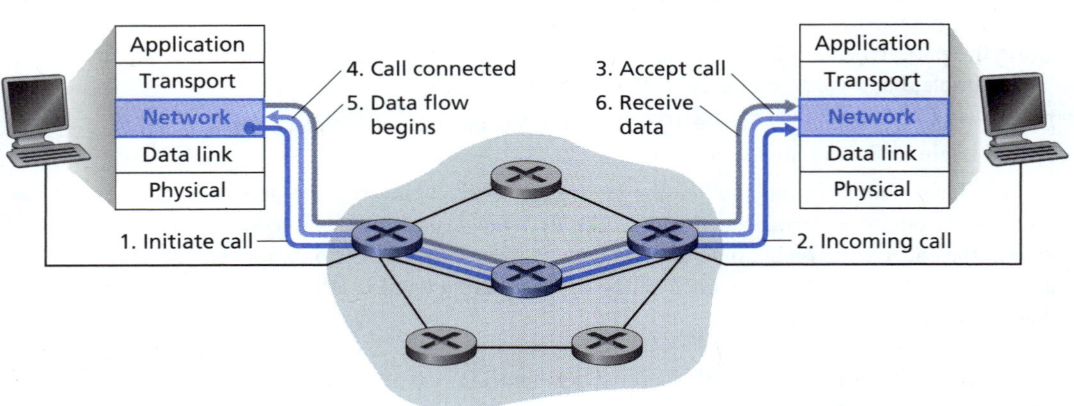

Figure 10.4 ♦ Virtual-circuit setup

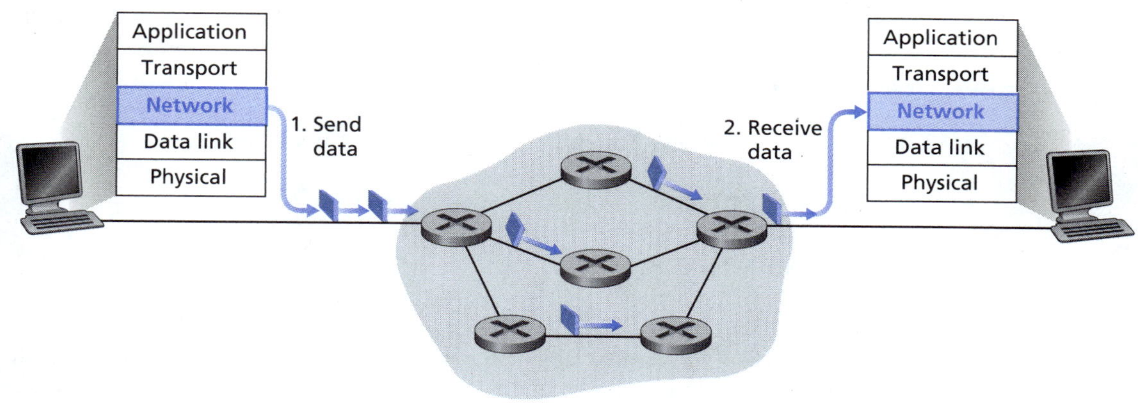

Figure 10.5 ♦ Datagram network

packet's destination address to lookup the appropriate output link interface in the forwarding table. The router then forwards the packet to that output link interface.

To get some further insight into the lookup operation, let's look at a specific example. Suppose that all destination addresses are 32 bits (which just happens to be the length of the destination address in an IP datagram). A brute-force implementation of the forwarding table would have one entry for every possible destination address. Since there are more than 4 billion possible addresses, this option is totally out the question—it would require a humongous forwarding table.

Now let's further suppose that our router has four links, numbered 0 through 3, and that packets are to be forwarded to the link interfaces as follows:

Destination Address Range	Link Interface
11001000 00010111 00010000 00000000 through 11001000 00010111 00010111 11111111	0
11001000 00010111 00011000 00000000 through 11001000 00010111 00011000 11111111	1
11001000 00010111 00011001 00000000 through 11001000 00010111 00011111 11111111	2
otherwise	3

Clearly, for this example, it is not necessary to have 4 billion entries in the router's forwarding table. We could, for example, have the following forwarding table with just four entries:

Prefix Match	Link Interface
11001000 00010111 00010	0
11001000 00010111 00011000	1
11001000 00010111 00011	2
otherwise	3

With this style of forwarding table, the router matches a **prefix** of the packet's destination address with the entries in the table; if there's a match, the router forwards the packet to link associated with the match. For example, suppose the packet's destination address is 11001000 00010111 00010110 10100001; because the 21-bit prefix of this address matches the first entry in the table, the router forwards the packet to link interface 0. If a prefix doesn't match any of the first three entries, then the router forwards the packet to interface 3. Although this sounds simple enough, there's an important subtlety here. You may have noticed that it is possible for a destination address to match more than one entry. For example, the first 24 bits of the address 11001000 00010111 00011000 10101010 match the second entry in the table, and the first 21 bits of the address match the third entry in the table. When there are multiple matches, the router uses the **longest prefix matching rule;** that is, it finds the longest matching entry in the table and forwards the packet to the link interface associated with the longest prefix match.

Of course, for longest prefix matching to be effective, each output link interface should be responsible for forwarding large blocks of contiguous destination addresses. We'll see in Section 10.4 that Internet addresses are typically assigned in a hierarchical fashion so that this contiguous property is prevalent in the forwarding tables of most routers. Nevertheless, there is some concern within the Internet research community that more and more holes are being punctured into the address space, causing the contiguous blocks to get smaller and smaller and the forwarding tables to get larger and larger. (See [Maennel 2002], [RFC 3221], and the Principles in Practice discussion in Section 10.4.)

Although routers in datagram networks maintain no connection state information, they nevertheless maintain forwarding state information in their forwarding tables. However, the time scale at which this forwarding state information changes is relatively slow. Indeed, in a datagram network the forwarding tables are modified by the routing algorithms, which typically update a forwarding table every one-to-five minutes or so. In a VC network, a forwarding table in a router is modified whenever a new connection is setup through the router or whenever an existing connection through the router is torn down. This could easily happen at a microsecond timescale in a backbone, tier-1 router.

Because forwarding tables in datagram networks can be modified at any time, a series of packets sent from one end system to another may follow different paths through the network and may arrive out of order. [Paxson 1997] and [Jaiswal 2003] present interesting measurement studies of packet reordering and other phenomena in the public Internet.

10.2.3 Origins of VC and Datagram Networks

The evolution of datagram and VC networks reflects their origins. The notion of a virtual circuit as a central organizing principle has its roots in the telephony world, which uses real circuits. With call setup and per-call state being maintained at the routers within the network, a VC network is arguably more complex than a datagram network (although see [Molinero 2002] for an interesting comparison of the complexity of circuit- versus packet-switched networks). This, too, is in keeping with its telephony heritage. Telephone networks, by necessity, had their complexity within the network, since they were connecting dumb end-system devices such as rotary telephones. (For those too young to know, a rotary phone is an analog telephone with no buttons—only a dial.)

The Internet as a datagram network, on the other hand, grew out of the need to connect computers together. Given more sophisticated end-system devices, the Internet architects chose to make the network-layer service model as simple as possible. As we have already seen, additional functionality (for example, in-order delivery, reliable data transfer, congestion control, and DNS name resolution) is then implemented at a higher layer, in the end systems. This inverts the model of the telephone network, with some interesting consequences.

- The resulting Internet network-layer service model, which makes minimal (no!) service guarantees (and hence imposes minimal requirements on the network layer), also makes it easier to interconnect networks that use very different link-layer technologies (for example, satellite, Ethernet, fiber, or radio) and have very different transmission rates and loss characteristics. We will address the interconnection of IP networks in detail in Section 10.4.
- Applications such as e-mail, the Web, and even a network layer–centric service such as the DNS, are implemented in hosts (servers) at the edge of the network. The ability to add a new service simply by attaching a host to the network and defining a new application-layer protocol (such as HTTP) has allowed new applications such as the Web to be deployed in the Internet in a remarkably short period of time.

As we'll see in Chapter 13, there is considerable debate in the Internet community about how the Internet's network-layer architecture should evolve in order to support real-time services such as multimedia. An interesting comparison of the

VC-oriented ATM network architecture and a proposed next generation Internet architecture is given in [Crowcroft 1995].

10.3 What's Inside a Router?

Now that we've seen an overview of the functions and services of the network layer, let's turn our attention to the network layer's **forwarding function**—the actual transfer of packets from a router's incoming links to the appropriate outgoing links. We already took a brief look at a few forwarding issues in Section 10.2, namely, addressing and longest prefix matching. In this section we'll look at specific router architectures for transferring packets from incoming links to outgoing links. Our coverage here is necessarily brief, as an entire course would be needed to cover router design in depth. Consequently, we'll make a special effort in this section to provide pointers to material that covers this topic in more depth. We mention here in passing that the words *forwarding* and *switching* are often used interchangeably by computer-networking researchers and practitioners; we'll use both terms in this textbook.

A high-level view of a generic router architecture is shown in Figure 10.6. Four components of a router can be identified.

- *Input ports.* The input port performs several functions. It performs the physical layer functions (the leftmost box of the input port and the rightmost box of the output port in Figure 10.6) of terminating an incoming physical link to a router. It performs the data link layer functions (represented by the middle boxes in the input and output ports) needed to interoperate with the data link layer functions at the remote side of

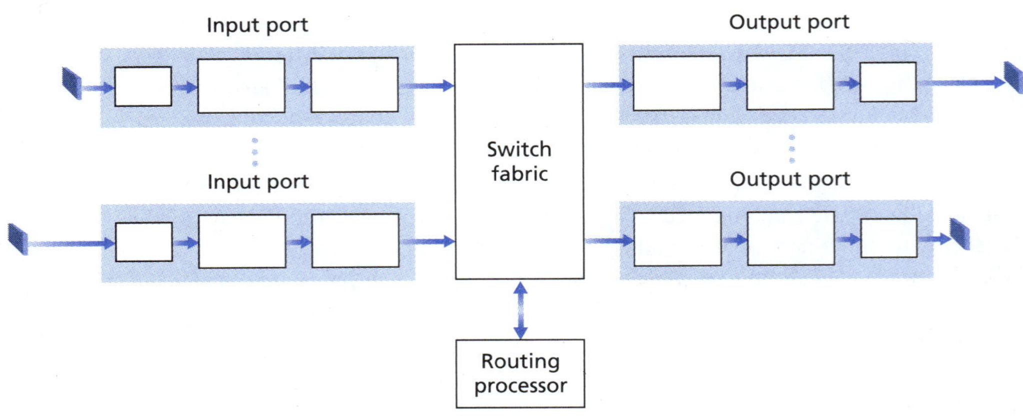

Figure 10.6 ♦ Router architecture

the incoming link. It also performs a lookup and forwarding function (the rightmost box of the input port and the leftmost box of the output port) so that a packet forwarded into the switching fabric of the router emerges at the appropriate output port. Control packets (for example, packets carrying routing protocol information) are forwarded from an input port to the routing processor. In practice, multiple ports are often gathered together on a single **line card** within a router.

- *Switching fabric.* The switching fabric connects the router's input ports to its output ports. This switching fabric is completely contained within the router—a network inside of a network router!
- *Output ports.* An output port stores the packets that have been forwarded to it through the switching fabric and then transmits the packets on the outgoing link. The output port thus performs the reverse data link and physical layer functionality of the input port. When a link is bidirectional (that is, carries traffic in both directions), an output port to the link will typically be paired with the input port for that link, on the same line card.
- *Routing processor.* The routing processor executes the routing protocols (for example, the protocols we study in Section 10.6), maintains the routing information and forwarding tables, and performs network management functions within the router.

In the following subsections, we'll look at input ports, the switching fabric, and output ports in more detail. [Chao 2001; Turner 1988; Giacopelli 1990; McKeown 1997a; Partridge 1998] provide a discussion of some specific router architectures. [McKeown 1997b] provides a particularly readable overview of modern router architectures, using the Cisco 12000 router as an example. For concreteness, the ensuing discussion assumes that the computer network is a packet network, and that forwarding decisions are based on the packet's destination address (rather than a VC number in a virtual-circuit network). However, the concepts and techniques are similar for a virtual-circuit network.

10.3.1 Input Ports

A more detailed view of input port functionality is given in Figure 10.7. As discussed above, the input port's line termination function and data link processing implement the physical and data link layers associated with an individual input link to the router. The lookup/forwarding module in the input port is central to the forwarding function of the router. In many routers, it is here that the router determines the output port to which an arriving packet will be forwarded via the switching fabric. The choice of the output port is made using the information contained in the forwarding table. Although the forwarding table is computed by the routing processor, a shadow copy of the forwarding table is typically stored at each input port and updated, as

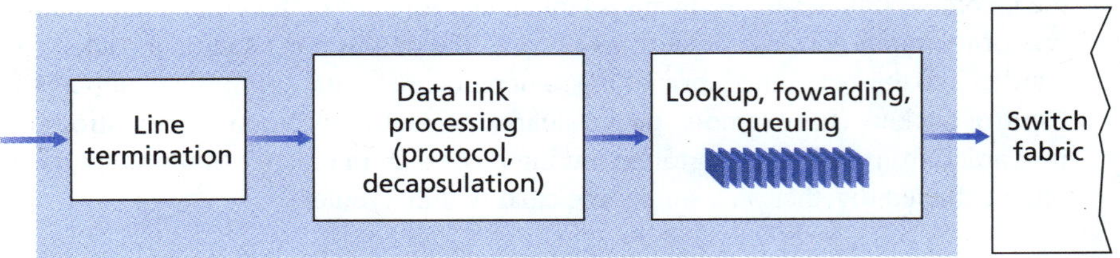

Figure 10.7 ♦ Input port processing

needed, by the routing processor. With local copies of the forwarding table, the forwarding decision can be made locally, at each input port, without invoking the centralized routing processor. Such *decentralized* forwarding avoids creating a forwarding processing bottleneck at a single point within the router.

In routers with limited processing capabilities at the input port, the input port may simply forward the packet to the centralized routing processor, which will then perform the forwarding table lookup and forward the packet to the appropriate output port. This is the approach taken when a workstation or a server serves as a

CASE HISTORY

CISCO SYSTEMS: DOMINATING THE NETWORK CORE

As of March 2004, Cisco employs more than 30,000 people and has a market capitalization of about $150 billion. Cisco currently dominates the Internet router market and in recent years has moved into the Internet telephony market, where it competes head-to-head with the telephone equipment companies, such as Lucent, Alcatel, Nortel, and Siemens. How did this gorilla of a networking company come to be? It all started in 1984 (only 20 years ago) in the living room of a Silicon Valley apartment.

Len Bosak and his wife Sandy Lerner were working at Stanford University when they had the idea to build and sell Internet routers to research and academic institutions. Sandy Lerner came up with the name Cisco (an abbreviation for San Francisco), and she also designed the company's bridge logo. Corporate headquarters was their living room, and they financed the project with credit cards and moonlighting consulting jobs. At the end of 1986, Cisco's revenues reached $250,000 a month. At the end of 1987, Cisco succeeded in attracting venture capital—$2 million dollars from Sequoia Capital in exchange for one third of the company. Over the next few years, Cisco continued to grow and grab more and more market share. At the same time, relations between Bosak/Lerner and Cisco management became strained. Cisco went public in 1990; in the same year Lerner and Bosak left the company.

router; here, the routing processor is really just the workstation's CPU, and the input port is really just a network interface card (for example, an Ethernet card).

Given the existence of a forwarding table, table lookup is conceptually simple—we just search through the forwarding table looking for the longest prefix match, as described in Section 10.2.2. In practice, however, life is not so simple. Perhaps the most important complicating factor is that backbone routers must operate at high speeds, performing millions of lookups per second. Indeed, it is desirable for the input port processing to be able to proceed at **line speed,** that is, for a lookup to be performed in less than the amount of time needed to receive a packet at the input port. In this case, input processing of a received packet can be completed before the next receive operation is complete. To get an idea of the performance requirements for a lookup, consider that a OC48 link runs at 2.5 Gbps. With packets 256 bytes long, this implies a lookup speed of approximately 1 million lookups per second.

Given the need to operate at today's high link speeds, a linear search through a large forwarding table is impossible. A more reasonable technique is to store the forwarding table entries in a tree data structure. Each level in the tree can be thought of as corresponding to a bit in the destination address. To look up an address, one simply starts at the root node of the tree. If the first address bit is a zero, then the left subtree will contain the forwarding table entry for the destination address; otherwise it will be in the right subtree. The appropriate subtree is then traversed using the remaining address bits—if the next address bit is a zero, the left subtree of the initial subtree is chosen; otherwise, the right subtree of the initial subtree is chosen. In this manner, one can look up the forwarding table entry in N steps, where N is the number of bits in the address. (Note that this is essentially a binary search through an address space of size 2^N.) An improvement over binary search techniques is described in [Srinivasan 1999], and a general survey of packet classification algorithms can be found in [Gupta 2001].

But even with $N = 32$ (for example, a 32-bit IP address) steps, the lookup speed via binary search is not fast enough for today's backbone routing requirements. For example, assuming a memory access at each step, fewer than a million address lookups per second could be performed with 40 ns memory access times. Several techniques have thus been explored to increase lookup speeds. **Content addressable memories (CAMs)** allow a 32-bit IP address to be presented to the CAM, which returns the content of the forwarding table entry for that address in essentially constant time. The Cisco 8500 series router [Cisco 8500 1999] has a 64K CAM for each input port.

Another technique for speeding up lookup is to keep recently accessed forwarding table entries in a cache [Feldmeier 1988]. Here, the concern is the potential size of the cache. Most recently, even faster data structures, which allow forwarding table entries to be located in $\log(N)$ steps [Waldvogel 1997], or which compress forwarding tables in novel ways [Brodnik 1997], have been proposed. A hardware-based approach to lookup that is optimized for the common case that the address being looked up has 24 or fewer significant bits is discussed in [Gupta 1998].

Once the output port for a packet has been determined via the lookup, the packet can be forwarded into the switching fabric. However, a packet may be temporarily blocked from entering the switching fabric (due to the fact that packets from other input ports are currently using the fabric). A blocked packet must thus be queued at the input port and then scheduled to cross the switching fabric at a later point in time. We'll take a closer look at the blocking, queuing, and scheduling of packets (at both input ports and output ports) within a router in Section 10.3.4.

10.3.2 Switching Fabric

The switching fabric is at the very heart of a router. It is through the switching fabric that the packets are actually switched (that is, forwarded) from an input port to an output port. Switching can be accomplished in a number of ways, as indicated in Figure 10.8.

- *Switching via memory.* The simplest, earliest routers were often traditional computers, with switching between input and output ports being done under direct

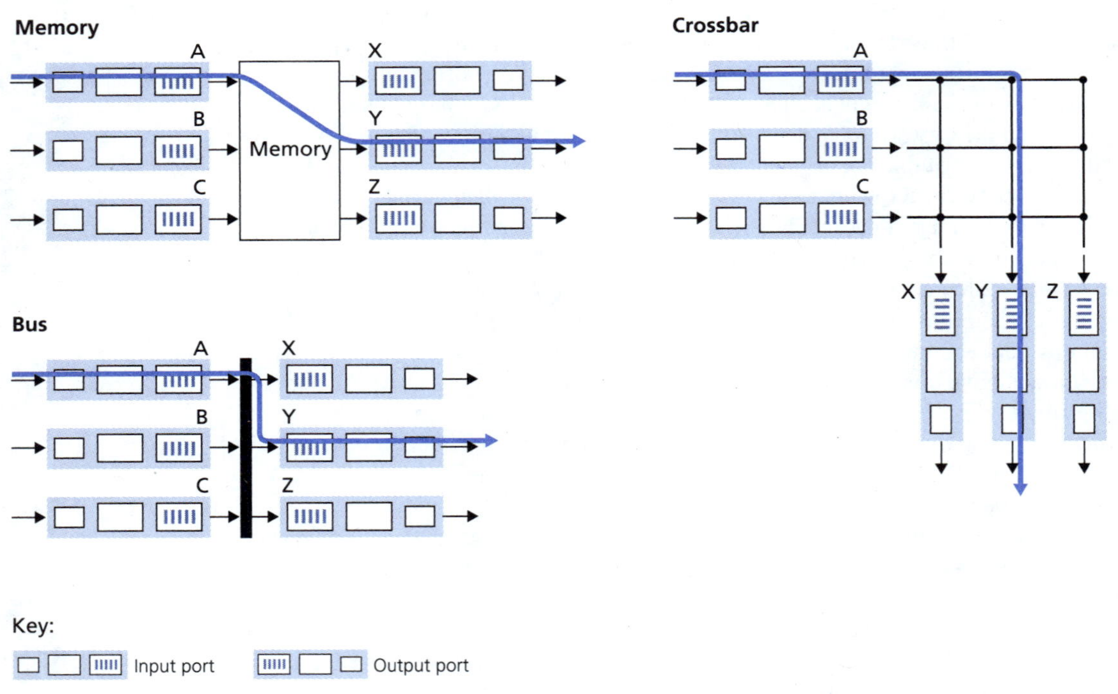

Figure 10.8 ♦ Three switching techniques

control of the CPU (routing processor). Input and output ports functioned as traditional I/O devices in a traditional operating system. An input port with an arriving packet first signaled the routing processor via an interrupt. The packet was then copied from the input port into processor memory. The routing processor then extracted the destination address from the header, looked up the appropriate output port in the forwarding table, and copied the packet to the output port's buffers. Note that if the memory bandwidth is such that B packets per second can be written into, or read from, memory, then the overall forwarding throughput (the total rate at which packets are transferred from input ports to output ports) must be less than $B/2$.

Many modern routers also switch via memory. A major difference from early routers, however, is that the lookup of the destination address and the storing of the packet into the appropriate memory location is performed by processors on the input line cards. In some ways, routers that switch via memory look very much like shared memory multiprocessors, with the processors on a line card switching packets into the memory of the appropriate output port. Cisco's Catalyst 8500 series switches [Cisco 8500 1999] and Bay Networks Accelar 1200 series routers forward packets via a shared memory. An abstract model for studying the properties of memory-based switching and a comparison with other forms of switching can be found in [Iyer 2002].

- *Switching via a bus.* In this approach, the input ports transfer a packet directly to the output port over a shared bus, without intervention by the routing processor (note that when switching via memory, the packet must also cross the system bus going to/from memory). Although the routing processor is not involved in the bus transfer, because the bus is shared only one packet at a time can be transferred over the bus. A packet arriving at an input port and finding the bus busy with the transfer of another packet is blocked from passing through the switching fabric and is queued at the input port. Because every packet must cross the single bus, the switching bandwidth of the router is limited to the bus speed.

  Given that bus bandwidths of over 1 Gbps are possible in today's technology, switching via a bus is often sufficient for routers that operate in access and enterprise networks (for example, local area and corporate networks). Bus-based switching has been adopted in a number of current router products, including the Cisco 1900 [Cisco Switches 1999], which switches packets over a 1 Gbps Packet Exchange Bus. 3Com's CoreBuilder 5000 system [Kapoor 1997] interconnects ports that reside on different switch modules over its PacketChannel data bus, with a bandwidth of 2 Gbps.

- *Switching via an interconnection network.* One way to overcome the bandwidth limitation of a single, shared bus is to use a more sophisticated interconnection network, such as those that have been used in the past to interconnect processors in a multiprocessor computer architecture. A crossbar switch is an interconnection network consisting of $2n$ buses that connect n input ports to n output ports, as shown in Figure 10.8. A packet arriving at an input port travels along the horizontal bus attached to the input port until it intersects with the vertical bus leading to the desired output port. If the vertical bus leading to the output port is free, the packet is transferred to the output port. If the vertical bus is being used to transfer a packet from another input port to this same output port, the arriving packet is blocked and must be queued at the input port.

Delta and Omega switching fabrics have also been proposed as an interconnection network between input and output ports. See [Tobagi 1990] for a survey of switch architectures. Cisco 12000 Family switches [Cisco 12000 1998] use an interconnection network, providing up to 60 Gbps through the switching fabric. One current trend in interconnection network design [Keshav 1998] is to fragment a variable-length IP packet into fixed-length cells, then tag and switch the fixed-length cells through the interconnection network. The cells are then reassembled into the original packet at the output port. The fixed-length cell and internal tag can considerably simplify and speed up the switching of the packet through the interconnection network.

10.3.3 Output Ports

Output port processing, shown in Figure 10.9, takes the packets that have been stored in the output port's memory and transmits them over the outgoing link. The data link protocol processing and line termination are the send-side link- and physical-layer functionality that interact with the input port on the other end of the outgoing link, as discussed above in Section 10.3.1. The queuing and buffer management functionality are needed when the switch fabric delivers packets to the output port at a rate that exceeds the output link rate; we'll cover output port queuing below.

10.3.4 Where Does Queuing Occur?

If we look at the input and output port functionality and the configurations shown in Figure 10.8, it is evident that packet queues can form at both the input ports *and* the output ports. It is important to consider these queues in a bit more detail, since as

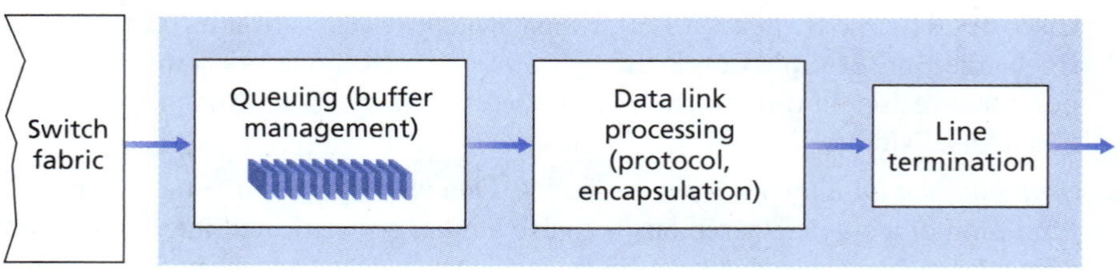

Figure 10.9 ♦ Output port processing

these queues grow large, the router's buffer space will eventually be exhausted and **packet loss** will occur. Recall that in our earlier discussions, we said that packets were lost within the network or dropped at a router. It is here, at these queues within a router, where such packets are actually dropped and lost. The actual location of packet loss (either at the input port queues or the output port queues) will depend on the traffic load, the relative speed of the switching fabric, and the line speed, as discussed below.

Suppose that the input line speeds and output line speeds are all identical, and that there are *n* input ports and *n* output ports. Define the **switching fabric speed** as the rate at which the switching fabric can move packets from input ports to output ports. If the switching fabric speed is at least *n* times as fast as the input line speed, then no queuing can occur at the input ports. This is because even in the worst case, where all *n* input lines are receiving packets, the switch will be able to transfer *n* packets from input port to output port in the time it takes each of the *n* input ports to (simultaneously) receive a *single* packet. But what can happen at the output ports? Let us suppose still that the switching fabric is at least *n* times as fast as the line speeds. In the worst case, the packets arriving at each of the *n* input ports will be destined to the *same* output port. In this case, in the time it takes to receive (or send) a single packet, *n* packets will arrive at this output port. Since the output port can transmit only a single packet in a unit of time (the packet transmission time), the *n* arriving packets will have to queue (wait) for transmission over the outgoing link. Then *n* more packets can possibly arrive in the time it takes to transmit just one of the *n* packets that had previously been queued. And so on. Eventually, the number of queued packets can grow large enough to exhaust the memory space at the output port, in which case packets are dropped.

Output port queuing is illustrated in Figure 10.10. At time *t,* a packet has arrived at each of the incoming input ports, each destined for the uppermost outgoing port. Assuming identical line speeds and a switch operating at three times the line speed, one time unit later (that is, in the time needed to receive or send a packet), all three original packets have been transferred to the outgoing port and are queued awaiting transmission. In the next time unit, one of these three packets will have been transmitted over the outgoing link. In our example, two *new* packets have arrived at the incoming side of the switch; one of these packets is destined for this uppermost output port.

A consequence of output port queuing is that a **packet scheduler** at the output port must choose one packet among those queued for transmission. This selection might be done on a simple basis, such as first-come-first-served (FCFS) scheduling, or a more sophisticated scheduling discipline such as weighted fair queuing (WFQ), which shares the outgoing link fairly among the different end-to-end connections that have packets queued for transmission. Packet scheduling plays a crucial role in providing **quality-of-service guarantees**. We'll thus cover packet scheduling extensively in Chapter 13. A discussion of output port packet scheduling disciplines is [Cisco Queue 1995].

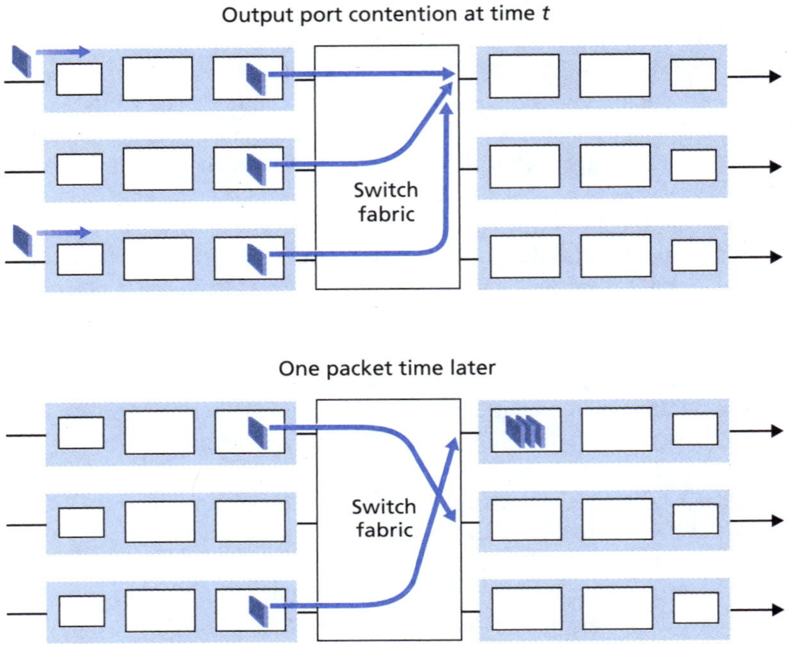

Figure 10.10 ♦ Output port queuing

Similarly, if there is not enough memory to buffer an incoming packet, a decision must be made to either drop the arriving packet (a policy known as **drop-tail**) or remove one or more already-queued packets to make room for the newly arrived packet. In some cases, it may be advantageous to drop (or mark the header of) a packet *before* the buffer is full in order to provide a congestion signal to the sender. A number of packet-dropping and -marking policies (which collectively have become known as **active queue management (AQM)** algorithms) have been proposed and analyzed [Labrador 1999, Hollot 2002]. One of the most widely studied and implemented AQM algorithms is the **Random Early Detection (RED)** algorithm. Under RED, a weighted average is maintained for the length of the output queue. If the average queue length is less than a minimum threshold, min_{th}, when a packet arrives, the packet is admitted to the queue. Conversely, if the queue is full or the average queue length is greater than a maximum threshold, max_{th}, when a packet arrives, the packet is marked or dropped. Finally, if the packet arrives to find an average queue length in the interval [min_{th}, max_{th}], the packet is marked or dropped with a probability that is typically some function of the average queue length, min_{th}, and max_{th}. A number of probabilistic marking/dropping functions have been proposed, and various versions of RED have been analytically modeled, simulated, and/or implemented. [Christiansen 2001] and [Floyd 2004] provide overviews and pointers to additional reading.

If the switch fabric is not fast enough (relative to the input line speeds) to transfer *all* arriving packets through the fabric without delay, then packet queuing can also occur at the input ports, as packets must join input port queues to wait their turn to be transferred through the switching fabric to the output port. To illustrate an important consequence of this queuing, consider a crossbar switching fabric and suppose that (1) all link speeds are identical, (2) that one packet can be transferred from any one input port to a given output port in the same amount of time it takes for a packet to be received on an input link, and (3) packets are moved from a given input queue to their desired output queue in an FCFS manner. Multiple packets can be transferred in parallel, as long as their output ports are different. However, if two packets at the front of two input queues are destined for the same output queue, then one of the packets will be blocked and must wait at the input queue—the switching fabric can transfer only one packet to a given output port at a time.

Figure 10.11 shows an example in which two packets (shaded dark blue) at the front of their input queues are destined for the same upper-right output port. Suppose that the switch fabric chooses to transfer the packet from the front of the upper-left queue. In this case, the dark blue packet in the lower-left queue must wait. But not only must this dark blue packet wait, so too must the light blue packet that is queued behind that packet in the lower-left queue, even though there is *no* contention for the middle-right output port (the destination for the light blue packet). This phenomenon is known as **head-of-the-line (HOL) blocking** in an input-queued switch—a queued packet in an input queue must wait for transfer through the fabric (even though its output port is free) because it is blocked by another packet at the head of the line. [Karol 1987] shows that due to HOL blocking, the input queue will grow to unbounded length (informally, this is equivalent to saying that significant packet loss will occur) under certain assumptions as soon as the packet arrival rate on the input links reaches only 58 percent of their capacity. A number of solutions to HOL blocking are discussed in [McKeown 1997b].

10.4 The Internet Protocol (IP): Forwarding and Addressing in the Internet

Our discussion of network-layer addressing and forwarding thus far has been without reference to any specific computer network. In this section, we'll turn our attention to how addressing and forwarding are done in the Internet. We'll see that Internet addressing and forwarding are important components of the Internet Protocol (IP). There are two versions of IP in use today. We'll first examine the widely

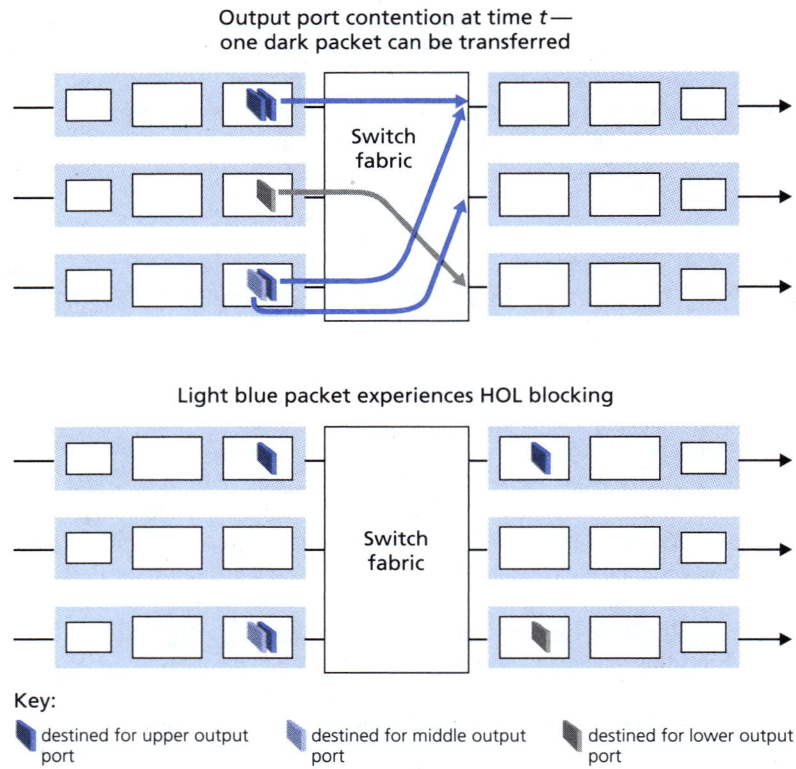

Figure 10.11 ♦ HOL blocking at an input queued switch

deployed IP protocol version 4, which is usually referred to simply as IPv4 [RFC 791]. We'll examine IP version 6 [RFC 2373; RFC 2460], which has been proposed to replace IPv4, at the end of this section.

But before beginning our foray into IP, let's take a step back and consider the components that make up the Internet's network layer. As shown in Figure 10.12, the Internet's network layer has three major components. The first component is the IP protocol, the topic of this section. The second major component is the routing component, which determines the path a datagram follows from source to destination. We mentioned earlier that routing protocols compute the forwarding tables that are used to forward packets through the network. We'll study the Internet's routing protocols in Section 10.6. The final component of the network layer is a facility to report errors in datagrams and respond to requests for certain network-layer information. We'll cover the Internet's network-layer error- and information-reporting protocol, the Internet Control Message Protocol (ICMP), in Section 10.4.3.

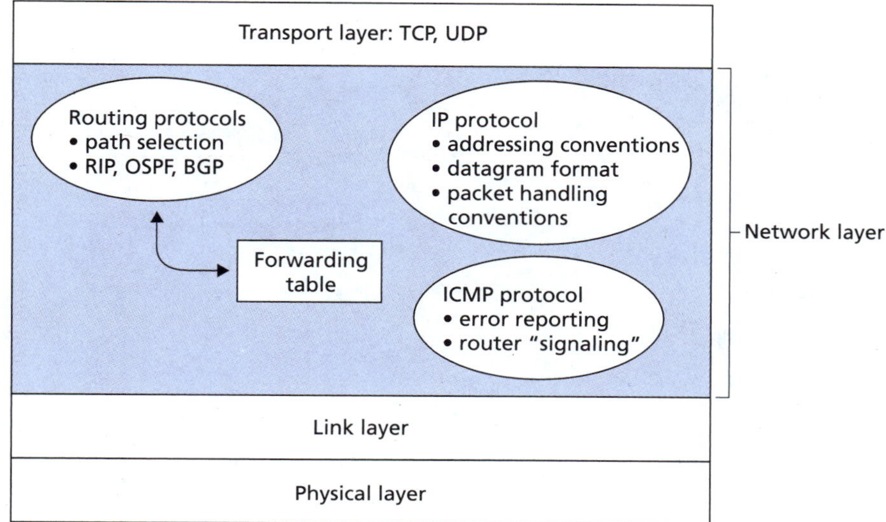

Figure 10.12 ♦ A look inside the Internet's network layer

10.4.1 Datagram Format

Recall that a network-layer packet is referred to as a *datagram*. We begin our study of IP with an overview of the syntax and semantics of the IPv4 datagram. You might be thinking that nothing could be drier than the syntax and semantics of a packet's bits. Nevertheless, the datagram plays a central role in the Internet—every networking student and professional needs to see it, absorb it, and master it. The IPv4 datagram format is shown in Figure 10.13. The key fields in the IPv4 datagram are the following:

- *Version number.* These 4 bits specify the IP protocol version of the datagram. By looking at the version number, the router can determine how to interpret the remainder of the IP datagram. Different versions of IP use different datagram formats. The datagram format for the current version of IP, IPv4, is shown in Figure 10.13. The datagram format for the new version of IP (IPv6) is discussed in at the end of this section.
- *Header length.* Because an IPv4 datagram can contain a variable number of options (which are included in the IPv4 datagram header) these 4 bits are needed to determine where in the IP datagram the data actually begins. Most IP datagrams do not contain options so the typical IP datagram has a 20-byte header.
- *Type of service.* The type of service (TOS) bits were included in the IPv4 header to allow different types of IP datagrams (for example, datagrams particularly requiring

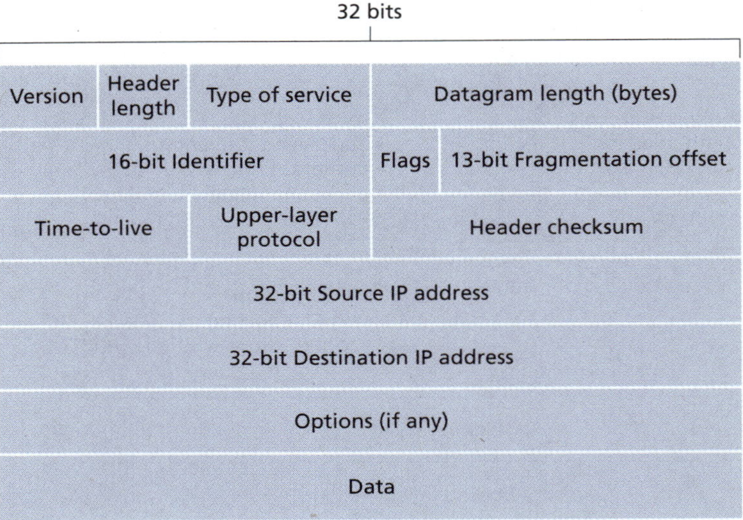

Figure 10.13 ♦ IPv4 datagram format

low delay, high throughput, or reliability) to be distinguished from each other. For example, it might be useful to distinguish real-time datagrams (such as those used by an IP telephony application) from non-real-time traffic (for example, FTP). One major routing vendor (Cisco) interprets the first three TOS bits as defining differential levels of service that can be provided by the router. The specific level of service to be provided is a policy issue determined by the router's administrator. We'll explore the topic of differentiated service in detail in Chapter 13.

- *Datagram length.* This is the total length of the IP datagram (header plus data), measured in bytes. Since this field is 16 bits long, the theoretical maximum size of the IP datagram is 65,535 bytes. However, datagrams are rarely larger than 1,500 bytes.
- *Identifier, flags, fragmentation offset.* These three fields have to do with so-called IP fragmentation, a topic we will consider in depth shortly. Interestingly, the new version of IP, IPv6, does not allow for fragmentation at routers.
- *Time-to-live.* The time-to-live (TTL) field is included to ensure that datagrams do not circulate forever (due to, for example, a long-lived routing loop) in the network. This field is decremented by one each time the datagram is processed by a router. If the TTL field reaches 0, the datagram must be dropped.
- *Protocol.* This field is used only when an IP datagram reaches its final destination. The value of this field indicates the specific transport-layer protocol to

which the data portion of this IP datagram should be passed. For example, a value of 6 indicates that the data portion is passed to TCP, while a value of 17 indicates that the data is passed to UDP. For a list of all possible values, see [RFC 1700; RFC 3232]. Note that the protocol number in the IP datagram has a role that is analogous to the role of the port number field in the transport-layer segment. The protocol number is the glue that binds the network and transport layers together, whereas the port number is the glue that binds the transport and application layers together. We'll see in Chapter 11 that the link-layer frame also has a special field that binds the link layer to the network layer.

- *Header checksum.* The header checksum aids a router in detecting bit errors in a received IP datagram. The header checksum is computed by treating each 2 bytes in the header as a number and summing these numbers using 1s complement arithmetic. As discussed, the 1s complement of this sum, known as the Internet checksum, is stored in the checksum field. A router computes the header checksum for each received IP datagram and detects an error condition if the checksum carried in the datagram header does not equal the computed checksum. Routers typically discard datagrams for which an error has been detected. Note that the checksum must be recomputed and stored again at each router, as the TTL field, and possibly options fields as well, may change. An interesting discussion of fast algorithms for computing the Internet checksum is [RFC 1071]. A question often asked at this point is, why does TCP/IP perform error checking at both the transport and network layers? There are several reasons for this repetition. First, note that only the IP header is checksummed at the IP layer, while the TCP/UDP checksum is computed over the entire TCP/UDP segment. Second, TCP/UDP and IP do not necessarily both have to belong to the same protocol stack. TCP can, in principle, run over a different protocol (for example, ATM) and IP can carry data that will not be passed to TCP/UDP.
- *Source and destination IP addresses.* When a source creates a datagram, it inserts its IP address into the source IP address field and inserts the address of the ultimate destination into the destination IP address field. Often the source host determines the destination address via a DNS lookup. We'll discuss IP addressing in detail in Section 10.4.2.
- *Options.* The options fields allow an IP header to be extended. Header options were meant to be used rarely—hence the decision to save overhead by not including the information in options fields in every datagram header. However, the mere existence of options does complicate matters—since datagram headers can be of variable length, one cannot determine a priori where the data field will start. Also, since some datagrams may require options processing and others may not, the amount of time needed to process an IP datagram at a router can vary greatly. These considerations become particularly important for IP processing in high-performance routers and hosts. For these reasons and others, IP options were dropped in the IPv6 header, as discussed in Section 10.4.4.

- *Data (payload).* Finally, we come to the last and most important field—the *raison d'être* for the datagram in the first place! In most circumstances, the data field of the IP datagram contains the transport-layer segment (TCP or UDP) to be delivered to the destination. However, the data field can carry other types of data, such as ICMP messages (discussed in Section 10.4.3).

Note that an IP datagram has a total of 20 bytes of header (assuming no options). If the datagram carries a TCP segment, then each (nonfragmented) datagram carries a total of 40 bytes of header (20 bytes of IP header plus 20 bytes of TCP header) along with the application-layer message.

IP Datagram Fragmentation

We'll see in Chapter 11 that not all link-layer protocols can carry network-layer packets of the same size. Some protocols can carry big datagrams, whereas other protocols can carry only little packets. For example, Ethernet frames can carry up to 1,500 bytes of data, whereas frames for some wide-area links can carry no more than 576 bytes. The maximum amount of data that a link-layer frame can carry is called the maximum transmission unit (MTU). Because each IP datagram is encapsulated within the link-layer frame for transport from one router to the next router, the MTU of the link-layer protocol places a hard limit on the length of an IP datagram. Having a hard limit on the size of an IP datagram is not much of a problem. What is a problem is that each of the links along the route between sender and destination can use different link-layer protocols, and each of these protocols can have different MTUs.

To understand the forwarding issue better, imagine that *you* are a router that interconnects several links, each running different link-layer protocols with different MTUs. Suppose you receive an IP datagram from one link. You check your forwarding table to determine the outgoing link, and this outgoing link has an MTU that is smaller than the length of the IP datagram. Time to panic—how are you going to squeeze this oversized IP datagram into the payload field of the link-layer frame? The solution is to fragment the data in the IP datagram into two or more smaller IP datagrams, then send these smaller datagrams over the outgoing link. Each of these smaller datagrams is referred to as a **fragment.**

Fragments need to be reassembled before they reach the transport layer at the destination. Indeed, both TCP and UDP are expecting to receive complete, unfragmented segments from the network layer. The designers of IPv4 felt that reassembling datagrams in the routers would introduce significant complication into the protocol and put a damper on router performance. (If you were a router, would you want to be reassembling fragments on top of everything else you had to do?) Sticking to the principle of keeping the network core simple, the designers of IPv4 decided to put the job of datagram reassembly in the end systems rather than in network routers.

When a destination host receives a series of datagrams from the same source, it needs to determine whether any of these datagrams are fragments of some original, larger datagram. If some datagrams are fragments, it must further determine when it has received the last fragment and how the fragments it has received should be pieced back together to form the original datagram. To allow the destination host to perform these reassembly tasks, the designers of IP (version 4) put *identification, flag,* and *fragmentation offset* fields in the IP datagram. When a datagram is created, the sending host stamps the datagram with an identification number as well as source and destination addresses. Typically, the sending host increments the identification number for each datagram it sends. When a router needs to fragment a datagram, each resulting datagram (that is, fragment) is stamped with the source address, destination address, and identification number of the original datagram. When the destination receives a series of datagrams from the same sending host, it can examine the identification numbers of the datagrams to determine which of the datagrams are actually fragments of the same larger datagram. Because IP is an unreliable service, one or more of the fragments may never arrive at the destination. For this reason, in order for the destination host to be absolutely sure it has received the last fragment of the original datagram, the last fragment has a flag bit set to 0, whereas all the other fragments have this flag bit set to 1. Also, in order for the destination host to determine whether a fragment is missing (and also to be able to reassemble the fragments in their proper order), the offset field is used to specify where the fragment fits within the original IP datagram.

Figure 10.14 illustrates an example. A datagram of 4,000 bytes (20 bytes of IP header plus 3,980 bytes of IP payload) arrives at a router and must be forwarded to a link with an MTU of 1,500 bytes. This implies that the 3,980 data bytes in the original datagram must be allocated to three separate fragments (each of which is also an IP datagram). Suppose that the original datagram is stamped with an identification number of 777. The characteristics of the three fragments are shown in Table 10.2. The values in Table 10.2 reflect the requirement that the amount of original payload data in all but the last fragment be a multiple of 8 bytes, and that the offset value be specified in units of 8-byte chunks.

The payload of the datagram is passed to the transport layer at the destination only after the IP layer has fully reconstructed the original IP datagram. If one or more of the fragments does not arrive at the destination, the incomplete datagram is discarded and not passed to the transport layer. But, as we learned in the previous chapter, if TCP is being used at the transport layer, then TCP will recover from this loss by having the source retransmit the data in the original datagram.

At this book's Web site, we provide a Java applet that generates fragments. You provide the incoming datagram size, the MTU, and the incoming datagram identification. It automatically generates the fragments for you. See http://www.awl.com/kurose-ross.

Fragment	Bytes	ID	Offset	Flag
1st fragment	1,480 bytes in the data field of the IP datagram	identification = 777	offset = 0 (meaning the data should be inserted beginning at byte 0)	flag = 1 (meaning there is more)
2nd fragment	1,480 bytes of data	identification = 777	offset = 185 (meaning the data should be inserted beginning at byte 1,480. Note that 185 · 8 = 1,480)	flag = 1 (meaning there is more)
3rd fragment	1,020 bytes (= 3,980–1,480–1,480) of data	identification = 777	offset = 370 (meaning the data should be inserted beginning at byte 2,960. Note that 370 · 8 = 2,960)	flag = 0 (meaning this is the last fragment)

Table 10.2 ♦ IP fragments

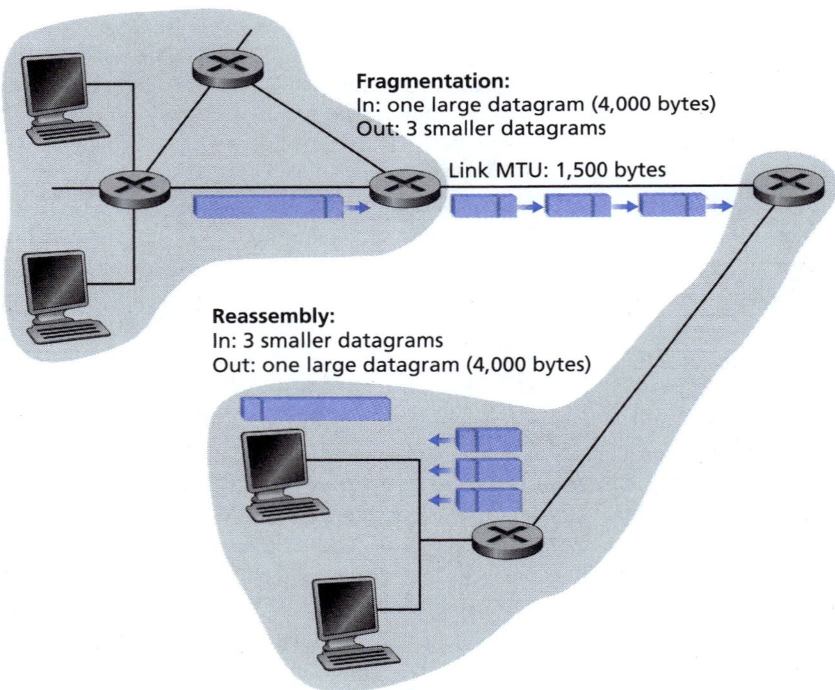

Figure 10.14 ♦ IP fragmentation and reassembly

10.4.2 IPv4 Addressing

We now turn our attention to IPv4 addressing. Although you may be thinking that addressing must be a straightforward topic, hopefully by the end of this chapter you'll be convinced that Internet addressing is not only a juicy, subtle, and interesting topic but also one that is of central importance to the Internet. Excellent treatments of IPv4 addressing are [Semeria 1996] and the first chapter in [Stewart 1999].

Before discussing IP addressing, however, we'll need to say a few words about how hosts and routers are connected into the network. A host typically has only a single link into the network; when IP in the host wants to send a datagram, it does so over this link. The boundary between the host and the physical link is called an **interface.** Now consider a router and its interfaces. Because a router's job is to receive a datagram on one link and forward the datagram on some other link, a router necessarily has two or more links to which it is connected. The boundary between the router and any one of its links is also called an interface. A router thus has multiple interfaces, one for each of its links. Because every host and router is capable of sending and receiving IP datagrams, IP requires each host and router interface to have its own IP address. Thus, an IP address is technically associated with an interface, rather than with the host or router containing that interface.

Each IP address is 32 bits long (equivalently, 4 bytes), and there are thus a total of 2^{32} possible IP addresses. By approximating 2^{10} by 10^3, it is easy to see that there are about 4 billion possible IP addresses. These addresses are typically written in so-called **dotted-decimal notation,** in which each byte of the address is written in its decimal form and is separated by a period (dot) from other bytes in the address. For example, consider the IP address 193.32.216.9. The 193 is the decimal equivalent of the first 8 bits of the address; the 32 is the decimal equivalent of the second 8 bits of the address, and so on. Thus, the address 193.32.216.9 in binary notation is

11000001 00100000 11011000 00001001

Each interface on every host and router in the global Internet must have an IP address that is globally unique (except for interfaces behind NATs, as discussed at the end of this section). These addresses cannot be chosen in a willy-nilly manner, however. A portion of an interface's IP address will be determined by the subnet to which it is connected.

Figure 10.15 provides an example of IP addressing and interfaces. In this figure, one router (with three interfaces) is used to interconnect seven hosts. Take a close look at the IP addresses assigned to the host and router interfaces; there are several things to notice. The three hosts in the upper-left portion of Figure 10.15, and the router interface to which they are connected, all have an IP address of the form 223.1.1.xxx. That is, they all have the same leftmost 24 bits in their IP address. The four interfaces are also interconnected to each other by a network *that contains no routers*. (This network could be, for example, an Ethernet LAN, in which case the interfaces would be interconnected by an Ethernet hub or an Ethernet switch; see Chapter 11.) In IP terms, this network interconnecting three host interfaces and one router interface forms a **subnet** [RFC 950]. (A subnet also called an *IP network* or simply a *network* in the Internet literature.) IP addressing assigns an address to this subnet: 223.1.1.0/24, where the /24 notation, sometimes known as a **subnet mask,** indicates that the leftmost 24 bits of the 32-bit quantity define the subnet address. The subnet 223.1.1.0/24 thus consists of the three host interfaces (223.1.1.1, 223.1.1.2, and 223.1.1.3) and one router interface (223.1.1.4). Any additional hosts attached to the 223.1.1.0/24 subnet would be *required* to have an address of the form 223.1.1.xxx. There are two additional subnets shown in Figure 10.15: the 223.1.2.0/24 network and the 223.1.3.0/24 subnet. Figure 10.16 illustrates the three IP subnets present in Figure 10.15.

The IP definition of a subnet is not restricted to Ethernet segments that connect multiple hosts to a router interface. To get some insight here, consider Figure 10.17, which shows three routers that are interconnected with each other by point-to-point links. Each router has three interfaces, one for each point-to-point link and one for the broadcast link that directly connects the router to a pair of hosts. What subnets are present here? Three subnets, 223.1.1.0/24, 223.1.2.0/24, and 223.1.3.0/24 are similar to the subnets we encountered in Figure 10.15. But note that there are three additional subnets in this example as well: one subnet, 223.1.9.0/24, for the interfaces that connect routers R1 and R2; another subnet, 223.1.8.0/24, for the interfaces that

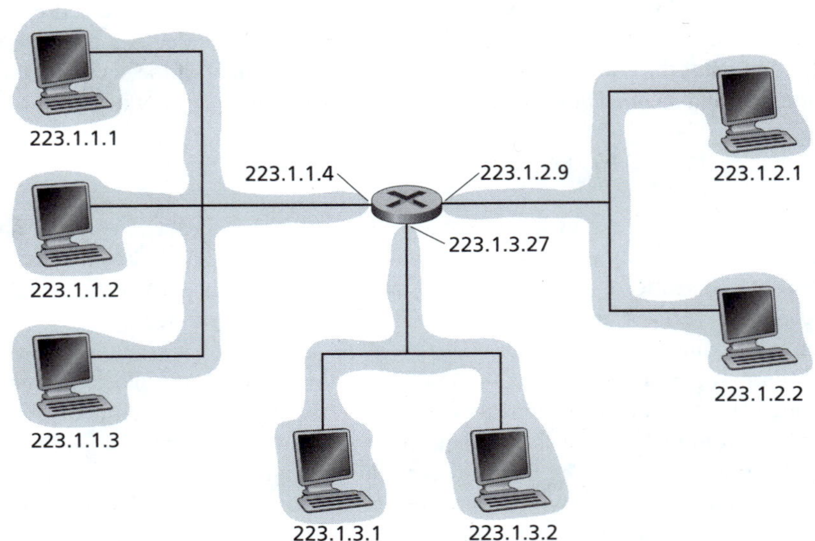

Figure 10.15 ♦ Interface addresses and subnets

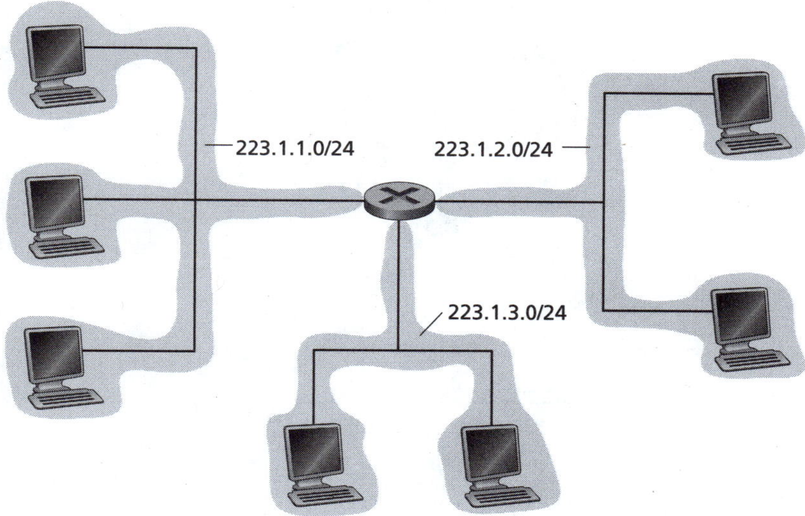

Figure 10.16 ♦ Subnet addresses

connect routers R2 and R3; and a third subnet, 223.1.7.0/24, for the interfaces that connect routers R3 and R1. For a general interconnected system of routers and hosts, we can use the following recipe to define the subnets in the system.

> *To determine the subnets, detach each interface from its host or router, creating islands of isolated networks, with interfaces terminating the endpoints of the isolated networks. Each of these isolated networks is called a* ***subnet.***

If we apply this procedure to the interconnected system in Figure 10.17, we get six islands or subnets.

From the discussion above, it's clear that an organization (such as a company or academic institution) with multiple Ethernet segments and point-to-point links will have multiple subnets, with all of the devices on a given subnet having the same subnet address. In principle, the different subnets could have quite different subnet addresses. In practice, however, their subnet addresses often have much in common. To understand why, let's next turn our attention to how addressing is handled in the global Internet.

The Internet's address assignment strategy is known as **Classless Interdomain Routing** (**CIDR**—pronounced *cider*) [RFC 1519]. CIDR generalizes the notion of subnet addressing. As with subnet addressing, the 32-bit IP address is divided into two parts and again has the dotted-decimal form *a.b.c.d/x*, where *x* indicates the number of bits in the first part of the address.

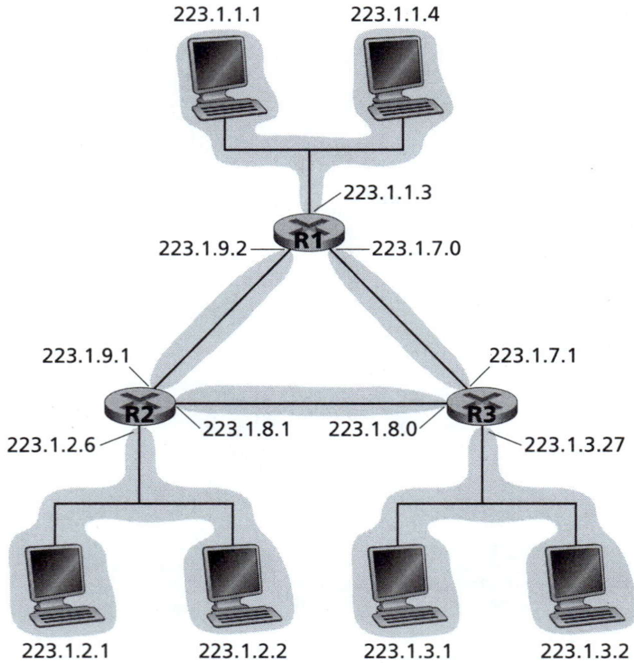

Figure 10.17 ♦ Three routers interconnecting six subnets

The *x* most significant bits of an address of the form *a.b.c.d/x* constitute the network portion of the IP address, and are often referred to as the **prefix** (or *network prefix*) of the address. An organization is typically assigned a block of contiguous addresses, that is, a range of addresses with a common prefix (see Principles in Practice sidebar). In this case, the IP addresses of devices within the organization will share the common prefix. When we cover the Internet's BGP routing protocol in Section 10.6, we'll see that only these *x* leading prefix bits are considered by routers outside the organization's network. That is, when a router outside the organization forwards a datagram whose destination address is inside the organization, only the leading *x* bits of the address need be considered. This considerably reduces the size of the forwarding table in these routers, since a *single* entry of the form *a.b.c.d/x* will be sufficient to forward packets to *any* destination within the organization.

The remaining 32-*x* bits of an address can be thought of as distinguishing among the devices *within* the organization, all of which have the same network prefix. These are the bits that will be considered when forwarding packets at routers *within* the organization. These lower-order bits may (or may not) have an additional subnetting structure, such as that discussed above. For example, suppose the first

21 bits of the CIDRized address *a.b.c.d/21* specify the organization's network prefix and are common to the IP addresses of all devices in that organization. The remaining 11 bits then identify the specific hosts in the organization. The organization's internal structure might be such that these 11 rightmost bits are used for subnetting within the organization, as discussed above. For example, *a.b.c.d/24* might refer to a specific subnet within the organization.

Before CIDR was adopted, the network portions of an IP address were constrained to be 8, 16, or 24 bits in length, an addressing scheme known as **classful addressing,** since subnets with an 8-, 16-, and 24-bit subnet addresses were known as class A, B, and C networks, respectively. The requirement that the subnet portion of an IP address be exactly 1, 2, or 3 bytes long turned out to be problematic for supporting the rapidly growing number of organizations with small and medium-sized subnets. A class C (/24) subnet could accommodate only up to $2^8 - 2 = 254$ hosts (two of the $2^8 = 256$ addresses are reserved for special use)—too small for many organizations. However, a class B (/16) subnet, which supports up 65,634 hosts, was too large. Under classful addressing, an organization with, say, 2,000 hosts was typically allocated a class B (/16) subnet address. This led to a rapid depletion of the class B address space and poor utilization of the assigned address space. For example, the organization that used a class B address for its 2,000 hosts was allocated enough of the address space for up to 65,534 interfaces—leaving more than 63,000 addresses that could not be used by other organizations.

We would be remiss if we did not mention yet another type of IP address, the IP broadcast address 255.255.255.255. When a host emits a datagram with destination address 255.255.255.255, the message is delivered to all hosts on the same subnet. Routers optionally forward the message into neighboring subnets as well (although they usually don't). In Chapter 11 we'll look at an example of how IP broadcast is used when discussing the DHCP protocol.

Having now studied IP addressing in detail, we need to know how hosts and subnets get their addresses in the first place. Let's begin by looking at how an organization gets a block of addresses for its devices, and then look at how a device (such as a host) is assigned an address from with the organization's block of addresses.

Obtaining a Block of Addresses

In order to obtain a block of IP addresses for use within an organization's subnet, a network administrator might first contact its ISP, which would provide addresses from a larger block of addresses that had already been allocated to the ISP. For example, the ISP may itself have been allocated the address block 200.23.16.0/20. The ISP, in turn, could divide its address block into eight equal-sized contiguous address blocks and give one of these address blocks out to each of up to eight organizations that are supported by this ISP, as shown below. (We have underlined the subnet part of these addresses for your convenience.)

ISP's block	200.23.16.0/20	11001000 00010111 00010000 00000000
Organization 0	200.23.16.0/23	11001000 00010111 00010000 00000000
Organization 1	200.23.18.0/23	11001000 00010111 00010010 00000000
Organization 2	200.23.20.0/23	11001000 00010111 00010100 00000000
. . .	. . .	. . .
Organization 7	200.23.30.0/23	11001000 00010111 00011110 00000000

PRINCIPLES IN PRACTICE

This example of an ISP that connects eight organizations to the Internet nicely illustrates how carefully allocated CIDRized addresses facilitate routing. Suppose, as shown in Figure 10.18, that the ISP (which we'll call Fly-By-Night-ISP) advertises to the outside world that it should be sent any datagrams whose first 20 address bits match 200.23.16.0/20. The rest of the world need not know that within the address block 200.23.16.0/20 there are in fact eight other organizations, each with their own subnets. This ability to use a single prefix to advertise multiple networks is often referred to as **address aggregation** (also **route aggregation** or **route summarization**).

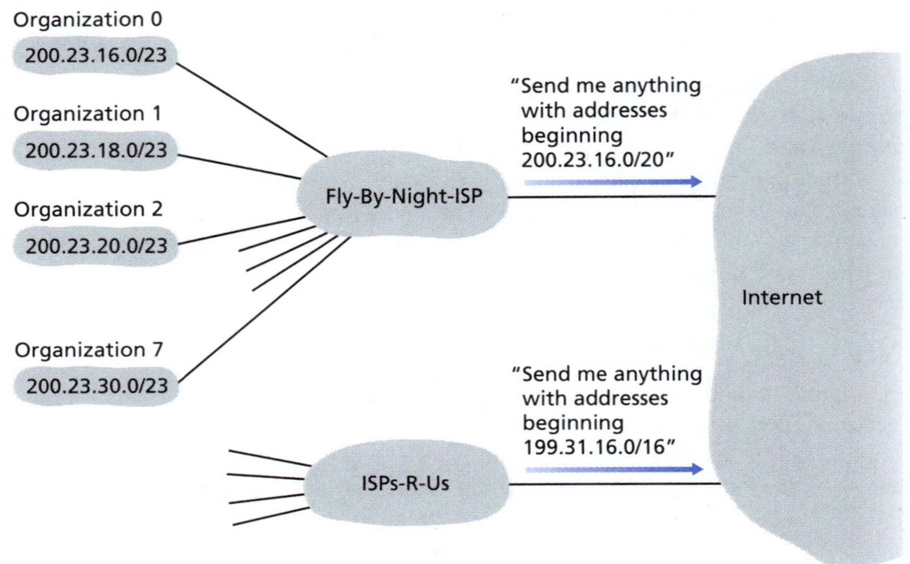

Figure 10.18 ♦ Hierarchical addressing and route aggregation

Address aggregation works extremely well when addresses are allocated in blocks to ISPs and then from ISPs to client organizations. But what happens when addresses are not allocated in such a hierarchical manner? What would happen, for example, if Fly-by-Night-ISP acquires ISPs-R-Us and then has Organization 1 connect to the Internet through its subsidiary ISPs-R-Us? As shown in Figure 10.18, the subsidiary ISPs-R-Us owns the address block 199.31.0.0/16, but Organization 1's IP addresses are unfortunately outside of this address block. What should be done here? Certainly, Organization 1 could renumber all of its routers and hosts to have addresses within the ISPs-R-Us address block. But this is a costly solution, and Organization 1 might well be re-assigned to another subsidiary in the future. The solution typically adopted is for Organization 1 to keep its IP addresses in 200.23.18.0/23. In this case, as shown in Figure 10.19, Fly-By-Night-ISP continues to advertise the address block 200.23.16.0/20 and ISPs-R-Us continues to advertise 199.31.0.0/16. However, ISPs-R-Us now *also* advertises the block of addresses for Organization 1, 200.23.18.0/23. When other routers in the larger Internet see the address blocks 200.23.16.0/20 (from Fly-By-Night-ISP) and 200.23.18.0/23 (from ISPs-R-Us) and want to route to an address in the block 200.23.18.0/23, they will use longest prefix matching (see Section 10.2.2), and route toward ISPs-R-Us, as it advertises the longest (most specific) address prefix that matches the destination address.

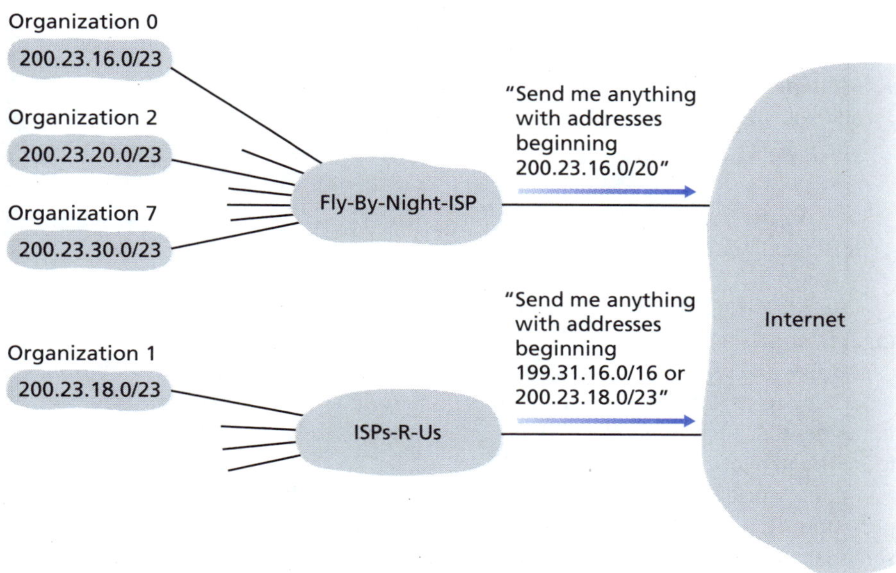

Figure 10.19 ♦ ISPs-R-Us has a more specific route to Organization 1

While obtaining a set of addresses from an ISP is one way to get a block of addresses, it is not the only way. Clearly, there must also be a way for the ISP itself to get a block of addresses. Is there a global authority that has ultimate responsibility for managing the IP address space and allocating address blocks to ISPs and other organizations? Indeed there is! IP addresses are managed under the authority of the Internet Corporation for Assigned Names and Numbers (ICANN) [ICANN 2004], based on guidelines set forth in RFC 2050. The role of the nonprofit ICANN organization [NTIA 1998] is not only to allocate IP addresses, but also to manage the DNS root servers. It also has the very contentious job of assigning domain names and resolving domain name disputes. The ICANN allocates addresses to regional Internet registries (for example, ARIN, RIPE, APNIC, and LACNIC, which together form the Address Supporting Organization of ICANN [ASO-ICANN 2004]), which handle the allocation/management of addresses within their regions.

Obtaining a Host Address

Once an organization has obtained a block of addresses, it can assign individual IP addresses to the host and router interfaces in its organization. For the router interface addresses, the system administrator manually configures the IP addresses into the router (often remotely, with a network management tool). There are two ways in which a host can be assigned an IP address:

- *Manual configuration.* A system administrator manually configures the IP address into the host (typically in a file).
- *Dynamic Host Configuration Protocol (DHCP) [RFC 2131].* DHCP allows a host to obtain (be allocated) an IP address automatically, as well as to learn additional information, such as its subnet mask, the address of its first-hop router (often called the default gateway), and the address of its local DNS server.

Because of DHCP's ability to automate the network-related aspects of connecting a host into a network, it is often referred to as a **plug-and-play protocol.** This capability makes it *very* attractive to the network administrator who would otherwise have to perform these tasks manually! DHCP is also enjoying widespread use in residential Internet access networks and in wireless LANs, where hosts join and leave the network frequently.

A network administrator can configure DHCP so that a given host receives a persistent IP address, so that each time the host joins the network it is assigned the same IP address. But many organizations and residential ISPs do not have enough IP addresses for all of their hosts. When this is the case, DHCP is used to assign each of its connecting hosts a **temporary IP address.** As an example, consider a residential ISP that has 2,000 customers, but no more than 400 of these customers are ever online at the same time. To handle all of its 2,000 customers, the ISP doesn't need a block of 2,000 addresses. Instead, by using a DHCP server to assign addresses dynamically, it only needs a block of 512 addresses (for example, a block of the form a.b.c.d/23). As the hosts join and leave, the DHCP server needs to update its list of available IP addresses. Each time a host joins, the DHCP server allocates an arbitrary address from its current pool of available addresses; each time a host leaves, an address is returned to the pool.

Another important reason why DHCP has found such widespread use is the advent of mobile computing. Consider, for example, the student who carries a laptop from a dormitory room to a library to a classroom. It is likely that in each location, the student will be connecting into a new subnet and hence will need a new IP address at each location. DHCP is ideally suited to this situation, as there are many users coming and going, and addresses are needed for only a limited amount of time.

The DHCP protocol actually straddles the boundary between the network and link layers in the five-layer Internet protocol stack. We'll therefore delay a detailed discussion of how the DHCP service is implemented until Chapter 11, which covers the link layer.

Network Address Translation (NAT)

Given our discussion about Internet addresses and the IPv4 datagram format, we're now well aware that every IP-capable device needs an IP address. With the proliferation of small office, home office (SOHO) subnets, this would seem to imply that whenever a SOHO wants to install a LAN to connect multiple machines, a range of addresses would need to be allocated by the ISP to cover all of the SOHO's machines. If the subnet grew bigger (for example, the kids at home have not only their own computers, but have bought handheld PDAs, IP-capable phones, and networked Game Boys as well), a larger block of addresses would have to be allocated. But what if the ISP had already allocated the contiguous portions of the SOHO network's current address range? And what typical homeowner wants (or should need) to know how to manage IP addresses in the first place? Fortunately, there is a simpler approach to address allocation that has found increasingly widespread use in such scenarios: **network address translation (NAT)** [RFC 2663; RFC 3022].

Figure 10.20 shows the operation of a NAT-enabled router. The NAT-enabled router, residing in the home, has an interface that is part of the home network on the right of Figure 10.20. Addressing within the home network is exactly as we have seen above—all four interfaces in the home network have the same subnet address of 10.0.0/24. The address space 10.0.0.0/8 is one of three portions of the IP address space that is reserved in [RFC 1918] for a private network or a **realm** with private addresses, such as the home network in Figure 10.20. A *realm with private addresses* refers to a network whose addresses only have meaning to devices within that network. To see why this is important, consider the fact that there are hundreds of thousands of home networks, many using the same address space, 10.0.0.0/24. Devices within a given home network can send packets to each other using 10.0.0.0/24 addressing. However, packets forwarded *beyond* the home network into the larger global Internet clearly cannot use these addresses (as either a source or a destination address) because there are hundreds of thousands of networks using this block of addresses. That is, the 10.0.0.0/24 addresses can only have meaning within the given home network. But if private addresses only have meaning within a given network, how is addressing handled when packets are sent to or received from the global Internet, where addresses are necessarily unique? The answer lies in understanding NAT.

The NAT-enabled router does not *look* like a router to the outside world. Instead the NAT router behaves to the outside world as a *single* device with a *single* IP address. In Figure 10.20, all traffic leaving the home router for the larger Internet has a source IP address of 138.76.29.7, and all traffic entering the home must have a destination address of 138.76.29.7. In essence, the NAT-enabled router is hiding the details of the home network from the outside world. (As an aside, you might wonder where the home network computers get their addresses and where the router gets its single IP address. Often, the answer is the same—DHCP! The router gets its address from the ISP's DHCP server, and the router runs a DHCP server to provide addresses to computers within the NAT-DHCP-router-controlled home network's address space.)

If all datagrams arriving at the NAT router from the WAN have the same destination IP address (specifically, that of the WAN-side interface of the NAT router), then how does the router know the internal host to which it should forward a given datagram? The trick is to use a **NAT translation table** at the NAT router, and to include port numbers as well as IP addresses in the table entries.

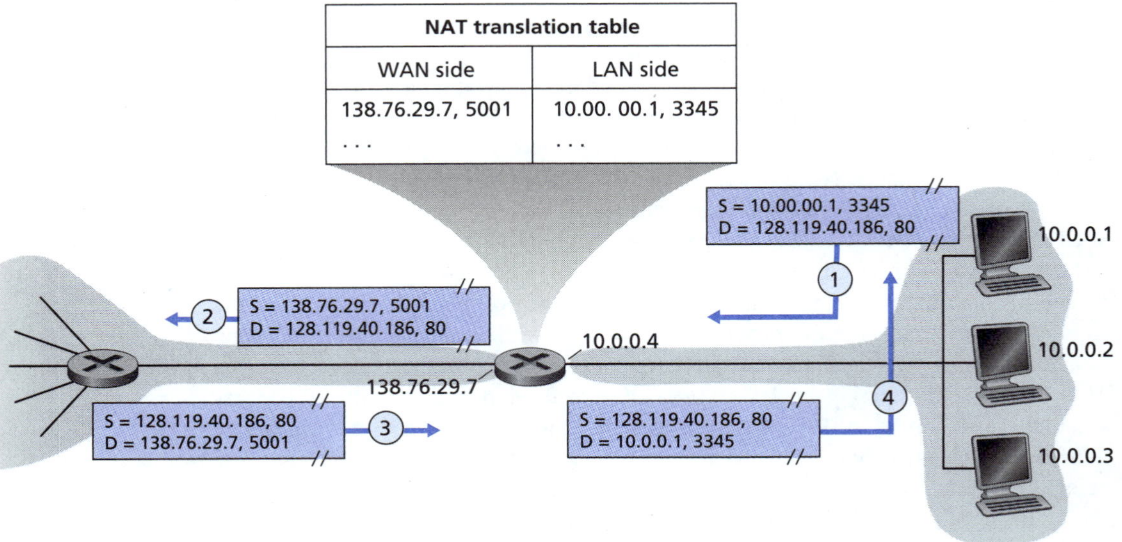

Figure 10.20 ♦ Network address translation

Consider the example in Figure 10.20. Suppose a user sitting in a home network behind host 10.0.0.1 requests a Web page on some Web server (port 80) with IP address 128.119.40.186. The host 10.0.0.1 assigns the (arbitrary) source port number 3345 and sends the datagram into the LAN. The NAT router receives the datagram, generates a new source port number 5001 for the datagram, replaces the source IP address with its WAN-side IP address 138.76.29.7, and replaces the original source port number 3345 with the new source port number 5001. When generating a new source port number, the NAT router can select any source port number that is not currently in the NAT translation table. (Note that because a port number field is 16 bits long, the NAT protocol can support over 60,000 simultaneous connections with a single WAN-side IP address for the router!) NAT in the router also adds an entry to its NAT translation table. The Web server, blissfully unaware that the arriving datagram containing the HTTP request has been manipulated by the NAT router, responds with a datagram whose destination address is the IP address of the NAT router, and whose destination port number is 5001. When this datagram arrives at the NAT router, the router indexes the NAT translation table using the destination IP address and destination port number to obtain the appropriate IP address (10.0.0.1) and destination port number (3345) for the browser in the home network. The router then rewrites the datagram's destination address and destination port number, and forwards the datagram into the home network.

NAT has enjoyed widespread deployment in recent years. But we should mention that many purists in the IETF community loudly object to NAT. First, they argue, port numbers are meant to be used for addressing processes, not for addressing hosts. (This violation can indeed cause problems for servers running on the home network, since server processes wait for incoming requests at well-known port numbers.) Second, they argue, routers are supposed to process packets only up to layer 3. Third, they argue, the NAT protocol violates the so-called end-to-end argument; that is, hosts should be talking directly with each other, without interfering nodes modifying IP addresses and port numbers. And fourth, they argue, we should use IPv6 (see Section 10.4.4) to solve the shortage of IP addresses, rather than recklessly patching up the problem with a stopgap solution like NAT. But like it or not, NAT has become an important component of the Internet.

Yet another major problem with NAT is that it interferes with P2P applications, including P2P file sharing applications and P2P voice-over-IP applications. Recall that in a P2P application, any participating Peer A should be able to initiate a TCP connection to any other participating Peer B. The essence of the problem is that if Peer B is behind a NAT, it cannot act as a server and accept TCP connections (unless the NAT is specifically configured for the P2P application). As we'll see in the homework problems, this NAT problem can be circumvented if Peer A first contacts Peer B through an intermediate Peer C which is not behind a NAT and to which B has established an on-going TCP connection. Peer A can then ask Peer B, via Peer C, to initiate a TCP connection directly back to Peer A. Once the direct P2P TCP connection is established between Peers A and B, the two peers can exchange messages or files. This hack, called **connection reversal,** is actually used by many P2P applications. But if both Peer A and Peer B are behind their own NATs, then, for all practical purposes, it is impossible to establish a TCP connection between the two peers without application-specific NAT configuration.

Our discussion of NAT here has been necessarily brief. There are many other important aspects of NAT, including static versus dynamic NAT, and the effects of NAT on higher-layer protocols and on security. For more details, and a discussion of the pros and cons of NAT, see [Cisco NAT 2004; Phifer 2000].

10.4.3 Internet Control Message Protocol (ICMP)

Recall that the network layer of the Internet has three main components: the IP protocol, discussed in the previous section; the Internet routing protocols (including RIP, OSPF, and BGP), which are covered in Section 10.6; and ICMP, which is the subject of this section.

ICMP, specified in RFC 792, is used by hosts and routers to communicate network-layer information to each other. The most typical use of ICMP is for error reporting. For example, when running a Telnet, FTP, or HTTP session, you may have encountered an error message such as "Destination network unreachable." This message had its origins in ICMP. At some point, an IP router was unable to find a path to the host specified in your Telnet, FTP, or HTTP application. That router created and sent a type-3 ICMP message to your host indicating the error.

ICMP is often considered part of IP but architecturally lies just above IP, as ICMP messages are carried inside IP datagrams. That is, ICMP messages are carried as IP payload, just as TCP or UDP segments are carried as IP payload. Similarly, when a host receives an IP datagram with ICMP specified as the upper-layer protocol, it demultiplexes the datagram's contents to ICMP, just as it would demultiplex a datagram's content to TCP or UDP.

ICMP messages have a type and a code field, and contain the header and the first 8 bytes of the IP datagram that caused the ICMP message to be generated in the first place (so that the sender can determine the datagram that caused the error). Selected ICMP message types are shown in Figure 10.21. Note that ICMP messages are used not only for signaling error conditions.

The well-known ping program sends an ICMP type 8 code 0 message to the specified host. The destination host, seeing the echo request, sends back a type 0 code 0 ICMP echo reply. Most TCP/IP implementations support the `ping` server directly in the operating system; that is, the server is not a process. Chapter 11 of [Stevens 1990] provides the source code for the `ping` client program. Note that the client program needs to be able to instruct the operating system to generate an ICMP message of type 8 code 0.

Another interesting ICMP message is the source quench message. This message is seldom used in practice. Its original purpose was to perform congestion control—to allow a congested router to send an ICMP source quench message to a host to force that host to reduce its transmission rate. We have seen that TCP has its own congestion-control mechanism that operates at the transport layer, without the use of network-layer feedback such as the ICMP source quench message.

We introduced the Traceroute program, which allows us to trace a route from a host to any host in the world. Interestingly, Traceroute is implemented with ICMP messages. To determine the names and addresses of the routers between source and destination, Traceroute in the source sends a series of ordinary IP datagrams to the destination. Each of these datagrams carries a UDP segment with an unlikely UDP port number. The first of these datagrams has a TTL of 1, the second of 2, the third of 3, and so on. The source also starts timers for each of the datagrams. When the *n*th datagram arrives at the *n*th router, the *n*th router observes that the TTL of the datagram has just expired. According to the rules of the IP protocol, the router discards the datagram and sends an ICMP warning message to the source (type 11 code 0). This warning message includes the name of the router and its IP

ICMP Type	Code	Description
0	0	echo reply (to ping)
3	0	destination network unreachable
3	1	destination host unreachable
3	2	destination protocol unreachable
3	3	destination port unreachable
3	6	destination network unknown
3	7	destination host unknown
4	0	source quench (congestion control)
8	0	echo request
9	0	router advertisement
10	0	router discovery
11	0	TTL expired
12	0	IP header bad

Figure 10.21 ♦ ICMP message types

address. When this ICMP message arrives back at the source, the source obtains the round-trip time from the timer and the name and IP address of the *n*th router from the ICMP message.

How does a Traceroute source know when to stop sending UDP segments? Recall that the source increments the TTL field for each datagram it sends. Thus, one of the datagrams will eventually make it all the way to the destination host. Because this datagram contains a UDP segment with an unlikely port number, the destination host sends a port unreachable ICMP message (type 3 code 3) back to the source. When the source host receives this particular ICMP message, it knows it does not need to send additional probe packets. (The standard Traceroute program actually sends sets of three packets with the same TTL; thus the Traceroute output provides three results for each TTL.)

In this manner, the source host learns the number and the identities of routers that lie between it and the destination host and the round-trip time between the two hosts. Note that the Traceroute client program must be able to instruct the operating system to generate UDP datagrams with specific TTL values and must also be able to be notified by its operating system when ICMP messages arrive. Now that you understand how Traceroute works, you may want to go back and play with it some more.

10.4.4 IPv6

In the early 1990s, the Internet Engineering Task Force began an effort to develop a successor to the IPv4 protocol. A prime motivation for this effort was the realization that the 32-bit IP address space was beginning to be used up, with new subnets and IP nodes being attached to the Internet (and being allocated unique IP addresses) at a breathtaking rate. To respond to this need for a large IP address space, a new IP protocol, IPv6, was developed. The designers of IPv6 also took this opportunity to tweak and augment other aspects of IPv4, based on the accumulated operational experience with IPv4.

The point in time when IPv4 addresses would be completely allocated (and hence no new subnets could attach to the Internet) was the subject of considerable debate. Based on current trends in address allocation at the time, the estimates of the two leaders of the IETF's Address Lifetime Expectations working group were that addresses would become exhausted in 2008 and 2018, respectively [Solensky 1996]. In 1996, the American Registry for Internet Numbers (ARIN) reported that all of the IPv4 class A addresses had been assigned, 62 percent of the class B addresses had been assigned, and 37 percent of the class C addresses had been assigned [ARIN 1996]. Although these estimates and numbers suggested that a considerable amount of time might be left until the IPv4 address space was exhausted, it was realized that considerable time would be needed to deploy a new technology on such an extensive scale, and so the Next Generation IP (IPng) effort [Bradner 1996; RFC 1752] was begun. The result of this effort was the specification of IP version 6 (IPv6) [RFC 2460]. (An often-asked question is what happened to IPv5. It was initially envisioned that the ST-2 protocol would become IPv5, but ST-2 was later dropped in favor of the RSVP protocol, that we'll discuss in Chapter 13.)

Excellent sources of information about IPv6 are The IP Next Generation Homepage [Hinden 2004] and a book on the subject by Huitema [Huitema 1998].

IPv6 Datagram Format

The format of the IPv6 datagram is shown in Figure 10.22. The most important changes introduced in IPv6 are evident in the datagram format:

- *Expanded addressing capabilities.* IPv6 increases the size of the IP address from 32 to 128 bits. This ensures that the world won't run out of IP addresses. Now, every grain of sand on the planet can be IP-addressable. In addition to unicast and multicast addresses, IPv6 has introduced a new type of address, called an **anycast address,** which allows a datagram to be delivered to any one of a group of hosts. (This feature could be used, for example, to send an HTTP GET to the nearest of a number of mirror sites that contain a given document.)
- *A streamlined 40-byte header.* As discussed below, a number of IPv4 fields have been dropped or made optional. The resulting 40-byte fixed-length header allows for faster processing of the IP datagram. A new encoding of options allows for more flexible options processing.
- *Flow labeling and priority.* IPv6 has an elusive definition of a **flow.** RFC 1752 and RFC 2460 state that this allows "labeling of packets belonging to particular

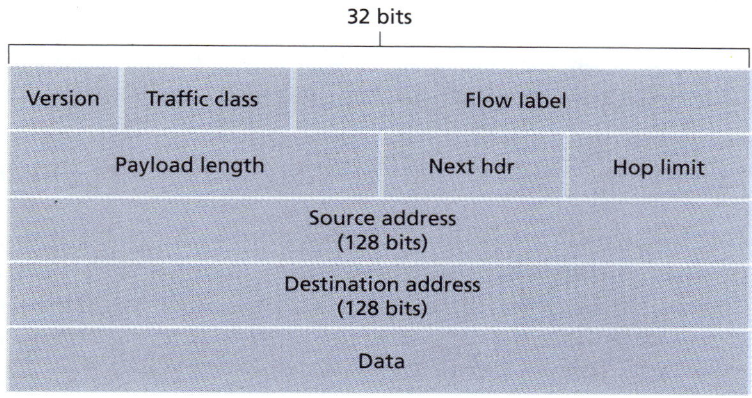

Figure 10.22 ♦ IPv6 datagram format

flows for which the sender requests special handling, such as a nondefault quality of service or real-time service." For example, audio and video transmission might likely be treated as a flow. On the other hand, the more traditional applications, such as file transfer and e-mail, might not be treated as flows. It is possible that the traffic carried by a high-priority user (for example, someone paying for better service for their traffic) might also be treated as a flow. What is clear, however, is that the designers of IPv6 foresee the eventual need to be able to differentiate among the flows, even if the exact meaning of a flow has not yet been determined. The IPv6 header also has an 8-bit traffic class field. This field, like the TOS field in IPv4, can be used to give priority to certain datagrams within a flow, or it can be used to give priority to datagrams from certain applications (for example, ICMP) over datagrams from other applications (for example, network news).

As noted above, a comparison of Figure 10.22 with Figure 10.13 reveals the simpler, more streamlined structure of the IPv6 datagram. The following fields are defined in IPv6:

- *Version.* This 4-bit field identifies the IP version number. Not surprisingly, IPv6 carries a value of 6 in this field. Note that putting a 4 in this field does not create a valid IPv4 datagram. (If it did, life would be a lot simpler—see the discussion below regarding the transition from IPv4 to IPv6.)
- *Traffic class.* This 8-bit field is similar in spirit to the TOS field we saw in IPv4.
- *Flow label.* As discussed above, this 20-bit field is used to identify a flow of datagrams.
- *Payload length.* This 16-bit value is treated as an unsigned integer giving the number of bytes in the IPv6 datagram following the fixed-length, 40-byte datagram header.
- *Next header.* This field identifies the protocol to which the contents (data field) of this datagram will be delivered (for example, to TCP or UDP). The field uses the same values as the protocol field in the IPv4 header.
- *Hop limit.* The contents of this field are decremented by one by each router that forwards the datagram. If the hop limit count reaches zero, the datagram is discarded.
- *Source and destination addresses.* The various formats of the IPv6 128-bit address are described in RFC 2373.
- *Data.* This is the payload portion of the IPv6 datagram. When the datagram reaches its destination, the payload will be removed from the IP datagram and passed on to the protocol specified in the next header field.

The discussion above identified the purpose of the fields that are included in the IPv6 datagram. Comparing the IPv6 datagram format in Figure 10.22 with the IPv4 datagram format that we saw in Figure 10.13, we notice that several fields appearing in the IPv4 datagram are no longer present in the IPv6 datagram:

- *Fragmentation/Reassembly.* IPv6 does not allow for fragmentation and reassembly at intermediate routers; these operations can be performed only by the source and destination. If an IPv6 datagram received by a router is too large to be forwarded over the outgoing link, the router simply drops the datagram and sends a "Packet Too Big" ICMP error message (see below) back to the sender. The sender can then resend the data, using a smaller IP datagram size. Fragmentation and reassembly is a time-consuming operation; removing this functionality from the routers and placing it squarely in the end systems considerably speeds up IP forwarding within the network.
- *Header checksum.* Because the transport layer (for example, TCP and UDP) and data link (for example, Ethernet) protocols in the Internet layers perform checksumming, the designers of IP probably felt that this functionality was sufficiently redundant in the network layer that it could be removed. Once again, fast processing of IP packets was a central concern. Recall from our discussion of IPv4 in Section 10.4.1, that since the IPv4 header contains a TTL field (similar to the hop limit field in IPv6), the IPv4 header checksum needed to be recomputed at every router. As with fragmentation and reassembly, this too was a costly operation in IPv4.
- *Options.* An options field is no longer a part of the standard IP header. However, it has not gone away. Instead, the options field is one of the possible next headers pointed to from within the IPv6 header. That is, just as TCP or UDP protocol headers can be the next header within an IP packet, so too can an options field. The removal of the options field results in a fixed-length, 40-byte IP header.

Recall from our discussion in Section 10.4.3 that the ICMP protocol is used by IP nodes to report error conditions and provide limited information (for example, the echo reply to a ping message) to an end system. A new version of ICMP has been defined for IPv6 in RFC 2463. In addition to reorganizing the existing ICMP type and code definitions, ICMPv6 also added new types and codes required by the new IPv6 functionality. These include the "Packet Too Big" type, and an "unrecognized IPv6 options" error code. In addition, ICMPv6 subsumes the functionality of the Internet Group Management Protocol (IGMP) that we'll study in Section 10.7. IGMP, which is used to manage a host's joining and leaving of multicast groups, was previously a separate protocol from ICMP in IPv4.

Transitioning from IPv4 to IPv6

Now that we have seen the technical details of IPv6, let us consider a very practical matter: How will the public Internet, which is based on IPv4, be transitioned to

IPv6? The problem is that while new IPv6-capable systems can be made backward-compatible, that is, can send, route, and receive IPv4 datagrams, already deployed IPv4-capable systems are not capable of handling IPv6 datagrams. Several options are possible.

One option would be to declare a flag day—a given time and date when all Internet machines would be turned off and upgraded from IPv4 to IPv6. The last major technology transition (from using NCP to using TCP for reliable transport service) occurred almost 20 years ago. Even back then [RFC 801], when the Internet was tiny and still being administered by a small number of "wizards," it was realized that such a flag day was not possible. A flag day involving hundreds of millions of machines and millions of network administrators and users is even more unthinkable today. RFC 2893 describes two approaches (which can be used either alone or together) for gradually integrating IPv6 hosts and routers into an IPv4 world (with the long-term goal, of course, of having all IPv4 nodes eventually transition to IPv6).

Probably the most straightforward way to introduce IPv6-capable nodes is a **dual-stack** approach, where IPv6 nodes also have a complete IPv4 implementation as well. Such a node, referred to as an IPv6/IPv4 node in RFC 2893, has the ability to send and receive both IPv4 and IPv6 datagrams. When interoperating with an IPv4 node, an IPv6/IPv4 node can use IPv4 datagrams; when interoperating with an IPv6 node, it can speak IPv6. IPv6/IPv4 nodes must have both IPv6 and IPv4 addresses. They must furthermore be able to determine whether another node is IPv6-capable or IPv4-only. This problem can be solved using the DNS, which can return an IPv6 address if the node name being resolved is IPv6-capable, or otherwise return an IPv4 address. Of course, if the node issuing the DNS request is only IPv4-capable, the DNS returns only an IPv4 address.

In the dual-stack approach, if either the sender or the receiver is only IPv4-capable, an IPv4 datagram must be used. As a result, it is possible that two IPv6-capable nodes can end up, in essence, sending IPv4 datagrams to each other. This is illustrated in Figure 10.23. Suppose Node *A* is IPv6-capable and wants to send an IP datagram to Node F, which is also IPv6-capable. Nodes A and B can exchange an IPv6 datagram. However, Node B must create an IPv4 datagram to send to C. Certainly, the data field of the IPv6 datagram can be copied into the data field of the IPv4 datagram and appropriate address mapping can be done. However, in performing the conversion from IPv6 to IPv4, there will be IPv6-specific fields in the IPv6 datagram (for example, the flow identifier field) that have no counterpart in IPv4. The information in these fields will be lost. Thus, even though E and F can exchange IPv6 datagrams, the arriving IPv4 datagrams at E from D do not contain all of the fields that were in the original IPv6 datagram sent from A.

An alternative to the dual-stack approach, also discussed in RFC 2893, is known as **tunneling.** Tunneling can solve the problem noted above, allowing, for example, E to receive the IPv6 datagram originated by A. The basic idea behind tunneling is the following. Suppose two IPv6 nodes (for example, B and E in Fig-

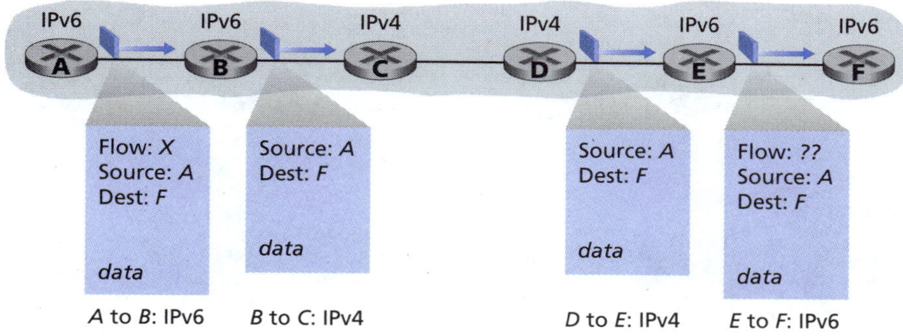

Figure 10.23 ♦ A dual-stack approach

ure 10.23) want to interoperate using IPv6 datagrams but are connected to each other by intervening IPv4 routers. We refer to the intervening set of IPv4 routers between two IPv6 routers as a **tunnel,** as illustrated in Figure 10.24. With tunneling, the IPv6 node on the sending side of the tunnel (for example, B) takes the *entire* IPv6 datagram and puts it in the data (payload) field of an IPv4 datagram. This IPv4 datagram is then addressed to the IPv6 node on the receiving side of the tunnel (for example, E) and sent to the first node in the tunnel (for example, C). The intervening IPv4 routers in the tunnel route this IPv4 datagram among themselves, just as they would any other datagram, blissfully unaware that the IPv4 datagram itself contains a complete IPv6 datagram. The IPv6 node on the receiving side of the tunnel eventually receives the IPv4 datagram (it is the destination of the IPv4 datagram!), determines that the IPv4 datagram contains an IPv6 datagram, extracts the IPv6 datagram, and then routes the IPv6 datagram exactly as it would if it had received the IPv6 datagram from a directly connected IPv6 neighbor.

We end this section by noting that the adoption of IPv6 has been slow to take off [Lawton 2001]. Recall that one of the main motivations for IPv6 was the depletion of available IPv4 addresses. We saw in Section 10.4.2 that advances such as CIDRized IPv4 addresses, DHCP, and NAT have all contributed toward solving this problem, at least in the short term. It is possible, however, that the proliferation of devices such as IP-enabled phones and other portable devices may provide the needed push for more widespread deployment of IPv6. Europe's Third Generation Partnership Program [3GPP 2004] has specified IPv6 as the standard addressing scheme for mobile multimedia. Even if IPv6 hasn't been widely deployed in the first nine years of its young life, a long-term view is clearly called for. Today's phone number system took several decades to take hold, but it has been in place now for nearly half a century with no sign of going away. Similarly, it may take some time for IPv6 to take hold, but it too may then be around for a long time thereafter. Brian Carpenter, former chair of the Internet Architecture Board [IAB 2004] and author of

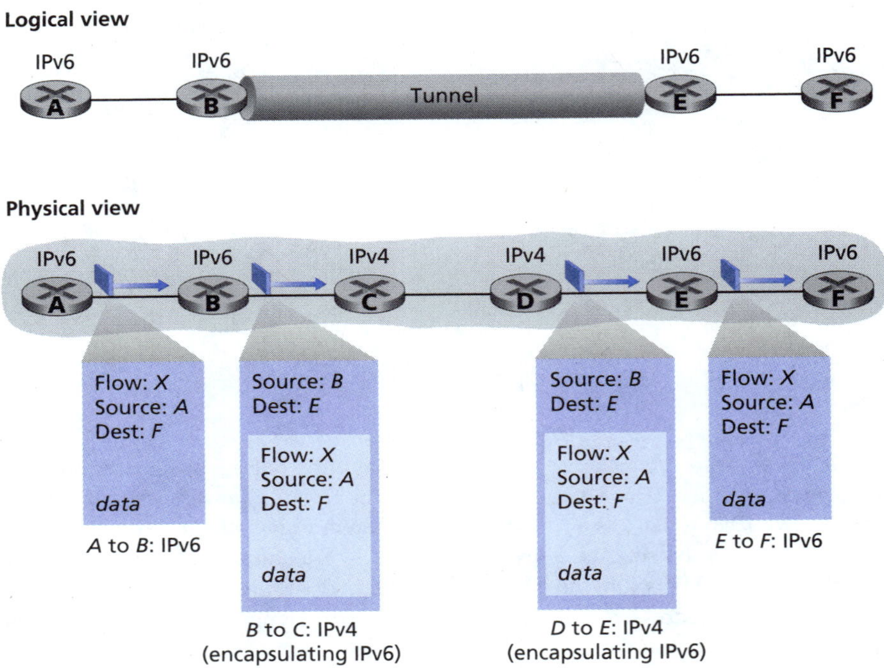

Figure 10.24 ♦ Tunneling

several IPv6-related RFCs, says, "I have always looked at this as a 15-year process starting in 1995." [Lawton 2001]. By Carpenter's dates, we're nearing the two-thirds point!

One important lesson that we can learn from the IPv6 experience is that it is enormously difficult to change network-layer protocols. Since the early 1990s, numerous new network-layer protocols have been trumpeted as the next major revolution for the Internet, but most of these protocols have had limited penetration to date. These protocols include IPv6, multicast protocols (Section 10.7), and resource reservation protocols (Chapter 13). Indeed, introducing new protocols into the network layer is like replacing the foundation of a house—it is difficult to do without tearing the whole house down or at least temporarily relocating the house's residents. On the other hand, the Internet has witnessed rapid deployment of new protocols at the application layer. The classic examples, of course, are the Web, instant messaging, and P2P file sharing. Other examples include audio and video streaming and distributed games. Introducing new application-layer protocols is like adding a new layer of paint to a house—it is relatively easy to do, and if you choose an attractive color, others in the neighborhood will copy you. In summary, in the future we can expect to see changes in the Internet's network layer, but these changes will likely occur on a time scale that is much slower than the changes that will occur at the application layer.

10.5 Routing Algorithms

So far in this chapter, we've mostly explored the network layer's forwarding function. We learned that when a packet arrives to a router, the router indexes a forwarding table and determines the link interface to which the packet is to be directed. We also learned that routing algorithms, operating in network routers, exchange and compute the information that is used to configure these forwarding tables. The interplay between routing algorithms and forwarding tables was shown in Figure 10.2. Having explored forwarding in some depth we now turn our attention to the other major topic of this chapter, namely, the network layer's critical routing function. Whether the network layer provides a datagram service (in which case different packets between a given source-destination pair may take different routes) or a VC service (in which case all packets between a given source and destination will take the same path), the network layer must nonetheless determine the path that packets take from senders to receivers. We'll see that the job of routing is to determine good paths (equivalently, routes), from senders to receivers, through the network of routers.

Typically a host is attached directly to one router, the **default router** for the host (also called the **first-hop router** for the host). Whenever a host emits a packet, the packet is transferred to its default router. We refer to the default router of the source host as the **source router** and the default router of the destination host as the **destination router.** The problem of routing a packet from source host to destination host clearly boils down to the problem of routing the packet from source router to destination router, which is the focus of this section.

The purpose of a routing algorithm is then simple: given a set of routers, with links connecting the routers, a routing algorithm finds a "good" path from source router to destination router. Typically, a good path is one that has the least cost. We'll see, however, that in practice, real-world concerns such as policy issues (for example, a rule such as "router *x*, belonging to organization *Y*, should not forward any packets originating from the network owned by organization *Z*") also come into play to complicate the conceptually simple and elegant algorithms whose theory underlies the practice of routing in today's networks.

A graph is used to formulate routing problems. Recall that a **graph** $G = (N,E)$ is a set N of nodes and a collection E of edges, where each edge is a pair of nodes from N. In the context of network-layer routing, the nodes in the graph represent routers—the points at which packet-forwarding decisions are made—and the edges connecting these nodes represent the physical links between these routers. Such a graph abstraction of a computer network is shown in Figure 10.25. To view some graphs representing real network maps, see [Dodge 2004, Cheswick 2000]; for a discussion of how well different graph-based models model the Internet, see [Zegura 1997, Faloutsos 1999].

As shown in Figure 10.25, an edge also has a value representing its cost. Typically, an edge's cost may reflect the physical length of the corresponding link (for example, a transoceanic link might have a higher cost than a short-haul terrestrial link), the link speed, or the monetary cost associated with a link. For our purposes, we'll simply take the edge costs as a given and won't worry about how they are determined. For any edge (x,y) in E, we denote $c(x,y)$ for the cost of the edge between nodes x and y. If the pair (x,y) does not belong to E, we set $c(x,y) = \infty$. Also, throughout we consider only undirected graphs (i.e., graphs whose edges do not have a direction), so that edge (x,y) is the same as edge (y,x) and that $c(x,y) = c(y,x)$. Also, a node y is said to be a **neighbor** of node x if (x,y) belongs to E.

Given that costs are assigned to the various edges in the graph abstraction, a natural goal of a routing algorithm is to identify the least costly paths between sources and destinations. To make this problem more precise, recall that a **path** in a graph $G = (N,E)$ is a sequence of nodes $(x_1, x_2,..., x_p)$ such that each of the pairs (x_1, x_2), (x_1, x_3),...,(x_{p-1}, x_p) are edges in E. The cost of a path $(x_1, x_2,..., x_p)$ is simply the sum of all the edge costs along the path, that is, $c(x_1, x_2) + c(x_2,x_3) + ...+ c(x_{p-1},x_p)$. Given any two nodes x and y, there are typically many paths between the two nodes, with each path having a cost. One or more of these paths is a **least-cost path.** The least-cost problem is therefore clear: Find a path between the source and destination that has least cost. In Figure 10.25, for example, the least-cost path between source node u and destination node w is (u, x, y, w) with a path cost of 3. Note that if all edges in the graph have the same cost, the least-cost path is also the **shortest path** (that is, the path with the smallest number of links between the source and the destination).

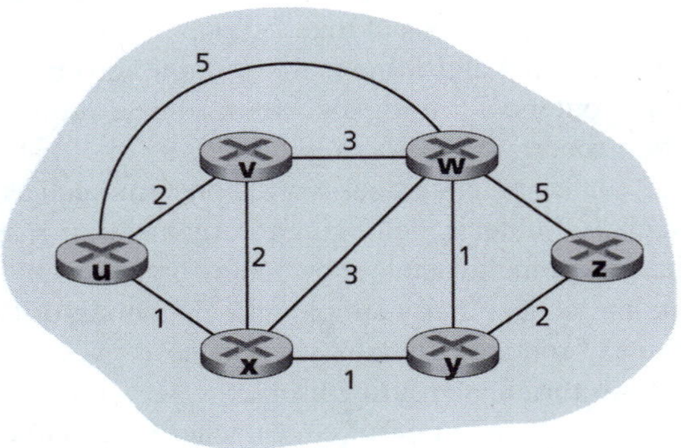

Figure 10.25 ♦ Abstract graph model of a computer network

As a simple exercise, try finding the least-cost path from nodes *u* to *z* in Figure 10.25 and reflect for a moment on how you calculated that path. If you are like most people, you found the path from *u* to *z* by examining Figure 10.25, tracing a few routes from *u* to *z*, and somehow convincing yourself that the path you had chosen had the least cost among all possible paths. (Did you check all of the 17 possible paths between *u* and *z*? Probably not!) Such a calculation is an example of a centralized routing algorithm—the routing algorithm was run in one location, your brain, with complete information about the network. Broadly, one way in which we can classify routing algorithms is according to whether they are global or decentralized.

- A **global routing algorithm** computes the least-cost path between a source and destination using complete, global knowledge about the network. That is, the algorithm takes the connectivity between all nodes and all link costs as inputs. This then requires that the algorithm somehow obtain this information before actually performing the calculation. The calculation itself can be run at one site (a centralized global routing algorithm) or replicated at multiple sites. The key distinguishing feature here, however, is that a global algorithm has complete information about connectivity and link costs. In practice, algorithms with global state information are often referred to as **link-state (LS) algorithms,** since the algorithm must be aware of the cost of each link in the network. We'll study LS algorithms in Section 10.5.1.
- In a **decentralized routing algorithm,** the calculation of the least-cost path is carried out in an iterative, distributed manner. No node has complete information about the costs of all network links. Instead, each node begins with only the knowledge of the costs of its own directly attached links. Then, through an iterative process of calculation and exchange of information with its neighboring nodes (that is, nodes that are at the other end of links to which it itself is attached), a node gradually calculates the least-cost path to a destination or set of destinations. The decentralized routing algorithm we'll study below in Section 10.5.2 is called a distance-vector (DV) algorithm, because each node maintains a vector of estimates of the costs (distances) to all other nodes in the network.

A second broad way to classify routing algorithms is according to whether they are static or dynamic. In **static routing algorithms,** routes change very slowly over time, often as a result of human intervention (for example, a human manually editing a router's forwarding table). **Dynamic routing algorithms** change the routing paths as the network traffic loads or topology change. A dynamic algorithm can be run either periodically or in direct response to topology or link cost changes. While dynamic algorithms are more responsive to network changes, they are also more susceptible to problems such as routing loops and oscillation in routes.

A third way to classify routing algorithms is according to whether they are load-sensitive or load-insensitive. In a **load-sensitive algorithm,** link costs vary dynamically to reflect the current level of congestion in the underlying link. If a high cost is associated with a link that is currently congested, a routing algorithm will tend to choose routes around such a congested link. While early ARPAnet routing algorithms were load-sensitive [McQuillan 1980], a number of difficulties were encountered [Huitema 1998]. Today's Internet routing algorithms (such RIP, OSPF, and BGP) are **load-insensitive,** as a link's cost does not explicitly reflect its current (or recent past) level of congestion.

10.5.1 The Link-State (LS) Routing Algorithm

Recall that in a link-state algorithm, the network topology and all link costs are known, that is, available as input to the LS algorithm. In practice this is accomplished by having each node broadcast link-state packets to *all* other nodes in the network, with each link-state packet containing the identities and costs of its attached links. In practice (for example, with the Internet's OSPF routing protocol, discussed in Section 10.6.1) this is often accomplished by a **link-state broadcast** algorithm [Perlman 1999]. We'll cover broadcast algorithms in Section 10.7. The result of the nodes' broadcast is that all nodes have an identical and complete view of the network. Each node can then run the LS algorithm and compute the same set of least-cost paths as every other node.

The link-state routing algorithm we present below is known as *Dijkstra's algorithm,* named after its inventor. A closely related algorithm is Prim's algorithm; see [Cormen 2001] for a general discussion of graph algorithms. Dijkstra's algorithm computes the least-cost path from one node (the source, which we will refer to as u) to all other nodes in the network. Dijkstra's algorithm is iterative and has the property that after the kth iteration of the algorithm, the least-cost paths are known to k destination nodes, and among the least-cost paths to all destination nodes, these k paths will have the k smallest costs. Let us define the following notation:

- $D(v)$: cost of the least-cost path from the source node to destination v as of this iteration of the algorithm.
- $p(v)$: previous node (neighbor of v) along the current least-cost path from the source to v.
- N': subset of nodes; v is in N' if the least cost from path the source to v is definitively known.

The global routing algorithm consists of an initialization step followed by a loop. The number of times the loop is executed is equal to the number of nodes in the network. Upon termination, the algorithm will have calculated the shortest paths from the source node u to every other node in the network.

Link-state (LS) Algorithm for Source Node *u*

```
1  Initialization:
2    N' = {u}
3    for all nodes v
4      if v is a neighbor of u
5        then D(v) = c(u,v)
6      else D(v) = ∞
7
8  Loop
9    find w not in N' such that D(w) is a minimum
10   add w to N'
11   update D(v) for each neighbor v of w and not in N':
12        D(v) = min( D(v), D(w) + c(w,v) )
13   /* new cost to v is either old cost to v or known
14    least path cost to w plus cost from w to v */
15 until N'= N
```

As an example, let's consider the network in Figure 10.25 and compute the least-cost paths from u to all possible destinations. A tabular summary of the algorithm's computation is shown in Table 10.3, where each line in the table gives the values of the algorithm's variables at the end of the iteration. Let's consider the few first steps in detail.

- In the initialization step, the currently known least-cost paths from u to its directly attached neighbors, v, x, and w, are initialized to 2, 1, and 5, respectively. Note in particular that the cost to w is set to 5 (even though we will soon see that a lesser-cost path does indeed exist) since this is the cost of the direct (one hop) link from u to w. The costs to y and z are set to infinity because they are not directly connected to u.
- In the first iteration, we look among those nodes not yet added to the set N' and find that node with the least cost as of the end of the previous iteration. That node is x, with a cost of 1, and thus x is added to the set N'. Line 12 of the LS algorithm is then performed to update $D(v)$ for all nodes v, yielding the results shown in the second line (Step 1) in Table 10.3. The cost of the path to v is unchanged. The cost of the path to w (which was 5 at the end of the initialization) through node x is found to have a cost of 4. Hence this lower-cost path is selected and w's predecessor along the shortest path from u is set to x. Similarly, the cost to y (through x) is computed to be 2, and the table is updated accordingly.
- In the second iteration, nodes v and y are found to have the least-cost paths (2), and we break the tie arbitrarily and add y to the set N' so that N' now contains u, x, and y. The cost to the remaining nodes not yet in N', that is, nodes v, w, and z,

are updated via line 12 of the LS algorithm, yielding the results shown in the third row in the Table 10.3.

- And so on. . . .

When the LS algorithm terminates, we have, for each node, its predecessor along the least-cost path from the source node. For each predecessor, we also have *its* predecessor, and so in this manner we can construct the entire path from the source to all destinations. The forwarding table in a node, say node *u*, can then be constructed from this information by storing, for each destination, the next-hop node on the least-cost path from *u* to the destination.

What is the computational complexity of this algorithm? That is, given *n* nodes (not counting the source), how much computation must be done in the worst case to find the least-cost paths from the source to all destinations? In the first iteration, we need to search through all *n* nodes to determine the node, *w*, not in N' that has the minimum cost. In the second iteration, we need to check $n - 1$ nodes to determine the minimum cost; in the third iteration $n - 2$ nodes, and so on. Overall, the total number of nodes we need to search through over all the iterations is $n(n + 1)/2$, and thus we say that the preceding implementation of the LS algorithm has worst-case complexity of order *n* squared: $O(n^2)$. (A more sophisticated implementation of this algorithm, using a data structure known as a heap, can find the minimum in line 9 in logarithmic rather than linear time, thus reducing the complexity.)

Before completing our discussion of the LS algorithm, let us consider a pathology that can arise. Figure 10.26 shows a simple network topology where link costs are equal to the load carried on the link, for example, reflecting the delay that would be experienced. In this example, link costs are not symmetric; that is, $c(u,v)$ equals $c(v,u)$ only if the load carried on both directions on the link (u,v) is the same. In this example, node *z* originates a unit of traffic destined for *w*, node *x* also originates a unit of traffic destined for *w*, and node *y* injects an amount of traffic equal to *e*, also destined for *w*. The initial routing is shown in Figure 10.26(a) with the link costs corresponding to the amount of traffic carried.

step	N′	D(v),p(v)	D(w),p(w)	D(x),p(x)	D(y),p(y)	D(z),p(z)
0	u	2,u	5,u	1,u	∞	∞
1	ux	2,u	4,x		2,x	∞
2	uxy	2,u	3,y			4,y
3	uxyv		3,y			4,y
4	uxyvw					4,y
5	uxyvwz					

Table 10.3 ♦ Running the link-state algorithm on the network in Figure 10.25

When the LS algorithm is next run, node *y* determines (based on the link costs shown in Figure 10.26(a)) that the clockwise path to *w* has a cost of 1, while the counterclockwise path to *w* (which it had been using) has a cost of 1 + *e*. Hence *y*'s least-cost path to *w* is now clockwise. Similarly, *x* determines that its new least-cost path to *w* is also clockwise, resulting in costs shown in Figure 10.26(b). When the LS algorithm is run next, nodes *x, y,* and *z* all detect a zero-cost path to *w* in the counterclockwise direction, and all route their traffic to the counterclockwise routes. The next time the LS algorithm is run, *x, y,* and *z* all then route their traffic to the clockwise routes.

What can be done to prevent such oscillations (which can occur in any algorithm, not just an LS algorithm, that uses a congestion or delay-based link metric)?

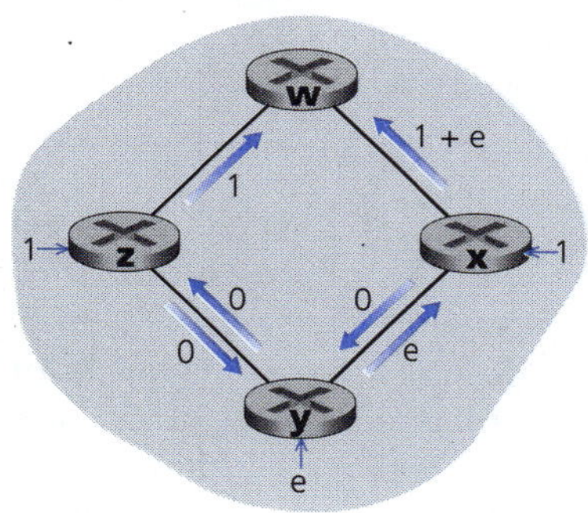

a. Initial routing

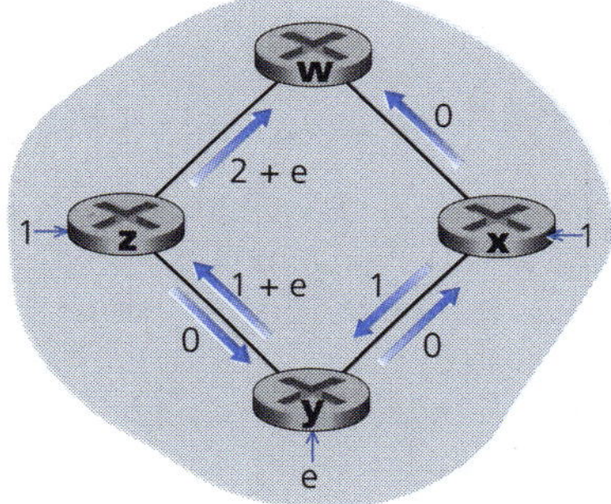

b. *x, y* detect better path to *w*, clockwise

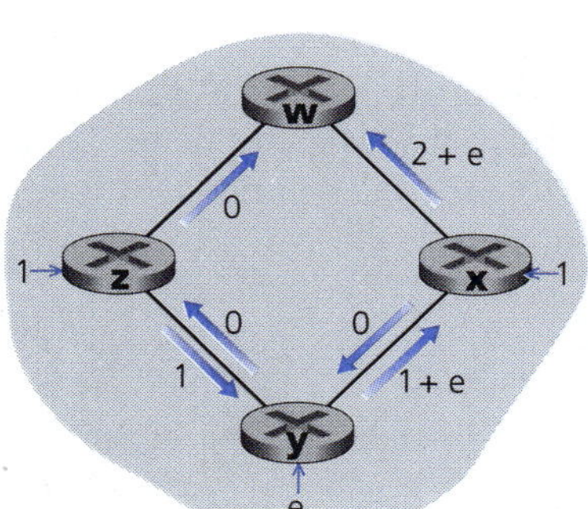

c. *x, y, z* detect better path to *w*, counterclockwise

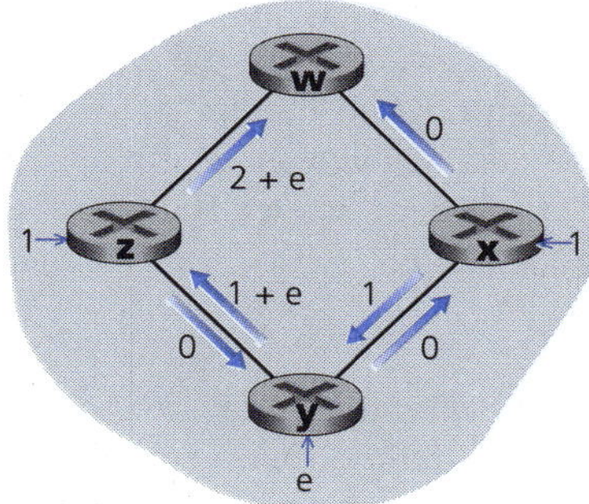

d. *x, y, z,* detect better path to *w*, clockwise

Figure 10.26 ♦ Oscillations with link-state routing

One solution would be to mandate that link costs not depend on the amount of traffic carried—an unacceptable solution since one goal of routing is to avoid highly congested (for example, high-delay) links. Another solution is to ensure that not all routers run the LS algorithm at the same time. This seems a more reasonable solution, since we would hope that even if routers ran the LS algorithm with the same periodicity, the execution instance of the algorithm would not be the same at each node. Interestingly, researchers have found that routers in the Internet can self-synchronize among themselves [Floyd Synchronization 1994]. That is, even though they initially execute the algorithm with the same period but at different instants of time, the algorithm execution instance can eventually become, and remain, synchronized at the routers. One way to avoid such self-synchronization is for each router to randomize the time it sends out a link advertisement.

Having studied the LS algorithm, let's consider the other major routing algorithm that is used in practice today—the distance-vector routing algorithm.

10.5.2 The Distance-Vector (DV) Routing Algorithm

Whereas the LS algorithm is an algorithm using global information, the **distance-vector (DV)** algorithm is iterative, asynchronous, and distributed. It is *distributed* in that each node receives some information from one or more of its *directly attached* neighbors, performs a calculation, and then distributes the results of its calculation back to its neighbors. It is *iterative* in that this process continues on until no more information is exchanged between neighbors. (Interestingly, the algorithm is also self-terminating—there is no signal that the computation should stop; it just stops.) The algorithm is *asynchronous* in that it does not require all of the nodes to operate in lockstep with each other. We'll see that an asynchronous, iterative, self-terminating, distributed algorithm is much more interesting and fun than a centralized algorithm!

Before we present the DV algorithm, it will prove beneficial to discuss an important relationship that exists among the costs of the least-cost paths. Let $d_x(y)$ be the cost of the least-cost path from node x to node y. Then the least costs are related by the celebrated Bellman-Ford equation, namely,

$$d_x(y) = min_v\{c(x,v) + d_v(y)\}, \tag{10.1}$$

where the min_v in the equation is taken over all of x's neighbors. The Bellman-Ford equation is rather intuitive. Indeed, after traveling from x to v, if we then take the least-cost path from v to y, the path cost will be $c(x,v) + d_v(y)$. Since we must begin by traveling to some neighbor v, the least cost from x to y is the minimum of $c(x,v) + d_v(y)$ taken over all neighbors v.

But for those who might be skeptical about the validity of the equation, let's check it for source node u and destination node z in Figure 10.25. The source node u has three neighbors: nodes v, x and w. By walking along various paths in the graph, it is easy to see that $d_v(z) = 5$, $d_x(z) = 3$ and $d_w(z) = 3$. Plugging these values into Equation 10.1, along with the costs $c(u,v) = 2$, $c(u,x) = 5$ and $c(u,w) = 1$, gives $d_u(z) = \min\{2 + 5, 5 + 3, 1 + 3\} = 4$, which is obviously true and which is exactly what the Dijskstra algorithm gave us for the same network. This quick verification should help relieve any skepticism you may have.

The Bellman-Ford equation is not just an intellectual curiosity. It actually has significant practical importance. In particular, the solution to the Bellman-Ford equation provides the entries in node x's forwarding table. To see this, let v^* be any neighboring node that achieves the minimum in Equation 10.1. Then, if node x wants to send a packet to node y along a least-cost path, it should first forward the packet to node v^*. Thus, node x's forwarding table would specify node v^* as the next-hop router for the ultimate destination y. Another important practical contribution of the Bellman-Ford equation is that it suggests the form of the neighbor-to-neighbor communication that will take place in the DV algorithm.

The basic idea is as follows. Each node x begins with $D_x(y)$, an estimate of the cost of the least-cost path from itself to node y, for all nodes in N. Let $\boldsymbol{D}_x = [D_x(y)$: y in $N]$ be node x's distance vector, which is the vector of cost estimates from x to all other nodes, y, in N. With the DV algorithm, each node x maintains the following routing data:

- For each neighbor v, the cost $c(x,v)$ from x to directly attached neighbor, v
- Node x's distance vector, that is, $\boldsymbol{D}_x = [D_x(y)$: y in $N]$, containing x's estimate of its cost to all destinations, y, in N
- The distance vectors of each of its neighbors, that is, $\boldsymbol{D}_v = [D_v(y)$: y in $N]$ for each neighbor v of x

In the distributed, asynchronous algorithm, from time to time, each node sends a copy of its distance vector to each of its neighbors. When a node x receives a new distance vector from any of its neighbors v, it saves v's distance vector, and then uses the Bellman-Ford equation to update its own distance vector as follows:

$$D_x(y) = min_v\{c(x,v) + D_v(y)\} \quad \text{for each node } y \text{ in } N$$

If node x's distance vector has changed as a result of this update step, node x will then send its updated distance vector to each of its neighbors, which can in turn update their own distance vectors. Miraculously enough, as long as all the nodes continue to exchange their distance vectors in an asynchronous fashion, each cost estimate $D_x(y)$ converges to $d_x(y)$, the actual cost of least-cost path from node x to node y [Bersekas 1992]!

Distance Vector (DV) Algorithm

At each node, *x*:

```
1   Initialization:
2      for all destinations y in N:
3         Dx(y) = c(x,y)    /* if y is not a neighbor than c(x,y) = ∞ /*
4      for each neighbor w
5         Dw(y) = ∞ for all destinations y in N
6      for each neighbor w
7         send distance vector Dx =  [Dx(y): y in N] to w
8
9   loop
10     wait (until I see a link cost change to some neighbor w or
11           until I receive a distance vector from some neighbor w)
12
13     for each y in N:
14        Dx(y) = minv{c(x,v) + Dv(y)}
15
16     if Dx(y) changed for any destination y
17        send distance vector Dx =  [Dx(y): y in N] to all neighbors
18
19  forever
```

The DV algorithm shows how a node x updates its distance vector estimate when it either sees a cost change in one of its directly attached links or receives a distance vector update from some neighbor. But to update its own forwarding table for a given destination y, what node x really needs to know is not the shortest-path distance to y but instead the neighboring node $v^*(y)$ that is the next-hop router along the shortest path to y. As you might expect, the next-hop router $v^*(y)$ is the neighbor v that achieves the minimum in Line 14 of the DV algorithm. (If there are multiple neighbors v that achieve the minimum, then $v^*(y)$ can be any of the minimizing neighbors.) Thus, in Lines 13–14, for each destination y, node x also determines $v^*(y)$ and updates its forwarding table for destination y.

Recall that the LS algorithm is a global algorithm in the sense that it requires each node to first obtain a complete map of the network before running the Dijkstra algorithm. The DV algorithm is *decentralized* and does not use such global information. Indeed, the only information a node will have is the costs of the links to its directly attached neighbors and information it receives from these neighbors. Each node waits for an update from any neighbor (Lines 10–11), calculates its new distance vector when receiving an update (Line 14) and distributes its new distance vector to its neighbors (Lines 16–17). The DV algorithm is used in many routing protocols in practice, including the Internet's RIP and BGP, ISO IDRP, Novell IPX, and the original ARPAnet.

Figure 10.27 illustrates the operation of the DV algorithm for the simple three-node network shown at the top of the figure. The operation of the algorithm is illustrated in a synchronous manner, where all nodes simultaneously receive distance vectors from their neighbors, compute their new distance vectors, and inform their neighbors if their distance vectors have changed. After studying this example, you should convince yourself that the algorithm operates correctly in an asynchronous manner as well, with node computations and update generation/reception occurring at any time.

The leftmost column of the figure displays three initial **routing tables** for each of the three nodes. For example, the table in the upper-left corner is node x's initial routing table. Within a specific routing table, each row is a distance vector—specifically, each node's routing table includes its own distance vector and that of each of its neighbors. Thus, the first row in node x's initial routing table is $\boldsymbol{D}_x = [D_x(x), D_x(y), D_x(z)] = [0, 2, 7]$. The second and third rows in this table are the most recently received distance vectors from nodes y and z, respectively. Because at initialization, node x has not received anything from node y or z, the entries in the second and third rows are initialized to infinity.

After initialization, each node sends its distance vector to each of its two neighbors. This is illustrated in Figure 10.27 by the arrows from the first column of tables to the second column of tables. For example, node x sends its distance vector $\boldsymbol{D}_x = [0, 2, 7]$ to both nodes y and z. After receiving the updates, each node recomputes its own distance vector. For example, node x computes

$$D_x(x) = 0$$

$$D_x(y) = \min\{c(x,y) + D_y(y), c(x,z) + D_z(y)\} = \min\{2 + 0, 7 + 1\} = 2$$

$$D_x(z) = \min\{c(x,y) + D_y(z), c(x,z) + D_z(z)\} = \min\{2 + 1, 7 + 0\} = 3$$

The second column therefore displays, for each node, the node's new distance vector along with distance vectors just received from its neighbors. Note, for example, that node x's estimate for the least cost to node z, $D_x(z)$, has changed from 7 to 3. Also note that for both nodes y and z, node y achieves the corresponding minimums. Thus, at this stage of the algorithm, the next-hop routers are $v^*(y) = y$ and $v^*(z) = y$.

After the nodes recompute their distance vectors, they again send their updated distance vectors to their neighbors (if there has been a change). This is illustrated in Figure 10.27 by the arrows from the second column of tables to the third column of tables. Note that only nodes x and z send updates: node y's distance vector didn't change so node y doesn't send an update. After receiving the updates, the nodes then recompute their distance vectors and update their routing tables, which are shown in the third column.

The process of receiving updated distance vectors from neighbors, recomputing routing table entries, and informing neighbors of changed costs of the least-cost path

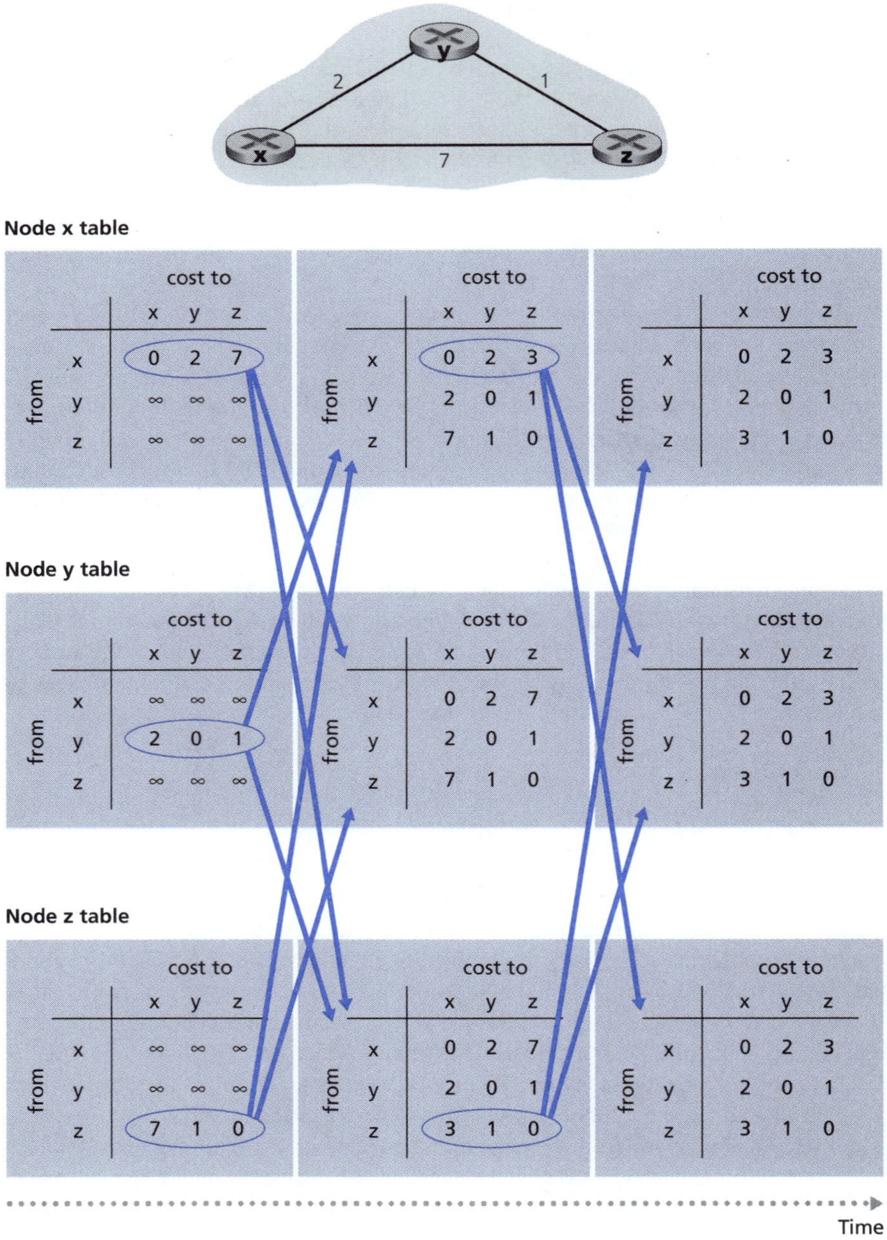

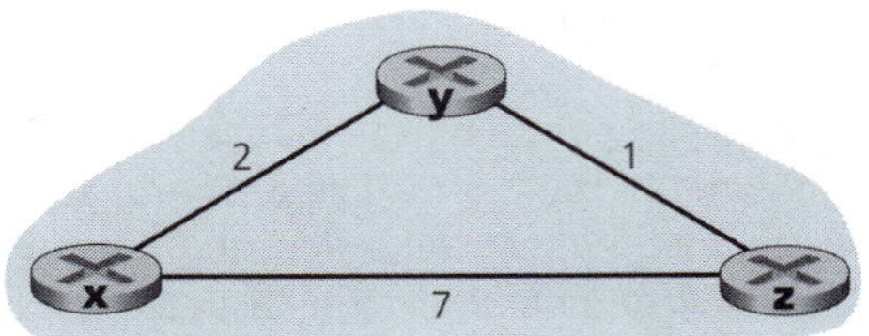

Node x table

from \ cost to	x	y	z
x	0	2	7
y	∞	∞	∞
z	∞	∞	∞

from \ cost to	x	y	z
x	0	2	3
y	2	0	1
z	7	1	0

from \ cost to	x	y	z
x	0	2	3
y	2	0	1
z	3	1	0

Node y table

from \ cost to	x	y	z
x	∞	∞	∞
y	2	0	1
z	∞	∞	∞

from \ cost to	x	y	z
x	0	2	7
y	2	0	1
z	7	1	0

from \ cost to	x	y	z
x	0	2	3
y	2	0	1
z	3	1	0

Node z table

from \ cost to	x	y	z
x	∞	∞	∞
y	∞	∞	∞
z	7	1	0

from \ cost to	x	y	z
x	0	2	7
y	2	0	1
z	3	1	0

from \ cost to	x	y	z
x	0	2	3
y	2	0	1
z	3	1	0

Time

Figure 10.27 ♦ Distance vector (DV) algorithm

to a destination continues until no update messages are sent. At this point, since no update messages are sent, no further routing table calculations will occur and the algorithm will enter a quiescent state; that is, all nodes will be performing the wait in Lines 10–11 of the DV algorithm. The algorithm remains in the quiescent state until a link cost changes, as discussed next.

Distance-Vector Algorithm: Link-Cost Changes and Link Failure

When a node running the DV algorithm detects a change in the link cost from itself to a neighbor (Lines 10–11), it updates its distance vector (Lines 13–14) and, if there's a change in the cost of the least-cost path, informs its neighbors (Lines 16–17) of its new distance vector. Figure 10.28(a) illustrates a scenario where the link cost from *y* to *x* changes from 4 to 1. We focus here only on *y* and *z*'s distance table entries to destination *x*. The DV algorithm causes the following sequence of events to occur:

- At time t_0, *y* detects the link-cost change (the cost has changed from 4 to 1), updates its distance vector, and informs its neighbors of this change since its distance vector has changed.
- At time t_1, *z* receives the update from *y* and updates its table. It computes a new least cost to *x* (it has decreased from a cost of 5 to a cost of 2) and sends its new distance vector to its neighbors.
- At time t_2, *y* receives *z*'s update and updates its distance table. *y*'s least costs do not change and hence *y* does not send any message to *z*. The algorithm comes to a quiescent state.

Thus, only two iterations are required for the DV algorithm to reach a quiescent state. The good news about the decreased cost between *x* and *y* has propagated quickly through the network.

Let's now consider what can happen when a link cost *increases.* Suppose that the link cost between *x* and *y* increases from 4 to 60, as shown in Figure 10.28(b).

1. Before the link cost changes, $D_y(x) = 4$, $D_y(z) = 1$, $D_z(y) = 1$, and $D_z(x) = 5$. At time t_0, *y* detects the link-cost change (the cost has changed from 4 to 60). *y* computes its new minimum-cost path to *x* to have a cost of

$$D_y(x) = \min\{c(y,x) + D_x(x),\ c(y,z) + D_z(x)\} = \{60 + 0,\ 1 + 5\} = 6$$

   Of course, with our global view of the network, we can see that this new cost via *z* is *wrong.* But the only information node *y* has is that its direct cost to *x* is 60 and that *z* has last told *y* that *z* could get to *x* with a cost of 5. So in order to get to *x*, *y* would now route through *z*, fully expecting that *z* will be able to get to *x* with a cost of 5. As of t_1 we have a **routing loop**—in order to get to *x*, *y*

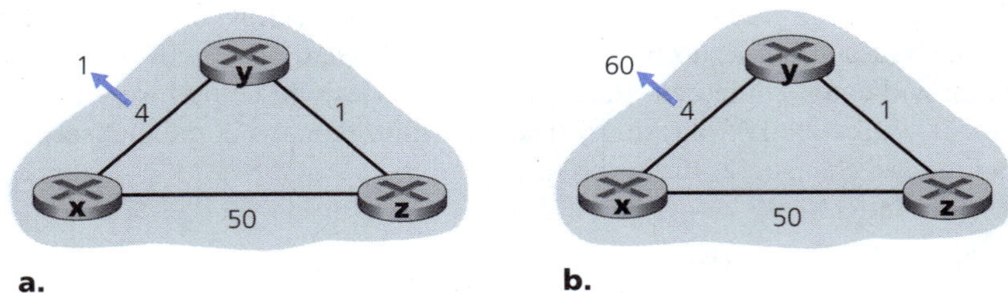

Figure 10.28 ♦ Changes in link cost

routes through z, and z routes through y. A routing loop is like a black hole—a packet destined for x arriving at y or z as of t_1 will bounce back and forth between these two nodes forever (or until the forwarding tables are changed).

2. Since node y has computed a new minimum cost to x, it informs z of its new distance vector at time t_1.
3. Sometime after t_1, z receives y's new distance vector, which indicates that y's minimum cost to x is 6. z knows it can get to y with a cost of 1 and hence computes a new least cost to x of $D_z(x) = \min\{50 + 0, 1 + 6\} = 7$. Since z's least cost to x has increased, it then informs y of its new distance vector at t_2.
4. In a similar manner, after receiving z's new distance vector, y determines $D_y(x) = 8$ and sends z its distance vector. z then determines $D_z(x) = 9$ and sends y its distance vector, and so on.

How long will the process continue? You should convince yourself that the loop will persist for 44 iterations (message exchanges between y and z)—until z eventually computes the cost of its path via y to be greater than 50. At this point, z will (finally!) determine that its least-cost path to x is via its direct connection to x. y will then route to x via z. The result of the bad news about the increase in link cost has indeed traveled slowly! What would have happened if the link cost $c(y,x)$ had changed from 4 to 10,000 and the cost $c(z,x)$ had been 9,999? Because of such scenarios, the problem we have seen is sometimes referred to as the count-to-infinity problem.

Distance-Vector Algorithm: Adding Poisoned Reverse

The specific looping scenario just described can be avoided using a technique known as *poisoned reverse*. The idea is simple—if z routes through y to get to destination x, then z will advertise to y that its distance to x is infinity, that is, z will advertise to y that $D_z(x) = \infty$ (even though z knows $D_z(x) = 5$ in truth). z will continue telling this little white lie to y as long as it routes to x via y. Since y believes that z has no path to x, y will never attempt to route to x via z, as long as z continues to route to x via y (and lies about doing so).

Let's now see how poisoned reverse solves the particular looping problem we encountered before in Figure 10.28(b). As a result of the poisoned reverse, *y*'s distance table indicates $D_z(x) = \infty$. When the cost of the (x,y) link changes from 4 to 60 at time t_0, *y* updates its table and continues to route directly to *x*, albeit at a higher cost of 60, and informs *z* of its new cost to *x*, that is, $D_y(x) = 60$. After receiving the update at t_1, *z* immediately shifts its route to *x* to be via the direct (x,y) link at a cost of 50. Since this is a new least-cost path to *x*, and since the path no longer passes through *y*, *z* now informs *y* that $D_z(x) = 50$ at t_2. After receiving the update from *z*, *y* updates its distance table with $D_y(x) = 51$. Also, since *z* is now on *y*'s least-cost path to *x*, *y* poisons the reverse path from *z* to *x* by informing *z* at time t_3 that $D_y(x) = \infty$ (even though *y* knows that $D_y(x) = 51$ in truth).

Does poisoned reverse solve the general count-to-infinity problem? It does not. You should convince yourself that loops involving three or more nodes (rather than simply two immediately neighboring nodes will not be detected by the poisoned reverse technique.

A Comparison of LS and DV Routing Algorithms

The DV and LS algorithms take complementary approaches towards computing routing. In the DV algorithm, each node talks to *only* its directly connected neighbors, but it provides its neighbors with least-cost estimates from itself to *all* the nodes (that it knows about) in the network. In the LS algorithm, each node talks with *all* other nodes (via broadcast), but it tells them *only* the costs of its directly connected links. Let's conclude our study of LS and DV algorithms with a quick comparison of some of their attributes. Recall that *N* is the set of nodes (routers) and *E* is the set of edges (links).

- *Message complexity.* We have seen that LS requires each node to know the cost of each link in the network. This requires O(|N| |E|) messages to be sent. Also, whenever a link cost changes, the new link cost must be sent to all nodes. The DV algorithm requires message exchanges between directly connected neighbors at each iteration. We have seen that the time needed for the algorithm to converge can depend on many factors. When link costs change, the DV algorithm will propagate the results of the changed link cost only if the new link cost results in a changed least-cost path for one of the nodes attached to that link.
- *Speed of convergence.* We have seen that our implementation of LS is an $O(|N|^2)$ algorithm requiring O(N| |E|)) messages. The DV algorithm can converge slowly and can have routing loops while the algorithm is converging. DV also suffers from the count-to-infinity problem.
- *Robustness.* What can happen if a router fails, misbehaves, or is sabotaged? Under LS, a router could broadcast an incorrect cost for one of its attached links (but no others). A node could also corrupt or drop any packets it received as part of an LS broadcast. But an LS node is computing only its own forwarding tables; other nodes

> are performing the similar calculations for themselves. This means route calculations are somewhat separated under LS, providing a degree of robustness. Under DV, a node can advertise incorrect least-cost paths to any or all destinations. (Indeed, in 1997, a malfunctioning router in a small ISP provided national backbone routers with erroneous routing information. This caused other routers to flood the malfunctioning router with traffic and caused large portions of the Internet to become disconnected for up to several hours [Neumann 1997].) More generally, we note that, at each iteration, a node's calculation in DV is passed on to its neighbor and then indirectly to its neighbor's neighbor on the next iteration. In this sense, an incorrect node calculation can be diffused through the entire network under DV.

In the end, neither algorithm is an obvious winner over the other; indeed, both algorithms are used in the Internet.

Other Routing Algorithms

The LS and DV algorithms we have studied are not only widely used in practice, they are essentially the *only* routing algorithms used in practice today in the Internet. Nonetheless, many routing algorithms have been proposed by researchers over the past 30 years, ranging from the extremely simple to the very sophisticated and complex. A broad class of routing algorithms is based on viewing packet traffic as flows between sources and destinations in a network. In this approach, the routing problem can be formulated mathematically as a constrained optimization problem known as a network flow problem [Bertsekas 1991]. Yet another set of routing algorithms we mention here are those derived from the telephony world. These **circuit-switched routing algorithms** are of interest to packet-switched data networking in cases where per-link resources (for example, buffers, or a fraction of the link bandwidth) are to be reserved for each connection that is routed over the link. While the formulation of the routing problem might appear quite different from the least-cost routing formulation we have seen in this chapter, there are a number of similarities, at least as far as the path-finding algorithm (routing algorithm) is concerned. See [Ash 1998; Ross 1995; Girard 1990] for a detailed discussion of this research area.

10.5.3 Hierarchical Routing

In our study of LS and DV algorithms, we've viewed the network simply as a collection of interconnected routers. One router was indistinguishable from another in the sense that all routers executed the same routing algorithm to compute routing paths through the entire network. In practice, this model and its view of a homogenous set of routers all executing the same routing algorithm is a bit simplistic for at least two important reasons:

- *Scale.* As the number of routers becomes large, the overhead involved in computing, storing, and communicating routing information (for example, LS updates or least-cost path changes) becomes prohibitive. Today's public Internet consists of hundreds of millions of hosts. Storing routing information to each of these hosts would clearly require enormous amounts of memory. The overhead required to broadcast LS updates among all of the routers in the public Internet would leave no bandwidth left for sending data packets! A distance vector algorithm that iterated among such a large number of routers would surely never converge. Clearly, something must be done to reduce the complexity of route computation in networks as large as the public Internet.
- *Administrative autonomy.* Although researchers tend to ignore issues such as a company's desire to run its routers as it pleases (for example, to run whatever routing algorithm it chooses) or to hide aspects of its networks' internal organization from the outside, these are important considerations. Ideally, an organization should be able to run and administer its network as it wishes, while still being able to connect its network to other outside networks.

Both of these problems can be solved by organizing routers into **autonomous systems (ASs),** with each AS consisting of a group of routers that are typically under the same administrative control (e.g., operated by the same ISP or belonging to the same company network). Routers within the same AS all run the same routing algorithm (for example, an LS or DV algorithm) and have information about each other—exactly as was the case in our idealized model in the preceding section. The routing algorithm running within an autonomous system is called an **intra-autonomous system routing protocol.** It will be necessary, of course, to connect ASs to each other, and thus one or more of the routers in an AS will have the added task of being responsible for forwarding packets to destinations outside the AS; these routers are called **gateway routers.**

Figure 10.29 provides a simple example with three ASs: AS1, AS2, and AS3. In this figure, the heavy lines represent direct link connections between pairs of routers. The thinner lines hanging from the routers represent subnets that are directly connected to the routers. AS1 has four routers—1a, 1b, 1c, and 1d—which run the intra-AS routing protocol used within AS1. Thus, each of these four routers knows how to forward packets along the optimal path to any destination within AS1. Similarly, autonomous systems AS2 and AS3 each have three routers. Note that the intra-AS routing protocols running in AS1, AS2, and AS3 need not be the same. Also note that the routers 1b, 1c, 2a, and 3a are all gateway routers.

It should now be clear how the routers in an AS determine routing paths for source-destination pairs that are internal to the AS. But there is still a big missing piece to the end-to-end routing puzzle. How does a router, within some AS, know how to route a packet to a destination that is outside the AS? It's easy to answer this question if the AS has only one gateway router that connects to only one other AS.

In this case, because the AS's intra-AS routing algorithm has determined the least-cost path from each internal router to the gateway router, each internal router knows how it should forward the packet. The gateway router, upon receiving the packet, forwards the packet on the one link that leads outside the AS. The AS on the other side of the link then takes over the responsibility of routing the packet to its ultimate destination. As an example, suppose router 2b in Figure 10.29 receives a packet whose destination is outside of AS2. Router 2b will then either forward the packet to router 2a or 2c, as specified by router 2b's forwarding table, which was configured by AS2's intra-AS routing protocol. The packet will eventually arrive to the gateway router 2a, which will forward the packet to 1b. Once the packet has left 2a, AS2's job is done with this one packet.

So the problem is easy when the source AS has only one link that leads outside the AS. But what if the source AS has two or more links (through one or more gateway routers) that lead outside the AS? Then the problem of knowing where to forward the packet becomes significantly more challenging. For example, consider a router in AS1 and suppose it receives a packet whose destination is outside the AS. The router should clearly forward the packet to one of its two gateway routers, 1b or 1c, but which one? To solve this problem, AS1 needs (1) to learn which destinations are reachable via AS2 and which destinations are reachable via AS3 and (2) to propagate this reachability information to all the routers within AS1, so that each router can configure its forwarding table to handle external-AS destinations. These two

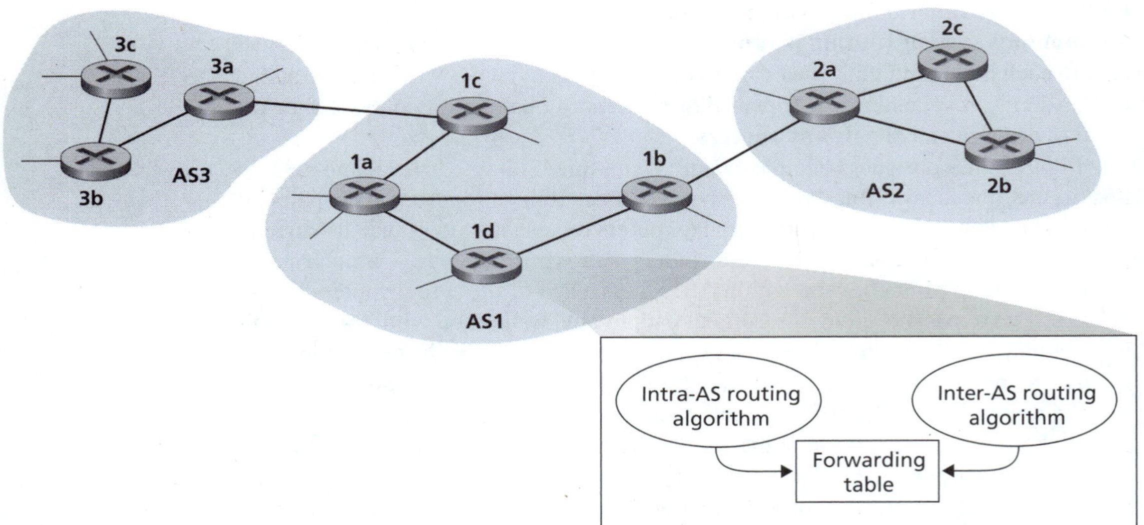

Figure 10.29 ♦ An example of interconnected autonomous systems

tasks—obtaining reachability information from neighboring ASs and propagating the reachability information to all routers internal to the AS—are handled by the **inter-AS routing protocol.** Since the inter-AS routing protocol involves communication between two ASs, the two communicating ASs must run the same inter-AS routing protocol. In fact, in the Internet all ASs run the same inter-AS routing protocol, called BGP4, which is discussed in the next section. As shown in Figure 10.29, each router receives information from an intra-AS routing protocol and an inter-AS routing protocol, and uses the information from both protocols to configure its forwarding table.

As an example, consider a subnet *x* (identified by its CDIRized address), and suppose that AS1 learns from the inter-AS routing protocol that subnet *x* is reachable from AS3 but is *not* reachable from AS2. AS1 then propagates this information to all of its routers. When router 1d learns that subnet *x* is reachable from AS3, and hence from gateway 1c, it then determines, from the information provided by the intra-AS routing protocol, the router interface that is on the least-cost path from router 1d to gateway router 1c. Say this is interface *I*. The router 1d can then put the entry (*x*, *I*) into its forwarding table. (This example, and others presented in this section, get the general ideas across but are simplifications of what really happens in the Internet. In the next section we'll provide a more detailed description, albeit more complicated, when we discuss BGP.)

Following up on the previous example, now suppose that AS2 and AS3 connect to other ASs, which are not shown in the diagram. Also suppose that AS1 learns from the inter-AS routing protocol that subnet *x* is reachable both from AS2, via gateway 1b, and from AS3, via gateway 1c. AS1 would then propagate this information to all its routers, including router 1d. In order to configure its forwarding table, router 1d would have to determine to which gateway router, 1b or 1c, it should direct packets that are destined for subnet *x*. One approach, which is often employed in practice, is to use **hot-potato routing.** In hot-potato routing, the AS gets rid of the packet (the hot potato) as quickly as possible (more precisely, as inexpensively as possible). This is done by having a router send the packet to the gateway router that has the smallest router-to-gateway cost among all gateways with a path to the destination. In the context of the current example, hot-potato routing, running in 1d, would use information from the intra-AS routing protocol to determine the path costs to 1b and 1c, and then choose the path with the least cost. Once this path is chosen, router 1d adds an entry for subnet *x* in its forwarding table. Figure 10.30 summarizes the actions taken at router 1d for adding the new entry for *x* to the forwarding table.

When an AS learns about a destination from a neighboring AS, the AS can advertise this routing information to some of its other neighboring ASs. For example, suppose AS1 learns from AS2 that subnet *x* is reachable via AS2. AS1 could then tell AS3 that *x* is reachable via AS1. In this manner, if AS3 needs to route a packet destined to *x*, AS3 would forward the packet to AS1, which would in turn forward the packet to AS2. As we'll see in our discussion of BGP, an AS has quite a bit of flexibility in deciding which destinations it advertises to its neighboring ASs.

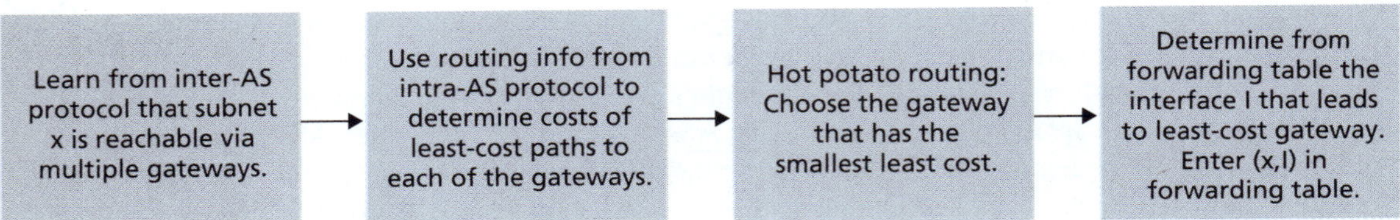

Figure 10.30 ♦ Steps in adding an outside-AS destination in a router's forwarding table

This is a *policy* decision, typically depending more on economic issues than on technical issues.

Recall that the Internet consists of a hierarchy of interconnected ISPs. So what is the relationship between ISPs and ASs? You might think that the routers in an ISP, and the links that interconnect them, constitute a single AS. Although this is often the case, many ISPs partition their network into multiple ASs. For example, some tier-1 ISPs use one AS for their entire network; others break up their ISP into tens of interconnected ASs.

In summary, the problems of scale and administrative authority are solved by defining autonomous systems. Within an AS, all routers run the same intra-autonomous system routing protocol. Among themselves, the ASs run the same inter-AS routing protocol. The problem of scale is solved because an intra-AS router need only know about routers within its AS. The problem of administrative authority is solved since an organization can run whatever intra-AS routing protocol it chooses; however, each pair of connected ASs needs to run the same inter-AS routing protocol to exchange reachability information.

In the following section, we'll examine two intra-AS routing protocols (RIP and OSPF) and the inter-AS routing protocol (BGP) that are used in today's Internet. These case studies will nicely round out our study of hierarchical routing.

10.6 Routing in the Internet

Having studied Internet addressing and the IP protocol, we now turn our attention to the Internet's routing protocols; their job is to determine the path taken by a datagram between source and destination. We'll see that the Internet's routing protocols embody many of the principles we learned earlier in this chapter. The link-state and distance-vector approaches studied in Sections 10.5.1 and 10.5.2, and the notion of an autonomous system considered in Section 10.5.3 are all central to how routing is done in today's Internet.

Recall from Section 10.5.3 that an autonomous system (AS) is a collection of routers under the same administrative and technical control, and that all run the same routing protocol among themselves. Each AS, in turn, typically contains multiple subnets (where we use the term subnet in the precise, addressing sense in Section 10.4.2).

10.6.1 Intra-AS Routing in the Internet: RIP

An intra-AS routing protocol is used to determine how routing is performed within an autonomous system (AS). Intra-AS routing protocols are also known as **interior gateway protocols.** Historically, two routing protocols have been used extensively for routing within an autonomous system in the Internet: the **Routing Information Protocol (RIP)** and **Open Shortest Path First (OSPF).** A routing protocol closely related to OSPF is the **IS-IS** protocol [RFC 1142, Perlman 1999]. We first discuss RIP and then consider OSPF.

RIP was one of the earliest intra-AS Internet routing protocols and is still in widespread use today. It traces its origins and its name to the Xerox Network Systems (XNS) architecture. The widespread deployment of RIP was due in great part to its inclusion in 1982 of the Berkeley Software Distribution (BSD) version of UNIX supporting TCP/IP. RIP version 1 is defined in RFC 1058, with a backward-compatible version 2 defined in RFC 2453.

RIP is a distance-vector protocol that operates in a manner very close to the idealized DV protocol we examined in Section 10.5.2. The version of RIP specified in RFC 1058 uses hop count as a cost metric; that is, each link has a cost of 1. In the DV algorithm in Section 10.5.2, for simplicity, costs were defined between pairs of routers. In RIP (and also in OSPF), costs are actually from source router to a destination subnet. RIP uses the term *hop,* which is the number of subnets traversed along the shortest path from source router to destination subnet, including the destination subnet. Figure 10.31 illustrates an AS with six leaf subnets. The table in the figure indicates the number of hops from the source A to all the leaf subnets.

The maximum cost of a path is limited to 15, thus limiting the use of RIP to autonomous systems that are fewer than 15 hops in diameter. Recall that in DV protocols, neighboring routers exchange distance vectors with each other. The distance vector for any one router is the current estimate of the shortest path distances from that router to the subnets in the AS. In RIP, routing updates are exchanged between neighbors approximately every 30 seconds using a **RIP response message.** The response message sent by a router or host contains a list of up to 25 destination subnets within the AS, as well as the sender's distance to each of those subnets. Response messages are also known as **RIP advertisements.**

Let's take a look at a simple example of how RIP advertisements work. Consider the portion of an AS shown in Figure 10.32. In this figure, lines connecting the routers denote subnets. Only selected routers (*A, B, C,* and *D*) and subnets (*w, x, y,*

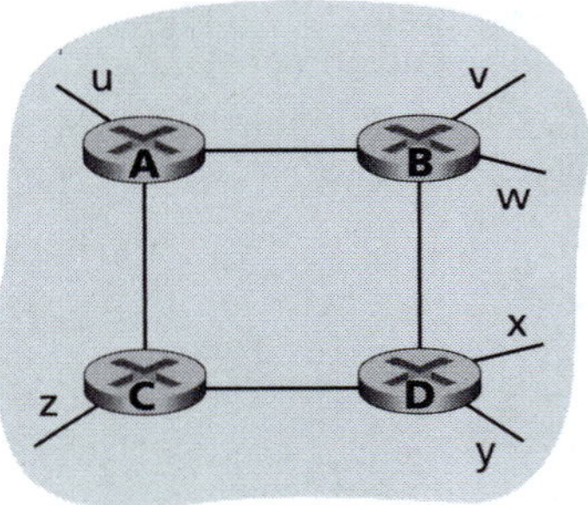

Destination	Hops
u	1
v	2
w	2
x	3
y	3
z	2

Figure 10.31 ♦ Number of hops from source router A to various subnets

and *z*) are labeled. Dotted lines indicate that the AS continues on; thus this autonomous system has many more routers and links than are shown.

Each router maintains a RIP table known as a **routing table.** A router's routing table includes both the router's distance vector and the router's forwarding table. Figure 10.33 shows the routing table for router *D*. Note that the routing table has three columns. The first column is for the destination subnet, the second column indicates the identity of the next router along the shortest path to the destination subnet, and the third column indicates the number of hops (that is, the number of subnets that have to be traversed, including the destination subnet) to get to the destination subnet along the shortest path. For this example, the table indicates that to send a datagram from router *D* to destination subnet *w*, the datagram should first be forwarded to neighboring router *A;* the table also indicates that destination subnet *w* is two hops away along the shortest path. Similarly, the table indicates that subnet *z* is seven hops away via router *B*. In principle, a routing table will have one row for each subnet in the AS, although RIP version 2 allows subnet entries to be aggregated using route aggregation techniques similar to those we examined in Section 10.4. The table in Figure 10.33, and the subsequent tables to come, are only partially complete.

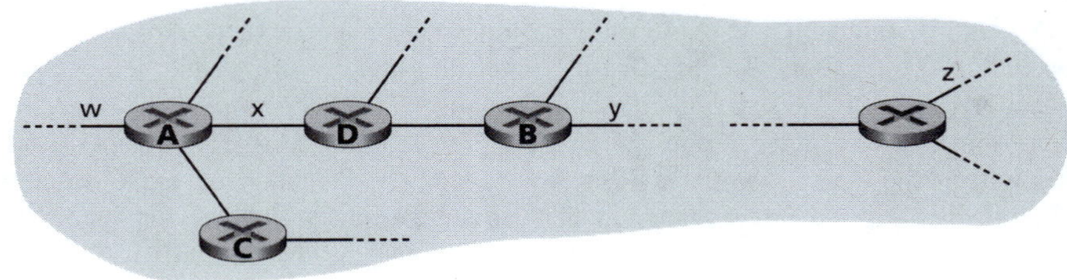

Figure 10.32 ♦ A portion of an autonomous system

Destination Subnet	Next Router	Number of Hops to Destination
w	A	2
y	B	2
z	B	7
x	—	1
....	....	....

Figure 10.33 ♦ Routing table in router *D* before receiving advertisement from router *A*

Now suppose that 30 seconds later, router *D* receives from router *A* the advertisement shown in Figure 10.34. Note that this advertisement is nothing other than the routing table information from router *A*! This information indicates, in particular, that subnet *z* is only four hops away from router *A*. Router *D*, upon receiving this advertisement, merges the advertisement (Figure 10.34) with the old routing table (Figure 10.33). In particular, router *D* learns that there is now a path through router *A* to subnet *z* that is shorter than the path through router *B*. Thus, router *D* updates its routing table to account for the shorter shortest path, as shown in Figure 10.35. How is it, you might ask, that the shortest path to subnet *z* has become shorter? Possibly, the decentralized distance vector algorithm is still in the process of converging (see Section 10.5.2), or perhaps new links and/or routers were added to the AS, thus changing the shortest paths in the AS.

Let's next consider a few of the implementation aspects of RIP. Recall that RIP routers exchange advertisements approximately every 30 seconds. If a router does not hear from its neighbor at least once every 180 seconds, that neighbor is considered to be no longer reachable; that is, either the neighbor has died or the connecting link has gone down. When this happens, RIP modifies the local routing table and

Destination Subnet	Next Router	Number of Hops to Destination
z	C	4
w	—	1
x	—	1
....	....	....

Figure 10.34 ♦ Advertisement from router A

Destination Subnet	Next Router	Number of Hops to Destination
w	A	2
y	B	2
z	A	5
....	....	....

Figure 10.35 ♦ Routing table in router *D* after receiving advertisement from router *A*

then propagates this information by sending advertisements to its neighboring routers (the ones that are still reachable). A router can also request information about its neighbor's cost to a given destination using RIP's request message. Routers send RIP request and response messages to each other over UDP using port number 520. The UDP segment is carried between routers in a standard IP datagram. The fact that RIP uses a transport-layer protocol (UDP) on top of a network-layer protocol (IP) to implement network-layer functionality (a routing algorithm) may seem rather convoluted (it is!). Looking a little deeper at how RIP is implemented will clear this up.

Figure 10.36 sketches how RIP is typically implemented in a UNIX system, for example, a UNIX workstation serving as a router. A process called routed (pronounced "route dee") executes RIP, that is, maintains routing information and exchanges messages with routed processes running in neighboring routers. Because RIP is implemented as an application-layer process (albeit a very special one that is able to manipulate the routing tables within the UNIX kernel), it can send and receive messages over a standard socket and use a standard transport protocol. As shown, RIP is implemented as an application-layer protocol running over UDP.

10.6.2 Intra-AS Routing in the Internet: OSPF

Like RIP, OSPF routing is widely used for intra-AS routing in the Internet. OSPF and its closely related cousin, IS-IS, are typically deployed in upper-tier ISPs whereas RIP is deployed in lower-tier ISPs and enterprise networks. The Open in OSPF indicates that the routing protocol specification is publicly available (for example, as opposed to Cisco's EIGRP protocol). The most recent version of OSPF, version 2, is defined in RFC 2328, a public document.

OSPF was conceived as the successor to RIP and as such has a number of advanced features. At its heart, however, OSPF is a link-state protocol that uses flooding of link-state information and a Dijkstra least-cost path algorithm. With

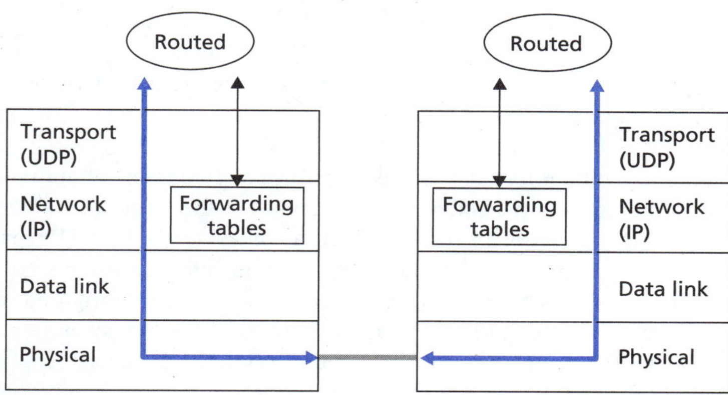

Figure 10.36 ♦ Implementation of RIP as the *routed* daemon

OSPF, a router constructs a complete topological map (that is, a graph) of the entire autonomous system. The router then locally runs Dijkstra's shortest-path algorithm to determine a shortest-path tree to all subnets, with itself as the root node. Individual link costs are configured by the network administrator (see Principles and Practice: Setting OSPF Weights). The administrator might choose to set all link costs to 1, thus achieving minimum-hop routing, or might choose to set the link weights to be inversely proportional to link capacity in order to discourage traffic from using low-bandwidth links. OSPF does not mandate a policy for how link weights are set (that is the job of the network administrator), but instead provides the mechanisms (protocol) for determining least-cost path routing for the given set of link weights.

With OSPF, a router broadcasts routing information to *all* other routers in the autonomous system, not just to its neighboring routers. A router broadcasts link-state information whenever there is a change in a link's state (for example, a change in cost or a change in up/down status). It also broadcasts a link's state periodically (at least once every 30 minutes), even if the link's state has not changed. RFC 2328 notes that "this periodic updating of link state advertisements adds robustness to the link state algorithm." OSPF advertisements are contained in OSPF messages that are carried directly by IP, with an upper-layer protocol of 89 for OSPF. Thus, the OSPF protocol must itself implement functionality such as reliable message transfer and link-state broadcast. The OSPF protocol also checks that links are operational (via a HELLO message that is sent to an attached neighbor) and allows an OSPF router to obtain a neighboring router's database of network-wide link state.

Some of the advances embodied in OSPF include the following:

- *Security.* Exchanges between OSPF routers (for example, link-state updates) are authenticated. With authentication, only trusted routers can participate in the OSPF protocol within a an AS, thus preventing malicious intruders (or networking students taking their newfound knowledge out for a joyride) from injecting incorrect information into router tables. By default, OSPF packets between routers are not authenticated and could be forged. Two types of authentication can be configured—simple and MD5. With simple authentication, the same password is configured on each router. When a router sends an OSPF packet, it includes the password in plaintext. Clearly, simple authentication is not secure. MD5 authentication is based on shared secret keys that are configured in all the routers. Each router computes an MD5 hash for each OSPF packet based on the content of the packet and the configured secret key. Then it includes the resulting hash value in the OSPF packet. The receiving router, using the preconfigured secret key, will compute an MD5 hash of the packet and compare it with the hash value that the packet carries, thus verifying the packet's authenticity. Sequence numbers are also used with MD5 authentication to protect against replay attacks.
- *Multiple same-cost paths.* When multiple paths to a destination have the same cost, OSPF allows multiple paths to be used (that is, a single path need not be chosen for carrying all traffic when multiple equal-cost paths exist).
- *Integrated support for unicast and multicast routing.* Multicast OSPF (MOSPF) [RFC 1584] provides simple extensions to OSPF to provide for multicast routing (a topic we cover in more depth in Section 10.7.2). MOSPF uses the existing OSPF link database and adds a new type of link-state advertisement to the existing OSPF link-state broadcast mechanism.
- *Support for hierarchy within a single routing domain.* Perhaps the most significant advance in OSPF is the ability to structure an autonomous system hierarchically. Section 10.5.3 has already looked at the many advantages of hierarchical routing structures. We cover the implementation of OSPF hierarchical routing in the remainder of this section.

An OSPF autonomous system can be configured into areas. Each area runs its own OSPF link-state routing algorithm, with each router in an area broadcasting its link state to all other routers in that area. The internal details of an area thus remain invisible to all routers outside the area. Intra-area routing involves only those routers within the same area.

Within each area, one or more **area border routers** are responsible for routing packets outside the area. Exactly one OSPF area in the AS is configured to be the **backbone** area. The primary role of the backbone area is to route traffic between the other areas in the AS. The backbone always contains all area border routers in the AS and may contain nonborder routers as well. Inter-area routing within the AS requires that the packet be first routed to an area border router (intra-area routing), then routed through the backbone to the area border router that is in the destination area, and then routed to the final destination.

A diagram of a hierarchically structured OSPF network is shown in Figure 10.37. We can identify four types of OSPF routers in Figure 10.37:

- *Internal routers.* These routers are in nonbackbone areas and perform only intra-AS routing.
- *Area border routers.* These routers belong to both an area and the backbone.
- *Backbone routers (nonborder routers).* These routers perform routing within the backbone but themselves are not area border routers. Within a nonbackbone area, internal routers learn of the existence of routes to other areas from information (essentially a link-state advertisement, but advertising the cost of a route to another area, rather than a link cost) broadcast within the area by its backbone routers.
- *Boundary routers.* A boundary router exchanges routing information with routers belonging to other autonomous systems. This router might, for example, use BGP to perform inter-AS routing. It is through such a boundary router that other routers learn about paths to external networks.

OSPF is a relatively complex protocol, and our coverage here has been necessarily brief; [Huitema 1998; Moy 1998; RFC 2328] provide additional details.

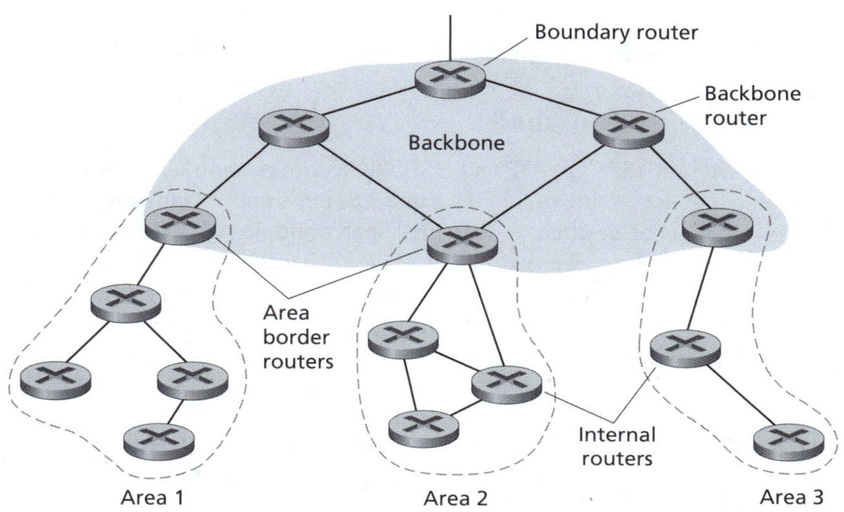

Figure 10.37 ♦ Hierarchically structured OSPF AS with four areas

PRINCIPLES IN PRACTICE

SETTING OSPF LINK WEIGHTS

Our discussion of link-state routing has implicitly assumed that link weights are set, a routing algorithm such as OSPF is run, and traffic flows according to the routing tables computed by the LS algorithm. In terms of cause and effect, the link weights are given (i.e., they come first) and result (via Dijkstra's algorithm) in routing paths that minimize overall cost. In this viewpoint, link weights reflect the cost of using a link (e.g., if link weights are inversely proportional to capacity, then the use of high capacity links would have smaller weights and thus be more attractive from a routing standpoint) and Disjkstra's algorithm serves to minimize overall cost.

In practice, the cause and effect relationship between link weights and routing paths may be reversed, with network operators configuring link weights in order to obtain routing paths that achieve certain traffic engineering goals [Fortz 2000, Fortz 2002]. For example, suppose a network operator has an estimate of traffic flow entering the network at each ingress point and destined for each egress point. The operator may then want to put in place a specific routing of ingress-to-egress flows that minimizes the maximum utilization over all of the network's links. But with a routing algorithm such as OSPF, the operator's main "knobs" for tuning the routing of flows through the network are the links weights. Thus, in order to achieve the goal of minimizing the maximum link utilization, the operator must find the set of link weights that achieve this goal. This is a reversal of the cause and effect relationship—the desired routing of flows is known, and the OSPF link weights must be found such that the OSPF routing algorithm results in this desired routing of flows.

10.6.3 Inter–Autonomous System Routing: BGP

We just learned how ISPs use RIP and OSPF to determine optimal paths for source-destination pairs that are internal to the same AS. Let's now examine how paths are determined for source-destination pairs that span multiple ASs. The **Border Gateway Protocol** version 4, specified in RFC 1771 (see also [RFC 1772; RFC 1773]), is the *de facto* standard inter-AS routing protocol in today's Internet. It is commonly referred to as BGP4 or simply as **BGP.** As an inter-AS routing protocol (see Section 10.5.3), BGP provides each AS a means to

1. Obtain subnet reachability information from neighboring ASs.
2. Propagate the reachability information to all routers internal to the AS.
3. Determine "good" routes to subnets based on the reachability information and on AS policy.

In particular, BGP allows each subnet to advertise its existence to the rest of the Internet. A subnet screams "I exist and I am here," and BGP makes sure that all the

ASs in the Internet know about the subnet and how to get there. If it weren't for BGP, each subnet would be isolated—alone and unknown by the rest of the Internet.

BGP Basics

BGP is extremely complex; entire books have been devoted to the subject. Furthermore, even after having read the books and RFCs, you may find it difficult to fully master BGP without having practiced BGP for many months (if not years) as a designer or administrator of an upper-tier ISP. Nevertheless, because BGP is an absolutely critical protocol for the Internet—in essence, it is the protocol that glues the whole thing together—we need to acquire at least a rudimentary understanding of how it works. We begin by describing how BGP might work in the context of the simple example network we studied earlier in Figure 10.29. In this description, we build on our discussion of hierarchical routing in Section 10.5.3; we encourage you to review that material.

In BGP, pairs of routers exchange routing information over semi-permanent TCP connections using port 179. The semi-permanent TCP connections for the network in Figure 10.29 are shown in Figure 10.38. There is typically one such BGP TCP connection for each link that directly connects two routers in two different ASs; thus, in Figure 10.38, there is a TCP connection between gateway routers 3a and 1c and another TCP connection between gateway routers 1b and 2a. There are also semipermanent BGP TCP connections between routers within an AS. In particular, Figure 10.38 displays a common configuration of one TCP connection for each pair of routers internal to an AS, creating a mesh of TCP connections within each AS. For each TCP connection, the two routers at the end the connection are called **BGP peers,** and the TCP connection along with all the BGP messages sent over the connection is called a **BGP session.** Furthermore, a BGP session that spans two ASs is called an **external BGP (eBGP) session,** and a BGP session between routers in the same AS is called an **internal BGP (iBGP) session.** In Figure 10.38, the eBGP sessions are shown with the long dashes; the iBGP sessions are shown with the short dashes. Note that BGP session lines in Figure 10.38 do not always correspond to the physical links in Figure 10.29.

BGP allows each AS to learn which destinations are reachable via its neighboring ASs. In BGP, destinations are not hosts but instead are CDIRized **prefixes,** with each prefix representing a subnet or a collection of subnets. Thus, for example, suppose there are four subnets attached to AS2: 138.16.64/24, 138.16.65/24, 138.16.66/24, and 138.16.67/24. Then AS2 could aggregate the prefixes for these four subnets and use BGP to advertise the single prefix to 138.16.64/22 to AS1. As another example, suppose that only the first three of those four subnets are in AS2 and the fourth subnet, 138.16.67/24, is in AS3. Then, as described in the Principles and Practice in Section 10.4.2, because routers use longest-prefix matching for forwarding datagrams, AS3 could advertise to AS1 the more specific prefix 138.16.67/24 and AS2 could *still* advertise to AS1 the aggregated prefix

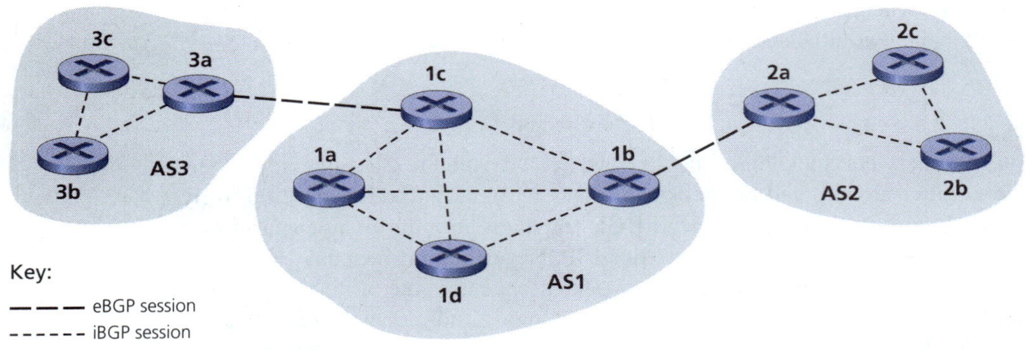

Figure 10.38 ♦ eBGP and iBGP sessions

138.16.64/22. We can think of each prefix advertisement as a promise. When one AS advertises a prefix to another AS, the advertising AS is promising that it will forward any datagram destined for the prefix along a path toward the prefix.

Let's now examine how BGP would distribute prefix reachability information over the BGP sessions shown in Figure 10.38. As you might expect, using the eBGP session between the gateway routers 3a and 1c, AS3 sends AS1 the list of prefixes that are reachable from AS3; and AS1 sends AS3 the list of prefixes that are reachable from AS1. Similarly, AS1 and AS2 exchange prefix reachability information through their gateway routers 1b and 2a. Also as you may expect, when a gateway router (in any AS) receives eBGP-learned prefixes, the gateway router uses its iBGP sessions to distribute the prefixes to the other routers in the AS. Thus, not only will non-eBGP routers in AS1 learn about AS3's prefixes, but so will the gateway router 1b learn about them. The gateway router 1b (in AS1) can therefore re-advertise AS3's prefixes to AS2. When a router (gateway or not) learns about a new prefix, it creates an entry for the prefix in its forwarding table, as described in Section 10.5.3.

Path Attributes and BGP Routes

Having now a preliminary understanding of BGP, let's get a little deeper into it (while still brushing some of less important details under the rug!). In BGP, an autonomous system is identified by its globally unique **autonomous system number (ASN)** [RFC 1930]. (Technically, not every AS has an ASN. In particular, a so-called stub AS that carries only traffic for which it is a source or destination will not typically have an ASN; we ignore this technicality in our discussion in order to better see the forest for the trees.) AS numbers, like IP addresses, are assigned by ICANN regional registries [ICANN 2004].

When a router advertises a prefix across a BGP session, it includes with the prefix a number of **BGP attributes.** In BGP jargon, a prefix along with its attributes is called a **route.** Thus, BGP peers advertise routes to each other. Two of the more important attributes are AS-PATH and NEXT-HOP:

- *AS-PATH*. This attribute contains the ASs through which the advertisement for the prefix has passed. When a prefix is passed into an AS, the AS adds its ASN to the AS-PATH attribute. For example, consider Figure 10.38 and suppose that prefix 138.16.64/24 is first advertised from AS2 to AS1; if AS1 then advertises the prefix to AS3, the AS-PATH would be AS2 AS1. Routers use the AS-PATH attribute to detect and prevent looping advertisements; specifically, if a router sees that its AS is contained in the path list, it will reject the advertisement. As we'll soon discuss, routers also use the AS-PATH attribute in choosing among multiple paths to the same prefix.
- *NEXT-HOP*. A pair of ASs, say AS A and AS B, may have multiple physical links that directly connect them. Thus, when a packet is forwarded from AS A to AS B, it could be sent over any one of the links that directly connect the ASs. When a gateway router in AS B sends a router advertisement to a gateway router in AS A, it includes in the advertisement its IP address (more specifically, the IP address of the interface that leads to the gateway router in AS A). A router in AS A may receive from eBGP and iBGP multiple routes to the same prefix, each passing through a different next-hop router. When configuring its forwarding table, this router would have to select among the multiple routes.

BGP also includes attributes that allow routers to assign preference metrics to the routes, and an attribute that indicates how the prefix was inserted into BGP at the origin AS. For a full discussion of route attributes, see [Griffin 2002; Stewart 1999; Halabi 2000; Feamster 2004].

When a gateway router receives a router advertisement, it uses its **import policy** to decide whether to accept or filter the route and whether to set certain attributes such as the router preference metrics. The import policy may filter a route because the AS may not want to send traffic over one of the ASs in the route's AS-PATH. The gateway router may also filter a route because it already knows of a preferable route to the same prefix.

BGP Route Selection

As described earlier in this section, BGP uses eBGP and iBGP to distribute routes to all the routers within ASs. From this distribution, a router may learn about more than one route to any one prefix, in which case the router must select one of the possible routes. The inputs into this route selection process is the set of all routes that have been learned and accepted by the router. If there are two or more routes to the same prefix, then BGP sequentially invokes the following elimination rules until one route remains.

- Routes are assigned a local preference value as one of their attritbutes. The local preference of a route could have been set by the router or could have been learned by another router in the same AS. This is a policy decision that is left up to the AS's network administrator. (We will shortly discuss BGP policy issues in some detail.) The routes with the highest local preference values are selected.
- From the remaining routes (all with the same local preference value), the route with the shortest AS-PATH is selected. If this rule were the only rule for route selection, then BGP would be using a DV algorithm for path determination, where the distance metric uses the number of AS hops rather than the number of router hops.
- From the remaining routes (all with the same local preference value and the same AS-PATH length), the route with the closest NEXT-HOP router is selected. Here, closest means the router for which the cost of the least-cost path, determined by the intra-AS algorithm, is the smallest. This process is often referred to as hot-potato routing.
- If more than one route still remains, the router uses BGP identifiers to select the route; see [Stewart 1999].

The elimination rules are even more complicated than described above. To avoid nightmares about BGP, it's best to learn about BGP selection rules in small doses!

Routing Policy

Let's illustrate some of the basic concepts of BGP routing with a simple example. Figure 10.39 shows six interconnected autonomous systems: A, B, C, W, X, and Y. It is important to note that A, B, C, W, X, and Y are ASs, not routers. Let's assume that autonomous systems W, X, and Y are stub networks and that A, B, and C are backbone provider networks. All traffic entering a **stub network** must be destined for that network, and all traffic leaving a stub network must have originated in that network. W and Y are clearly stub networks. X is a **multi-homed stub network,** since it is connected to the rest of the network via two different providers (a scenario that is becoming increasingly common in practice). However, like W and Y, X itself must be the source/destination of all traffic leaving/entering X. But how will this stub network behavior be implemented and enforced? How will X be prevented from forwarding traffic between B and C? This can easily be accomplished by controlling the manner in which BGP routes are advertised. In particular, X will function as a stub network if it advertises (to its neighbors B and C) that it has no paths to any other destinations except itself. That is, even though X may know of a path,

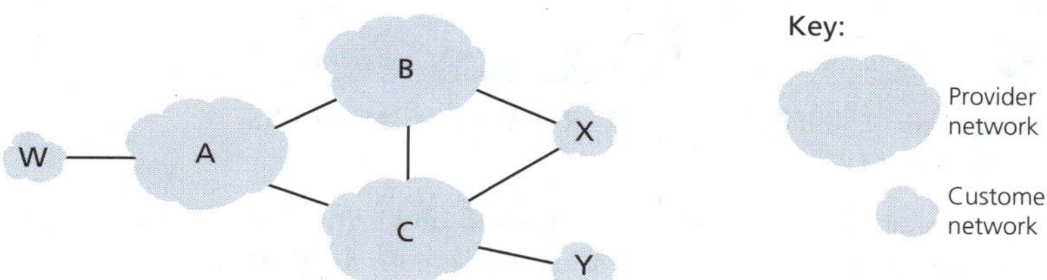

Figure 10.39 ♦ A simple BGP scenario

say XCY, that reaches network Y, it will *not* advertise this path to B. Since B is unaware that X has a path to Y, B would never forward traffic destined to Y (or C) via X. This simple example illustrates how a selective route advertisement policy can be used to implement customer/provider routing relationships.

Let's next focus on a provider network, say AS B. Suppose that B has learned (from A) that A has a path AW to W. B can thus install the route BAW into its routing information base. Clearly, B also wants to advertise the path BAW to its customer, X, so that X knows that it can route to W via B. But should B advertise the path BAW to C? If it does so, then C could route traffic to W via CBAW. If A, B, and C are all backbone providers, than B might rightly feel that it should not have to shoulder the burden (and cost!) of carrying transit traffic between A and C. B might rightly feel that it is A and C's job (and cost!) to make sure that C can route to/from A's customers via a direct connection between A and C. There are currently no official standards that govern how backbone ISPs route among themselves. However, a rule of thumb followed by commercial ISPs is that any traffic flowing across an ISP's backbone network must have either a source or a destination (or both) in a network that is a customer of that ISP; otherwise the traffic would be getting a free ride on the ISP's network. Individual peering agreements (that would govern questions such as those raised above) are typically negotiated between pairs of ISPs and are often confidential; [Huston 1999a] provides an interesting discussion of peering agreements. For a detailed description of how routing policy reflects commercial relationships among ISPs see [Gao 2001].

As noted above, BGP is the *de facto* standard for inter-AS routing for the public Internet. To see the contents of various BGP routing tables (large!) extracting from routers in tier-1 ISPs, see http://www.routeviews.org. BGP routing tables often contain tens of thousands of prefixes and corresponding attributes. Statistics about the size and characteristics of BGP routing tables are presented in [Huston 2001].

This completes our brief introduction to BGP. Understanding BGP is important because it plays a central role in the Internet. We encourage you to see the references [Griffin 2002; Stewart 1999; Labovitz 1997; Halabi 2000; Huitema 1998; Gao 2001; Feamster 2004] to learn more about BGP.

PRINCIPLES IN PRACTICE

WHY ARE THERE DIFFERENT INTER-AS AND INTRA-AS ROUTING PROTOCOLS?

Having now studied the details of specific inter-AS and intra-AS routing protocols deployed in today's Internet, let's conclude by considering perhaps the most fundamental question we could ask about these protocols in the first place (hopefully, you have been wondering this all along, and have not lost the forest for the trees!): Why are different inter-AS and intra-AS routing protocols used?

The answer to this question gets at the heart of the differences between the goals of routing within an AS and among ASs:

- *Policy.* Among ASs, policy issues dominate. It may well be important that traffic originating in a given AS not be able to pass through another specific AS. Similarly, a given AS may well want to control what transit traffic it carries between other ASs. We have seen that BGP carries path attributes and provides for controlled distribution of routing information so that such policy-based routing decisions can be made. Within an AS, everything is nominally under the same administrative control, and thus policy issues play a much less important role in choosing routes within the AS.
- *Scale.* The ability of a routing algorithm and its data structures to scale to handle routing to/among large numbers of networks is a critical issue in inter-AS routing. Within an AS, scalability is less of a concern. For one thing, if a single administrative domain becomes too large, it is always possible to divide it into two ASs and perform inter-AS routing between the two new ASs. (Recall that OSPF allows such a hierarchy to be built by splitting an AS into areas.)
- *Performance.* Because inter-AS routing is so policy oriented, the quality (for example, performance) of the routes used is often of secondary concern (that is, a longer or more costly route that satisfies certain policy criteria may well be taken over a route that is shorter but does not meet that criteria). Indeed, we saw that among ASs, there is not even the notion of cost (other than AS hop count) associated with routes. Within a single AS, however, such policy concerns are of less importance, allowing routing to focus more on the level of performance realized on a route.

10.7 Broadcast and Multicast Routing

Thus far in this chapter, our focus has been on routing protocols that support unicast (i.e., point-to-point) communication, in which a single source node sends a packet to a single destination node. In this section, we turn our attention to broadcast and multicast routing protocols. In **broadcast routing,** the network layer provides a service of delivering a packet sent from a source node to all other nodes in the network; **multicast routing** enables a single source node to send a copy of a packet to a subset of the other network nodes. In Section 10.7.1 we'll consider broadcast routing algorithms and their embodiment in routing protocols. We'll examine multicast routing in Section 10.7.2.

10.7.1 Broadcast Routing Algorithms

Perhaps the most straightforward way to accomplish broadcast communication is for the sending node to send a separate copy of the packet to each destination, as shown in Figure 10.40(a). Given *N* destination nodes, the source node simply makes *N* copies of the packet, addresses each copy to a different destination, and then transmits the *N* copies to the *N* destinations using unicast routing. This **N-way-unicast** approach to broadcasting is simple—no new network-layer routing protocol, packet-duplication, or forwarding functionality is needed. There are, however, several drawbacks to this approach. The first drawback is its inefficiency. If the source node is connected to the rest of the network via a single link, then *N* separate copies of the (same) packet will traverse this single link. It would clearly be more efficient to send only a single copy of a packet over this first hop and then have the node at the other end of the first hop make and forward any additional needed copies. That is, it would be more efficient for the network nodes themselves (rather than just the source node) to create duplicate copies of a packet. For example, in Figure 10.40(b), only a single copy of a packet traverses the R1-R2 link. That packet is then duplicated at R2, with a single copy being sent over links R2-R3 and R2-R4.

The additional drawbacks of *N*-way-unicast are perhaps more subtle, but no less important. An implicit assumption of *N*-way-unicast is that broadcast recipients, and their addresses, are known to the sender. But how is this information obtained? Most likely, additional protocol mechanisms (such as a broadcast membership or

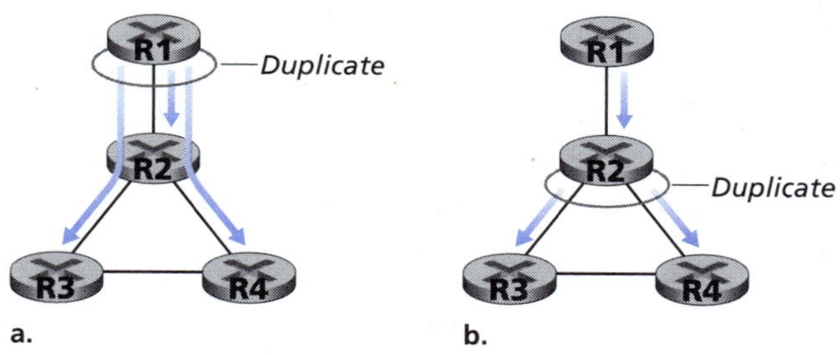

Figure 10.40 ♦ Source-duplication versus in-network duplication

destination-registration protocol) would be required. This would add more overhead and, importantly, additional complexity to a protocol that had initially seemed quite simple. A final drawback of N-way-unicast relates to the purposes for which broadcast is to be used. In Section 10.5, we learned that link-state routing protocols use broadcast to disseminate the link-state information that is used to compute unicast routes. Clearly, in situations where broadcast is used to create and update unicast routes, it would be unwise (at best!) to rely on the unicast routing infrastructure to achieve broadcast.

Given the several drawbacks of N-way-unicast broadcast, approaches in which the network nodes themselves play an active role in packet duplication, packet forwarding, and computation of the broadcast routes are clearly of interest. We'll examine several such approaches below and again adopt the graph notation introduced in Section 10.5. We again model the network as a graph, $G = (N,E)$, where N is a set of nodes and a collection E of edges, where each edge is a pair of nodes from N. We'll be a bit sloppy with our notation and use N to refer to both the set of nodes, as well as the cardinality ($|N|$) or size of that set when there is no confusion.

Uncontrolled Flooding

The most obvious technique for achieving broadcast is a **flooding** approach in which the source node sends a copy of the packet to all of its neighbors. When a node receives a broadcast packet, it duplicates the packet and forwards it to all of its neighbors (except the neighbor from which it received the packet). Clearly, if the graph is connected, this scheme will eventually deliver a copy of the broadcast packet to all nodes in the graph. Although this scheme is simple and elegant, it has a fatal flaw (before you read on, see if you can figure out this fatal flaw): If the graph has cycles, then one or more copies of each broadcast packet will cycle indefinitely. For example, in Figure 10.40, R2 will flood to R3, R3 will flood to R4, R4 will flood to R2, and R2 will flood (again!) to R3, and so on. This simple scenario results in the endless cycling of two broadcast packets, one clockwise, and one counterclockwise. But there can be an even more calamitous fatal flaw: When a node is connected to more than two other nodes, it will create and forward multiple copies of the broadcast packet, each of which will create multiple copies of themselves (at other nodes with more then two neighbors), and so on. This **broadcast storm,** resulting from the endless multiplication of broadcast packets, would eventually result in so many broadcast packets being created that the network would be rendered useless. (See the homework questions at the end of the chapter for a problem analyzing the rate at which such a broadcast storm grows.)

Controlled Flooding

The key to avoiding a broadcast storm is for a node to judiciously choose when to flood a packet and (e.g., if it has already received and flooded an earlier copy of a packet) when not to flood a packet. In practice, this can be done in one of several ways.

In **sequence-number-controlled flooding,** a source node puts its address (or other unique identifier) as well as a **broadcast sequence number** into a broadcast packet, then sends the packet to all of its neighbors. Each node maintains a list of the source address and sequence number of each broadcast packet it has already received, duplicated, and forwarded. When a node receives a broadcast packet, it first checks whether the packet is in this list. If so, the packet is dropped; if not, the packet is duplicated and forwarded to all the node's neighbors (except the node from which the packet has just been received). The Gnutella protocol uses sequence-number-controlled flooding to broadcast queries in its overlay network. (In Gnutella, message duplication and forwarding is performed at the application layer, rather than at the network layer.)

A second approach to controlled flooding is known as **reverse path forwarding (RPF)** [Dalal 1978], also sometimes referred to as reverse path broadcast (RPB). The idea behind RPF is simple, yet elegant. When a router receives a broadcast packet with a given source address, it transmits the packet on all of its outgoing links (except the one on which it was received) only if the packet arrived on the link that is on its own shortest unicast path back to the source. Otherwise, the router simply discards the incoming packet without forwarding it on any of its outgoing links. Such a packet can be dropped because the router knows it either will receive, or has already received, a copy of this packet on the link that is on its own shortest path back to the sender. (You might want to convince yourself that this will, in fact, happen and that looping and broadcast storms will not occur.) Note that RPF does not use unicast routing to actually deliver a packet to a destination, nor does it require that a router know the complete shortest path from itself to the source. RPF need only know the next neighbor on its unicast shortest path to the sender; it uses this neighbor's identity only to determine whether or not to flood a received broadcast packet.

Figure 10.41 illustrates RPF. Suppose that the links drawn with thick lines represent the least-cost paths from the receivers to the source (A). Node *A* initially broadcasts a source-*A* packet to nodes *C* and *B*. Node *B* will forward the source-A packet it has received from *A* (since *A* is on its least-cost path to *A*) to both *C* and *D*. *B* will ignore (drop, without forwarding) any source-A packets it receives from any other nodes (for example, from routers *C* or *D*). Let us now consider node *C*, which will receive a source-*A* packet directly from A as well as from B. Since *B* is not on *C*'s own shortest path back to *A*, *C* will ignore any source-*A* packets it receives from *B*. On the other hand, when C receives a source-A packet directly from *A*, it will forward the packet to nodes *B*, *E*, and *F*.

Spanning-Tree Broadcast

While sequence-number controlled flooding and RPF avoid broadcast storms, they do not completely avoid the transmission of redundant broadcast packets. For example, in Figure 10.42, nodes *B*, *C*, *D*, *E*, and *F* receive either one or two redundant packets. Ideally, every node should receive only one copy of the broadcast packet.

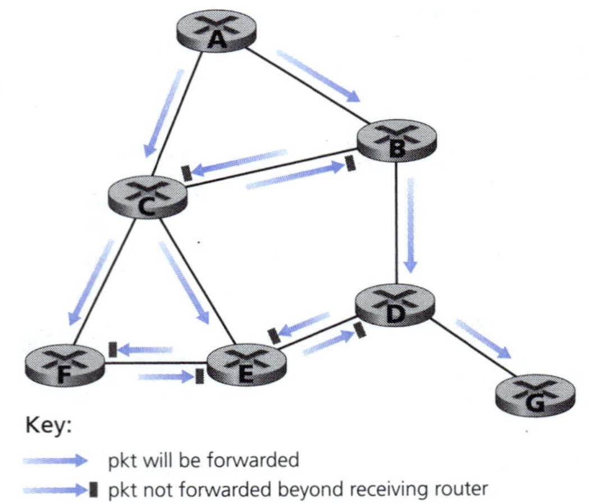

Figure 10.41 ♦ Reverse path forwarding

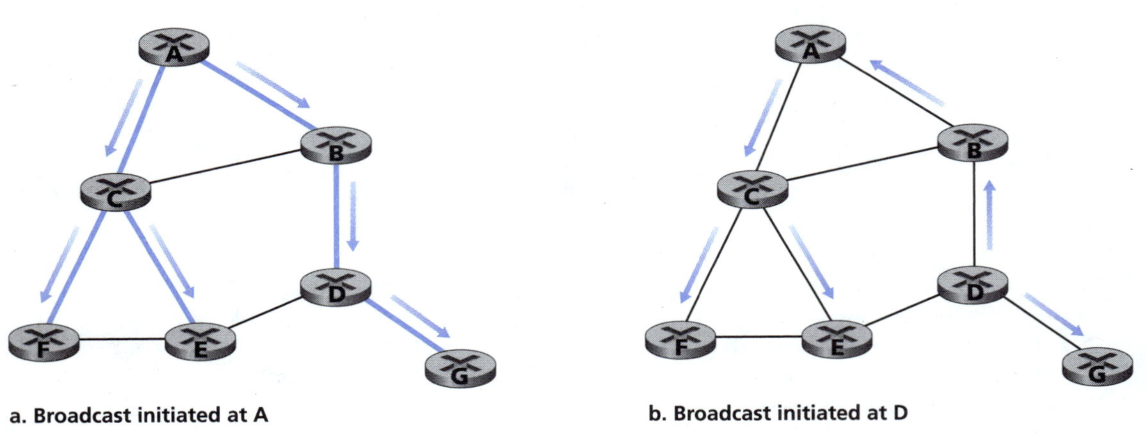

Figure 10.42 ♦ Broadcast along a spanning tree

Examining the tree consisting of the nodes connected by thick lines in Figure 10.42(a), you can see that if broadcast packets were forwarded only along links within this tree, each and every network node would receive exactly one copy of the broadcast packet—exactly the solution we were looking for! This tree is an example of a **spanning tree**—a tree that contains each and every node in a graph. More formally, a spanning tree of a graph $G = (N,E)$ is a graph $G' = (N,E')$ such that E' is a subset of E, G' is connected, G' contains no cycles, and G' contains all the original nodes in *G*. If each link has an associated cost and the cost of a tree is the sum of the link costs, then a spanning tree whose cost is the minimum of all of the graph's spanning trees is called (not surprisingly) a **minimum spanning tree.**

Thus, another approach to providing broadcast is for the network nodes to first construct a spanning tree. When a source node wants to send a broadcast packet, it sends the packet out on all of the incident links that belong to the spanning tree. A node receiving a broadcast packet then forwards the packet to all its neighbors in the spanning tree (except the neighbor from which it received the packet). Not only does spanning tree eliminate redundant broadcast packets, but once in place, the spanning tree can be used by any node to begin a broadcast, as shown in Figures 10.42(a) and 10.42(b). Note that a node need not be aware of the entire tree; it simply needs to know which of its neighbors in *G* are spanning-tree neighbors.

The main complexity associated with the spanning-tree approach is the creation and maintenance of the spanning tree. Numerous distributed spanning-tree algorithms have been developed [Gallager 1983, Gartner 2003]. We consider only one simple algorithm here. In the **center-based approach** to building a spanning tree, a center node (also known as a **rendezvous point** or a **core**) is defined. Nodes then unicast tree-join messages addressed to the center node. A tree-join message is forwarded using unicast routing toward the center until it either arrives at a node that already belongs to the spanning tree or arrives at the center. In either case, the path that the tree-join message has followed defines the branch of the spanning tree between the edge node that initiated the tree-join message and the center. One can think of this new path as being grafted onto the existing spanning tree.

Figure 10.43 illustrates the construction of a center-based spanning tree. Suppose that node *E* is selected as the center of the tree. Suppose that node *F* first joins the tree

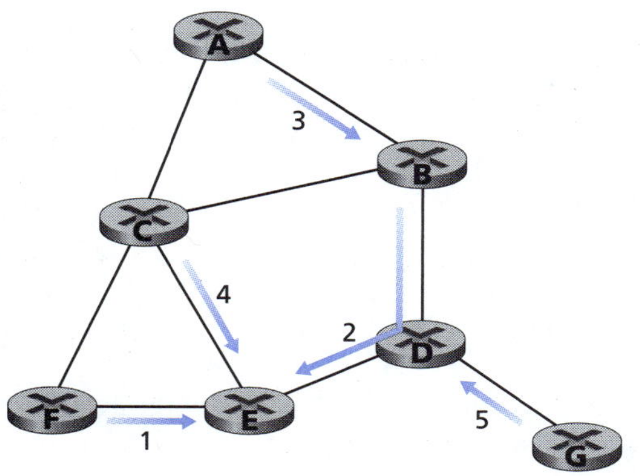

a. Stepwise construction of spanning tree

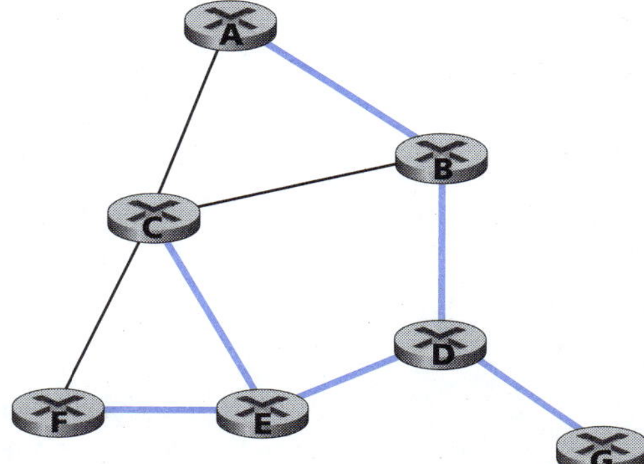

b. Constructed spanning tree

Figure 10.43 ♦ Center-based construction of a spanning tree

and forwards a tree-join message to *E*. The single link *EF* becomes the initial spanning tree. Node *B* then joins the spanning tree by sending its tree-join message to *E*. Suppose that the unicast path route to *E* from *B* is via *D*. In this case, the tree-join message results in the path *BDE* being grafted onto the spanning tree. Node *A* next joins the spanning group by forwarding its tree-join message towards *E*. If *A*'s unicast path to *E* is through *B*, then since *B* has already joined the spanning tree, the arrival of *A*'s tree-join message at *B* will result in the *AB* link being immediately grafted onto the spanning tree. Node *C* joins the spanning tree next by forwarding its tree-join message directly to *E*. Finally, because the unicast routing from *G* to *E* must be via node *D*, when *G* sends its tree-join message to *E*, the *GD* link is grafted onto the spanning tree at node *D*.

Broadcast Algorithms in Practice

Broadcast protocols are used in practice at both the application and network layers. As discussed, Gnutella [Gnutella 2004] uses application-level broadcast in order to broadcast queries for content among Gnutella peers. Here, a link between two distributed application-level peer processes in the Gnutella network is actually a TCP connection. Gnutella uses a form of sequence-number-controlled flooding in which a 16-bit identifier and a 16-bit payload descriptor (which identifies the Gnutella message type) are used to detect whether a received broadcast query has been previously received, duplicated, and forwarded. As discussed, Gnutella also uses a time-to-live (TTL) field to limit the number of hops over which a flooded query will be forwarded. When a Gnutella process receives and duplicates a query, it decrements the TTL field before forwarding the query. Thus, a flooded Gnutella query will only reach peers that are within a given number (the initial value of TTL) of application-level hops from the query initiator. Gnutella's flooding mechanism is thus sometimes referred to as *limited-scope flooding*.

A form of sequence-number controlled flooding is also used to broadcast link-state advertisements (LSAs) in the OSPF [RFC 2328, Perlman 1999] routing algorithm, and in the Intermediate-System-to-Intermediate-System (IS-IS) routing algorithm [RFC 1142, Perlman 1999]. OSPF uses a 32-bit sequence number, as well as a 16-bit age field to identify link-state advertisements (LSAs). Recall that an OSPF node broadcasts LSAs for its attached links periodically, when a link cost to a neighbor changes, or when a link goes up/down. LSA sequence numbers are used to detect duplicate LSAs, but also serve a second important function in OSPF. With flooding, it is possible for an LSA generated by the source at time t to arrive *after* a newer LSA that was generated by the same source at time $t + \delta$. The sequence numbers used by the source node allow an older LSA to be distinguished from a newer LSA. The age field serves a purpose similar to that of a TTL value. The initial age field value is set to zero and is incremented at each hop as it flooded, and is also incremented as it sits in a router's memory waiting to be flooded. Although we have only briefly described the LSA flooding algorithm here, we note that designing LSA broadcast protocols can be very tricky business indeed. [RFC 789; Perlman 1999, Section 12.2.3.3] describe an incident in which incorrectly transmitted LSAs by two malfunctioning routers caused an early version of an LSA flooding algorithm to take down the entire ARPAnet!

10.7.2 Multicast

We've seen in the previous section that with broadcast service, packets are delivered to each and every node in the network. In this section we turn our attention to **multicast** service, in which a multicast packet is delivered to only a *subset* of network nodes. A number of emerging network applications require the delivery of packets from one or more senders to a group of receivers. These applications include bulk data transfer (for example, the transfer of a software upgrade from the software developer to users needing the upgrade), streaming continuous media (for example, the transfer of the audio, video, and text of a live lecture to a set of distributed lecture participants), shared data applications (for example, a whiteboard or teleconferencing application that is shared among many distributed participants), data feeds (for example, stock quotes), Web cache updating, and interactive gaming (for example, distributed interactive virtual environments or multiplayer games such as Quake).

In multicast communication, we are immediately faced with two problems—how to identify the receivers of a multicast packet and how to address a packet sent to these receivers. In the case of unicast communication, the IP address of the receiver (destination) is carried in each IP unicast datagram and identifies the single recipient; in the case of broadcast, *all* nodes need to receive the broadcast packet, so no destination addresses are needed. But in the case of multicast, we now have multiple receivers. Does it make sense for each multicast packet to carry the IP addresses of all of the multiple recipients? While this approach might be workable with a small number of recipients, it would not scale well to the case of hundreds or thousands of receivers; the amount of addressing information in the datagram would swamp the amount of data actually carried in the packet's payload field. Explicit identification of the receivers by the sender also requires that the sender know the identities and addresses of all of the receivers. We will see shortly that there are cases where this requirement might be undesirable.

For these reasons, in the Internet architecture (and other network architectures such as ATM [Black 1995]), a multicast packet is addressed using **address indirection.** That is, a single identifier is used for the group of receivers, and a copy of the packet that is addressed to the group using this single identifier is delivered to all of the multicast receivers associated with that group. In the Internet, the single identifier that represents a group of receivers is a class D multicast address. The group of receivers associated with a class D address is referred to as a **multicast group.** The multicast group abstraction is illustrated in Figure 10.44. Here, four hosts (shown in shaded blue) are associated with the multicast group address of 226.17.30.197 and will receive all datagrams addressed to that multicast address. The difficulty that we must

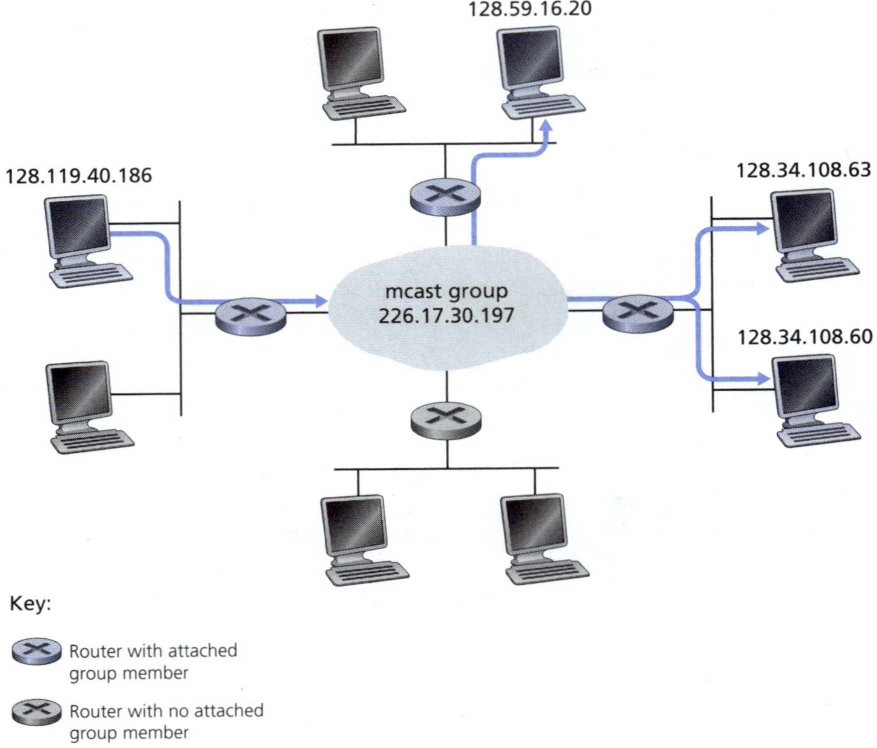

Figure 10.44 ♦ The multicast group: A datagram addressed to the group is delivered to all members of the multicast group

still address is the fact that each host has a unique IP unicast address that is completely independent of the address of the multicast group in which it is participating.

While the multicast group abstraction is simple, it raises a host (pun intended) of questions. How does a group get started and how does it terminate? How is the group address chosen? How are new hosts added to the group (either as senders or receivers)? Can anyone join a group (and send to, or receive from, that group) or is group membership restricted and, if so, by whom? Do group members know the identities of the other group members as part of the network-layer protocol? How do the network nodes interoperate with each other to deliver a multicast datagram to all group members? For the Internet, the answers to all of these questions involve the Internet Group Management Protocol [RFC 3376]. So, let us next consider the IGMP and then return to these broader questions.

Internet Group Management Protocol

The IGMP protocol version 3 [RFC 3376] operates between a host and its directly attached router (informally, we can think of the directly attached router as the first-hop router that a host would see on a path to any other host outside its own local network, or the last-hop router on any path to that host), as shown in Figure 10.45. Figure 10.45 shows three first-hop multicast routers, each connected to its attached hosts via one outgoing local interface. This local interface is attached to a LAN in this example, and while each LAN has multiple attached hosts, at most a few of these hosts will typically belong to a given multicast group at any given time.

IGMP provides the means for a host to inform its attached router that an application running on the host wants to join a specific multicast group. Given that the scope of IGMP interaction is limited to a host and its attached router, another protocol is clearly required to coordinate the multicast routers (including the attached routers) throughout the Internet, so that multicast datagrams are routed to their final destinations. This latter functionality is accomplished by network-layer multicast routing algorithms, such as PIM, DVMRP, and MOSPF. Network-layer multicast in the Internet thus consists of two complementary components: IGMP and multicast routing protocols.

Although IGMP's name suggests it manages the group of hosts joined to a multicast group, the name is a bit misleading since IGMP operates *locally*, between a host and an attached router. Despite its name, IGMP is *not* a protocol that operates

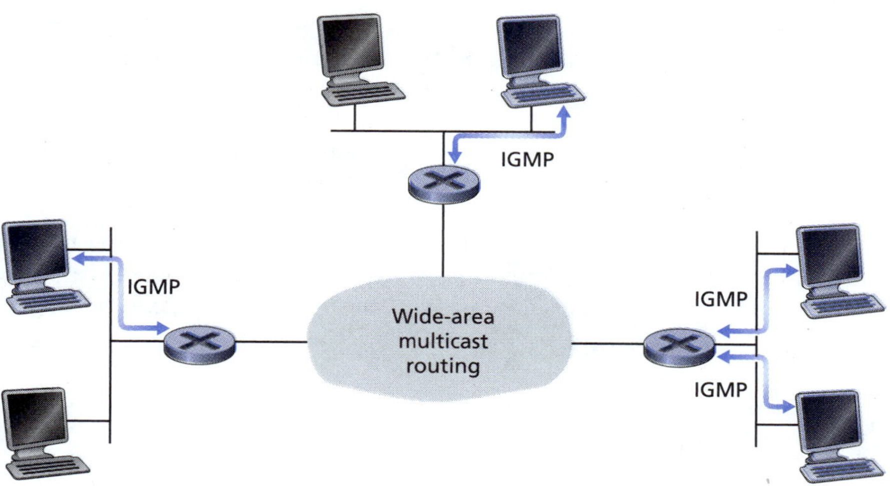

Figure 10.45 ♦ The two components of network-layer multicast: IGMP and multicast routing protocols

among all the hosts that have joined a multicast group. Indeed, there is no network-layer multicast group membership protocol that operates among all the Internet hosts in a group. There is no network-layer protocol, for example, that allows a host to determine the identities of all of the other hosts, network-wide, that have joined the multicast group. (See the homework problems for a further exploration of the consequences of this design choice.)

IGMP has only three message types. The IGMP message format is summarized in Figure 10.46. Like ICMP, IGMP messages are carried (encapsulated) within an IP datagram, with an IP protocol number of 2. A general `membership_query` message is sent by a router to all hosts on an attached interface (for example, to all hosts on a local area network) to determine the set of all multicast groups that have been joined by the hosts on that interface. A router can also determine whether a specific multicast group has been joined by hosts on an attached interface using a specific `membership_query`. The specific query includes the multicast address of the group being queried in the multicast group address field of the IGMP `membership_query` message, as shown in Figure 10.46. Hosts respond to a `membership_query` message with an IGMP `membership_report` message, as illustrated in Figure 10.47. `Membership_report` messages can also be generated by a host when an application first joins a multicast group without waiting for a `membership_query` message from the router.

The final type of IGMP message is the `leave_group` message. Interestingly, this message is optional. But if it is optional, how does a router detect that there are no longer any hosts on an attached interface that are joined to a given multicast group? The answer to this question lies in the use of the IGMP `membership_query` message. The router *infers* that no hosts are joined to a given multicast group when no host responds to a `membership_query` message with the given group address. This is an example of what is sometimes called **soft state** in an Internet protocol. In a soft-state protocol, the state (in this case of IGMP, the fact that there are hosts joined to a given multicast group) is removed via a time-out event (in this case, via a periodic `membership_query` message from the router) if it is not explicitly refreshed (in this case, by a `membership_report` message from an attached host). It has been argued that soft-state protocols result in simpler control than hard-state protocols, which not only require state to be explicitly added and removed, but also require mechanisms to recover from the situation

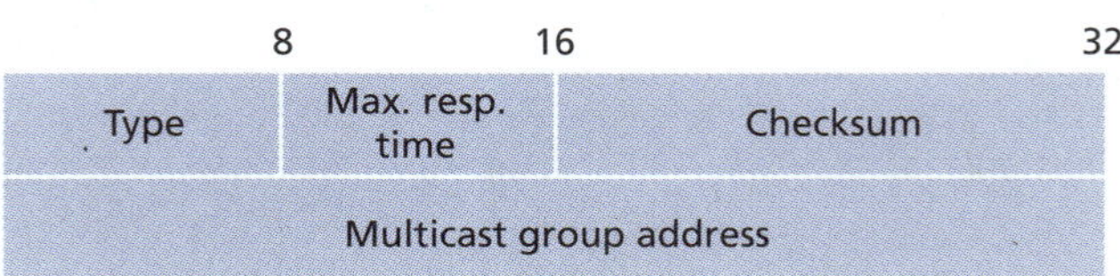

Figure 10.46 ♦ IGMP message format

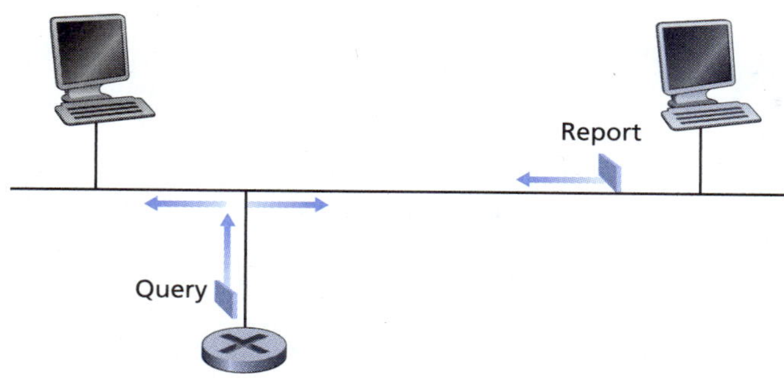

Figure 10.47 ♦ IGMP member query and membership report

where the entity responsible for removing state has terminated prematurely or failed [Sharma 1997]. Interesting discussions of soft state can be found in [Raman 1999; Ji 2003]; see also the sidebar in Section 13.9.

Having examined the protocol for joining and leaving multicast groups, we are now in a better position to reflect on the current Internet multicast service model, which is based on the work of Steve Deering [RFC 1112; Deering 1990]. In this multicast service model, any host can join a multicast group at the network layer. A host simply issues a `membership_report` IGMP message to its attached router. That router, working in concert with other Internet routers, will soon begin delivering multicast datagrams to the host. Joining a multicast group is thus receiver-driven. A sender need not be concerned with explicitly adding receivers to the multicast group, but neither can it control who joins the group and therefore who receives datagrams sent to that group. Similarly, in early versions of IGMP, a receiver could not specify a set of specific sources from which it wanted to receive (or avoid receiving) multicast packets; IGMPv3 provides for this specification.

In many ways, the current Internet multicast service model reflects the same philosophy as the Internet unicast service model—an extremely simple network layer with additional functionality (such as group membership) being provided in the upper-layer protocols in the hosts at the edges of the network. This philosophy has been unquestionably successful for the unicast case; whether the minimalist network-layer philosophy will be equally successful for the multicast service model remains an open question. A number of alternate multicast service models have recently been proposed presented in [Holbrook 1999, RFC 3569]. An interesting discussion of the current Internet multicast service model and deployment issues is [Diot 2000].

Multicast Routing Algorithms

Figure 10.48 illustrates the setting for the **multicast routing problem.** We consider a single multicast group and assume that any router that has an attached host that has joined this group may either send or receive traffic addressed to this group. In Figure 10.48, hosts joined to the multicast group are shaded in color; their immediately attached router is also shaded in color. As shown in Figure 10.48, among the population of multicast routers, only a subset of these routers (those with attached hosts that are joined to the multicast group) actually need to receive the multicast traffic. In Figure 10.48, only routers *A, B, E,* and *F* need to receive the multicast traffic. Since none of the hosts attached to router *D* are joined to the multicast group and since router *C* has no attached hosts, neither *C* nor *D* needs to receive the multicast group traffic.

The goal of multicast routing then is to find a tree of links that connects all of the routers that have attached hosts belonging to the multicast group. Multicast packets will then be routed along this tree from the sender to all of the hosts belonging to the multicast tree. Of course, the tree may contain routers that do not have attached hosts belonging to the multicast group (for example, in Figure 10.48, it is impossible to connect routers *A, B, E,* and *F* in a tree without involving either router *C* and/or *D*).

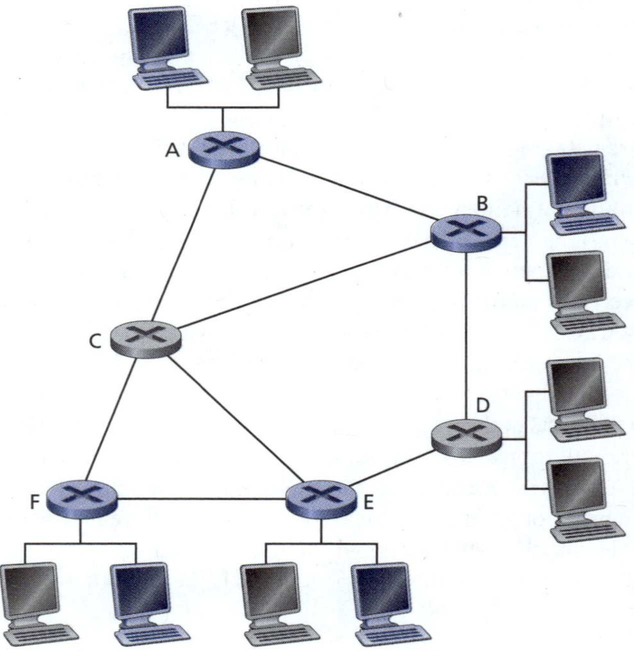

Figure 10.48 ♦ Multicast hosts, their attached routers, and other routers

In practice, two approaches have been adopted for determining the multicast routing tree, both of which we have already studied in the context of broadcast routring. The two approaches differ according to whether a single group-shared tree is used to distribute the traffic for *all* senders in the group, or whether a source-specific routing tree is constructed for each individual sender.

- *Multicast routing using a group-shared tree.* As in the case of spanning-tree broadcast, multicast routing over a group-shared tree is based on building a tree that includes all edge routers with attached hosts belonging to the multicast group. In practice, a center-based approach is used to construct the multicast routing tree, with edge routers with attached hosts belonging to the multicast group sending (via unicast) join messages addressed to the center node. As in the broadcast case, a join message is forwarded using unicast routing toward the center until it either arrives at a router that already belongs to the multicast tree or arrives at the center. All routers along the path that the join message follows will then forward received multicast packets to the edge router that initiated the multicast join. A critical question for center-based tree multicast routing is the process used to select the center. Center-selection algorithms are discussed in [Wall 1980; Thaler 1997; Estrin 1997].
- *Multicast routing using a source-based tree.* While group-shared tree multicast routing constructs a single, shared routing tree to route packets from *all* senders, the second approach constructs a multicast routing tree for *each* source in the multicast group. In practice, an RPF algorithm (with source node x) is used to construct a multicast forwarding tree for multicast datagrams originating at source x. The RPF algorithm we have studied requires a bit of tweaking for use in multicast. To see why, consider router D in Figure 10.49. Under broadcast RPF, it would forward packets to router G, even though router G has no attached hosts that are joined to the multicast group. While this is not so bad for this case where D has only a single downstream router, G, imagine what would happen if there were thousands of routers downstream from D! Each of these thousands of routers would receive unwanted multicast packets. (This scenario is not as far-fetched as it might seem. The initial MBone [Casner 1992; Macedonia 1994], the first global multicast network, suffered from precisely this problem at first.). The solution to the problem of receiving unwanted multicast packets under RPF is known as **pruning.** A multicast router that receives multicast packets and has no attached hosts joined to that group will send a prune message to its upstream router. If a router receives prune messages from each of its downstream routers, then it can forward a prune message upstream.

Multicast Routing in the Internet

The first multicast routing protocol used in the Internet and the most widely supported multicast routing algorithm is the **Distance-Vector Multicast Routing**

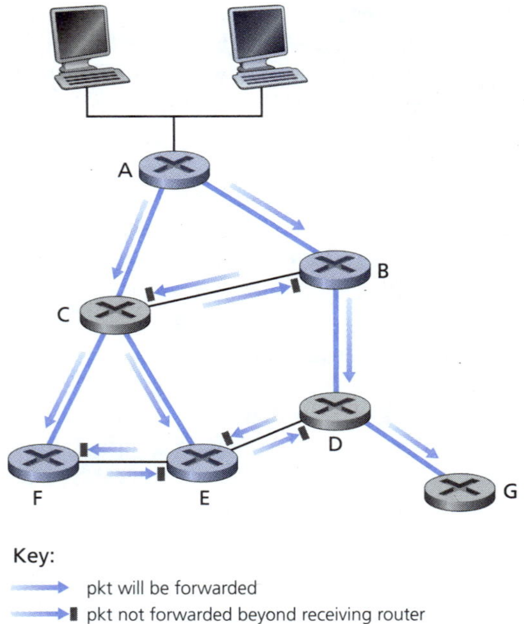

Figure 10.49 ♦ Reverse path forwarding, the multicast case

Protocol (DVMRP) [RFC 1075]. DVMRP implements source-based trees with reverse path forwarding and pruning. DVMRP uses a distance vector algorithm that allows each router to compute the outgoing link (next hop) that is on its shortest path back to each possible source. This information is then used in the RPF algorithm, as discussed above. A public copy of DVMRP software is available at [mrouted 1996].

In addition to computing next-hop information, DVMRP also computes a list of dependent downstream routers for pruning purposes. When a router has received a prune message from all of its dependent downstream routers for a given group, it will propagate a prune message upstream to the router from which it receives its multicast traffic for that group. A DVMRP prune message contains a prune lifetime (with a default value of two hours) that indicates how long a pruned branch will remain pruned before being automatically restored. DVMRP graft messages are sent by a router to its upstream neighbor to force a previously pruned branch to be added back on to the multicast tree.

The second widely used Internet multicast routing protocol is the **Protocol-Independent Multicast (PIM) routing protocol** [Deering 1996; RFC 2362; Estrin 1998b], which explicitly envisions two multicast distribution scenarios. In **dense mode,** multicast group members are densely located; that is, many or most of the routers in the area need to be involved in routing multicast datagrams. In **sparse mode,** the number of routers with attached group members is small with respect to the total number of routers; group members are widely dispersed. PIM accommodates this dense versus sparse dichotomy by offering two explicit modes of operation: dense mode and sparse mode. PIM dense mode is a flood-and-prune reverse path forwarding technique similar in spirit to DVMRP. PIM sparse mode is a center-based approach, similar to the core-based tree (CBT) multicast routing protocol [RFC 2201; RFC 2189]. One novel feature of PIM is that it gives us the ability to switch from a group-shared tree to a source-specific tree after joining the rendezvous point. A source-specific tree may be preferred due to the decreased traffic concentration that occurs when multiple source-specific trees are used (see homework problems). In PIM sparse mode, the router that receives a datagram to send from one of its attached hosts will unicast the datagram to the rendezvous point. The rendezvous point (RP) then multicasts the datagram via the group-shared tree. The RP notifies the sender that it must stop sending to the RP whenever there are no routers joined to the tree (that is, no one is listening).

In our discussion above, we have assumed that all routers are running the same multicast routing protocol. As we saw with unicasting, this will typically be the case within a single autonomous system (AS). However, different ASs may choose to run different multicast routing protocols. Interoperability rules have been defined for the major Internet multicast routing protocols [RFC 2715]. (The rules are particularly messy due to the very different approaches taken to multicast routing by sparse- and dense-mode protocols.) What is still missing, however, is an inter-AS multicast routing protocol to route multicast datagrams among different ASs. To date, DVMRP has served as the *de facto* inter-AS multicast routing protocol.

Finally we mention that to date IP multicast has not yet taken off in a big way. Many video streaming companies and content distribution companies instead use overlays to create application-layer multicast distribution networks. As with IPv6, IP multicast has struggled—and continues to struggle—to make significant inroads in the Internet.

10.8 Summary

In this chapter, we began our journey into the network core. We learned that the network layer involves each and every host and router in the network. Because of this, network-layer protocols are among the most challenging in the protocol stack.

We learned that a router may need to process millions of flows of packets between different source-destination pairs at the same time. To permit a router to process such a large number of flows, network designers have learned over the years that the router's tasks should be as simple as possible. Many measures can be taken to make the router's job easier, including using a datagram network layer rather than a virtual circuit network layer, using a streamlined and fixed-sized header (as in

IPv6), eliminating fragmentation (also done in IPv6), and providing the one and only best-effort service. Perhaps the most important trick here is *not* to keep track of individual flows, but instead base routing decisions solely on hierarchically structured destination addresses in the packets. It is interesting to note that the postal service has been using this approach for many years.

In this chapter, we also looked at the underlying principles of routing algorithms. We learned how routing algorithms abstract the computer network to a graph with nodes and links. With this abstraction, we can exploit the rich theory of shortest-path routing in graphs, which has been developed over the past 40 years in the operations research and algorithms communities. We saw that there are two broad approaches, a centralized (global) approach, in which each node obtains a complete map of the network and independently applies a shortest-path routing algorithm; and a decentralized approach, in which individual nodes have only a partial picture of the entire network, yet the nodes work together to deliver packets along the shortest routes. We also studied how hierarchy is used to deal with the problem of scale by partitioning large networks into independent administrative domains called autonomous systems (ASs). Each AS independently routes its datagrams through the AS, just as each country independently routes its postal mail through the country. We learned how centralized, decentralized, and hierarchical approaches are embodied in the principal routing protocols in the Internet: RIP, OSPF, and BGP. We concluded our study of routing algorithms by considering broadcast and multicast routing.

Having completed our study of the network layer, our journey now takes us one step further down the protocol stack, namely, to the link layer. Like the network layer, the link layer is also part of the network core. But we will see in the next chapter that the link layer has the much more localized task of moving packets between nodes on the same link or LAN. Although this task may appear on the surface to be trivial compared with that of the network layer's tasks, we will see that the link layer involves a number of important and fascinating issues that can keep us busy for a long time.

Homework Problems and Questions

Chapter 10 Review Questions

SECTIONS 10.1–10.2

1. Let's review some of the terminology used in this textbook. Recall that the name of a transport-layer packet is *segment* and that the name of a link-layer packet is *frame*. What is the name of a network-layer packet? Recall that both routers and link-layer switches are called *packet switches*. What is the fundamental difference between a router and link-layer switch? Recall that we use the term *routers* for both datagram networks and VC networks.

2. What are the two most important network-layer functions in a datagram network? What are three most important network-layer functions in a circuit-switched network?
3. What is the difference between routing and forwarding?
4. Do the routers in both datagram networks and virtual-circuit networks use forwarding tables? If so, describe the forwarding tables for both classes of networks.
5. Describe some hypothetical services that the network layer can provide to a single packet. Do the same for a flow of packets. Are any of your hypothetical services provided by the Internet's network layer? Are any provided by ATM's CBR service model? Are any provided by ATM's ABR service model?
6. List some applications that would benefit from ATM's CBR service model.

SECTION 10.3

7. Discuss why each input port in a high-speed router stores a shadow copy of the forwarding table.
8. Three types of switching fabrics are discussed in Section 10.3. List and briefly describe each type.
9. Describe how packet loss can occur at input ports. Describe how packet loss at input ports can be eliminated (without using infinite buffers).
10. Describe how packet loss can occur at output ports.
11. What is HOL blocking? Does it occur in input ports or output ports?

SECTION 10.4

12. Do routers have IP addresses? If so, how many?
13. What is the 32-bit binary equivalent of the IP address 223.1.3.27?
14. Visit a host that uses DHCP to obtain its IP address, network mask, default router, and IP address of its local DNS server. List these values.
15. Suppose there are three routers between a source host and a destination host. Ignoring fragmentation, an IP datagram sent from the source host to the destination host will travel over how many interfaces? How many forwarding tables will be indexed to move the datagram from the source to the destination?
16. Suppose an application generates chunks of 40 bytes of data every 20 msec, and each chunk gets encapsulated in a TCP segment and then an IP datagram. What percentage of each datagram will be overhead, and what percentage will be application data?
17. Suppose Host A sends Host B a TCP segment encapsulated in an IP datagram. When Host B receives the datagram, how does the network layer in Host B know it should pass the segment (that is, the payload of the datagram) to TCP rather than to UDP or to something else?

18. Suppose you purchase a wireless router and connect it to your cable modem. Also suppose that your ISP dynamically assigns your connected device (that is, your wireless router) one IP address. Also suppose that you have five PCs at home that use 802.11 to wirelessly connect to your wireless router. How are IP addresses assigned to the five PCs? Does the wireless router use NAT? Why or why not?
19. Compare and contrast the IPv4 and the IPv6 header fields. Do they have any fields in common?
20. It has been said that when IPv6 tunnels through IPv4 routers, IPv6 treats the IPv4 tunnels as link-layer protocols. Do you agree with this statement? Why or why not?

SECTION 10.5

21. Compare and contrast link state and distance vector routing algorithms.
22. Discuss how a hierarchical organization of the Internet has made it possible to scale to millions of users.
23. Is it necessary that every autonomous system use the same intra-AS routing algorithm? Why or why not?

SECTION 10.6

24. Consider Figure 10.31. Starting with the original table in *D*, suppose that *D* receives from *A* the following advertisement:

Destination Subnet	Next Router	Number of Hops to Destination
z	C	10
w	—	1
x	—	1
....	....	....

Will the table in *D* change? If so how?

25. Compare and contrast the advertisements used by RIP and OSPF.
26. Fill in the blank: RIP advertisements typically announce the number of hops to various destinations. BGP updates, on the other hand, announce the __________ to the various destinations.
27. Why are different inter-AS and intra-AS protocols used in the Internet?
28. Why are policy considerations as important for intra-AS protocols, such as OSPF and RIP, as they are for an inter-AS routing protocol like BGP?
29. Define and contrast the following terms: *subnet, prefix,* and *BGP route*.

30. How does BGP use the NEXT-HOP attribute? How does it use the AS-PATH attribute?
31. Describe how a network administrator of an upper-tier ISP can implement policy when configuring BGP.

SECTION 10.7

32. What is an important difference between implementing the broadacst abstraction via multiple unicasts, and a single network- (router-) supported broadcast?
33. For each of the three general approaches we studied for broadcast communication (uncontrolled flooding, controlled flooding, and spanning-tree broadcast), are the following statements true or false? You may assume that no packets are lost due to buffer overflow and all packets are delivered on a link in the order in which they were sent.
    a. A node may receive multiple copies of the same packet.
    b. A node may forward multiple copies of a packet over the same outgoing link.
34. When a host joins a multicast group, must it change its IP address to that of the multicast group it is joining?
35. What are the roles played by the IGMP protocol and a wide-area multicast routing protocol?
36. What is the difference between a group-shared tree and a source-based tree in the context of multicast routing?

Problems

1. Consider some of the pros and cons of virtual-circuit and datagram networks.
    a. Suppose that in the network layer, routers were subjected to stressful conditions that might cause them to fail fairly often. At a high level, what actions would need to be taken on such router failure? Does this argue in favor of VC or datagram architecture?
    b. Suppose that in order to provide a guarantee regarding the level of performance (for example, delay) that would be seen along a source-to-destination path, the network requires a sender to declare its peak traffic rate. If the declared peak traffic rate and the existing declared traffic rates are such that there is no way to get traffic from the source to the destination that meets the required delay requirements, the source is not allowed access to the network. Would such an approach be more easily accomplished within a VC or a datagram architecture?

2. Consider a virtual-circuit network. Suppose the VC number is a 16-bit field.
   a. What is the maximum number of virtual circuits that can be carried over the link?
   b. Suppose a central node determines paths and VC numbers at connection setup. Suppose the same VC number is used on each link along the VC's path. Describe how the central node might determine the VC number at connection setup. Is it possible that there are fewer VCs in progress than the maximum as determined in part (a) yet there is no common free VC number?
   c. Suppose that different VC numbers are permitted in each link along a VC's path. During connection setup, after an end-to-end path is determined, describe how the links can choose their VC numbers and configure their forwarding tables in a decentralized manner, without reliance on a central node.
3. A bare-bones forwarding table in a VC network has four columns. What is the meaning of the values in each of these columns? A bare-bones forwarding table in a datagram network has two columns. What is the meaning of the values in each of these columns?
4. Consider a VC network with a 2-bit field for the VC number. Suppose that the network wants to set up a virtual circuit over four links: link A, link B, link C, and link D. Suppose that each of these links is currently carrying two other virtual circuits, and the VC numbers of these other VCs are as follows:

Link A	Link B	Link C	Link D
00	01	10	11
01	10	11	00

   In answering the following questions, keep in mind that each of the existing VCs may only traverse one of the four links.
   a. If each VC is required to use the same VC number on all links along its path, what VC number could be assigned to the new VC?
   b. If each VC is permitted to have a different VC numbers in the different links along its path (so that forwarding table must perform VC number translation), how many different combinations of four VC numbers (one for each of the four links) could be used?
5. In the text we have used the term *connection-oriented service* to describe the transport layer and *connection service* for the network layer. Why the subtle shades in terminology?
6. In Section 10.3, we noted that there can be no input queuing if the switching fabric is n times faster than the input line rates, assuming n input lines all have the same line rate. Explain (in words) why this should be so.

7. Consider a datagram network using 32-bit host addresses. Suppose a router has four links, numbered 0 through 3, and packets are to be forwarded to the link interfaces as follows:

Destination Address Range	Link Interface
11100000 00000000 00000000 00000000 through 11100000 11111111 11111111 11111111	0
11100001 00000000 00000000 00000000 through 11100001 00000000 11111111 11111111	1
11100001 00000001 00000000 00000000 through 11100001 11111111 11111111 11111111	2
otherwise	3

a. Provide a forwarding table that has four entries, uses longest-prefix matching, and forwards packets to the correct link interfaces.

b. Describe how your forwarding table determines the appropriate link interface for datagrams with destination addresses:

11001000 10010001 01010001 01010101
11100001 00000000 11000011 00111100
11100001 10000000 00010001 01110111

8. Consider a datagram network using 8-bit host addresses. Suppose a router uses longest prefix matching and has the following forwarding table:

Prefix Match	Interface
00	0
01	1
10	2
11	3

For each of the four interfaces, give the associated range of destination host addresses and the number of addresses in the range.

9. Consider a datagram network using 8-bit host addresses. Suppose a router uses longest prefix matching and has the following forwarding table:

Prefix Match	Interface
1	0
11	1
111	2
otherwise	3

For each of the four interfaces, give the associated range of destination host addresses and the number of addresses in the range.

10. Consider a router that interconnects three subnets: Subnet 1, Subnet 2, and Subnet 3. Suppose all of the interfaces in each of these three subnets are required to have the prefix 223.1.17/24. Also suppose that Subnet 1 is required to support up to 125 interfaces, and Subnets 2 and 3 are each required to support up to 60 interfaces. Provide three network addresses (of the form a.b.c.d/x) that satisfy these constraints.
11. In Section 10.2.2 an example forwarding table (using longest prefix matching) is given. Rewrite this forwarding table using the a.b.c.d/x notation instead of the binary string notation.
12. In Problem 7 you are asked to provide a forwarding table (using longest prefix matching). Rewrite this forwarding table using the a.b.c.d/x notation instead of the binary string notation.
13. Consider a subnet with prefix 101.101.101.64/26. Give an example of one IP address (of form xxx.xxx.xxx.xxx) that can be assigned to this network. Suppose an ISP owns the block of addresses of the form 101.101.128/17. Suppose it wants to create four subnets from this block, with each block having the same number of IP addresses. What are the prefixes (of form a.b.c.d/x) for the four subnets?
14. Consider the topology shown in Figure 10.17. Denote the three subnets with hosts (starting clockwise at 12:00) as Networks A, B, and C. Denote the subnets without hosts as Networks D, E, and F.
    a. Assign network addresses to each of these six subnets, with the following constraints: All addresses must be allocated from 214.97.254/17; Subnet A should have enough addresses to support 250 interfaces; Subnet B should have enough addresses to support 120 interfaces; and Subnet C should have enough addresses to support 120 interfaces. Of course, subnets D, E and F should each be able to support two interfaces. For each subnet, the assignment should take the form a.b.c.d/x or a.b.c.d/x – e.f.g.h/y.
    b. Using your answer to part (a), provide the forwarding tables (using longest prefix matching) for each of the three routers.

15. Consider sending a 3,000-byte datagram into a link that has an MTU of 500 bytes. Suppose the original datagram is stamped with the identification number 422. How many fragments are generated? What are their characteristics?
16. Suppose datagrams are limited to 1,500 bytes (including header) between source Host A and destination Host B. Assuming a 20-byte IP header, how many datagrams would be required to send an MP3 consisting of 4 million bytes?
17. Consider the network setup in Figure 10.20. Suppose that the ISP instead assigns the router the address 126.13.89.67 and that network address of the home network is 192.168/16.
    a. Assign addresses to all interfaces in the home network.
    b. Suppose each host has two ongoing TCP connections, all to port 80 at host 128.119.40.86. Provide the six corresponding entries in the NAT translation table.
18. In this problem we'll explore the impact of NATs on P2P applications. Suppose a peer with user name Arnold discovers through querying that a peer with user name Bernard has a file it wants to download. Also suppose that Bernard is behind a NAT whereas Arnold isn't. Let 138.76.29.7 be the WAN-side address of the NAT and let 10.0.0.1 be the internal IP address for Bernard. Assume that the NAT is not specifically configured for the P2P application.
    a. Discuss why Arnold's peer cannot initiate a TCP connection to Bernard's peer, even if Arnold knows the WAN-side address of the NAT, 138.76.29.7.
    b. Now suppose that Bernard has established an ongoing TCP connection to another peer, Cindy, which is not behind a NAT. Also suppose that Arnold learned from Cindy that Bernard has the desired file and that Arnold can establish (or already has established) a TCP connection with Cindy. Describe how Arnold can use these two TCP connections (one from Bernard to Cindy and the other from Arnold to Cindy) to instruct Bernard to initiate a direct TCP connection (that is, not passing through Cindy) back to Arnold. This technique is sometimes called *connection reversal*. Note that even though Bernard is behind a NAT, Arnold can use this direct TCP connection to request the file, and Bernard can use the connection to deliver the file.
19. Following up on the previous problem, now suppose that both Arnold and Bernard are behind NATs. Try to devise a technique that will allow Arnold to establish a TCP connection with Bernard without application-specific NAT configuration. If you have difficulty devising such a technique, discuss why.
20. Looking at Figure 10.25, enumerate the paths from u to z that do not contain any loops.

21. Consider the following network. With the indicated link costs, use Dijkstra's shortest-path algorithm to compute the shortest path from x to all network nodes. Show how the algorithm works by computing a table similar to Table 10.3.

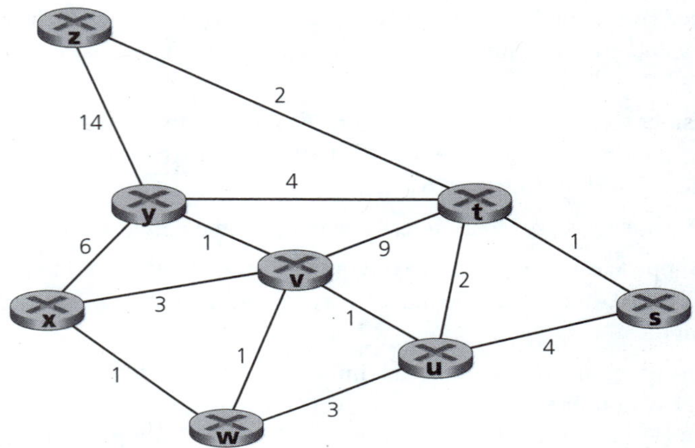

22. Consider the network shown in Problem 21. Using Dijkstra's algorithm, and showing your work using a table similar to Table 10.3, do the following.
    a. Compute the shortest path from s to all network nodes.
    b. Compute the shortest path from t to all network nodes.
    c. Compute the shortest path from u to all network nodes.
    d. Compute the shortest path from v to all network nodes.
    e. Compute the shortest path from w to all network nodes.
    f. Compute the shortest path from y to all network nodes.
    g. Compute the shortest path from z to all network nodes.
23. Consider the network shown below, and assume that each node initially knows the costs to each of its neighbors. Consider the distance vector algorithm and show the distance table entries at node z.

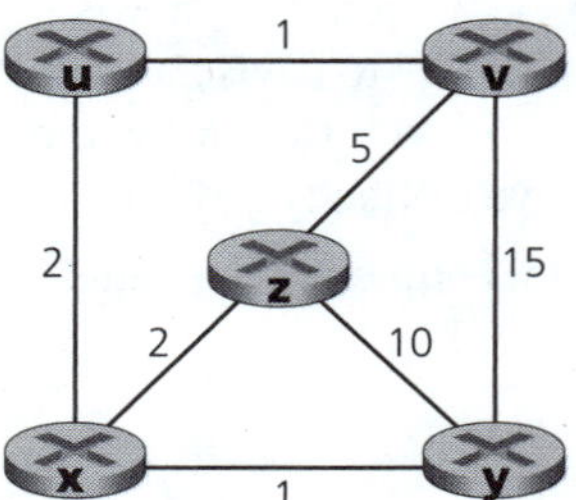

24. Consider a general topology (that is, not the specific network shown above) and a synchronous version of the distance vector algorithm. Suppose that at each iteration, a node exchanges its distance vectors with its neighbors and receives their distance vectors. Assuming that the algorithm begins with each node knowing only the costs to its immediate neighbors, what is the maximum number of iterations required before the distributed algorithm converges? Justify your answer.
25. Consider the network fragment shown below. x has only two attached neighbors, w and y. w has a minimum-cost path to destination u (not shown) of 5, and y has a minimum-cost path to u of 6. The complete paths from w and y to u (and between w and y) are not shown. All link costs in the network have strictly positive integer values.

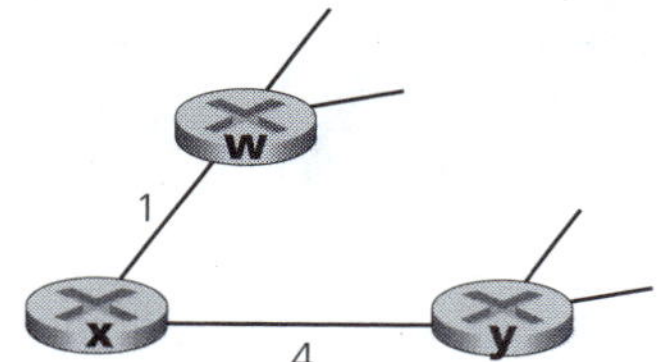

   a. Give x's distance vector for destinations w, y, and u.
   b. Give a link-cost change for either $c(x,w)$ or $c(x,y)$ such that x will inform its neighbors of a new minimum-cost path to u as a result of executing the distance vector algorithm.
   c. Give a link-cost change for either $c(x,w)$ or $c(x,y)$ such that x will *not* inform its neighbors of a new minimum-cost path to u as a result of executing the distance vector algorithm.
26. Consider the three-node topology shown in Figure 10.27. Rather than having the link costs shown in Figure 10.27, the link costs are $c(x,y) = 5$, $c(y,z) = 6$, $c(z,x) = 2$. Compute the distance tables after the initialization step and after each iteration of a synchronous version of the distance vector algorithm (as we did in our earlier discussion of Figure 10.27).
27. Describe how loops in paths can be detected in BGP.
28. Consider the following network. ISP B provides national backbone service to regional ISP A. ISP C provides national backbone service to regional ISP D. B and C peer with each other in two places using BGP. Consider traffic going from A to D. B would prefer to hand that traffic over to C on the West Coast (so that C would have to absorb the cost of carrying the traffic cross-country), while C would prefer to get the traffic via its East Coast peering point with B (so that B would have carried the traffic across the country). What BGP

mechanism might C use, so that B would hand over A-to-D traffic at their East Coast peering point? To answer this question, you will need to dig into the BGP specification.

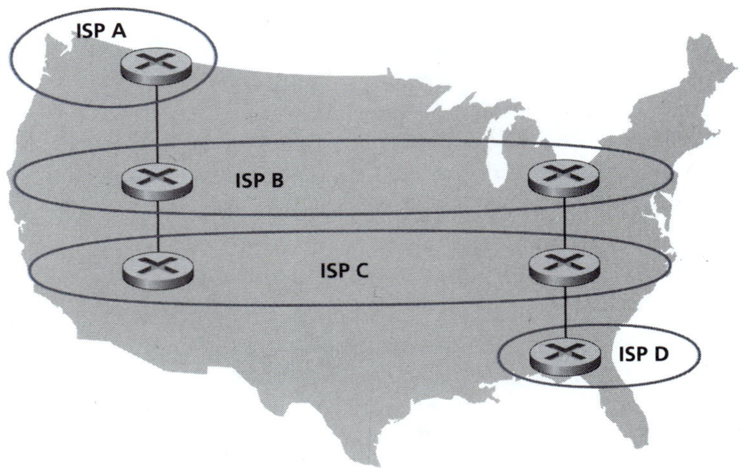

29. In Figure 10.39, consider the path information that reaches stub networks W, X, and Y. Based on the information available at W and X, what are their respective views of the network topology? Justify your answer. The topology view at Y is shown below.

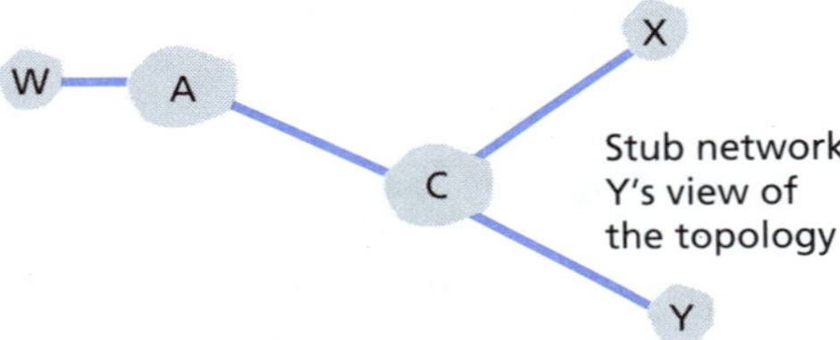

30. Consider the eight-node network (with nodes labeled *s* to *z*) in Problem 21. Show the minimal-cost tree rooted at *s* that includes (as end hosts) nodes *u*, *v*, *w*, and *y*. Informally argue why your tree is a minimal-cost tree.
31. Consider the two basic approaches identified for achieving broadcast: unicast emulation and network-layer (i.e., router-assisted) broadcast, and suppose spanning-tree broadcast is used to achive network-layer broadcast. Consider a single sender and 32 receivers. Suppose the sender is connected to the receivers by a binary tree of routers. What is the cost of sending a broadcast packet, in the cases of unicast emulation and network-layer broadcast, for this topology? Here, each

time a packet (or copy of a packet) is sent over a single link, it incurs a unit of cost. What topology for interconnecting the sender, receivers, and routers will bring the cost of unicast emulation and true network-layer broadcast as far apart as possible? You can choose as many routers as you'd like.

32. Consider the operation of the reverse path forwarding (RPF) algorithm in Figure 10.41. Using the same topology, find a set of paths from all nodes to the source node *A* (and indicate these paths in a graph using thicker-shaded lines as in Figure 10.41 such that if these paths were the least-cost paths, then node *B* would receive a copy of *A*'s broadcast message from nodes *A*, *C*, and *D* under RPF.
33. Consider the topology shown in Figure 10.41. Suppose that all links have unit coast and that node *E* is the broadcast source. Using arrows like those shown in Figure 10.41, indicate links over which packets will be forwarded using RPF, and links over which packets will not be forwarded, given that node *E* is the source.
34. Consider the topology shown in Figure 10.43, and suppose that each link has unit cost. Suppose node *C* is chosen as the center in a center-based multicast routing algorithm. Assuming that each attached router uses its least-cost path to node *C* to send join messages to *C*, draw the resulting center-based routing tree. Is the resulting tree a minimum-cost tree? Justify your answer.
35. In Section 10.5.1 we studied Dijkstra's link-state routing algorithm for computing the unicast paths that are individually the least-cost paths from the source to all destinations. The union of these paths might be thought of as forming a **least-unicast-cost path tree** (or a shortest unicast path tree, if all link costs are identical). By constructing a counterexample, show that the least-cost path tree is *not* always the same as a minimum spanning tree.
36. Consider a network in which all nodes are connected to three other nodes. In a single time step, a node can receive all transmitted broadcast packets from its neighbors, duplicate the packets, and send them to all of its neighbors (except to the node that sent a given packet). At the next time step, neighboring nodes can receive, duplicate, and forward these packets, and so on. Suppose that uncontrolled flooding is used to provide broadcast in such a network. At time step *t,* how many copies of the broadcast packet will be transmitted, assuming that during time step 1, a single broadcast packet is transmitted by the source node to its three neighbors.
37. We saw in Section 10.7 that there is no network-layer protocol that can be used to identify the hosts participating in a multicast group. Given this, how can multicast applications learn the identities of the hosts that are participating in a multicast group?
38. Design (give a pseudocode description of) an application-level protocol that maintains the host addresses of all hosts participating in a multicast group. Specifically identify the network service (unicast or multicast) that is used by your protocol, and indicate whether your protocol is sending messages in-band

or out-of-band (with respect to the application data flow among the multicast group participants) and why.

39. What is the size of the multicast address space? Suppose now that two multicast groups randomly choose a multicast address. What is the probability that they choose the same address? Suppose now that 1,000 multicast groups are ongoing at the same time and choose their multicast group addresses at random. What is the probability that they interfere with each other?

Discussion Questions

1. Find three companies that are currently selling high-speed router products. Compare the products.
2. Use the whois service at the American Registry for Internet Numbers (http://www.arin.net/whois) to determine the IP address blocks for three universities. Can the whois services be used to determine with certainty the location of a specific IP address?
3. Is it possible to write the ping client program (using ICMP messages) in Java? Why or why not?
4. In Section 10.4, we indicated that deployment of IPv6 has been slow. Why has it been slow? What is needed to accelerate its deployment?
5. Discuss some of the problems NATs create for IPsec security (see [Phifer 2000]).
6. Suppose ASs X and Z are not directly connected but instead are connected by AS Y. Further suppose that X has a peering agreement with Y, and that Y has a peering agreement with Z. Finally, suppose that Z wants to transit all of Y's traffic but does not want to transit X's traffic. Does BGP allow Z to implement this policy?
7. In Section 10.7 we identified a number of multicast applications. Which of these applications are well suited for the minimalist Internet multicast service model? Why? Which applications are not particularly well suited for this service model?

Programming Assignment

In this programming assignment, you will be writing a "distributed" set of procedures that implement a distributed asynchronous distance vector routing for the network shown below.

You are to write the following routines that will "execute" asynchronously within the emulated environment provided for this assignment. For node 0, you will write the routines:

- *rtinit0()*. This routine will be called once at the beginning of the emulation. *rtinit0()* has no arguments. It should initialize your distance table in node 0 to reflect the direct costs of 1, 3, and 7 to nodes 1, 2, and 3, respectively. In the figure above, all links are bidirectional and the costs in both directions are identical. After initializing the distance table and any other data structures needed by your node 0 routines, it should then send its directly connected neighbors (in this case, 1, 2, and 3) the cost of its minimum-cost paths to all other network nodes. This minimum-cost information is sent to neighboring nodes in a routing update packet by calling the routine *tolayer2()*, as described in the full assignment. The format of the routing update packet is also described in the full assignment.
- *rtupdate0(struct rtpkt *rcvdpkt)*. This routine will be called when node 0 receives a routing packet that was sent to it by one of its directly connected neighbors. The parameter **rcvdpkt* is a pointer to the packet that was received. *rtupdate0()* is the "heart" of the distance vector algorithm. The values it receives in a routing update packet from some other node *i* contain *i*'s current shortest-path costs to all other network nodes. *rtupdate0()* uses these received values to update its own distance table (as specified by the distance vector algorithm). If its own minimum cost to another node changes as a result of the update, node 0 informs its directly connected neighbors of this change in minimum cost by sending them a routing packet. Recall that in the distance vector algorithm, only directly connected nodes will exchange routing packets. Thus, nodes 1 and 2 will communicate with each other, but nodes 1 and 3 will not communicate with each other.

Similar routines are defined for nodes 1, 2, and 3. Thus, you will write eight procedures in all: *rtinit0()*, *rtinit1()*, *rtinit2()*, *rtinit3()*, *rtupdate0()*, *rtupdate1()*, *rtupdate2()*, and *rtupdate3()*. These routines will together implement a distributed, asynchronous computation of the distance tables for the topology and costs shown in the figure on the preceding page.

You can find the full details of the programming assignment, as well as C code that you will need to create the simulated hardware/software environment at http://www.awl.com/kurose-ross. A Java version of the assignment is also available.

Ethereal Lab

In the companion Web site for this textbook, http://www.awl.com/kurose-ross, you'll find two Ethereal lab assignments. The first lab examines the operation of IP protocol, and the IP datagram format in particular. The second lab explores the use of the ICMP protocol in the ping and traceroute commands.

AN INTERVIEW WITH...

Vinton G. Cerf

Vinton G. Cerf is senior vice president of Architecture and Technology for WorldCom. He is widely known as the co-designer of the TCP/IP protocols and the architecture of the Internet. As vice president of MCI Digital Information Services from 1982 to 1986, he led the engineering of MCI Mail, the first commercial e-mail service to be connected to the Internet. During his tenure from 1976 to 1982 with the US Department of Defense's Advanced Research Projects Agency (DARPA), he played a key role leading the development of Internet and Internet-related data packet and security technologies. Vinton holds a BS in Mathematics from Stanford University and a PhD in computer science from UCLA.

What brought you to specialize in networking?

I was working as a programmer at UCLA in the late 1960s. My job was supported by the US Defense Advanced Research Projects Agency (called ARPA then, called DARPA now). I was working in the laboratory of Professor Leonard Kleinrock on the Network Measurement Center of the newly-created ARPANET. The first node of the ARPANET was installed at UCLA on September 1, 1969. I was responsible for programming a computer that was used to capture performance information about the ARPANET and to report this information back for comparison with mathematical models and predictions of the performance of the network.

Several of the other graduate students and I were made responsible for working on the so-called host-level protocols of the ARPANET—the procedures and formats that would allow many different kinds of computers on the network to interact with each other. It was a fascinating exploration into a new world (for me) of distributed computing and communication.

Did you imagine that IP would become as pervasive as it is today when you first designed the protocol?

When Bob Kahn and I first worked on this in 1973, I think we were mostly very focused on the central question: how can we make heterogeneous packet networks interoperate with one another, assuming we cannot actually change the networks themselves. We hoped that we could find a way to permit an arbitrary collection of packet-switched networks to be interconnected in a transparent fashion, so that host computers could communicate end-to-end without having to do any translations in between. I think we knew that we were dealing with powerful and expandable technology but I doubt we had a clear image of what the world would be like with hundreds of millions of computers all interlinked on the Internet.

What do you now envision for the future of networking and the Internet? What major challenges/obstacles do you think lie ahead in their development?

I believe the Internet itself and networks in general will continue to proliferate. Already there is convincing evidence that there will be billions of Internet-enabled devices on the Internet, including appliances like cell phones, refrigerators, personal digital assistants, home servers, televisions, as well as the usual array of laptops, servers, and so on. Big challenges include support for mobility, battery life, capacity of the access links to the network, and ability to scale the optical core of the network up in an unlimited fashion. Designing an interplanetary extension of the Internet is a project in which I am deeply engaged at the Jet Propulsion Laboratory. We will need to cut over from IPv4 [32-bit addresses] to IPv6 [128 bits]. The list is long!

Who has inspired you professionally?

My colleague Bob Kahn; my thesis advisor, Gerald Estrin; my best friend, Steve Crocker (we met in high school and he introduced me to computers in 1960!); and the thousands of engineers who continue to evolve the Internet today.

Do you have any advice for students entering the networking/Internet field?

Think outside the limitations of existing systems—imagine what might be possible; but then do the hard work of figuring out how to get there from the current state of affairs. Dare to dream: a half dozen colleagues and I at the Jet Propulsion Laboratory have been working on the design of an interplanetary extension of the terrestrial Internet. It may take decades to implement this, mission by mission, but to paraphrase: “A man’s reach should exceed his grasp, or what are the heavens for?”

CHAPTER 11

The Link Layer and Local Area Networks

In the previous chapter we learned that the network layer provides a communication service between two hosts. As shown in Figure 11.1, this communication path consists of a series of communication links, starting at the source host, passing through a series of routers, and ending at the destination host. As we continue to proceed down the protocol stack, from the network layer to the link layer, we naturally wonder how packets are sent across the individual links within the end-to-end communication path. How are the network-layer datagrams encapsulated in the link-layer frames for transmission over a single link? Can link-layer protocols provide router-to-router reliable data transfer? Can different link-layer protocols be used in the different links along the communication path? We will answer these and other important questions in this chapter.

In discussing the link layer, we will find that there are two fundamentally different types of link-layer channels. The first type consists of broadcast channels, which are common in local area networks (LANs), wireless LANs, satellite networks, and hybrid fiber coaxial cable (HFC) access networks. For a broadcast channel, many hosts are connected to the same communication channel, and a so-called medium access protocol is needed to coordinate transmissions and avoid collisions. The second type of link-layer channel is the point-to-point communication link, such as between two routers or between a residential dial-up modem and an ISP router. Coordinating access to a point-to-point link is trivial, but there are still

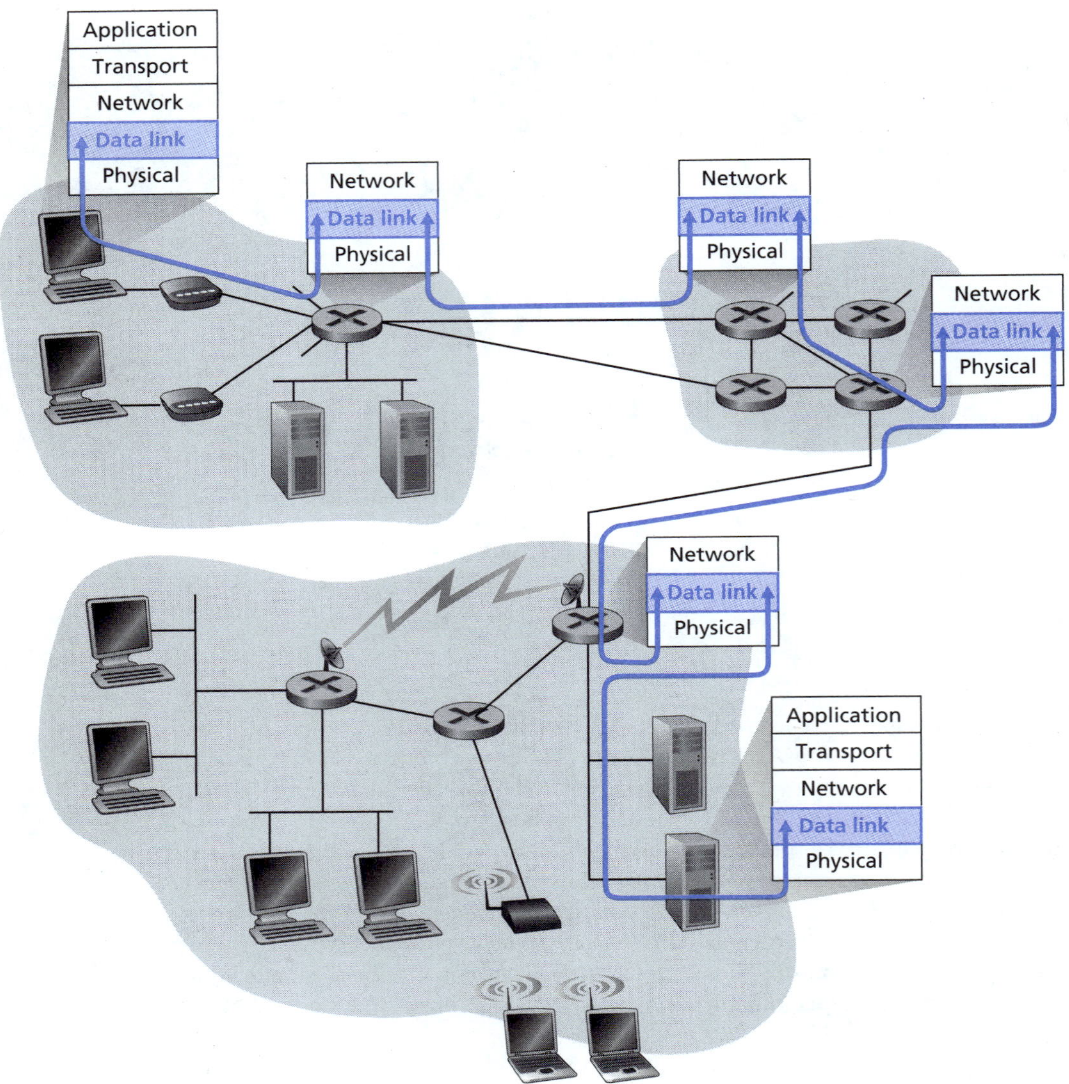

Figure 11.1 ♦ The link layer

important issues surrounding framing, reliable data transfer, error detection, and flow control.

We'll explore several important link-layer technologies in this chapter. We'll take an in-depth look at Ethernet, by far the most prevalent wired LAN technology. We'll also look at point-to-point protocol (PPP), the protocol of choice for dial-up residential hosts.

Although Wi-Fi, and more generally wireless LANs, are certainly link-layer topics, they are not covered in this chapter. This is not because Wi-Fi is an unimportant topic—quite the opposite, as the Wi-Fi revolution is dramatically changing how people access and use the Internet. Wi-Fi is instead covered in depth in Chapter 12, which is devoted to wireless computer networking and mobility.

11.1 Link Layer: Introduction and Services

Let's begin with some useful terminology. We'll find it convenient in this chapter to refer to the hosts and the routers simply as **nodes** since, as we'll see shortly, we will not be particularly concerned whether a node is a router or a host. We will also refer to the communication channels that connect adjacent nodes along the communication path as **links**. In order for a datagram to be transferred from source host to destination host, it must be moved over each of the *individual links* in the end-to-end path. Over a given link, a transmitting node encapsulates the datagram in a link-layer frame and transmits the frame into the link; and a receiving node receives the frame and extracts the datagram.

11.1.1 The Services Provided by the Link Layer

A link-layer protocol is used to move a datagram over an individual link. The **link-layer protocol** defines the format of the packets exchanged between the nodes at the ends of the link, as well as the actions taken by these nodes when the packets are sent and received. Recall that the units of data exchanged by a link-layer protocol are called **frames**, and that each link-layer frame typically encapsulates one network-layer datagram. As we'll see shortly, the actions taken by a link-layer protocol when sending and receiving frames include error detection, retransmission, flow control, and random access. Examples of link-layer protocols include Ethernet, 802.11 wireless LANs (also known as Wi-Fi), token ring, and PPP; in many contexts, ATM can be considered a link-layer protocol as well. We'll cover many of these protocols in detail in the latter half of this chapter.

Whereas the network layer has the end-to-end job of moving transport-layer segments from the source host to the destination host, a link-layer protocol has the node-to-node job of moving network-layer datagrams over a *single link* in the path. An important characteristic of the link layer is that a datagram may be handled by different link-layer protocols on the different links in the path. For example, a datagram may be handled by Ethernet on the first link, PPP on the last link, and a link-layer WAN protocol in the intermediate links. It is important to note that the services provided by the link-layer protocols may be different. For example, a link-layer protocol may or may not provide reliable delivery. Thus, the network layer must be able to accomplish its end-to-end job in the presence of a heterogeneous set of individual link-layer services.

In order to gain insight into the link layer and how it relates to the network layer, let's consider a transportation analogy. A travel agent who is planning a trip for a tourist traveling from Princeton, New Jersey, to Lausanne, Switzerland decides that it is most convenient for the tourist to take a limousine from Princeton to JFK airport, then a plane from JFK airport to Geneva's airport, and finally a train from Geneva's airport to Lausanne's train station. Once the travel agent makes the three reservations, it is the responsibility of the Princeton limousine company to get the tourist from Princeton to JFK; it is the responsibility of the airline company to get the tourist from JFK to Geneva; and it is the responsibility of the Swiss train service to get the tourist from Geneva to Lausanne. Each of the three segments of the trip is "direct" between two "adjacent" locations. Note that the three transportation segments are managed by different companies and use entirely different transportation modes (limousine, plane, and train). Although the transportation modes are different, they each provide the basic service of moving passengers from one location to an adjacent location. In this transportation analogy, the tourist is a datagram, each transportation segment is a communication link, the transportation mode is a link-layer protocol, and the travel agent is a routing protocol.

Although the basic service of any link layer is to move a datagram from one node to an adjacent node over a single communication link, the details of the provided service can vary from one link-layer protocol to the next. Possible services that can be offered by a link-layer protocol include:

- *Framing.* Almost all link-layer protocols encapsulate each network-layer datagram within a link-layer frame before transmission over the link. A frame consists of a data field, in which the network-layer datagram is inserted, and a number of header fields. (A frame may also include trailer fields; however, we will refer to both header and trailer fields as header fields.) The structure of the frame is specified by the link-layer protocol. We'll see several different frame formats when we examine specific link-layer protocols in the second half of this chapter.
- *Link Access.* A medium access control (MAC) protocol specifies the rules by which a frame is transmitted onto the link. For point-to-point links that have a single sender at one end of the link and a single receiver at the other end of the link, the MAC protocol is simple (or nonexistent)—the sender can send a frame whenever the link is idle. The more interesting case is when multiple nodes share a single broadcast link—the so-called multiple access problem. Here, the MAC

protocol serves to coordinate the frame transmissions of the many nodes; we cover MAC protocols in detail in Section 11.3.

- *Reliable delivery.* When a link-layer protocol provides reliable delivery service, it guarantees to move each network-layer datagram across the link without error. Recall that certain transport-layer protocols (such as TCP) also provide a reliable delivery service. Similar to a transport-layer reliable delivery service, a link-layer reliable delivery service is achieved with acknowledgments and retransmissions. A link-layer reliable delivery service is often used for links that are prone to high error rates, such as a wireless link, with the goal of correcting an error locally—on the link where the error occurs—rather than forcing an end-to-end retransmission of the data by a transport- or application-layer protocol. However, link-layer reliable delivery can be considered an unnecessary overhead for low bit-error links, including fiber, coax, and many twisted-pair copper links. For this reason, many wired link-layer protocols do not provide a reliable delivery service.
- *Flow control.* The nodes on each side of a link have a limited amount of frame buffering capacity. This is a potential problem, as a receiving node may receive frames at a rate faster than it can process them. Without flow control, the receiver's buffer can overflow and frames can get lost. Similar to the transport layer, a link-layer protocol can provide flow control in order to prevent the sending node on one side of a link from overwhelming the receiving node on the other side of the link.
- *Error detection.* A node's receiver can incorrectly decide that a bit in a frame is zero when it was transmitted as a one, and vice versa. Such bit errors are introduced by signal attenuation and electromagnetic noise. Because there is no need to forward a datagram that has an error, many link-layer protocols provide a mechanism to detect the presence of one or more errors. This is done by having the transmitting node set error-detection bits in the frame, and having the receiving node perform an error check. Error detection is a very common service among link-layer protocols. Recall from Chapter 10 that the Internet's transport layer and network layers also provide a limited form of error detection. Error detection in the link layer is usually more sophisticated and is implemented in hardware.
- *Error correction.* Error correction is similar to error detection, except that a receiver not only detects whether errors have been introduced in the frame but also determines exactly where in the frame the errors have occurred (and then corrects these errors). Some protocols (such as ATM) provide link-layer error correction for the packet header rather than for the entire packet. We cover error detection and correction in Section 11.2.
- *Half-duplex and full-duplex.* With full-duplex transmission, the nodes at both ends of a link may transmit packets at the same time. With half-duplex transmission, a node cannot both transmit and receive at the same time.

As noted above, many of the services provided by the link layer have strong parallels with services provided at the transport layer. For example, both the link layer and the transport layer can provide reliable delivery. Although the mechanisms used to provide reliable delivery in the two layers are similar, the two reliable delivery services are not the same. A transport protocol provides reliable delivery between two processes on an end-to-end basis; a reliable link-layer protocol provides the reliable delivery service between two nodes connected by a single link. Similarly, both link-layer and transport-layer protocols can provide flow control and error detection; again, flow control in a transport-layer protocol is provided on an end-to-end basis, whereas it is provided in a link-layer protocol on a node-to-adjacent-node basis.

11.1.2 Adapters Communicating

For a given communication link, the link-layer protocol is, for the most part, implemented in an **adapter**. An adapter is a board (or a PCMCIA card) that typically contains RAM, DSP chips, a host bus interface, and a link interface. Adapters are also commonly known as **network interface cards (NICs)**. As shown in Figure 11.2, the network layer in the transmitting node (that is, a host or router) passes a network-layer datagram to the adapter that handles the sending side of the communication link. The adapter encapsulates the datagram in a frame and then transmits the frame into the communication link. At the other side, the receiving adapter receives the entire frame, extracts the network-layer datagram, and passes it to the network layer. If the link-layer protocol provides error detection, then it is the sending adapter that sets the error detection bits and it is the receiving adapter that performs error checking. If the link-layer protocol provides reliable delivery, then the mechanisms for reliable delivery (for example, sequence numbers, timers, and acknowledgments) are implemented entirely in the adapters. If the link-layer protocol uses random access (see Section 11.3), then the random access protocol is implemented entirely in the adapters.

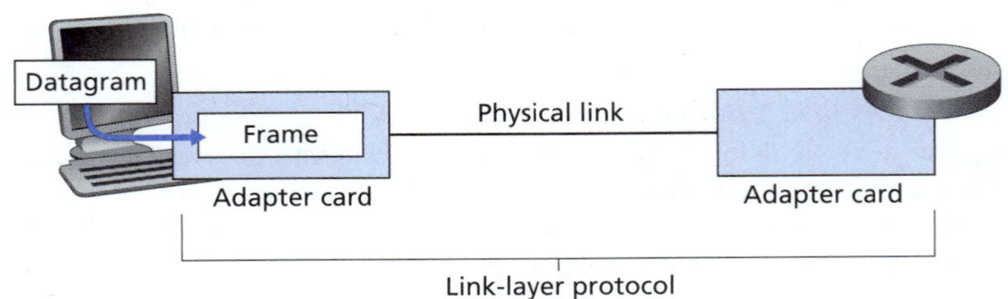

Figure 11.2 ♦ The link-layer protocol for a communication link is implemented in the adapters at the two ends of the link.

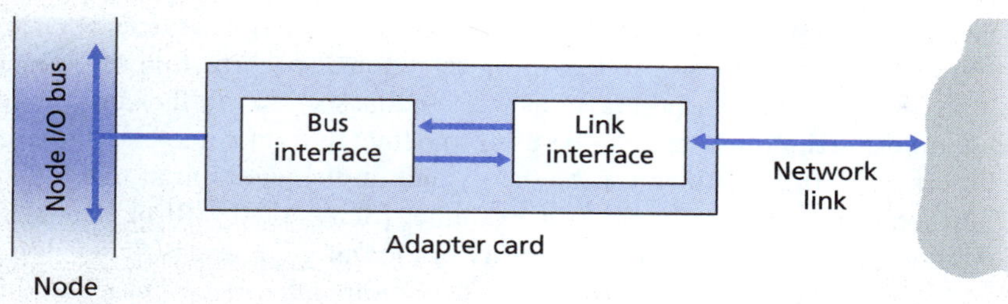

Figure 11.3 ♦ The adapter is a semi-autonomous unit.

An adapter is a semi-autonomous unit. For example, an adapter can receive a frame, determine if the frame is in error, and discard the frame without notifying other components (e.g., a central processing unit) in the node in which it is housed (which we will refer to as the adapter's *parent* node). When receiving a frame, an adapter will interrupt its parent node only if it wants to pass a network-layer datagram up the protocol stack. Similarly, when a node passes a datagram down the protocol stack to an adapter, the node fully delegates to the adapter the task of transmitting the datagram across that link. An adapter is semi-autonomous, not fully autonomous. Although we have shown the adapter as a separate box in Figure 11.3, the adapter is typically housed in the same physical box as the rest of the node, shares power and buses with the rest of the node, and is ultimately under the control of the node.

As shown in Figure 11.3, the main components of an adapter are the bus interface and the link interface. The bus interface is responsible for communicating with the adapter's parent node. It transfers data and control information between the adapter and the parent node. The link interface is responsible for implementing the link-layer protocol. In addition to framing and deframing datagrams, it may provide error detection, random access, and other link-layer functions. It also includes the transmit and receive circuitry. For popular link-layer technologies, such as Ethernet and Wi-Fi, the link interface is implemented by chip sets that can be bought on the commodity market. For this reason, Ethernet and Wi-Fi adapters are incredibly cheap—often less than $20. You can learn more about adapter architecture for 10, 100, and 1,000 Mbps Ethernet and for 155 Mbps ATM by visiting the 3Com adapter page [3Com 2004].

11.2 Error-Detection and -Correction Techniques

In the previous section, we noted that **bit-level error detection and correction**—detecting and correcting the corruption of bits in a link-layer frame sent from one node to another physically connected neighboring node—are two services often provided by the link layer. We saw in that error-detection and -correction services are also often offered at the transport layer as well. In this section, we'll examine a few of the simplest techniques that can be used to detect and, in some cases, correct such bit errors. A full treatment of the theory and implementation of this topic is itself the topic of many textbooks (for example, [Schwartz 1980] or [Bertsekas 1991]), and our treatment here is necessarily brief. Our goal here is to develop an intuitive feel for the capabilities that error-detection and -correction techniques provide, and to see how a few simple techniques work and are used in practice in the link layer.

Figure 11.4 illustrates the setting for our study. At the sending node, data, *D*, to be protected against bit errors, is augmented with error-detection and -correction bits (*EDC*). Typically, the data to be protected includes not only the datagram passed down from the network layer for transmission across the link, but also link-level addressing information, sequence numbers, and other fields in the link frame header. Both *D* and *EDC* are sent to the receiving node in a link-level frame. At the receiving node, a sequence of bits, *D′* and *EDC′* are received. Note that *D′* and *EDC′* may differ from the original *D* and *EDC* as a result of in-transit bit flips.

The receiver's challenge is to determine whether or not *D′* is the same as the original *D*, given that it has only received *D′* and *EDC′*. The exact wording of the

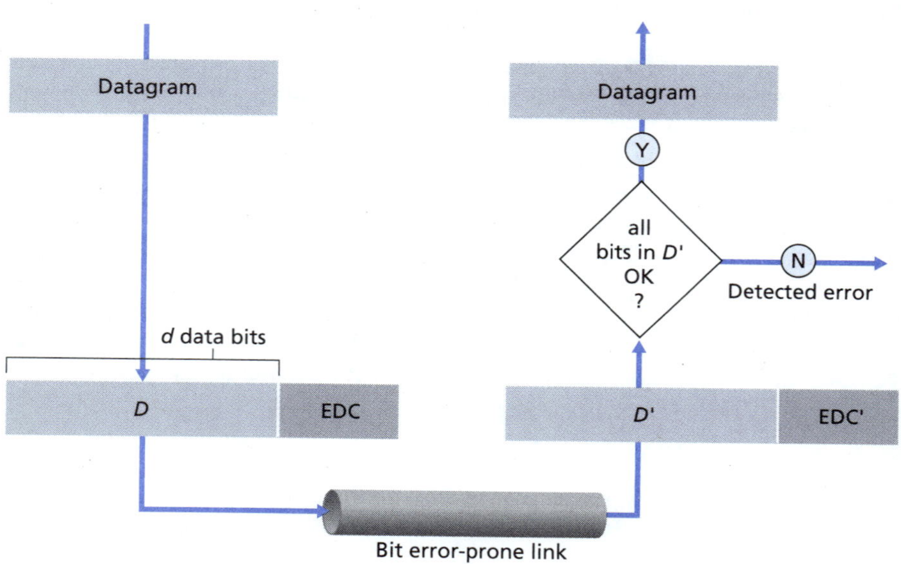

Figure 11.4 ♦ Error-detection and -correction scenario

receiver's decision in Figure 11.4 (we ask whether an error is detected, not whether an error has occurred!) is important. Error-detection and -correction techniques allow the receiver to sometimes, *but not always,* detect that bit errors have occurred. Even with the use of error detection bits there still may be **undetected bit errors**; that is, the receiver may be unaware that the received information contains bit errors. As a consequence, the receiver might deliver a corrupted datagram to the network layer, or be unaware that the contents of a field in the frame's header has been corrupted. We thus want to choose an error-detection scheme that keeps the probability of such occurrences small. Generally, more sophisticated error-detection and -correction techniques (that is, those that have a smaller probability of allowing undetected bit errors) incur a larger overhead—more computation is needed to compute and transmit a larger number of error-detection and -correction bits.

Let's now examine three techniques for detecting errors in the transmitted data—parity checks (to illustrate the basic ideas behind error detection and correction), checksumming methods (which are more typically employed in the transport layer), and cyclic redundancy checks (which are more typically employed in the link layer in the adapters).

11.2.1 Parity Checks

Perhaps the simplest form of error detection is the use of a single **parity bit**. Suppose that the information to be sent, D in Figure 11.4, has d bits. In an even parity scheme, the sender simply includes one additional bit and chooses its value such that the total number of 1s in the $d + 1$ bits (the original information plus a parity bit) is even. For odd parity schemes, the parity bit value is chosen such that there is an odd number of 1s. Figure 11.5 illustrates an even parity scheme, with the single parity bit being stored in a separate field.

Receiver operation is also simple with a single parity bit. The receiver need only count the number of 1s in the received $d + 1$ bits. If an odd number of 1-valued bits are found with an even parity scheme, the receiver knows that at least one bit error has occurred. More precisely, it knows that some *odd* number of bit errors have occurred.

But what happens if an even number of bit errors occurs? You should convince yourself that this would result in an undetected error. If the probability of bit errors

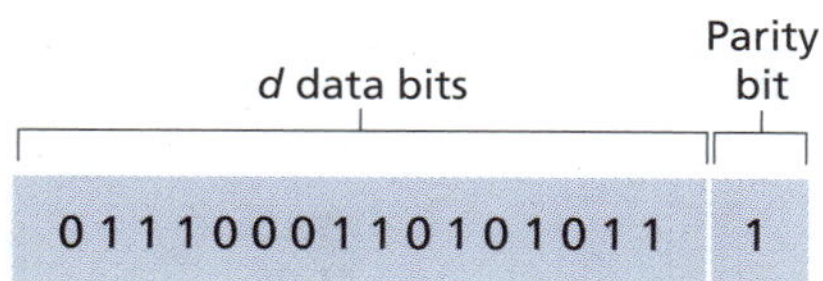

Figure 11.5 ♦ One-bit even parity

is small and errors can be assumed to occur independently from one bit to the next, the probability of multiple bit errors in a packet would be extremely small. In this case, a single parity bit might suffice. However, measurements have shown that, rather than occurring independently, errors are often clustered together in "bursts." Under burst error conditions, the probability of undetected errors in a frame protected by single-bit parity can approach 50 percent [Spragins 1991]. Clearly, a more robust error-detection scheme is needed (and, fortunately, is used in practice!). But before examining error-detection schemes that are used in practice, let's consider a simple generalization of one-bit parity that will provide us with insight into error-correction techniques.

Figure 11.6 shows a two-dimensional generalization of the single-bit parity scheme. Here, the d bits in D are divided into i rows and j columns. A parity value is computed for each row and for each column. The resulting $i + j + 1$ parity bits comprise the link-layer frame's error-detection bits.

Suppose now that a single bit error occurs in the original d bits of information. With this **two-dimensional parity** scheme, the parity of both the column and the

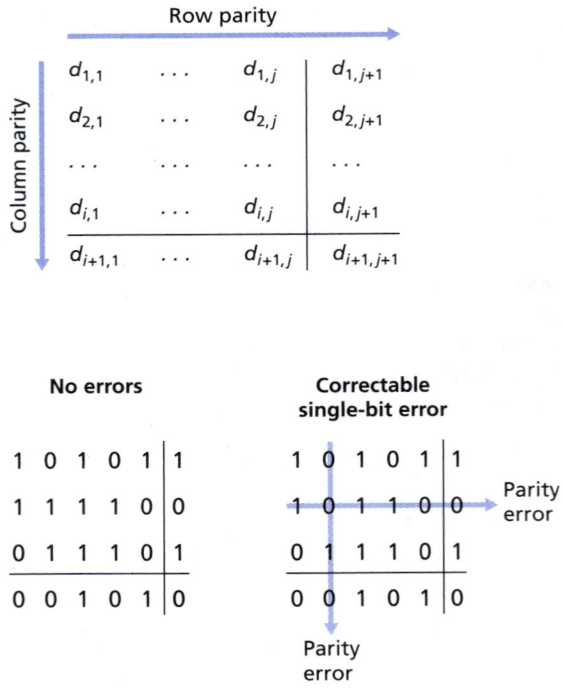

Row parity

Column parity

$d_{1,1}$	...	$d_{1,j}$	$d_{1,j+1}$
$d_{2,1}$	...	$d_{2,j}$	$d_{2,j+1}$
...	...	...	...
$d_{i,1}$	...	$d_{i,j}$	$d_{i,j+1}$
$d_{i+1,1}$	...	$d_{i+1,j}$	$d_{i+1,j+1}$

No errors

1	0	1	0	1	1
1	1	1	1	0	0
0	1	1	1	0	1
0	0	1	0	1	0

Correctable single-bit error

1	0	1	0	1	1
1	0	1	1	0	0
0	1	1	1	0	1
0	0	1	0	1	0

Parity error (row)

Parity error (column)

Figure 11.6 ♦ Two-dimensional even parity

row containing the flipped bit will be in error. The receiver can thus not only *detect* the fact that a single bit error has occurred, but can use the column and row indices of the column and row with parity errors to actually identify the bit that was corrupted and *correct* that error! Figure 11.6 shows an example in which the 1-valued bit in position (2,2) is corrupted and switched to a 0—an error that is both detectable and correctable at the receiver. Although our discussion has focused on the original *d* bits of information, a single error in the parity bits themselves is also detectable and correctable. Two-dimensional parity can also detect (but not correct!) any combination of two errors in a packet. Other properties of the two-dimensional parity scheme are explored in the problems at the end of the chapter.

The ability of the receiver to both detect and correct errors is known as **forward error correction (FEC)**. These techniques are commonly used in audio storage and playback devices such as audio CDs. In a network setting, FEC techniques can be used by themselves, or in conjunction with the ARQ techniques. FEC techniques are valuable because they can decrease the number of sender retransmissions required. Perhaps more important, they allow for immediate correction of errors at the receiver. This avoids having to wait for the round-trip propagation delay needed for the sender to receive a NAK packet and for the retransmitted packet to propagate back to the receiver—a potentially important advantage for real-time network applications [Rubenstein 1998]. Recent work examining the use of FEC in error-control protocols includes [Biersack 1992; Nonnenmacher 1998; Byers 1998; Shacham 1990].

11.2.2 Checksumming Methods

In checksumming techniques, the *d* bits of data in Figure 11.4 are treated as a sequence of *k*-bit integers. One simple checksumming method is to simply sum these *k*-bit integers and use the resulting sum as the error detection bits. The so-called **Internet checksum** is based on this approach—bytes of data are treated as 16-bit integers and summed. The 1's complement of this sum then forms the Internet checksum that is carried in the segment header. As discussed, the receiver checks the checksum by taking the 1's complement of the sum of the received data (including the checksum) and checking whether the result is all 1 bits. If any of the bits are 0, an error is indicated. RFC 1071 discusses the Internet checksum algorithm and its implementation in detail. In the TCP and UDP protocols, the Internet checksum is computed over all fields (header and data fields included). In other protocols, for example, XTP [Strayer 1992], one checksum is computed over the header and another checksum is computed over the entire packet.

Checksumming methods require relatively little packet overhead. For example, the checksums in TCP and UDP use only 16 bits. However, they provide relatively weak protection against errors as compared with cyclic redundancy check, which is discussed below and which is often used in the link layer. A natural question at this point is, Why is checksumming used at the transport layer and cyclic redundancy check used at the link layer? Recall that the transport layer is typically implemented in software in a host as part of the host's operating system. Because transport-layer error detection is implemented in software, it is important to have a simple and fast error-detection scheme such as checksumming. On the other hand, error detection at the link layer is implemented in dedicated hardware in adapters, which can rapidly perform the more complex CRC operations.

The principal reason checksumming is used at the transport layer and the stronger CRC is used at the link layer is that checksumming is easy to implement in software.

McAuley [McAuley 1994] describes improved weighted checksum codes that are suitable for high-speed software implementation and Feldmeier [Feldmeier 1995] presents fast software implementation techniques for not only weighted checksum codes, but CRC (see below) and other codes as well.

11.2.3 Cyclic Redundancy Check (CRC)

An error-detection technique used widely in today's computer networks is based on **cyclic redundancy check (CRC) codes.** CRC codes are also known as **polynomial codes**, since it is possible to view the bit string to be sent as a polynomial whose coefficients are the 0 and 1 values in the bit string, with operations on the bit string interpreted as polynomial arithmetic.

CRC codes operate as follows. Consider the d-bit piece of data, D, that the sending node wants to send to the receiving node. The sender and receiver must first agree on an $r + 1$ bit pattern, known as a **generator**, which we will denote as G. We will require that the most significant (leftmost) bit of G be a 1. The key idea behind CRC codes is shown in Figure 11.7. For a given piece of data, D, the sender will choose r additional bits, R, and append them to D such that the resulting $d + r$ bit pattern (interpreted as a binary number) is exactly divisible by G using modulo-2 arithmetic. The process of error checking with CRCs is thus simple: The receiver divides the $d + r$ received bits by G. If the remainder is nonzero, the receiver knows that an error has occurred; otherwise the data is accepted as being correct.

All CRC calculations are done in modulo-2 arithmetic without carries in addition or borrows in subtraction. This means that addition and subtraction are identical,

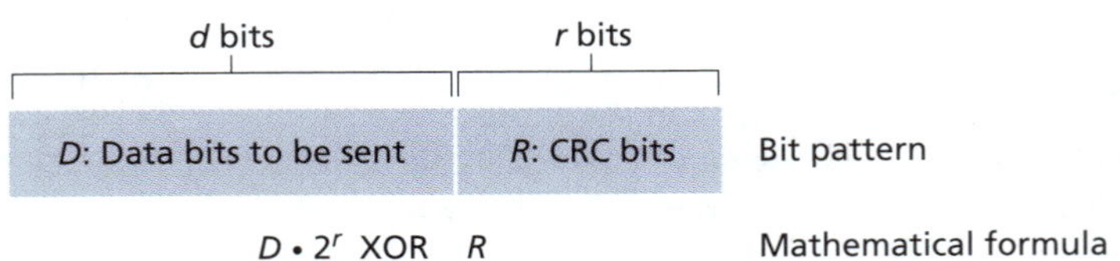

Figure 11.7 ♦ CRC codes

and both are equivalent to the bitwise exclusive-or (XOR) of the operands. Thus, for example,

```
1011 XOR 0101 = 1110
1001 XOR 1101 = 0100
```

Also, we similarly have

```
1011 – 0101 = 1110
1001 – 1101 = 0100
```

Multiplication and division are the same as in base-2 arithmetic, except that any required addition or subtraction is done without carries or borrows. As in regular binary arithmetic, multiplication by 2^k left shifts a bit pattern by k places. Thus, given D and R, the quantity $D \cdot 2^r$ XOR R yields the $d + r$ bit pattern shown in Figure 11.7. We'll use this algebraic characterization of the $d + r$ bit pattern from Figure 11.7 in our discussion below.

Let us now turn to the crucial question of how the sender computes R. Recall that we want to find R such that there is an n such that

$$D \cdot 2^r \text{ XOR } R = nG$$

That is, we want to choose R such that G divides into $D \cdot 2^r$ XOR R without remainder. If we XOR (that is, add modulo-2, without carry) R to both sides of the above equation, we get

$$D \cdot 2^r = nG \text{ XOR } R$$

This equation tells us that if we divide $D \cdot 2^r$ by G, the value of the remainder is precisely R. In other words, we can calculate R as

$$R = \text{remainder}\frac{D \cdot 2^r}{G}$$

Figure 11.8 illustrates this calculation for the case of $D = 101110$, $d = 6$, $G = 1001$, and $r = 3$. The 9 bits transmitted in this case are 101110 011. You should check these calculations for yourself and also check that indeed $D \cdot 2^r = 101011 \cdot G$ XOR R.

International standards have been defined for 8-, 12-, 16-, and 32-bit generators, G. An 8-bit CRC is used to protect the 5-byte header in ATM cells. The CRC-32 32-bit standard, which has been adopted in a number of link-level IEEE protocols, uses a generator of

$$G_{\text{CRC-32}} = 100000100110000010001110110110111$$

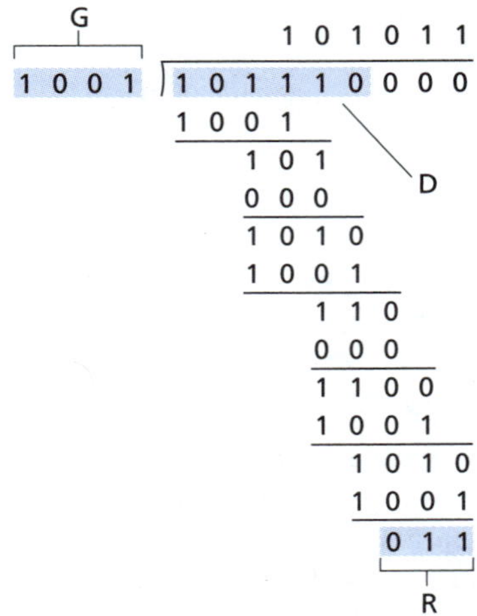

Figure 11.8 ♦ A sample CRC calculation

Each of the CRC standards can detect burst errors of fewer than $r + 1$ bits. (This means that all consecutive bit errors of r bits or fewer will be detected.) Furthermore, under appropriate assumptions, a burst of length greater than $r + 1$ bits is detected with probability $1 - 0.5^r$. Also, each of the CRC standards can detect any odd number of bit errors. The theory behind CRC codes and even more powerful codes is beyond the scope of this text. The text [Schwartz 1980] provides an excellent introduction to this topic.

11.3 Multiple Access Protocols

In the introduction to this chapter, we noted that there are two types of network links: point-to-point links and broadcast links. A **point-to-point link** consists of a single sender at one end of the link and a single receiver at the other end of the link. Many link-layer protocols have been designed for point-to-point links; the point-to-point protocol (PPP) is one such protocol that we'll cover later in this chapter. The second type of link, a **broadcast link**, can have multiple sending and receiving nodes all connected to the same, single, shared broadcast channel. The term *broadcast* is used here because when any one node transmits a frame, the channel broadcasts the frame and each of the other nodes receives a copy. Ethernet and wireless LANs are examples of broadcast link-layer technologies. In this section we'll take a step back from specific link-layer protocols and first examine a problem of central importance to the link layer: how to coordinate the access of multiple sending and receiving nodes to a shared broadcast channel—the **multiple access problem**. Broadcast channels are often used in LANs, networks that are geographically concentrated in a single building (or on a corporate or university campus). Thus, we'll also look at how multiple access channels are used in LANs at the end of this section.

We are all familiar with the notion of broadcasting—television has been using it since its invention. But traditional television is a one-way broadcast (that is, one fixed node transmitting to many receiving nodes), while nodes on a computer network broadcast channel can both send and receive. Perhaps a more apt human analogy for a broadcast channel is a cocktail party, where many people gather in a large room (the air providing the broadcast medium) to talk and listen. A second good analogy is something many readers will be familiar with—a classroom—where teacher(s) and student(s) similarly share the same, single, broadcast medium. A central problem in both scenarios is that of determining who gets to talk (that is, transmit into the channel), and when. As humans, we've evolved an elaborate set of protocols for sharing the broadcast channel:

"Give everyone a chance to speak."

"Don't speak until you are spoken to."

"Don't monopolize the conversation."

"Raise your hand if you have a question."

"Don't interrupt when someone is speaking."

"Don't fall asleep when someone is talking."

Computer networks similarly have protocols—so-called **multiple access protocols**—by which nodes regulate their transmission onto the shared broadcast channel. As shown in Figure 11.9, multiple access protocols are needed in a wide variety of network settings, including both wired and wireless local area networks, and satellite networks. Although technically each node accesses the broadcast channel through its adapter, in this section we will refer to the *node* as the sending and receiving device. In practice, hundreds or even thousands of nodes can directly communicate over a broadcast channel.

Because all nodes are capable of transmitting frames, more than two nodes can transmit frames at the same time. When this happens, all of the nodes receive multiple frames at the same time; that is, the transmitted frames **collide** at all of the receivers. Typically, when there is a collision, none of the receiving nodes can make any sense of any of the frames that were transmitted; in a sense, the signals of the colliding frames become inextricably tangled together. Thus, all the frames involved in the collision are lost, and the broadcast channel is wasted during the collision interval. Clearly, if many nodes want to transmit frames frequently, many transmissions will result in collisions, and much of the bandwidth of the broadcast channel will be wasted.

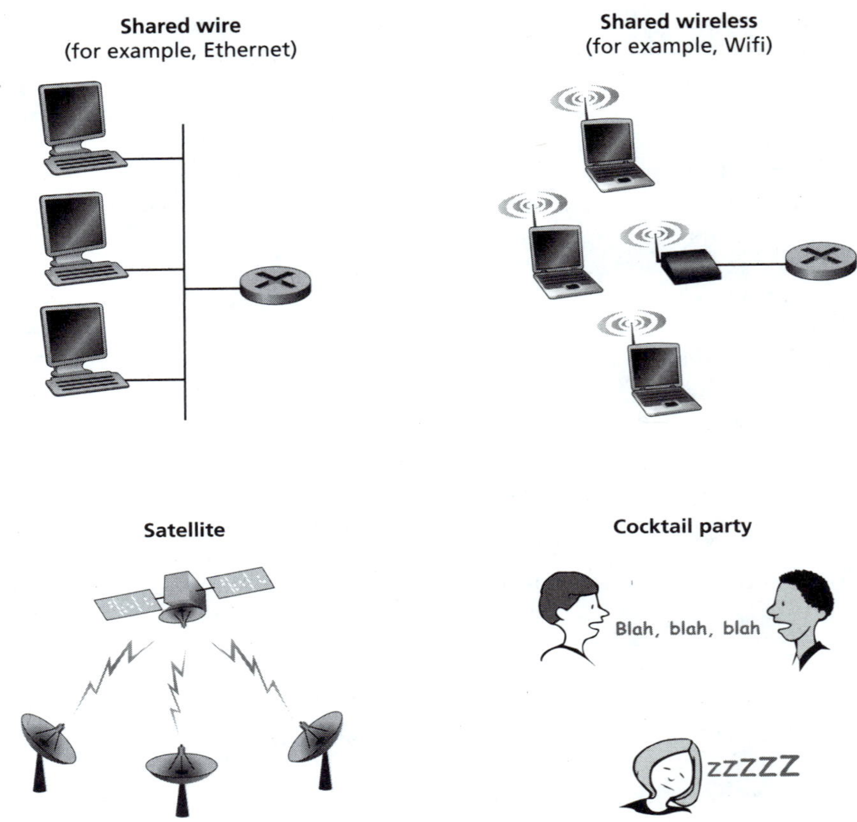

Figure 11.9 ♦ Various multiple access channels

In order to ensure that the broadcast channel performs useful work when multiple nodes are active, it is necessary to somehow coordinate the transmissions of the active nodes. This coordination job is the responsibility of the multiple access protocol. Over the past 30 years, thousands of papers and hundreds of PhD dissertations have been written on multiple access protocols; a comprehensive survey of this body of work is [Rom 1990]. Furthermore, active research in multiple access protocols continues due to the continued emergence of new types of links, particularly new wireless links.

Over the years, dozens of multiple access protocols have been implemented in a variety of link-layer technologies. Nevertheless, we can classify just about any multiple access protocol as belonging to one of three categories: **channel partitioning protocols**, **random access protocols**, and **taking-turns protocols**. We'll cover these categories of multiple access protocols in the following three subsections.

Let us conclude this overview by noting that, ideally, a multiple access protocol for a broadcast channel of rate *R* bits per second should have the following desirable characteristics:

1. When only one node has data to send, that node has a throughput of *R* bps.
2. When *M* nodes have data to send, each of these nodes has a throughput of *R*/*M* bps. This need not necessarily imply that each of the *M* nodes always has an instantaneous rate of *R*/*M*, but rather that each node should have an average transmission rate of *R*/*M* over some suitably defined interval of time.
3. The protocol is decentralized; that is, there are no master nodes that can fail and bring down the entire system.
4. The protocol is simple, so that it is inexpensive to implement.

11.3.1 Channel Partitioning Protocols

Recall from our early discussion that time-division multiplexing (TDM) and frequency-division multiplexing (FDM) are two techniques that can be used to partition a broadcast channel's bandwidth among all nodes sharing that channel. As an example, suppose the channel supports *N* nodes and that the transmission rate of the channel is *R* bps. TDM divides time into **time frames** and further divides each time frame into *N* **time slots**. (The TDM time frame should not be confused with the link-layer unit of data exchanged between sending and receiving adapters, which is also called a frame. In order to reduce confusion, in this subsection we refer to the link-layer unit of data exchanged as a packet.) Each slot time is then assigned to one of the *N* nodes. Whenever a node has a packet to send, it transmits the packet's bits during its assigned time slot in the revolving TDM frame. Typically, slot sizes are chosen so that a single packet can be transmitted during a slot time. Figure 11.10 shows a simple four-node TDM example. Returning to our cocktail party analogy, a TDM-regulated cocktail party would allow one partygoer to speak for a fixed period of time, then allow another partygoer to speak for the same amount of time, and so on. Once everyone had had a chance to talk, the pattern would repeat.

TDM is appealing because it eliminates collisions and is perfectly fair: Each node gets a dedicated transmission rate of *R*/*N* bps during each frame time. However, it has two major drawbacks. First, a node is limited to an average rate of *R*/*N* bps even when it is the only node with packets to send. A second drawback is that a node must always wait for its turn in the transmission sequence—again, even when it is the only node with a frame to send. Imagine the partygoer who is the only one with anything to say (and imagine that this is the even rarer circumstance where everyone at the party wants to hear what that one person has to say). Clearly, TDM would be a poor choice for a multiple access protocol for this particular party.

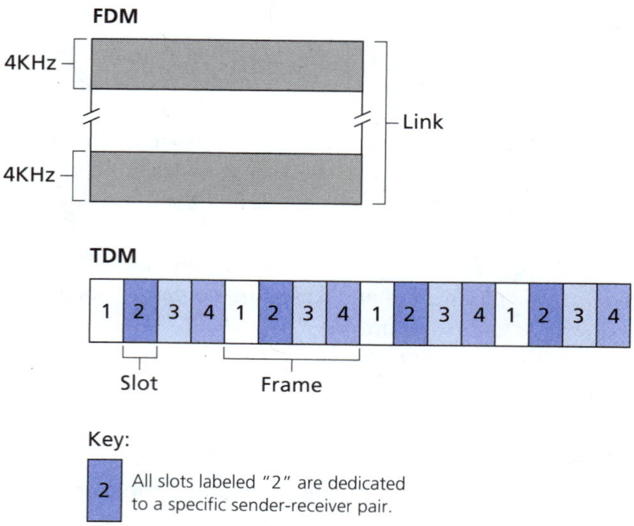

Figure 11.10 ♦ A four-node TDM and FDM example

While TDM shares the broadcast channel in time, FDM divides the R bps channel into different frequencies (each with a bandwidth of R/N) and assigns each frequency to one of the N nodes. FDM thus creates N smaller channels of R/N bps out of the single, larger R bps channel. FDM shares both the advantages and drawbacks of TDM. It avoids collisions and divides the bandwidth fairly among the N nodes. However, FDM also shares a principal disadvantage with TDM—a node is limited to a bandwidth of R/N, even when it is the only node with packets to send.

A third channel-partitioning protocol is **code division multiple access (CDMA)**. While TDM and FDM assign time slots and frequencies, respectively, to the nodes, CDMA assigns a different *code* to each node. Each node then uses its unique code to encode the data bits it sends. If the codes are chosen carefully, CDMA networks have the wonderful property that different nodes can transmit *simultaneously* and yet have their respective receivers correctly receive a sender's encoded data bits (assuming the receiver knows the sender's code) in spite of interfering transmissions by other nodes. CDMA has been used in military systems for some time (due to its anti-jamming properties) and now has widespread civilian use, particularly in wireless multiple access channels. Because CDMA's use is so tightly tied to wireless channels, we'll save our discussion of the technical details of CDMA until Chapter 12. For now, it will suffice to know that CDMA codes, like time slots in TDM and frequencies in FDM, can be allocated to the multiple access channel users.

11.3.2 Random Access Protocols

The second broad class of multiple access protocols are random access protocols. In a random access protocol, a transmitting node always transmits at the full rate of the channel, namely, R bps. When there is a collision, each node involved in the collision repeatedly retransmits its frame (that is, packet) until the frame gets through without a collision. But when a node experiences a collision, it doesn't necessarily retransmit the frame right away. *Instead it waits a random delay before retransmitting the frame*. Each node involved in a collision chooses independent random delays. Because the random delays are independently chosen, it is possible that one of the nodes will pick a delay that is sufficiently less than the delays of the other colliding nodes and will therefore be able to sneak its frame into the channel without a collision.

There are dozens if not hundreds of random access protocols described in the literature [Rom 1990; Bertsekas 1991]. In this section we'll describe a few of the most commonly used random access protocols—the ALOHA protocols [Abramson 1970; Abramson 1985] and the carrier sense multiple access (CSMA) protocols [Kleinrock 1975b]. Later, in Section 11.5, we'll cover the details of Ethernet [Metcalfe 1976], a popular and widely deployed CSMA protocol.

Slotted ALOHA

Let's begin our study of random access protocols with one of the most simple random access protocols, the slotted ALOHA protocol. In our description of slotted ALOHA, we assume the following:

- All frames consist of exactly L bits.
- Time is divided into slots of size L/R seconds (that is, a slot equals the time to transmit one frame).
- Nodes start to transmit frames only at the beginnings of slots.
- The nodes are synchronized so that each node knows when the slots begin.
- If two or more frames collide in a slot, then all the nodes detect the collision event before the slot ends.

Let p be a probability, that is, a number between 0 and 1. The operation of slotted ALOHA in each node is simple:

- When the node has a fresh frame to send, it waits until the beginning of the next slot and transmits the entire frame in the slot.
- If there isn't a collision, the node has successfully transmitted its frame and thus need not consider retransmitting the frame. (The node can prepare a new frame for transmission, if it has one.)

- If there is a collision, the node detects the collision before the end of the slot. The node retransmits its frame in each subsequent slot with probability p until the frame is transmitted without a collision.

By retransmitting with probability p, we mean that the node effectively tosses a biased coin; the event heads corresponds to "retransmit," which occurs with probability p. The event tails corresponds to "skip the slot and toss the coin again in the next slot"; this occurs with probability $(1 - p)$. All nodes involved in the collision toss their coins independently.

Slotted ALOHA would appear to have many advantages. Unlike channel partitioning, slotted ALOHA allows a node to transmit continuously at the full rate, R, when that node is the only active node. (A node is said to be active if it has frames to send.) Slotted ALOHA is also highly decentralized, because each node detects collisions and independently decides when to retransmit. (Slotted ALOHA does, however, require the slots to be synchronized in the nodes; shortly we'll discuss an unslotted version of the ALOHA protocol, as well as CSMA protocols, none of which require such synchronization and are therefore fully decentralized.) Slotted ALOHA is also an extremely simple protocol.

Slotted ALOHA works well when there is only one active node, but how efficient is it when there are multiple active nodes? There are two possible efficiency concerns here. First, as shown in Figure 11.11, when there are multiple active nodes, a certain fraction of the slots will have collisions and will therefore be "wasted." The second concern is that another fraction of the slots will be *empty* because all active nodes refrain from transmitting as a result of the probabilistic transmission policy. The only "unwasted" slots will be those in which exactly one node transmits. A slot in which exactly one node transmits is said to be a **successful slot**. The **efficiency** of a slotted multiple access protocol is defined to be the long-run fraction of successful slots in the case when there are a large number of active nodes, each always having a large number of frames to send. Note that if no form of access control were used, and each node were to immediately retransmit after each collision, the efficiency would be zero. Slotted ALOHA clearly increases the efficiency beyond zero, but by how much?

We now proceed to outline the derivation of the maximum efficiency of slotted ALOHA. To keep this derivation simple, let's modify the protocol a little and assume that each node attempts to transmit a frame in each slot with probability p. (That is, we assume that each node always has a frame to send and that the node transmits with probability p for a fresh frame as well as for a frame that has already suffered a collision.) Suppose there are N nodes. Then the probability that a given slot is a successful slot is the probability that one of the nodes transmits and that the remaining $N - 1$ nodes do not transmit. The probability that a given node transmits is p; the probability that the remaining nodes do not transmit is $(1 - p)^{N-1}$. Therefore the probability a given node has a success is $p(1 - p)^{N-1}$. Because there are N nodes, the probability that an arbitrary node has a success is $Np(1 - p)^{N-1}$.

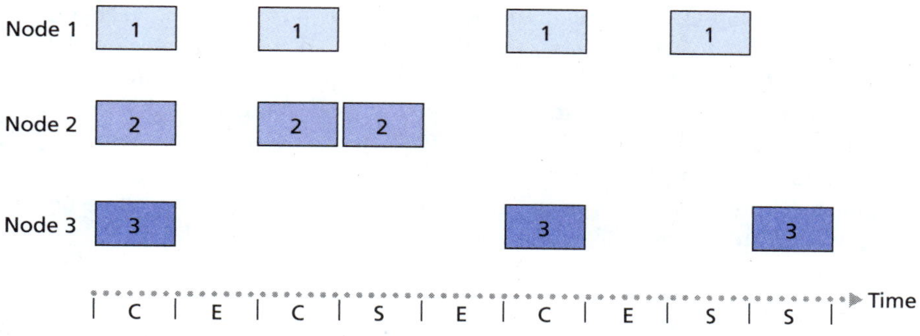

Figure 11.11 ♦ Nodes 1, 2, and 3 collide in the first slot. Node 2 finally succeeds in the fourth slot, node 1 in the eighth slot, and node 3 in the ninth slot.

Thus, when there are N active nodes, the efficiency of slotted ALOHA is $Np(1 - p)^{N-1}$. To obtain the *maximum* efficiency for N active nodes, we have to find the p^* that maximizes this expression. (See the homework problems for a general outline of this derivation.) And to obtain the maximum efficiency for a large number of active nodes, we take the limit of $Np^*(1 - p^*)^{N-1}$ as N approaches infinity. (Again, see the homework problems.) After performing these calculations, we'll find that the maximum efficiency of the protocol is given by $1/e = 0.37$. That is, when a large number of nodes have many frames to transmit, then (at best) only 37 percent of the slots do useful work. Thus the effective transmission rate of the channel is not R bps but only 0.37 R bps! A similar analysis also shows that 37 percent of the slots go empty and 26 percent of slots have collisions. Imagine the poor network administrator who has purchased a 100-Mbps slotted ALOHA system, expecting to be able to use the network to transmit data among a large number of users at an aggregate rate of, say, 80 Mbps! Although the channel is capable of transmitting a given frame at the full channel rate of 100 Mbps, in the long run, the successful throughput of this channel will be less than 37 Mbps.

ALOHA

The slotted ALOHA protocol required that all nodes synchronize their transmissions to start at the beginning of a slot. The first ALOHA protocol [Abramson 1970] was actually an unslotted, fully decentralized protocol. In pure ALOHA, when a frame first arrives (that is, a network-layer datagram is passed down from the network layer at the sending node), the node immediately transmits the frame in its entirety into the broadcast channel. If a transmitted frame experiences a collision with one or more other transmissions, the node will then immediately (after completely transmitting its collided frame) retransmit the frame with probability p. Otherwise, the node waits for a frame transmission time. After this wait, it then transmits the frame with probability p, or waits (remaining idle) for another frame time with probability $1 - p$.

To determine the maximum efficiency of pure ALOHA, we focus on an individual node. We'll make the same assumptions as in our slotted ALOHA analysis and take the frame transmission time to be the unit of time. At any given time, the probability that a node is transmitting a frame is p. Suppose this frame begins transmission at time t_0. As shown in Figure 11.12, in order for this frame to be successfully transmitted, no other nodes can begin their transmission in the interval of time $[t_0 - 1, t_0]$. Such a transmission would overlap with the beginning of the transmission of node i's frame. The probability that all other nodes do not begin a transmission in this interval is $(1 - p)^{N-1}$. Similarly, no other node can begin a transmission while node i is transmitting, as such a transmission would overlap with the latter part of node i's transmission. The probability that all other nodes do not begin a transmission in this interval is also $(1 - p)^{N-1}$. Thus, the probability that a given node has a successful transmission is $p(1 - p)^{2(N-1)}$. By taking limits as in the slotted ALOHA case, we find that the maximum efficiency of the pure ALOHA protocol is only $1/(2e)$—exactly half that of slotted ALOHA. This then is the price to be paid for a fully decentralized ALOHA protocol.

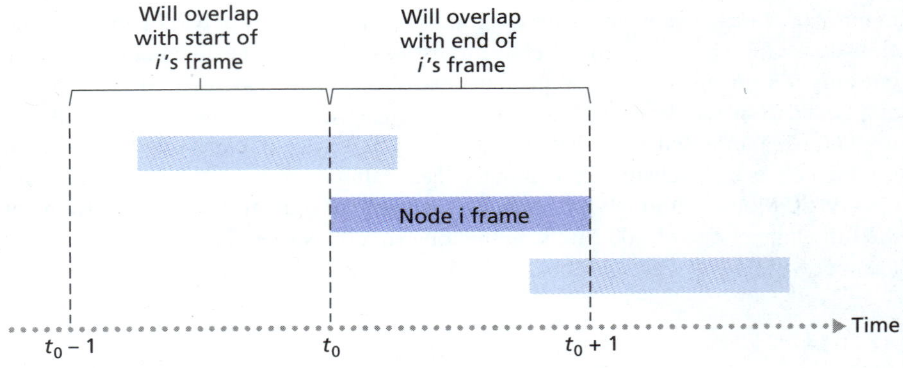

Figure 11.12 ♦ Interfering transmissions in pure ALOHA

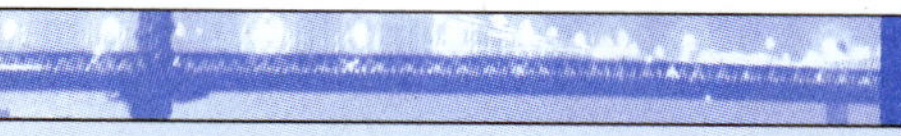

CASE HISTORY

NORM ABRAMSON AND ALOHANET

Norm Abramson, a PhD engineer, had a passion for surfing and an interest in packet switching. This combination of interests brought him to the University of Hawaii in 1969. Hawaii consists of many mountainous islands, making it difficult to install and operate land-based networks. When not surfing, Abramson thought about how to design a network that does packet switching over radio. The network he designed had one central host and several secondary nodes scattered over the Hawaiian Islands. The network had two channels, each using a different frequency band. The downlink channel broadcasted packets from the central host to the secondary hosts; and the upstream channel sent packets from the secondary hosts to the central host. In addition to sending informational packets, the central host also sent on the downstream channel an acknowledgment for each packet successfully received from the secondary hosts.

Because the secondary hosts transmitted packets in a decentralized fashion, collisions on the upstream channel inevitably occurred. This observation led Abramson to devise the pure ALOHA protocol, as described in this chapter. In 1970, with continued funding from ARPA, Abramson connected his ALOHAnet to the ARPAnet. Abramson's work is important not only because it was the first example of a radio packet network, but also because it inspired Bob Metcalfe. A few years after Abramson invented it, Metcalfe modified the ALOHA protocol to create the CSMA/CD protocol and the Ethernet LAN.

Carrier Sense Multiple Access (CSMA)

In both slotted and pure ALOHA, a node's decision to transmit is made independently of the activity of the other nodes attached to the broadcast channel. In particular, a node neither pays attention to whether another node happens to be transmitting when it begins to transmit, nor stops transmitting if another node begins to interfere with its transmission. In our cocktail party analogy, ALOHA protocols are quite like a boorish partygoer who continues to chatter away regardless of whether other people are talking. As humans, we have human protocols that allow us not only to behave with more civility, but also to decrease the amount of time spent "colliding" with each other in conversation and, consequently, to increase the amount of data we exchange in our conversations. Specifically, there are two important rules for polite human conversation:

- *Listen before speaking.* If someone else is speaking, wait until they are finished. In the networking world, this is called **carrier sensing**—a node listens to the channel before transmitting. If a frame from another node is currently being transmitted into the channel, a node then waits ("backs off") a random amount of time and then again senses the channel. If the channel is sensed to be idle, the node then begins frame transmission. Otherwise, the node waits another random amount of time and repeats this process.

- *If someone else begins talking at the same time, stop talking.* In the networking world, this is called **collision detection**—a transmitting node listens to the channel while it is transmitting. If it detects that another node is transmitting an interfering frame, it stops transmitting and uses some protocol to determine when it should next attempt to transmit.

These two rules are embodied in the family of **carrier sense multiple access (CSMA)** and **CSMA with collision detection (CSMA/CD)** protocols [Kleinrock 1975b; Metcalfe 1976; Lam 1980; Rom 1990]. Many variations on CSMA and CSMA/CD have been proposed. You can consult these references for the details of these protocols. We'll study the CSMA/CD scheme used in Ethernet in detail in Section 11.5. Here, we'll consider a few of the most important, and fundamental, characteristics of CSMA and CSMA/CD.

The first question that you might ask about CSMA is why, if all nodes perform carrier sensing, do collisions occur in the first place? After all, a node will refrain from transmitting whenever it senses that another node is transmitting. The answer to the question can best be illustrated using space-time diagrams [Molle 1987]. Figure 11.13 shows a space-time diagram of four nodes (A, B, C, D) attached to a linear broadcast bus. The horizontal axis shows the position of each node in space; the vertical axis represents time.

At time t_0, node B senses the channel is idle, as no other nodes are currently transmitting. Node B thus begins transmitting, with its bits propagating in both directions along the broadcast medium. The downward propagation of B's bits in Figure 11.13 with increasing time indicates that a nonzero amount of time is needed for B's bits actually to propagate (albeit at near the speed of light) along the broadcast medium. At time t_1 ($t_1 > t_0$), node D has a frame to send. Although node B is currently transmitting at time t_1, the bits being transmitted by B have yet to reach D, and thus D senses the channel idle at t_1. In accordance with the CSMA protocol, D thus begins transmitting its frame. A short time later, B's transmission begins to interfere with D's transmission at D. From Figure 11.13, it is evident that the end-to-end **channel propagation delay** of a broadcast channel—the time it takes for a signal to propagate from one of the nodes to another—will play a crucial role in determining its performance. The longer this propagation delay, the larger the chance that a carrier-sensing node is not yet able to sense a transmission that has already begun at another node in the network.

In Figure 11.13, nodes do not perform collision detection; both B and D continue to transmit their frames in their entirety even though a collision has occurred. When a node performs collision detection, it ceases transmission as soon as it

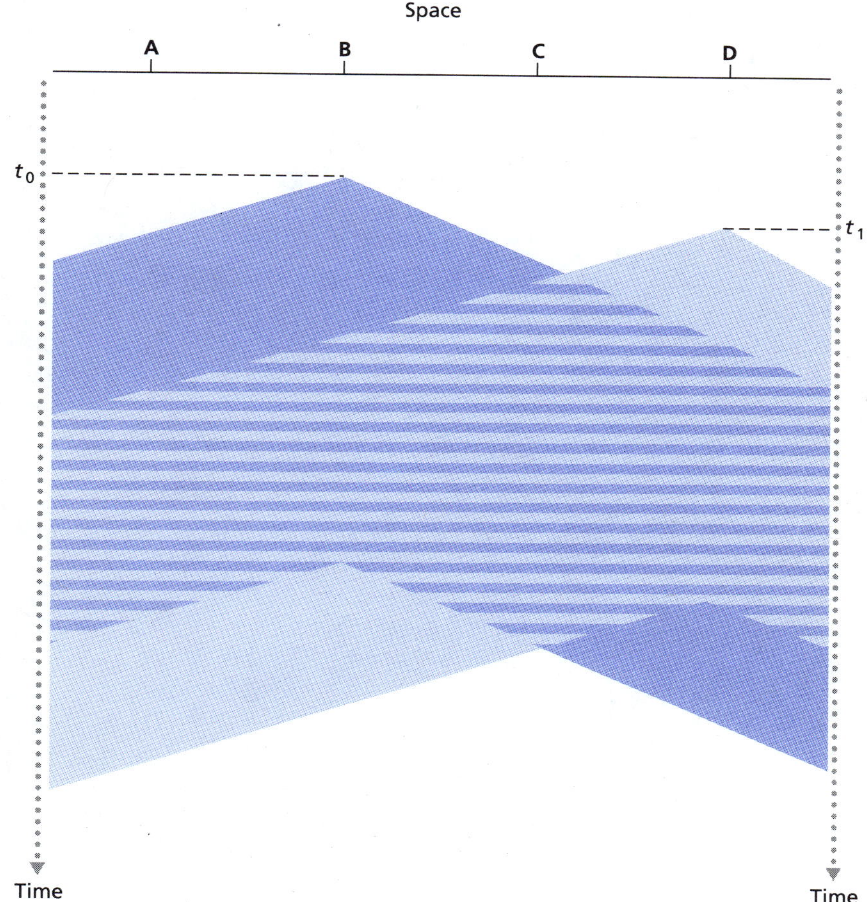

Figure 11.13 ♦ Space-time diagram of two CSMA nodes with colliding transmissions

detects a collision. Figure 11.14 shows the same scenario as in Figure 11.13, except that the two nodes each abort their transmission a short time after detecting a collision. Clearly, adding collision detection to a multiple access protocol will help protocol performance by not transmitting a useless, damaged (by interference with a frame from another node) frame in its entirety. The Ethernet protocol we will study in Section 11.5 is a CSMA protocol that uses collision detection.

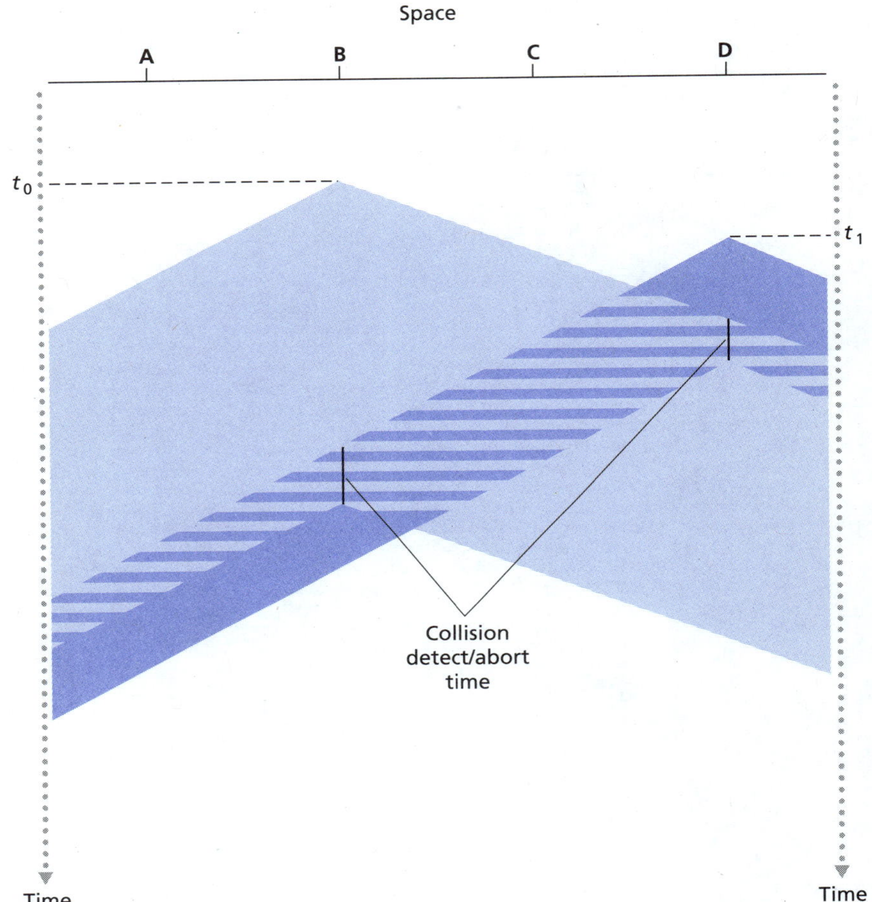

Figure 11.14 ♦ CSMA with collision detection

11.3.3 Taking-Turns Protocols

Recall that two desirable properties of a multiple access protocol are (1) when only one node is active, the active node has a throughput of *R* bps, and (2) when *M* nodes are active, then each active node has a throughput of nearly *R*/*M* bps. The ALOHA and CSMA protocols have this first property but not the second. This has motivated researchers to create another class of protocols—the **taking-turns protocols**. As with random access protocols, there are dozens of taking-turns protocols, and each one of these protocols has many variations. We'll discuss two of the more important protocols here. The first one is the **polling protocol**. The polling protocol requires one of the nodes to be designated as a master node. The master node **polls** each of the nodes in a round-robin fashion. In particular, the master node first sends a message to node 1, saying that it (node 1) can transmit up to some maximum number of frames. After node 1 transmits some frames, the master node tells node 2 it (node 2) can transmit up to the maximum number of frames. (The master node can determine when a node has finished sending its frames by observing the lack of a signal on the channel.) The procedure continues in this manner, with the master node polling each of the nodes in a cyclic manner.

The polling protocol eliminates the collisions and the empty slots that plague the random access protocols. This allows polling to achieve a much higher efficiency. But it also has a few drawbacks. The first drawback is that the protocol introduces a polling delay—the amount of time required to notify a node that it can transmit. If, for example, only one node is active, then the node will transmit at a rate less than R bps, as the master node must poll each of the inactive nodes in turn each time the active node has sent its maximum number of frames. The second drawback, which is potentially more serious, is that if the master node fails, the entire channel becomes inoperative.

The second taking-turn protocol is the **token-passing protocol**. In this protocol there is no master node. A small, special-purpose frame known as a **token** is exchanged among the nodes in some fixed order. For example, node 1 might always send the token to node 2, node 2 might always send the token to node 3, node N might always send the token to node 1. When a node receives a token, it holds onto the token only if it has some frames to transmit; otherwise, it immediately forwards the token to the next node. If a node does have frames to transmit when it receives the token, it sends up to a maximum number of frames and then forwards the token to the next node. Token passing is decentralized and highly efficient. But it has its problems as well. For example, the failure of one node can crash the entire channel. Or if a node accidentally neglects to release the token, then some recovery procedure must be invoked to get the token back in circulation. Over the years many token-passing protocols have been developed, and each one had to address these as well as other sticky issues; we'll mention two of these protocols, FDDI and IEEE 802.5, in the following section.

11.3.4 Local Area Networks (LANs)

Multiple access protocols are used in conjunction with many different types of broadcast channels. They have been used for satellite and wireless channels, whose nodes transmit over a common frequency spectrum. They are currently used in the upstream channel for cable access to the Internet, and they are extensively used in local area networks (LANs).

Recall that a LAN is a computer network concentrated in a geographical area, such as in a building or on a university campus. When a user accesses the Internet from a university or corporate campus, the access is almost always by way of a

LAN—specifically, the access is from host to LAN to router to Internet, as shown in Figure 11.15. The transmission rate, *R*, of most LANs is very high. Even in the early 1980s, 10 Mbps LANs were common; today, 100 Mbps LANs are common, and 1 Gbps and 10 Gbps LANs are available.

In the 1980s and the early 1990s, two classes of LAN technologies were popular in the workplace. The first class consists of the Ethernet LANs (also known as 802.3 LANs [Spurgeon 2004]), which are random-access based. The second class of LAN technologies consists of token-passing technologies, including **token ring** (also known as IEEE 802.5) and **fiber distributed data interface (FDDI)** (Jain 1994). Because we'll explore the Ethernet technologies in some detail in Section 11.5, we focus our discussion here on the token-passing LANs. Our discussion of token-passing technologies is intentionally brief, because relentless Ethernet competition has made these technologies nearly extinct. Nevertheless, in order to provide examples of token-passing technology and to give a little historical perspective, it is useful to say a few words about token rings.

In a token ring LAN, the *N* nodes of the LAN (hosts and routers) are connected in a ring by direct links. The topology of the token ring defines the token-passing order. When a node obtains the token and sends a frame, the frame propagates around the entire ring, thereby creating a virtual broadcast channel. The destination node reads the frame from the link-layer medium as the frame propagates by. The

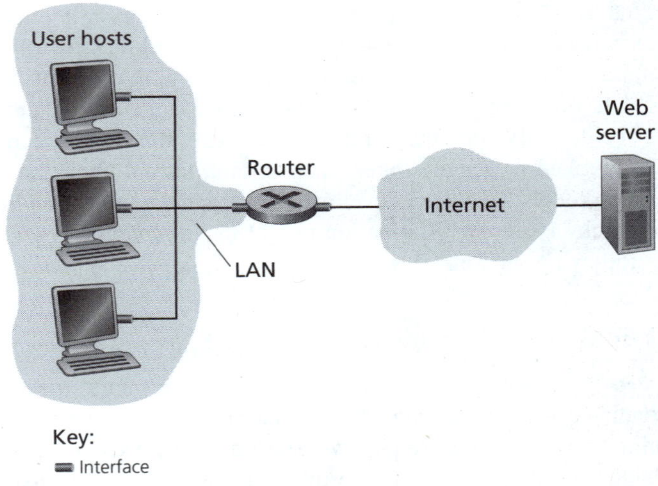

Figure 11.15 ♦ User hosts access an Internet Web server through a LAN. The broadcast channel between a user host and the router consists of one link.

node that sends the frame has the responsibility of removing the frame from the ring. FDDI was designed for geographically larger LANs, including **metropolitan area networks (MANs)**. For geographically large LANs (spread out over several kilometers) it is inefficient to let a frame propagate back to the sending node once the frame has passed the destination node. FDDI has the destination node remove the frame from the ring. (Strictly speaking, FDDI is thus not a pure broadcast channel, as every node does not receive every transmitted frame.)

11.4 Link-Layer Addressing

Nodes—that is hosts and routers—have link-layer addresses. Now you might find this surprising, remembering from Chapter 10 that nodes have network-layer addresses as well. You might be asking, why in the world do we need to have addresses at both the network and link layers? In addition to describing the syntax and function of the link-layer addresses, in this section we hope to shed some light on why the two layers of addresses are useful and, in fact, indispensable.

Additionally, we will cover two critical and address-related topics in this section. The first is the Address Resolution Protocol (ARP), which provides a mechanism for nodes to translate IP addresses to link-layer addresses. The second is Dynamic Host Configuration Protocol (DHCP). We discussed the DHCP service in Chapter 10; here, we'll leverage our knowledge about link-layer addresses to describe how the DHCP service is implemented.

11.4.1 MAC Addresses

In truth, it is not a node (that is, host or router) that has a link-layer address but instead a node's adapter that has a link-layer address. This is illustrated in Figure 11.16. A link-layer address is variously called a **LAN address**, a **physical address,** or a **MAC address**. Because MAC address seems to be the most popular term, we'll henceforth refer to link-layer addresses as MAC addresses. For most LANs (including Ethernet and 802.11 wireless LANs), the MAC address is 6 bytes long, giving 2^{48} possible MAC addresses. As shown in Figure 11.16, these 6-byte addresses are typically expressed in hexadecimal notation, with each byte of the address expressed as a pair of hexadecimal numbers. An important fact about MAC addresses is that they are permanent—when an adapter is manufactured, a MAC address is burned into the adapter's ROM.

One interesting property of MAC addresses is that no two adapters have the same address. This might seem surprising given that adapters are manufactured in many countries by many companies. How does a company manufacturing adapters in Taiwan make sure that it is using different addresses from a company manufacturing adapters in Belgium? The answer is that the IEEE manages the MAC address

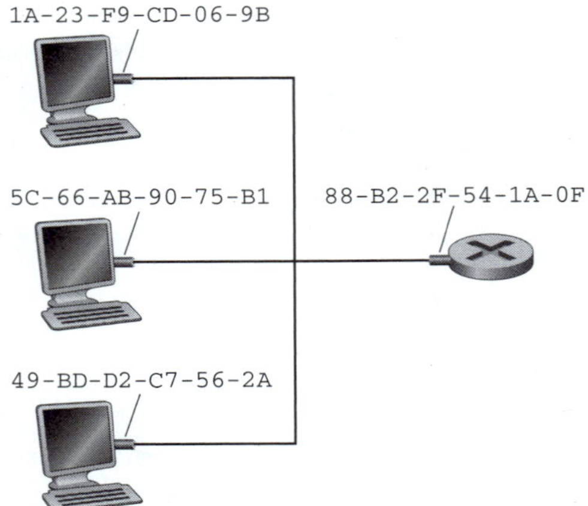

Figure 11.16 ♦ Each adapter connected to a LAN has a unique MAC address.

space. In particular, when a company wants to manufacture adapters, it purchases a chunk of the address space consisting of 2^{24} addresses for a nominal fee. IEEE allocates the chunk of 2^{24} addresses by fixing the first 24 bits of a MAC address and letting the company create unique combinations of the last 24 bits for each adapter.

An adapter's MAC address has a flat structure (as opposed to a hierarchical structure) and doesn't change no matter where the adapter goes. A portable computer with an Ethernet card always has the same MAC address, no matter where the computer goes. A PDA with an 802.11 interface always has the same MAC address, no matter where the PDA goes. Recall that, in contrast, an IP address has a hierarchical structure (that is, a network part and a host part), and a node's IP address needs to be changed when the host moves. An adapter's MAC address is analogous to a person's social security number, which also has a flat addressing structure and which doesn't change no matter where the person goes. An IP address is analogous to a person's postal address, which is hierarchical and which needs to be changed whenever a person moves. Just as a person may find it useful to have both a postal address and a Social Security number, it is useful for a node to have both a network-layer address and a MAC address.

As we described at the beginning of this section, when an adapter wants to send a frame to some destination adapter, the sending adapter inserts the destination adapter's MAC address into the frame and then sends the frame into the LAN. If the LAN is a broadcast LAN (such as 802.11 and many Ethernet LANs), the frame is received and processed by all other adapters on the LAN. In particular, each adapter that receives the frame will check to see whether destination MAC address in the frame matches its own MAC address. If there is a match, the adapter extracts the

PRINCIPLES IN PRACTICE

KEEPING THE LAYERS INDEPENDENT

There are several reasons why nodes have MAC addresses in addition to network-layer addresses. First, LANs are designed for arbitrary network-layer protocols, not just for IP and the Internet. If adapters were assigned IP addresses rather than "neutral" MAC addresses, then adapters would not easily be able to support other network-layer protocols (for example, IPX or DECnet). Second, if adapters were to use network-layer addresses instead of MAC addresses, the network-layer address would have to be stored in the adapter RAM and reconfigured every time the adapter was moved (or powered up). Another option is not to use any addresses in the adapters and have each adapter pass the data (typically, an IP datagram) of each frame it receives up the protocol stack to its parent node. The parent node could then check for a matching network-layer address. One problem with this option is that the parent node would be interrupted by every frame sent on the LAN, including by frames that were destined for other nodes on the same broadcast LAN. In summary, in order for the layers to be largely independent building blocks in a network architecture, many layers need to have their own addressing scheme. We have now seen three types of addresses: host names for the application layer, IP addresses for the network layer, and MAC addresses for the link layer.

enclosed datagram and passes the datagram up the protocol stack to its parent node. If there isn't a match, the adapter discards the frame, without passing the network-layer datagram up the protocol stack. Thus, only the adaptor in the destination node will interrupt its parent node when it receives a frame.

However, sometimes a sending adapter *does* want all the other adapters on the LAN to receive and *process* the frame it is about to send. In this case, the sending adapter inserts a special MAC **broadcast address** into the destination address field of the frame. For LANs that use 6-byte addresses (such as Ethernet and token-passing LANs), the broadcast address is a string of 48 consecutive 1s (that is, FF-FF-FF-FF-FF-FF in hexadecimal notation).

11.4.2 Address Resolution Protocol (ARP)

Because there are both network-layer addresses (for example, Internet IP addresses) and link-layer addresses (that is, MAC addresses), there is a need to translate between them. For the Internet, this is the job of the **address resolution protocol (ARP)** [RFC 826].

To understand the need for a protocol such as ARP, consider the network shown in Figure 11.17. In this simple example, each node has a single IP address, and each node's adapter has a single MAC address. As usual, IP addresses are shown in dotted-decimal notation and MAC addresses are shown in hexadecimal notation. Now suppose that the node with IP address 222.222.222.220 wants to send an IP datagram to node 222.222.222.222. (For example, destination node 222.222.222.222 may be a Web server, and the sending node 222.222.222.220 may have determined the Web server's IP address from DNS.) In this example, both the source and destination nodes are in the same network (LAN). To send a datagram, the source node must give its adapter not only the IP datagram but also the MAC address for destination node 222.222.222.222. Given the IP datagram and the MAC address, the sending node's adapter will construct a link-layer frame containing the destination node's MAC address and send the frame into the LAN.

The important question addressed in this section is, How does the sending node determine the MAC address for the destination node with IP address 222.222.222.222? As you might have guessed, it uses ARP. An ARP module in the sending node takes as input any IP address on the same LAN and returns the corresponding MAC address. In the example at hand, the sending node 222.222.222.220 provides its ARP module the IP address 222.222.222.222, and the ARP module returns the corresponding MAC address 49-BD-D2-C7-56-2A.

So we see that ARP resolves an IP address to a MAC address. In many ways it is analogous to DNS, which resolves hostnames to IP addresses. However, one important difference between the two resolvers is that DNS resolves hostnames for hosts anywhere in the Internet, whereas ARP resolves IP addresses only for nodes

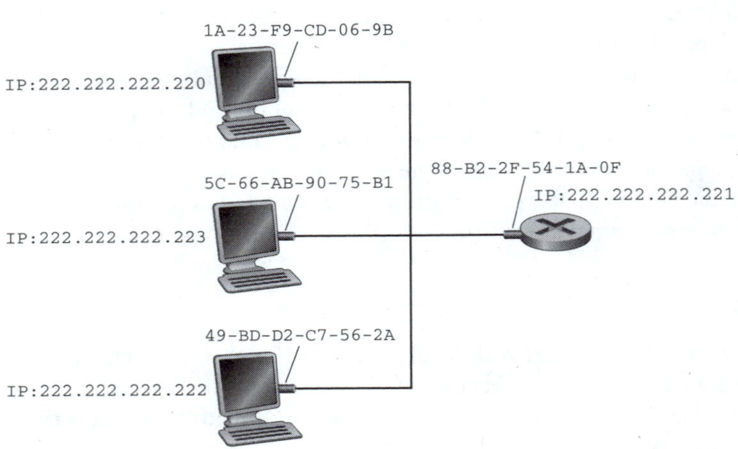

Figure 11.17 ♦ Each node on a LAN has an IP address, and each node's adapter has a MAC address.

IP Address	MAC Address	TTL
222.222.222.221	88-B2-2F-54-1A-0F	13:45:00
222.222.222.223	5C-66-AB-90-75-B1	13:52:00

Figure 11.18 ♦ A possible ARP table in node 222.222.222.220

on the same subnet. If a node in California were to try to use ARP to resolve the IP address for a node in Mississippi, ARP would return with an error.

Now that we have explained what ARP does, let's look at how it works. Each node (host or router) has in its RAM an **ARP table**, which contains mappings of IP addresses to MAC addresses. Figure 11.18 shows what an ARP table in node 222.222.222.220 might look like. The ARP table also contains a time-to-live (TTL) value, which indicates when each mapping will be deleted from the table. Note that the table does not necessarily contain an entry for every node on the subnet; some nodes may have had entries that have expired, whereas other nodes may never have been entered into the table. A typical expiration time for an entry is 20 minutes from when an entry is placed in an ARP table.

Now suppose that node 222.222.222.220 wants to send a datagram that is IP-addressed to another node on that subnet. The sending node needs to obtain the MAC address of the destination node, given the IP address of that node. This task is easy if the sending node's ARP table has an entry for the destination node. But what if the ARP table doesn't currently have an entry for the destination node? In particular, suppose node 222.222.222.220 wants to send a datagram to node 222.222.222.222. In this case, the sending node uses the ARP protocol to resolve the address. First, the sending node constructs a special packet called an **ARP packet**. An ARP packet has several fields, including the sending and receiving IP and MAC addresses. Both ARP query and response packets have the same format. The purpose of the ARP query packet is to query all the other nodes on the subnet to determine the MAC address corresponding to the IP address that is being resolved.

Returning to our example, node 222.222.222.220 passes an ARP query packet to the adapter along with an indication that the adapter should send the packet to the MAC broadcast address, namely, FF-FF-FF-FF-FF-FF. The adapter encapsulates the ARP packet in a link-layer frame, uses the broadcast address for the frame's destination address, and transmits the frame into the subnet. Recalling our Social Security number/postal address analogy, note that an ARP query is equivalent to a person shouting out in a crowded room of cubicles in some company (say, AnyCorp): "What is the Social Security number of the person whose postal address is Cubicle 13, Room 112, AnyCorp, Palo Alto, California?" The frame containing the ARP query is received by all the other adapters on the subnet, and (because of the broadcast address) each adapter passes the ARP packet within the frame up to its parent node. Each node checks to see if its IP address matches the destination IP address in the ARP packet. The (at most) one node with a match sends back to the querying node a response ARP packet with the desired mapping. The querying node 222.222.222.220 can then update its ARP table and send its IP datagram.

There are a couple of interesting things to note about the ARP protocol. First, the query ARP message is sent within a broadcast frame, whereas the response ARP message is sent within a standard frame. Before reading on you should think about why this is so. Second, ARP is plug-and-play; that is, a node's ARP table gets built automatically—it doesn't have to be configured by a system administrator. And if a node becomes disconnected from the subnet, its entry is eventually deleted from the tables of the nodes remaining in the subnet.

Sending a Datagram to a Node Off the Subnet

It should now be clear how ARP operates when a node wants to send a datagram to another node *on the same subnet.* (Subnets are precisely defined in Section 10.4.2.) But now let's look at the more complicated situation when a node on a subnet wants to send a network-layer datagram to a node *off the subnet* (that is, across a router onto another subnet). Let us discuss this issue in the context of Figure 11.19, which shows a simple network consisting of two subnets interconnected by a router.

There are several interesting things to note about Figure 11.19. First, there are two types of nodes: hosts and routers. Each host has exactly one IP address and one adapter. But, as discussed in Chapter 10, a router has an IP address for *each* of its interfaces. For each router interface there is also an ARP module (in the router) and an adapter. Because the router in Figure 11.19 has two interfaces, it has two IP addresses, two ARP modules, and two adapters. Of course, each adapter in the network has its own MAC address.

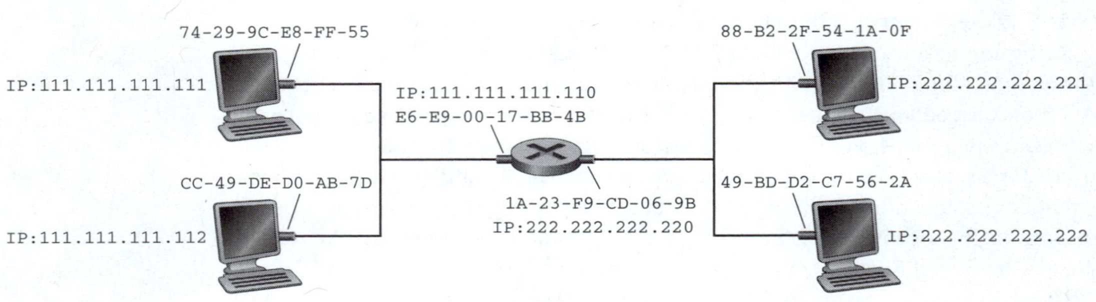

Figure 11.19 ♦ Two subnets interconnected by a router

Also note that Subnet 1 has the network address 111.111.111/24 and that Subnet 2 has the network address 222.222.222/24. Thus all of the interfaces connected to Subnet 1 have addresses of the form 111.111.111.xxx and all of the interfaces connected to Subnet 2 have the form 222.222.222.xxx.

Now let us examine how a host on Subnet 1 would send a datagram to a host on Subnet 2. Specifically, suppose that host 111.111.111.111 wants to send an IP datagram to a host 222.222.222.222. The sending host passes the datagram to its adapter, as usual. But the sending host must also indicate to its adapter an appropriate destination MAC address. What MAC address should the adapter use? One might be tempted to guess that the appropriate MAC address is that of the adapter for host 222.222.222.222, namely, 49-BD-D2-C7-56-2A. This guess, however, would be wrong. If the sending adapter were to use that MAC address, then none of the adapters on Subnet 1 would bother to pass the IP datagram up to its network layer, since the frame's destination address would not match the MAC address of any adapter on Subnet 1. The datagram would just die and go to datagram heaven.

If we look carefully at Figure 11.19, we see that in order for a datagram to go from 111.111.111.111 to a node on Subnet 2, the datagram must first be sent to the router interface 111.111.111.110. Thus, the appropriate MAC address for the frame is the address of the adapter for router interface 111.111.111.110, namely, E6-E9-00-17-BB-4B. How does the sending host acquire the MAC address for 111.111.111.110? By using ARP, of course! Once the sending adapter has this MAC address, it creates a frame and sends the frame into Subnet 1. The router adapter on Subnet 1 sees that the link-layer frame is addressed to it, and therefore passes the frame to the network layer of the router. Hooray! The IP datagram has successfully been moved from source host to the router! But we are not finished. We still have to move the datagram from the router to the destination. The router now has to determine the correct interface on which the datagram is to be forwarded. As discussed in Chapter 10, this is done by consulting a forwarding table in the router. The forwarding table tells the router that the datagram is to be forwarded via router interface 222.222.222.220. This interface then passes the datagram to its adapter, which encapsulates the datagram in a new frame and sends the frame into Subnet 2. This time, the destination MAC address of the frame is indeed the MAC address of the ultimate destination. And how does the router obtain this destination MAC address? From ARP, of course!

ARP for Ethernet is defined in RFC 826. A nice introduction to ARP is given in the TCP/IP tutorial, RFC 1180. We'll explore ARP in more detail in the homework problems.

11.4.3 Dynamic Host Configuration Protocol

In Chapter 10, when discussing IP addresses, we briefly considered the service provided by DHCP, a protocol that is extensively used in corporate, university, and home-network LANs to dynamically assign IP addresses to hosts. Having described the service in Chapter 10, we'll now use our newly acquired knowledge about MAC addresses to describe how DHCP actually works.

DHCP is a client-server protocol. A client is typically a newly arriving host wanting to obtain network configuration information, including an IP address for itself. In the simplest case, each subnet (in the addressing sense described in Section 10.4.2) will have a DHCP server. If no server is present on the subnet, a DHCP relay agent (typically a router) that knows the address of a DHCP server for that network is needed. Figure 11.20 shows a DHCP server attached to subnet 223.1.2/24, with the router serving as the relay agent for arriving clients attached to subnets 223.1.1/24 and 223.1.3/24.

For a newly arriving host, the DHCP protocol is a four-step process:

- *DHCP server discovery.* The first task of a newly arriving host is to find a DHCP server with which to interact. This is done using a **DHCP discover message**, which a client sends within a UDP packet to port 67. The UDP packet is encapsulated in an IP datagram. But to whom should this datagram be sent? The host doesn't even know the IP address of the network to which it is attaching, much less the address of a DHCP server for this network. Given this, the DHCP client

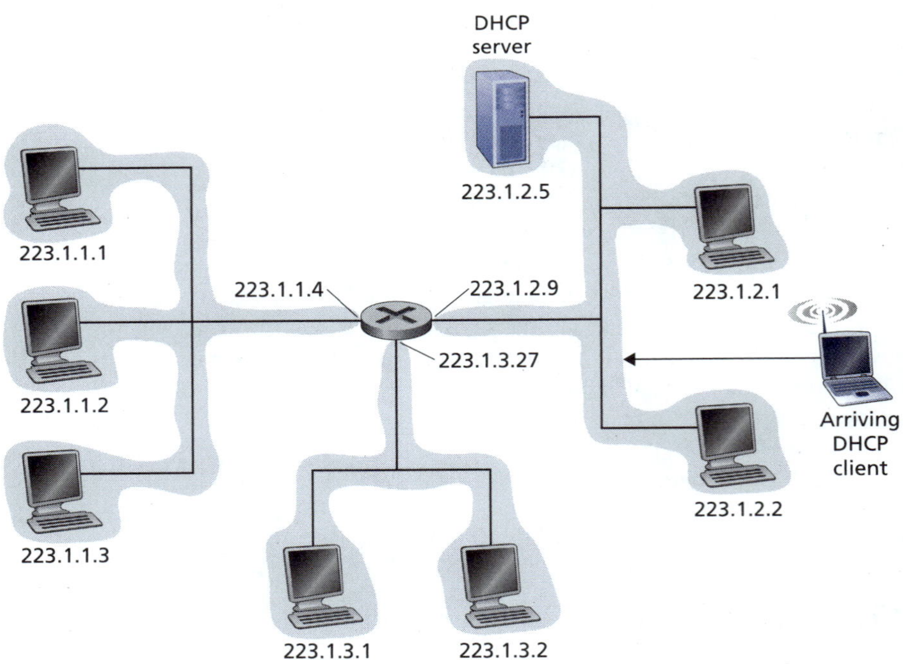

Figure 11.20 ♦ DHCP client-server scenario

creates an IP datagram containing its DHCP discover message along with the broadcast destination IP address of 255.255.255.255 and a "this host" source IP address of 0.0.0.0. The DHCP client passes the IP datagram to its adapter, which encapsulates the datagram in a link-layer frame. This link-layer frame includes the MAC broadcast address (FF-FF-FF-FF-FF-FF) in the destination address field. The DHCP client then sends the broadcast frame, containing the discovery message, into the subnet. This broadcast frame will be received by all adapters on the network. If a DHCP server is attached to the same subnet, it will process the encapsulated discovery message (see below); if a DHCP relay agent is attached to the subnet, it will forward the frame to the network with a DHCP server. (This relayed frame will have a different source MAC address.) The discovery message contains a transaction ID that allows subsequent responses to be matched to the discovery request.

- *DHCP server offer(s).* A DHCP server receiving a DHCP discover message responds to the client with a **DHCP offer message**. Since several DHCP servers can be present on the subnet, the client may find itself in the enviable position of being able to choose from among several offers. Each server offer message contains the transaction ID of the received discover message, the proposed IP address for the client, the network mask, and an IP **address lease time**—the amount of time for which the IP address will be valid. It is common for the server to set the lease time to several hours or days [Droms 1999]. The link-layer frame containing the IP datagram containing the UDP segment containing the DHCP offer message is then sent to the arriving client.
- *DHCP request.* The newly arriving client will choose from among one or more server offers and respond to its selected offer with a DHCP request message, echoing back the configuration parameters.
- *DHCP ACK.* The server responds to the DHCP request message with a DHCP ACK message, confirming the requested parameters.

Once the client receives the DHCP ACK, the interaction is complete and the client can use the DHCP-allocated IP address for the lease duration. Since a client may want to use its address beyond the lease's expiration, DHCP also provides a mechanism that allows a client to renew its lease on an IP address.

A simple DHCP client-server interaction is shown in Figure 11.21 for the network setting shown in Figure 11.20. In this figure, `yiaddr` (as in "your Internet address") indicates the address being allocated to the newly arriving client.

The value of DHCP's plug-and-play capability is clear. Consider the student who moves from classroom to library to dorm room with a laptop, joins a new subnet, and thus obtains a new IP address at each location. It is unimaginable that a system administrator would have to reconfigure laptops at each location, and few students (except those taking a computer networking class!) would have the expertise to configure

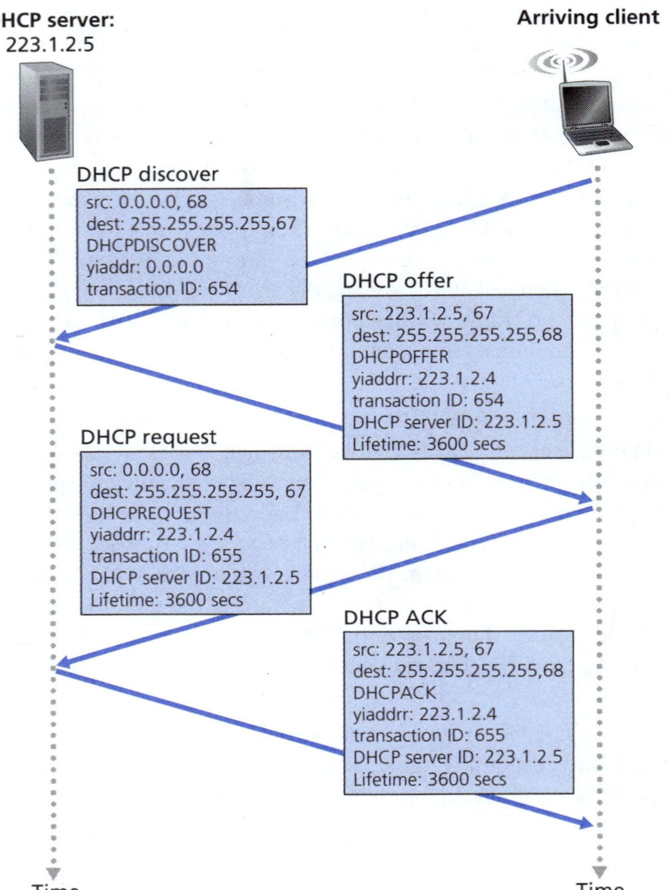

Figure 11.21 ♦ DHCP client-server interaction

their laptops manually. From a mobility aspect, however, DHCP does have shortcomings. Since a new IP address is obtained from DHCP each time a node connects to a new subnet, a connection to a remote application cannot be maintained as a mobile node moves between subnets. We will examine mobile IP—a recent extension to the IP infrastructure that allows a mobile node to use its single permanent address as it moves between subnets—in Chapter 12.

Additional details about DHCP can be found in [Droms 1999] and [dhc 2004]. An open source reference implementation of DHCP is available from the Internet Systems Consortium [ISC 2004].

11.5 Ethernet

Ethernet has pretty much taken over the wired LAN market. In the 1980s and the early 1990s, Ethernet faced many challenges from other LAN technologies, including token ring, FDDI, and ATM. Some of these other technologies succeeded in capturing a part of the LAN market for a few years. But since its invention in the mid-1970s, Ethernet has continued to evolve and grow and has held on to its dominant position. Today, Ethernet is by far the most prevalent wired LAN technology, and it is likely to remain so for the foreseeable future. One might say that Ethernet has been to local area networking what the Internet has been to global networking.

There are many reasons for Ethernet's success. First, Ethernet was the first widely deployed high-speed LAN. Because it was deployed early, network administrators became intimately familiar with Ethernet—its wonders and its quirks—and were reluctant to switch over to other LAN technologies when they came on the scene. Second, token ring, FDDI, and ATM were more complex and expensive than Ethernet, which further discouraged network administrators from switching over. Third, the most compelling reason to switch to another LAN technology (such as FDDI or ATM) was usually the higher data rate of the new technology; however, Ethernet always fought back, producing versions that operated at equal data rates or higher. Switched Ethernet was also introduced in the early 1990s, which further increased its effective data rates. Finally, because Ethernet has been so popular, Ethernet hardware (in particular, adapters, hubs, and switches) has become a commodity and is remarkably cheap.

The original Ethernet LAN was invented in the mid-1970s by Bob Metcalfe and David Boggs. Figure 11.22 shows Metcalfe's schematic for Ethernet. In this figure

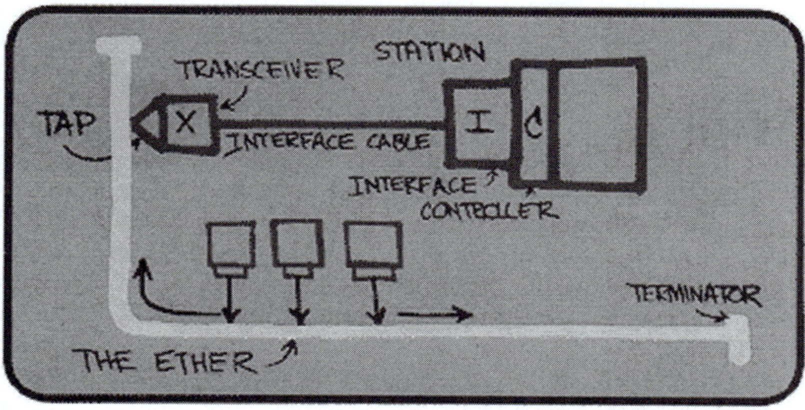

Figure 11.22 ♦ The original Metcalfe design led to the 10Base5 Ethernet standard, which included an interface cable that connected the Ethernet adapter to an external transceiver.

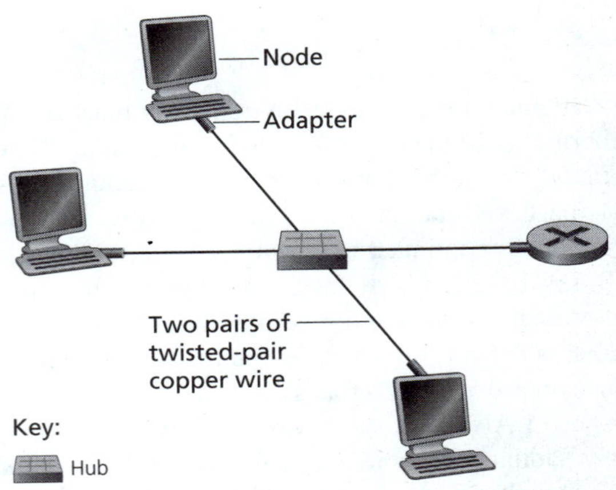

Figure 11.23 ♦ Star topology for Ethernet. Nodes are interconnected with a hub.

you'll notice that the original Ethernet LAN used a bus to interconnect the nodes. This bus topology actually persisted throughout the 1980s and much of the 1990s; in particular, the Ethernet 10Base2 technology, using a thin coaxial cable for the bus, was immensely popular in the 1990s. However, except for an occasional legacy installation, almost all Ethernet installations today use a star topology, as shown in Figure 11.23. At the center of the star topology is a **hub** or a **switch**. We'll discuss hubs and switches in some detail soon. An excellent source of online information about Ethernet is Spurgeon's Ethernet Web site [Spurgeon 2004].

11.5.1 Ethernet Frame Structure

The Ethernet frame is shown in Figure 11.24. We can learn a lot about Ethernet by examining the Ethernet frame. To give this discussion about Ethernet frames a tangible context, let's consider sending an IP datagram from one host to another host, with both hosts on the same Ethernet LAN (for example, the Ethernet LAN in Figure 11.23.) Although the payload of our Ethernet frame is an IP datagram, we note in passing that an Ethernet frame can carry other network-layer packets as well. Let the sending adapter, adapter A, have the MAC address AA-AA-AA-AA-AA-AA and the receiving adapter, adapter B, have the MAC address BB-BB-BB-BB-BB-BB. The sending adapter encapsulates the IP datagram within an Ethernet frame and passes the frame to the physical layer. The receiving adapter receives the frame from the physical layer, extracts the IP datagram, and passes the IP datagram to the network layer. In this context, let us now examine the six fields of the Ethernet frame, as shown in Figure 11.24.

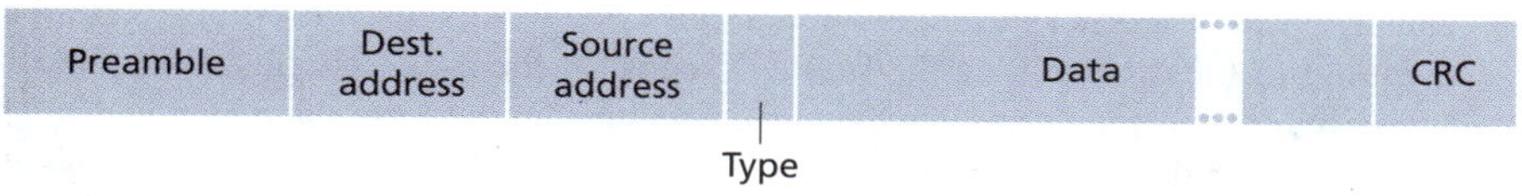

Figure 11.24 ♦ Ethernet frame structure

- *Data Field (46 to 1,500 bytes).* This field carries the IP datagram. The maximum transfer unit (MTU) of Ethernet is 1,500 bytes. This means that if the IP datagram exceeds 1,500 bytes, then the host has to fragment the datagram, as discussed in Section 10.4.1. The minimum size of the data field is 46 bytes. This means that if the IP datagram is less than 46 bytes, the data field has to be "stuffed" to fill it out to 46 bytes. When stuffing is used, the data passed to the network layer contains the stuffing as well as an IP datagram. The network layer uses the length field in the IP datagram header to remove the stuffing.
- *Destination Address (6 bytes).* This field contains the MAC address of the destination adapter, BB-BB-BB-BB-BB-BB. When adapter B receives an Ethernet frame whose destination address is either BB-BB-BB-BB-BB-BB or the MAC broadcast address, it passes the contents of the frame's data field to the network layer; if it receives a frame with any other MAC address, it discards the frame.
- *Source Address (6 bytes).* This field contains the MAC address of the adapter that transmits the frame onto the LAN, in this example, AA-AA-AA-AA-AA-AA.
- *Type Field (2 bytes).* The type field permits Ethernet to multiplex network-layer protocols. To understand this, we need to keep in mind that hosts can use other network-layer protocols besides IP. In fact, a given host may support multiple network-layer protocols using different protocols for different applications. For this reason, when the Ethernet frame arrives at adapter B, adapter B needs to know to which network-layer protocol it should pass (that is, demultiplex) the contents of the data field. IP and other network-layer protocols (for example, Novell IPX or AppleTalk) each have their own, standardized type number. Furthermore, the ARP protocol (discussed in the previous section) has its own type number. Note that the type field is analogous to the protocol field in the network-layer datagram and the port-number fields in the transport-layer segment; all of these fields serve to glue a protocol at one layer to a protocol at the layer above.
- *Cyclic Redundancy Check (CRC) (4 bytes).* As discussed in Section 11.2.3, the purpose of the CRC field is to allow the receiving adapter, adapter B, to detect whether any errors have been introduced into the frame, that is, if bits in the frame have been toggled. Causes of bit errors include attenuation in signal strength and ambient electromagnetic energy that leaks into the Ethernet cables and interface cards. Error detection is performed as follows. When host A

constructs the Ethernet frame, it calculates a CRC field, which is obtained from a mapping of the other bits in the frame (except for the preamble bits). When host B receives the frame, it applies the same mapping to the frame and checks to see if the result of the mapping is equal to what is in the CRC field. This operation at the receiving host is called the **CRC check**. If the CRC check fails (that is, if the result of the mapping does not equal the contents of the CRC field), then host B knows that there is an error in the frame.

- *Preamble (8 bytes).* The Ethernet frame begins with an 8-byte preamble field. Each of the first 7 bytes of the preamble has a value of 10101010; the last byte is 10101011. The first 7 bytes of the preamble serve to "wake up" the receiving adapters and to synchronize their clocks to that of the sender's clock. Why should the clocks be out of synchronization? Keep in mind that adapter A aims to transmit the frame at 10 Mbps, 100 Mbps, or 1 Gbps, depending on the type of Ethernet LAN. However, because nothing is absolutely perfect, adapter A will not transmit the frame at exactly the target rate; there will always be some *drift* from the target rate, a drift which is not known *a priori* by the other adapters on the LAN. A receiving adapter can lock onto adapter A's clock simply by locking onto the bits in the first 7 bytes of the preamble. The last 2 bits of the eighth byte of the preamble (the first two consecutive 1s) alert adapter B that the "important stuff" is about to come. When host B sees the two consecutive 1s, it knows that the next 6 bytes are the destination address. An adapter can tell when a frame ends by simply detecting absence of current.

Ethernet uses baseband transmission; that is, the adapter sends a digital signal directly into the broadcast channel. The interface card does not shift the signal into another frequency band, as is done in ADSL and cable modem systems. Many Ethernet technologies (e.g., 10BaseT) also use Manchester encoding, as shown in Figure 11.25. With Manchester encoding, each bit contains a transition; a 1 has a transition from up to down, whereas a 0 has a transition from down to up. The reason for Manchester encoding is that the clocks in the sending and receiving adapters are not perfectly synchronized. By including a transition in the middle of each bit, the receiving host can synchronize its clock to that of the sending host. Once the receiving adapter's clock is synchronized, the receiver can delineate each bit and determine whether it is a 1 or 0. Manchester encoding is a physical-layer operation rather than a link-layer operation; however, we have briefly described it here because it is used extensively in Ethernet.

An Unreliable Connectionless Service

All of the Ethernet technologies provide **connectionless service** to the network layer. That is, when adapter A wants to send a datagram to adapter B, adapter A encapsulates the datagram in an Ethernet frame and sends the frame into the LAN, without first handshaking with adapter B. This layer-2 connectionless service is analogous to IP's layer-3 datagram service and UDP's layer-4 connectionless service.

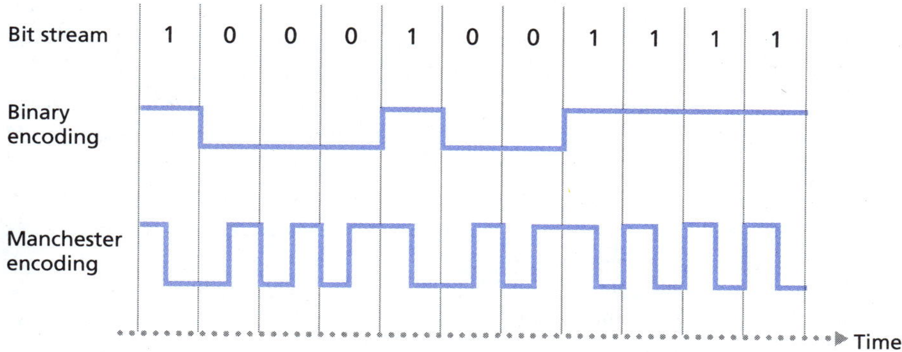

Figure 11.25 ♦ Manchester encoding

CASE HISTORY

BOB METCALFE AND ETHERNET

As a PhD student at Harvard University in the early 1970s, Bob Metcalfe worked on the ARPAnet at MIT. During his studies, he also became exposed to Abramson's work on ALOHA and random access protocols. After completing his PhD and just before beginning a job at Xerox Palo Alto Research Center (Xerox PARC), he visited Abramson and his University of Hawaii colleagues for three months, getting a first-hand look at ALOHAnet. At Xerox PARC, Metcalfe became exposed to Alto computers, which in many ways were the forerunners of the personal computers of the 1980s. Metcalfe saw the need to network these computers in an inexpensive manner. So armed with his knowledge about ARPAnet, ALOHAnet, and random access protocols, Metcalfe—along with colleague David Boggs—invented Ethernet.

Metcalfe and Boggs's original Ethernet ran at 2.94 Mbps and linked up to 256 hosts separated by up to one mile. Metcalfe and Boggs succeeded at getting most of the researchers at Xerox PARC to communicate through their Alto computers. Metcalfe then forged an alliance between Xerox, Digital, and Intel to establish Ethernet as a 10 Mbps Ethernet standard, ratified by the IEEE. Xerox did not show much interest in commercializing Ethernet. In 1979, Metcalfe formed his own company, 3Com, which developed and commercialized networking technology, including Ethernet technology. In particular, 3Com developed and marketed Ethernet cards in the early 1980s for the immensely popular IBM PCs. Metcalfe left 3Com in 1990, when it had 2,000 people and $400 million dollars in revenue. As of November 2003, 3Com employed over 2,900 people worldwide.

All of the Ethernet technologies provide an **unreliable service** to the network layer. Specifically, when adapter B receives a frame from adapter A, it runs the frame through a CRC check, but neither sends an acknowledgment when a frame passes the CRC check nor sends a negative acknowledgment when a frame fails the CRC check. When a frame fails the CRC check, adapter B simply discards the frame. Thus, Adapter A has no idea whether its transmitted frame passed the CRC check. This lack of reliable transport (at the link layer) helps to make Ethernet simple and cheap. But it also means that the stream of datagrams passed to the network layer can have gaps.

If there are gaps due to discarded Ethernet frames, does the application at Host B see gaps as well? As we learned in, this depends solely on whether the application is using UDP or TCP. If the application is using UDP, then the application in Host B will indeed suffer from gaps in the data. On the other hand, if the application is using TCP, then TCP in Host B will not acknowledge the data contained in discarded frames, causing TCP in Host A to retransmit. Note that when TCP retransmits data, the data will eventually return to the Ethernet adapter at which it was discarded. Thus, in this sense, Ethernet does retransmit data, although Ethernet is unaware of whether it is transmitting a brand-new datagram with brand-new data, or a datagram that contains data that has already been transmitted at least once.

11.5.2 CSMA/CD: Ethernet's Multiple Access Protocol

When the nodes are interconnected with a hub (as opposed to a link-layer switch), the Ethernet LAN is a true broadcast LAN – that is, when an adapter transmits a frame, all of the adapters on the LAN receive the frame. Because Ethernet can employ broadcast, it needs a multiple access protocol. Ethernet uses the celebrated CSMA/CD multiple access protocol. Recall from Section 11.3 that CSMA/CD does the following:

1. An adapter may begin to transmit at any time; that is, no slots are used.
2. An adapter never transmits a frame when it senses that some other adapter is transmitting; that is, it uses carrier sensing.
3. A transmitting adapter aborts its transmission as soon as it detects that another adapter is also transmitting; that is, it uses collision detection.
4. Before attempting a retransmission, an adapter waits a random time that is typically small compared with the time to transmit a frame.

These mechanisms give CSMA/CD much better performance than slotted ALOHA in a LAN environment. In fact, if the maximum propagation delay between stations is very small, the efficiency of CSMA/CD can approach 100 percent. But note that the second and third mechanisms listed above require each Ethernet adapter to be able to (1) sense when some other adapter is transmitting and (2) detect a collision while it is transmitting. Ethernet adapters perform these two tasks by measuring voltage levels before and during transmission.

Each adapter runs the CSMA/CD protocol without explicit coordination with the other adapters on the Ethernet. Within a specific adapter, the CSMA/CD protocol works as follows:

1. The adapter obtains a network-layer datagram from its parent node, prepares an Ethernet frame, and puts the frame in an adapter buffer.
2. If the adapter senses that the channel is idle (that is, there is no signal energy entering the adapter from the channel for 96 bit times), it starts to transmit the frame. If the adapter senses that the channel is busy, it waits until it senses no signal energy (plus 96 bit times) and then starts to transmit the frame.
3. While transmitting, the adapter monitors for the presence of signal energy coming from other adapters. If the adapter transmits the entire frame without detecting signal energy from other adapters, the adapter is finished with the frame.
4. If the adapter detects signal energy from other adapters while transmitting, it stops transmitting its frame and instead transmits a 48-bit jam signal.
5. After aborting (that is, transmitting the jam signal), the adapter enters an **exponential backoff** phase. Specifically, when transmitting a given frame, after experiencing the *n*th collision in a row for this frame, the adapter chooses a value for K at random from $\{0,1,2, \ldots, 2^{m-1}\}$ where $m = \min(n,10)$. The adapter then waits $K \cdot 512$ bit times and then returns to Step 2.

A few comments about the CSMA/CD protocol are certainly in order. The purpose of the jam signal is to make sure that all other transmitting adapters become aware of the collision. Let's look at an example. Suppose adapter A begins to transmit a frame, and just before A's signal reaches adapter B, adapter B begins to transmit. So B will have transmitted only a few bits when it aborts its transmission. These few bits will indeed propagate to A, but they may not constitute enough energy for A to detect the collision. To make sure that A detects the collision (so that it too can also abort), B transmits the 48-bit jam signal.

Next consider the exponential backoff algorithm. The first thing to notice here is that a bit time (that is, the time to transmit a single bit) is very short; for a 10 Mbps Ethernet, a bit time is 0.1 microsecond. Now let's look at an example. Suppose that an adapter attempts to transmit a frame for the first time and while transmitting it detects a collision. The adapter then chooses $K = 0$ with probability 0.5 or chooses $K = 1$ with probability 0.5. If the adapter chooses $K = 0$, then it immediately jumps to Step 2 after transmitting the jam signal. If the adapter chooses $K = 1$, it waits 51.2 microseconds before returning to Step 2. After a second collision, K is chosen with equal probability from $\{0,1,2,3\}$. After three collisions, K is chosen with equal probability from $\{0,1,2,3,4,5,6,7\}$. After 10 or more collisions, K is chosen with equal probability from {0,1,2, . . . , 1023}. Thus the size of the sets from which K is chosen grows exponentially with the number of collisions (until $n = 10$); it is for this reason that Ethernet's backoff algorithm is referred to as *exponential backoff*.

The Ethernet standard imposes limits on the distance between any two nodes. These limits ensure that if adapter A chooses a lower value of K than all the other adapters involved in a collision, then adapter A will be able to transmit its frame without experiencing a new collision. We will explore this property in more detail in the homework problems.

Why use exponential backoff? Why not, for example, select K from {0,1,2,3,4,5,6,7} after every collision? The reason is that when an adapter experiences its first collision, it has no idea how many adapters are involved in the collision. If there are only a small number of colliding adapters, it makes sense to choose K from a small set of small values. On the other hand, if many adapters are involved in the collision, it makes sense to choose K from a larger, more dispersed set of values (why?). By increasing the size of the set after each collision, the adapter appropriately adapts to these different scenarios.

We also note here that each time an adapter prepares a new frame for transmission, it runs the CSMA/CD algorithm presented above. In particular, the adapter does not take into account any collisions that may have occurred in the recent past. So it is possible that an adapter with a new frame will immediately be able to sneak in a successful transmission while several other adapters are in the exponential backoff state.

Ethernet Efficiency

When only one node has a frame to send, the node can transmit at the full rate of the Ethernet technology (either 10 Mbps, 100 Mbps, or 1 Gbps). However, if many nodes have frames to transmit, the effective transmission rate of the channel can be much less. We define the **efficiency of Ethernet** to be the long-run fraction of time during which frames are being transmitted on the channel without collisions when there is a large number of active nodes, with each node having a large number of frames to send. In order to present a closed-form approximation of the efficiency of Ethernet, let t_{prop} denote the maximum time it takes signal energy to propagate between any two adapters. Let t_{trans} be the time to transmit a maximum-size Ethernet frame (approximately 1.2 msecs for a 10 Mbps Ethernet). A derivation of the efficiency of Ethernet is beyond the scope of this book (see [Lam 1980] and [Bertsekas 1991]). Here we simply state the following approximation:

$$\text{Efficiency} = \frac{1}{1 + 5t_{prop}/t_{trans}}$$

We see from this formula that as t_{prop} approaches 0, the efficiency approaches 1. This matches our intuition that if the propagation delay is zero, colliding nodes will abort immediately without wasting the channel. Also, as t_{trans} becomes very large, efficiency approaches 1. This is also intuitive because when a frame grabs the channel, it will hold on to the channel for a very long time; thus the channel will be doing productive work most of the time.

11.5.3 Ethernet Technologies

In 2004 the most common Ethernet technologies are 10BaseT and 100BaseT, which uses twisted-pair copper wire in a star topology and have transmission rates of 10 Mbps and 100 Mbps, respectively. These Ethernet technologies are standardized by the IEEE 802.3 working groups. For this reason, an Ethernet LAN is often referred to as an 802.3 LAN.

Figure 11.26 illustrates 10BaseT/100BaseT technology. Each adapter on each node has a direct, point-to-point connection to the hub. This connection consists of two pairs of twisted-pair copper wire, one for transmitting and the other for receiving. At the end of the connection there is an RJ-45 connector, which resembles the RJ-11 connector used for ordinary telephones. The T in 10BaseT and 100BaseT stands for "twisted pair." For both 10BaseT and 100BaseT, the maximum length of the connection between an adapter and the hub is 100 meters; thus, the maximum length between any two nodes is 200 meters. As we will discuss in the next section, this maximum distance can be increased by deploying tiers of hubs or switches and by fiber links.

A **hub** is a physical-layer device that acts on individual bits rather than on frames. It has two or more interfaces. When a bit, representing a zero or a one, arrives from one interface, the hub simply re-creates the bit, boosts its energy

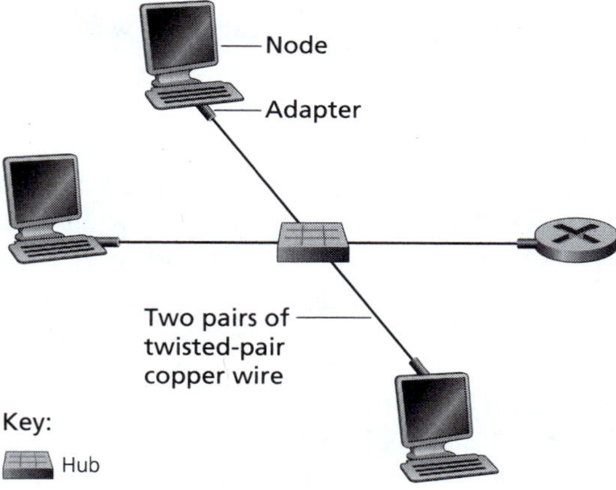

Figure 11.26 ♦ Star topology for 10BaseT and 100BaseT

strength, and transmits the bit onto all the other interfaces. It is important to keep in mind that hubs do not implement carrier sensing or any other part of CSMA/CD; a hub repeats an incoming bit on all outgoing interfaces even if there is signal energy on some of the interfaces. Because hubs broadcast bits, each adapter on a 10/100 BaseT Ethernet can (1) sense the channel to determine whether it is idle and (2) detect a collision while it is transmitting.

Hubs also provide network management features. For example, if an adapter malfunctions and continually sends Ethernet frames (called a *jabbering adapter*), a 10/100 BaseT network will continue to function, because the hub will detect the problem and internally disconnect the malfunctioning adapter. With this feature, the network administrator doesn't have to get out of bed and drive back to work in order to correct the problem. Also, most hubs can gather information and report the information to a host that connects directly to the hub. As discussed in this monitoring host provides a graphical interface that displays statistics and graphs, such as bandwidth usage, collision rates, average frame sizes, and so on. Network administrators can use this information not only to debug and correct problems, but also to plan how the LAN should evolve in the future.

Many Ethernet adapters today are 10/100 Mbps adapters. This means that they can be used for both 10BaseT and 100BaseT Ethernets. 100BaseT typically uses category-5 twisted pair (a high-quality twisted pair of wires with many twists). Unlike 10BaseT, 100BaseT does not use Manchester encoding but instead uses a more efficient encoding called 4B5B: Every group of five clock periods is used to send 4 bits in order to provide enough transitions to allow clock synchronization.

We briefly mention at this point that both 10 Mbps and 100 Mbps Ethernet technologies can employ fiber links. A fiber link is often used to interconnect to hubs that are in different buildings on the same campus. Fiber is expensive because of the cost of its connectors, but it has excellent noise immunity. The IEEE 802 standards permit a LAN to have a larger geographical reach when fiber is used to connect backbone nodes.

Gigabit Ethernet and 10 Gbps Ethernet

Gigabit Ethernet is an extension to the highly successful 10 Mbps and 100 Mbps Ethernet standards. Offering a raw data rate of 1,000 Mbps, Gigabit Ethernet maintains full compatibility with the huge installed base of Ethernet equipment. The standard for Gigabit Ethernet, referred to as IEEE 802.3z, does the following:

- Uses the standard Ethernet frame format (Figure 11.24) and is backward compatible with 10BaseT and 100BaseT technologies. This allows for easy integration of Gigabit Ethernet with the existing installed base of Ethernet equipment.
- Allows for point-to-point links as well as shared broadcast channels. Point-to-point links use switches (see Section 11.6), whereas broadcast channels use hubs,

as described above for 10BaseT and 100BaseT. In Gigabit Ethernet jargon, hubs are called *buffered distributors*.

- Uses CSMA/CD for shared broadcast channels. In order to have acceptable efficiency, the maximum distance between nodes must be severely restricted.
- Allows for full-duplex operation at 1,000 Mbps in both directions for point-to-point channels.

Like 10BaseT and 100BaseT, Gigabit Ethernet has a star topology with a hub or switch at its center. (Ethernet switches will be discussed in Section 11.6.) Gigabit Ethernet often serves as a backbone for interconnecting multiple 10 Mbps and 100 Mbps Ethernet LANs. Initially operating over optical fiber, Gigabit Ethernet is now able to run over category 5 UTP cabling.

With products that emerged in 2001, 10 Gigabit Ethernet further extended the popular Ethernet technology. Additionally, the 10 Gigabit Ethernet standard, 802.3ae, extends Ethernet technology to point-to-point wide-area-network (WAN) links. See Spurgeon's Ethernet Web site [Spurgeon 2004] for good information and links about Gigabit and 10 Gigabit Ethernet.

11.6 Interconnections: Hubs and Switches

Institutions—including companies, universities, and high schools—typically consist of many departments, each managing its own Ethernet LAN. Naturally, an institution will want its departments to interconnect their departmental LAN segments. In this section we consider two approaches to connecting LANs: hubs and switches. Both are in widespread use today.

11.6.1 Hubs

The simplest way to interconnect LANs is to use hubs. Figure 11.27 shows how three academic departments in a university might interconnect their LANs. In this figure, each of the three departments has a 10BaseT Ethernet that provides network access to the faculty, staff, and students of the department. Each host in a department has a point-to-point connection to the departmental hub. A fourth hub, called a **backbone hub**, has point-to-point connections to the departmental hubs, interconnecting the LANs of the three departments. The design shown in Figure 11.27 is a **multi-tier hub design** because the hubs are arranged in a hierarchy. It is also possible to create multi-tier designs with more than two tiers—for example, one tier for the departments, one tier for the schools within the university (engineering school, business school, and so on), and one tier at the highest university level.

In a multi-tier design, we refer to the entire interconnected network as a LAN, and we refer to each of the departmental portions of the LAN (that is, the departmental hub

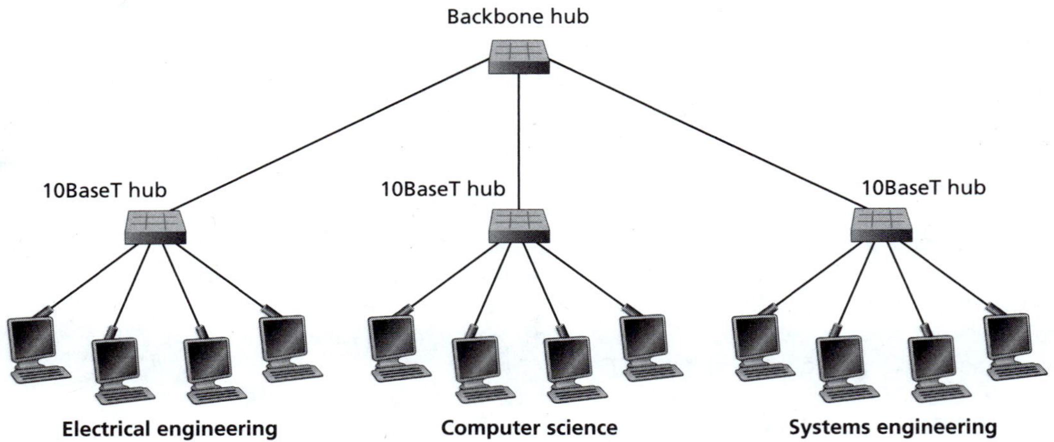

Figure 11.27 ♦ Three departmental Ethernets interconnected with a hub.

and the hosts that connect to the hub) as a **LAN segment**. It is important to note that all of the LAN segments in Figure 11.27 belong to the same **collision domain**; that is, whenever two or more nodes on the LAN segments transmit at the same time, there will be a collision and all of the transmitting nodes will enter exponential backoff.

Interconnecting departmental LANs with a backbone hub has many benefits. First and foremost, it provides interdepartmental communication among the hosts in the various departments. Second, it extends the maximum distance between any pair of nodes on the LAN. For example, with 10BaseT the maximum distance between a node and its hub is 100 meters; therefore, in a single LAN segment the maximum distance between any pair of nodes is 200 meters. By interconnecting the hubs, this maximum distance can be extended, since the distance between directly connected hubs can also be 100 meters when using twisted pair (and more when using fiber). A third benefit is that the multi-tier design provides a degree of graceful degradation. Specifically, if any one of the departmental hubs starts to malfunction, the backbone hub can detect the problem and disconnect the departmental hub from the LAN; in this manner, the remaining departments can continue to operate and communicate while the faulty departmental hub gets repaired.

Although a backbone hub is a useful interconnection device, it has three serious limitations that hinder its deployment. First, and perhaps most important, when departmental LANs are interconnected with a hub, the (previously independent) collision domains of the departments are transformed into one large, common collision domain. Let us explore this issue in the context of Figure 11.27. Before interconnecting the three departments, each departmental LAN had a maximum throughput of 10 Mbps, so that the maximum aggregate throughput of the three

LANs was 30 Mbps. But once the three LANs are interconnected with a hub, all of the hosts in the three departments belong to the same collision domain, and the maximum aggregate throughput is reduced to 10 Mbps.

A second limitation is that if the various departments use different Ethernet technologies, then it may not be possible to interconnect the departmental hubs with a backbone hub. For example, if some departments use 10BaseT and the remaining departments use 100BaseT, then it is impossible to interconnect all the departments without some frame buffering at the interconnection point; since a hub is essentially a repeater that does not buffer frames, it cannot interconnect LAN segments operating at different rates.

A third limitation is that each of the Ethernet technologies (10Base2, 10BaseT, 100BaseT, and so on) has restrictions on the maximum allowable number of nodes in a collision domain, the maximum distance between two hosts in a collision domain, and the maximum allowable number of tiers in a multi-tier design. These restrictions constrain both the total number of hosts that can connect to a multi-tier LAN as well as the geographical reach of the multi-tier LAN.

11.6.2 Link-Layer Switches

In contrast to hubs, which are physical-layer devices, link-layer switches—simply called **switches**—operate on Ethernet frames and thus are layer-2 devices. In fact, as full-fledged packet switches, switches forward frames based on LAN destination addresses. When a frame comes into a switch interface, the switch examines the layer-2 destination address of the frame and attempts to forward the frame on the interface that leads to the destination.

Figure 11.28 shows how the three academic departments of our previous example might be interconnected with a switch. The three numbers next to the switch are the interface numbers for the three switch interfaces. When the departments are interconnected by a switch, as in Figure 11.28, we again refer to the entire interconnected network as a LAN, and we again refer to each of the departmental portions of the network as LAN segments. But in contrast to the multi-tier hub design in Figure 11.27, each LAN segment is now an isolated collision domain.

Switches can overcome many of the problems that plague hubs. First, switches permit interdepartmental communication while preserving isolated collision domains for each of the departments. Second, switches can interconnect different LAN technologies, including 10BaseT, 100BaseT, and Gigabit Ethernet. Third, there is no limit to how large a LAN can be when switches are used to interconnect LAN segments; in theory, using switches, it is possible to build a LAN that spans the entire globe. Also, as we'll discuss at the end of this section, switches operate in full duplex and provide cut-through switching.

Figure 11.29 shows how an institution with several departments and several critical servers might deploy a combination of hubs, switches, and routers. In Figure 11.29, each of the three departments has its own 10 Mbps Ethernet segment with its

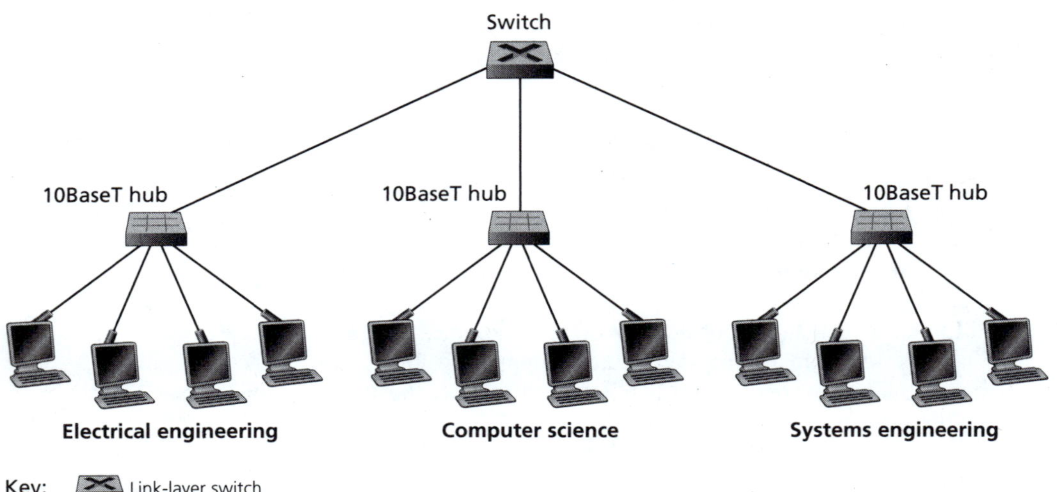

Figure 11.28 ♦ Three departmental LANs interconnected with a switch.

own hub. Because each departmental hub has a connection to the switch, all intradepartmental traffic is confined to the Ethernet segment of the department. The Web and mail servers each have dedicated 100 Mbps access to the switch. Finally, a router, leading to the Internet, has dedicated 100 Mbps access to the switch. Note that this switch has at least three 10 Mbps interfaces and three 100 Mbps interfaces.

Switch Forwarding and Filtering

Filtering is the ability of a switch to determine whether a frame should be forwarded to some interface or should just be dropped. **Forwarding** is the ability to determine the interfaces to which a frame should be directed, and then directing the frame to those interfaces. Switch filtering and forwarding are done with a **switch table**. The switch table contains entries for some, but not necessarily all, of the nodes on a LAN. An entry in the switch table contains (1) the MAC address of a node, (2) the switch interface that leads toward the node, and (3) the time at which the entry for the node was placed in the table. An example switch table for the LAN in Figure 11.28 is shown in Figure 11.30. Although this description of frame forwarding may sound similar to our discussion of datagram forwarding in Chapter 10, we'll see shortly that there are important differences. We note here that the addresses used by switches are MAC addresses rather than network-layer addresses. We will also see shortly that a switch table is constructed in a very different manner from routing tables.

To understand how switch filtering and forwarding works, suppose a frame with destination address DD-DD-DD-DD-DD-DD arrives at the switch on interface *x*.

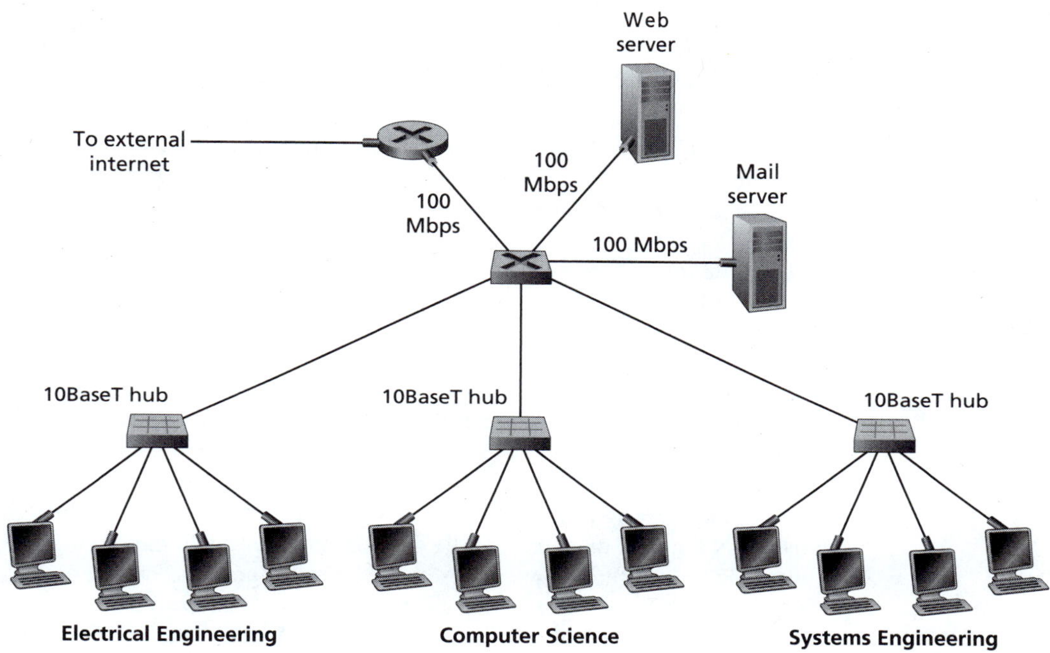

Figure 11.29 ♦ An institutional network using a combination of hubs, Ethernet switches, and a router

The switch indexes its table with the MAC address DD-DD-DD-DD-DD-DD and finds its corresponding interface *y* that is known to lead to destination address DD-DD-DD-DD-DD-DD. (We'll see shortly what happens if the address DD-DD-DD-DD-DD-DD is not in the table.)

Address	Interface	Time
62-FE-F7-11-89-A3	1	9:32
7C-BA-B2-B4-91-10	3	9:36
....	....	....

Figure 11.30 ♦ Portion of a switch table for the LAN in Figure 11.28

- If x equals y, then the frame is coming from a LAN segment that contains adapter DD-DD-DD-DD-DD-DD. There being no need to forward the frame to any of the other interfaces, the switch performs the filtering function by discarding the frame.
- If x does not equal y, then the frame needs to be forwarded to the LAN segment attached to interface y. The switch performs its forwarding function by putting the frame in an output buffer that precedes interface y.

These simple rules allow a switch to preserve separate collision domains for each of the different LAN segments connected to its interfaces. The rules also allow two sets of nodes on different LAN segments to communicate simultaneously without interfering with each other.

Let's walk through these rules for the network in Figure 11.28 and its switch table in Figure 11.30. Suppose that a frame with destination address 62-FE-F7-11-89-A3 arrives at the switch from interface 1. The switch examines its table and sees that the destination is on the LAN segment connected to interface 1 (that is, the Electrical Engineering LAN). This means that the frame has already been broadcast on the LAN segment that contains the destination. The switch therefore filters (that is, discards) the frame. Now suppose a frame with the same destination address arrives from interface 2. The switch again examines its table and sees that the destination is in the direction of interface 1; it therefore forwards the frame to the output buffer preceding interface 1. It should be clear from this example that as long as the switch table is complete and accurate, the switch isolates the departmental collision domains while permitting the departments to communicate.

Hubs versus Switches

Recall that when a hub forwards a frame onto a link, it just sends the bits onto the link without bothering to sense whether another transmission is currently taking place on the link. In contrast, when a switch wants to forward a frame onto a link, it runs the CSMA/CD algorithm discussed in Section 11.3. In particular, the switch refrains from transmitting if it senses that some other node on the LAN segment into which it wants to send a frame is transmitting; furthermore, the switch uses exponential backoff when one of its transmissions results in a collision. Thus switch interfaces behave very much like node adapters. But, technically speaking, they are *not* node adapters because neither a switch nor its interfaces have MAC addresses. Recall that a node (that is, a host or router) adapter always inserts its MAC address into the source address of every frame it transmits. A switch, on the other hand, does not change the source address of the frame.

One significant feature of switches is that they can be used to combine Ethernet segments using different Ethernet technologies. For example, if in Figure 11.28 Electrical Engineering has a 10Base2 Ethernet, Computer Science has a 100BaseT

Ethernet, and Systems Engineering has a 10BaseT Ethernet, then a switch can be purchased that can interconnect the three LANs. With Gigabit Ethernet switches, it is possible to have an additional 1 Gbps connection to a router, which in turn connects to a larger university network. As we mentioned earlier, this feature of being able to interconnect different link rates is not available with hubs.

Also, when switches are used as interconnection devices, there is no theoretical limit to the geographical reach of a LAN. In theory, we can build a LAN that spans the globe by interconnecting hubs in a long, linear topology, with each pair of neighboring hubs interconnected by a switch. With this design, each of the hubs has its own collision domain, and there is no limit on how long the LAN can be. We shall see shortly, however, that it is undesirable to build very large networks exclusively using switches as interconnection devices—large networks need routers as well.

Self-Learning

A switch has the wonderful property (particularly for the already-overworked network administrator) that its table is built automatically, dynamically, and autonomously—without any intervention from a network administrator or from a configuration protocol. In other words, switches are **self-learning**. This capability is accomplished as follows:

1. The switch table is initially empty.
2. When a frame arrives on one of the interfaces and the frame's destination address is not in the table, the switch forwards copies of the frame to the output buffers preceding *all* of the other interfaces. (At each of these other interfaces, the frame is transmitted into that LAN segment using CSMA/CD.)
3. For each incoming frame received on an interface, the switch stores in its table (1) the MAC address in the frame's *source address field,* (2) the interface from which the frame arrived, (3) the current time. In this manner the switch records in its table the LAN segment on which the sending node resides. If every node in the LAN eventually sends a frame, then every node will eventually get recorded in the table.
4. When a frame arrives on one of the interfaces and the frame's destination address is in the table, the switch forwards the frame to the appropriate interface.
5. The switch deletes an address in the table if no frames are received with that address as the source address after some period of time (the **aging time**). In this manner, if a PC is replaced by another PC (with a different adapter), the MAC address of the original PC will eventually be purged from the switch table.

Let's walk through the self-learning property for the network in Figure 11.28 and its corresponding switch table in Figure 11.30. Suppose at time 9:39 a frame

Address	Interface	Time
01-12-23-34-45-56	2	9:39
62-FE-F7-11-89-A3	1	9:32
7C-BA-B2-B4-91-10	3	9:36
....	....	....

Figure 11.31 ♦ Switch learns about the location of an adapter with address 01-12-23-34-45-56

with source address 01-12-23-34-45-56 arrives from interface 2. Suppose that this address is not in the switch table. Then the switch adds a new entry to the table, as shown in Figure 11.31.

Continuing with this same example, suppose that the aging time for this switch is 60 minutes, and no frames with source address 62-FE-F7-11-89-A3 arrive to the switch between 9:32 and 10:32. Then at time 10:32, the switch removes this address from its table.

Switches are **plug-and-play devices** because they require no intervention from a network administrator or user. A network administrator wanting to install a switch need do nothing more than connect the LAN segments to the switch interfaces. The administrator need not configure the switch tables at the time of installation or when a host is removed from one of the LAN segments.

Dedicated Access and Full Duplex

A switch with a large number of interfaces facilitates direct connections between hosts and the switch. When a host has a direct connection to a switch (rather than a shared LAN connection), the host is said to have **dedicated access**. In Figure 11.32, a switch provides dedicated access to six hosts.

A switch and the hosts directly connected to the switch operate in the full-duplex mode. Let's see how this done. To make the discussion concrete, suppose that each connection in the network in Figure 11.32 uses two pairs of twisted-pair cooper wire (as in 10BaseT and 100BaseT), one pair for transmitting from host to switch, and the other pair for transmitting from switch to host. Because of the dedicated access, when Host A transmits a frame on its upstream wire pair, there is no possibility that the frame will collide with a transmission from some other host or from the switch. Similarly, because switches "store and forward," the switch will transmit at most one frame at a time onto any one of the downstream wire pairs. Thus with direct upstream and downstream connections, neither collision detection nor carrier sensing are needed. In fact, each link becomes a point-to-point link, obviating the need for a medium-access protocol whatsoever! Thus, by disabling in each adapter the carrier sensing, the collision detection, and the looping back of transmitted data onto the

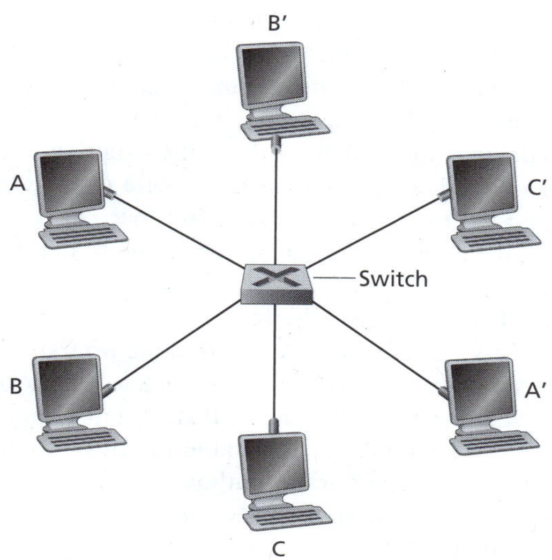

Figure 11.32 ♦ A switch providing dedicated Ethernet access to six hosts

receiver input, a full-duplex channel is created between each host and the switch. For example, in Figure 11.32, host A can send a file to A′ while B is sending a file to B′ and C is sending a file to C′. If each host has a 10 Mbps adapter card, then the aggregate throughput during the three simultaneous file transfers is 30 Mbps. If A and A′ have 100 Mbps adapters and the remaining hosts have 10 Mbps adapters, then the aggregate throughput during the three simultaneous file transfers is 120 Mbps.

Cut-Through Switching

In addition to large numbers of interfaces, support for multitudes of physical media types and transmission rates, and enticing network management features, switch manufacturers often tout that their switches use **cut-through switching** rather than store-and-forward packet switching, used by routers. The difference between store-and-forward and cut-through switching is subtle. To understand this difference, consider a packet that is being forwarded through a packet switch (that is, a router or switch). As discussed in Section 10.4, the packet arrives at the switch on an *input port* and leaves the switch on an *output port*. At the output port, there may or may not be other packets queued in the output port's buffer. When there are packets in the output buffer, there is absolutely no difference between store-and-forward and cut-through switching. The two switching techniques differ only when the output buffer is empty.

Recall that when a packet is forwarded through a store-and-forward packet switch, the packet is first gathered and stored in its entirety before the packet switch begins to transmit it on the outbound link. In the case that the output buffer becomes empty before the whole packet has arrived to the switch, this gathering generates a store-and-forward delay at the switch—a delay that contributes to the total end-to-end delay. An upper bound on this delay is L/R, where L is the length of the packet and R is transmission rate of the *inbound* link. Note that a packet incurs a store-and-forward delay only if the output buffer becomes empty before the entire packet arrives to the switch.

With cut-through switching, if the buffer becomes empty before the entire packet has arrived, the switch can start to transmit the front of the packet while the back of the packet continues to arrive. Of course, before the packet on the outbound link is transmitted, the portion of the packet that contains the destination address must first arrive. (This small delay is inevitable for all types of switching, as the switch must determine the appropriate outbound link.) In summary, with cut-through switching, a packet need not be fully stored before it is forwarded; instead the packet is forwarded through the switch when the output link is free. If the output link is a multiple access network that is shared with other hosts (for example, the output link connects to a hub), then the switch must also sense the link as idle before it can cut-through a packet.

To shed some insight on the difference between store-and-forward and cut-through switching, let us recall the caravan analogy. In this analogy, there is a highway with occasional tollbooths, with each tollbooth having a single attendant. On the highway there is a caravan of 10 cars traveling together, each at the same constant speed. The cars in the caravan are the only cars on the highway. Each tollbooth services the cars at a constant rate, so that when the cars leave the tollbooth they are equally spaced apart. As before, we can think of the caravan as being a packet, each car in the caravan as being a bit, and the tollbooth service rate as the link transmission rate. Consider now what the cars in the caravan do when they arrive to a tollbooth. If each car proceeds directly to the tollbooth on arrival, then the tollbooth is a cut-through tollbooth. If, on the other hand, each car waits at the entrance until all the remaining cars in the caravan have arrived, then the tollbooth is a store-and-forward tollbooth. The store-and-forward tollbooth clearly delays the caravan more than the cut-through tollbooth.

A cut-through switch can reduce a packet's end-to-end delay, but by how much? As we mentioned above, the maximum store-and-forward delay is L/R, where L is the packet size and R is the rate of the inbound link. The maximum delay is approximately 1.2 msec for 10 Mbps Ethernet and 0.12 msec for 100 Mbps Ethernet (corresponding to a maximum-size Ethernet packet). Thus, a cut-through switch reduces the delay by only 0.12 to 1.2 msec, and this reduction occurs only when the outbound link is lightly loaded. How significant is this delay? Probably not very much in most practical applications, so you may want to think twice about selling the family house before investing in the cut-through feature.

Switches Versus Routers

As we learned in Chapter 10, routers are store-and-forward packet switches that forward packets using network-layer addresses. Although a switch is also a store-and-forward packet switch, it is fundamentally different from a router in that it forwards packets using MAC addresses. Whereas a router is a layer-3 packet switch, a switch is a layer-2 packet switch.

Even though switches and routers are fundamentally different, network administrators must often choose between them when installing an interconnection device. For example, for the network in Figure 11.28, the network administrator could have just as easily used a router instead of a switch. Indeed, a router would have also kept the three collision domains separate while permitting interdepartmental communication. Given that both switches and routers are candidates for interconnection devices, what are the pros and cons of the two approaches?

First consider the pros and cons of switches. As mentioned above, switches are plug-and-play, a property that is cherished by all the overworked network administrators of the world. Switches can also have relatively high packet filtering and forwarding rates—as shown in Figure 11.33, switches have to process packets only up through layer 2, whereas routers have to process frames up through layer 3. On the other hand, the topology of a switched network is restricted to a spanning tree. Also a large switched network would require large ARP tables in the nodes and would generate substantial ARP traffic and processing. Furthermore, switches do not offer any protection against broadcast storms—if one host goes haywire and transmits an endless stream of Ethernet broadcast frames, the switches will forward all of these frames, causing the entire network to collapse.

Now consider the pros and cons of routers. Because network addressing is often hierarchical (and not flat, as is MAC addressing), packets do not normally cycle through routers even when the network has redundant paths. (However, packets can cycle when router tables are misconfigured; but as we learned in Chapter 10, IP uses a special datagram header field to limit the cycling.) Thus, packets are not restricted to a spanning tree and can use the best path between source and destination. Because routers do not have the spanning tree restriction, they have allowed the Internet to be built with a rich topology that includes, for example, multiple active links between Europe and North America. Another feature of routers is that they provide firewall protection against layer-2 broadcast storms. Perhaps the most significant drawback of routers, though, is that they are not plug-and-play—they and the hosts that connect to them need their IP addresses to be configured. Also, routers often have a larger per-packet processing time than switches, because they have to process up through the layer-3 fields. Finally, there are two different ways to pronounce the word *router*, either as "rootor" or as "rowter," and people waste a lot of time arguing over the proper pronunciation [Perlman 1999].

Given that both switches and routers have their pros and cons, when should an institutional network (for example, university campus network or a corporate

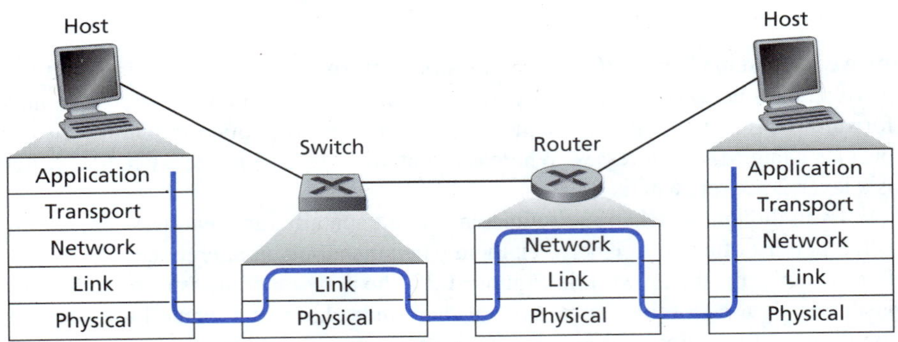

Figure 11.33 ♦ Packet processing in switches, routers, and hosts

campus network) use switches, and when should it use routers? Typically, small networks consisting of a few hundred hosts have a few LAN segments. Switches suffice for these small networks, as they localize traffic and increase aggregate throughput without requiring any configuration of IP addresses. But larger networks consisting of thousands of hosts typically include routers within the network (in addition to switches). The routers provide a more robust isolation of traffic, control broadcast storms, and use more "intelligent" routes among the hosts in the network.

We have learned in this section that hubs, switches, and routers can all be used as interconnection devices for hosts and LAN segments. Table 11.1 provides a summary of the features of each of these interconnection devices. The Cisco Web site provides numerous comparisons of the different interconnection technologies [Cisco Switches 2004].

	Hubs	Routers	Switches
Traffic isolation	No	Yes	Yes
Plug and play	Yes	No	Yes
Optimal routing	No	Yes	No
Cut-through	Yes	No	Yes

Table 11.1 ♦ Comparison of the typical features of popular interconnection devices

11.7 PPP: The Point-to-Point Protocol

Most of our discussion of link-layer protocols thus far has focused on protocols for broadcast channels. In this section we cover a link-layer protocol for point-to-point links—PPP, the point-to-point protocol. Because PPP is typically the protocol of choice for a dial-up link from a residential host, it is undoubtedly one of the most widely deployed link-layer protocols today. The other important link-layer protocol in use today is the high-level data link control (HDLC) protocol; see [Spragins 1991] for a discussion of HDLC. Our discussion here of the simpler PPP protocol will allow us to explore many of the most important features of a point-to-point link-layer protocol.

As its name implies, the point-to-point protocol (PPP) [RFC 1661; RFC 2153] is a link-layer protocol that operates over a **point-to-point link**—a link directly connecting two nodes, one on each end of the link. The point-to-point link over which PPP operates might be a serial dial-up telephone line (for example, a 56K modem connection), a SONET/SDH link, an X.25 connection, or an ISDN circuit. As noted above, PPP has become the protocol of choice for connecting home users to their ISPs over a dial-up connection.

Before diving into the details of PPP, it is instructive to examine the original requirements that the IETF placed on the design of PPP [RFC 1547]:

- *Packet framing.* The PPP protocol link-layer sender must be able to take a network-level packet and encapsulate it within the PPP link-layer frame such that the receiver will be able to identify the start and end of both the link-layer frame and the network-layer packet within the frame.
- *Transparency.* The PPP protocol must not place any constraints on data appearing on the network-layer packet (headers or data). Thus, for example, PPP cannot forbid the use of certain bit patterns in the network-layer packet. We'll return to this issue shortly in our discussion of byte stuffing.
- *Multiple network-layer protocols.* The PPP protocol must be able to support multiple network-layer protocols (for example, IP and DECnet) running over the same physical link at the same time. Just as the IP protocol is required to multiplex different transport-level protocols (for example, TCP and UDP) over a single end-to-end connection, so too must PPP be able to multiplex different network-layer protocols over a single point-to-point connection. This requirement means that at a minimum, PPP will likely require a protocol type field or some similar mechanism so the receiving-side PPP can demultiplex a received frame up to the appropriate network-layer protocol.
- *Multiple types of links.* In addition to being able to carry multiple higher-level protocols, PPP must also be able to operate over a wide variety of link types, including links that are either serial (transmitting a bit at a time in a given direction) or parallel (transmitting bits in parallel), synchronous (transmitting a clock

signal along with the data bits) or asynchronous, low-speed or high-speed, electrical or optical.

- *Error detection.* A PPP receiver must be able to detect bit errors in the received frame.
- *Connection liveness.* PPP must be able to detect a failure at the link level (for example, the inability to transfer data from the sending side of the link to the receiving side of the link) and signal this error condition to the network layer.
- *Network-layer address negotiation.* PPP must provide a mechanism for the communicating network layers (for example, IP) to learn or configure each other's network-layer address.
- *Simplicity.* PPP was required to meet a number of additional requirements beyond those listed above. On top of all of these requirements, first and foremost is simplicity. RFC 1547 states, "The watchword for a point-to-point protocol should be simplicity." A tall order indeed, given all of the other requirements placed on the design of PPP! More than fifty RFCs now define the various aspects of this "simple" protocol.

While it may appear that many requirements were placed on the design of PPP, the situation could actually have been much more difficult! The design specifications for PPP also explicitly note protocol functionality that PPP was *not* required to implement:

- *Error correction.* PPP is required to detect bit errors but is *not* required to correct them.
- *Flow control.* A PPP receiver is expected to be able to receive frames at the full rate of the underlying physical layer. If a higher layer cannot receive packets at this full rate, it is then up to the higher layer to drop packets or throttle the sender at the higher layer. That is, rather than having the PPP sender throttle its own transmission rate, it is the responsibility of a higher-level protocol to throttle the rate at which packets are delivered to PPP for sending.
- *Sequencing.* PPP is *not* required to deliver frames to the link receiver in the same order in which they were sent by the link sender. It is interesting to note that while this flexibility is compatible with the IP service model (which allows IP packets to be delivered end-to-end in any order), other network-layer protocols that operate over PPP do require sequenced end-to-end packet delivery.
- *Multipoint links.* PPP need only operate over links that have a single sender and a single receiver. Other link-layer protocols (e.g., HDLC) can accommodate multiple receivers (e.g., an Ethernet-like scenario) on a link.

Having now considered the design goals (and nongoals) for PPP, let us see how the design of PPP met these goals.

11.7.1 PPP Data Framing

Figure 11.34 shows a PPP data frame that uses HDLC-like framing [RFC 1662]. The PPP frame contains the following fields:

- *Flag field.* Every PPP frame begins and ends with a 1-byte flag field with a value of 01111110.
- *Address field.* The only possible value for this field is 11111111.
- *Control field.* The only possible value for this field is 00000011. Because both the address and control fields can take only a fixed value, you might wonder why the fields are defined in the first place. The PPP specification [RFC 1662] states that other values "may be defined at a later time," although none has been defined to date. Because these fields take fixed values, PPP allows the sender to simply not send the address and control bytes, thus saving 2 bytes of overhead in the PPP frame.
- *Protocol.* The protocol field tells the PPP receiver the upper-layer protocol to which the received encapsulated data (that is, the contents of the PPP frame's info field) belongs. On receipt of a PPP frame, the PPP receiver will check the frame for correctness and then pass the encapsulated data on to the appropriate protocol. RFC 1700 and RFC 3232 define the 16-bit protocol codes used by PPP. Of interest to us is the IP protocol (that is, the data encapsulated in the PPP frame in an IP datagram), which has a value of 21 hexadecimal; other network-layer protocols such as AppleTalk (29) and DECnet (27); the PPP link control protocol (C021 hexadecimal) that we discuss in detail in the following section; and the IP Control Protocol (IPCP) (8021). This last protocol is called by PPP when a link is first activated in order to configure the IP-level connection between the IP-capable devices on each end of the link (see below).
- *Information.* This field contains the encapsulated packet (data) that is being sent by an upper-layer protocol (for example, IP) over the PPP link. The default maximum length of the information field is 1,500 bytes, although this can be changed when the link is first configured, as discussed below.
- *Checksum.* The checksum field is used to detect bit errors in a transmitted frame. It uses either a 2- or 4-byte HDLC-standard cyclic redundancy check.

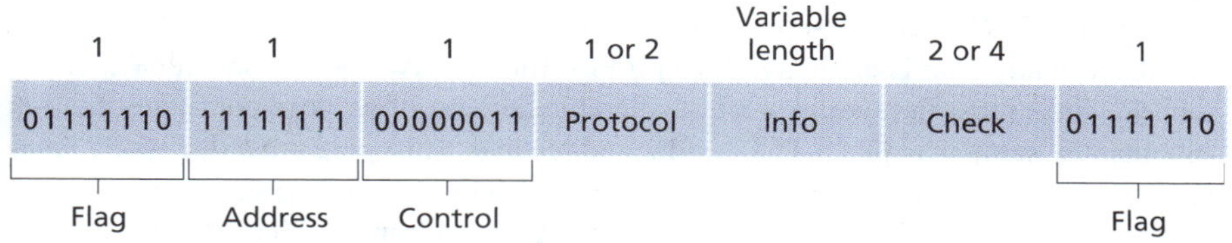

Figure 11.34 ♦ PPP data frame format

Byte Stuffing

Before closing our discussion of PPP framing, let us consider a problem that arises when any protocol uses a specific bit pattern in a flag field to delineate the beginning or end of the frame. What happens if the flag pattern itself occurs elsewhere in the packet? For example, what happens if the flag field value of 01111110 appears in the information field? Will the receiver incorrectly detect the end of the PPP frame?

One way to solve this problem would be for PPP to forbid the upper-layer protocol from sending data containing the flag field bit pattern. The PPP requirement of transparency discussed above obviates this possibility. An alternative solution, and the one taken in PPP and many other protocols, is to use a technique known as **byte stuffing**.

PPP defines a special control escape byte, 01111101. If the flag sequence, 01111110 appears anywhere in the frame, except in the flag field, PPP precedes that instance of the flag pattern with the control escape byte. That is, it "stuffs" (adds) a control escape byte into the transmitted data stream, before the 01111110, to indicate that the following 011111110 is *not* a flag value but is, in fact, actual data. A receiver that sees a 01111110 preceded by a 01111101 will, of course, remove the stuffed control escape to reconstruct the original data. Similarly, if the control escape byte bit pattern itself appears as actual data, it too must be preceded by a stuffed control escape byte. Thus, when the receiver sees a single control escape byte by itself in the data stream, it knows that the byte was stuffed into the data stream. A pair of control escape bytes occurring back to back means that one instance of the control escape byte appears in the original data being sent. Figure 11.35 illustrates PPP byte stuffing. (Actually, PPP also XORs the data byte being escaped with 20 hexadecimal, a detail we omit here for simplicity.)

11.7.2 PPP Link-Control Protocol (LCP) and Network-Control Protocols

Thus far, we have seen how PPP frames the data being sent over the point-to-point link. But how does the link get initialized when a host or router on one end of the PPP link is first turned on? The initialization, maintenance, error reporting, and shutdown of a PPP link is accomplished using PPP's **link-control protocol (LCP)** and family of PPP network-control protocols.

Before any data is exchanged over a PPP link, the two peers (one at each end of the PPP link) must first perform a considerable amount of work to configure the link, in much the same way that a TCP sender and receiver must perform a three-way handshake to set the parameters of the TCP connection before TCP data segments are transmitted. Figure 11.36 illustrates the state transition diagram for the LCP protocol for configuring, maintaining, and terminating the PPP link.

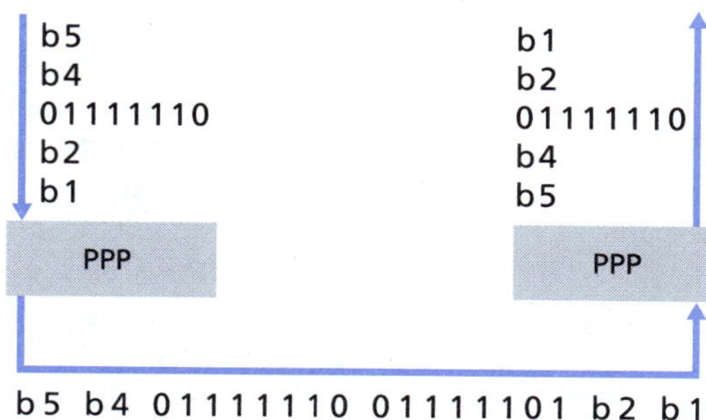

Figure 11.35 ♦ Byte stuffing

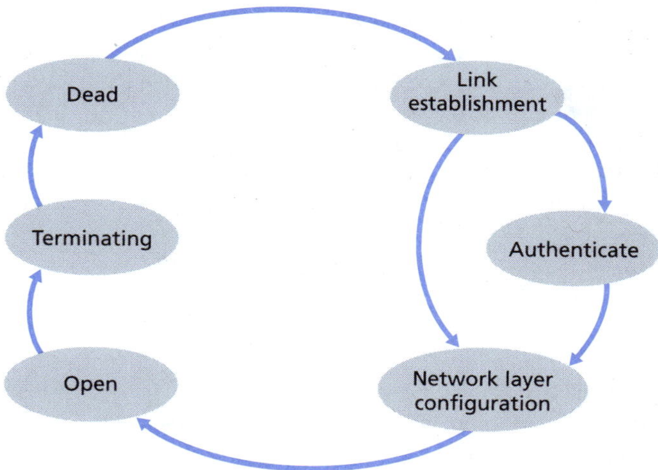

Figure 11.36 ♦ PPP link-control protocol states

The PPP link always begins and ends in the dead state. When an event such as a carrier detection or network administrator intervention indicates that a physical layer is present and ready to be used, PPP enters the link-establishment state. In this state, one end of the link sends its desired link configuration options using an LCP `configure-request` frame (a PPP frame with the protocol field set to LCP and the PPP information field containing the specific configuration request). The other side then responds with a `configure-ack` frame (all options acceptable), a `configure-nak` frame (all options understood but not acceptable), or a `configure-reject` frame (options not recognizable or not acceptable for negotiation). LCP configuration options include a maximum frame size for the link, the specification of an authentication protocol (if any) to be used, and an option to skip the use of the address and control fields in PPP frames.

Once the link has been established, link options negotiated, and the authentication (if any) performed, the two sides of the PPP link then exchange network layer–specific network-control packets with each other. If IP is running over the PPP link, the IP control protocol [RFC 1332] is used to configure the IP protocol modules at each end of the PPP link. IPCP data are carried within a PPP frame (with a protocol field value of 8021), just as LCP data are carried in a PPP frame. IPCP allows the two IP modules to exchange or configure their IP addresses and negotiate whether or not IP datagrams will be sent in compressed form. Similar network-control protocols are defined for other network-layer protocols, such as DECnet [RFC 1762] and AppleTalk [RFC 1378]. Once the network layer has been configured, PPP may then begin sending network-layer datagrams—the link is in the opened state and data has begun to flow across the PPP link. The LCP `echo-request` frame and `echo-reply` frame can be exchanged between the two PPP endpoints in order to check the status of the link.

The PPP link remains configured for communication until an LCP `terminate-request` packet is sent. If a `terminate-request` LCP frame is sent by one end of the PPP link and replied to with a `terminate-ack` LCP frame, the link then enters the dead state.

In summary, PPP is a link-layer protocol by which two communicating link-level peers, one on each end of a point-to-point link, exchange PPP frames containing network-layer datagrams. The principal components of PPP are:

- *Framing.* A method for encapsulating data in a PPP frame, identifying the beginning and end of the frame, and detecting errors in the frame.
- *Link-control protocol.* A protocol for initializing, maintaining, and taking down the PPP link.
- *Network-control protocols.* A family of protocols, one for each upper-layer network protocol, that allows the network-layer modules to configure themselves before network-level datagrams begin flowing across the PPP link.

11.8 Link Virtualization: A Network as a Link Layer

Because this chapter concerns link-layer protocols, and given that we're now nearing the chapter's end, let's reflect on how our understanding of the term *link* has evolved. We began this chapter by viewing the link as a physical wire connecting two communicating hosts, as illustrated in Figure 11.2. In studying multiple access protocols (Figure 11.9), we saw that multiple hosts could be connected by a shared wire and that the "wire" connecting the hosts could be radio spectra or other media. This led us to consider the link a bit more abstractly as a channel, rather than as a wire. In our study of Ethernet LANs (Figures 11.26–11.28) we saw that the interconnecting media could actually be a rather complex switched infrastructure. Throughout this evolution, however, the hosts themselves maintained the view that the interconnecting medium was simply a link-layer channel connecting two or more hosts. We saw, for example, that an Ethernet host can be blissfully unaware of whether it is connected to other LAN hosts by a single short LAN segment (Figure 11.9) or by a geographically dispersed switched LAN (Figure 11.28).

In Section 11.7 we saw that the PPP protocol is often used over a modem connection between two hosts. Here, the link connecting the two hosts is actually the telephone network—a logically separate, global telecommunications network with its own switches, links, and protocol stacks for data transfer and signaling. From the Internet link-layer point of view, however, the dial-up connection through the telephone network is viewed as a simple "wire." In this sense, the Internet virtualizes the telephone network, viewing the telephone network as a link-layer technology providing link-layer connectivity between two Internet hosts. You may recall from our discussion of overlay networks that an overlay network similarly views the Internet as a means for providing connectivity between overlay nodes, seeking to overlay the Internet in the same way that the Internet overlays the telephone network.

In this section, we'll consider asynchronous transfer mode (ATM) and Multiprotocol Label Switching (MPLS) networks. Unlike the circuit-switched telephone network, both ATM and MPLS are packet-switched, virtual-circuit networks in their own right. They have their own packet formats and forwarding behaviors. Thus, from a pedagogical viewpoint, a discussion of ATM and MPLS fits well into a study of either the network layer or the link layer. From an Internet viewpoint, however, we can consider ATM and MPLS, like the telephone network and switched-Ethernets, as link-layer technologies that serve to interconnect IP devices. Thus, we'll consider both MPLS and ATM in our discussion of the link layer. Frame-relay networks can also be used to interconnect IP devices, though they represent a slightly older (but still deployed) technology and will not be covered here; see the very readable book [Goralski 1999] for details. Our treatment of ATM and MPLS will be necessarily brief, as entire books could be (and have been) written on these networks. We'll focus here primarily on how these networks serve to interconnect IP devices, although we'll dive a bit deeper into the underlying technologies as well.

11.8.1 Asynchronous Transfer Mode (ATM) Networks

The standards for **asynchronous transfer mode (ATM)** networks were first developed in the mid-1980s, with the goal of designing a single networking technology that would transport real-time audio and video as well as text, e-mail, and image files. Two groups, the ATM Forum [ATM 2004] and the International Telecommunications Union [ITU 2004], were involved in the development of ATM standards. They defined a complete end-to-end standard, ranging from the specification of the application interface to ATM down to the bit-level framing of ATM data over various fiber, copper, and radio physical layers. In practice, ATM has been used primarily within telephone and IP networks, serving, for example, as a link-layer technology to connect IP routers, as discussed above.

Principal Characteristics of ATM

As discussed in Section 10.1, ATM supports several service models, including constant bit rate service, variable bit rate service, available bit rate service, and unspecified bit rate service. ATM is a packet-switched, virtual-circuit (VC) network architecture. Recall that we've considered VCs at some length in Section 10.2.1. ATM's overall architecture is organized into three layers, as shown in Figure 11.37.

The **ATM adaptation layer (AAL)** is roughly analogous to the Internet's transport layer and is present only at the ATM devices at the edge of the ATM network. On the sending side, the AAL is passed data from a higher-level application or protocol (such as IP, if ATM is being used to connected IP devices). On the receiving side it passes data up to the higher layer protocol or application. AALs have been defined for constant bit rate services and circuit emulation (AAL1), for variable-bit-rate services such as variable-bit-rate video (AAL2), and for data services such as IP-datagram transport (AAL5). Among the services performed by the AAL are error detection and segmentation/reassembly. The unit of data handled by the AAL is referred to by the rather generic name of **AAL protocol data unit (PDU),** which is roughly equivalent to a UDP or TCP segment.

The AAL5 PDU is shown in Figure 11.38. The PDU's fields are relatively straightforward. The PAD ensures that the PDU is an integer multiple of 48 bytes, because the PDU will be segmented to fit into the 48-byte payloads of the underlying ATM packets (known as *ATM cells*). The length field identifies the size of the PDU payload, so that the PAD can be removed at the receiver. The CRC field

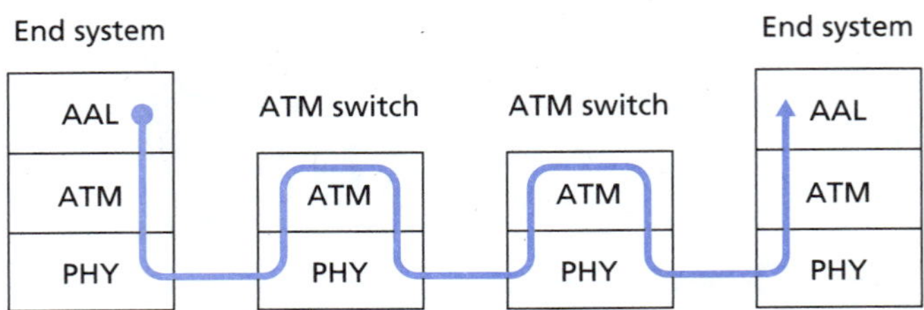

Figure 11.37 ♦ The three ATM layers. The AAL layer is only present at the edges of the ATM network.

Figure 11.38 ♦ AAL5 PDU

provides for error detection using the same cyclic redundancy check as Ethernet. The payload field can be up to 65,535 bytes long.

Let's now drop down one layer and consider the **ATM layer**, which lies at the heart of the ATM architecture. The ATM layer defines the structure of the ATM cell and the meaning of the fields within the cell. The ATM cell is as important to an ATM network as the IP datagram is to an IP network. The first 5 bytes of the cell constitute the ATM header; the remaining 48 bytes constitute the ATM payload. Figure 11.39 shows the structure of the ATM cell header.

The fields in the ATM cell have the following functions:

- **Virtual-channel identifier (VCI).** Indicates the virtual channel to which the cell belongs. As with most network technologies that use virtual circuits, a cell's VCI is translated from link to link (see Section 10.2.1).
- **Payload type (PT).** Indicates the type of payload contained in the cell. There are several data payload types, several maintenance payload types, and an idle cell payload type. The PT field also includes a bit that serves to indicate the last cell in a fragmented AAL PDU.
- **Cell-loss priority (CLP) bit.** Can be set by the source to differentiate between high-priority traffic and low-priority traffic. If congestion occurs and an ATM switch must discard cells, the switch can use this bit to first discard low-priority traffic.
- **Header error control (HEC) byte.** Error-detection bits that protect the cell header.

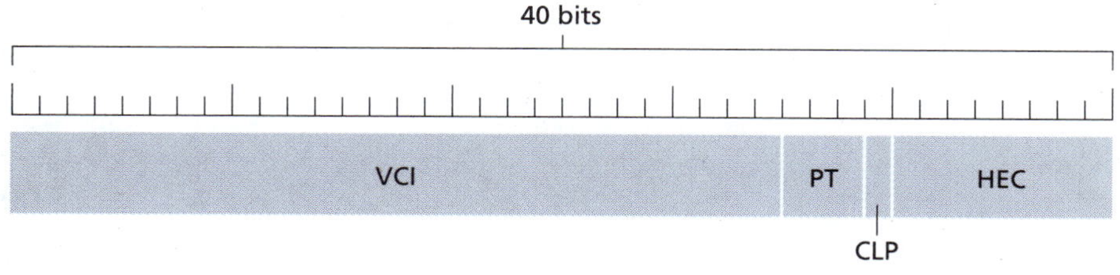

Figure 11.39 ♦ The format of the ATM cell header

Before a source can begin sending cells to a destination, the ATM network must first establish a **virtual channel (VC)** from source to destination. A virtual channel is nothing more than a virtual circuit, as described in Section 10.2.1. Each VC is a path consisting of a sequence of links between source and destination. A **virtual channel identifier (VCI)** is associated with each link on the VC. Whenever a VC is established or torn down, VC translation tables must be updated (see Section 10.3.1.). If permanent VCs are used, there is no need for dynamic VC establishment and teardown. When dynamic VC establishment and teardown are called for, the Q.2931 protocol [Black 1997, ITU-T Q.2931] provides signaling needed among the ATM switches and end systems.

The **ATM physical layer** is at the very bottom of the ATM protocol stack, and deals with voltages, bit timings, and framing on the physical medium. A good deal of the physical layer depends on the link's physical characteristics. There are two broad classes of physical layers: Those that have a transmission frame structure (for example, T1, T3, SONET, or SDH) and those that do not. If the physical layer has a frame structure, then it is responsible for generating and delineating frames. The use of the term *frames* here should not be confused with the link-layer (e.g., Ethernet) frames used in the earlier sections of this chapter. The transmission frame here is a physical-layer TDM-like mechanism for organizing the bits sent on a link. Some possible physical layers include:

- SONET/SDH (synchronous optical network/synchronous digital hierarchy) over single-mode fiber. Like T1 and T3, SONET and SDH have frame structures that establish bit synchronization between the transmitter and receiver at the two ends of the link. There are several standardized rates, including:

  OC-1: 51.84 Mbps

  OC-3: 155.52 Mbps

  OC-12: 622.08 Mbps

  OC-48: 2.5 Gbps
- T1/T3 frames over fiber, microwave, and copper.
- Cell-based with no frames. In this case, the clock at receiver is derived from a transmitted signal.

IP over ATM

Now let's consider how an ATM network can be used to provide connectivity between IP devices. Figure 11.40 shows an ATM backbone with four entry/exit points for Internet IP traffic. Note that each entry/exit point is a router. An ATM backbone can span an entire continent and may have tens or even hundreds of ATM switches. Most ATM backbones have a permanent VC between each pair of entry/exit points. By using permanent VCs, ATM cells are routed from entry point to exit point without having to establish and tear down VCs dynamically. Permanent VCs, however, are feasible only

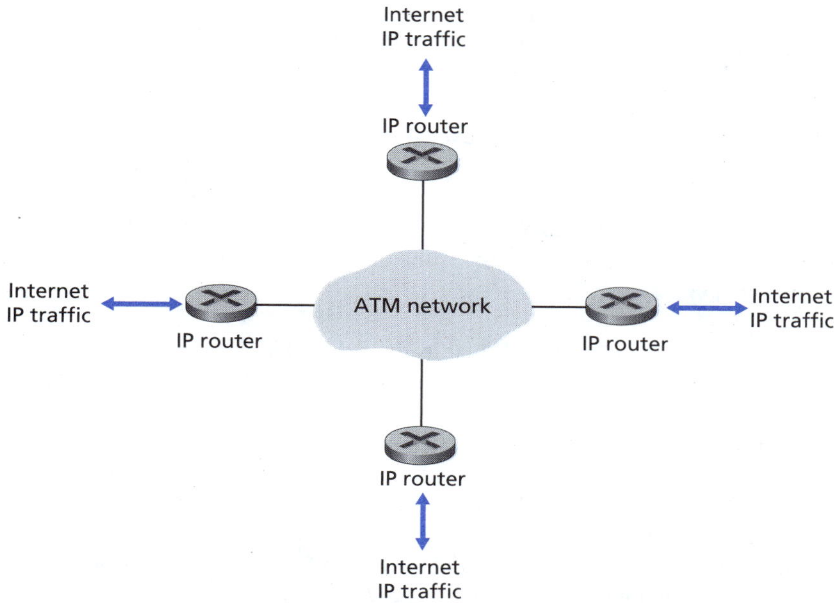

Figure 11.40 ♦ ATM network in the core of an Internet backbone

when the number of entry/exit points is relatively small. For n entry points, $n(n-1)$ permanent VCs are needed to directly connect n entry/exit points.

Each router interface that connects to the ATM network will need two addresses, in much the same way that an IP host has two addresses for an Ethernet interface: an IP address and a MAC address. Similarly, an ATM interface will have an IP address and an ATM address. Consider now an IP datagram crossing the ATM network shown in Figure 11.40. In the simplest case, the ATM network appears as a single logical link—ATM interconnects these four routers just as Ethernet can be used to connect four routers. Let us refer to the router at which the datagram enters the ATM network as the "entry router" and the router at which the datagram leaves the network as the "exit router." The entry router does the following:

1. Examines the destination address of the datagram.
2. Indexes its routing table and determines the IP address of the exit router (that is, the next router in the datagram's route).
3. To get the datagram to the exit router, the entry router views ATM as just another link-layer protocol. To move the datagram to the next router, we must determine the physical address of the next-hop router. Recall from our discussion in Section 11.4.2, that this is done using ARP. In the case of an ATM

interface, the entry router indexes an ATM ARP table with the IP address of the exit router and determines the ATM address of the exit router. The ATMARP protocol is described in [RFC 2225].
4. IP in the entry router then passes the datagram along with the ATM address of the exit router down to the link layer (that is, ATM).

After these four steps have been completed, the job of moving the datagram to the exit router is out of the hands of IP and in the hands of ATM. ATM must now move the datagram to the ATM destination address obtained in Step 3 above. This task has two subtasks:

1. Determine the VCI for the VC that leads to the ATM destination address.
2. Segment the datagram into cells at the sending side of the VC (that is, at the entry router), and reassemble the cells into the original datagram at the receiving side of the VC (that is, at the exit router).

The first subtask is straightforward. The interface at the sending side maintains a table that maps ATM addresses to VCIs. Because we're assuming that the VCs are permanent, this table is static and up-to-date. (If the VCs were not permanent, then the ATM Q.2931 signaling protocol would be needed to establish and tear down the VCs dynamically.) The second task merits more careful consideration. One approach is to use IP fragmentation, as discussed in Section 10.4. With IP fragmentation, the sending router would first break the original datagram into fragments, with each fragment being no more than 48 bytes, so that the fragment could fit into the payload of the ATM cell. But this fragmentation approach has a big problem—each IP fragment typically has 20 bytes of header, so that an ATM cell carrying a fragment would have 25 bytes of "overhead" and only 28 bytes of useful information. ATM thus uses AAL5 to provide more efficient segmentation/reassembly of a datagram.

The ATM network then moves each cell across the network to the ATM destination address. At each ATM switch between the ATM source and the ATM destination, the ATM cell is processed by the ATM physical and ATM layers, but not by the AAL layer. At each switch the VCI is typically translated (see Section 10.2.1) and the HEC is recalculated. When the cells arrive at the ATM destination address, they are directed to an AAL buffer that has been allocated to the particular VC. The AAL5 PDU is then reconstructed and the IP datagram is extracted and passed up the protocol stack to the IP layer.

11.8.2 Multiprotocol Label Switching (MPLS)

Multiprotocol Label Switching (MPLS) evolved from number of industry efforts in the mid-to-late 1990s to improve the forwarding speed of IP routers by adopting a key concept from the world of virtual-circuit networks: a fixed-length label. The goal was not to abandon the destination-based IP datagram-forwarding infrastructure for one based on fixed-length labels and virtual circuits, but to augment it by selectively labeling datagrams and allowing routers to forward datagrams based on fixed-length labels (rather than destination IP addresses) when possible. Importantly, these techniques work hand-in-hand with IP, using IP addressing and routing. The IETF unified these efforts in the MPLS protocol [RFC 3031, RFC 3032], effectively blending VC techniques into a routed datagram network.

Let's begin our study of MPLS by considering the format of a link-layer frame that is handled by an MPLS-capable router. Figure 11.41 shows that a link-layer frame transmitted on a PPP link or LAN (such as Ethernet) has a small MPLS header added between the layer-2 (i.e., PPP or Ethernet) header and layer-3 (i.e., IP) header. RFC 3032 defines the format of MPLS header for such links; headers are defined for ATM and frame-relayed networks as well in other RFCs. Among the fields in the MPLS header are the label (which serves the role of the virtual circuit identifier that we encountered back in Section 10.2.1), 3 bits reserved for experimental use, a single S bit, which is used to indicate the end of a series of "stacked" MPLS headers (an advanced topic that we'll not cover here), and a time-to-live field.

It's immediately evident from Figure 11.41 that an MPLS-enhanced frame can only be sent between routers that are both MPLS capable (since an non-MPLS-capable router would be quite confused when it found an MPLS header where it had expected to find the IP header!). An MPLS-capable router is often referred to as a **label-switched router**, since it forwards an MPLS frame by looking up the MPLS label in its forwarding table and then immediately passing the datagram to the appropriate output interface. Thus, the MPLS-capable router need *not* extract the destination address and perform a lookup of the longest prefix match in the forwarding table. But how does a router know if its neighbor is indeed MPLS capable, and how does a router know what label to associate with the given IP destination? To answer these questions, we'll need to take a look at the interaction among a group of MPLS-capable routers.

In the example in Figure 11.42, routers R1 through R4 are MPLS-capable. R5 and R6 are standard IP routers. R1 has advertised to R2 and R3 that it (R1) can route to destination A, and that a received frame with MPLS label 6 will be forwarded to

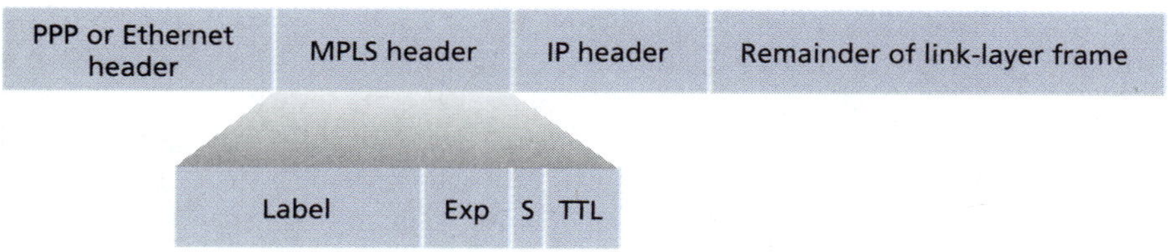

Figure 11.41 ♦ MPLS header: Located between link- and network-layer headers

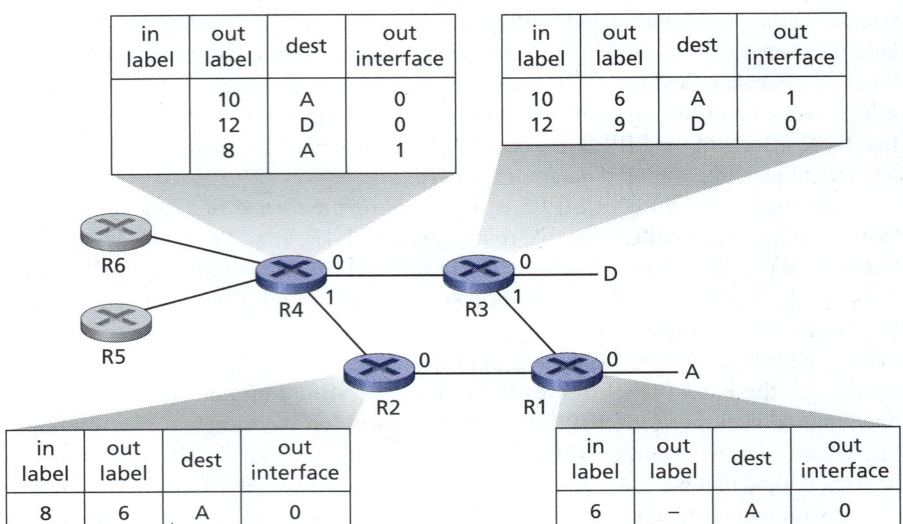

Figure 11.42 ♦ MPLS-enhanced forwarding

destination A. Router R3 has advertised to router R4 that it can route to destinations A and D, and that incoming frames with MPLS labels 10 and 12 respectively will be switched toward those destinations. Router R2 has also advertised to router R4 that it (R2) can reach destination A, and that a received frame with MPLS label 8 with be switched toward A. Note that Router R4 is now in the interesting position having *two* MPLS paths to reach A via interface 0 with outbound MPLS label 10, and via interface 1 with an MPLS label of 8. The broad picture painted in Figure 11.42 is that IP R4, R5, A, and D are connected together via an MPLS infrastructure (MPLS-capable routers R1, R2, R3, and R4) in much the same way that a switched LAN or an ATM network can connect together IP devices. And like a switched LAN or ATM network, the MPLS-capable routers R1 through R4 do so *without ever touching the IP header of a packet*.

In our discussion above, we've not specified the specific protocol used to distribute labels between among the MPLS-capable routers, as the details of this signaling are well beyond the scope of this book. We note, however, that the IETF working group on MPLS has specified in RFC 3468 that an extension of the RSVP protocol (which we'll study in Chapter 13), known as RSVP-TE [RFC 3209] will be the focus of its efforts for MPLS signaling. Thus, the interested reader is encouraged to consult RFC 3209.

Thus far, the emphasis of our discussion of MPLS has been on the fact that MPLS performs switching based on labels, without needing to consider the IP address of a packet. The true advantages of MPLS and the reason for current interest in MPLS, however, lie not in the potential increases in switching speeds, but rather in the new traffic management capabilities that MPLS enables. As noted above, R4 has *two* MPLS paths to A. If forwarding were performed up at the IP layer on the basis of IP address, the IP routing protocols we studied in Chapter 10 would specify only a single, least cost path to A. Thus, MPLS provides the ability to forward packets along routes that would not be possible using standard IP routing protocols. This is one simple form of **traffic engineering** using MPLS [RFC 3346, Xiao 2000], in which a network operator can override normal IP routing and force some of the traffic headed toward a given destination along one path, and other traffic destined toward the same destination along another path (whether for policy, performance, or some other reason).

It is also possible to use MPLS for many other purposes as well. It can be used to perform fast restoration of MPLS forwarding paths, e.g., to reroute traffic over a precomputed failover path in response to link failure [Kar 2000, Huang 2002, RFC 3469]. MPLS can also be used to implement the differentiated service framework ("diff-serv") that we will study in Chapter 13. Finally, we note that MPLS can, and has, been used to implement so-called **virtual private networks** (VPN). In implementing a VPN for a customer, an ISP uses its MPLS-enabled network to connect together the customer's various networks. MPLS can be used to isolate both the resources and addressing used by the customer's VPN from that of other users crossing the ISP's network; see [DeClercq 2002] for details.

Our discussion of MPLS has been necessarily brief, and we encourage you to consult the references we've mentioned. We note that with so many possible uses for MPLS, it appears that it is rapidly becoming the Swiss Army knife of Internet traffic engineering!

11.9 Summary

In this chapter, we've examined the link layer—its services, the principles underlying its operation, and a number of important specific protocols that use these principles in implementing link-layer services.

We saw that the basic service of the link layer is to move a network-layer datagram from one node (router or host) to an adjacent node. We saw that all link-layer protocols operate by encapsulating a network-layer datagram within a link-layer frame before transmitting the frame over the link to the adjacent node. Beyond this common framing function, however, we learned that different link-layer protocols provide very different link access, delivery (reliability, error detection/correction), flow control, and transmission (e.g., full-duplex versus half-duplex) services. These differences are due in part to the wide variety of link types over which link-layer protocols must operate. A simple point-to-point link has a single sender and receiver communicating over a single "wire." A multiple access link is shared among many senders and receivers; consequently, the link-layer protocol for a multiple access channel has a protocol (its multiple access protocol) for coordinating link access. In the cases of ATM and MPLS, the "link" connecting two adjacent nodes (for example, two IP routers that are adjacent in an IP sense—that they are next-hop IP routers toward some destination) may actually be a *network* in and of itself. In one sense, the idea of a network being considered as a link should not seem odd. A telephone link connecting a home modem/computer to a remote modem/router, for example, is actually a path through a sophisticated and complex telephone *network*.

Among the principles underlying link-layer communication, we examined error-detection and correction techniques, multiple access protocols, link-layer addressing, and the construction of extended LANs via hubs, and switches. In the case of error detection/correction, we examined how it is possible to add additional bits to a frame's header in order to detect, and in some cases correct, bit-flip errors that might occur when the frame is transmitted over the link. We covered simple parity and checksumming schemes, as well as the more robust cyclic redundancy check. We then moved on to the topic of multiple access protocols. We identified and studied three broad approaches for coordinating access to a broadcast channel: channel partitioning approaches (TDM, FDM, CDMA), random access approaches (the ALOHA protocols and CSMA protocols), and taking-turns approaches (polling and token passing). We saw that a consequence of having multiple nodes share a single broadcast channel was the need to provide node addresses at the link layer. We learned that physical addresses were quite different from network-layer addresses and that, in the case of the Internet, a special protocol (ARP—the address resolution protocol) is used to translate between these two forms of addressing. We then examined how nodes sharing a broadcast channel form a LAN and how multiple LANs can be connected together to form larger LANs—all *without* the intervention of network-layer routing to interconnect these local nodes.

We also covered a number of specific link-layer protocols in detail—Ethernet and PPP. We ended our study of the link layer by focusing on how ATM and MPLS networks provide link-layer services when they interconnect IP routers. Having covered the link layer, *our journey down the protocol stack is now over*! Certainly, the physical layer lies below the data link layer, but the details of the physical layer are probably best left for another course (for example, in communication theory, rather than computer networking). We have, however, touched upon several aspects of the physical layer in this chapter (for example, our brief discussions of Manchester encoding in Section 11.5). We consider the physical layer again when we consider wireless link characteristics in the next chapter.

Although our journey down the protocol stack is over, our study of computer networking is not yet at an end. In the following four chapters we cover wireless networking, multimedia networking, network security, and network management. These four topics do not fit conveniently into any one layer; indeed, each topic crosscuts many layers. Understanding these topics (billed as advanced topics in some networking texts) thus requires a firm foundation in all layers of the protocol stack—a foundation that our study of the data link layer has now completed!

Homework Problems and Questions

Chapter 11 Review Questions

SECTIONS 11.1–11.2

1. If all the links in the Internet were to provide the reliable delivery service, would the TCP reliable delivery service be redundant? Why or why not?
2. What are some of the possible services that a link-layer protocol can offer to the network layer? Which of these link-layer services have corresponding services in IP? In TCP?

SECTION 11.3

3. Suppose two nodes start to transmit at the same time a packet of length L over a broadcast channel of rate R. Denote the propagation delay between the two nodes as t_{prop}. Will there be a collision if $t_{prop} < L/R$? Why or why not?
4. In Section 11.3, we listed four desirable characteristics of a broadcast channel. Which of these characteristics does slotted ALOHA have? Which of these characteristics does token passing have?
5. Describe polling and token-passing protocols using the analogy of cocktail party interactions.
6. Why would the token-ring protocol be inefficient if a LAN had a very large perimeter?

SECTION 11.4

7. How big is the MAC address space? The IPv4 address space? The IPv6 address space?
8. Suppose nodes A, B, and C each attach to the same broadcast LAN (through their adapters). If A sends thousands of IP datagrams to B with each encapsulating frame addressed to the MAC address of B, will C's adapter process these frames? If so, will C's adapter pass the IP datagrams in these frames to C (that is, the adapter's parent node)? How would your answers change if A sent frames with the MAC broadcast address?
9. Why is an ARP query sent within a broadcast frame? Why is an ARP response sent within a frame with a specific destination MAC address?
10. For the network in Figure 11.19, the router has two ARP modules, each with its own ARP table. Is it possible that the same MAC address appears in both tables?

SECTION 11.5

11. Compare the frame structures for 10BaseT, 100BaseT, and Gigabit Ethernet. How do they differ?
12. Suppose a 10 Mbps adapter sends into a channel an infinite stream of 1s using Manchester encoding. The signal emerging from the adapter has how many transitions per second?
13. In CSMA/CD, after the fifth collision, what is the probability that a node chooses $K = 4$? The result $K = 4$ corresponds to a delay of how many seconds on a 10 Mbps Ethernet?

Problems

1. Suppose the information content of a packet is the bit pattern 1010101010101011 and an even parity scheme is being used. What would the value of the checksum field be for the case of a two-dimensional parity scheme? Your answer should be such that a minimum-length checksum field is used.
2. Show (give an example other than the one in Figure 11.6) that two-dimensional parity checks can correct and detect a single bit error. Show (give an example) of a double-bit error that can be detected but not corrected.
3. Suppose the information portion of a packet (D in Figure 11.4) contains 10 bytes consisting of the 8-bit unsigned binary representation of the integers 0 through 9. Compute the Internet checksum for this data.
4. Consider the 4-bit generator, G, shown in Figure 11.8, and suppose that D has the value 10101010. What is the value of R?
5. In Section 11.3, we provided an outline of the derivation of the efficiency of slotted ALOHA. In this problem we'll complete the derivation.
   a. Recall that when there are N active nodes the efficiency of slotted ALOHA is $Np(1 - p)^{N-1}$. Find the value of p that maximizes this expression.
   b. Using the value of p found in (a), find the efficiency of slotted ALOHA by letting N approach infinity. *Hint*: $(1 - 1/N)^N$ approaches $1/e$ as N approaches infinity.
6. Show that the maximum efficiency of pure ALOHA is $1/(2e)$. *Note*: This problem is easy if you have completed the problem above!
7. Graph the efficiency of slotted ALOHA and pure ALOHA as a function of p for $N = 100$.
8. Consider a broadcast channel with N nodes and a transmission rate of R bps. Suppose the broadcast channel uses polling (with an additional polling node)

for multiple access. Suppose the amount of time from when a node completes transmission until the subsequent node is permitted to transmit (that is, the polling delay) is t_{poll}. Suppose that within a polling round, a given node is allowed to transmit at most Q bits. What is the maximum throughput of the broadcast channel?

9. Consider three LANs interconnected by two routers, as shown in the diagram below.
   a. Redraw the diagram to include adapters.
   b. Assign IP addresses to all of the interfaces. For Subnet 1 use addresses of the form 111.111.111.xxx; for Subnet 2 uses addresses of the form 122.222.222.xxx; and for Subnet 3 use addresses of the form 133.133.133.xxx.
   c. Assign MAC addresses to all of the adapters.
   d. Consider sending an IP datagram from Host A to Host F. Suppose all of the ARP tables are up to date. Enumerate all the steps as done for the single-router example in Section 11.4.2.
   e. Repeat (d), now assuming that the ARP table in the sending host is empty (and the other tables are up to date).

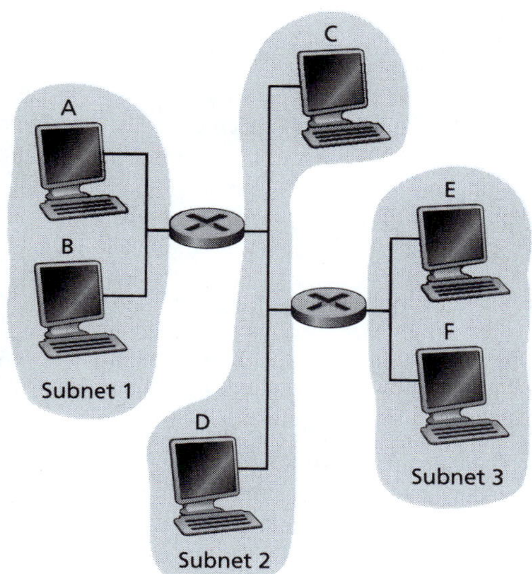

10. Recall that with the CSMA/CD protocol, the adapter waits $K \cdot 512$ bit times after a collision, where K is drawn randomly. For $K = 100$, how long does the adapter wait until returning to Step 2 for a 10 Mbps Ethernet? For a 100 Mbps Ethernet?

11. Suppose nodes A and B are on the same 10 Mbps Ethernet segment, and the propagation delay between the two nodes is 225 bit times. Suppose node A begins transmitting a frame and, before it finishes, node B begins transmitting a frame. Can A finish transmitting before it detects that B has transmitted? Why or why not? If the answer is yes, then A incorrectly believes that its frame was successfully transmitted without a collision. *Hint*: Suppose at time $t = 0$ bit times, A begins transmitting a frame. In the worst case, A transmits a minimum-sized frame of 512 + 64 bit times. So A would finish transmitting the frame at $t =$ 512 + 64 bit times. Thus, the answer is no, if B's signal reaches A before bit time $t = 512 + 64$ bits. In the worst case, when does B's signal reach A?

12. Suppose nodes A and B are on the same 10 Mbps Ethernet segment and the propagation delay between the two nodes is 225 bit times. Suppose A and B send frames at the same time, the frames collide, and then A and B choose different values of K in the CSMA/CD algorithm. Assuming no other nodes are active, can the retransmissions from A and B collide? For our purposes, it suffices to work out the following example. Suppose A and B begin transmission at $t = 0$ bit times. They both detect collisions at $t = 225$ bit times. They finish transmitting a jam signal at $t = 225 + 48 = 273$ bit times. Suppose $K_A = 0$ and $K_B = 1$. At what time does B schedule its retransmission? At what time does A begin transmission? (*Note*: The nodes must wait for an idle channel after returning to Step 2—see protocol.) At what time does A's signal reach B? Does B refrain from transmitting at its scheduled time?

13. Consider a 100 Mbps 100BaseT Ethernet. In order to have an efficiency of 0.50, what should be the maximum distance between a node and the hub? Assume a frame length of 64 bytes and that there are no repeaters. Does this maximum distance also ensure that a transmitting node A will be able to detect whether any other node transmitted while A was transmitting? Why or why not? How does your maximum distance compare with the actual 100 Mbps standard?

14. In this problem you will derive the efficiency of a CSMA/CD-like multiple access protocol. In this protocol, time is slotted and all adapters are synchronized to the slots. Unlike slotted ALOHA, however, the length of a slot (in seconds) is much less than a frame time (the time to transmit a frame). Let S be the length of a slot. Suppose all frames are of constant length $L = kRS$, where R is the transmission rate of the channel and k is a large integer. Suppose there are N nodes, each with an infinite number of frames to send. We also assume that $t_{prop} < S$, so that all nodes can detect a collision before the end of a slot time. The protocol is as follows:

    - If, for a given slot, no node has possession of the channel, all nodes contend for the channel; in particular, each node transmits in the slot with probability p. If exactly one node transmits in the slot, that node takes possession of the channel for the subsequent $k - 1$ slots and transmits its entire frame.

- If some node has possession of the channel, all other nodes refrain from transmitting until the node that possesses the channel has finished transmitting its frame. Once this node has transmitted its frame, all nodes contend for the channel.

Note that the channel alternates between two states: the productive state, which lasts exactly k slots, and the nonproductive state, which lasts for a random number of slots. Clearly, the channel efficiency is the ratio of $k/(k + x)$, where x is the expected number of consecutive unproductive slots.

a. For fixed N and p, determine the efficiency of this protocol.

b. For fixed N, determine the p that maximizes the efficiency.

c. Using the p (which is a function of N) found in (b), determine the efficiency as N approaches infinity.

d. Show that this efficiency approaches 1 as the frame length becomes large.

15. Suppose two nodes, A and B, are attached to opposite ends of a 900 m cable, and that they each have one frame of 1,000 bits (including all headers and preambles) to send to each other. Both nodes attempt to transmit at time $t = 0$. Suppose there are four repeaters between A and B, each inserting a 20-bit delay. Assume the transmission rate is 10 Mbps, and CSMA/CD with backoff intervals of multiples of 512 bits is used. After the first collision, A draws $K = 0$ and B draws $K = 1$ in the exponential backoff protocol. Ignore the jam signal and the 96-bit time delay.

    a. What is the one-way propagation delay (including repeater delays) between A and B in seconds? Assume that the signal propagation speed is $2 \cdot 10^8$ m/sec.

    b. At what time (in seconds) is A's packet completely delivered at B?

    c. Now suppose that only A has a packet to send and that the repeaters are replaced with switches. Suppose that each switch has a 20-bit processing delay in addition to a store-and-forward delay. At what time, in seconds, is A's packet delivered at B?

16. Recall that ATM uses 53-byte packets consisting of 5 header bytes and 48 payload bytes. Fifty-three bytes is unusually small for fixed-length packets; most networking protocols (IP, Ethernet, Frame Relay, and so forth) use packets that are, on average, significantly larger. One of the drawbacks of a small packet size is that a large fraction of link bandwidth is consumed by overhead bytes; in the case of ATM, almost 10 percent of the bandwidth is "wasted" by the ATM header. In this problem we investigate why such a small packet size was chosen. To this end, suppose that the ATM cell consists of P bytes (possibly different from 48) and 5 bytes of header.

    a. Consider sending a digitally encoded voice source directly over ATM. Suppose the source is encoded at a constant rate of 64 kbps. Assume each cell is entirely filled before the source sends the cell into the network. The time required to fill a cell is the **packetization delay**. In terms of L, determine the packetization delay in milliseconds.

b. Packetization delays greater than 20 msec can cause a noticeable and unpleasant echo. Determine the packetization delay for L = 1,500 bytes (roughly corresponding to a maximum-sized Ethernet packet) and for L = 48 (corresponding to an ATM cell).

c. Calculate the store-and-forward delay at a single ATM switch for a link rate of R = 155 Mbps (a popular link speed for ATM) for L = 1,500 bytes, and for L = 48 bytes.

d. Comment on the advantages of using a small cell size.

17. Consider the MPLS network shown in Figure 11.42, and suppose that routers R5 and R6 are now MPLS enabled. Suppose that we want to perform traffic engineering so that packets from R6 destined for A are switched to A via R6-R4-R3-R1, and packets from R5 destined for A are switched via R5-R4-R2-R1. Show the MPLS tables in R5 and R6, as well as the modified table in R4, that would make this possible.

Discussion Questions

You are encouraged to surf the Web in seeking answers to the following questions.

1. Roughly, what is the current price range of a 10/100 Mbps adapter? Of a Gigabit Ethernet adapter? How do these prices compare with a 56 kbps dial-up modem or with an ADSL modem?
2. Hubs and switches are often priced by number of interfaces (also called *ports* in LAN jargon). Roughly, what is the current per-interface price range for a 10 Mbps hub? For a 100 Mbps hub? For a switch consisting of only 10 Mbps interfaces? For a switch consisting of only 100 Mbps interfaces?
3. Many of the functions of an adapter can be performed in software that runs on the node's CPU. What are the advantages and disadvantages of moving this functionality from the adapter to the node?
4. Search the Web for the protocol numbers used in an Ethernet frame for an IP datagram and for an ARP packet.
5. Read references [Xiao 2000, Huang 2002, and RFC 3346] on traffic engineering using MPLS. List a set of goals for traffic engineering. Which of these goals can only be met with MPLS, and which of these goals are met by using existing (non-MPLS) protocols? In the latter case, what advantages does MPLS offer?

Ethereal Lab

In the companion Web site for this textbook, http://www.awl.com/kurose-ross, you'll find two Ethereal lab assignments for this chapter The first lab examines the operation of the IEEE 802.3 protocol and the Ethernet frame format. The second lab explores the use of the DHCP protocol that we studied in Section 11.4.3.

AN INTERVIEW WITH...

Simon S. Lam

Simon S. Lam is Professor and Regents Chair in Computer Sciences at the University of Texas at Austin. From 1971 to 1974, he was with the ARPA Network Measurement Center at UCLA, where he worked on satellite and radio packet switching. He led a research group that invented secure sockets and prototyped the first secure sockets layer (named Secure Network Programming) in 1993. His research interests are in design and analysis of network protocols and security services. He received his BSEE from Washington State University and his MS and PhD from UCLA.

Why did you decide to specialize in networking?

When I arrived at UCLA as a new graduate student in Fall 1969, my intention was to study control theory. Then I took the queueing theory classes of Leonard Kleinrock and was very impressed by him. For a while, I was working on adaptive control of queueing systems as a possible thesis topic. In early 1972, Larry Roberts initiated the ARPANET Satellite System project (later called Packet Satellite). Professor Kleinrock asked me to join the project. The first thing we did was to introduce a simple, yet realistic, backoff algorithm to the slotted Aloha protocol. Shortly thereafter, I found many interesting research problems, such as Aloha's instability problem and need for adaptive backoff, which would form the core of my thesis.

You were active in the early days of the Internet in the 1970s, beginning with your student days at UCLA. What was it like then? Did people have any inkling of what the Internet would become?

The atmosphere was really no different from other system-building projects I have seen in industry and academia. The initially stated goal of the ARPANET was fairly modest, that is., to provide access to expensive computers from remote locations so that many more scientists could use them. However, with the startup of the Packet Satellite project in 1972 and the Packet Radio project in 1973, ARPA's goal had expanded substantially. By 1973, ARPA was building three different packet networks at the same time and it became necessary for Vint Cerf and Bob Kahn to develop an interconnection strategy.

Back then, all of these progressive developments in networking were viewed (I believe) as logical rather than magical. No one could have envisioned the scale of the Internet and power of personal computers today. It was a decade before appearance of the first PCs. To put things in perspective, most students submitted their computer programs as decks of punched cards for batch processing. Only some students had direct access to computers, which were typically housed in a restricted area. Modems were slow and still a rarity. As a graduate student, I had only a phone on my desk, and I used pencil and paper to do most of my work.

Where do you see the field of networking and the Internet, heading in the future?

In the past, the simplicity of Internet's IP protocol was its greatest strength in vanquishing competition and becoming the de facto standard for internetworking. Unlike competitors, such as X.25 in the 1980s and ATM in the 1990s, IP can run on top of any link-layer networking technology because it offers only a best-effort datagram service. Thus any packet network can connect to the Internet.

Unfortunately, IP's greatest strength is now a shortcoming. IP is like a straitjacket that confines the Internet's development to specific directions. The IP layer is too economically important to tinker with to support new functionalities, such as multicast and QoS. In recent years, many researchers have redirected their efforts to the application and transport layers for multicast and QoS support. Most of the other current Internet research topics, such as security and P2P systems, involve the application layer only. There is also a great deal of research on wireless ad hoc networks, sensor networks, and satellite networks. These networks can be viewed either as standalone systems or link-layer systems, which can flourish because they are outside of the IP straitjacket.

Many people are excited about the possibility of P2P systems as a platform for novel Internet applications. However, P2P systems are highly inefficient in their use of Internet resources. A concern of mine is whether the transmission and switching capacity of the Internet core will continue to increase faster than the traffic demand on the Internet as it grows to interconnect all kinds of devices and support future P2P-enabled applications. Without substantial overprovisioning of capacity, ensuring network stability in the presence of malicious attacks and congestion would be a major task.

What is the most challenging part of your job?

The most challenging part of my job as a professor is teaching and motivating *every* student in my class, and *every* doctoral student under my supervision, rather than just the high achievers. The very bright and motivated may require a little guidance but not much else. I often learn more from these students than they learn from me. Educating and motivating the underachievers present a major challenge.

What impacts do you foresee technology having on learning in the future?

Eventually, almost all human knowledge will be accessible through the Internet, which will be the most powerful tool for learning. This vast knowledge base will have the potential of leveling the playing field for students all over the world. For example, motivated students in any country will be able to access the best class Web sites, multimedia lectures, and teaching materials. Already, it was said that the IEEE and ACM digital libraries have accelerated the development of computer science researchers in China. In time, the Internet will transcend all geographic barriers to learning.

CHAPTER 12

Wireless and Mobile Networks

In the telephony world, the past 10 years have arguably been the decade of cellular telephony. The number of worldwide mobile cellular subscribers increased from 34 million in 1993 to more than 1 billion in 2003, with the number of cellular subscribers now surpassing the number of main telephone lines [ITU Statistics 2004]. The many advantages of cell phones are evident to all—anywhere, anytime, untethered access to the global telephone network via a highly portable lightweight device. With the advent of laptops, palmtops, PDAs and their promise of anywhere, anytime, untethered access to the global Internet, is a similar explosion in the use of wireless Internet devices just around the corner?

Regardless of the future growth of wireless Internet devices, it's already clear that wireless networks and the mobility-related services they enable are here to stay. From a networking standpoint, the challenges posed by these networks, particularly at the data link and network layers, are so different from traditional wired computer networks that an individual chapter devoted to the study of wireless and mobile networks (i.e., *this* chapter) is appropriate.

We'll begin this chapter with a discussion of mobile users, wireless links and networks, and their relationship to the larger (typically wired) networks to which they connect. We'll draw a distinction between the challenges posed by the *wireless* nature of the communication links in such networks, and by the *mobility* that these wireless links enable. Making this important distinction—between wireless and mobility—will allow us to better isolate, identify, and master the key concepts in each area. Note that there are indeed many networked environments in which the network nodes are wireless but not mobile (e.g., wireless home or office networks with stationary workstations and large displays), and limited forms of mobility that do not require wireless links (e.g., a worker who uses a wired laptop at home, shuts down the laptop, drives to work, and attaches the laptop to the company's wired network). Of course, many of the most exciting networked environments are those in which users are both wireless *and* mobile—for example, a scenario in which a mobile user (say in the back seat of a car) maintains a voice-over-IP call and multiple ongoing TCP connections while racing down the autobahn at 160 kilometers per hour. It is here, at the intersection of wireless and mobility, that we'll find the most interesting technical challenges!

We'll begin by first illustrating the setting in which we'll consider wireless communication and mobility—a network in which wireless (and possibly mobile) users are connected into the larger network infrastructure by a wireless link at the network's edge. We'll then consider the characteristics of this wireless link in Section 12.2. We include a brief introduction to Code Division Multiple Access (CDMA), a shared-medium access protocol that is often used in wireless networks, in Section 12.2. In Section 12.3, we'll examine the link-level aspects of the IEEE 802.11 (Wi-Fi) wireless LAN standard in some depth; we'll also say a few words about Bluetooth. In Section 12.4 we provide an overview of cellular Internet access, including the emerging 3G cellular technologies that provide both voice and high-speed Internet access. In Section 12.5, we'll turn our attention to mobility, focusing on the problems of locating a mobile user, routing to the mobile user, and "handing off" the mobile user who dynamically moves from one point of attachment to the network to another. We'll examine how these mobility services are implemented in the mobile IP standard and in GSM, in Sections 12.6 and 12.7, respectively. Finally, we'll consider the impact of wireless links and mobility on transport-layer protocols and networked applications in Section 12.8.

12.1 Introduction

Figure 12.1 shows the setting in which we'll consider the topics of wireless data communication and mobility. We'll begin by keeping our discussion general enough to cover a wide range of networks, including both wireless LANs such as IEEE 802.11 and cellular networks such as a 3G network; we'll dive down into a more detailed discussion of specific wireless architectures in later sections. We can identify the following elements in a wireless network:

- *Wireless hosts.* As in the case of wired networks, hosts are the end-system devices that run applications. A **wireless host** might be a laptop, palmtop, PDA, phone, or desktop computer. The hosts themselves may or may not be mobile.

CASE HISTORY

PUBLIC WI-FI ACCESS: COMING SOON TO A CORNER NEAR YOU?

Only five years ago, wireless computer networks were somewhat of an oddity. Although massive investment was pouring into licensing radio spectrum for 3G systems (see Case History: 3G Cellular Mobile Versus Wireless LANS), 3G systems were (and still are) only at early stages of deployment. At the time, a few early adopters were beginning to try out the just-standardized IEEE 802.11 wireless LAN technology. What a difference five years can make! Today many corporations, universities, and homes have their own wireless IEEE 802.11 LANs. Even more remarkably, the number of wireless hot spots—public locations where users can find 802.11 wireless access—is rapidly expanding. The Gartner Group estimates there were 71,000 public hot spots in 2003, a nearly fifty-fold increase since 2001. In the United States, eateries such as Starbucks and McDonalds offer Wi-Fi access in a number of locations. In New York City, Verizon Communications has located Wi-Fi access points at over one thousand of its public phone booths and has connected the phone booths to the Internet [Verizon 2004], providing Wi-Fi access to passersby and nearby businesses. In early 2004, T-Mobile [T-Mobile 2004] provided more that 4,000 public Wi-Fi hotspots in locations such as airports, restaurants, and bookstores. A recent startup, Cometa, announced plans in 2003 to set up 20,000 commercial Wi-Fi hotspots in 50 metropolitan areas by 2005. With this level of activity, the dream of nearly ubiquitous, anytime, untethered access to the global Internet may be closer than we think!

- *Wireless links.* A host connects to a base station (defined below) or to another wireless host through a **wireless communication link**. Different wireless link technologies have different transmission rates and can transmit over different distances. Figure 12.2 shows a few of the key characteristics of the more popular wireless link standards. We'll cover these standards later in the first half of this chapter; we'll also consider other wireless link characteristics (such as their bit error rates and their causes) in Section 12.2.
- In Figure 12.1, wireless links connect hosts located at the edge of the network into the larger network infrastructure. We hasten to add that wireless links are also sometimes used *within* a network and to connect routers, switches, and other network equipment. However, our focus in this chapter will be on the use of wireless communication around the edges of the network, as it is here that many of the most exciting technical challenges, and most of the growth, are occurring.
- *Base station.* The **base station** is a key part of the wireless network infrastructure. Unlike the wireless host and wireless link, a base station has no obvious counterpart in a wired network. A base station is responsible for sending and receiving data (e.g., packets) to and from a wireless host that is associated with

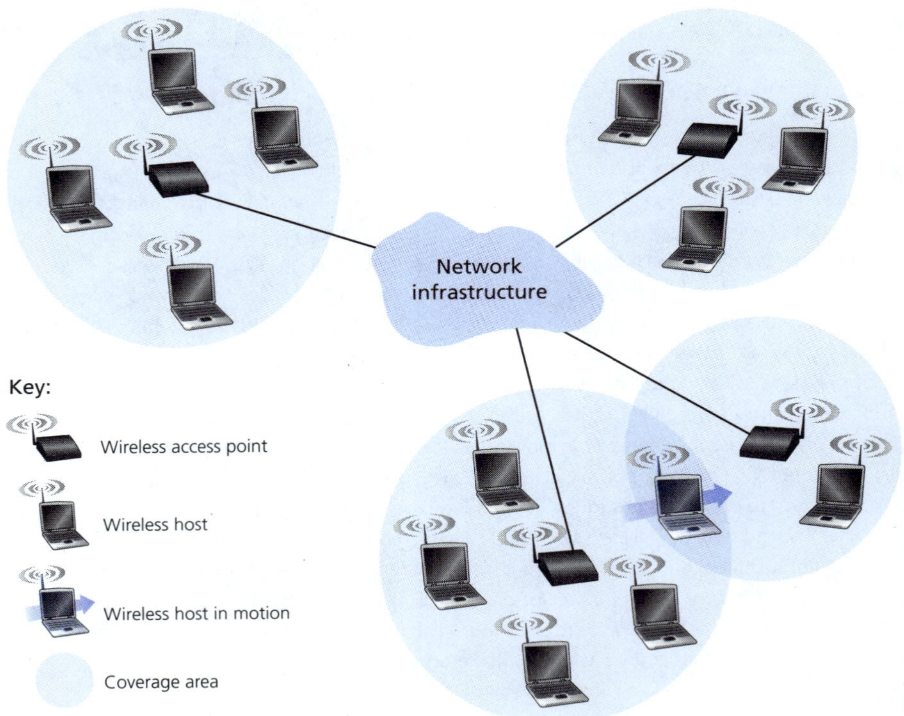

Figure 12.1 ♦ Elements of a wireless network

that base station. A base station will often be responsible for coordinating the transmission of multiple wireless hosts with which it is associated. When we say a wireless host is "associated" with a base station, we mean that (1) the host is within wireless communication distance of the base station, and (2) the host uses that base station to relay data between it (the host) and the larger network. **Cell towers** in cellular networks and **access points** in an 802.11 wireless LANs are examples of base stations.

In Figure 12.1, the base station is connected to the larger network (i.e., the Internet, corporate, or home network, or telephone network), thus functioning as a link-layer relay between the wireless host and the rest of the world with which the host communicates.

Hosts associated with a base station are often referred to as operating in **infrastructure mode**, since all traditional network services (e.g., address assignment and routing) are provided by the network to which a host is connected via the base station. In **ad hoc networks**, wireless hosts have no such infrastructure with which to connect. In the absence of such infrastructure, the hosts themselves must provide for services such as routing, address assignment, DNS-like name translation, and more. In this book, we'll focus our attention primarily on infrastructure-mode networks.

When a mobile host moves beyond the range of one base station and into the range of another, it will change its point of attachment into the larger network (i.e., change the base station with which it is associated)—a process referred to as **handoff**. Such mobility raises many challenging questions. If a host can move, how does one find its current location in the network so that data can be forwarded to the mobile host? How is addressing performed, given that a host can be in one of many possible locations? If the host moves *during* a TCP connection or phone call, how is data routed so that the connection continues uninterrupted? These and many (many!) other questions make wireless and mobile networking an area of exciting networking research.

- *Network infrastructure.* This is the larger network with which a wireless host may wish to communicate.

Let's now dig deeper into the technical challenges that arise in wireless and mobile networks. We'll begin by first considering the individual wireless link, deferring our discussion of mobility until later in this chapter.

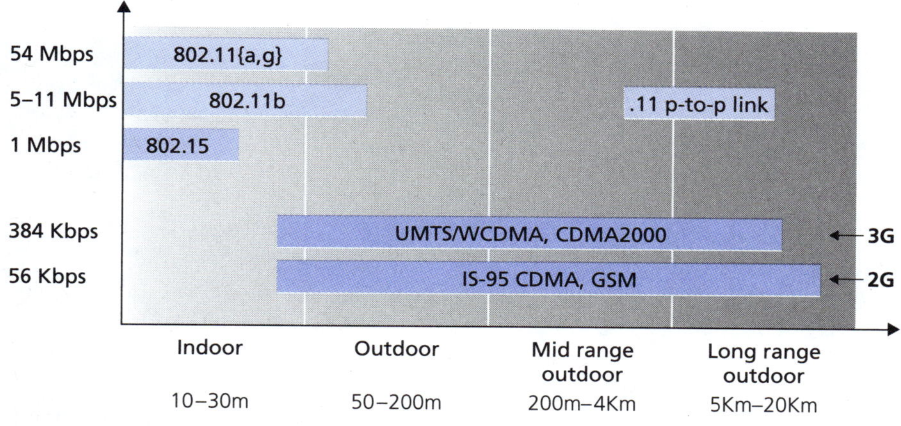

Figure 12.2 ♦ Link characteristics of selected wireless network standards

12.2 Wireless Links and Network Characteristics

Let's begin by considering a simple wired network, say a home network, with a wired Ethernet switch (see Section 11.6) interconnecting the hosts. If we replace the wired Ethernet with a wireless 802.11 network, a wireless NIC card would replace the wired Ethernet cards at the hosts, and an access point would replace the Ethernet switch, but virtually no changes would be needed at the network layer or above. This suggests that we focus our attention on the link layer when looking for important differences between wired and wireless networks. Indeed, we can find a number of important differences between a wired link and a wireless link:

- *Decreasing signal strength.* Electromagnetic radiation attenuates as it passes through matter (e.g., a radio signal passing through a wall). Even in free space, the signal will disperse, resulting in decreased signal strength (sometimes referred to as **path loss**) as the distance between sender and receiver increases.
- *Interference from other sources.* Radio sources transmitting in the same frequency band will interfere with each other. For example, 2.4 GHz wireless phones and 802.11b wireless LANs transmit in the same frequency band. Thus, the 802.11b wireless LAN user talking on a 2.4GHz wireless phone can expect that neither the network nor the phone will perform particularly well. In addition to interference from transmitting sources, electromagnetic noise within the environment (e.g., a nearby motor, a microwave) can result in interference.
- *Multipath propagation.* **Multipath propagation** occurs when portions of the electromagnetic wave reflect off objects and the ground, taking paths of different lengths between a sender and receiver. This results in the blurring of the received signal at the receiver. Moving objects between the sender and receiver can cause multipath propagation to change over time.

The discussion above suggests that bit errors will be more common in wireless links than in wired links. For this reason, it is perhaps not surprising that wireless link protocols (such as the 802.11 protocol we'll examine in the following section) employ not only powerful CRC error detection codes, but also link-level ARQ protocols that retransmit corrupted frames.

A higher and time-varying bit error rate are not the only differences between a wired and wireless link. Recall that in the case of wired broadcast links, all nodes receive the transmissions from all other nodes. In the case of wireless links, the situation is not as simple, as shown in Figure 12.3. Suppose that Station A is transmitting to Station B. Suppose also that Station C is transmitting to Station B. With the so-called **hidden terminal problem**, physical obstructions in the environment (for example, a mountain or a building) may prevent A and C from hearing each other's transmissions, even though A's and C's transmissions are indeed interfering at the destination, B. This is shown in Figure 12.3(a). A second scenario that results in undetectable collisions at the receiver results from the **fading** of a signal's strength as it propagates through the wireless medium. Figure 12.3(b) illustrates the case where A and C are placed such that their signals are not strong enough to detect each other's transmissions, yet their transmissions *are* strong enough to interfere with each other at station B. As we'll see in Section 12.3, the hidden terminal problem and fading make multiple access in a wireless network considerably more complex than in a wired network.

12.2.1 CDMA

Recall from Chapter 11 that when hosts communicate over a shared medium, a protocol is needed so that the signals sent by multiple senders do not interfere at the receivers. In Chapter 11 we described three classes of medium access protocols: channel partitioning, random access, and taking turns. Code division multiple access (CDMA) is yet a fourth type of a shared-medium access protocol, one that is prevalent in wireless LAN and cellular technologies. Because CDMA is so important in the wireless world, we'll take a quick look at CDMA now, before getting into specific wireless access technologies in the subsequent sections.

In a CDMA protocol, each bit being sent is encoded by multiplying the bit by a signal (the code) that changes at a much faster rate (known as the **chipping rate**) than the original sequence of data bits. Figure 12.4 shows a simple, idealized CDMA encoding/decoding scenario. Suppose that the rate at which original data bits reach the CDMA encoder defines the unit of time; that is, each original data bit to be transmitted requires a one-bit slot time. Let d_i be the value of the data bit for

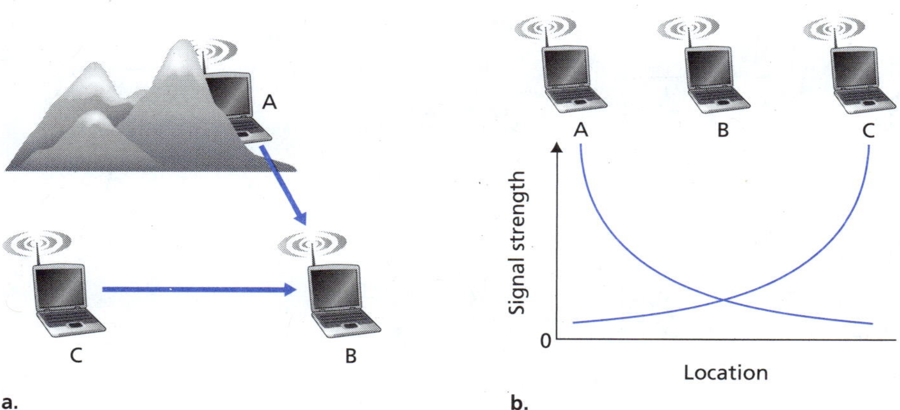

Figure 12.3 ♦ Hidden terminal problem (a) and fading (b)

the ith bit slot. For mathematical convenience, we represent a data bit with a 0 value as –1. Each bit slot is further subdivided into M mini-slots; in Figure 12.4, $M = 8$, although in practice M is much larger. The CDMA code used by the sender consists of a sequence of M values, c_m, $m = 1, \ldots, M$, each taking a +1 or –1 value. In the example in Figure 12.4, the M-bit CDMA code being used by the sender is (1, 1, 1, –1, 1, –1, –1, –1).

To illustrate how CDMA works, let us focus on the ith data bit, d_i. For the mth mini-slot of the bit-transmission time of d_i, the output of the CDMA encoder, $Z_{i,m}$, is the value of d_i multiplied by the mth bit in the assigned CDMA code, c_m:

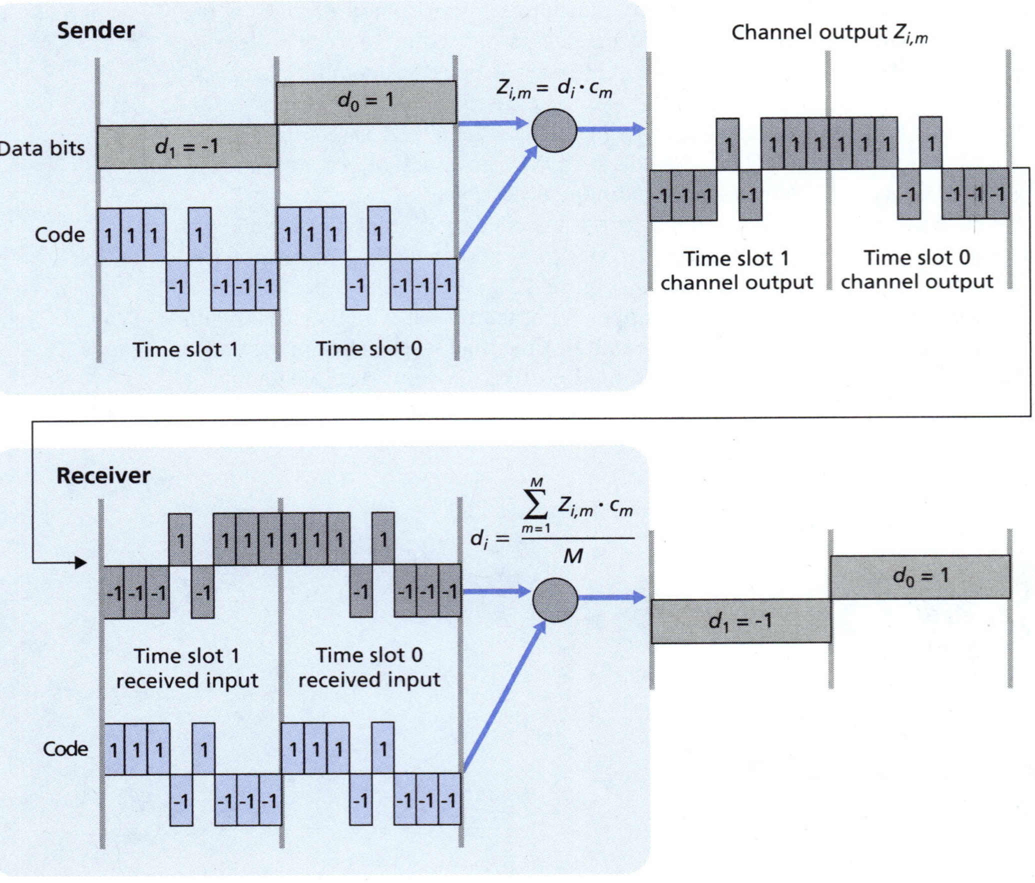

Figure 12.4 ♦ A simple CDMA example: sender encoding, receiver decoding

$$Z_{i,m} = d_i \cdot c_m \tag{12.1}$$

In a simple world, with no interfering senders, the receiver would receive the encoded bits, $Z_{i,m}$, and recover the original data bit, d_i, by computing:

$$d_i = \frac{1}{M} \sum_{m=1}^{M} Z_{i,m} \cdot c_m \tag{12.2}$$

The reader might want to work through the details of the example in Figure 12.4 to see that the original data bits are indeed correctly recovered at the receiver using Equation 12.2.

The world is far from ideal, however, and as noted above, CDMA must work in the presence of interfering senders that are encoding and transmitting their data using a different assigned code. But how can a CDMA receiver recover a sender's original data bits when those data bits are being tangled with bits being transmitted by other senders? CDMA works under the assumption that the interfering transmitted bit signals are additive. This means, for example, that if three senders send a 1 value, and a fourth sender sends a –1 value during the same mini-slot, then the received signal at all receivers during that mini-slot is a 2 (since 1 + 1 + 1 – 1 = 2). In the presence of multiple senders, sender s computes its encoded transmissions, $Z^s_{i,m}$, in exactly the same manner as in Equation 12.1. The value received at a receiver during the mth mini-slot of the ith bit slot, however, is now the *sum* of the transmitted bits from all N senders during that mini-slot:

$$Z^*_{i,m} = \sum_{s=1}^{N} Z^s_{i,m}$$

Amazingly, if the senders' codes are chosen carefully, each receiver can recover the data sent by a given sender out of the aggregate signal simply by using the sender's code in exactly the same manner as in Equation 12.2:

$$d_i = \frac{1}{M} \sum_{m=1}^{M} Z^*_{i,m} \cdot c \tag{12.3}$$

Figure 12.5 illustrates a two-sender CDMA example. The M-bit CDMA code being used by the upper sender is (1, 1, 1, –1, 1, –1, –1, –1), while the CDMA code being used by the lower sender is (1, –1, 1, 1, 1,–1, 1, 1). Figure 12.5 illustrates a receiver recovering the original data bits from the upper sender. Note that the receiver is able to extract the data from sender 1 in spite of the interfering transmission from sender 2.

Recall our cocktail analogy from Chapter 11. A CDMA protocol is similar to having partygoers speaking in multiple languages; in such circumstances humans are actually quite good at locking into the conversation in the language they understand, while filtering out the remaining conversations. We see here that

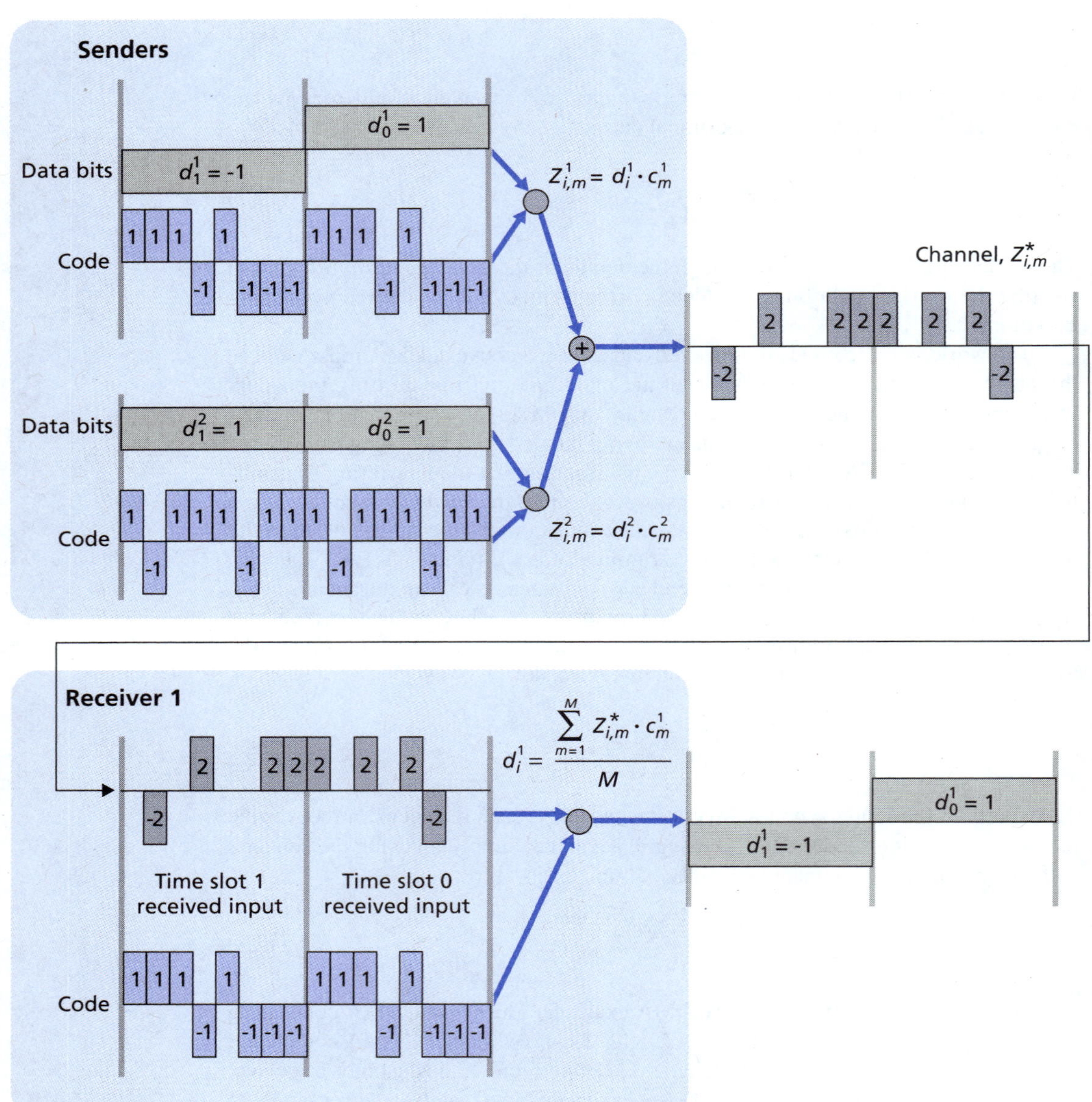

Figure 12.5 ♦ A two-sender CDMA example

CDMA is a partitioning protocol in that it partitions the codespace (as opposed to time or frequency) and assigns each node a dedicated piece of the codespace.

Our discussion here of CDMA is necessarily brief; in practice a number of difficult issues must be addressed. First, in order for the CDMA receivers to be able to extract a particular sender's signal, the CDMA codes must be carefully chosen. Second, our discussion has assumed that the received signal strengths from various senders are the same; in reality this can be difficult to achieve. There is a considerable body of literature addressing these and other issues related to CDMA; see [Pickholtz 1982; Viterbi 1995] for details.

12.3 Wi-Fi: 802.11 Wireless LANs

Pervasive in the workplace, the home, educational institutions, cafés, airports, and street corners, wireless LANs are now one of the most important access network technologies in the Internet today. Although many technologies and standards for wireless LANs were developed in the 1990s, one particular class of standards has clearly emerged as the winner: the **IEEE 802.11 wireless LAN**, also known as **Wi-Fi**. In this section, we'll take a close look at 802.11 wireless LANs, examining the 802.11 frame structure, the 802.11 medium access protocol, and the internetworking of 802.11 LANs with wired Ethernet LANs.

There are several 802.11 standards for wireless LAN technology, including 802.11b, 802.11a, and 802.11g. Table 12.1 summarizes the main characteristics of these standards. As of this writing (spring 2004), the 802.11b wireless LANs are by far the most prevalent. However, 802.11a and 802.11g products are also widely available, and these higher-speed wireless LANs should enjoy significant deployment in the coming years.

The three 802.11 standards share many characteristics. They all use the same medium access protocol, CSMA/CA, which we'll discuss shortly. All three use the same frame structure for their link-layer frames as well. All three standards have the

Standard	Frequency Range	Data Rate
802.11b	2.4-2.485 GHz	up to 11 Mbps
802.11a	5.1-5.8 GHz	up to 54 Mbps
802.11g	2.4-2.485 GHz	up to 54 Mbps

Table 12.1 ♦ Summary of IEEE 802.11 Standards

ability to reduce their transmission rate in order to reach out over greater distances. And all three standards allow for both "infrastructure mode" and "ad hoc mode," as we'll also shortly discuss. However, as shown in Table 12.1, the three standards have some major differences at the physical layer.

The 802.11b wireless LAN has a data rate of 11 Mbps, which is more than sufficient for most home networks with broadband cable or DSL Internet access. 802.11b LANs operate in the unlicensed frequency band of 2.4-2.485 GHz, competing for frequency spectrum with 2.4 GHz phones and microwave ovens. 802.1la wireless LANs can run at significantly higher bit rates, but do so at higher frequencies. By operating at a higher frequency, however, 802.11a LANs have a shorter transmission distance for a given power level and suffer more from multipath propagation. 802.11g LANs, operating in the same lower frequency band as 802.11b yet with the higher-speed transmission rates of 802.11a, should allow users to eat their cake and have it too.

12.3.1 The 802.11 Architecture

Figure 12.6 illustrates the principal components of the 802.11 wireless LAN architecture. The fundamental building block of the 802.11 architecture is the **basic service set (BSS)**. A BSS contains one or more wireless stations and a central **base station**, known as an **access point (AP)** in 802.11 parlance. Figure 12.6 shows the AP in each of two BSSs connecting to an interconnection device (such as a hub, switch or router), which in turn leads to the Internet. In a typical home network, there is one AP and one router (often packaged with a cable or ADSL modem, all in the same box) that connects the BSS to the Internet.

As with Ethernet devices, each 802.11 wireless station has a 6-byte MAC address that is stored in the firmware of the station's adaptor (that is, 802.11 network interface card). Each AP also has a MAC address for its wireless interface. As with Ethernet, these MAC addresses are administered by IEEE and are (in theory) globally unique.

As noted in Section 12.1, wireless LANs that deploy APs are often referred to as **infrastructure wireless LANs**, with the "infrastructure" being the APs along with the wired Ethernet infrastructure that interconnect the APs and a router. Figure 12.7 shows that IEEE 802.11 stations can also group themselves together to form an ad hoc network—a network with no central control and with no connections to the "outside world." Here, the network is formed "on the fly," by mobile devices that have found themselves in proximity to each other, that have a need to communicate, and that find no preexisting network infrastructure in their location. An ad hoc network might be formed when people with laptops get together (for example, in a conference room, a train, or a car) and want to exchange data in the absence of a centralized AP. There has been tremendous interest in ad hoc networking, as communicating portable devices continue to proliferate. In this section, though, we'll focus our attention on infrastructure wireless LANs.

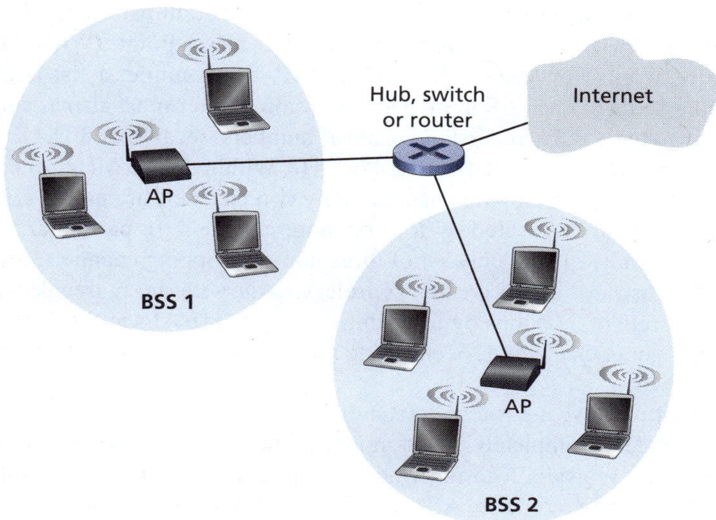

Figure 12.6 ♦ IEEE 802.11 LAN architecture

Channels and Association

In 802.11, each wireless station needs to associate with an AP before it can send or receive 802.11 frames containing network-layer data. Although all of the 802.11 standards use association, we'll discuss this topic specifically in the context of IEEE 802.11b.

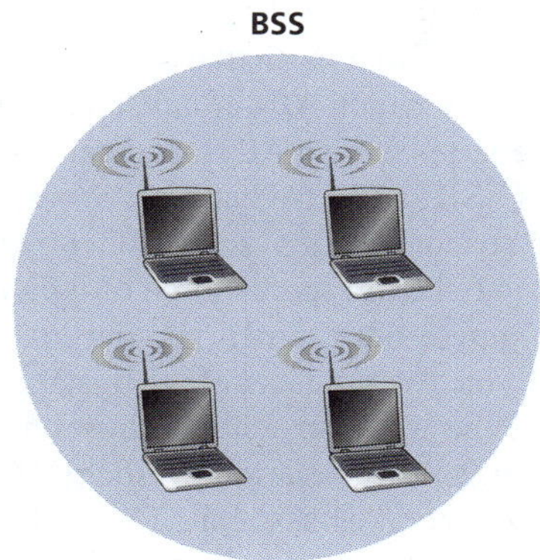

Figure 12.7 ♦ An IEEE 802.11 ad hoc network

When a network administrator installs an AP, the administrator assigns a one- or two-word **Service Set Identifier (SSID)** to the access point. (When you "view available networks" in Microsoft Windows XP, for example, a list is displayed showing the SSID of each AP in range.) The administrator must also assign a channel number to the AP. To understand channel numbers, recall that 802.11b operates in the frequency range of 2.4 GHZ to 2.485 GHz. Within this 85 MHz band, 802.11b defines 11 partially overlapping channels. Any two channels are non-overlapping if and only if they are separated by four or more channels. In particular, the set of channels 1, 6, and 11 is the only set of three non-overlapping channels. This means that an administrator could create a wireless LAN with an aggregate maximum transmission rate of 33 Mbps by installing three 802.11b APs at the same physical location, assigning channels 1, 6, and 11 to the APs, and interconnecting each of the APs with a switch.

Now that we have a basic understanding of 802.11 channels, let's describe an interesting (and not completely uncommon) situation—that of a Wi-Fi jungle. A **Wi-Fi jungle** is any physical location where a wireless station receives a sufficiently strong signal from two or more APs. For example, in many cafés in New York City, a wireless station can pick up a signal from numerous nearby APs. One of the APs might be managed by the café, while the other APs might be in residential apartments near the café. Each of these APs would likely be located in a different subnet and would have been independently assigned a channel.

Now suppose you enter such a Wi-Fi jungle with your portable computer, seeking wireless Internet access and a blueberry muffin. Suppose there are five APs in the jungle. To gain Internet access, your wireless station will need to join exactly one of the subnets and hence need to **associate** with exactly one of the APs. Associating means the wireless station creates a virtual wire between itself and the AP. Specifically, only the associated AP will send data frames (that is, frames containing data, such as a datagram) to your wireless station, and your wireless station will send data frames into the Internet only through the associated AP. But how does your wireless station associate with a particular AP? And more fundamentally, how does your wireless station know which APs, if any, are out there in the jungle?

The 802.11 standard requires that an AP periodically send **beacon frames**, each of which includes the AP's SSID and MAC address. Your wireless station, knowing that APs are sending out beacon frames, scans the 11 channels, seeking beacon frames from any APs that may be out there (some of which may be transmitting on the same channel—it's a jungle out there!). Having learned about available APs from the beacon frames, you (or your wireless host) select one of the APs for association. After selecting the AP, your wireless host and the chosen AP dialogue with each other using the 802.11 association protocol. If all goes well in this dialogue, your wireless station becomes associated with the selected AP. Implicitly, during the association phase, your wireless station is joining the subnet to which the selected AP belongs. Just after the association phase, the wireless station will typically send a DHCP discovery message (see Section 11.4.3) into the subnet via the associated AP in order to obtain an IP address in the AP's subnet. At this point, the rest of the Internet now views your computer simply as a host in the AP's subnet.

In order to create an association with a particular AP, the wireless station may be required to authenticate itself to the AP. 802.11 wireless LANs provide a number of alternatives for authentication and access. One approach, used by many companies, is to permit access to a wireless network based on a station's MAC address. A second approach, used by many Internet cafés, employs user names and passwords. In both cases, the AP typically communicates with an authentication server, relaying information between the wireless endpoint station and the authentication server using a protocol such as RADIUS [RFC 2138] or DIAMETER [RFC 3588]. Separating the authentication server from the AP allows one authentication server to serve many APs, centralizing the (often sensitive) decisions of authentication and access within the single server, and keeping AP costs and complexity low. We'll see that the new IEEE 802.11i protocol defining security aspects of the 802.11 protocol family takes precisely this approach.

12.3.2 The 802.11 MAC Protocol

Once a wireless station is associated with an AP, it can start sending and receiving data frames to and from the access point. But because multiple stations may want to transmit data frames at the same time over the same channel, a multiple access protocol is needed to coordinate the transmissions. Here, a **station** is either a wireless station or an AP. As discussed in Chapter 11 and Section 12.2.1, broadly speaking there are four classes of multiple access protocols: channel partitioning, random access, taking turns, and CDMA. Inspired by the huge success of Ethernet and its random access protocol, the designers of 802.11 chose a random access protocol for 802.11 wireless LANs. This random access protocol is referred to as **CSMA with collision avoidance**, or more succinctly as **CSMA/CA**. As with Ethernet's CSMA/CD, the "CSMA" in CSMA/CA stands for "carrier sense multiple access," meaning that each station senses the channel before transmitting, and refrains from transmitting when the channel is sensed busy. Although both Ethernet and 802.11 use carrier-sensing random access, the two MAC protocols have important differences. First, instead of using collision detection, 802.11 uses collision avoidance techniques. Second, because of the relatively high bit-error rates of wireless channels, 802.11 (unlike Ethernet) uses a link-layer acknowledgement/retransmission (ARQ) scheme. We'll describe 802.11's collision avoidance and link-layer acknowledgment schemes below.

Recall from Sections 11.3 and 11.5 that with Ethernet's collision-detection algorithm, an Ethernet station listens to the channel as it transmits. If, while transmitting, it detects that another station is also transmitting, it aborts its transmission and tries to transmit again after waiting a small, random amount of time. Unlike the 802.3 Ethernet protocol, the 802.11 MAC protocol does *not* implement collision detection. There are two important reasons for this:

- The ability to detect collisions requires the ability to send (the station's own signal) and receive (to determine whether another station is also transmitting) at the same time. Because the strength of the received signal is typically very small compared to the strength of transmitted signal at the 802.11 adapter, it is costly to build hardware that can detect a collision.
- More importantly, even if the adapter could transmit and listen at the same time (and presumably abort transmission when it senses a busy channel), the adapter would still not be able to detect all collisions due to the hidden terminal problem and fading, as discussed in Section 12.2.

Because 802.11wireless LANs do not use collision detection, once a station begins to transmit a frame, *it transmits the frame in its entirety*; that is, once a station gets started, there is no turning back. As one might expect, transmitting entire frames (particularly long frames) when collisions are prevalent can significantly degrade a multiple access protocol's performance. In order to reduce the likelihood of collisions, 802.11 employs several collision avoidance techniques, which we'll shortly discuss.

Before considering collision avoidance, however, we'll first need to examine 802.11's **link-layer acknowledgment** scheme. Recall from Section 12.2 that when a station in a wireless LAN sends a frame, the frame may not reach the destination station intact for a variety of reasons. To deal with this non-negligible chance of failure, the 802.11 MAC uses link-layer acknowledgments. As shown in Figure 12.8, when the destination station receives a frame that passes the CRC check, it waits a short period of time known as the **Short Inter-frame Spacing (SIFS)** and then sends back an acknowledgment frame. If the transmitting station does not receive an acknowledgment within a given amount of time, it assumes that an error has occurred and retransmits the frame, again using the CSMA/CA protocol to access the channel. If an acknowledgment is not received after some fixed number of retransmissions, the transmitting station gives up and discards the frame.

Having discussed how 802.11 uses link-layer acknowledgments, we're now in a position to describe the 802.11 CSMA/CA protocol. Suppose that a station (wireless station or an AP) has a frame to transmit.

1. If initially the station senses the channel idle, it transmits its frame after a short period of time known as the **Distributed Inter-frame Space (DIFS)**; see Figure 12.8.
2. Otherwise, the station chooses a random backoff value and counts down this value when the channel is sensed idle. When the channel is sensed busy, the counter value remains frozen.
3. When the counter reaches zero (note that this can only occur when the channel is sensed idle), the station transmits the entire frame and then waits for an acknowledgement.

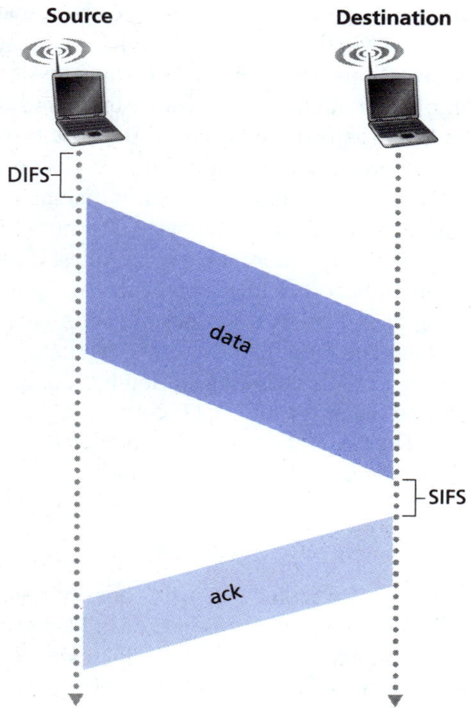

Figure 12.8 ♦ 802.11 uses link-layer acknowledgments

4. If an acknowledgment is received, the transmitting station knows that its frame has been correctly received at the destination station. If the station has another frame to send, it begins the CSMA/CA protocol at step 2. If the acknowledgment isn't received, the transmitting station reenters the backoff phase in step 2, with the random value chosen from a larger interval.

The observant reader may have noted that in step 2, the station chooses a random backoff value and begins a countdown, effectively delaying its transmission even if the channel is sensed idle. Under Ethernet's CSMA/CD multiple access protocol (Section 11.5.2), however, a station begins transmitting as soon as the channel is sensed idle. Why do CSMA/CD and CDMA/CA take such different approaches here?

To answer this question, let's consider a scenario in which two stations each have a data frame to transmit, but neither station transmits immediately because each senses that a third station is already transmitting. With Ethernet's CSMA/CD, the two stations would each transmit as soon as they detect that the third station has finished transmitting. This would cause a collision, which isn't a serious issue in CSMA/CD, since both stations would abort their transmissions and thus avoid the useless transmission of the remainder of a frame that has suffered a collision. In 802.11, however, the situation is quite different. Because 802.11 does not detect a collision and abort transmission, a frame suffering a collision will be transmitted in its entirety. The goal in 802.11 is thus to avoid collisions whenever possible. In 802.11, if the two stations sense the channel busy, they both immediately enter random backoff, hopefully choosing different backoff values. If these values are indeed different, once the channel becomes idle, one of the two stations will begin transmitting before the other, and (if the two stations are not hidden from each other) the "losing station" will hear the "winning station's" signal, freeze its counter, and refrain from transmitting until the winning station has completed its transmission. In this manner, a costly collision is avoided. Of course, collisions can still occur with 802.11 in this scenario: The two stations could be hidden from each other, or the two stations could choose identical random backoff values.

Dealing with Hidden Terminals: RTS and CTS

The 802.11 MAC protocol also includes a nifty (but optional) reservation scheme that helps avoid collisions even in the presence of hidden terminals. Let's investigate this scheme in the context of Figure 12.9, which shows two wireless stations and one access point. Both of the wireless stations are within range of the AP (whose coverage is shown as a shaded circle) and both have associated with the AP. However, due to fading, the signal ranges of wireless stations are limited to the interiors of the shaded circles shown in Figure 12.9. Thus, each of the wireless stations is hidden from the other, although neither is hidden from the AP.

Let's now consider why hidden terminals can be problematic. Suppose Station H1 is transmitting a frame and halfway through H1's transmission, the network layer at Station H2 passes a frame (which we will refer to as a DATA frame here) to the 802.11 MAC. H2, not hearing the transmission from H1 will first wait a short random amount of time and then transmit the DATA frame, resulting in a collision. The channel will therefore be wasted during the entire period of H1's transmission as well as during H2's transmission.

In order to avoid this problem, the IEEE 802.11 protocol allows a station to use a short **Request to Send (RTS)** control frame and a short **Clear to Send (CTS)** control frame to *reserve* access to the channel. When a sender wants to send a DATA frame, it can first send an RTS frame to the AP, indicating the total time required to transmit the DATA frame and the acknowledgement (ACK) frame. When the AP receives the RTS frame, it responds by broadcasting a CTS frame. This CTS frame serves two purposes: It gives the sender explicit permission to send and also instructs the other stations not to send for the reserved duration.

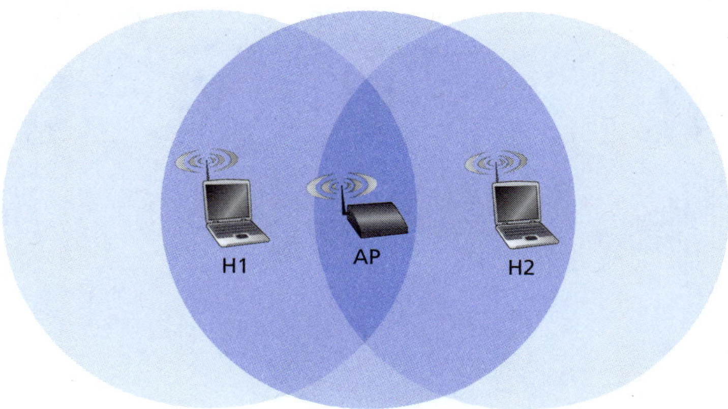

Figure 12.9 ♦ Hidden terminal example: H1 is hidden from H2, and vice versa

Thus, in Figure 12.10, before transmitting a DATA frame, H1 first broadcasts an RTS frame, which is heard by all stations in its circle, including the AP. The AP then responds with a CTS frame, which is heard by all stations within its range, including H1 and H2. Station H2, having heard the CTS, refrains from transmitting for the time specified in the CTS frame. The RTS, CTS, DATA, and ACK frames are shown in Figure 12.10.

The use of the RTS and CTS frames can improve performance in two important ways:

- The hidden station problem is mitigated, since a long DATA frame is transmitted only after the channel has been reserved.
- Because the RTS and CTS frames are short, a collision involving an RTS or CTS frame will last only for the duration of the short RTS or CTS frame. Once the RTS and CTS frames are correctly transmitted, the following DATA and ACK frames should be transmitted without collisions.

You are encouraged to check out the 802.11 applet in the textbook's companion Web site. This interactive applet illustrates the CSMA/CA protocol, including the RTS/CTS exchange sequence.

Although the RTS/CTS exchange can help reduce collisions, it also introduces delay and consumes channel resources. For this reason, the RTS/CTS exchange is only used (if at all) to reserve the channel for the transmission of a long DATA frame. In practice, each wireless station can set an RTS threshold such that the

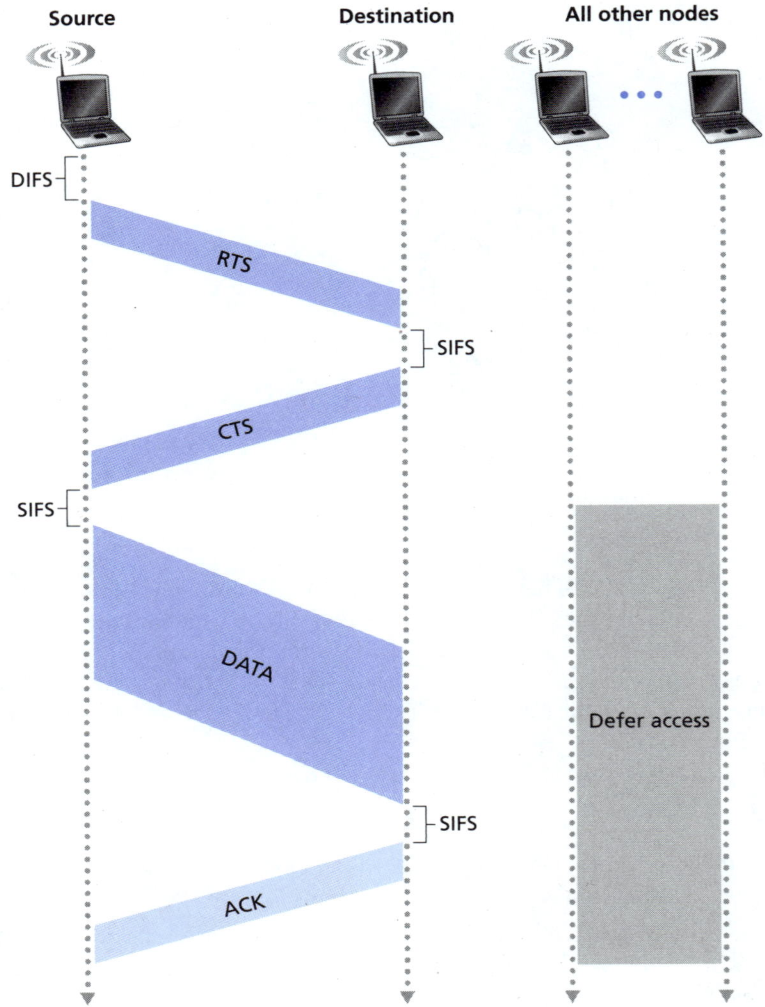

Figure 12.10 ♦ Collision avoidance using the RTS and CTS frames

RTS/CTS sequence is used only when the frame is longer than the threshold. For many wireless stations, the default RTS threshold value is larger than the maximum frame length, so the RTS/CTS sequence is skipped for all DATA frames sent.

Using 802.11 as a Point-to-Point Link

Our discussion so far has focused on the use of 802.11 in a multiple access setting. We should mention that if two nodes each have a directional antenna, they can point their directional antennae at each other and run the 802.11 protocol over what is an essentially a point-to-point link. Given the low cost of commodity 802.11 hardware, the use of directional antennae and an increased transmission power allow 802.11 to be used as an inexpensive means of providing wireless point-to-point connections over tens of kilometers distance. [Bhagwat 2003] describes such a multi-hop wireless network operating in the rural Ganges plains in India that contains point-to-point 802.11 links.

12.3.3 The IEEE 802.11 Frame

Although the 802.11 frame shares many similarities with an Ethernet frame, it also contains a number of fields that are specific to its use for wireless links. The 802.11 frame is shown in Figure 12.11. The numbers above each of the fields in the frame represent the lengths of the fields in *bytes*; the numbers above each of the subfields in the frame control field represent the lengths of the subfields in *bits*. Let's now examine the fields in the frame as well as some of the more important subfields in the frame's control field.

Payload and CRC Fields

At the heart of the frame is the payload, which typically consists of an IP datagram or an ARP packet. Although the field is permitted to be as long as 2,312 bytes, it is typically fewer than 1,500 bytes, holding an IP datagram or an ARP packet. As with an Ethernet frame, an 802.11 frame includes a cyclic redundancy check (CRC) so

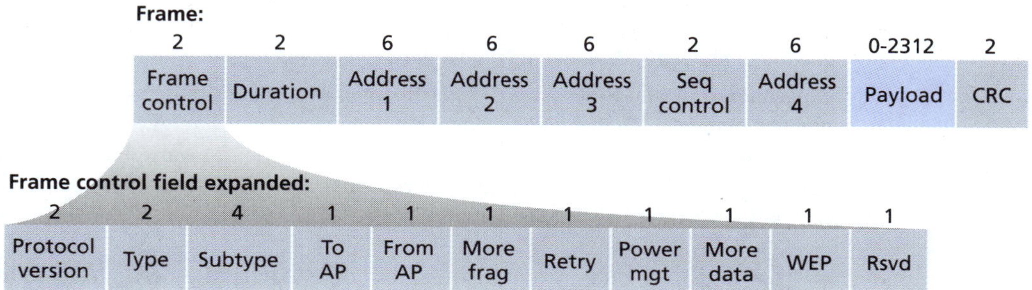

Figure 12.11 ♦ The 802.11 frame

that the receiver can detect bit errors in the received frame. As we've seen, bit errors are much more common in wireless LANs than in wired LANs, so the CRC is even more useful here.

Address Fields

Perhaps the most striking difference in the 802.11 frame is that it has *four* address fields, each of which can hold a 6-byte MAC address. But why four address fields? Doesn't a source MAC field and destination MAC field suffice, as they do for Ethernet? It turns out that three address fields are needed for internetworking purposes—specifically, for moving the network-layer datagram from a wireless station through an AP to a router interface. The fourth address field is used in ad hoc networks, but not in infrastructure networks. Since we are only considering infrastructure networks here, let's focus our attention on the first three address fields. The 802.11 standard defines these fields as follows:

- Address 2 is the MAC address of the station that transmits the frame. Thus, if a wireless station transmits the frame, that station's MAC address is inserted in the address 2 field. Similarly, if an AP transmits the frame, the AP's MAC address is inserted in the address 2 field.
- Address 1 is the MAC address of the wireless station that is to receive the frame. Thus if a mobile wireless station transmits the frame, address 1 contains the MAC address of the destination AP. Similarly, if an AP transmits the frame, address 1 contains the MAC address of the destination wireless station.
- To understand address 3, recall that the BSS (consisting of the AP and wireless stations) is part of a subnet, and that this subnet connects to other subnets via some router interface. Address 3 contains the MAC address of this router interface.

To gain further insight into the purpose of address 3, let's walk through an internetworking example in the context of Figure 12.12. In this figure, there are two APs, each of which is responsible for a number of wireless stations. Each of the APs has a direct connection to a router, which in turn connects to the global Internet. We should keep in mind that an AP is a link-layer device, and thus neither "speaks" IP nor understands IP addresses. Consider now moving a datagram from the router interface R1 to the wireless Station H1. The router is not aware that there is an AP between it and H1; from the router's perspective, H1 is just a host in one of the subnets to which it (the router) is connected.

- The router, which knows the IP address of H1 (from the destination address of the datagram), uses ARP to determine the MAC address of H1, just as in an ordinary Ethernet LAN. After obtaining H1's MAC address, router interface R1 encapsulates the datagram within an Ethernet frame. The source address field of

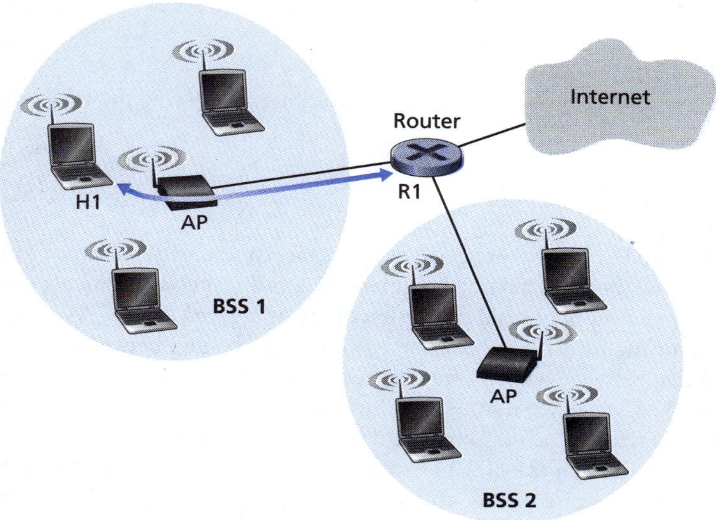

Figure 12.12 ♦ The use of address fields in 802.11 frames: Moving a frame between H1 and R1

this frame contains R1's MAC address and the destination address field contains H1's MAC address.

- When the Ethernet frame arrives at the AP, the AP converts the 802.3 Ethernet frame to an 802.11 frame before transmitting the frame into the wireless channel. The AP fills in address 1 and address 2 with H1's MAC address and its own MAC address, respectively, as described above. For address 3, the AP inserts the MAC address of R1. In this manner, H1 can to determine (from address 3) the MAC address of the router interface that sent the datagram into the subnet.

Now consider what happens when the wireless station H1 responds by moving a datagram from H1 to R1.

- H1 creates an 802.11 frame, filling the fields for address 1 and address 2 with the AP's MAC address and H1's MAC address, respectively, as described above. For address 3, H1 inserts R1's MAC address.
- When the AP receives the 802.11 frame, it converts the frame to an Ethernet frame. The source address field for this frame is H1's MAC address, and the destination address field is R1's MAC address. Thus, address 3 allows the AP to

determine the appropriate destination MAC address when constructing the Ethernet frame.

In summary, address 3 plays a crucial role for internetworking the BSS with a wired LAN.

Sequence Number, Duration, and Frame Control Fields

Recall that in 802.11, whenever a station correctly receives a frame from another station, it sends back an acknowledgment. Because acknowledgments can get lost, the sending station may send multiple copies of a given frame. As we saw in our discussion of the rdt2.1 protocol, the use of sequence numbers allows the receiver to distinguish between a newly transmitted frame and the retransmission of a previous frame. The sequence number field in the 802.11 frame thus serves exactly the same purpose here at the link layer as it did in the transport layer.

Keep in mind that the 802.11 protocol allows a transmitting station to reserve the channel for a period of time that includes the time to transmit its data frame and the time to transmit an acknowledgment. This duration value is included in the frame's duration field (both for data frames and for the RTS and CTS frames).

As shown in Figure 12.11, the frame control field includes many subfields. We'll say just a few words about some of the more important subfields; for a more complete discussion, you are encouraged to consult the 802.11 specification [Held 2001; Crow 1997; IEEE 802.11 1999]. The *type* and *subtype* fields are used to distinguish the association, RTS, CTS, ACK, and data frames. The *to* and *from* fields are used to define the meanings of the different address fields. (These meanings change depending on whether ad hoc or infrastructure modes are used and, in the case of infrastructure mode, whether a wireless station or an AP is sending the frame.) Finally the WEP field indicates whether encryption is being used or not.

12.3.4 Mobility in the Same IP Subnet

In order to increase the physical range of a wireless LAN, companies and universities will often deploy multiple BSSs within the same IP subnet. This naturally raises the issue of mobility among the BSSs—how do wireless stations seamlessly move from one BSS to another while maintaining ongoing TCP sessions? As we'll see in this subsection, mobility can be handled in a relatively straightforward manner when the BSSs are part of the subnet. When stations move between subnets, more sophisticated mobility management protocols will be needed, such as those we'll study in Sections 12.5 and 12.6.

Let's now look at a specific example of mobility between BSSs in the same subnet. Figure 12.13 shows two interconnected BSSs with a host, H1, moving from

BSS1 to BSS2. Because in this example the interconnection device that connects the two BSSs is *not* a router, all of the stations in the two BSSs, including the APs, belong to the same IP subnet. Thus, when H1 moves from BSS1 to BSS2, it may keep its IP address and all of its ongoing TCP connections. If the interconnection device were a router, then H1 would either have to change its IP address, and either drop its ongoing TCP connections, or make use of a network-layer mobility protocol, such as mobile IP, as discussed in Section 12.6.

But what specifically happens when H1 moves from BSS1 to BSS2? As H1 wanders away from AP1, H1 detects a weakening signal from AP1 and starts to scan for a stronger signal. H1 receives beacon frames from AP2 (which in many corporate and university settings will have the same SSID as AP1). H1 then disassociates with AP1 and associates with AP2, while keeping its IP address and maintaining its ongoing TCP sessions.

This all works fine if the interconnection device is a hub. But if the device is a switch—as it often is—then special care must be taken. As you may recall from Chapter 11, switches are "self-learning" and automatically build their forwarding tables. This self-learning feature nicely handles occasional moves (for example, when an employee gets transferred from one department to another); however, switches were not designed to support highly mobile users who want to maintain TCP connections while moving between BSSs. To appreciate the problem here, recall that before the move, the switch has an entry in its forwarding table that pairs H1's MAC address and the outgoing switch interface through which H1 can be reached. If H1 is initially in BSS1, then a datagram destined to H1 will be directed to via AP1. Once H1 associates with BSS2, however, its frames should be directed to AP2. One solution (a bit of a hack, really) is for AP2 to send a broadcast Ethernet

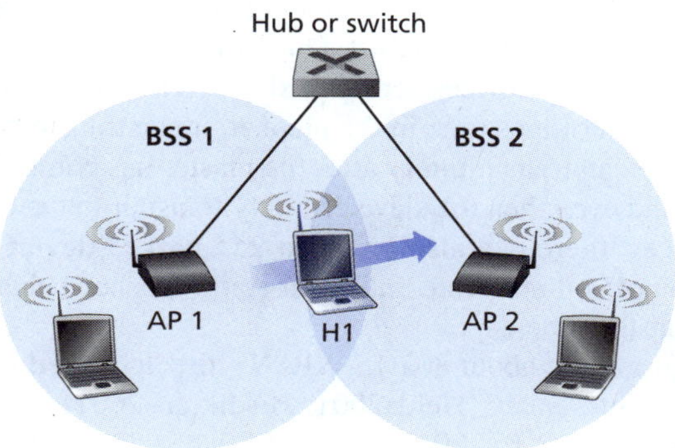

Figure 12.13 ♦ Mobility in the same subnet

frame with H1's source address to the switch just after the new association. When the switch receives the frame, it updates its forwarding table, allowing H1 to be reached via AP2. The 802.11f standards group is developing an inter-AP protocol to handle these and related issues.

12.3.5 802.15 and Bluetooth

As noted in Figure 12.2, the IEEE 801.11 Wi-Fi standard is aimed at communication among devices separated by up to 100 meters, while network access over cellular telephony networks spans the range of tens of kilometers. Before delving into the details of these longer distance cellular wireless networks, let's briefly consider the 802.15 **wireless personal area network (WPAN)** standard, a cousin of 802.11 in the IEEE 802 family that is meant to provide connectivity among personal devices separated by up to 10 meters or so. 802.15 is essentially a low-power, short-range, low-rate "cable replacement" technology for interconnecting notebooks, peripheral devices, cellular phones, and PDAs, whereas 802.11 is a higher-power, medium-range, higher-rate "access" technology.

An IEEE 802.15 network operates over a short range, at low power, and at low cost. The link and physical layers of 802.15 are based on the earlier **Bluetooth** specification for personal area networks [Held 2001, Bisdikian 2001]. 802.15 networks operate in the 2.4 GHz unlicensed radio band in a TDM manner, with time slots of 625 microseconds. During each time slot, a sender transmits on one of 79 channels, with the channel changing in a known but pseudo-random manner from slot to slot. This form of channel hopping, known as **frequency-hopping spread spectrum (FHSS)** spreads transmissions in time over the frequency spectrum. 802.15 can provide data rates up to 721 kbps.

802.15 networks are ad hoc networks: No network infrastructure (e.g., an access point) is needed to interconnect 802.15 devices. Thus, 802.15 devices must organize themselves. 802.15 devices are first organized into a **piconet** of up to eight active devices, as shown in Figure 12.14. One of these devices is designated as the master, with the remaining devices acting as slaves. The master node truly rules the piconet—its clock determines time in the piconet, it can transmit in each odd number slot, and a slave can transmit only after the master has communicated with it in the previous slot and even then the slave can only transmit to the master. In addition to the slave devices, there can also be up to 255 parked devices in the network. These devices cannot communicate until their status has been changed from parked to active by the master node.

For more information about 802.15 WPANs, the interested reader should consult the Bluetooth references [Held 2001, Bisdikian 2001] or the official IEEE 802.15 Web site [IEEE 802.15 2004].

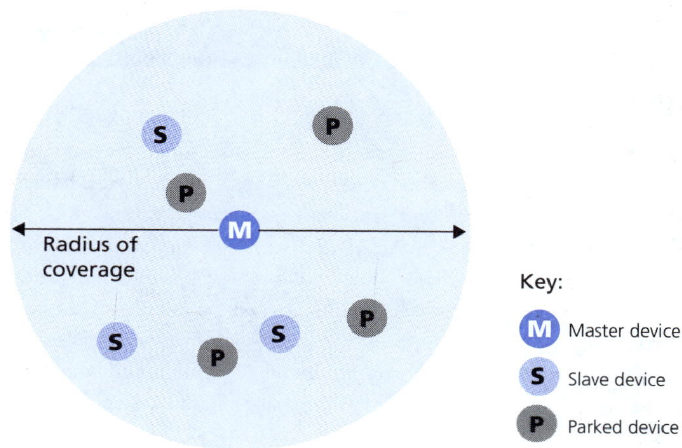

Figure 12.14 ♦ An 802.15 piconet

12.4 Cellular Internet Access

In the previous section we examined how an Internet host can access the Internet when inside a Wi-Fi hotspot, that is, when it is within the vicinity of an 802.11 access point. But most Wi-Fi hot spots have a small coverage area of between 10 and 100 meters in diameter. What do we do then when we have a desperate need for wireless Internet access and we cannot access a Wi-Fi hotspot?

Given that cellular telephony is now ubiquitous in many areas throughout the world, a natural strategy is to extend cellular networks so that they support not only voice telephony but wireless Internet access as well. Ideally, this Internet access would be at a reasonably high speed and would provide for seamless mobility, allowing users to maintain their TCP sessions while traveling, for example, on a bus or a train. With sufficiently high upstream and downstream bit rates, the user could even maintain video-conferencing sessions while roaming about. This scenario is not that far-fetched. As of Spring 2004 many cellular telephony providers offer their subscribers a cellular Internet access service for under $100 per month with typical downstream and upstream bit rates in the low hundreds of kilobits per second.

In this section, we provide a brief overview of current and emerging cellular Internet access technologies. Our focus here will again be on the wireless first hop between the cellular phone and the wired telephone network infrastructure; in Section 12.7 we'll consider how calls are routed to a user moving between base stations. Our brief discussion will necessarily provide only a simplified and high-level

CASE HISTORY

3G CELLULAR MOBILE VERSUS WIRELESS LANS

Many cellular mobile phone operators are deploying 3G cellular mobile systems with 2 Mbps indoor and 384 kbps outdoor data rates. The 3G systems are being deployed in licensed radio-frequency bands, with some operators paying as much as $2,000 per subscriber to governments for the licenses. The 3G systems will allow users to access the Internet from remote outdoor locations while on the move, in a manner similar to today's cellular phone access. For example, 3G technology will permit a user to access road map information while driving a car, or movie theater information while sunbathing on a beach. Nevertheless, many experts today are beginning to question whether 3G technology will be successful, given its cost and its competition from wireless LAN technology [Weinstein 2002]. In particular, these experts argue:

- The emerging wireless LAN infrastructure will become nearly ubiquitous. IEEE 802.11 wireless LANs, operating at 11 Mbps and higher, are enjoying widespread deployment, as noted in an earlier sidebar (Public Wi-Fi Access). Soon almost all portable computers and PDAs will have factory-equipped 802.11 LAN cards. Furthermore, emerging Internet appliances—such as wireless cameras and picture frames—will also use the small and low-powered wireless LAN cards.
- The bulk of the wireless data traffic will originate or terminate in local environments. Assuming that the wireless traffic originating/terminating from shopping malls, office buildings, and so on is carried by the inexpensive wireless LANs, there will be relatively little traffic for the expensive 3G systems.
- Wireless LAN base stations could also handle mobile phone appliances. This allows low-cost data access for cellular mobile appliances as well as wireless LAN appliances. Thus, a cell phone without a wireless LAN card, but present in a local environment, will be able to bypass the operators' 3G systems to access the Internet.

Of course, many other experts believe that 3G will not only be a major success, but will also dramatically revolutionize the way we work and live. Of course, both Wi-Fi and 3G may become prevalent wireless technologies, with roaming wireless devices automatically selecting the access technology that provides the best service in their current physical location (see the discussion of 4G wireless access in this section).

description of cellular technologies. Modern cellular communications, of course, has great breadth and depth, with many universities offering several courses on the topic. Readers seeking a deeper understanding are encouraged to see [Goodman 1997; Scourias 1997; Korhonen 2003; Kaaranen 2001; Lin 2001], as well as the particularly excellent and exhaustive reference [Mouly 1992].

12.4.1 An Overview of Cellular Architecture

The term *cellular* refers to the fact that a geographical area is partitioned into a number of geographic coverage areas, known as **cells**, as shown in left side of Figure 12.15. Each cell contains a base station, which transmits signals to, and receives signals from, the mobile stations in its cell. The coverage area of a cell depends on many factors, including the transmitting power of the base station, the transmitting power of the mobile station, obstructing buildings in the cell, and the height of base station antennae. Although Figure 12.15 shows each cell containing one base station residing in the middle of the cell, many systems today place the base stations at corners where three cells intersect, so that a single base station with directional antennas can service three cells.

Basic Network Architecture

As shown in Figure 12.15, each base station is connected to a wide-area network—such as the Public Switched Telephone Network (PSTN) or directly to the Internet—via a

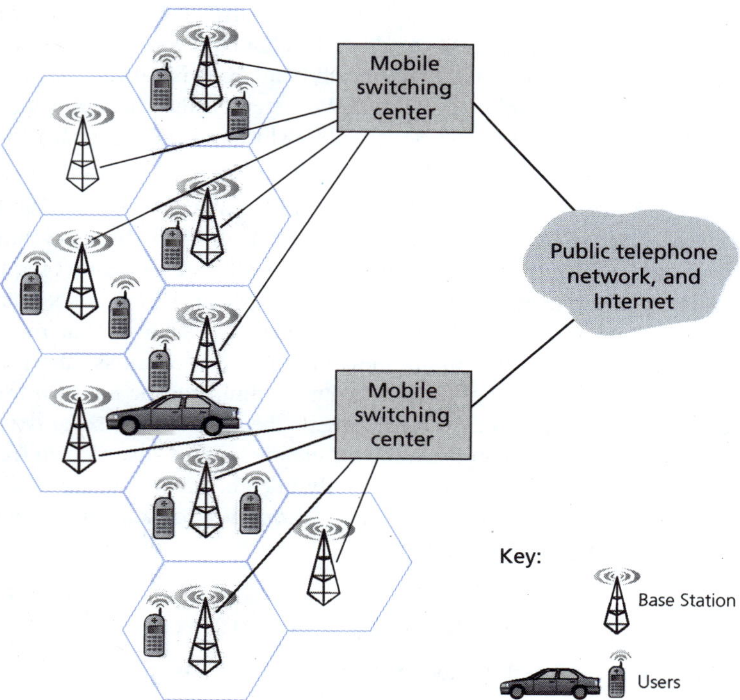

Figure 12.15 ♦ Components of a cellular network architecture

wired infrastructure. Specifically, Figure 12.15 shows that each base station is connected to a **mobile switching center (MSC)**, which manages call establishment and teardown to and from mobile users. An MSC contains much of functionality that is found in an ordinary telephone switching center (such as a PBX or central office), but augmented with the additional functionality required to handle the mobility of its users.

Air Interface Access Techniques

Typically many simultaneous calls take place in a given cell. These calls need to share the portion of the radio spectrum that is allocated to the cellular service provider. Most cellular systems today use one of two broad approaches for sharing radio spectrum:

- *A combination of frequency division multiplexing (FDM) and time division multiplexing (TDM).* Recall with pure FDM, the channel is partitioned into a number of frequency bands, with each band devoted to a call. Also recall that with pure TDM, time is partitioned into frames with each frame is further partitioned into slots, with each call being assigned the use a particular slot in the revolving frame. In combined FDM/TDM systems, the channel is partitioned into a number of frequency sub-bands; within each sub-band, time is partitioned into frames and slots. Thus, for a combined FDM/TDM system, if the channel is partitioned into F sub-bands and time is partitioned into T slots, then the channel will be able to support $F \cdot T$ simultaneous calls.
- *Code division multiple access (CDMA).* Recall from Section 12.2.1 that CDMA does not partition in frequency or in time. Instead, all users share the same radio frequency at the same time. Each user in a cell is allocated a distinct sequence of bits, called a chipping sequence. As we saw in Section 12.2.1, when the sender and receiver use the same chipping sequence, the receiver can recover the sender's transmission from among the simultaneous transmissions from other senders. A major advantage of CDMA is that it eliminates the need for frequency allocation. When using an FDM/TDM system, the receivers are sensitive to interference from other signals in the same frequency band. Thus, a given frequency can be reused in an FDM/TDM system only in cells that are located sufficiently far apart to avoid such interference. Such **frequency reuse** is not a major concern when designing CDMA systems.

12.4.2 Cellular Standards and Technologies: A Brief Survey

When people talk about cellular technology, they often classify the technology as belonging to one of several "generations." The earlier generations were designed primarily for voice traffic; the more recent cellular systems support Internet access as well as voice. Because this book is about computer networking and not voice telephony, we are, of course, more interested in recent generations of cellular systems. But because the recent generations directly evolved from the earlier generations, we nevertheless begin our survey with a brief discussion of first- and second-generation wireless systems.

In surveying the generations, we'll be quickly running through an alphabet soup of jargon for the various technologies. As a reader, you shouldn't feel obligated to fully absorb or memorize all the terms and acronyms in this alphabet soup. The purpose of this survey is to put the various wireless generations into perspective as well as to provide a quick reference guide for the various terms and acronyms.

First generation (1G) systems were analog FDMA systems designed for voice-only communication. These 1G systems are almost extinct now, having been replaced by the digital 2G systems.

Second Generation (2G)

Second generation systems, although digital, were also designed for voice communication. But because the current 2.5G and 3G systems, designed to handle data communications, have grown out of the 2G, it's important to say a few words about 2G. A 2G cell phone converts an analog voice signal into digital format before modulating and then transmitting the signal into the air. The digital technology in 2G has many advantages over the analog 1G technology, including increased service capacity within a cell, improved security to reduce fraud, and more advanced services such as caller ID and messaging. Most of today's cellular providers use 2G technology. Various 2G standards and technologies have been widely deployed, including:

- *Interim Standard 136 (**IS-136**) TDMA.* This is a combined FDM/TDM system that evolved from 1G FDMA technology. It has been widely deployed in North America.
- *Global System for Mobile Communications (**GSM**).* In the 1980s Europeans recognized the need for a pan-European digital system that would replace their incompatible 1G systems, providing seamless mobility between countries as well as features and capabilities not possible with analog systems. This need led to the GSM standard for cellular communications. Europeans deployed GSM technology with great success in the early 1990s. GSM then spread into Asia and North America, and is now the now the most widely deployed cellular communications standard. The GSM standard for 2G cellular systems uses combined FDM/TDM for the air interface. GSM systems consist of 200 kHz frequency bands, with each band supporting 8 TDM calls. GSM encodes speech at 13 kbps and 12.2 kbps.
- ***IS-95** CDMA.* Unlike IS-136 and GSM, which use FDM/TDM, IS-95 CDMA uses code division multiple access (see Section 12.2.1). The company Qualcomm demonstrated the viability of CDMA for cellular telephony in the late 1980s;

since then many IS-95 systems have been deployed, particularly in North America and Korea.

Transition from Second Generation to Third Generation (2.5G)

2G systems such as IS-95, GSM, and IS-136 are optimized for voice service and are not particularly well adapted for data communications. In the 1990s, standard organizations recognized the need for a 3G cellular technology that was appropriate for both voice and data communications (including Internet access). However, because broad deployment of 3G technology takes many years, companies developed interim protocols and standards that enable data transmission over the existing 2G infrastructure. Such systems have been collectively dubbed "2.5G cellular systems." These include:

- ***General Packet Radio Service (GPRS)***. GPRS evolved from GSM. For data services, GSM effectively emulates a modem between the user device and the destination data network—that is, GSM uses circuit switching for its data as well as voice traffic. As we learned, circuit switching is highly inefficient for bursty data. Furthermore, standard GSM supports data rates only up to 9.6 kbps, which is intolerably slow for just about anything besides plain text. GPRS is an interim solution that provides more efficient packet-based data service at higher data rates (typically in the 40 kbps to 60 kbps range). GPRS service is provided by an underlying GSM network. However, unlike vanilla GSM, a mobile GPRS station can use more than one time slot within a given channel in an on-demand basis. With GPRS, a number of slots are set aside for data communications and allocated dynamically to the mobile stations as a function their instantaneous demands.
- ***Enhanced Data Rates for Global Evolution (EDGE)***. The main goal of EDGE is to increase the data rate capabilities of a GSM/GPRS network, that is, to better exploit the 200 KHz GSM channel with its eight-slot TDMA frames. This is done primarily by replacing GSM's modulation scheme with a more powerful scheme. In theory, EDGE can provide users with 384 kbps for data communications. An excellent overview of EDGE is [Ericsson 2004].
- ***CDMA2000, Phase 1***. This 2.5G technology evolved from IS-95. It can provide packet-data services up to 144.4 kbps and sets the stage for 3G deployment of CDMA2000, Phase 2.

Third Generation (3G)

3G cellular systems are required to provide telephone service as well as data communications at significantly higher speeds than their 2G counterparts. In particular, 3G systems are mandated to provide:

- 144 kbps at driving speeds
- 384 kbps for outside stationary use or walking speeds
- 2 Mbps for indoors

There are two major (and competing) standards in the 3G arena:

- ***Universal Mobile Telecommunications Service (UMTS)***. UMTS is an evolution of GSM to support 3G capabilities. The UMTS network architecture borrows heavily from the established GSM network architecture. However, UMTS's radio access is significantly different from the FDMA/TDMA scheme used in GSM. Specifically, UMTS uses a CDMA technique called Direct Sequence Wideband CDMA (DS-WCDMA). Not surprisingly, since UMTS has its roots in GSM, UMTS is being broadly deployed in Europe
- ***CDMA-2000***. CDMA-2000 is an evolution of the IS-95 2G system and is backward compatible with IS-95. As you would expect from its name, it also uses CDMA as part of its air interface. CDMA-2000 is being deployed in North America and parts of Asia.

Fourth Generation (4G)

Now that we have examined both wireless LAN technology and the gamut of the cellular access technologies, let's take a step back and reflect on what we, as users, would ideally like for wireless Internet access. Here is a wish list that may come to mind:

- We would like ubiquitous wireless Internet access. Whether at home, in the office, in a car, in a café, or on a beach, we'd like to be able to access the Internet.
- As a function of our physical location and the speed at which we're moving, we'd like to be able to access the Internet at the highest possible rate. For example, if we're on a street corner where both 11 Mbps 802.11b and 384 kbps 3G access are available, we would like our system to automatically select 802.11b, the system that offers the highest bit rate at that time and place.
- As we roam throughout this heterogeneous environment, we are automatically and transparently switched from one access technology to another (for example, from 802.11 to 3G), depending on availability, without any user intervention.
- Of course, as we roam about, we want to maintain our ongoing TCP connections. Furthermore, we'd like the system to know where we are, so that new calls can continue to reach us as we move.
- We'd like the system to support voice and real-time video over IP, so that we can all wear Dick Tracy watches and video conference with our friends and colleagues, no matter where we are.

And of course we'd like this for free (or more realistically, at least at low cost). Although this may sound like a wireless nirvana, the good news is that most of the critical technology components are already available. It is really now an issue of integrating protocols and technologies to make this wish list a reality. These components include access technologies such as 802.11 and 3G, as well as mobility management protocols (see Sections 12.5, 12.6, and 12.7), encryption and authentication protocols, and the multimedia networking protocols (such as SIP for voice-over-IP, discussed in Chapter 13).

12.5 Mobility Management: Principles

Having now covered the *wireless* nature of the communication links in a wireless network, it's now time to turn our attention to the *mobility* that these wireless links enable. In the broadest sense, a mobile node is one that changes its point of attachment into the network over time. Because the term *mobility* has taken on many meanings in both the computer and telephony worlds, it will serve us well first to consider several dimensions of mobility in some detail.

- *From the network layer's standpoint, how mobile is a user?* A physically mobile user will present a very different set of challenges to the network layer, depending on how he or she moves between points of attachment to the network. At one end of the spectrum in Figure 12.16, a user may carry a laptop with a wireless network interface card around in a building. As we saw in Section 12.3.4, this user is *not* mobile from a network-layer perspective. Moreover, if the user associates with the same access point regardless of location, the user is not even mobile from the perspective of the link layer.

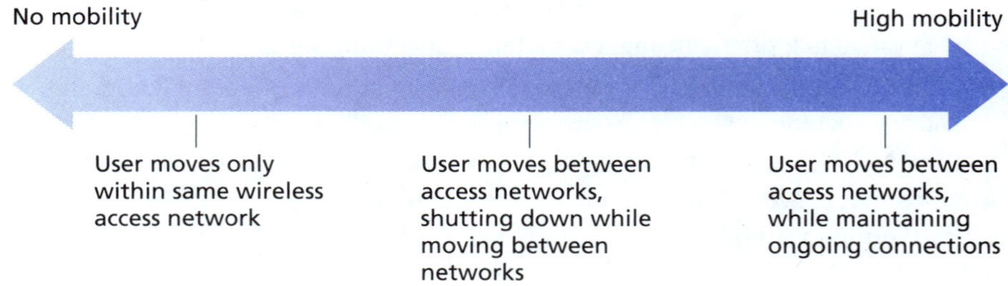

Figure 12.16 ♦ Various degrees of mobility, from the network layer's point of view

At the other end of the spectrum, consider the user zooming along the autobahn in a BMW at 150 kilometers per hour, passing through multiple wireless access networks and wanting to maintain an uninterrupted TCP connection to a remote application throughout the trip. This user is *definitely* mobile! In between these extremes is a user who takes a laptop from one location (e.g., office or dormitory) into another (e.g., coffeeshop, classroom) and wants to connect into the network in the new location. This user is also mobile (although less so than the BMW driver!) but does not need to maintain an ongoing connection while moving between points of attachment to the network. Figure 12.16 illustrates this spectrum of user mobility from the network layer's perspective.

- *How important is it for the mobile node's address to always remain the same?* With mobile telephony, your phone number—essentially the network-layer address of your phone—remains the same as you travel from one provider's mobile phone network to another. Must a laptop similarly maintain the same IP address while moving between IP networks?

  The answer to this question will depend strongly on the applications being run. For the BMW driver who wants to maintain an uninterrupted TCP connection to a remote application while zipping along the autobahn, it would be convenient to maintain the same IP address. Recall that an Internet application needs to know the IP address and port number of the remote entity with which it is communicating. If a mobile entity is able to maintain its IP address as it moves, mobility becomes invisible from the application standpoint. There is great value to this transparency—an application need not be concerned with a potentially changing IP address, and the same application code serves mobile and nonmobile connections alike. We'll see in the following section that mobile IP provides this transparency, allowing a mobile node to maintain its permanent IP address while moving among networks.

  On the other hand, a less glamorous mobile user might simply want to turn off an office laptop, bring that laptop home, power up, and work from home. If the laptop functions primarily as a client in client-server applications (e.g., send/read e-mail, browse the Web, Telnet to a remote host) from home, the particular IP address used by the laptop is not that important. In particular, one could get by fine with an address that is temporarily allocated to the laptop by the ISP serving the home. We saw in Section 11.4.3 that DHCP already provides this functionality.

- *What supporting wired infrastructure is available?* In all of our scenarios above, we've implicitly assumed that there is a fixed infrastructure to which the mobile user can connect, for example, the home's ISP network, the wireless access network in the office, or the wireless access networks lining the autobahn. What if no such infrastructure exists? If two users are within communication proximity of each other, can they establish a network connection in the absence of any other network-layer infrastructure? Ad hoc networking provides precisely these capabilities. This rapidly developing area is at the cutting edge of mobile networking research and is beyond the scope of this book. [Perkins 2000] and the IETF Mobile Ad Hoc Network (manet) working group Web pages [manet 2004] provide thorough treatments of the subject.

In order to illustrate the issues involved in allowing a mobile user to maintain ongoing connections while moving between networks, let's consider a human analogy. A twenty-something adult moving out of the family home becomes mobile, living in a series of dormitories and/or apartments, and often changing addresses. If an old friend wants to get in touch, how can that friend find the address of her mobile friend? One common way is to contact the family, since a mobile adult will often register his or her current address with the family (if for no other reason than so that the parents can send money to help pay the rent!). The family home, with its permanent address, becomes that one place that others can go as a first step in communicating with the mobile adult. Later communication from the friend may be either indirect (for example, with mail being sent first to the parents' home and then forwarded to the mobile adult) or direct (for example, with the friend using the address obtained from the parents to send mail directly to her mobile friend).

In a network setting, the permanent home of a mobile node (such as a laptop or PDA) is known as the **home network**, and the entity within the home network that performs the mobility management functions discussed below on behalf of the mobile node is known as the **home agent**. The network in which the mobile node is currently residing is known as the **foreign** (or **visited**) **network**, and the entity within the foreign network that helps the mobile node with the mobility management functions discussed below is known as a **foreign agent**. For mobile professionals, their home network might likely be their company network, while the visited network might be the network of a colleague they are visiting. A **correspondent** is the entity wishing to communicate with the mobile node. Figure 12.17 illustrates these concepts, as well as addressing concepts considered below. In Figure 12.17, note that agents are shown as being collocated with routers (e.g., as processes running on routers), but alternatively they could be executing on other hosts or servers in the network.

12.5.1 Addressing

We noted above that in order for user mobility to be transparent to network applications, it is desirable for a mobile node to keep its address as it moves from one network to another. When a mobile node is resident in a foreign network, all traffic addressed to the node's permanent address now needs to be routed to the foreign network. How can this be done? One option is for the foreign network to advertise to all other networks that the mobile node is resident in its network. This could be via the usual exchange of intradomain and interdomain routing information and would require few changes to the existing routing infrastructure. The foreign network could simply advertise to its neighbors that it has a highly specific route to the mobile node's permanent address (that is, essentially inform other networks that it

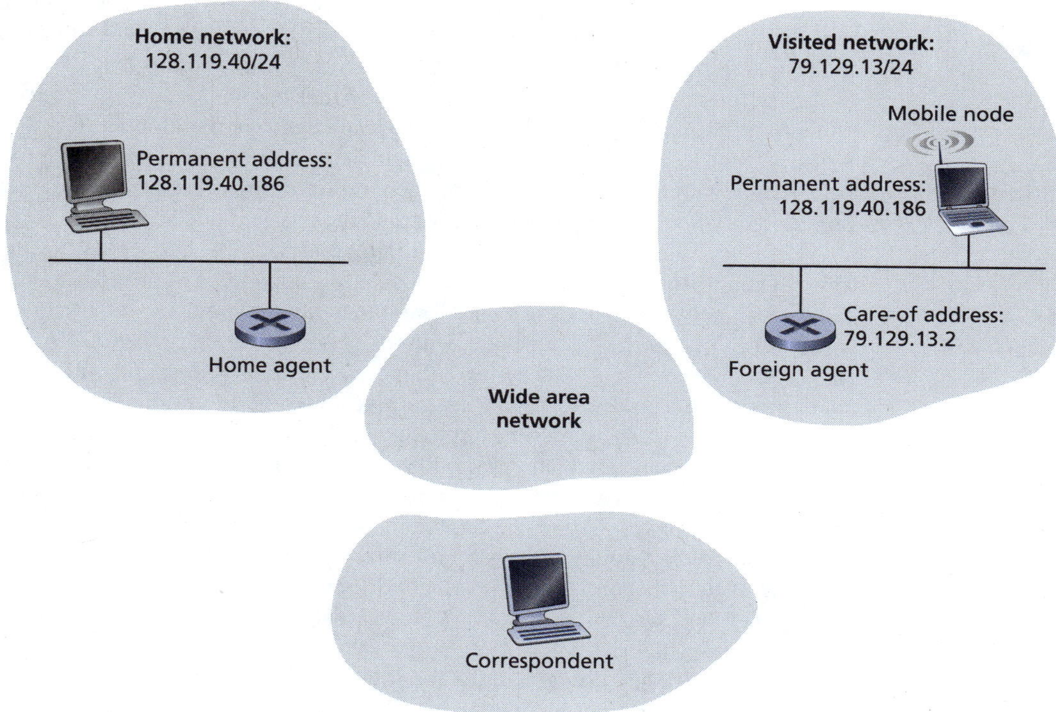

Figure 12.17 ♦ Initial elements of a mobile network architecture

has the correct path for routing datagrams to the mobile node's permanent address; see Section 10.4). These neighbors would then propagate this routing information throughout the network as part of the normal procedure of updating routing information and fowarding tables. When the mobile node leaves one foreign network and joins another, the new foreign network would advertise a new, highly specific route to the mobile node, and the old foreign network would withdraw its routing information regarding the mobile node.

This solves two problems at once, and it does so without making significant changes to the network-layer infrastructure. Other networks know the location of the mobile node, and it is easy to route datagrams to the mobile node, since the forwarding tables will direct datagrams to the foreign network. A significant drawback, however, is that of scalability. If mobility management were to be the responsibility of network routers, the routers would have to maintain forwarding table entries for potentially millions of mobile nodes, and update these entries as nodes move. Some additional drawbacks are explored in the problems at the end of this chapter.

An alternative approach (and one that has been adopted in practice) is to push mobility functionality from the network core to the network edge—a recurring theme in our study of Internet architecture. A natural way to do this is via the mobile node's home network. In much the same way that parents of the mobile twenty-something track their child's location, the home agent in the mobile node's home network can track the foreign network in which the mobile node resides. A protocol between the mobile node (or a foreign agent representing the mobile node) and the home agent will certainly be needed to update the mobile node's location.

Let's now consider the foreign agent in more detail. The conceptually simplest approach, shown in Figure 12.17, is to locate foreign agents at the edge routers in the foreign network. One role of the foreign agent is to create a so-called **care-of address (COA)** for the mobile node, with the network portion of the COA matching that of the foreign network. There are thus two addresses associated with a mobile mode, its **permanent address** (analogous to our mobile youth's family's home address) and its COA, sometimes known as a **foreign address** (analogous to the address of the house in which our mobile youth is currently residing). In the example in Figure 12.17, the permanent address of the mobile node is 128.119.40.186. When visiting network 79.129.13/24, the mobile node has a COA of 79.129.13.2. A second role of the foreign agent is to inform the home agent that the mobile node is resident in its (the foreign agent's) network and has the given COA. We'll see shortly that the COA will be used to "reroute" datagrams to the mobile node via its foreign agent.

Although we have separated the functionality of the mobile node and the foreign agent, it is worth noting that the mobile node can also assume the responsibilities of the foreign agent. For example, the mobile node could obtain a COA in the foreign network (for example, using a protocol such as DHCP) and itself inform the home agent of its COA.

12.5.2 Routing to a Mobile Node

We have now seen how a mobile node obtains a COA and how the home agent can be informed of that address. But having the home agent know the COA solves only part of the problem. How should datagrams be addressed and forwarded to the mobile node? Since only the home agent (and not network-wide routers) knows the location of the mobile node, it will no longer suffice to simply address a datagram to the mobile node's permanent address and send it into the network-layer infrastructure. Something more must be done. Two approaches can be identified, which we will refer to as indirect and direct routing.

Indirect Routing to a Mobile Node

Let's first consider a correspondent that wants to send a datagram to a mobile node. In the **indirect routing** approach, the correspondent simply addresses the datagram to the mobile node's permanent address and sends the datagram into the network, blissfully unaware of whether the mobile node is resident in its home network or is visiting a foreign network; mobility is thus completely transparent to the correspondent. Such datagrams are first routed, as usual, to the mobile node's home network. This is illustrated in step 1 in Figure 12.18.

Let's now turn our attention to the home agent. In addition to being responsible for interacting with a foreign agent to track the mobile node's COA, the home agent has another very important function. Its second job is to be on the lookout for arriving datagrams addressed to nodes whose home network is that of the home agent but that are currently resident in a foreign network. The home agent intercepts these datagrams and then forwards them to a mobile node in a two-step process. The datagram is first forwarded to the foreign agent, using the mobile node's COA (step 2 in Figure 12.18), and then forwarded from the foreign agent to the mobile node (step 3 in Figure 12.18).

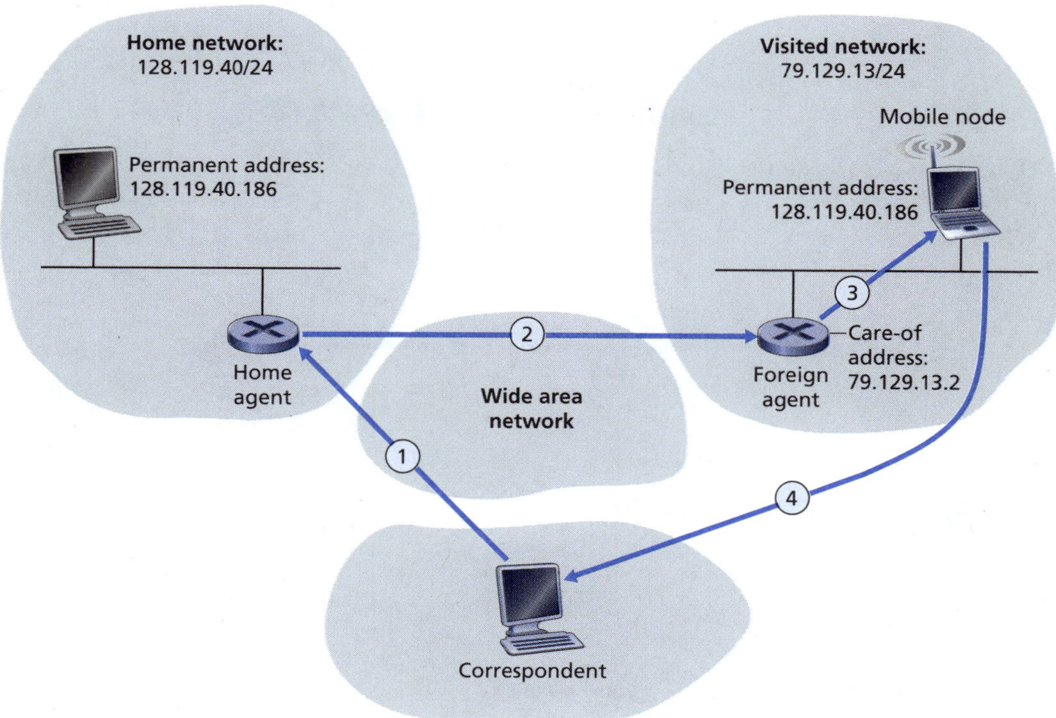

Figure 12.18 ♦ Indirect forwarding to a mobile node

It is instructive to consider this rerouting in more detail. The home agent will need to address the datagram using the mobile node's COA, so that the network layer will route the datagram to the foreign network. On the other hand, it is desirable to leave the correspondent's datagram intact, since the application receiving the datagram should be unaware that the datagram was forwarded via the home agent. Both goals can be satisfied by having the home agent **encapsulate** the correspondent's original complete datagram within a new (larger) datagram. This larger datagram is addressed and delivered to the mobile node's COA. The foreign agent, who "owns" the COA will receive and decapsulate the datagram, that is, remove the correspondent's original datagram from within the larger encapsulating datagram and forward (step 3 in Figure 12.18) the original datagram to the mobile node. Figure 12.19 shows a correspondent's original datagram being sent to the home network, an encapsulated datagram being sent to the foreign agent, and the original datagram being delivered to the mobile node. The sharp reader will note that the encapsulation/decapsulation described here is identical to the notion of tunneling, discussed in Chapter 10 in the context of IP multicast and IPv12.

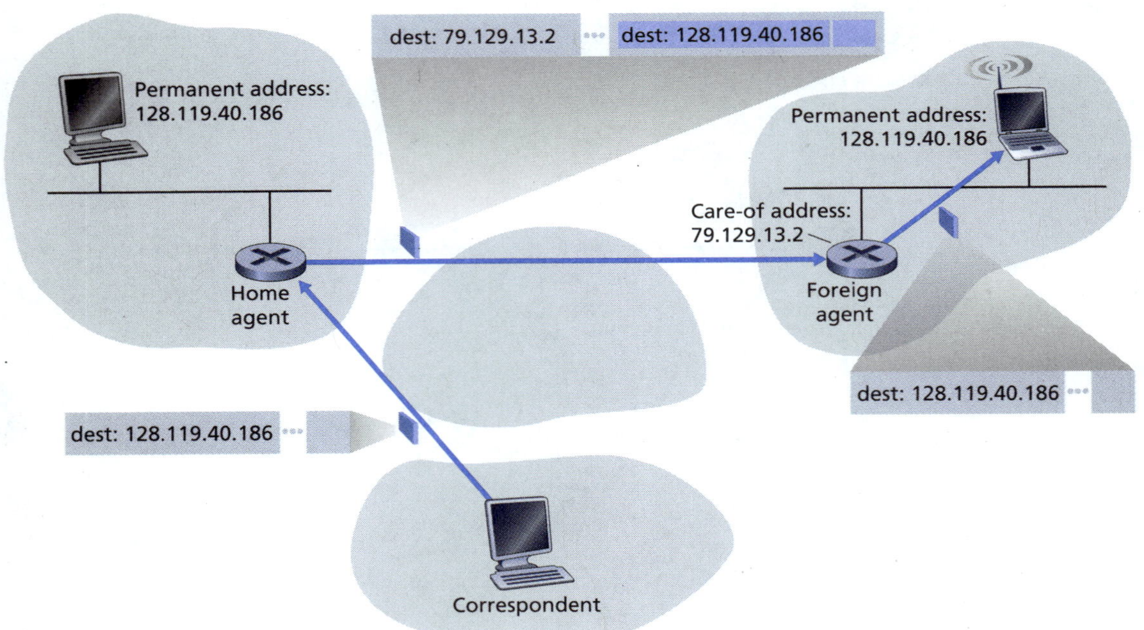

Figure 12.19 ♦ Encapsulation and decapsulation

Let's next consider how a mobile node sends datagrams to a correspondent. This is quite simple, as the mobile node can address its datagram *directly* to the correspondent (using its own permanent address as the source address, and the correspondent's address as the destination address). Since the mobile node knows the correspondent's address, there is no need to route the datagram back through the home agent. This is shown as step 4 in Figure 12.18.

Let's summarize our discussion of indirect routing by listing the new network-layer functionality required to support mobility.

- *A mobile-node–to–foreign-agent protocol.* The mobile node will register with the foreign agent when attaching to the foreign network. Similarly, a mobile node will deregister with the foreign agent when it leaves the foreign network.
- *A foreign-agent–to–home-agent registration protocol.* The foreign agent will register the mobile node's COA with the home agent. A foreign agent need not explicitly deregister a COA when a mobile node leaves its network, because the subsequent registration of a new COA, when the mobile node moves to a new network, will take care of this.
- *A home-agent datagram encapsulation protocol.* Encapsulation and forwarding of the correspondent's original datagram within a datagram addressed to the COA.
- *A foreign-agent decapsulation protocol.* Extraction of the correspondent's original datagram from the encapsulating datagram, and the forwarding of the original datagram to the mobile node.

The discussion above provides all the pieces—foreign agents, the home agent, and indirect forwarding—needed for a mobile node to maintain an ongoing connection while moving among networks. As an example of how these pieces fit together, assume the mobile node is attached to foreign network A, has registered a COA in network A with its home agent, and is receiving datagrams that are being indirectly routed through its home agent. The mobile node now moves to foreign network B and registers with the foreign agent in network B, which informs the home agent of the mobile node's new COA. From this point on, the home agent will reroute datagrams to foreign network B. As far as a correspondent is concerned, mobility is transparent—datagrams are routed via the same home agent both before and after the move. As far as the home agent is concerned, there is no disruption in the flow of datagrams—arriving datagrams are first forwarded to foreign network A; after the change in COA, datagrams are forwarded to foreign network B. But will the mobile node see an interrupted flow of datagrams as it moves between networks? As long as the time between the mobile node's disconnection from network A (at which point it can no longer receive datagrams via A) and its attachment to network B (at which point it will register a new COA with its home agent) is small, few datagrams will be lost. Recall that end-to-end connections can suffer datagram loss due to network congestion. Hence occasional datagram loss within a connection when a node moves between networks is by no means a catastrophic problem. If loss-free communication is required, upper-layer mechanisms will recover from datagram loss, whether such loss results from network congestion or from user mobility.

An indirect routing approach is used in the mobile IP standard [RFC 3220], as discussed in the Section 12.6.

Direct Routing to a Mobile Node

The indirect routing approach illustrated in Figure 12.18 suffers from an inefficiency known as the **triangle routing problem**—datagrams addressed to the mobile node must be routed first to the home agent and then to the foreign network, even when a much more efficient route exists between the correspondent and the mobile node. In the worst case, imagine a mobile user who is visiting the foreign network of a colleague. The two are sitting side by side and exchanging data over the network. Datagrams from the correspondent (in this case the colleague of the visitor) are routed to the mobile user's home agent and then back again to the foreign network!

Direct routing overcomes the inefficiency of triangle routing, but does so at the cost of additional complexity. In the direct routing approach, a **correspondent agent** in the correspondent's network first learns the COA of the mobile node. This can be done by having the correspondent agent query the home agent, assuming that (as in the case of indirect routing), the mobile node has an up-to-date value for its COA registered with its home agent). It is also possible for the correspondent itself to perform the function of the correspondent agent, just as a mobile node could perform the function of the foreign agent.) This is shown as steps 1 and 2 in Figure 12.20. The correspondent agent then tunnels datagrams directly to the mobile node's COA, in a manner analogous to the tunneling performed by the home agent, steps 3 and 4 in Figure 12.20.

While direct routing overcomes the triangle routing problem, it introduces two important additional challenges:

- A ***mobile-user location protocol*** is needed for the correspondent agent to query the home agent to obtain the mobile node's COA (steps 1 and 2 in Figure 12.20).
- When the mobile node moves from one foreign network to another, how will data now be forwarded to the new foreign network? In the case of indirect routing, this problem was easily solved by updating the COA maintained by the home agent. However, with direct routing, the home agent is queried for the COA by the correspondent agent only once, at the beginning of the session. Thus, updating the COA at the home agent, while necessary, will not be enough to solve the problem of routing data to the mobile node's new foreign network.

One solution would be to create a new protocol to notify the correspondent of the changing COA. An alternate solution, and one that we'll see is adopted in

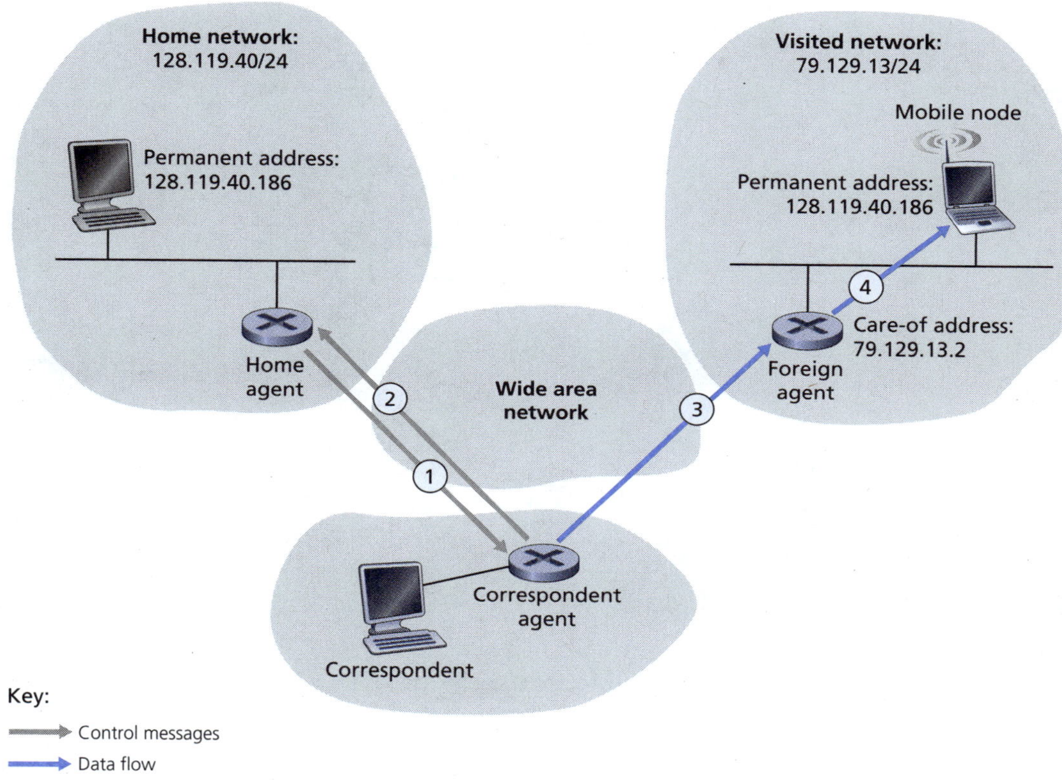

Figure 12.20 ♦ Direct routing to a mobile user

practice in GSM networks, works as follows. Suppose data is currently being forwarded to the mobile node in the foreign network where the mobile node was located when the session first started (step 1 in Figure 12.21). We'll identify the foreign agent in that foreign network where the mobile node was first found as the **anchor foreign agent**. When the mobile node moves to a new foreign network (step 2 in Figure 12.21), the mobile node registers with the new foreign agent (step 3), and the new foreign agent provides the anchor foreign agent with the mobile node's new COA (step 4). When the anchor foreign agent receives an encapsulated datagram for a departed mobile node it can then re-encapsulate the datagram and forward it to the mobile node (step 5) using the new COA. If the mobile node later moves yet again to a new foreign network, the foreign agent in that new visited network would then contact the anchor foreign agent in order to set up forwarding to this new foreign network.

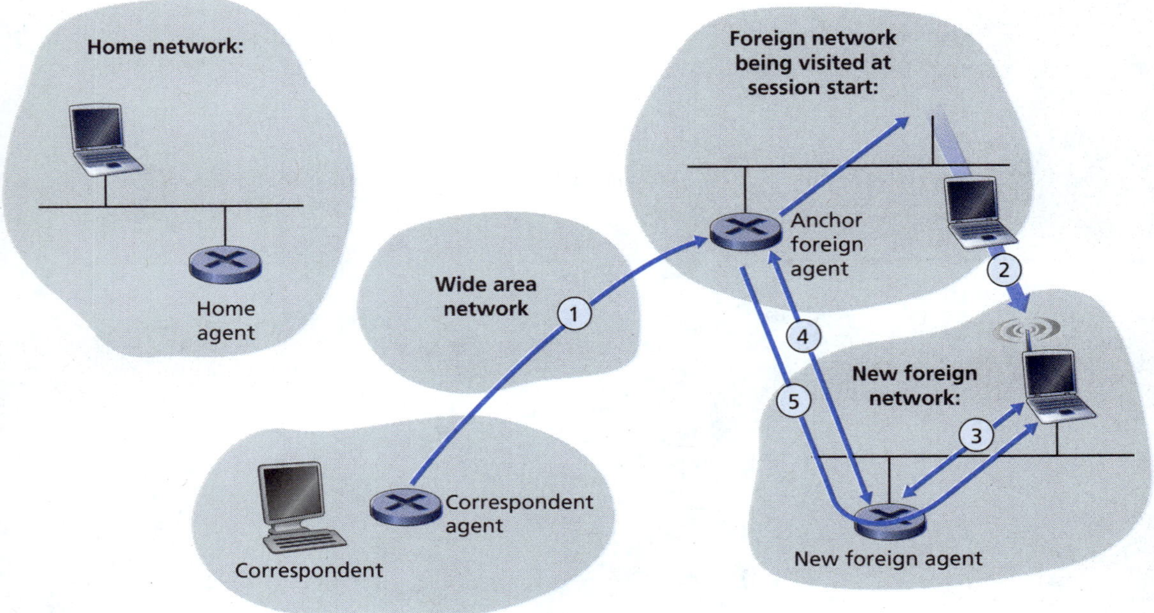

Figure 12.21 ♦ Mobile transfer between networks with direct routing

12.6 Mobile IP

The Internet architecture and protocols for supporting mobility, collectively known as mobile IP, are defined primarily in RFC 3220. Mobile IP is a flexible standard, supporting many different modes of operation, for example, operation with or without a foreign agent, multiple ways for agents and mobile nodes to discover each other, use of single or multiple COAs, and multiple forms of encapsulation. As such, mobile IP is a complex standard, and would require an entire book to describe in detail; indeed one such book is [Perkins 1998b]. Our modest goal here is to provide an overview of the most important aspects of mobile IP and to illustrate its use in a few common-case scenarios.

The mobile IP architecture contains many of the elements we have considered above, including the concepts of home agents, foreign agents, care-of addresses, and encapsulation/decapsulation. The current standard [RFC 3220] specifies the use of indirect routing to the mobile node.

The mobile IP standard consists of three main pieces:

- *Agent discovery.* Mobile IP defines the protocols used by a home or foreign agent to advertise its services to mobile nodes, and protocols for mobile nodes to solicit the services of a foreign or home agent.
- *Registration with the home agent.* Mobile IP defines the protocols used by the mobile node and/or foreign agent to register and deregister COAs with a mobile node's home agent.
- *Indirect routing of datagrams.* The standard also defines the manner in which datagrams are forwarded to mobile nodes by a home agent, including rules for forwarding datagrams, rules for handling error conditions, and several forms of encapsulation [RFC 2003, RFC 2004].

Security considerations are prominent throughout the mobile IP standard. For example, authentication of a mobile node is clearly needed to ensure that a malicious user does not register a bogus care-of address with a home agent, which could cause all datagrams addressed to an IP address to be redirected to the malicious user. Mobile IP achieves security using many of the mechanisms that we will examine, so we will not address security considerations in our discussion below.

Agent Discovery

A mobile IP node arriving to a new network, whether attaching to a foreign network or returning to its home network, must learn the identity of the corresponding foreign or home agent. Indeed it is the discovery of a new foreign agent, with a new network address, that allows the network layer in a mobile node to learn that it has moved into a new foreign network. This process is known as **agent discovery**. Agent discovery can be accomplished in one of two ways: via agent advertisement or via agent solicitation.

With **agent advertisement**, a foreign or home agent advertises its services using an extension to the existing router discovery protocol [RFC 1256]. The agent periodically broadcasts an ICMP message with a type field of 9 (router discovery) on all links to which it is connected. The router discovery message contains the IP address of the router (that is, the agent), thus allowing a mobile node to learn the agent's IP address. The router discovery message also contains a mobility agent advertisement extension that contains additional information needed by the mobile node. Among the more important fields in the extension are the following:

- *Home agent bit (H).* Indicates that the agent is a home agent for the network in which it resides.
- *Foreign agent bit (F).* Indicates that the agent is a foreign agent for the network in which it resides.
- *Registration required bit (R).* Indicates that a mobile user in this network *must* register with a foreign agent. In particular, a mobile user cannot obtain a care-of

address in the foreign network (for example, using DHCP) and assume the functionality of the foreign agent for itself, without registering with the foreign agent.

- *M, G encapsulation bits.* Indicate whether a form of encapsulation other than IP-in-IP encapsulation will be used.
- *Care-of address (COA) fields.* A list of one or more care-of addresses provided by the foreign agent. In our example below, the COA will be associated with the foreign agent, who will receive datagrams sent to the COA and then forward them to the appropriate mobile node. The mobile user will select one of these addresses as its COA when registering with its home agent.

Figure 12.22 illustrates some of the key fields in the agent advertisement message.

With **agent solicitation**, a mobile node wanting to learn about agents without waiting to receive an agent advertisement can broadcast an agent solicitation message, which is simply an ICMP message with type value 10. An agent receiving the solicitation will unicast an agent advertisement directly to the mobile node, which can then proceed as if it had received an unsolicited advertisement.

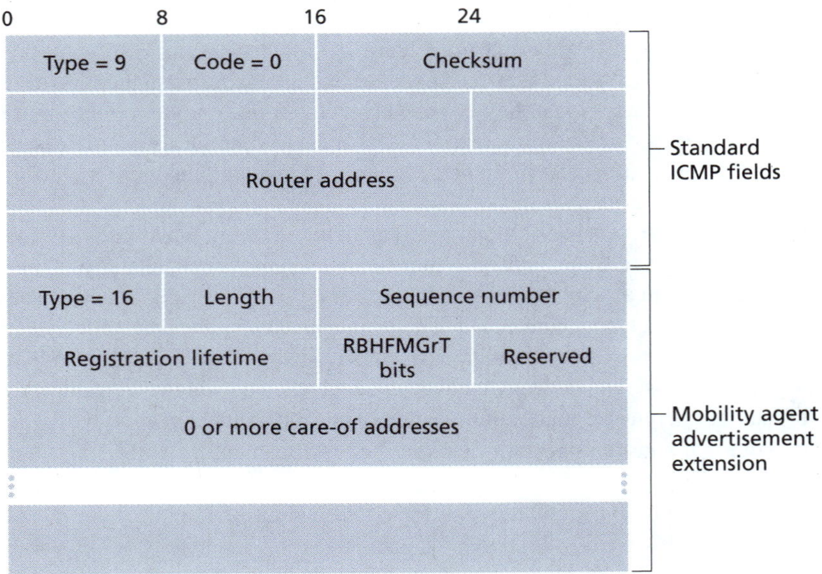

Figure 12.22 ♦ ICMP router discovery message with mobility agent advertisement extension

Registration with the Home Agent

Once a mobile IP node has received a COA, that address must be registered with the home agent. This can be done either via the foreign agent (who then registers the COA with the home agent) or directly by the mobile IP node itself. We consider the former case below. Four steps are involved.

1. Following the receipt of a foreign agent advertisement, a mobile node sends a mobile IP registration message to the foreign agent. The registration message is carried within a UDP datagram and sent to port 434. The registration message carries a COA advertised by the foreign agent, the address of the home agent (HA), the permanent address of the mobile node (MA), the requested lifetime of the registration, and a 64-bit registration identification. The requested registration lifetime is the number of seconds that the registration is to be valid. If the registration is not renewed at the home agent within the specified lifetime, the registration will become invalid. The registration identifier acts like a sequence number and serves to match a received registration reply with a registration request, as discussed below.
2. The foreign agent receives the registration message and records the mobile node's permanent IP address. The foreign agent now knows that it should be looking for datagrams containing an encapsulated datagram whose destination address matches the permanent address of the mobile node. The foreign agent then sends a mobile IP registration message (again, within a UDP datagram) to port 434 of the home agent. The message contains the COA, HA, MA, encapsulation format requested, requested registration lifetime, and registration identification.
3. The home agent receives the registration request and checks for authenticity and correctness. The home agent binds the mobile node's permanent IP address with the COA; in the future, datagrams arriving at the home agent and addressed to the mobile node will now be encapsulated and tunneled to the COA. The home agent sends a mobile IP registration reply containing the HA, MA, actual registration lifetime, and the registration identification of the request that is being satisfied with this reply.
4. The foreign agent receives the registration reply and then forwards it to the mobile node.

At this point registration is complete, and the mobile node can receive datagrams sent to its permanent address. Figure 12.23 illustrates these steps. Note that the home agent specifies a lifetime that is smaller than the lifetime requested by the mobile node.

A foreign agent need not explicitly deregister a COA when a mobile node leaves its network. This will occur automatically, when the mobile node moves to a new network (whether another foreign network or its home network) and registers a new COA.

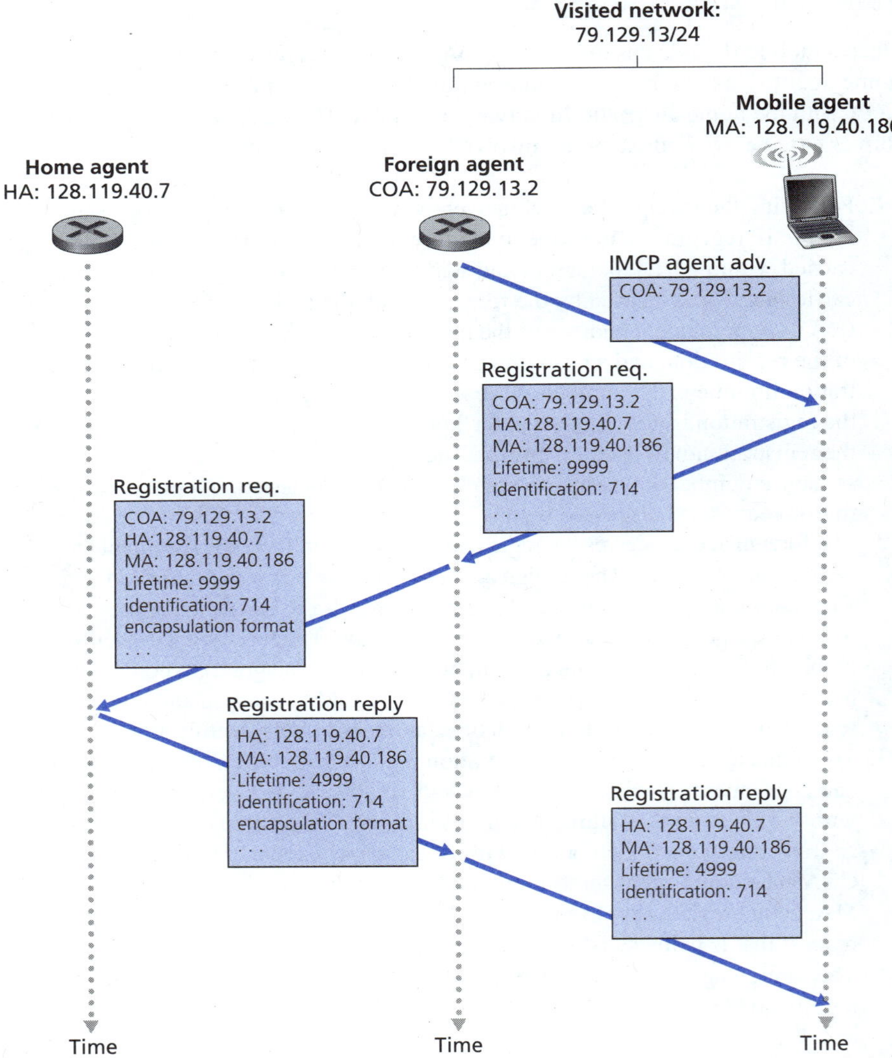

Figure 12.23 ♦ Agent advertisement and mobile IP registration

The mobile IP standard allows many additional scenarios and capabilities in addition to those described above. The interested reader should consult [Perkins 1998b; RFC 3220].

12.7 Managing Mobility in Cellular Networks

Having examined how mobility is managed in IP networks, let's now turn our attention to networks with an even longer history of supporting mobility—cellular telephony networks. Whereas we focused on the first-hop wireless link in cellular networks in Section 12.4, we'll focus here on mobility, using the GSM cellular network architecture [Goodman 1997; Mouly 1992; Scourias 1997; Kaaranen 2001, Korhonen 2002] as our case study, since it is a mature and widely deployed technology. As in the case of mobile IP, we'll see that a number of the fundamental principles we identified in Section 12.5 are embodied in GSM's network architecture.

Like mobile IP, GSM adopts an indirect routing approach (see Section 12.5.2), first routing the correspondent's call to the mobile's home network and from there to the visited network. In GSM terminology, the mobile's home network is referred to as the mobile's **home public land mobile network (home PLMN)**. Since the PLMN acronym is a bit of a mouthful, and mindful of our quest to avoid an alphabet soup of acronyms, we'll refer to the GSM home PLMN simply as the **home network**. The home network is the cellular provider with which the mobile user has a subscription (i.e., the provider that bills the user for monthly cellular service). The visited PLMN, which we'll refer to simply as the **visited network**, is the network in which the mobile is currently residing

As in the case of mobile IP, the responsibilities of the home and visited networks are quite different.

- The home network maintains a database known as the **home location register (HLR)**, which contains the permanent cell phone number and subscriber profile information for each of its subscribers. Importantly, the HLR also contains information about the current locations of these subscribers. That is, if a mobile user is currently roaming in another provider's cellular network, the HLR contains enough information to obtain (via a process we'll describe shortly) an address in the visited network to which a call to the mobile user should be routed. As we'll see, a special switch in the home network, known as the **Gateway Mobile Services Switching Center (GMSC)** is contacted by a correspondent when a call is placed to a mobile user. Again, in our quest to avoid an alphabet soup of acronyms, we'll refer to the GMSC here by a more descriptive term, **home MSC**.
- The visited network maintains a database known as the **visitor location register (VLR)**. The VLR contains an entry for each mobile user that is *currently* in the portion of the network served by the VLR. VLR entries thus come and go as mobile users enter and leave the network. A VLR is usually co-located with the mobile switching center (MSC) that coordinates the setup of a call to and from the visited network.

In practice, a provider's cellular network will serve as a home network for its subscribers and as a visited network for mobile users whose subscription is with a different cellular provider.

12.7.1 Routing Calls to a Mobile User

We're now in a position to describe how a call is placed to a mobile GSM user in a visited network. We'll consider a simple example below; more complex scenarios are described in [Mouly 1992]. The steps, as illustrated in Figure 12.24, are as follows:

1. The correspondent dials the mobile user's phone number. This number itself does not refer to a particular telephone line or location (after all, the phone number is fixed and the user is mobile!). The leading digits in the number are sufficient to globally identify the mobile's home network. The call is routed from the correspondent through the public switched telephone network to the home MSC in the mobile's home network. This is the first leg of the call.
2. The home MSC receives the call and interrogates the HLR to determine the location of the mobile user. In the simplest case, the HLR returns the **mobile**

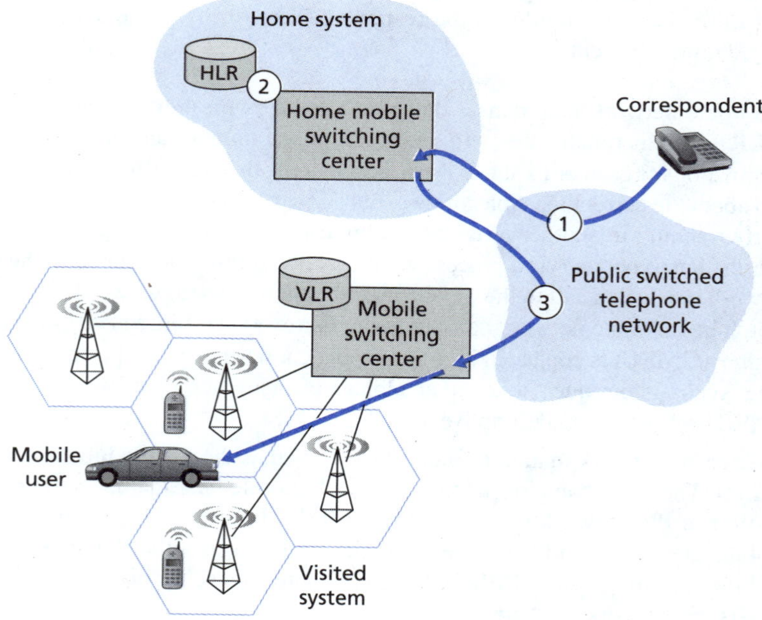

Figure 12.24 ♦ Placing a call to a mobile user: indirect routing

station roaming number (MSRN), which we will refer to as the **roaming number**. Note that this number is different from the mobile's permanent phone number, which is associated with the mobile's home network. The roaming number is ephemeral: It is temporarily assigned to a mobile when it enters a visited network. The roaming number serves a role similar to that of the care-of-address in mobile IP and, like the COA, is invisible to the correspondent and the mobile. If HLR does not have the roaming number, it returns the address of the VLR in the visited network. In this case (not shown in Figure 12.24), the home MSC will need to query the VLR to obtain the roaming number of the mobile node. But how does the HLR get the roaming number or the VLR address in the first place? What happens to these values when the mobile user moves to another visited network? We'll consider these important questions shortly.

3. Given the roaming number, the home MSC sets up the second leg of the call through the network to the MSC in the visited network. The call is completed, being routed from the correspondent to the home MSC, and from there to the visited MSC, and from there to the base station serving the mobile user.

An unresolved question in step 2 is how the HLR obtains information about the location of the mobile user. When a mobile telephone is switched on or enters a part of a visited network that is covered by a new VLR, the mobile must register with the visited network. This is done through the exchange of signaling messages between the mobile and the VLR. The visited VLR, in turn, sends a location update request message to the mobile's HLR. This message informs the HLR of either the roaming number at which the mobile can be contacted, or the address of the VLR (which can then later be queried to obtain the mobile number). As part of this exchange, the VLR also obtains subscriber information from the HLR about the mobile and determines what services (if any) should be accorded the mobile user by the visited network.

12.7.2 Handoffs in GSM

A **handoff** occurs when a mobile station changes its association from one base station to another during a call. As shown in Figure 12.25, a mobile's call is initially (before handoff) routed to the mobile through one base station (which we'll refer to as the old base station), and after handoff is routed to the mobile through another base station (which we'll refer to as the new base station). Note that a handoff between base stations results not only in the mobile transmitting/receiving to/from a new base station, but also in the rerouting of the ongoing call from a switching point within the network to the new base station. Let's initially assume that the old and new base stations share the same MSC, and that the rerouting occurs at this MSC.

There may be several reasons for handoff to occur, including (1) the signal between the current base station and the mobile may have deteriorated to such an extent that the call is in danger of being dropped, and (2) a cell may have become a

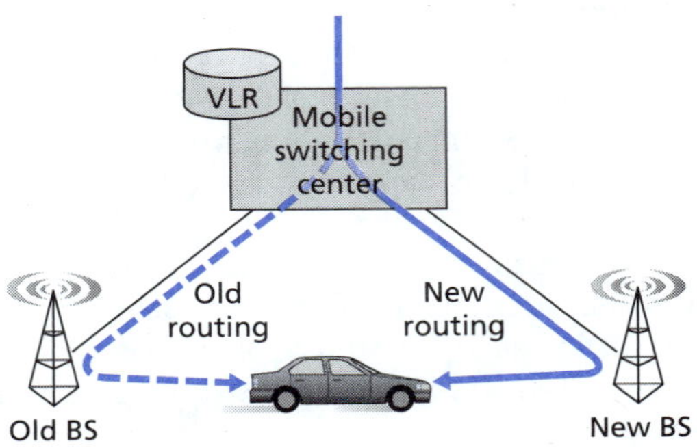

Figure 12.25 ♦ Handoff scenario between base stations with a common MSC

overloaded, handling a large number of calls. This congestion may be alleviated by handing off mobiles to less congested nearby cells.

While it is associated with a base station, a mobile periodically measures the strength of a beacon signal from its current base station as well as beacon signals from nearby base stations that it can "hear." These measurements are reported once or twice a second to the mobile's current base station. Handoff in GSM is initiated by the old base station based on these measurements, the current loads of mobiles in nearby cells, and other factors [Mouly 1992]. The GSM standard does not specify the specific algorithm to be used by a base station to determine whether or not to perform handoff.

Figure 12.26 illustrates the steps involved when a base station does decide to handoff a mobile user:

1. The old base station (BS) informs the visited MSC that a handoff is to be performed and the BS (or possible set of BSs) to which the mobile is to be handed off.
2. The visited MSC initiates path setup to the new BS, allocating the resources needed to carry the rerouted call, and signaling the new BS that a handoff is about to occur.
3. The new BS allocates and activates a radio channel for use by the mobile.
4. The new BS signals back to the visited MSC and the old BS that the visited-MSC-to-new-BS path has been established and that the mobile should be informed of the impending handoff. The new BS provides all of the information that the mobile will need to associate with the new BS.
5. The mobile is informed that it should perform a handoff. Note that up until this point, the mobile has been blissfully unaware that the network has been laying the groundwork (e.g., allocating a channel in the new BS and allocating a path from the visited MSC to the new BS) for a handoff.

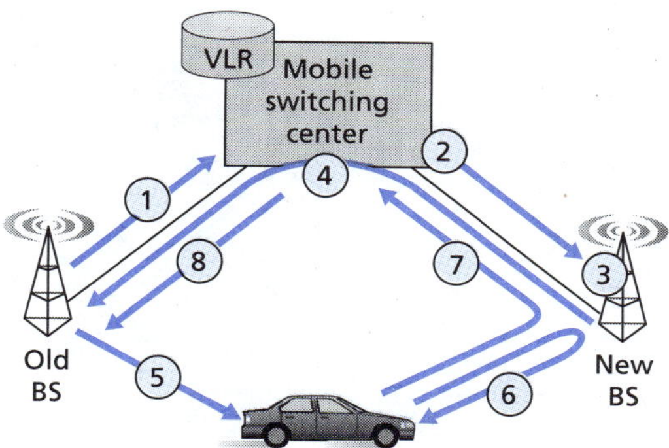

Figure 12.26 ♦ Steps in accomplishing a handoff between base stations with a common MSC

6. The mobile and the new BS exchange one or more messages to fully activate the new channel in the new BS.
7. The mobile sends a handoff complete message to the new BS, which is forwarded up to the visited MSC. The visited MSC then reroutes the on-going call to the mobile via the new BS.
8. The resources allocated along the path to the old BS are then released.

Let's conclude our discussion of handoff by considering what happens when the mobile moves to a BS that is associated with a *different* MSC than the old BS, and what happens when this inter-MSC handoff occurs more than once. As shown in Figure 12.27, GSM defines the notion of an **anchor MSC**. The anchor MSC is the MSC visited by the mobile when a call first begins; the anchor MSC thus remains unchanged during the call. Throughout the call's duration and regardless of the number of inter-MSC transfers performed by the mobile, the call is routed from the home MSC to the anchor MSC, and then from the anchor MSC to the visited MSC where the mobile is currently located. When a mobile moves from the coverage area of one MSC to another, the ongoing call is rerouted from the anchor MSC to the new visited MSC containing the new base station. Thus, at all times there are at most three MSCs (the home MSC, the anchor MSC, and the visited MSC) between the correspondent and the mobile. Figure 12.27 illustrates the routing of a call among the MSCs visited by a mobile user.

Rather than maintaining a single MSC-hop from the anchor MSC to the current MSC, an alternative approach would have been to simply chain the MSCs visited by the mobile, having an old MSC forward the ongoing call to the new MSC each time the mobile moves to a new MSC. Such MSC-chaining can in fact occur in IS-41 cellular networks, with an optional path minimization step to remove MSCs between the anchor MSC and the current visited MSC [Lin 2001].

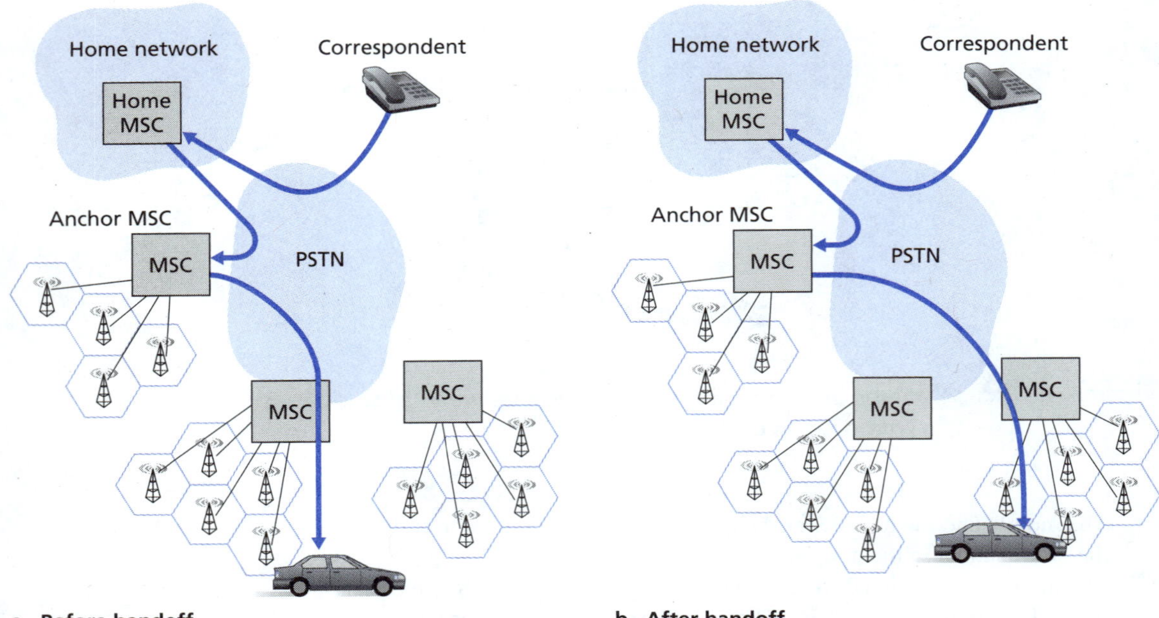

Figure 12.27 ♦ Rerouting via the anchor MSC

Let's wrap up our discussion of GSM mobility management with a comparison of mobility management in GSM and Mobile IP. The comparison in Table 12.2 indicates that although IP and cellular networks are fundamentally different in many ways, they share a surprising number of common functional elements and overall approaches in handling mobility.

12.8 Wireless and Mobility: Impact on Higher-layer Protocols

In this chapter, we've seen that wireless networks differ significantly from their wired counterparts at both the link layer (as a result wireless channel characteristics such as fading, multipath, and hidden terminals) and at the network layer (as a result of mobile users who change their points of attachment to the network). But are there important differences at the transport and application layers? It's tempting to think that these differences will be minor, since the network layer provides the same best-effort delivery service model to upper layers in both wired and wireless networks.

GSM element	Comment on GSM element	Mobile IP element
Home system	Network to which the mobile user's permanent phone number belongs	Home network
Gateway mobile switching center or simply home MSC, Home location register (HLR)	Home MSC: point of contact to obtain routable address of mobile user. HLR: database in home system containing permanent phone number, profile information, current location of mobile user, subscription information	Home agent
Visited system	Network other than home system where mobile user is currently residing	Visited network
Visited mobile services switching center, Visitor location record (VLR)	Visited MSC: responsible for setting up calls to/from mobile nodes in cells associated with MSC. VLR: temporary database entry in visited system, containing subscription information for each visiting mobile user	Foreign agent
Mobile station roaming number (MSRN) or simply roaming number	Routable address for telephone call segment between home MSC and visited MSC, visible to neither the mobile nor the correspondent.	Care-of-address

Table 12.2 ♦ Commonalities between mobile IP and GSM mobility

Similarly, if protocols such as TCP or UDP are used to provide transport-layer services to applications in both wired and wireless networks, then the application layer should remain unchanged as well. In one sense our intuition is right—TCP and UDP can (and do) operate in networks with wireless links. On the other hand, transport protocols in general, and TCP in particular, can sometimes have very different performance in wired and wireless networks, and it is here, in terms of performance, that differences are manifested. Let's see why.

Recall that TCP retransmits a segment that is either lost or corrupted on the path between sender and receiver. In the case of mobile users, loss can result from either network congestion (router buffer overflow) or from handoff (e.g., from delays in rerouting segments to a mobile's new point-of-attachment to the network). In all cases, TCP's receiver-to-sender ACK indicates only that a segment was not received intact; the sender is unaware of whether the segment was lost due to congestion, during handoff, or due to detected bit errors. In all cases, the sender's response is the same—to retransmit the segment. TCP's congestion control response is *also* the same in all cases—TCP decreases its congestion window. By unconditionally decreasing its congestion window, TCP implicitly assumes that segment loss results from congestion rather than corruption or handoff. We saw in Section 12.2 that bit errors are much more common in wireless networks than in wired networks. When such bit errors occur or when handoff loss occurs, there's really no reason for the TCP sender to decrease its congestion window (and thus decrease its sending rate). Indeed, it may well be the case that router buffers are empty and packets are flowing along the end-end path unimpeded by congestion.

Researchers realized in the early to mid 1990s that given high bit-error rates on wireless links and the possibility of handoff loss, TCP's congestion control response could be problematic in a wireless setting. Two broad classes of approaches are possible for dealing with this problem [Balakrishnan 1995]:

- *Local recovery.* The goal of local recovery approaches is to recover from bit errors when and where (e.g., at the wireless link) they occur. This includes (1) protocols that recover from loss or corruption at the link layer (e.g., the 802.11 ARQ protocol we studied in Section 12.3, or more sophisticated approaches that use both ARQ and FEC [Ayanoglu 1995]); (2) transport-layer protocols that split a TCP connection into two segments, one from the source to the wireless link, and one from the wireless link to the destination [Bakre 1995; Brown 1997]; and (3) TCP-aware link-layer protocols [Balakrishnan 1995; Liu 2002].
- *TCP sender awareness of wireless links.* In the local recovery approaches, the TCP sender is blissfully unaware that its segments are traversing a wireless link. An alternative approach is for the TCP sender and receiver to be aware of the existence of a wireless link, to distinguish between congestive losses occurring in the wired network and corruption/loss occurring at the wireless link, and to invoke congestion control only in response to congestive wired-network losses. [Balakrishnan 1995] investigates various types of TCP, assuming that end systems can make this distinction. [Wei 2004] investigates techniques for distinguishing between losses on the wired and wireless segments of an end-end path.

Our treatment of TCP over wireless links has been necessarily brief here. We encourage you to consult the references for details of this ongoing area of research.

Having considered transport layer protocols, let us next consider the effect of wireless and mobility on application-layer protocols. Here, an important consideration is that wireless links often have relatively low bandwidths, as we saw in Figure 12.2. As a result, applications that operate over wireless links, particularly over cellular wireless links, must treat bandwidth as a scare commodity. For example, a Web server serving content to a Web browser executing on 3G phone will likely not be able to provide the same image-rich content that it gives to a browser operating over a wired connection. Although wireless links do provide challenges at the application layer, the mobility they enable also makes possible a rich set of location-aware and context-aware applications [Chen 2000]. More generally, wireless and mobile networks will play a key role in realizing the ubiquitous computing environments of the future [Weiser 1991]. It's fair to say that we've only seen the tip of the iceberg when it comes to impact of wireless and mobile networks on networked applications and their protocols!

12.9 Summary

Wireless and mobile networks have revolutionized telephony and are having an increasingly profound impact in the world of computer networks as well. With their anytime, anywhere, untethered access into the global network infrastructure, they are not only making network access more ubiquitous, they are also enabling an exciting new set of location-dependent services. Given the growing importance of wireless and networks, this chapter has focused on the principles, common link technologies, and network architectures for supporting wireless and mobile communication.

We began this chapter with an introduction to wireless and mobile networks, drawing an important distinction between the challenges posed by the *wireless* nature of the communication links in such networks, and by the *mobility* that these wireless links enable. This allowed us to better isolate, identify, and master the key concepts in each area. We focused first on wireless communication, considering the characteristics of a wireless link in Section 12.2. In Sections 12.3 and 12.4, we examined the link-level aspects of the IEEE 802.11 (Wi-Fi) wireless LAN standard, and cellular Internet access. We then turned our attention to the issue of mobility. In Section 12.5 we identified several forms of mobility, with points along this spectrum posing different challenges and admitting different solutions. We considered the problems of locating and routing to a mobile user, as well as approaches for handing off the mobile user who dynamically moves from one point of attachment to the network to another. We examined how these issues were addressed in the mobile IP standard and in GSM, in Sections 12.6 and 12.7, respectively. Finally, we considered the impact of wireless links and mobility on transport-layer protocols and networked applications in Section 12.8.

Although we have devoted an entire chapter to the study of wireless and mobile networks, an entire book (or more) would be required to fully explore this exciting and rapidly expanding field. We encourage you to delve more deeply into this field by consulting the many references provided in this chapter.

Homework Problems and Questions

Chapter 12 • Review Questions

1. Describe the role of the beacon frames in 802.11.
2. Discuss the methods that are available to authenticate users for 802.11 networks.
3. True or false: Before a 802.11 station transmits a data frame, it must first send an RTS frame and receive a corresponding CTS frame.
4. Why are acknowledgments used in 802.11 but not in wired Ethernet?

5. True or false: Ethernet and 802.11 use the same frame structure.
6. Describe how the RTS threshold works.
7. Suppose the IEEE 802.11 RTS and CTS frames were as long as the standard DATA and ACK frames. Would there be any advantage to using the CTS and RTS frames? Why or why not?
8. Section 12.3.4 discusses 802.11 mobility, in which a wireless station moves from one BSS to another within the same subnet. When the APs are interconnected with a switch, an AP may need to send a frame with a spoofed MAC address to get the switch to forward frames properly. Why?
9. We learned in Section 12.3.2 that there are two major 3G standards: UMTS and CDMA-2000. These two standards each owe their lineage to which 2G and 2.5G standards?

Problems

1. Consider the single-sender CDMA example in Figure 12.4. What would be the sender's output (for the 2 data bits shown) if the sender's CDMA code were (1, –1, 1, –1, 1, –1, 1, –1)?
2. Consider sender 2 in Figure 12.5. What is the sender's output to the channel (before it is added to the signal from sender 1), $Z^2_{i,m}$?
3. Suppose that the receiver in Figure 12.5 wanted to receive the data being sent by sender 2. Show (by calculation) that the receiver is indeed able to recover sender 2's data from the aggregate channel signal by using sender 2's code.
4. Suppose there are two ISPs providing Wi-Fi access in a particular café, with each ISP operating its own AP and having its own IP address block.
   a. Further suppose that by accident, each ISP has configured its AP to operate over channel 11. Will the 802.11 protocol completely break down in this situation? Discuss what happens when two stations, each associated with a different ISP, attempt to transmit at the same time.
   b. Now suppose that one AP operates over channel 1 and the other over channel 11.
5. In step 4 of the CSMA/CA protocol, a station that successfully transmits a frame begins the CSMA/CA protocol for a second frame at step 2, rather than at step 1. What rationale might the designers of CSMA/CA have had in mind by having such a station not transmit the second frame immediately (if the channel is sensed idle)?
6. Suppose an 802.11b station is configured to always reserve the channel with the RTS/CTS sequence. Suppose this station suddenly wants to transmit 1,000

bytes of data, and all other stations are idle at this time. As a function of SIFS and DIFS, and ignoring propagation delay and assuming no bit errors, calculate the time required to transmit the frame and receive the acknowledgment.

7. In Section 12.5, one proposed solution that allowed mobile users to maintain their IP addresses as they moved among foreign networks was to have a foreign network advertise a highly specific route to the mobile user and use the existing routing infrastructure to propagate this information throughout the network. We identified scalability as one concern. Suppose that when a mobile user moves from one network to another, the new foreign network advertises a specific route to the mobile user, and the old foreign network withdraws its route. Consider how routing information propagates in a distance vector algorithm (particularly for the case of interdomain routing among networks that span the globe).
   a. Will other routers be able to route datagrams immediately to the new foreign network as soon as the foreign network begins advertising its route?
   b. Is it possible for different routers to believe that different foreign networks contain the mobile user?
   c. Discuss the timescale over which other routers in the network will eventually learn the path to the mobile users.
8. Suppose the correspondent in Figure 12.17 were mobile. Sketch the additional network-layer infrastructure that would be needed to route the datagram from the original mobile user to the (now mobile) correspondent. Show the structure of the datagram(s) between the original mobile user and the (now mobile) correspondent, as in Figure 12.18.
9. In mobile IP, what effect will mobility have on end-to-end delays of datagrams between the source and destination?
10. Consider the chaining example discussed at the end of Section 12.7.2. Suppose a mobile user visits foreign networks A, B, and C, and that a correspondent begins a connection to the mobile user when it is resident in foreign network A. List the sequence of messages between foreign agents, and between foreign agents and the home agent as the mobile user moves from network A to network B to network C. Next, suppose chaining is not performed, and the correspondent (as well as the home agent) must be explicitly notified of the changes in the mobile user's care-of address. List the sequence of messages that would need to be exchanged in this second scenario.
11. Consider two mobile nodes in a foreign network having a foreign agent. Is it possible for the two mobile nodes to use the same care-of address in mobile IP? Explain your answer.
12. In our discussion of how the VLR updated the HLR with information about the mobiles current location, what are the advantages and disadvantages of providing the MSRN as opposed to the address of the VLR to the HLR?

Discussion Questions

1. List five products on the market today that provide a Bluetooth or 802.15 interface.
2. Is the 3G wireless service available in your region? How is it priced? What applications are being supported?
3. As a user of IEEE 802.11, what kinds of problems have you observed? How can 802.11 designs evolve to overcome these problems?

Ethereal Lab

In the companion Web site for this textbook, http://www.awl.com/kurose-ross, you'll find an Ethereal lab for this chapter that captures and studies the 802.11 frames exchanged between a wireless laptop and an access point.

Charlie Perkins

Charles E. Perkins is a Nokia Fellow in the Communication System Laboratory at Nokia Research Center, investigating mobile wireless networking and dynamic configuration protocols. He is the editor of several ACM and IEEE journals for areas related to wireless networking. He serves as document editor for the mobile-IP working group of the Internet Engineering Task Force (IETF), and has written or cowritten standards-track documents in the mobileip, manet, IPv6, and seamoby (Seamless Mobility) working groups. He is also associate editor for *Mobile Communications and Computing* Review, the official publication of ACM SIGMOBILE, and has served on the editorial staff for *IEEE Internet Computing* magazine. Charles has written and edited books on Mobile IP and Ad Hoc Networking, and has published a number of papers and award-winning articles in the areas of mobile networking, ad hoc networking, route optimization for mobile networking, resource discovery, and automatic configuration for mobile computers.

Why did you decide to specialize in wireless/mobility?

My involvement with wireless networking and mobility was a natural outgrowth of project work at IBM Research in the late 1980s. We had radio links and were trying to build a "ThinkPad" style of device (like, a Palm Pilot) with wireless connectivity and handwriting recognition.

We built a simple solution (later called "Mobile IP") and noticed that it worked. This is, of course, unusual compared to most research solutions. Using our experience with Mobile IP, we engineered a quick and effective modification to RIP that accomplished ad hoc. This also worked pretty well. By "working," I mean that the applications ran just fine without any modifications, and the network didn't bog down from our new designs. These properties go under the names "application transparency" and "scalability."

Of course, working in the lab is amazingly different than commercial success, and both of these technologies still have a lot of unmet commercial potential.

What was your first job in the computer industry?

I worked at TRW Controls, in Houston, Texas. It was a drastic change from university study.

One thing I learned at TRW Controls is how poor the support software is for even the most critical utility control systems. These systems were meant to control the flow of electricity in huge power networks, and the underlying software was built in ways that would raise the hair on your neck. Plus, the schedules were always compressed, and the programmers were deeply cynical about the intentions of management and their working conditions. The whole system needed to be redesigned from the ground up. I don't have much reason to believe that things have changed during the last 30 years, especially given recent events surrounding the blackout of 2003. In fact, given deregulation, it's almost certainly worse. I was very happy to leave TRW Controls and join Tektronix (Tek Labs).

What is the most challenging part of your job?

The most challenging part of my job is to understand what I should be doing to help my company. Also, I take it as part of my job to shape the wireless technologies that I come into contact with, into providing better service and a more enjoyable daily experience for people. My company is in the business of "connecting people," and I hope to help make those connections as harmonious and smooth as possible. Doing this in a way to also maximize the profit potential of the technologies we develop makes every day into a new challenge. Specifically in the area of wireless, I believe that security technology has to be developed to be desirable and appreciated (like a raincoat) instead of burdensome and dreaded (as it mostly is today).

On a more detailed technical level, where in fact I am much more comfortable, I try to solve network protocol problems in a way that places the least burden on the wireless devices (and their batteries!) and presents the users with the least inconvenience. Interconnecting today's wireless telephones with the Internet by way of new high-speed wireless technologies is terrifically interesting technically, and offers unlimited potential for commercial success for those who can find the right paths forward.

What do you see for the future of wireless?

The entire wireless industry is undergoing tremendous changes and there is no end in sight. New high-speed wireless technologies are emerging and may have unforeseen practical effects that could fundamentally change society. Our current expectations of privacy and the limitations on our ability to communicate with each other (voice, image, and data) could be unrecognizable within ten years. As enterprises convert more and more to wireless communications, it is quite possible that new security measures will be taken that would significantly change our workplace experience.

It seems pretty clear that we will get more spectrum allocated to various schemes for radio communications. These can be very high speed. Soon, I expect it will be quite feasible for communities to offer their citizens complete high-speed wireless communications, as if a whole town were a local area network. This could have the effect of reinvigorating the sense of community which has long been lost in our society, at least in the United States. Of course, the community would still demand access to the Internet. Disk storage is getting so inexpensive, that one can imagine high-speed wireless access to untold libraries of humanity's intellectual treasures, as well as the latest news.

Wireless will likely accelerate the growth of the Internet. As wireless devices get cheaper and cheaper, we will see Internet communications everywhere (earrings, multiplayer games, subway fare readers). This will motivate new applications and new security solutions.

These are predictions that have often been made, but only within the last few years has the technology become available. Now the huge barrier will be rights management and access controls. If citizens do not engage in the process of formulating their rights in these matters, the long-held dreams will still remain dreams. Or, worse, they may be replaced by new nightmares. The Internet is everyone's business, and wireless brings it right up front and personal. I'm there to help it be the wonderful tool it should be.

CHAPTER 13

Multimedia Networking

Having completed our journey down the protocol stack in the first part of this book, we now have a strong grounding in the principles and practice of computer networking. This foundation will serve us well as we turn to a topic that cuts across many layers of the protocol stack: multimedia networking.

The last few years have witnessed an explosive growth in the development and deployment of networked applications that transmit and receive audio and video over the Internet. New multimedia networking applications (also referred to as continuous-media applications)—streaming video, IP telephony, Internet radio, teleconferencing, interactive games, virtual worlds, distance learning, and much more—seem to be announced daily. The service requirements of these applications differ significantly from those of the elastic applications (e-mail, Web, remote login, file sharing). In particular, many multimedia applications are highly sensitive to end-to-end delay and delay variation but can tolerate occasional loss of data. In the first half of this chapter we'll examine how multimedia applications can be designed to make the best of the best-effort Internet, which provides no end-to-end delay guarantees. In the second half of this chapter we'll examine a number of activities that are currently under way to extend the Internet architecture to provide explicit support for the service requirements of multimedia applications.

13.1 Multimedia Networking Applications

In our discussion of application service requirements in, we identified a number of axes along which these requirements can be classified. Two of these axes—timing considerations and tolerance of data loss—are particularly important for networked multimedia applications. Timing considerations are important because many multimedia applications are highly **delay-sensitive.** We will see shortly that in many multimedia applications, packets that incur a sender-to-receiver delay of more than a few hundred milliseconds are essentially useless. On the other hand, networked multimedia applications are for the most part **loss-tolerant**—occasional loss only causes occasional glitches in the audio/video playback, and these losses can often be partially or fully concealed. These delay-sensitive but loss-tolerant characteristics are clearly different from those of elastic applications such as the Web, e-mail, FTP, and Telnet. For elastic applications, long delays are annoying but not particularly harmful, and the completeness and integrity of the transferred data is of paramount importance.

13.1.1 Examples of Multimedia Applications

The Internet carries a large variety of exciting multimedia applications. In this subsection, we consider three broad classes of multimedia applications: streaming stored audio/video, streaming live audio/video, and real-time interactive audio/video.

In this chapter we do *not* cover download-and-then-play applications, such as fully downloading an MP3 over a P2P file-sharing application before playing back the MP3. Indeed, download-and-then-play applications are elastic, file-transfer applications without any special delay requirements. We examined file transfer (HTTP and FTP) and P2P file-sharing systems.

Streaming Stored Audio and Video

In this class of applications, clients request on-demand compressed audio or video files that are stored on servers. Stored audio files might contain audio from a professor's lecture (you are urged to visit the Web site for this book to try this out), rock songs, symphonies, archives of famous radio broadcasts, or archived historical recordings. Stored video files might contain video of a professor's lecture, full-length movies, prerecorded television shows, documentaries, video archives of historical events, cartoons, or music video clips. This class of applications has three key distinguishing features.

- *Stored media.* The multimedia content has been prerecorded and is stored at the server. As a result, a user may pause, rewind, fast-forward, or index through the multimedia content. The time from when a client makes such a request until the action manifests itself at the client should be on the order of one to ten seconds for acceptable responsiveness.

- *Streaming.* In a streaming stored audio/video application, a client typically begins playout of the audio/video a few seconds after it begins receiving the file from the server. This means that the client will be playing out audio/video from one location in the file while it is receiving later parts of the file from the server. This technique, known as **streaming,** avoids having to download the entire file (and incurring a potentially long delay) before beginning playout. There are many streaming multimedia products, including RealPlayer from RealNetworks [RealNetworks 2004], Apple's QuickTime [QuickTime 2004], and Microsoft's Windows Media [Microsoft Media Player 2004].
- *Continuous playout.* Once playout of the multimedia content begins, it should proceed according to the original timing of the recording. This places critical delay constraints on data delivery. Data must be received from the server in time for its playout at the client. Although stored media applications have continuous playout requirements, their end-to-end delay constraints are nevertheless less stringent than those for live, interactive applications such as Internet telephony and video conferencing (see below).

Streaming Live Audio and Video

This class of applications is similar to traditional broadcast radio and television, except that transmission takes place over the Internet. These applications allow a user to receive a *live* radio or television transmission emitted from any corner of the world. (For example, one of the authors of this book often listens to his favorite Philadelphia radio stations when traveling. The other author regularly listened to live broadcasts of his university's beloved basketball team while he was living in France for a year.)

Since streaming live audio/video is not stored, a client cannot fast-forward through the media. However, with local storage of received data, other interactive operations such as pausing and rewinding through live multimedia transmissions are possible in some applications. Live, broadcast-like applications often have many clients who are receiving the same audio/video program. Distribution of live audio/video to many receivers can be efficiently accomplished using the IP multicasting techniques described in Section 10.7. At the time of this writing, however, live audio/video distribution is more often accomplished through multiple separate unicast streams. As with streaming stored multimedia, continuous playout is required, although the timing constraints are less stringent than for real-time interactive applications. Delays of up to tens of seconds from when the user requests the delivery/playout of a live transmission to when playout begins can be tolerated.

CASE HISTORY

REALNETWORKS: BRINGING AUDIO TO THE INTERNET FOREGROUND

RealNetworks, a pioneer in streaming audio and video products, was the first company to bring audio to the Internet mainstream. The company began under the name Progressive Networks in 1995. Its initial product—the RealAudio system— included an audio encoder, an audio server, and an audio player. The RealAudio system enabled users to browse, select, and play back audio content on demand, as easily as using a standard video cassette player/recorder. It quickly became popular for providers of entertainment, information, and news content to deliver audio-on-demand services that can be accessed and played back immediately. In early 1997, RealNetworks expanded its product line to include video as well as audio. RealNetwork products currently incorporate the RTP and RTSP protocols.

Over the past few years, RealNetworks has seen tough competition from Microsoft, which began to market its own streaming media products in the late 1990's. RealNetworks and Microsoft have diverged on some of the underlying technology choices in their players. Waging the tug of war in the marketplace and in Internet standards groups, both companies are seeking to have their own formats and protocols become the standard for the Internet.

Real-Time Interactive Audio and Video

This class of applications allows people to use audio/video to communicate with each other in real time. Real-time interactive audio over the Internet is often referred to as **Internet phone**, since, from the user's perspective, it is similar to the traditional circuit-switched telephone service. Internet phone can potentially provide private branch exchange (PBX), local, and long-distance telephone service at very low cost. It can also facilitate the deployment of new services that are not easily supported by the traditional circuit-switched networks, including Web-phone integration, group real-time communication, directory services, caller filtering, and more. There are hundreds of Internet telephone products currently available [VON 2004]. For example, users of Microsoft's Instant Messenger can make PC-to-phone and PC-to-PC voice calls. With real-time interactive video, also called video conferencing, individuals communicate visually as well as orally. There are also many real-time interactive video products currently available for the Internet, including Microsoft's NetMeeting. Note that in a real-time interactive audio/video application, a user can speak or move at any time. For a conversation with interaction among multiple speakers, the delay from when a user speaks or moves until the action is manifested at the receiving hosts should be less than a few hundred milliseconds. For voice, delays smaller than 150 milliseconds are not perceived by a human listener, delays between 150 and 400 milliseconds can be acceptable, and delays exceeding 400 milliseconds can result in frustrating, if not completely unintelligible, voice conversations.

13.1.2 Hurdles for Multimedia in Today's Internet

Recall that the IP protocol deployed in the Internet today provides a **best-effort service** to all the datagrams it carries. In other words, the Internet makes its best

CASE HISTORY

VOICE OVER THE INTERNET

Given the worldwide popularity of the telephone system, many Internet visionaries have repeatedly predicted since the late 1980s that the next Internet killer application would be some sort of voice application. These predictions were accompanied by Internet telephony research and product development. For example, researchers created Internet phone prototypes in the 1980s, building on research on packetized voice transmission from the 1970's [Cohen 1977, RFC 741], years before the Web was popularized. And numerous startups produced PC-to-PC Internet phone products throughout the 1990s. But none of these prototypes or products really caught on with mainstream Internet users (even though some were bundled with popular browsers). Not until 1999 did voice communication begin to be popularized in the Internet.

The PC-to-phone application began to see significant usage in the late 1990s. This application allows an Internet user with an Internet connection and a microphone to call any ordinary telephone. Net2Phone [Net2Phone 2004] and Dialpad [Dialpad 2004] are two companies that have provided PC-to-phone service. These PC-to-phone services are low-cost and are hence popular with people who love to talk but are on a tight budget. Furthermore, a number of companies offer PC-to-phone-like services to the enterprise. As we'll discuss in this chapter, for a PC-to-phone call, the call is routed over the Internet from a PC to a gateway, and over circuit-switched telephone networks from the gateway to the telephone (fixed or mobile). For communication over the Internet between the PC and gateway, a number of popular protocols are often used, including RTP, SIP, and H.323, all of which are discussed in this chapter. A second class of applications is phone-to-Internet-to-phone, allowing consumers to make long-distance calls at lower cost while using traditional phone handsets on both ends. Many of the prepaid phone cards that can be purchased at newspaper stands and drugstores use the phone-to-Internet-to-phone mode. A third class of applications is asynchronous voice over the Internet [Wimba 2004]. Most major networking equipment companies—including Cisco, Lucent, and Alcatel—offer complete product lines for voice over IP for telephone operators and business customers [VON 2004].

effort to move each datagram from sender to receiver as quickly as possible, but it does not make any promises whatsoever about the end-to-end delay for an individual packet. Nor does the service make any promises about the variation of packet delay within a packet stream. Because TCP and UDP run over IP, it follows that neither of these transport protocols makes any delay guarantees to invoking applications. Due to the lack of any special effort to deliver packets in a timely manner, it is an extremely challenging problem to develop successful multimedia networking applications for the Internet. To date, multimedia over the Internet has achieved significant but limited success. For example, streaming stored audio/video with user-interactivity delays of five to ten seconds is now commonplace in the Internet. But during peak traffic periods, performance may be unsatisfactory, particularly when intervening links are congested (such as congested transoceanic links).

Internet phone and real-time interactive video has, to date, been less successful than streaming stored audio/video. Indeed, real-time interactive voice and video impose rigid constraints on packet delay and packet jitter. **Packet jitter** is the variability of packet delays within the same packet stream. Real-time voice and video can work well in regions where bandwidth is plentiful, and hence delay and jitter are minimal. But quality can deteriorate to unacceptable levels as soon as the real-time voice or video packet stream hits a moderately congested link.

The design of multimedia applications would certainly be more straightforward if there were some sort of first-class and second-class Internet services, whereby first-class packets were limited in number and received priority service in router queues. Such a first-class service could be satisfactory for delay-sensitive applications. But to date, the Internet has mostly taken an egalitarian approach to packet scheduling in router queues. All packets receive equal service; no packets, including delay-sensitive audio and video packets, receive special priority in the router queues. No matter how much money you have or how important you are, you must join the end of the line and wait your turn! In the latter half of this chapter, we'll examine proposed architectures that aim to remove this restriction.

So for the time being we have to live with best-effort service. But given this constraint, we can make several design decisions and employ a few tricks to improve the user-perceived quality of a multimedia networking application. For example, we can send the audio and video over UDP, and thereby circumvent TCP's low throughput when TCP enters its slow-start phase. We can delay playback at the receiver by 100 msecs or more in order to diminish the effects of network-induced jitter. We can timestamp packets at the sender so that the receiver knows when the packets should be played back. For stored audio/video we can prefetch data during playback when client storage and extra bandwidth are available. We can even send redundant information in order to mitigate the effects of network-induced packet loss. We'll investigate many of these techniques in the rest of the first half of this chapter.

13.1.3 How Should the Internet Evolve to Support Multimedia Better?

Today there is a tremendous—and sometimes ferocious—debate about how the Internet should evolve in order to better accommodate multimedia traffic with its rigid timing constraints. At one extreme, some researchers argue that fundamental changes should be made to the Internet so that applications can explicitly reserve end-to-end bandwidth. These researchers believe that if a user wants to make, for example, an Internet phone call from Host A to Host B, then the user's Internet phone application should be able to reserve bandwidth explicitly in each link along a route between the two hosts. But permitting applications to make reservations and requiring the network to honor the reservations requires some big changes. First we need a protocol that, on the behalf of applications, reserves link bandwidth on the path from the senders to their receivers. Second, we must modify scheduling policies in the router queues so that bandwidth reservations can be honored. With these new scheduling policies, not all packets get equal treatment; instead, those that reserve (and pay) more get more. Third, in order to honor reservations, the applications must give the network a description of the traffic that they intend to send into the network. The network must then police each application's traffic to make sure that it abides by the description. Finally, the network must have a means of determining whether it has sufficient available bandwidth to support any new reservation request. These mechanisms, when combined, require new and complex software in the hosts and routers as well as new types of services. We'll look into these mechanisms in more detail, when we examine the Intserv model in Section 13.8.

At the other extreme, some researchers argue that it isn't necessary to make any fundamental changes to best-effort service and the underlying Internet protocols. Instead they advocate a laissez-faire approach:

- As demand increases, the ISPs (both top-tier and lower-tier ISPs) will scale their networks to meet the demand. Specifically, ISPs will add more bandwidth and switching capacity to provide satisfactory delay and packet-loss performance within their networks. The ISPs will thereby provide better service to their customers (users and customer ISPs), translating to higher revenues through more customers and higher service fees. As discussed, ISPs can also install caches in their networks, which bring stored content (Web pages as well as stored audio and video) closer to the users, thereby reducing traffic in higher-tier ISPs.
- Content distribution networks (CDNs), replicate stored content and put the replicated content at the edges of the Internet. Given that a large fraction of the traffic flowing through the Internet is stored content (Web pages, MP3s, video), CDNs can significantly alleviate the traffic loads on the ISPs and the peering interfaces between ISPs. Furthermore, CDNs provide a differentiated service to content providers: content providers that pay for a CDN service can deliver content faster and more effectively. We'll study CDNs later in this chapter in Section 13.5.

- To deal with live streaming traffic (such as a sporting event), which is being sent to millions of users simultaneously, **multicast overlay networks** can be deployed. A multicast overlay network consists of servers scattered throughout the ISP network (and potentially throughout the entire Internet). These servers and the logical links between them collectively form an overlay network, which multicasts (see Section 10.7) traffic from the source to the millions of users. Unlike multicast IP, for which the multicast function is handled by routers at the IP layer, overlay networks multicast at the application layer. For example, the source host might send the stream to three overlay servers; each of the overlay servers may forward the stream to three more overlay servers; the process continues, creating a distribution tree on top of the underlying IP network with routers and hosts. By multicasting popular live traffic through overlay networks, overall traffic loads in the Internet can be reduced over the case of unicast distribution.

Between the reservation camp and the laissez-faire camp there is a yet a third camp—the differentiated services (Diffserv) camp. This camp wants to make relatively small changes at the network and transport layers, and introduce simple pricing and policing schemes at the edge of the network (that is, at the interface between the user and the user's ISP). The idea is to introduce a small number of traffic classes (possibly just two classes), assign each datagram to one of the classes, give datagrams different levels of service according to their class in the router queues, and charge users according to the class of packets that they are sending into the network. We'll cover differentiated services in Section 13.8.

13.1.4 Audio and Video Compression

Before audio and video can be transmitted over a computer network, it must be digitized and compressed. The need for digitization is obvious: computer networks transmit bits, so all transmitted information must be represented as a sequence of bits. Compression is important because uncompressed audio and video consume a tremendous amount of storage and bandwidth; removing the inherent redundancies in digitized audio and video signals can reduce the amount of data that needs to be stored and transmitted by orders of magnitude. As an example, a single image consisting of 1024 pixels (1024 pixels, with each pixel encoded into 24 bits (8 bits each for the colors red, green, and blue), requires 3 Mbytes of storage without compression. It would take seven minutes to send this image over a 64 kbps link. If the image is compressed at a modest 10:1 compression ratio, the storage requirement is reduced to 300 Kbytes and the transmission time also drops by a factor of ten.

The fields of audio and video compression are vast. They have been active areas of research for more than fifty years, and there are now literally hundreds of popular techniques and standards for both audio and video compression. Most universities offer entire courses on audio and video compression and often offer separate courses on each. We therefore provide here a brief and high-level introduction to the subject.

Audio Compression in the Internet

A continuously varying analog audio signal (which could emanate from speech or music) is normally converted to a digital signal as follows:

- The analog audio signal is first sampled at some fixed rate, for example, at 8,000 samples per second. The value of each sample is an arbitrary real number.
- Each of the samples is then rounded to one of a finite number of values. This operation is referred to as **quantization.** The number of finite values—called quantization values—is typically a power of two, for example, 256 quantization values.
- Each of the quantization values is represented by a fixed number of bits. For example, if there are 256 quantization values, then each value—and hence each sample—is represented by 1 byte. Each of the samples is converted to its bit representation. The bit representations of all the samples are concatenated together to form the digital representation of the signal.

As an example, if an analog audio signal is sampled at 8,000 samples per second and each sample is quantized and represented by 8 bits, then the resulting digital signal will have a rate of 64,000 bits per second. This digital signal can then be converted back—that is, decoded—to an analog signal for playback. However, the decoded analog signal is typically different from the original audio signal. By increasing the sampling rate and the number of quantization values, the decoded signal can approximate the original analog signal. Thus, there is a clear trade-off between the quality of the decoded signal and the storage and bandwidth requirements of the digital signal.

The basic encoding technique that we just described is called **pulse code modulation (PCM).** Speech encoding often uses PCM, with a sampling rate of 8,000 samples per second and 8 bits per sample, giving a rate of 64 kbps. The audio compact disk (CD) also uses PCM, with a sampling rate of 44,100 samples per second with 16 bits per sample; this gives a rate of 705.6 kbps for mono and 1.411 Mbps for stereo.

A bit rate of 1.411 Mbps for stereo music exceeds most access rates, and even 64 kbps for speech exceeds the access rate for a dial-up modem user. For these reasons, PCM-encoded speech and music are rarely used in the Internet. Instead compression techniques are used to reduce the bit rates of the stream. Popular compression techniques for speech include **GSM** (13 kbps), **G.729** (8 kbps), and **G.723.3** (both 6.4 and 5.3 kbps), and a large number of proprietary techniques, including those used by RealNetworks. A popular compression technique for near CD-quality stereo music is **MPEG 1 layer 3,** more commonly known as **MP3.** MP3 encoders typically compress to rates of 96 kbps, 128 kbps, and 160 kbps, and produce very little sound degradation. When an MP3 file is broken up into pieces, each piece is still playable. This headerless file format allows MP3 music files to be streamed across the Internet (assuming the playback bit rate and speed of the Internet connection are compatible). The MP3 compression standard is complex, using psychoacoustic masking, redundancy reduction, and bit reservoir buffering.

Video Compression in the Internet

A video is a sequence of images, typically being displayed at a constant rate, for example at 24 or 30 images per second. An uncompressed, digitally encoded image consists of an array of pixels, with each pixel encoded into a number of bits to represent luminance and color. There are two types of redundancy in video, both of which can be exploited for compression. Spatial redundancy is the redundancy within a given image. For example, an image that consists of mostly white space can be efficiently compressed. Temporal redundancy reflects repetition from image to subsequent image. If, for example, an image and the subsequent image are exactly the same, there is no reason to re-encode the subsequent image; it is more efficient simply to indicate during encoding that the subsequent image is exactly the same.

The MPEG compression standards are among the most popular compression techniques. These include **MPEG 1** for CD-ROM quality video (1.5 Mbps), **MPEG 2** for high-quality **DVD** video (3–6 Mbps), and **MPEG 4** for object-oriented video compression. The MPEG standard draws heavily on the JPEG standard for image compression by exploiting temporal redundancy across images in addition to the spatial redundancy exploited by JPEG. The **H.261** video compression standards are also very popular in the Internet. In addition there are numerous proprietary schemes, including Apple's QuickTime and Real Networks' encoders.

Readers interested in learning more about audio and video encoding are encouraged to see [Rao 1996] and [Solari 1997]. A good book on multimedia networking in general is [Crowcroft 1999].

13.2 Streaming Stored Audio and Video

In recent years, audio/video streaming has become a popular application and a significant consumer of network bandwidth. This trend is likely to continue for several reasons. First, the cost of disk storage continues to decrease rapidly, making room for storage-hungry multimedia files. Today, terabyte storage facilities are available, capable of holding thousands of MPEG 2 videos. Second, improvements in Internet infrastructure, such as high-speed residential access (that is, cable modems and ADSL, content-distribution techniques such as caching and CDNs (see Section 13.5), and new QoS-oriented Internet protocols (see Sections 13.6–13.9) will greatly facilitate the distribution of stored audio and video. And third, there is an enormous pent-up demand for high-quality video on demand, an application that combines two existing killer communication technologies—television and on-demand Web.

In audio/video streaming, clients request compressed audio/video files that reside on servers. As we'll soon discuss, these servers can be ordinary Web servers or can be special streaming servers tailored for the audio/video streaming application. Upon client request, the server directs an audio/video file to the client by sending the file into a socket. Both TCP and UDP socket connections are used in practice. Before being sent into the network, the audio/video file is segmented, and the segments are typically encapsulated with special headers appropriate for audio/video traffic. The **real-time protocol (RTP),** discussed in Section 13.4, is a public-domain standard for encapsulating such segments. Once the requested audio/video file starts to arrive, the client begins to render the file (typically) within a few seconds. Most existing products also provide for user interactivity, for example, pause/resume and temporal jumps within the audio/video file. This user interactivity also requires a protocol for client/server interaction. The **real-time streaming protocol (RTSP)**, discussed at the end of this section, is a public-domain protocol for providing user interactivity.

Users often request audio/video streaming through a Web client (that is, browser). But because audio/video playout is not integrated directly into today's Web clients, a separate **helper application** is required for playing out the audio/video. Helper applications are often called **media players,** the most popular of which are currently RealNetworks' RealPlayer and the Microsoft Windows Media Player. The media player performs several functions, including the following:

- *Decompression.* Audio/video is almost always compressed to save disk storage and network bandwidth. A media player must decompress the audio/video on the fly during playout.
- *Jitter removal.* Packet jitter is the variability of source-to-destination delays of packets within the same packet stream. Since audio and video must be played out with the same timing with which it was recorded, a receiver will buffer received packets for a short period of time to remove this jitter. We'll examine this topic in detail in Section 13.3.
- *Error correction.* Due to unpredictable congestion in the Internet, a fraction of packets in the packet stream can be lost. If this fraction becomes too large, user-perceived audio/video quality becomes unacceptable. To this end, many streaming systems attempt to recover from losses by either (1) reconstructing lost packets through the transmission of redundant packets, (2) having the client explicitly request retransmission of lost packets, or (3) masking loss by interpolating the missing data from the received data.

The media player has a graphical user interface with control knobs. This is the actual interface that the user interacts with. It typically includes volume controls, pause/resume buttons, sliders for making temporal jumps in the audio/video stream, and so on.

Plug-ins may be used to embed the user interface of the media player within the window of the Web browser. For such embeddings, the browser reserves screen space on the current Web page, and it is up to the media player to manage the screen space. But whether it appears in a separate window or within the browser window (as a plug-in), the media player program is executed separately from the browser.

13.2.1 Accessing Audio and Video Through a Web Server

Stored audio/video can reside either on a Web server that delivers the audio/video to the client over HTTP, or on an audio/video streaming server that delivers the audio/video over non-HTTP protocols (protocols that can be either proprietary or open standards). In this subsection, we examine delivery of audio/video from a Web server; in the next subsection, we examine delivery from a streaming server.

Consider first the case of audio streaming. When an audio file resides on a Web server, the audio file is an ordinary object in the server's file system, just as HTML and JPEG files are. When a user wants to hear the audio file, the user's host establishes a TCP connection with the Web server and sends an HTTP request for the object. Upon receiving a request, the Web server encapsulates the audio file in an HTTP response message and sends the response message back into the TCP connection. The case of video can be a little trickier, because the audio and video parts of the video may be stored in two files; that is, they may be two objects in the Web server's file system. In this case, two separate HTTP requests are sent to the server (over two separate TCP connections for HTTP/1.0), and the audio and video files arrive at the client in parallel. It is up to the client to manage the synchronization of the two streams. It is also possible that the audio and video are interleaved in the same file, so that only one object need be sent to the client. To keep our discussion simple, for the case of video we assume that the audio and video are contained in one file.

A naive architecture for audio/video streaming is shown in Figure 13.1. In this architecture:

- The browser process establishes a TCP connection with the Web server and requests the audio/video file with an HTTP request message.
- The Web server sends the audio/video file to the browser in an HTTP response message.
- The content-type header line in the HTTP response message indicates a specific audio/video encoding. The client browser examines the content type of the response message, launches the associated media player, and passes the file to the media player.
- The media player then renders the audio/video file.

Although this approach is very simple, it has a major drawback: the media player (that is, the helper application) must interact with the server through a Web browser as an intermediary. This can lead to many problems. In particular, when a browser is an

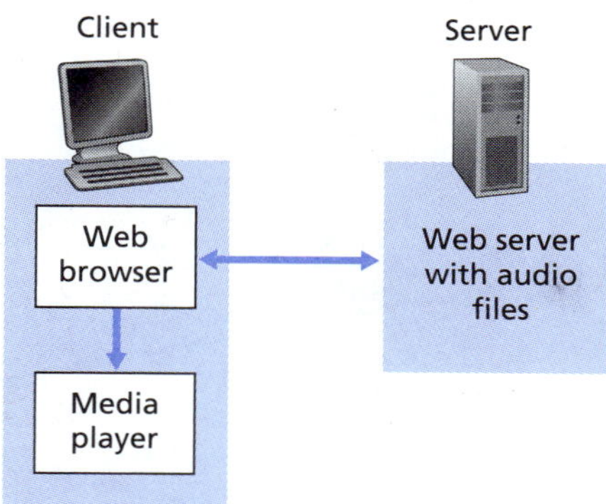

Figure 13.1 ♦ A naive implementation for audio streaming

intermediary, the entire object must be downloaded before the browser passes the object to a helper application. The resulting delay before playout can begin is typically unacceptable for audio/video clips of moderate length. For this reason, audio/video streaming implementations typically have the server send the audio/video file directly to the media player process. In other words, a direct socket connection is made between the server process and the media player process. As shown in Figure 13.2, this is typically done by making use of a **meta file,** a file that provides information (for example, URL or type of encoding) about the audio/video file that is to be streamed.

A direct TCP connection between the server and the media player is obtained as follows:

1. The user clicks on a hyperlink for an audio/video file.
2. The hyperlink does not point directly to the audio/video file, but instead to a meta file. The meta file contains the URL of the actual audio/video file. The HTTP response message that encapsulates the meta file includes a content-type header line that indicates the specific audio/video application.
3. The client browser examines the content-type header line of the response message, launches the associated media player, and passes the entire body of the response message (that is, the meta file) to the media player.
4. The media player sets up a TCP connection directly with the HTTP server. The media player sends an HTTP request message for the audio/video file into the TCP connection.
5. The audio/video file is sent within an HTTP response message to the media player. The media player streams out the audio/video file.

The importance of the intermediate step of acquiring the meta file is clear. When the browser sees the content type of the file, it can launch the appropriate media player, and thereby have the media player contact the server directly.

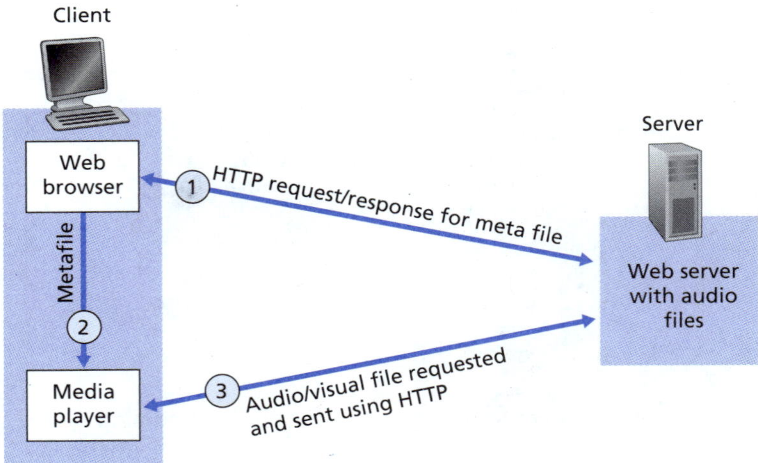

Figure 13.2 ♦ Web server sends audio/video directly to the media player

We have just learned how a meta file can allow a media player to communicate directly with a Web server that stores an audio/video file. Yet many companies that sell products for audio/video streaming do not recommend the architecture we just described. This is because the architecture has the media player communicate with the server over HTTP and hence also over TCP. HTTP is often considered insufficiently rich to allow for satisfactory user interaction with the server; in particular, HTTP does not easily allow a user (through the media player) to send pause/resume, fast-forward, and temporal jump commands to the server.

13.2.2 Sending Multimedia from a Streaming Server to a Helper Application

In order to get around HTTP and/or TCP, audio/video can be stored on and sent from a streaming server to the media player. This streaming server could be a proprietary streaming server, such as those marketed by RealNetworks and Microsoft, or could be a public-domain streaming server. With a streaming server, audio/video can be sent over UDP (rather than TCP) using application-layer protocols that may be better tailored than HTTP to audio/video streaming.

This architecture requires two servers, as shown in Figure 13.3. One server, the HTTP server, serves Web pages (including meta files). The second server, the **streaming server,** serves the audio/video files. The two servers can run on the same end system or on two distinct end systems. The steps for this architecture are similar to those described in the preceding subsection. However, now the media player requests the file from a streaming server rather than from a Web server, and now the media player and streaming server can interact using their own protocols. These protocols can allow for rich user interaction with the audio/video stream.

In the architecture of Figure 13.3, there are many options for delivering the audio/video from the streaming server to the media player. A partial list of the options is given below.

1. The audio/video is sent over UDP at a constant rate equal to the drain rate at the receiver (which is the encoded rate of the audio/video). For example, if the audio is compressed using GSM at a rate of 13 kbps, then the server clocks out the compressed audio file at 13 kbps. As soon as the client receives compressed audio/video from the network, it decompresses the audio/video and plays it back.
2. This is the same as the first option, but the media player delays playout for two to five seconds in order to eliminate network-induced jitter. The client accomplishes this task by placing the compressed media that it receives from the network into a **client buffer,** as shown in Figure 13.4. Once the client has prefetched a few seconds of the media, it begins to drain the buffer. For this, and the previous option, the fill rate $x(t)$ is equal to the drain rate d, except when there is packet loss, in which case $x(t)$ is momentarily less than d.
3. The media is sent over TCP. The server pushes the media file into the TCP socket as quickly as it can; the client (that is, media player) reads from the TCP socket as quickly as it can and places the compressed video into the media player buffer.

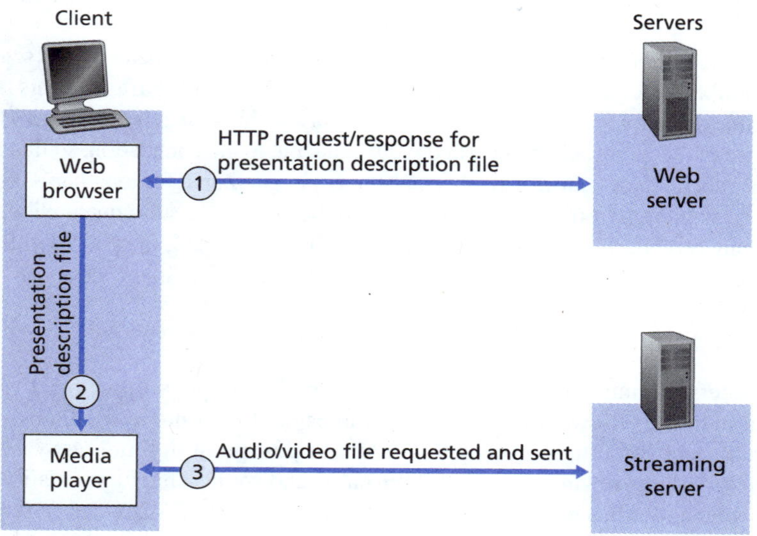

Figure 13.3 ♦ Streaming from a streaming server to a media player

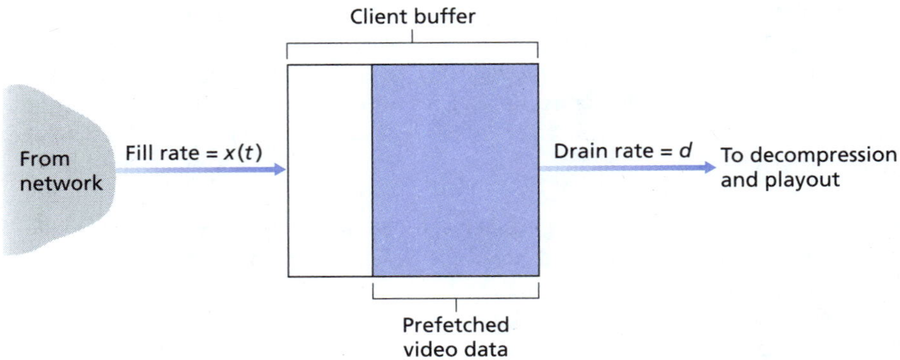

Figure 13.4 ♦ Client buffer being filled at rate $x(t)$ and drained at rate d

> After an initial two- to five-second delay, the media player reads from its buffer at a rate d and forwards the compressed media to decompression and playback. Because TCP retransmits lost packets, it has the potential to provide better sound quality than UDP. On the other hand, the fill rate $x(t)$ now fluctuates with time due to TCP congestion control and window flow control. In fact, after packet loss, TCP congestion control may reduce the instantaneous rate to less than d for long periods of time. This can empty the client buffer (a process known as **starvation**) and introduce undesirable pauses into the output of the audio/video stream at the client.

For the third option, the behavior of $x(t)$ will very much depend on the size of the client buffer (which is not to be confused with the TCP receive buffer). If this buffer is large enough to hold all of the media file (possibly within disk storage), then TCP will make use of all the instantaneous bandwidth available to the connection, so that $x(t)$ can become much larger than d. If $x(t)$ becomes much larger than d for long periods of time, then a large portion of media is prefetched into the client, and subsequent client starvation is unlikely. If, on the other hand, the client buffer is small, then $x(t)$ will fluctuate around the drain rate d. Risk of client starvation is much larger in this case.

13.2.3 Real-Time Streaming Protocol (RTSP)

Many Internet multimedia users (particularly those who grew up with a TV remote control in hand) will want to control the playback of continuous media by pausing playback, repositioning playback to a future or past point in time, fast-forwarding playback visually, rewinding playback visually, and so on. This functionality is similar to what a user has with a DVD player when watching a DVD video or with a CD player when listening to a music CD. To allow a user to control playback, the media player and server need a protocol for exchanging playback control information. The real-time streaming protocol (RTSP), defined in RFC 2326, is such a protocol.

Before getting into the details of RTSP, let us first indicate what RTSP does not do.

- RTSP does not define compression schemes for audio and video.
- RTSP does not define how audio and video are encapsulated in packets for transmission over a network; encapsulation for streaming media can be provided by RTP or by a proprietary protocol. (RTP is discussed in Section 13.4.) For example, RealNetworks' audio/video servers and players use RTSP to send control information to each other, but the media stream itself can be encapsulated in RTP packets or in some proprietary data format.
- RTSP does not restrict how streamed media is transported; it can be transported over UDP or TCP.
- RTSP does not restrict how the media player buffers the audio/video. The audio/video can be played out as soon as it begins to arrive at the client, it can be played out after a delay of a few seconds, or it can be downloaded in its entirety before playout.

So if RTSP doesn't do any of the above, what does it do? RTSP allows a media player to control the transmission of a media stream. As mentioned above, control actions include pause/resume, repositioning of playback, fast-forward, and rewind. RTSP is an **out-of-band protocol.** In particular, the RTSP messages are sent out-of-band, whereas the media stream, whose packet structure is not defined by RTSP, is considered "in-band." RTSP messages use a different port number, 544, from the media stream. The RTSP specification [RFC 2326] permits RTSP messages to be sent over either TCP or UDP.

Recall that the file transfer protocol (FTP) also uses the out-of-band notion. In particular, FTP uses two client/server pairs of sockets, each pair with its own port number: one client/server socket pair supports a TCP connection that transports control information; the other client/server socket pair supports a TCP connection that actually transports the file. The RTSP channel is in many ways similar to FTP's control channel.

Let's now walk through a simple RTSP example, which is illustrated in Figure 13.5. The Web browser first requests a presentation description file from a Web server. The presentation description file can have references to several continuous-media files as well as directives for synchronization of the continuous-media files. Each reference to a continuous-media file begins with the URL method, `rtsp://`. Below we provide a sample presentation file that has been adapted from [Schulzrinne 1997]. In this presentation, an audio and video stream are played in parallel and in lip sync (as part of the same group). For the audio stream, the media player can choose (switch) between two audio recordings, a low-fidelity recording and a high-fidelity recording. (The format of the file is similar to SMIL [SMIL 2004], which is used by many streaming products to define synchronized multimedia presentations.)

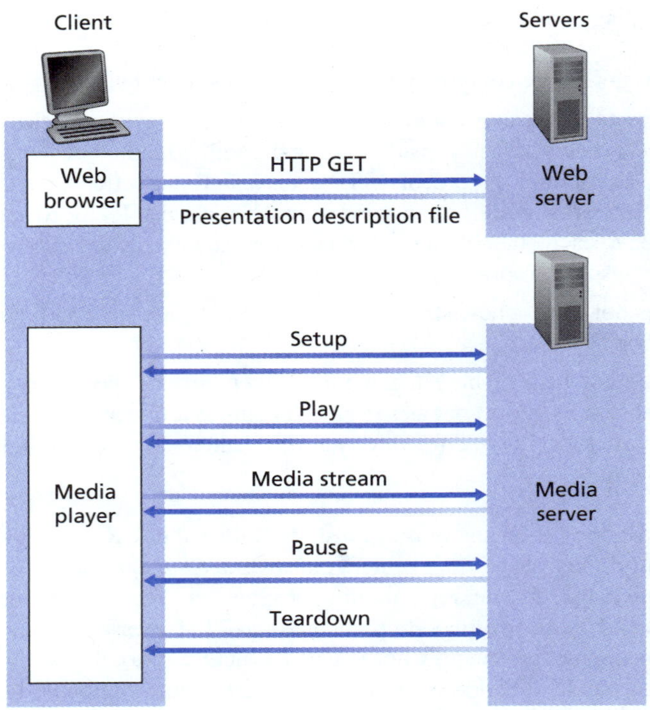

Figure 13.5 ♦ Interaction between client and server using RTSP.

```
<title>Twister</title>
<session>
   <group language=en lipsync>
      <switch>
         <track type=audio
               e="PCMU/8000/1"
               src="rtsp://audio.example.com/twister/audio.en/lofi">
         <track type=audio
               e="DVI4/16000/2" pt="90 DVI4/8000/1"
               src="rtsp://audio.example.com/twister/audio.en/hifi">
            </switch>
         <track type="video/jpeg"
               src="rtsp://video.example.com/twister/video">
   </group>
</session>
```

The Web server encapsulates the presentation description file in an HTTP response message and sends the message to the browser. When the browser receives the HTTP response message, the browser invokes a media player (that is, the helper application) based on the content-type field of the message. The presentation description file includes references to media streams, using the URL method `rtsp://`, as in the sample above. As shown in Figure 13.5, the player and the server then send each other a series of RTSP messages. The player sends an RTSP SETUP request, and the server responds with an RTSP OK message. The player sends an RTSP PLAY request, say, for low-fidelity audio, and the server responds with an RTSP OK message. At this point, the streaming server pumps the low-fidelity audio into its own in-band channel. Later, the media player sends an RTSP PAUSE request, and the server responds with an RTSP OK message. When the user is finished, the media player sends an RTSP TEARDOWN request, and the server confirms with an RTSP OK response.

Now let's take a brief look at the actual RTSP messages. The following is a simplified example of an RTSP session between a client (C:) and a sender (S:).

```
C: SETUP rtsp://audio.example.com/twister/audio RTSP/1.0
   Cseq: 1
   Transport: rtp/udp; compression; port=3056; mode=PLAY
S: RTSP/1.0 200 OK
   Cseq: 1
   Session: 4231
C: PLAY rtsp://audio.example.com/twister/audio.en/lofi RTSP/1.0
   Range: npt=0-
   Cseq: 2
   Session: 4231
S: RTSP/1.0 200 OK
   Cseq: 2
   Session: 4231
C: PAUSE rtsp://audio.example.com/twister/audio.en/lofi RTSP/1.0
   Range: npt=37
   Cseq: 3
   Session: 4231
S: RTSP/1.0 200 OK
   Cseq: 3
   Session: 4231
C: TEARDOWN rtsp://audio.example.com/twister/audio.en/lofi RTSP/1.0
   Cseq: 4
   Session: 4231
S: RTSP/1.0 200 OK
   Cseq: 4
   Session: 4231
```

It is interesting to note the similarities between HTTP and RTSP. All request and response messages are in ASCII text, the client employs standardized methods (SETUP, PLAY, PAUSE, and so on), and the server responds with standardized reply codes. One important difference, however, is that the RTSP server keeps track of the state of the client for each ongoing RTSP session. For example, the server keeps track of whether the client is in an initialization state, a play state, or a pause state (see the programming assignment for this chapter). The session and sequence numbers, which are part of each RTSP request and response, help the server keep track of the session state. The session number is fixed throughout the entire session; the client increments the sequence number each time it sends a new message; the server echoes back the session number and the current sequence number.

As shown in the example, the client initiates the session with the SETUP request, providing the URL of the file to be streamed and the RTSP version. The setup message includes the client port number to which the media should be sent. The setup message also indicates that the media should be sent over UDP using the RTP packetization protocol (to be discussed in Section 13.4). Notice that in this example, the player chose not to play back the complete presentation, but instead only the low-fidelity portion of the presentation.

RTSP is actually capable of doing much more than described in this brief introduction. In particular, RTSP has facilities that allow clients to stream toward the server (for example, for recording). RTSP has been adopted by RealNetworks, one of the industry leaders in audio/video streaming. Henning Schulzrinne makes available a Web page on RTSP [Schulzrinne-RTSP 2004].

At the end of this chapter, you will find a programming assignment for creating a video streaming system (both server and client) that leverages RTSP. This assignment involves writing code that actually constructs and sends RTSP messages at the client. The assignment provides the RTSP server code, which parses the RTSP messages and constructs appropriate responses. Readers interested in obtaining a deeper understanding of RTSP are highly encouraged to work through this interesting assignment.

13.3 Making the Best of the Best-Effort Service: An Internet Phone Example

The Internet's network-layer protocol, IP, provides a best-effort service. That is to say that the service makes its best effort to move each datagram from source to destination as quickly as possible. However, it does not make any promises whatsoever about the extent of the end-to-end delay for an individual packet, or about the extent of packet jitter and packet loss within the packet stream. The lack of guarantees about delay and packet jitter poses significant challenges to the design of real-time multimedia applications such as Internet phone and real-time video conferencing, which are acutely sensitive to packet delay, jitter, and loss. Fortunately, designers of these applications can introduce several useful mechanisms that can preserve good audio and video quality as long as delay, jitter, and loss are not excessive. In this section, we examine some of these mechanisms. To keep the discussion concrete, we discuss these mechanisms in the context of an **Internet phone application,** described below. The situation is similar for real-time video conferencing applications [Bolot 1994].

The speaker in our Internet phone example generates an audio signal consisting of alternating talk spurts and silent periods. In order to conserve bandwidth, our Internet phone application generates packets only during talk spurts. During a talk spurt the sender generates bytes at a rate of 8,000 bytes per second, and every 20 msecs the sender gathers bytes into chunks. Thus, the number of bytes in a chunk is (20 msecs) · (8,000 bytes/sec) = 160 bytes. A special header is attached to each chunk, the contents of which are discussed below. The chunk and its header are encapsulated in a UDP segment, via the call to the socket interface. Thus, during a talk spurt, a UDP segment is sent every 20 msec.

If each packet makes it to the receiver and has a small constant end-to-end delay, then packets arrive at the receiver periodically every 20 msecs during a talk spurt. In these ideal conditions, the receiver can simply play back each chunk as soon as it arrives. But unfortunately, some packets can be lost and most packets will not have the same end-to-end delay, even in a lightly congested Internet. For this reason, the receiver must take more care in determining (1) when to play back a chunk, and (2) what to do with a missing chunk.

13.3.1 The Limitations of a Best-Effort Service

We mentioned that best-effort service can lead to packet loss, excessive end-to-end delay, and packet jitter. Let's examine these issues in more detail.

Packet Loss

Consider one of the UDP segments generated by our Internet phone application. The UDP segment is encapsulated in an IP datagram. As the datagram wanders through the network, it passes through buffers (that is, queues) in the routers in order to access outbound links. It is possible that one or more of the buffers in the route from sender to receiver is full and cannot admit the IP datagram. In this case, the IP datagram is discarded, never to arrive at the receiving application.

Loss could be eliminated by sending the packets over TCP rather than over UDP. Recall that TCP retransmits packets that do not arrive at the destination. However, retransmission mechanisms are often considered unacceptable for interactive real-time audio applications such as Internet phone, because they increase end-to-end delay [Bolot 1996]. Furthermore, due to TCP congestion control, after packet loss the transmission rate at the sender can be reduced to a rate that is lower than the drain rate at the receiver. This can have a severe impact on voice intelligibility at the receiver. For these reasons, almost all existing Internet phone applications run over UDP and do not bother to retransmit lost packets.

But losing packets is not necessarily as disastrous as one might think. Indeed, packet loss rates between 1 and 20 percent can be tolerated, depending on how the voice is encoded and transmitted, and on how the loss is concealed at the receiver. For example, forward error correction (FEC) can help conceal packet loss. We'll see below that with FEC, redundant information is transmitted along with the original information so that some of the lost original data can be recovered from the redundant information. Nevertheless, if one or more of the links between sender and receiver is severely congested, and packet loss exceeds 10 to 20 percent (although these rates are rarely observed in well-provisioned networks [Boutremans 2002]), then there is really nothing that can be done to achieve acceptable audio quality. Clearly, best-effort service has its limitations.

End-to-End Delay

End-to-end delay is the accumulation of transmission, processing, and queuing delays in routers; propagation delays in the links; and end-system processing delays. For highly interactive audio applications, such as Internet phone, end-to-end delays smaller than 150 msecs are not perceived by a human listener; delays between 150 and 400 msecs can be acceptable but are not ideal; and delays exceeding 400 msecs can seriously hinder the interactivity in voice conversations. The receiving side of an Internet phone application will typically disregard any packets that are delayed more than a certain threshold, for example, more than 400 msecs. Thus, packets that are delayed by more than the threshold are effectively lost.

Packet Jitter

A crucial component of end-to-end delay is the random queuing delays in the routers. Because of these varying delays within the network, the time from when a packet is generated at the source until it is received at the receiver can fluctuate from packet to packet. This phenomenon is called **jitter.**

As an example, consider two consecutive packets within a talk spurt in our Internet phone application. The sender sends the second packet 20 msecs after sending the first packet. But at the receiver, the spacing between these packets can become greater than 20 msecs. To see this, suppose the first packet arrives at a nearly empty queue at a router, but just before the second packet arrives at the queue a large number of packets from other sources arrive at the same queue. Because the first packet suffers a small queuing delay and the second packet suffers a large queuing delay at this router, the first and second packets become spaced by more than 20 msecs. The spacing between consecutive packets can also become less than 20 msecs. To see this, again consider two consecutive packets within a talk spurt. Suppose the first packet joins the end of a queue with a large number of packets, and the second packet arrives at the queue before packets from other sources arrive at the queue. In this case, our two packets find themselves one right after the other in the queue. If the time it takes to transmit a packet on the router's outbound link is less than 20 msecs, then the first and second packets become spaced apart by less than 20 msecs.

The situation is analogous to driving cars on roads. Suppose you and your friend are each driving in your own cars from San Diego to Phoenix. Suppose you and your friend have similar driving styles, and that you both drive at 100 km/hour, traffic permitting. Finally, suppose your friend starts out one hour before you. Then, depending on intervening traffic, you may arrive at Phoenix more or less than one hour after your friend.

If the receiver ignores the presence of jitter and plays out chunks as soon as they arrive, then the resulting audio quality can easily become unintelligible at the receiver. Fortunately, jitter can often be removed by using **sequence numbers, timestamps,** and a **playout delay,** as discussed below.

13.3.2 Removing Jitter at the Receiver for Audio

For a voice application such as Internet phone or audio-on-demand, the receiver should attempt to provide synchronous playout of voice chunks in the presence of random network jitter. This is typically done by combining the following three mechanisms:

- *Prefacing each chunk with a* ***sequence number.*** The sender increments the sequence number by one for each of the packets it generates.
- *Prefacing each chunk with a* ***timestamp.*** The sender stamps each chunk with the time at which the chunk was generated.
- ***Delaying playout*** *of chunks at the receiver*. The playout delay of the received audio chunks must be long enough so that most of the packets are received before their scheduled playout times. This playout delay can either be fixed throughout the duration of the audio session or it may vary adaptively during the audio session lifetime. Packets that do not arrive before their scheduled playout times are considered lost and forgotten; as noted above, the receiver may use some form of speech interpolation to attempt to conceal the loss.

We now discuss how these three mechanisms, when combined, can alleviate or even eliminate the effects of jitter. We examine two playback strategies: fixed playout delay and adaptive playout delay.

Fixed Playout Delay

With the fixed-delay strategy, the receiver attempts to play out each chunk exactly q msecs after the chunk is generated. So if a chunk is timestamped at time t, the receiver plays out the chunk at time $t + q$, assuming the chunk has arrived by that time. Packets that arrive after their scheduled playout times are discarded and considered lost.

What is a good choice for q? Internet telephone can support delays up to about 400 msecs, although a more satisfying interactive experience is achieved with smaller values of q. On the other hand, if q is made much smaller than 400 msecs, then many packets may miss their scheduled playback times due to the network-induced packet jitter. Roughly speaking, if large variations in end-to-end delay are typical, it is preferable to use a large q; on the other hand, if delay is small and variations in delay are also small, it is preferable to use a small q, perhaps less than 150 msecs.

The trade-off between the playback delay and packet loss is illustrated in Figure 13.6. The figure shows the times at which packets are generated and played out for a single talk spurt. Two distinct initial playout delays are considered. As shown by the leftmost staircase, the sender generates packets at regular intervals—say, every 20 msecs. The first packet in this talk spurt is received at time r. As shown in the figure, the arrivals of subsequent packets are not evenly spaced due to the network jitter.

For the first playout schedule, the fixed initial playout delay is set to $p - r$. With this schedule, the fourth packet does not arrive by its scheduled playout time, and the receiver considers it lost. For the second playout schedule, the fixed initial playout delay is set to $p' - r$. For this schedule, all packets arrive before their scheduled playout times, and there is therefore no loss.

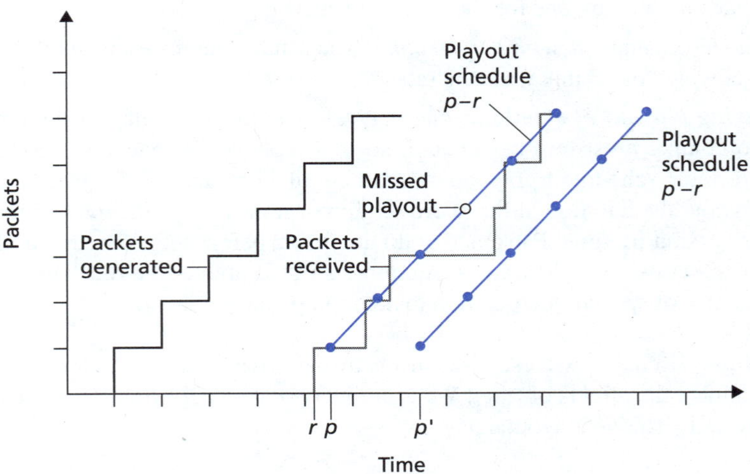

Figure 13.6 ♦ Packet loss for different fixed playout delays.

Adaptive Playout Delay

The example above demonstrates an important delay-loss trade-off that arises when designing a playout strategy with fixed playout delays. By making the initial playout delay large, most packets will make their deadlines and there will therefore be negligible loss; however, for interactive services such as Internet phone, long delays can become bothersome if not intolerable. Ideally, we would like the playout delay to be minimized subject to the constraint that the loss be below a few percent.

The natural way to deal with this trade-off is to estimate the network delay and the variance of the network delay, and to adjust the playout delay accordingly at the beginning of each talk spurt. This adaptive adjustment of playout delays at the beginning of the talk spurts will cause the sender's silent periods to be compressed and elongated; however, compression and elongation of silence by a small amount is not noticeable in speech.

Following [Ramjee 1994], we now describe a generic algorithm that the receiver can use to adaptively adjust its playout delays. To this end, let

t_i = the timestamp of the ith packet = the time the packet was generated by the sender

r_i = the time packet i is received by receiver

p_i = the time packet i is played at receiver

The end-to-end network delay of the ith packet is $r_i - t_i$. Due to network jitter, this delay will vary from packet to packet. Let d_i denote an estimate of the *average* network delay upon reception of the ith packet. This estimate is constructed from the timestamps as follows:

$$d_i = (1 - u)\, d_{i-1} + u\, (r_i - t_i)$$

where u is a fixed constant (for example, $u = 0.01$). Thus d_i is a smoothed average of the observed network delays $r_1 - t_1, \ldots, r_i - t_i$. The estimate places more weight on the recently observed network delays than on the observed network delays of the distant past. This form of estimate should not be completely unfamiliar; a similar idea is used to estimate round-trip times in TCP. Let v_i denote an estimate of the average deviation of the delay from the estimated average delay. This estimate is also constructed from the timestamps:

$$v_i = (1 - u)\, v_{i-1} + u\, | r_i - t_i - d_i |$$

The estimates d_i and v_i are calculated for every packet received, although they are used only to determine the playout point for the first packet in any talk spurt.

Once having calculated these estimates, the receiver employs the following algorithm for the playout of packets. If packet i is the first packet of a talk spurt, its playout time, p_i, is computed as:

$$p_i = t_i + d_i + Kv_i$$

where K is a positive constant (for example, $K = 4$). The purpose of the Kv_i term is to set the playout time far enough into the future so that only a small fraction of the arriving packets in the talk spurt will be lost due to late arrivals. The playout point for any subsequent packet in a talk spurt is computed as an offset from the point in time when the first packet in the talk spurt was played out. In particular, let

$$q_i = p_i - t_i$$

be the length of time from when the first packet in the talk spurt is generated until it is played out. If packet j also belongs to this talk spurt, it is played out at time

$$p_j = t_j + q_i$$

The algorithm just described makes perfect sense assuming that the receiver can tell whether a packet is the first packet in the talk spurt. If there is no packet loss, then the receiver can determine whether packet i is the first packet of the talk spurt by comparing the timestamp of the ith packet with the timestamp of the $(i - 1)$st packet. Indeed, if $t_i - t_{i-1} > 20$ msecs, then the receiver knows that ith packet starts a new talk spurt. But now suppose there is occasional packet loss. In this case, two successive packets received at the destination may have timestamps that differ by more than 20 msecs when the two packets belong to the same talk spurt. So here is where the sequence numbers are particularly useful. The receiver can use the sequence numbers to determine whether a difference of more than 20 msecs in timestamps is due to a new talk spurt or to lost packets.

13.3.3 Recovering from Packet Loss

We have discussed in some detail how an Internet phone application can deal with packet jitter. We now briefly describe several schemes that attempt to preserve acceptable audio quality in the presence of packet loss. Such schemes are called **loss recovery schemes.** Here we define packet loss in a broad sense: a packet is lost either if it never arrives at the receiver or if it arrives after its scheduled playout time. Our Internet phone example will again serve as a context for describing loss recovery schemes.

As mentioned at the beginning of this section, retransmitting lost packets is generally not appropriate in an interactive real-time application such as Internet phone. Indeed, retransmitting a packet that has missed its playout deadline serves absolutely no purpose. And retransmitting a packet that overflowed a router queue cannot normally be accomplished quickly enough. Because of these considerations, Internet phone applications often use some type of loss anticipation scheme. Two types of loss anticipation schemes are **forward error correction (FEC)** and **interleaving.**

Forward Error Correction (FEC)

The basic idea of FEC is to add redundant information to the original packet stream. For the cost of marginally increasing the transmission rate of the audio of the stream, the redundant information can be used to reconstruct approximations or exact versions of some of the lost packets. Following [Bolot 1996] and [Perkins 1998], we now outline two FEC mechanisms. The first mechanism sends a redundant encoded chunk after every n chunks. The redundant chunk is obtained by exclusive OR-ing the n original chunks [Shacham 1990]. In this manner if any one packet of the group of $n + 1$ packets is lost, the receiver can fully reconstruct the lost packet. But if two or more packets in a group are lost, the receiver cannot reconstruct the lost packets. By keeping $n + 1$, the group size, small, a large fraction of the lost packets can be recovered when loss is not excessive. However, the smaller the group size, the greater the relative increase of the transmission rate of the audio stream. In particular, the transmission rate increases by a factor of $1/n$; for example, if $n = 3$, then the transmission rate increases by 33 percent. Furthermore, this simple scheme increases the playout delay, as the receiver must wait to receive the entire group of packets before it can begin playout. For more practical details about how FEC works for multimedia transport see [RFC 2733].

The second FEC mechanism is to send a lower-resolution audio stream as the redundant information. For example, the sender might create a nominal audio stream and a corresponding low-resolution, low-bit rate audio stream. (The nominal stream could be a PCM encoding at 64 kbps, and the lower-quality stream could be a GSM encoding at 13 kbps.) The low-bit rate stream is referred to as the redundant stream. As shown in Figure 13.7, the sender constructs the nth packet by taking the nth chunk from the nominal stream and appending to it the $(n - 1)$st chunk from the redundant stream. In this manner, whenever there is nonconsecutive packet loss, the receiver can conceal the loss by playing out the low-bit rate encoded chunk that arrives with the subsequent packet. Of course, low-bit rate chunks give lower quality than the nominal chunks. However, a stream of mostly high-quality chunks, occasional low-quality chunks, and no missing chunks gives good overall audio quality. Note that in this scheme, the receiver only has to receive two packets before playback, so that the increased playout delay is small. Furthermore, if the low-bit rate encoding is much less than the nominal encoding, then the marginal increase in the transmission rate will be small.

In order to cope with consecutive loss, we can use a simple variation. Instead of appending just the $(n - 1)$st low-bit rate chunk to the nth nominal chunk, the sender

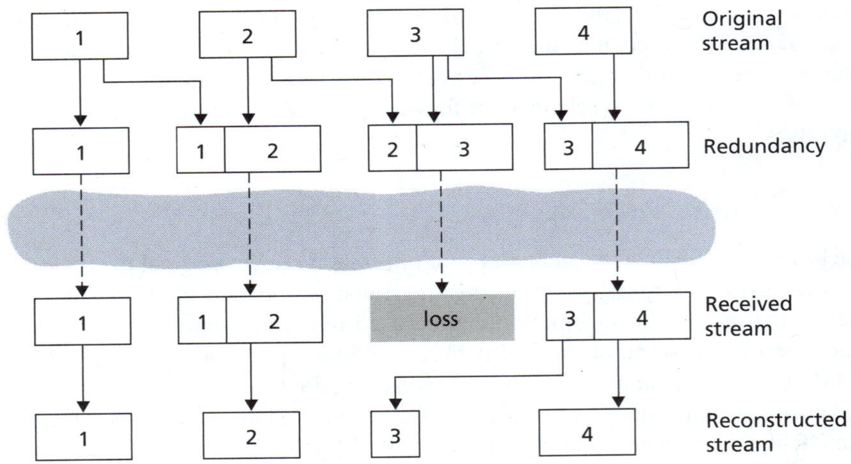

Figure 13.7 ♦ Piggybacking lower-quality redundant information

can append the $(n - 1)$st and $(n - 2)$nd low-bit rate chunk, or append the $(n - 1)$st and $(n - 3)$rd low-bit rate chunk, and so on. By appending more low-bit rate chunks to each nominal chunk, the audio quality at the receiver becomes acceptable for a wider variety of harsh best-effort environments. On the other hand, the additional chunks increase the transmission bandwidth and the playout delay.

Free Phone [Freephone 2004] and RAT [RAT 2004] are well-documented Internet phone applications that use FEC. They can transmit lower-quality audio streams along with the nominal audio stream, as described above. Also see [Rosenberg 2000].

Interleaving

As an alternative to redundant transmission, an Internet phone application can send interleaved audio. As shown in Figure 13.8, the sender resequences units of audio data before transmission, so that originally adjacent units are separated by a certain distance in the transmitted stream. Interleaving can mitigate the effect of packet losses. If, for example, units are 5 msecs in length and chunks are 20 msecs (that is, four units per chunk), then the first chunk could contain units 1, 5, 9, and 13; the second chunk could contain units 2, 6, 10, and 14; and so on. Figure 13.8 shows that the loss of a single packet from an interleaved stream results in multiple small gaps in the reconstructed stream, as opposed to the single large gap that would occur in a noninterleaved stream.

Interleaving can significantly improve the perceived quality of an audio stream [Perkins 1998]. It also has low overhead. The obvious disadvantage of interleaving is that it increases latency. This limits its use for interactive applications such as

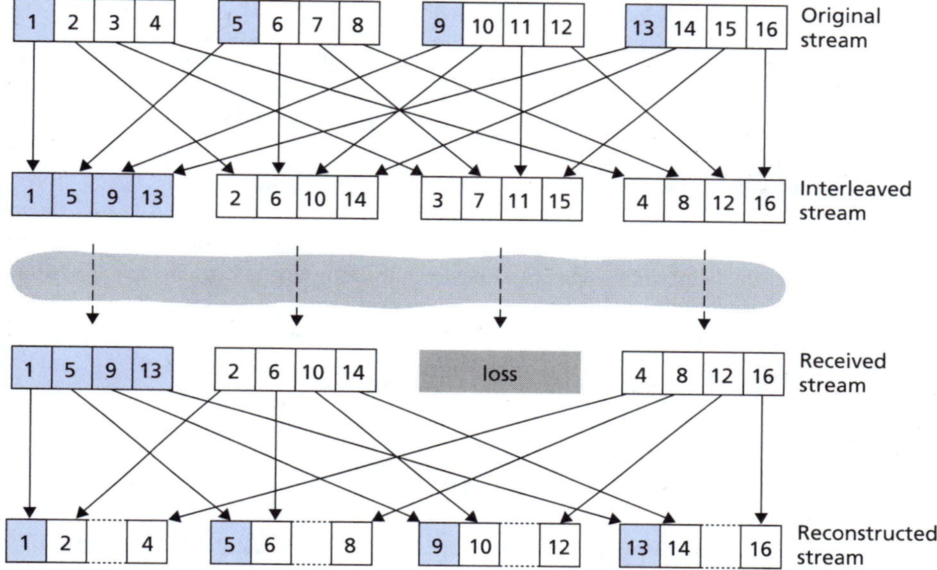

Figure 13.8 ♦ Sending interleaved audio

Internet phone, although it can perform well for streaming stored audio. A major advantage of interleaving is that it does not increase the bandwidth requirements of a stream.

Receiver-Based Repair of Damaged Audio Streams

Receiver-based recovery schemes attempt to produce a replacement for a lost packet that is similar to the original. As discussed in [Perkins 1998], this is possible since audio signals, and in particular speech, exhibit large amounts of short-term self-similarity. As such, these techniques work for relatively small loss rates (less than 15 percent), and for small packets (4–40 msecs). When the loss length approaches the length of a phoneme (5–100 msecs) these techniques break down, since whole phonemes may be missed by the listener.

Perhaps the simplest form of receiver-based recovery is packet repetition. Packet repetition replaces lost packets with copies of the packets that arrived immediately before the loss. It has low computational complexity and performs reasonably well. Another form of receiver-based recovery is interpolation, which uses audio before and after the loss to interpolate a suitable packet to cover the loss. Interpolation performs somewhat better than packet repetition but is significantly more computationally intensive [Perkins 1998].

13.3.4 Streaming Stored Audio and Video

Let us conclude this section with a few words about streaming stored audio and video. Streaming stored audio/video applications also typically use sequence numbers, timestamps, and playout delay to alleviate or even eliminate the effects of network jitter. However, there is an important difference between real-time interactive audio/video and streaming stored audio/video. Specifically, streaming of stored audio/video can tolerate significantly larger delays. Indeed, when a user requests an audio/video clip, the user may find it acceptable to wait five seconds or more before playback begins. And most users can tolerate similar delays after interactive actions such as a temporal jump within the media stream. This greater tolerance for delay gives the application developer greater flexibility when designing stored media applications.

13.4 Protocols for Real-Time Interactive Applications

Real-time interactive applications, including Internet phone and video conferencing, promise to drive much of the future Internet growth. It is therefore not surprising that standards bodies, such as the IETF and ITU, have been busy for many years (and continue to be busy!) at hammering out standards for this class of applications. With the appropriate standards in place for real-time interactive applications, independent companies will be able to create new and compelling products that interoperate with each other. In this section we examine RTP, SIP, and H.323 for real-time interactive applications. All three sets of standards are enjoying widespread implementation in industry products.

13.4.1 RTP

In the previous section we learned that the sender side of a multimedia application appends header fields to the audio/video chunks before passing them to the transport layer. These header fields include sequence numbers and timestamps. Since most multimedia networking applications can make use of sequence numbers and timestamps, it is convenient to have a standardized packet structure that includes fields for audio/video data, sequence number, and timestamp, as well as other potentially useful fields. RTP, defined in RFC 3550, is such a standard. RTP can be used for transporting common formats such as PCM, GSM, and MP3 for sound and MPEG and H.263 for video. It can also be used for transporting proprietary sound and video formats. Today, RTP enjoys widespread implementation in hundreds of products and research prototypes. It is also complementary to other important real-time interactive protocols, including SIP and H.323.

In this section we provide an introduction to RTP and to its companion protocol, RTCP. We also encourage you to visit Henning Schulzrinne's RTP site [Schulzrinne-RTP 2004], which provides a wealth of information on the subject. Also, you may want to visit the Free Phone site [Freephone 2004], which documents an Internet phone application that uses RTP.

RTP Basics

RTP typically runs on top of UDP. The sending side encapsulates a media chunk within an RTP packet, then encapsulates the packet in a UDP segment, and then hands the segment to IP. The receiving side extracts the RTP packet from the UDP segment, then extracts the media chunk from the RTP packet, and then passes the chunk to the media player for decoding and rendering.

As an example, consider the use of RTP to transport voice. Suppose the voice source is PCM-encoded (that is, sampled, quantized, and digitized) at 64 kbps. Further suppose that the application collects the encoded data in 20-msec chunks, that is, 160 bytes in a chunk. The sending side precedes each chunk of the audio data with an **RTP header** that includes the type of audio encoding, a sequence number, and a timestamp. The RTP header is normally 12 bytes. The audio chunk along with the RTP header form the **RTP packet.** The RTP packet is then sent into the UDP socket interface. At the receiver side, the application receives the RTP packet from its socket interface. The application extracts the audio chunk from the RTP packet and uses the header fields of the RTP packet to properly decode and play back the audio chunk.

If an application incorporates RTP—instead of a proprietary scheme to provide payload type, sequence numbers, or timestamps—then the application will more easily interoperate with other networked multimedia applications. For example, if two different companies develop Internet phone software and they both incorporate RTP into their product, there may be some hope that a user using one of the Internet phone products will be able to communicate with a user using the other Internet phone product. In Section 13.4.3 we'll see that RTP is often used in conjunction with the Internet telephony standards.

It should be emphasized that RTP does not provide any mechanism to ensure timely delivery of data or provide other quality-of-service (QoS) guarantees; it does not even guarantee delivery of packets or prevent out-of-order delivery of packets. Indeed, RTP encapsulation is seen only at the end systems. Routers do not distinguish between IP datagrams that carry RTP packets and IP datagrams that don't.

RTP allows each source (for example, a camera or a microphone) to be assigned its own independent RTP stream of packets. For example, for a video conference between two participants, four RTP streams could be opened—two streams for transmitting the audio (one in each direction) and two streams for transmitting the video (again, one in each direction). However, many popular encoding techniques—

including MPEG 1 and MPEG 2—bundle the audio and video into a single stream during the encoding process. When the audio and video are bundled by the encoder, then only one RTP stream is generated in each direction.

RTP packets are not limited to unicast applications. They can also be sent over one-to-many and many-to-many multicast trees. For a many-to-many multicast session, all of the session's senders and sources typically use the same multicast group for sending their RTP streams. RTP multicast streams belonging together, such as audio and video streams emanating from multiple senders in a video conference application, belong to an **RTP session.**

RTP Packet Header Fields

As shown in Figure 13.9, the four main RTP packet header fields are the payload type, sequence number, timestamp, and the source identifier fields.

The payload-type field in the RTP packet is 7 bits long. For an audio stream, the payload-type field is used to indicate the type of audio encoding (for example, PCM, adaptive delta modulation, linear predictive encoding) that is being used. If a sender decides to change the encoding in the middle of a session, the sender can inform the receiver of the change through this payload-type field. The sender may want to change the encoding in order to increase the audio quality or to decrease the RTP stream bit rate. Table 13.1 lists some of the audio payload types currently supported by RTP.

For a video stream, the payload type is used to indicate the type of video encoding (for example, motion JPEG, MPEG 1, MPEG 2, H.261). Again, the sender can change video encoding on the fly during a session. Table 13.2 lists some of the video payload types currently supported by RTP. The other important fields are the following.

- *Sequence number field.* The sequence number field is 16 bits long. The sequence number increments by one for each RTP packet sent, and may be used by the receiver to detect packet loss and to restore packet sequence. For example, if the receiver side of the application receives a stream of RTP packets with a gap between sequence numbers 86 and 89, then the receiver knows that packets 87 and 88 are missing. The receiver can then attempt to conceal the lost data.
- *Timestamp field.* The timestamp field is 32 bits long. It reflects the sampling instant of the first byte in the RTP data packet. As we saw in the preceding

Payload type	Sequence number	Timestamp	Synchronization source identifier	Miscellaneous fields

Figure 13.9 ♦ RTP header fields

Payload-Type Number	Audio Format	Sampling Rate	Rate
0	PCM μ-law	8 kHz	64 kbps
1	1016	8 kHz	4.8 kbps
3	GSM	8 kHz	13 kbps
7	LPC	8 kHz	2.4 kbps
9	G.722	16 kHz	48–64 kbps
14	MPEG Audio	90 kHz	—
15	G.728	8 kHz	16 kbps

Table 13.1 ♦ Audio Payload Types Supported by RTP

section, the receiver can use timestamps in order to remove packet jitter introduced in the network and to provide synchronous playout at the receiver. The timestamp is derived from a sampling clock at the sender. As an example, for audio the timestamp clock increments by one for each sampling period (for example, each 125 μsec for an 8 kHz sampling clock); if the audio application generates chunks consisting of 160 encoded samples, then the timestamp increases by 160 for each RTP packet when the source is active. The timestamp clock continues to increase at a constant rate even if the source is inactive.

- *Synchronization source identifier (SSRC).* The SSRC field is 32 bits long. It identifies the source of the RTP stream. Typically, each stream in an RTP session has a distinct SSRC. The SSRC is not the IP address of the sender, but instead is a number that the source assigns randomly when the new stream is started. The probability that two streams get assigned the same SSRC is very small. Should this happen, the two sources pick a new SSRC value.

Payload-Type Number	Video Format
26	Motion JPEG
31	H.261
32	MPEG 1 video
33	MPEG 2 video

Table 13.2 ♦ Some Video Payload Types Supported by RTP

Developing Software Applications with RTP

There are two approaches to developing an RTP-based networked application. The first approach is for the application developer to incorporate RTP by hand, that is, actually to write the code that performs RTP encapsulation at the sender side and RTP unraveling at the receiver side. The second approach is for the application developer to use existing RTP libraries (for C programmers) and Java classes (for Java programmers), which perform the encapsulation and unraveling for the application. Since you may be itching to write your first multimedia networking application using RTP, let us now elaborate a little on these two approaches. (The programming assignment at the end of this chapter will guide you through the creation of an RTP application.) We'll do this in the context of unicast communication (rather than for multicast).

Recall that the UDP API requires the sending process to set, for each UDP segment it sends, the destination IP address and the destination port number before popping the packet into the UDP socket. The UDP segment will then wander through the Internet and (if the segment is not lost due to, for example, router buffer overflow) will eventually arrive at the door of the receiving process for the application. This door is fully addressed by the destination IP address and the destination port number. In fact, any IP datagram containing this destination IP address and destination port number will be directed to the receiving process's UDP door. (The UDP API also lets the application developer set the UDP source port number; however, this value has no effect on which process the segment is sent to.) It is important to note that RTP does not mandate a specific port number. When the application developer creates an RTP application, the developer specifies the port numbers for the two sides of the application.

As part of the programming assignment for this chapter, you will write an RTP server that encapsulates stored video frames within RTP packets. You will do this by hand; that is, your application will grab a video frame, add the RTP headers to the frame to create an RTP packet, and then pass the RTP frame to the UDP socket. To do this, you will need to create placeholder fields for the various RTP headers, including a sequence-number field and a timestamp field. And for each RTP packet that is created, you will have to set the sequence number and the timestamp appropriately. You will explicitly code all of these RTP operations into the sender side of your application. As shown in Figure 13.10, your API to the network will be the standard UDP socket API.

An alternative approach (not done in the programming assignment) is to use a Java RTP class (or a C RTP library for C programmers) to implement the RTP operations. With this approach, as shown in Figure 13.11, the application developer is given the impression that RTP is part of the transport layer, with an RTP/UDP API between the application layer and the transport layer. Without getting into the nitty-gritty details (as they are class/library-dependent), when sending a chunk of media into the API, the sending side of the application needs to provide the interface with

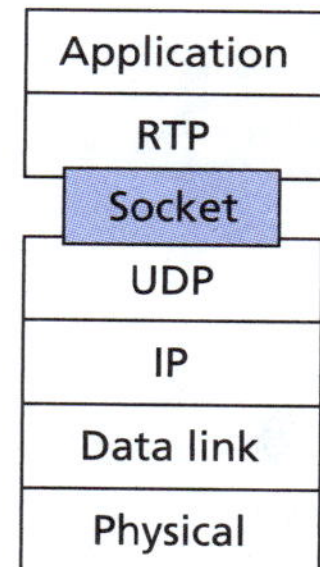

Figure 13.10 ♦ RTP is part of the application and lies above the UDP socket.

the media chunk itself, a payload-type number, an SSRC, and a timestamp, along with a destination port number and an IP destination address. We mention here that the Java Media Framework (JMF) includes a complete RTP implementation.

13.4.2 RTP Control Protocol (RTCP)

RFC 1889 also specifies RTCP, a protocol that a networked multimedia application can use in conjunction with RTP. As shown in the multicast scenario in Figure 13.12, RTCP packets are transmitted by each participant in an RTP session to all other participants in the session using IP multicast. For an RTP session, typically there is a single multicast address and all RTP and RTCP packets belonging to the session use the multicast address. RTP and RTCP packets are distinguished from each other through the use of distinct port numbers. (The RTCP port number is set to be equal to the RTP port number plus one.)

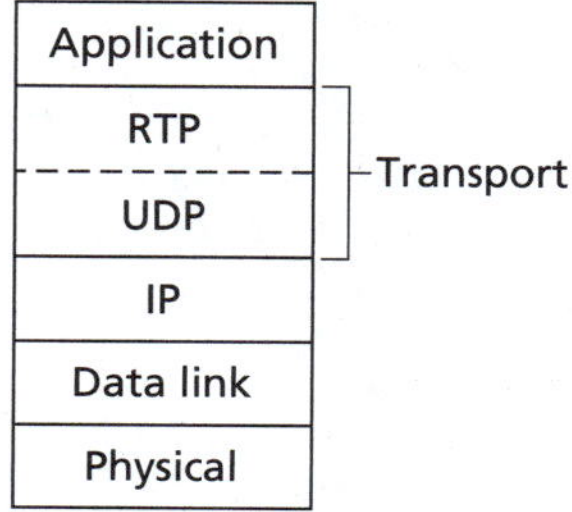

Figure 13.11 ♦ RTP can be viewed as a sublayer of the transport layer.

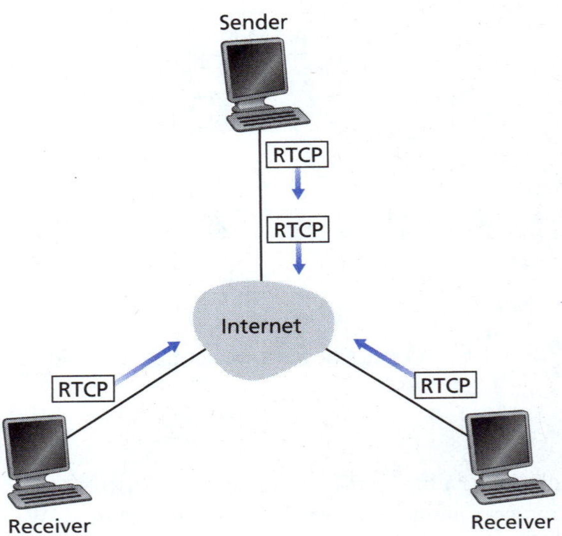

Figure 13.12 ♦ Both senders and receivers send RTCP messages.

RTCP packets do not encapsulate chunks of audio or video. Instead, RTCP packets are sent periodically and contain sender and/or receiver reports that announce statistics that can be useful to the application. These statistics include number of packets sent, number of packets lost, and interarrival jitter. The RTP specification [RFC 3550] does not dictate what the application should do with this feedback information; this is up to the application developer. Senders can use the feedback information, for example, to modify their transmission rates. The feedback information can also be used for diagnostic purposes; for example, receivers can determine whether problems are local, regional, or global.

RTCP Packet Types

For each RTP stream that a receiver receives as part of a session, the receiver generates a reception report. The receiver aggregates its reception reports into a single RTCP packet. The packet is then sent into the multicast tree that connects all the session's participants. The reception report includes several fields, the most important of which are listed below.

- The SSRC of the RTP stream for which the reception report is being generated.
- The fraction of packets lost within the RTP stream. Each receiver calculates the number of RTP packets lost divided by the number of RTP packets sent as part of the stream. If a sender receives reception reports indicating that the receivers

are receiving only a small fraction of the sender's transmitted packets, it can switch to a lower encoding rate, with the aim of decreasing network congestion and improving the reception rate.

- The last sequence number received in the stream of RTP packets.
- The interarrival jitter, which is a smoothed estimate of the variation in the interarrival time between successive packets in the RTP stream.

For each RTP stream that a sender is transmitting, the sender creates and transmits RTCP sender report packets. These packets include information about the RTP stream, including:

- The SSRC of the RTP stream
- The timestamp and wall clock time of the most recently generated RTP packet in the stream
- The number of packets sent in the stream
- The number of bytes sent in the stream

Sender reports can be used to synchronize different media streams within an RTP session. For example, consider a video conferencing application for which each sender generates two independent RTP streams, one for video and one for audio. The timestamps in these RTP packets are tied to the video and audio sampling clocks, and are not tied to the *wall clock time* (i.e., real time). Each RTCP sender report contains, for the most recently generated packet in the associated RTP stream, the timestamp of the RTP packet and the wall clock time when the packet was created. Thus the RTCP sender report packets associate the sampling clock with the real-time clock. Receivers can use this association in RTCP sender reports to synchronize the playout of audio and video.

For each RTP stream that a sender is transmitting, the sender also creates and transmits source description packets. These packets contain information about the source, such as the e-mail address of the sender, the sender's name, and the application that generates the RTP stream. It also includes the SSRC of the associated RTP stream. These packets provide a mapping between the source identifier (that is, the SSRC) and the user/host name.

RTCP packets are stackable; that is, receiver reception reports, sender reports, and source descriptors can be concatenated into a single packet. The resulting packet is then encapsulated into a UDP segment and forwarded into the multicast tree.

RTCP Bandwidth Scaling

You may have observed that RTCP has a potential scaling problem. Consider, for example, an RTP session that consists of one sender and a large number of receivers. If each of the receivers periodically generates RTCP packets, then the aggregate transmission rate of RTCP packets can greatly exceed the rate of RTP packets sent by the sender. Observe that the amount of RTP traffic sent into the multicast tree does not change as the number of receivers increases, whereas the amount of RTCP traffic grows linearly with the number of receivers. To solve this scaling problem, RTCP modifies the rate at which a participant sends RTCP packets into the multicast tree as a function of the number of participants in the session. Also, since each participant sends control packets to everyone else, each participant can estimate the total number of participants in the session [Friedman 1999].

RTCP attempts to limit its traffic to 5 percent of the session bandwidth. For example, suppose there is one sender, which is sending video at a rate of 2 Mbps. Then RTCP attempts to limit its traffic to 5 percent of 2 Mbps, or 100 kbps, as follows. The protocol gives 75 percent of this rate, or 75 kbps, to the receivers; it gives the remaining 25 percent of the rate, or 25 kbps, to the sender. The 75 kbps devoted to the receivers is equally shared among the receivers. Thus, if there are R receivers, then each receiver gets to send RTCP traffic at a rate of $75/R$ kbps, and the sender gets to send RTCP traffic at a rate of 25 kbps. A participant (a sender or receiver) determines the RTCP packet transmission period by dynamically calculating the average RTCP packet size (across the entire session) and dividing the average RTCP packet size by its allocated rate. In summary, the period for transmitting RTCP packets for a sender is

$$T = \frac{\text{number of senders}}{.25 \cdot .05 \cdot \text{session bandwidth}} (\text{avg. RTCP packet size})$$

And the period for transmitting RTCP packets for a receiver is

$$T = \frac{\text{number of receivers}}{.75 \cdot .05 \cdot \text{session bandwidth}} (\text{avg. RTCP packet size})$$

13.4.3 SIP

Imagine a world in which, when you are working on your PC, your phone calls arrive over the Internet to your PC. When you get up and start walking around, your new phone calls are automatically routed to your PDA. And when you are driving in your car, your new phone calls are automatically routed to some Internet appliance in your car. In this same world, while participating in a conference call, you can access an address book to call and invite other participants into the conference. The other participants may be at their PCs, or walking with their PDAs, or driving their cars—no matter where they are, your invitation is transparently routed to them. In this same world, when you browse an individual's homepage, there will be a link "Call Me"; clicking on this link establishes an Internet phone session between your PC and the owner of the homepage (wherever that person might be).

In this world, there is no longer a circuit-switched telephone network. Instead, all calls pass over the Internet—from end to end. In this same world, companies no longer use private branch exchanges (PBXs), that is, local circuit switches for handling intracompany telephone calls. Instead, the intracompany phone traffic flows over the company's high-speed LAN.

All of this may sound like science fiction. And, of course, today's circuit-switched networks and PBXs are not going to disappear completely in the near future [Jiang 2001]. Nevertheless, protocols and products exist to turn this vision into a reality. Among the most promising protocols in this direction is the Session Initiation Protocol (SIP), defined in [RFC 3261]. SIP is a lightweight protocol that does the following:

- It provides mechanisms for establishing calls between a caller and a callee over an IP network. It allows the caller to notify the callee that it wants to start a call. It allows the participants to agree on media encodings. It also allows participants to end calls.
- It provides mechanisms for the caller to determine the current IP address of the callee. Users do not have a single, fixed IP addresses because they may be assigned addresses dynamically (using DHCP) and because they may have multiple IP devices, each with a different IP address.
- It provides mechanisms for call management, such as adding new media streams during the call, changing the encoding during the call, inviting new participants during the call, call transfer, and call holding.

Setting Up a Call to a Known IP Address

To understand the essence of SIP, it is best to take a look at a concrete example. In this example, Alice is at her PC and she wants to call Bob, who is also working at his PC. Alice's and Bob's PCs are both equipped with SIP-based software for making and receiving phone calls. In this initial example, we'll assume that Alice knows the IP address of Bob's PC. Figure 13.13 illustrates the SIP call-establishment process.

In Figure 13.13, we see that an SIP session begins when Alice sends Bob an INVITE message, which resembles an HTTP request message. This INVITE message is sent over UDP to the well-known port 5060 for SIP. (SIP messages can also be sent over TCP.) The INVITE message includes an identifier for Bob (bob@193.64.210.89), an indication of Alice's current IP address, an indication that Alice desires to receive audio, which is to be encoded in format AVP 0 (PCM encoded μ-law) and encapsulated in RTP, and an indication that she wants to receive the RTP packets on port 38060. After receiving Alice's INVITE message, Bob sends an SIP response message, which resembles an HTTP response message. This response SIP message is also sent to the SIP port 5060. Bob's response includes a 200 OK as well as an indication of his IP address, his desired encoding and packetization for reception, and his port number to which the audio packets should be sent.

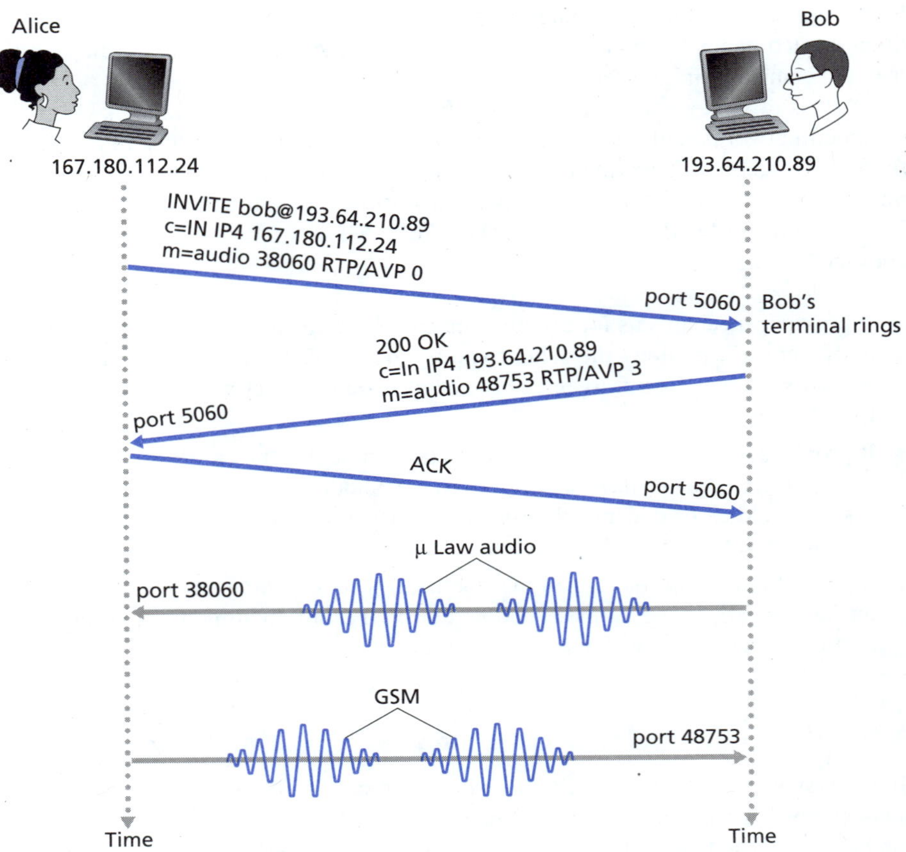

Figure 13.13 ♦ SIP call establishment when Alice knows Bob's IP address

Note that in this example Alice and Bob are going to use different audio-encoding mechanisms: Alice is asked to encode her audio with GSM whereas Bob is asked to encode his audio with PCM μ-law. After receiving Bob's response, Alice sends Bob an SIP acknowledgment message. After this SIP transaction, Bob and Alice can talk. (For visual convenience, Figure 13.13 shows Alice talking after Bob, but in truth they would normally talk at the same time.) Bob will encode and packetize the audio as requested and send the audio packets to port number 38060 at IP address 167.180.112.24. Alice will also encode and packetize the audio as requested and send the audio packets to port number 48753 at IP address 193.64.210.89.

From this simple example, we have learned a number of key characteristics of SIP. First, SIP is an out-of-band protocol: the SIP messages are sent and received in sockets that are different from those used for sending and receiving the media data. Second, the SIP messages themselves are ASCII-readable and resemble HTTP messages. Third, SIP requires all messages to be acknowledged, so it can run over UDP or TCP.

In this example, let's consider what would happen if Bob does not have a PCM μ-law codec for encoding audio. In this case, instead of responding with 200 OK, Bob would likely respond with a 600 Not Acceptable and list in the message all the codecs he can use. Alice would then choose one of the listed codecs and send another INVITE message, this time advertising the chosen codec. Bob could also simply reject the call by sending one of many possible rejection reply codes. (There are many such codes, including "busy," "gone," "payment required," and "forbidden.")

SIP Addresses

In the previous example, Bob's SIP address is sip:bob@193.64.210.89. However, we expect many—if not most—SIP addresses to resemble e-mail addresses. For example, Bob's address might be sip:bob@domain.com. When Alice's SIP device sends an INVITE message, the message would include this e-mail-like address; the SIP infrastructure would then route the message to the IP device that Bob is currently using (as we'll discuss below). Other possible forms for the SIP address could be Bob's legacy phone number or simply Bob's first/middle/last name (assuming it is unique).

An interesting feature of SIP addresses is that they can be included in Web pages, just as people's e-mail addresses are included in Web pages with the mailto URL. For example, suppose Bob has a personal homepage, and he wants to provide a means for visitors to the homepage to call him. He could then simply include the URL sip:bob@domain.com. When the visitor clicks on the URL, the SIP application in the visitor's device is launched and an INVITE message is sent to Bob.

SIP Messages

In this short introduction to SIP, we'll not cover all SIP message types and headers. Instead, we'll take a brief look at the SIP INVITE message, along with a few common header lines. Let us again suppose that Alice wants to initiate an IP phone call to Bob, and this time Alice knows only Bob's SIP address, bob@domain.com, and does not know the IP address of the device that Bob is currently using. Then her message might look something like this:

```
INVITE sip:bob@domain.com SIP/2.0
Via: SIP/2.0/UDP 167.180.112.24
From: sip:alice@hereway.com
To: sip:bob@domain.com
```

```
Call-ID: a2e3a@pigeon.hereway.com
Content-Type: application/sdp
Content-Length: 885

c=IN IP4 167.180.112.24
m=audio 38060 RTP/AVP 0
```

The INVITE line includes the SIP version, as does an HTTP request message. Whenever an SIP message passes through a SIP device (including the device that originates the message), it attaches a Via header, which indicates the IP address of the device. (We'll see soon that the typical INVITE message passes through many SIP devices before reaching the callee's SIP application.) Similar to an e-mail message, the SIP message includes a From header line and a To header line. The message includes a Call-ID, which uniquely identifies the call (similar to the message-ID in e-mail). It includes a Content-Type header line, which defines the format used to describe the content contained in the SIP message. It also includes a Content-Length header line, which provides the length in bytes of the content in the message. Finally, after a carriage return and line feed, the message contains the content. In this case, the content provides information about Alice's IP address and how Alice wants to receive the audio.

Name Translation and User Location

In the example in Figure 13.13, we assumed that Alice's SIP device knew the IP address where Bob could be contacted. But this assumption is quite unrealistic, not only because IP addresses are often dynamically assigned with DHCP, but also because Bob may have multiple IP devices (for example, different devices for his home, work, and car). So now let us suppose that Alice knows only Bob's e-mail address, bob@domain.com, and that this same address is used for SIP-based calls. In this case, Alice needs to obtain the IP address of the device that the user bob@domain.com is currently using. To find this out, Alice creates an INVITE message that begins with INVITE bob@domain.com SIP/2.0 and sends this message to an **SIP proxy.** The proxy will respond with an SIP reply that might include the IP address of the device that bob@domain.com is currently using. Alternatively, the reply might include the IP address of Bob's voicemail box, or it might include a URL of a Web page (that says "Bob is sleeping. Leave me alone!"). Also, the result returned by the proxy might depend on the caller: if the call is from Bob's wife, he might accept the call and supply his IP address; if the call is from Bob's mother-in-law, he might respond with the URL that points to the I-am-sleeping Web page!

Now, you are probably wondering, how can the proxy server determine the current IP address for bob@domain.com? To answer this question, we need to say a few words about another SIP device, the **SIP registrar.** Every SIP user has an associated registrar. Whenever a user launches an SIP application on a device, the application sends an SIP register message to the registrar, informing the registrar of its current IP address. For example, when Bob launches his SIP application on his PDA, the application would send a message along the lines of:

```
REGISTER sip:domain.com SIP/2.0
Via: SIP/2.0/UDP 193.64.210.89
From: sip:bob@domain.com
To: sip:bob@domain.com
Expires: 3600
```

Bob's registrar keeps track of Bob's current IP address. Whenever Bob switches to a new SIP device, the new device sends a new register message, indicating the new IP address. Also, if Bob remains at the same device for an extended period of time, the device will send refresh register messages, indicating that the most recently sent IP address is still valid. (In the example above, refresh messages need to be sent every 3600 seconds to maintain the address at the registrar server.) It is worth noting that the registrar is analogous to a DNS authoritative name server: the DNS server translates fixed host names to fixed IP addresses; the SIP registrar translates fixed human identifiers (for example, bob@domain.com) to dynamic IP addresses. Often SIP registrars and SIP proxies are run on the same host.

Now let's examine how Alice's SIP proxy server obtains Bob's current IP address. From the preceding discussion we see that the proxy server simply needs to forward Alice's INVITE message to Bob's registrar/proxy. The registrar/proxy could then forward the message to Bob's current SIP device. Finally, Bob, having now received Alice's INVITE message, could send an SIP response to Alice.

As an example, consider Figure 13.14, in which jim@umass.edu, currently working on 217.123.56.89, wants to initiate a voice-over-IP session with keith@upenn.edu, currently working on 197.87.54.21. The following steps are taken: (1) Jim sends an INVITE message to the umass SIP proxy. (2) The proxy does a DNS lookup on the SIP registrar upenn.edu (not shown in diagram) and then forwards the message to the registrar server. (3) Because keith@upenn.edu is no longer registered at the upenn registrar, the upenn registrar sends a redirect response, indicating that it should try keith@eurecom.fr. (4) The umass proxy sends an INVITE to the eurecom SIP registrar. (5) The eurecom registrar knows the IP address of keith@eurecom.fr and forwards the INVITE to the host 197.87.54.21, which is running Keith's SIP client. (6–8). A SIP response is sent back through registrars/proxies to the SIP client on 217.123.56.89. (9) Media is sent directly between the two clients. (There is also an SIP acknowledgment message, which is not shown.)

Our discussion of SIP has focused on call initiation for voice calls. SIP, being a signaling protocol for initiating and ending calls in general, can be used for video conference calls as well as for text-based sessions. In fact, SIP has become a fundamental component in many instant-messaging applications. Readers desiring to learn more about SIP are encouraged to visit Henning Schulzrinne's SIP Web site

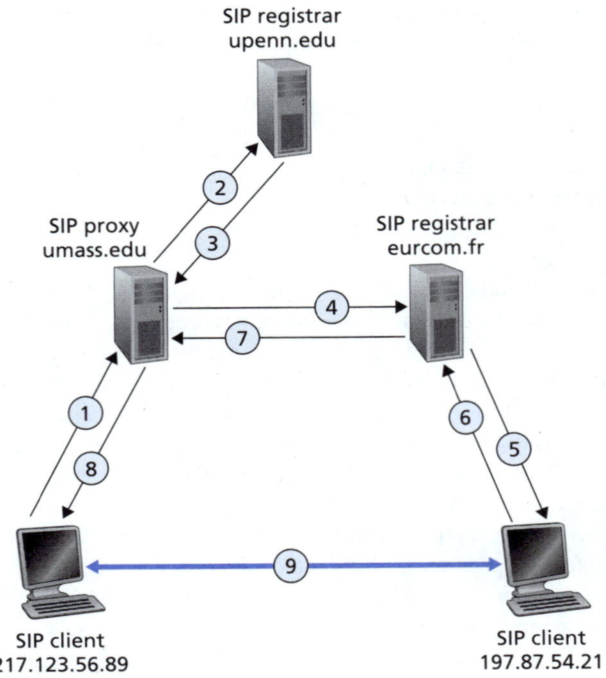

Figure 13.14 ♦ Session initiation, involving SIP proxies and registrars

[Schulzrinne-SIP 2004]. In particular, on this site you will find open source software for SIP clients and servers [SIP Software 2004].

13.4.4 H.323

As an alternative to SIP, H.323 is a popular standard for real-time audio and video conferencing among end systems on the Internet. As shown in Figure 13.15, the standard also covers how end systems attached to the Internet communicate with telephones attached to ordinary circuit-switched telephone networks. (SIP does this as well, although we did not discuss it.) The H.323 gatekeeper is a device similar to an SIP registrar.

The H.323 standard is an umbrella specification that includes the following specifications:

- A specification for how endpoints negotiate common audio/video encodings. Because H.323 supports a variety of audio and video encoding standards, a protocol is needed to allow the communicating endpoints to agree on a common encoding.

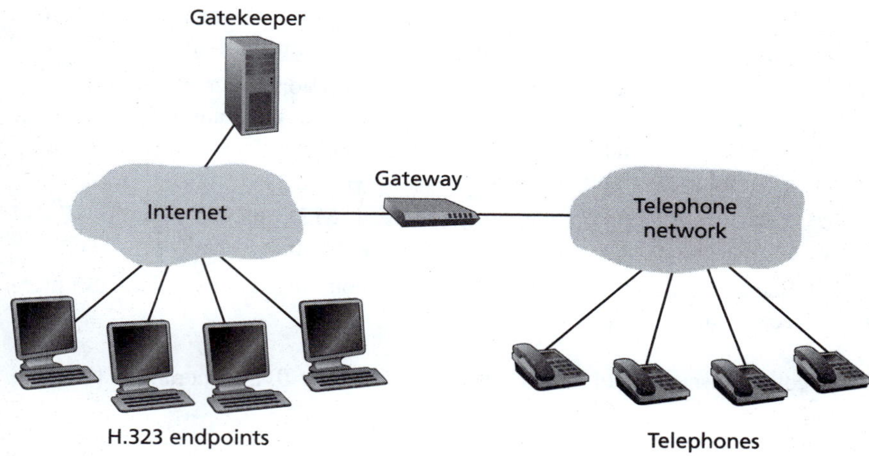

Figure 13.15 ♦ H.323 end systems attached to the Internet can communicate with telephones attached to a circuit-switched telephone network.

- A specification for how audio and video chunks are encapsulated and sent over the network. In particular, H.323 mandates RTP for this purpose.
- A specification for how endpoints communicate with their respective gatekeepers.
- A specification for how Internet phones communicate through a gateway with ordinary phones in the public circuit-switched telephone network.

Minimally, each H.323 endpoint *must* support the G.711 speech compression standard. G.711 uses PCM to generate digitized speech at either 56 kbps or 64 kbps. Although H.323 requires every endpoint to be voice capable (through G.711), video capabilities are optional. Because video support is optional, manufacturers of terminals can sell simpler speech terminals as well as more complex terminals that support both audio and video. Video capabilities for an H.323 endpoint are optional. However, if an endpoint does support video, then it must (at the very least) support the QCIF H.261 (176 x 144 pixels) video standard.

H.323 is a comprehensive umbrella standard, which, in addition to the standards and protocols described above, mandates an H.245 control protocol, a Q.931 signaling channel, and an RAS protocol for registration with the gatekeeper.

We conclude this section by highlighting some of the most important differences between H.323 and SIP.

- H.323 is a complete, vertically integrated suite of protocols for multimedia conferencing: signaling, registration, admission control, transport, and codecs.
- SIP, on the other hand, addresses only session initiation and management and is a single component. SIP works with RTP but does not mandate it. It works with G.711 speech codecs and QCIF H.261 video codecs but does not mandate them. It can be combined with other protocols and services.
- H.323 comes from the ITU (telephony), whereas SIP comes from the IETF and borrows many concepts from the Web, DNS, and Internet e-mail.
- H.323, being an umbrella standard, is large and complex. SIP uses the KISS principle: keep it simple, stupid.

For an excellent discussion of H.323, SIP, and voice-over-IP in general, see [Hersent 2000].

13.5 Distributing Multimedia: Content Distribution Networks

With video streaming rates ranging from hundreds of kbps for low-resolution video to several Mbps for DVD video, the task of streaming a stored video, on demand, to a large number of geographically distributed users seems a daunting challenge. The simplest approach would be to store the video in a single server and simply stream the video from a video server (or server farm) to a client for each client request as we discussed in Section 13.2. But there are two obvious problems with this solution. First, because a client may be very far from the server, server-to-client packets may pass through many ISPs, increasing the likelihood of significant delay and loss. Second, if the video is very popular, the video will likely be sent many times through the same ISPs (and over the same communication links), thereby consuming significant bandwidth. We discussed how caching can alleviate these problems. Although we discussed caching in terms of traditional Web content, it should be clear that caching is also appropriate for multimedia content such as stored audio and video. In this section we discuss **content distribution networks (CDNs)**, which provide an alternative approach to distributing stored multimedia content (as well as for distributing traditional Web content).

CDNs are based on the philosophy that if the client can't come to the content (because the best-effort path from server-to-client path cannot support streaming video), the content should be brought to the client. CDNs thus use a different model than Web caching. For a CDN, the paying customers are no longer the ISPs but the content providers. A content provider with a video to distribute (such as CNN) pays a CDN company (such as Akamai) to get its video to requesting users with the shortest possible delays.

A CDN company typically provides its content distribution service as follows:

1. The CDN company installs hundreds of **CDN servers** throughout the Internet. The CDN company typically places the CDN servers in a **data center.** A **data center,** owned and run by a third party, is typically a building filled with server hosts. These data centers are often in lower-tier ISPs, close to ISP access networks and the clients.
2. The CDN replicates its customers' content in the CDN servers. Whenever a customer updates its content, the CDN redistributes the fresh content to the CDN servers.
3. The CDN company provides a mechanism so that when a client requests content, the content is provided by the CDN server that can best deliver the content to the specific client. This server may be the closest CDN server to the client (perhaps in the same ISP as the client) or may be a CDN server with a congestion-free path to the client.

It is interesting to note that many independent companies are involved in the CDN paradigm. A content provider (such as CNN) distributes its content through a CDN company (such as Akamai). The CDN company buys CDN servers from a server vendor (such as Cisco or IBM) and installs the servers in hosting centers, owned by a hosting center company (such as AT&T). Thus, not counting the ISPs, there are four independent companies involved in the CDN paradigm!

Figure 13.16 shows the interaction between the content provider and the CDN company. The content provider first determines which of its objects (e.g., videos) it wants the CDN to distribute. (The content provider distributes the remaining objects without intervention from the CDN.) The content provider tags and then pushes this content to a CDN node, which in turn replicates and pushes the content to all its CDN servers. The CDN company may own a private network for pushing the content from the CDN node to the CDN servers. Whenever the content provider modifies a CDN-distributed object, it pushes the fresh version to the CDN node, which again immediately replicates and distributes the object to the CDN servers. It is important to keep in mind that each CDN server typically contains objects from many content providers.

Now comes the interesting question. When a browser in a user's host is instructed to retrieve a specific object (identified with a URL), how does the browser determine whether it should retrieve the object from the origin server or from one of the CDN servers? Typically, CDNs make use of DNS redirection in order to guide browsers to the correct server [Kangasharju 2000].

As an example, suppose the hostname of the content provider is `www.foo.com`. Suppose the name of the CDN company is `cdn.com`. Further suppose that the content provider only wants its video mpeg files to be distributed by the CDN; all other objects, including the base HTML pages, are distributed directly by the content provider. To accomplish this, the content provider modifies

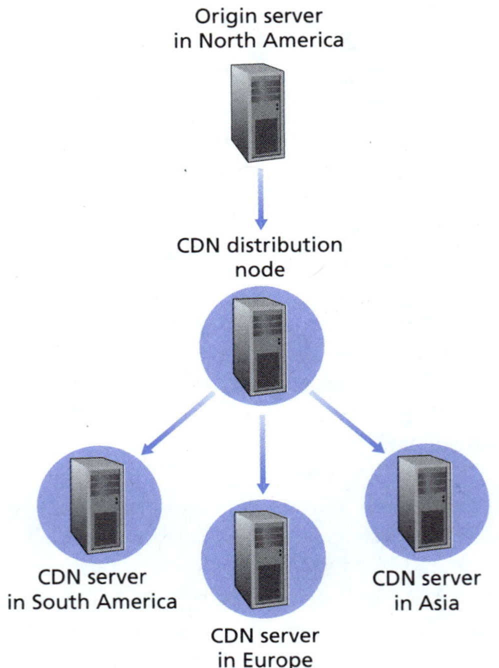

Figure 13.16 ♦ The CDN pushes content provider's tagged objects to its CDN servers.

all the HTML objects in the origin server so that the URLs of the video files are prefixed with `http://www.cdn.com`. Thus, if an HTML file at the content provider originally had a reference to `http://www.foo.com/sports/ruth.mpg`, the content provider would tag this object by replacing the reference in the HTML file with `http://www.cdn.com/www.foo.com/sports/ruth.mpg`.

When a browser requests a Web page containing the image ruth.mpg, the following actions occur:

1. The browser sends its request for the base HTML object to the origin server, `www.foo.com`, which sends the requested HTML object to the browser. The browser parses the HTML file and finds the reference to `http://www.cdn.com/www.foo.com/sports/ruth.mpg`.
2. The browser then does a DNS lookup on `www.cdn.com`, which is the hostname for the referenced URL. The DNS is configured so that all queries about `www.cdn.com` that arrive to a root DNS server are sent to an authoritative DNS server for `www.cdn.com`. When the authoritative DNS server receives

the query, it extracts the IP address of the requesting browser. Using an internal network map that it has constructed for the entire Internet, the CDN's DNS server returns the IP address of the CDN server that is likely the best for the requesting browser (often the closest CDN server to the browser).

3. DNS in the requesting client receives a DNS reply with the IP address. The browser then sends its HTTP request to the CDN server with that IP address. The browser obtains ruth.mpg from this CDN server. For subsequent requests from `www.cdn.com`, the client continues to use the same CDN server since the IP address for `www.cdn.com` is in the DNS cache (in the client host or in the local DNS name server).

In summary, as shown in Figure 13.17, the requesting host first goes to the origin Web server to get the base HTML object, then to the CDN's authoritative DNS server to get the IP address of the best CDN server, and finally to that CDN server to get the video. Note that no changes need be made to HTTP, DNS, or the browser to implement this distribution scheme.

What remains to explain is how a CDN company determines the "best" CDN server for the requesting host. Although each CDN company has its own proprietary way of doing this, it is not difficult to get a rough idea of what they do. For every access ISP in the Internet (containing potential requesting clients), the CDN company keeps track of the best CDN server for that access ISP. The CDN company determines the best CDN server based on its knowledge of Internet routing tables (specifically, BGP tables, which we discussed in Chapter 10), roundtrip time estimates, and other measurement data it has from its various servers to various access

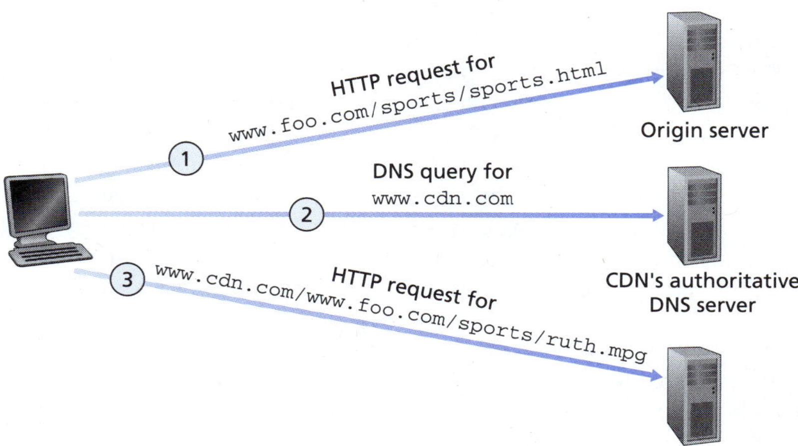

Figure 13.17 ♦ CDNs use DNS to direct requests to nearby CDN server.

networks; see [Verma 2001] for a discussion. In this manner, the CDN estimates which CDN server provides the best best-effort service to the ISP. The CDN does this for a large number of access ISPs in the Internet and uses this information to configure the authoritative DNS server.

CDNs are also often deployed by enterprises that have a large number of regional offices. An enterprise's regional offices are typically connected to the Internet (or to a private network) via relatively low-speed links (e.g., T1 links at 1.544 Mbps). Many such enterprises today need to distribute video e-learning or other corporate video material to their employees. To accomplish this task, an enterprise purchases CDN servers and installs them in its regional offices. When the enterprise has a new video to distribute, it pushes the video to all of its regional offices, and the employees are then served the video by their regional CDN server. In this manner, each video is sent over each regional office's access link only once, thereby not over-burdening the access links with repeated distributions of the same videos. Furthermore, enterprise CDNs often push the video from the central enterprise site to the regional CDN servers when distributing a high-bandwidth video will not interfere with other important traffic, such as at night.

13.6 Beyond Best Effort

In previous sections we learned how sequence numbers, timestamps, FEC, RTP, and H.323 can be used by multimedia applications in today's Internet. CDNs represent a system-wide solution for distributing multimedia content. But are these techniques alone enough to support reliable and robust multimedia applications, such as an IP telephony service that is equivalent to a service in today's telephone network? Before answering this question, let's recall again that today's Internet provides a best-effort service to all of its applications; that is, it does not make any promises about the QoS an application will receive. An application will receive whatever level of performance (for example, end-to-end packet delay and loss) that the network is able to provide at that moment. Recall also that today's public Internet does not allow delay-sensitive multimedia applications to request any special treatment. Because every packet, including delay-sensitive audio and video packets, is treated equally at the routers, all that's required to ruin the quality of an ongoing IP telephone call is enough interfering traffic (that is, network congestion) to noticeably increase the delay and loss seen by an IP telephone call.

In this section, we will identify *new* architectural components that can be added to the Internet architecture to shield an application from such congestion and thus make high-quality networked multimedia applications a reality. Many of the issues that we will discuss in this, and the remaining sections of this chapter, are currently, or recently have been under active discussion in the IETF Diffserv, Intserv, and RSVP working groups.

Figure 13.18 shows a simple network scenario we'll use to illustrate the most important architectural components that have been proposed in order to provide explicit support for the QoS needs of multimedia applications. Suppose that two application packet flows originate on Hosts H1 and H2 on one LAN and are destined for Hosts H3 and H4 on another LAN. The routers on the two LANs are connected by a 1.5 Mbps link. Let's assume the LAN speeds are significantly higher than 1.5 Mbps, and focus on the output queue of router R1; it is here that packet delay and packet loss will occur if the aggregate sending rate of the H1 and H2 exceeds 1.5 Mbps. Let's now consider several scenarios, each of which will provide us with important insight into the underlying principles for providing QoS guarantees to multimedia applications.

13.6.1 Scenario 1: A 1 Mbps Audio Application and an FTP Transfer

Scenario 1 is illustrated in Figure 13.19. Here, a 1 Mbps audio application (for example, a CD-quality audio call) shares the 1.5 Mbps link between R1 and R2 with an FTP application that is transferring a file from H2 to H4. In the best-effort Internet, the audio and FTP packets are mixed in the output queue at R1 and (typically) transmitted in a first-in-first-out (FIFO) order. In this scenario, a burst of packets from the FTP source could potentially fill up the queue, causing IP audio packets to be excessively delayed or lost due to buffer overflow at R1. How should we solve

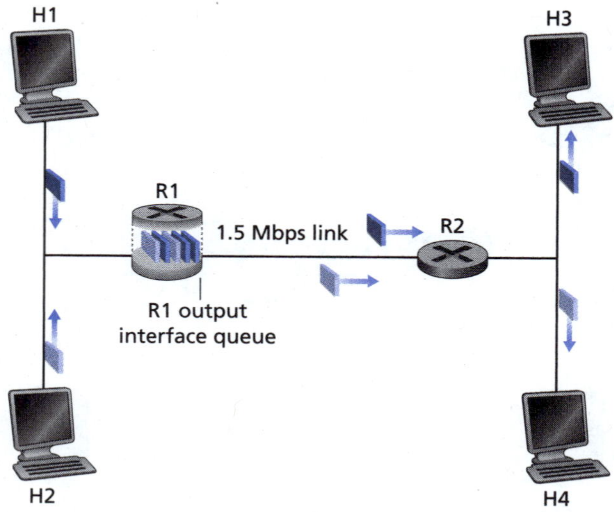

Figure 13.18 ♦ A simple network with two applications

this potential problem? Given that the FTP application does not have time constraints, our intuition might be to give strict priority to audio packets at R1. Under a strict priority scheduling discipline, an audio packet in the R1 output buffer would always be transmitted before any FTP packet in the R1 output buffer. The link from R1 to R2 would look like a dedicated link of 1.5 Mbps to the audio traffic, with FTP traffic using the R1-to-R2 link only when no audio traffic is queued.

In order for R1 to distinguish between the audio and FTP packets in its queue, each packet must be marked as belonging to one of these two classes of traffic. Recall from Section 10.4.1 that this was the original goal of the type-of-service (ToS) field in IPv4. As obvious as this might seem, this then is our first principle underlying the provision of QoS guarantees:

> **Principle 1:** Packet marking allows a router to distinguish among packets belonging to different classes of traffic.

13.6.2 Scenario 2: A 1 Mbps Audio Application and a High-Priority FTP Transfer

Our second scenario is only slightly different from scenario 1. Suppose now that the FTP user has purchased "platinum" (that is, high-priced) Internet access from its ISP, while the audio user has purchased cheap, low-budget Internet service that costs only a minuscule fraction of platinum service. Should the cheap user's audio packets be given priority over FTP packets in this case? Arguably not. In this case, it would seem more reasonable to distinguish packets on the basis of the sender's IP

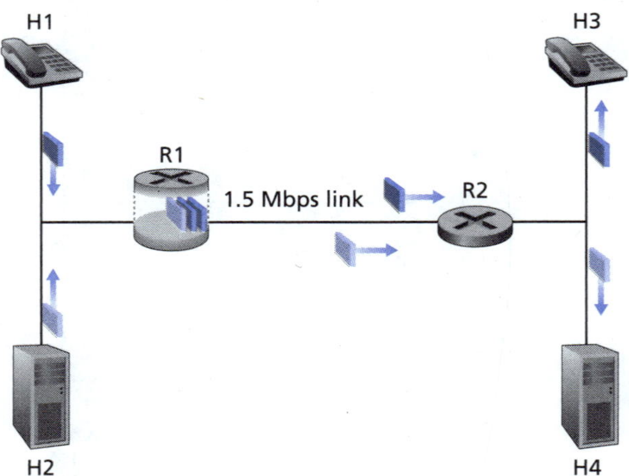

Figure 13.19 ♦ Competing audio and FTP Applications

address. More generally, we see that it is necessary for a router to *classify* packets according to some criteria. This then calls for a slight modification to principle 1:

> **Principle 1 (modified):** Packet classification allows a router to distinguish among packets belonging to different classes of traffic.

Explicit packet marking is one way in which packets may be distinguished. However, the marking carried by a packet does not, by itself, mandate that the packet will receive a given quality of service. Marking is but one *mechanism* for distinguishing packets. The manner in which a router distinguishes among packets by treating them differently is a *policy* decision.

13.6.3 Scenario 3: A Misbehaving Audio Application and an FTP Transfer

Suppose now that somehow (by use of mechanisms that we'll study in subsequent sections) the router knows it should give priority to packets from the 1 Mbps audio application. Since the outgoing link speed is 1.5 Mbps, even though the FTP packets receive lower priority, they will still, on average, receive 0.5 Mbps of transmission service. But what happens if the audio application starts sending packets at a rate of 1.5 Mbps or higher (either maliciously or due to an error in the application)? In this case, the FTP packets will starve, that is, they will not receive any service on the R1-to-R2 link. Similar problems would occur if multiple applications (for example, multiple audio calls), all with the same priority, were sharing a link's bandwidth; one noncompliant flow could degrade and ruin the performance of the other flows. Ideally, one wants a degree of *isolation* among flows, in order to protect one flow from another misbehaving flow. This, then, is a second underlying principle the provision of QoS guarantees.

> **Principle 2:** It is desirable to provide a degree of isolation among traffic flows, so that one flow is not adversely affected by another misbehaving flow.

In the following section, we will examine several specific mechanisms for providing this isolation among flows. We note here that two broad approaches can be taken. First, it is possible to police traffic flows, as shown in Figure 13.20. If a traffic flow must meet certain criteria (for example, that the audio flow not exceed a peak rate of 1 Mbps), then a policing mechanism can be put into place to ensure that these criteria are indeed observed. If the policed application misbehaves, the policing mechanism will take some action (for example, drop or delay packets that are in violation of the criteria) so that the traffic actually entering the network conforms to the criteria. The leaky bucket mechanism that we examine in the following section is perhaps the most widely used policing mechanism. In Figure 13.20, the packet classification and marking mechanism (Principle 1) and the policing mechanism (Principle 2) are co-located at the edge of the network, either in the end system or at an edge router.

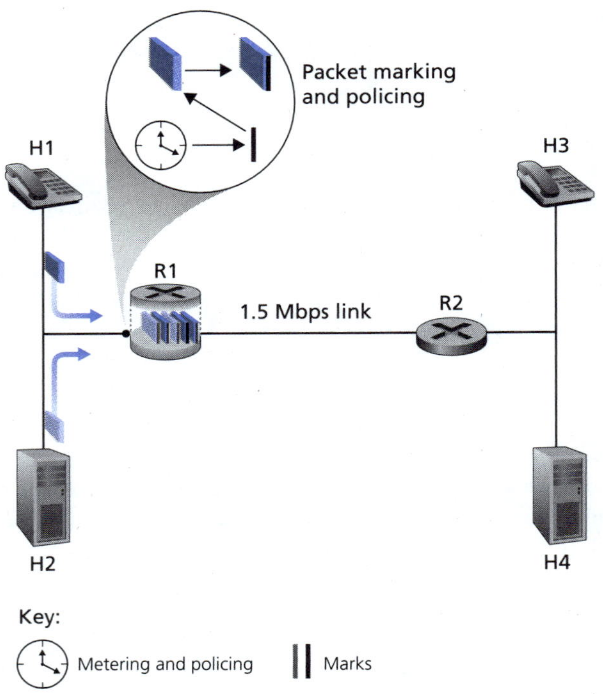

Figure 13.20 ♦ Policing (and marking) the audio and FTP traffic flows

An alternative approach for providing isolation among traffic flows is for the link-level packet-scheduling mechanism to explicitly allocate a fixed amount of link bandwidth to each application flow. For example, the audio flow could be allocated 1Mbps at R1, and the FTP flow could be allocated 0.5 Mbps. In this case, the audio and FTP flows see a logical link with capacity 1.0 and 0.5 Mbps, respectively, as shown in Figure 13.21.

With strict enforcement of the link-level allocation of bandwidth, a flow can use only the amount of bandwidth that has been allocated; in particular, it cannot utilize bandwidth that is not currently being used by the other applications. For example, if the audio flow goes silent (for example, if the speaker pauses and generates no audio packets), the FTP flow would still not be able to transmit more than 0.5 Mbps over the R1-to-R2 link, even though the audio flow's 1 Mbps bandwidth allocation is not being used at that moment. It is therefore desirable to use bandwidth as efficiently as possible, allowing one flow to use another flow's unused bandwidth at any given point in time. This is the third principle underlying the provision of QoS:

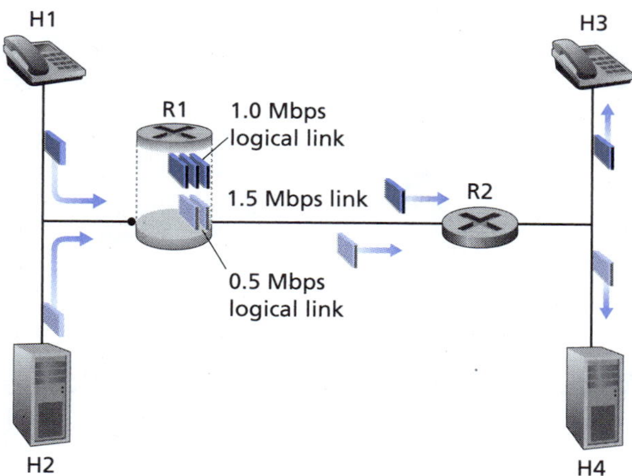

Figure 13.21 ♦ Logical isolation of audio and FTP application flows

> **Principle 3:** While providing isolation among flows, it is desirable to use resources (for example, link bandwidth and buffers) as efficiently as possible.

13.6.4 Scenario 4: Two 1 Mbps Audio Applications over an Overloaded 1.5 Mbps Link

In our final scenario, two 1 Mbps audio connections transmit their packets over the 1.5 Mbps link, as shown in Figure 13.22. The combined data rate of the two flows (2 Mbps) exceeds the link capacity. Even with classification and marking (Principle 1), isolation of flows (Principle 2), and sharing of unused bandwidth (Principle 3), of which there is none, this is clearly a losing proposition. There is simply not enough bandwidth to accommodate the applications' needs. If the two applications equally share the bandwidth, each would receive only 0.75 Mbps. Looked at another way, each application would lose 25 percent of its transmitted packets. This is such an unacceptably low QoS that the application is completely unusable; there's no need even to transmit any audio packets in the first place.

For a flow that needs a minimum QoS in order to be considered usable, the network should either allow or *block* the flow. The telephone network is an example of a network that performs such call blocking—if the required resources (an end-to-end circuit in the case of the telephone network) cannot be allocated to the call, the call is blocked (prevented from entering the network) and a busy signal is returned to the user. In our example, there is no gain in allowing a flow into the network if it will not receive a sufficient QoS to be considered usable. Indeed, there is a *cost* to

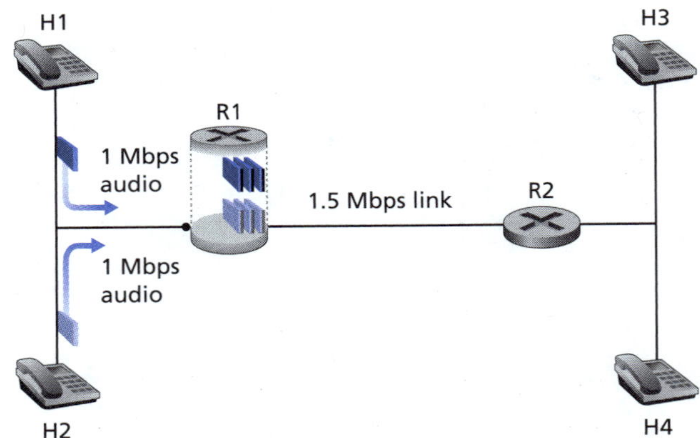

Figure 13.22 ♦ Two competing audio applications overloading the R1-to-R2 link

admitting a flow that does not receive its needed QoS, as network resources are being used to support a flow that provides no utility to the end user.

Implicit with the need to provide a guaranteed QoS to a flow is the need for the flow to declare its QoS requirements. This process of having a flow declare its QoS requirement, and then having the network either accept the flow (at the required QoS) or block the flow is referred to as the **call admission** process. The need for call admission is the fourth underlying principle in the provision of QoS guarantees:

> **Principle 4:** If sufficient resources will not always be available, a call admission process is needed in which flows declare their QoS requirements and are then either admitted to the network (at the required QoS) or blocked from the network (if the required QoS cannot be provided by the network).

In our discussion so far, we have identified four basic principles in providing QoS guarantees for multimedia applications. In the following section, we consider various mechanisms for implementing these principles. In the sections following that, we examine proposed Internet service models for providing QoS guarantees.

13.7 Scheduling and Policing Mechanisms

In the previous section, we identified the important underlying principles in providing QoS guarantees to networked multimedia applications. In this section, we will examine various mechanisms that are used to provide these QoS guarantees.

13.7.1 Scheduling Mechanisms

Recall from our discussion in Section 10.3 that packets belonging to various network flows are multiplexed and queued for transmission at the output buffers associated with a link. The manner in which queued packets are selected for transmission on the link is known as the **link-scheduling discipline.** We saw in the previous section that the link-scheduling discipline plays an important role in providing QoS guarantees. Let us now consider several of the most important link-scheduling disciplines in more detail.

First-In-First-Out (FIFO)

Figure 13.23 shows the queuing model abstractions for the FIFO link-scheduling discipline. Packets arriving at the link output queue wait for transmission if the link is currently busy transmitting another packet. If there is not sufficient buffering space to hold the arriving packet, the queue's **packet-discarding policy** then determines whether the packet will be dropped (lost) or whether other packets will be removed from the queue to make space for the arriving packet. In our discussion below we will ignore packet discard. When a packet is completely transmitted over the outgoing link (that is, receives service) it is removed from the queue.

The FIFO (also known as first-come-first-served, or FCFS) scheduling discipline selects packets for link transmission in the same order in which they arrived at the output link queue. We're all familiar with FIFO queuing from bus stops (particularly in England, where queuing seems to have been perfected) or other service centers, where arriving customers join the back of the single waiting line, remain in order, and are then served when they reach the front of the line.

Figure 13.24 shows the FIFO queue in operation. Packet arrivals are indicated by numbered arrows above the upper timeline, with the number indicating the order in which the packet arrived. Individual packet departures are shown below the lower timeline. The time that a packet spends in service (being transmitted) is indicated by the shaded rectangle between the two timelines. Because of the FIFO discipline, packets leave in the same order in which they arrived. Note that after the departure of packet 4, the link remains idle (since packets 1 through 4 have been transmitted and removed from the queue) until the arrival of packet 5.

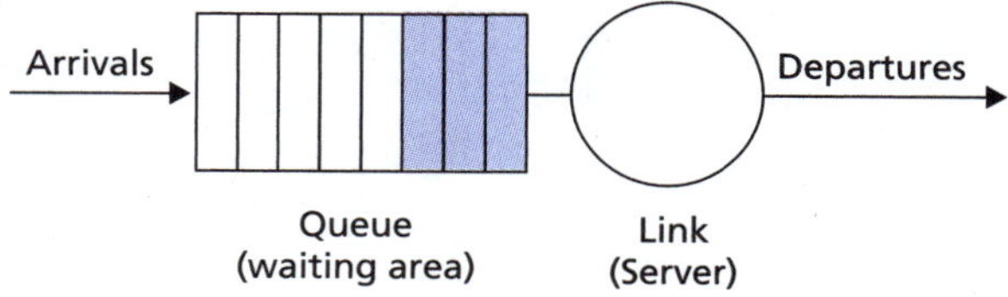

Figure 13.23 ♦ FIFO queuing abstraction

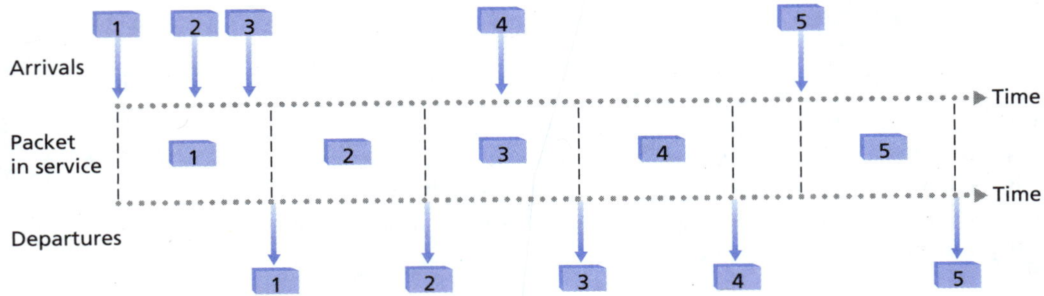

Figure 13.24 ♦ The FIFO queue in operation

Priority Queuing

Under **priority queuing,** packets arriving at the output link are classified into priority classes at the output queue, as shown in Figure 13.25. As discussed in the previous section, a packet's priority class may depend on an explicit marking that it carries in its packet header (for example, the value of the ToS bits in an IPv4 packet), its source or destination IP address, its destination port number, or other criteria. Each priority class typically has its own queue. When choosing a packet to transmit, the priority queuing discipline will transmit a packet from the highest priority class that has a nonempty queue (that is, has packets waiting for transmission). The choice among packets *in the same priority class* is typically done in a FIFO manner.

Figure 13.26 illustrates the operation of a priority queue with two priority classes. Packets 1, 3, and 4 belong to the high-priority class, and packets 2 and 5 belong to the low-priority class. Packet 1 arrives and, finding the link idle, begins

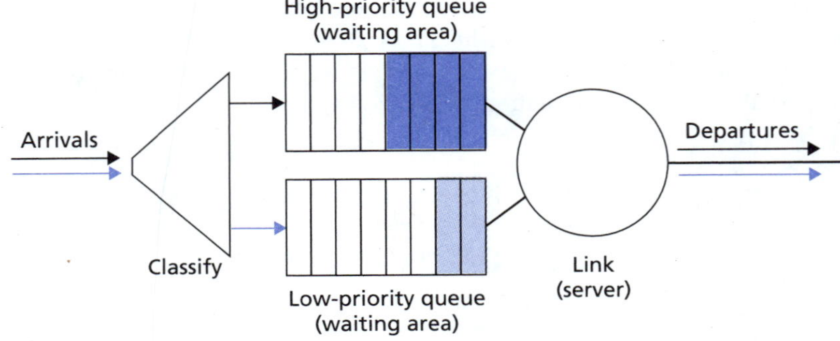

Figure 13.25 ♦ Priority queuing model

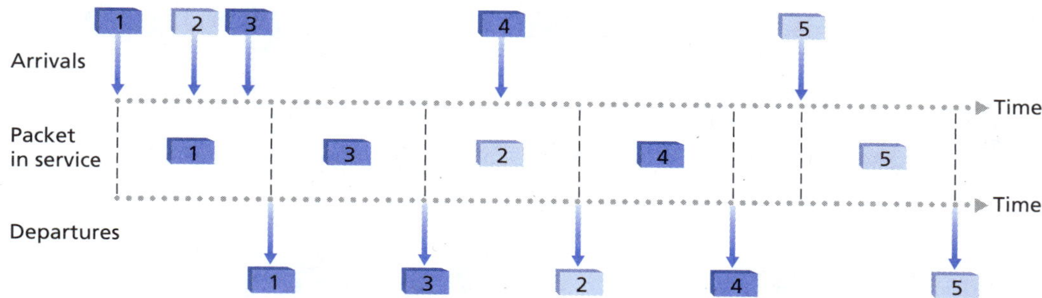

Figure 13.26 ♦ Operation of the priority queue

transmission. During the transmission of packet 1, packets 2 and 3 arrive and are queued in the low- and high-priority queues, respectively. After the transmission of packet 1, packet 3 (a high-priority packet) is selected for transmission over packet 2 (which, even though it arrived earlier, is a low-priority packet). At the end of the transmission of packet 3, packet 2 then begins transmission. Packet 4 (a high-priority packet) arrives during the transmission of packet 2 (a low-priority packet). Under a nonpreemptive priority queuing discipline, the transmission of a packet is not interrupted once it has begun. In this case, packet 4 queues for transmission and begins being transmitted after the transmission of packet 2 is completed.

Round Robin and Weighted Fair Queuing (WFQ)

Under the **round robin queuing discipline,** packets are sorted into classes as with priority queuing. However, rather than there being a strict priority of service among classes, a round robin scheduler alternates service among the classes. In the simplest form of round robin scheduling, a class 1 packet is transmitted, followed by a class 2 packet, followed by a class 1 packet, followed by a class 2 packet, and so on. A so-called work-conserving queuing discipline will never allow the link to remain idle whenever there are packets (of any class) queued for transmission. A **work-conserving round robin discipline** that looks for a packet of a given class but finds none will immediately check the next class in the round robin sequence.

Figure 13.27 illustrates the operation of a two-class round robin queue. In this example, packets 1, 2, and 4 belong to class 1, and packets 3 and 5 belong to the second class. Packet 1 begins transmission immediately upon arrival at the output queue. Packets 2 and 3 arrive during the transmission of packet 1 and thus queue for transmission. After the transmission of packet 1, the link scheduler looks for a class 2 packet and thus transmits packet 3. After the transmission of packet 3, the scheduler looks for a class 1 packet and thus transmits packet 2. After the transmission of packet 2, packet 4 is the only queued packet; it is thus transmitted immediately after packet 2.

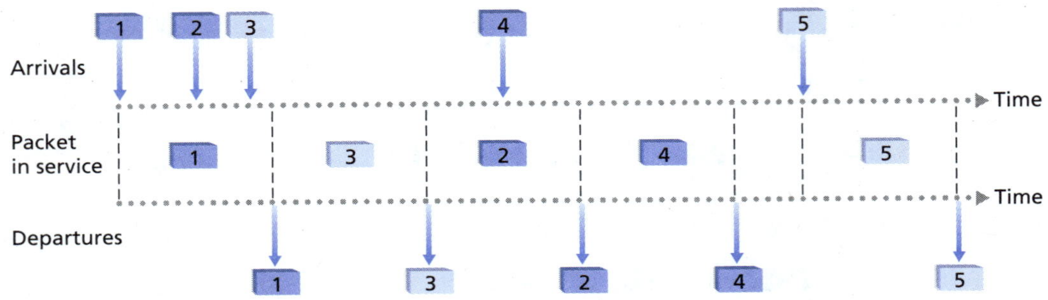

Figure 13.27 ♦ Operation of the two-class round robin queue

A generalized abstraction of round robin queuing that has found considerable use in QoS architectures is the so-called **weighted fair queuing** (WFQ) discipline [Demers 1990; Parekh 1993]. WFQ is illustrated in Figure 13.28. Arriving packets are classified and queued in the appropriate per-class waiting area. As in round robin scheduling, a WFQ scheduler will serve classes in a circular manner—first serving class 1, then serving class 2, then serving class 3, and then (assuming there are three classes) repeating the service pattern. WFQ is also a work-conserving queuing discipline and thus will immediately move on to the next class in the service sequence when it finds an empty class queue.

WFQ differs from round robin in that each class may receive a *differential* amount of service in any interval of time. Specifically, each class, *i*, is assigned a weight, w_i. Under WFQ, during any interval of time during which there are class *i* packets to send, class *i* will then be guaranteed to receive a fraction of service equal to $w_i/(\sum w_j)$, where the sum in the denominator is taken over all classes that also have

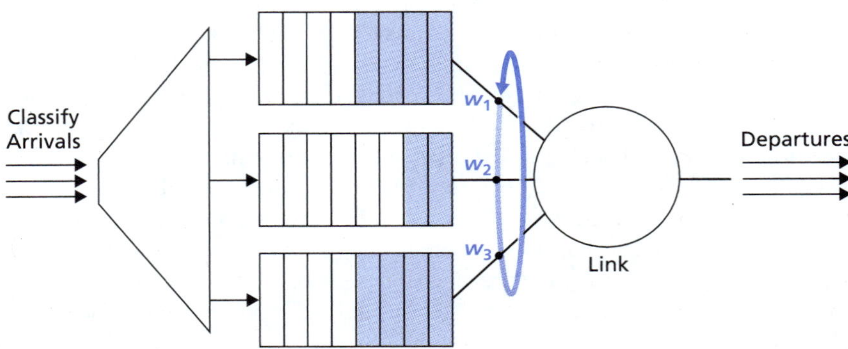

Figure 13.28 ♦ Weighted fair queuing (WFQ)

packets queued for transmission. In the worst case, even if all classes have queued packets, class i will still be guaranteed to receive a fraction $w_i/(\Sigma w_j)$ of the bandwidth. Thus, for a link with transmission rate R, class i will always achieve a throughput of at least $R \cdot w_i/(\Sigma w_j)$. Our description of WFQ has been an idealized one, as we have not considered the fact that packets are discrete units of data and a packet's transmission will not be interrupted to begin transmission of another packet; [Demers 1990] and [Parekh 1993] discuss this packetization issue. As we will see in the following sections, WFQ plays a central role in QoS architectures. It is also available in today's router products [Cisco QoS 2002]. (Intranets that use WFQ-capable routers can therefore provide QoS to their internal flows.)

13.7.2 Policing: The Leaky Bucket

In Section 13.6 we also identified policing, the regulation of the rate at which a flow is allowed to inject packets into the network, as one of the cornerstones of any QoS architecture. But what aspects of a flow's packet rate should be policed? We can identify three important policing criteria, each differing from the other according to the time scale over which the packet flow is policed:

- *Average rate.* The network may wish to limit the long-term average rate (packets per time interval) at which a flow's packets can be sent into the network. A crucial issue here is the interval of time over which the average rate will be policed. A flow whose average rate is limited to 100 packets per second is more constrained than a source that is limited to 6,000 packets per minute, even though both have the same average rate over a long enough interval of time. For example, the latter constraint would allow a flow to send 1,000 packets in a given second-long interval of time (subject to the constraint that the rate be less than 6,000 packets over a minute-long interval containing these 1,000 packets), while the former constraint would disallow this sending behavior.
- *Peak rate.* While the average rate constraint limits the amount of traffic that can be sent into the network over a relatively long period of time, a peak-rate constraint limits the maximum number of packets that can be sent over a shorter period of time. Using our example above, the network may police a flow at an average rate of 6,000 packets per minute, while limiting the flow's peak rate to 1,500 packets per second.
- *Burst size.* The network may also wish to limit the maximum number of packets (the "burst" of packets) that can be sent into the network over an extremely short interval of time. In the limit, as the interval length approaches zero, the burst size limits the number of packets that can be instantaneously sent into the network. Even though it is physically impossible to instantaneously send multiple packets into the network (after all, every link has a physical transmission rate that cannot be exceeded!), the abstraction of a maximum burst size is a useful one.

The leaky bucket mechanism is an abstraction that can be used to characterize these policing limits. As shown in Figure 13.29, a leaky bucket consists of a bucket that can hold up to b tokens. Tokens are added to this bucket as follows. New tokens, which may potentially be added to the bucket, are always being generated at a rate of r tokens per second. (We assume here for simplicity that the unit of time is a second.) If the bucket is filled with less than b tokens when a token is generated, the newly generated token is added to the bucket; otherwise the newly generated token is ignored, and the token bucket remains full with b tokens.

Let us now consider how the leaky bucket can be used to police a packet flow. Suppose that before a packet is transmitted into the network, it must first remove a token from the token bucket. If the token bucket is empty, the packet must wait for a token. (An alternative is for the packet to be dropped, although we will not consider that option here.) Let us now consider how this behavior polices a traffic flow. Because there can be at most b tokens in the bucket, the maximum burst size for a leaky-bucket-policed flow is b packets. Furthermore, because the token generation rate is r, the maximum number of packets that can enter the network of *any* interval of time of length t is $rt + b$. Thus, the token generation rate, r, serves to limit the long-term average rate at which packets can enter the network. It is also possible to use leaky buckets (specifically, two leaky buckets in series) to police a flow's peak rate in addition to the long-term average rate; see the homework problems at the end of this chapter.

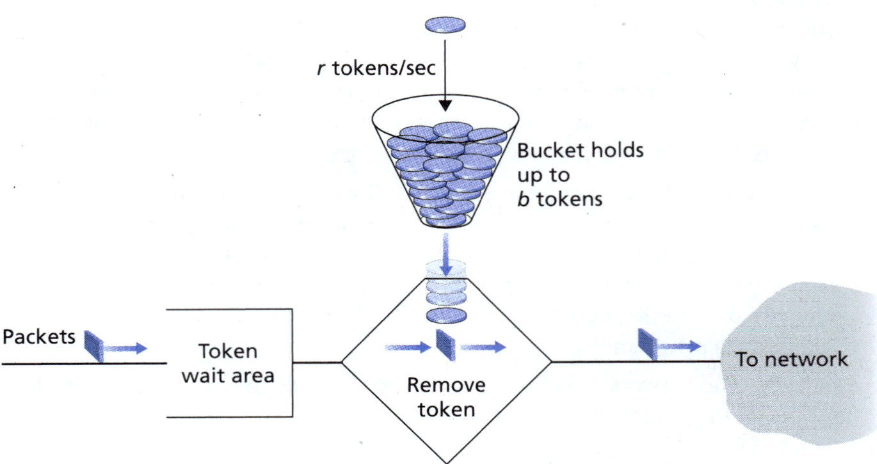

Figure 13.29 ♦ The leaky bucket policer

Leaky Bucket + Weighted Fair Queuing = Provable Maximum Delay in a Queue

In Section 13.8 we'll examine the so-called Intserv and Diffserv approaches for providing quality of service in the Internet. We'll see that both leaky bucket policing and WFQ scheduling can play an important role. Let us thus close this section by considering a router's output link that multiplexes n flows, each policed by a leaky bucket with parameters b_i and r_i, $i = 1, \ldots, n,$ using WFQ scheduling. We use the term *flow* here loosely to refer to the set of packets that are not distinguished from each other by the scheduler. In practice, a flow might be comprised of traffic from a single end-to-end connection (as in Intserv) or a collection of many such connections (as in Diffserv), see Figure 13.30.

Recall from our discussion of WFQ that each flow, i, is guaranteed to receive a share of the link bandwidth equal to at least $R \cdot w_i/(\sum w_j)$, where R is the transmission rate of the link in packets/sec. What then is the maximum delay that a packet will experience while waiting for service in the WFQ (that is, after passing through the leaky bucket)? Let us focus on flow 1. Suppose that flow 1's token bucket is initially full. A burst of b_1 packets then arrives to the leaky bucket policer for flow 1. These packets remove all of the tokens (without wait) from the leaky bucket and then join the WFQ waiting area for flow 1. Since these b_1 packets are served at a rate of at least $R \cdot w_i/(\sum w_j)$ packet/sec, the last of these packets will then have a maximum delay, d_{max}, until its transmission is completed, where

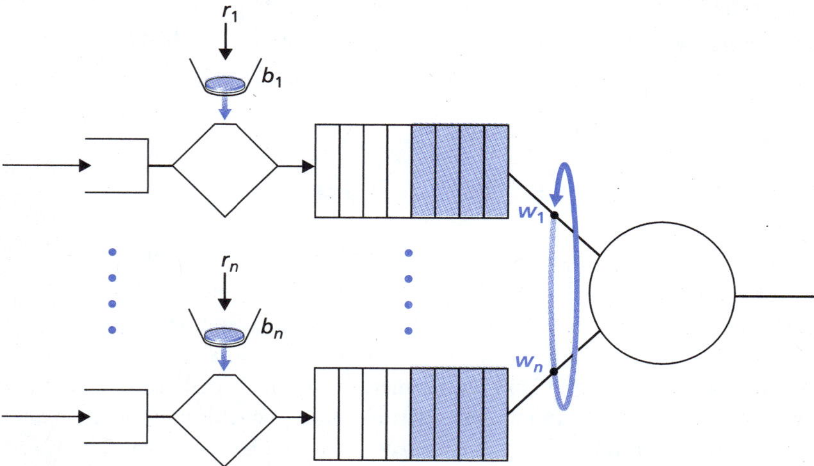

Figure 13.30 ♦ *n* multiplexed leaky bucket flows with WFQ scheduling

$$d_{max} = \frac{b_1}{R \cdot w_1/\Sigma w_j}$$

The rationale behind this formula is that if there are b_1 packets in the queue and packets are being serviced (removed) from the queue at a rate of at least $R \cdot w_1/(\Sigma w_j)$ packets per second, then the amount of time until the last bit of the last packet is transmitted cannot be more than $b_1/(R \cdot w_1/(\Sigma w_j))$. A homework problem asks you to prove that as long as $r_1 < R \cdot w_1/(\Sigma w_j)$, then d_{max} is indeed the maximum delay that any packet in flow 1 will ever experience in the WFQ queue.

13.8 Integrated Services and Differentiated Services

In the previous sections, we identified both the principles and the mechanisms used to provide quality of service in the Internet. In this section, we consider how these ideas are exploited in two architectures that have been proposed for providing quality of service in the Internet—the integrated services (**Intserv**) and differentiated services (**Diffserv**) architecture. As we will see, Intserv is a framework developed within the IETF to provide individualized QoS guarantees to individual application sessions. The goal of Diffserv is to provide the ability to handle different classes of traffic in different ways within the Internet. Although neither Intserv nor Diffserv have taken off and found widespread adoption (for reasons we will discuss), they represent the IETF's current standards for providing quality of service guarantees. Incorporating the principles and mechanisms we've studied in the previous sections, they are thus of interest to us.

13.8.1 Intserv

Two key features lie at the heart of the Intserv architecture:

- *Reserved resources.* A router is required to know what amounts of its resources (buffers, link bandwidth) are already reserved for ongoing sessions.
- *Call setup.* A session requiring QoS guarantees must first be able to reserve sufficient resources at each network router on its source-to-destination path to ensure that its end-to-end QoS requirement is met. This call setup (also known as call admission) process requires the participation of each router on the path. Each router must determine the local resources required by the session, consider the amounts of its resources that are already committed to other ongoing sessions, and determine whether it has sufficient resources to satisfy the per-hop QoS requirement of the session at this router without violating local QoS guarantees made to an already-admitted session.

Figure 13.31 depicts the call setup process. Let us now consider the steps involved in call admission in more detail:

1. *Traffic characterization and specification of the desired QoS.* In order for a router to determine whether or not its resources are sufficient to meet the QoS requirements of a session, that session must first declare its QoS requirement, as well as characterize the traffic that it will be sending into the network, and for which it requires a QoS guarantee. In the Intserv architecture, the so-called Rspec (R for reservation) defines the specific QoS being requested by a connection; the so-called Tspec (T for traffic) characterizes the traffic the sender will be sending into the network or that the receiver will be receiving from the network. The specific form of the Rspec and Tspec will vary, depending on the service requested, as discussed below. The Tspec and Rspec are defined in part in RFC 2210 and RFC 2215.
2. *Signaling for call setup.* A session's Tspec and Rspec must be carried to the routers at which resources will be reserved for the session. In the Internet, the RSVP protocol, which is discussed in detail shortly, is currently the signaling protocol of choice. RFC 2210 describes the use of the RSVP resource reservation protocol with the Intserv architecture.
3. *Per-element call admission.* Once a router receives the Tspec and Rspec for a session requesting a QoS guarantee, it can determine whether or not it can admit the call. This call admission decision will depend on the traffic specification, the

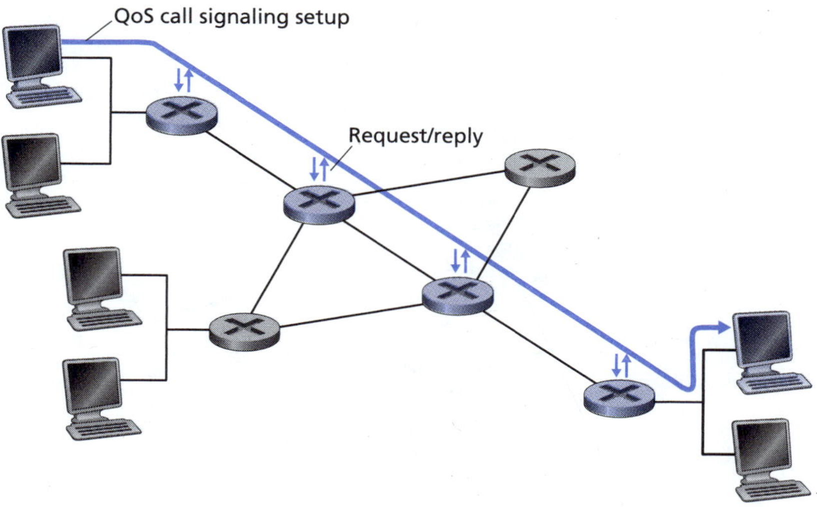

Figure 13.31 ♦ The call setup process

requested type of service, and the existing resource commitments already made by the router to ongoing sessions. Per-element call admission is shown in Figure 13.32.

The Intserv architecture defines two major classes of service: guaranteed service and controlled-load service. We will see shortly that each provides a very different form of a QoS guarantee.

Guaranteed Quality of Service

The guaranteed service specification, defined in RFC 2212, provides firm (mathematically provable) bounds on the queuing delays that a packet will experience in a router. While the details behind guaranteed service are rather complicated, the basic idea is really quite simple. To a first approximation, a source's traffic characterization is given by a leaky bucket (see Section 13.7) with parameters (r,b) and the requested service is characterized by a transmission rate, R, at which packets will be transmitted. In essence, a session requesting guaranteed service is requiring that the bits in its packet be guaranteed a forwarding rate of R bits/sec. Given that traffic is specified using a leaky bucket characterization, and a guaranteed rate of R is being requested, it is also possible to bound the maximum queuing delay at the router. Recall that with a leaky bucket traffic characterization, the amount of traffic (in bits) generated over any interval of length t is bounded by $rt + b$. Recall also from Section 13.7, that when a leaky bucket source is fed into a queue that guarantees that queued traffic will be serviced at least at a rate of R bits per second, the maximum queuing delay experienced by any packet will be bounded by b/R, as long as R is

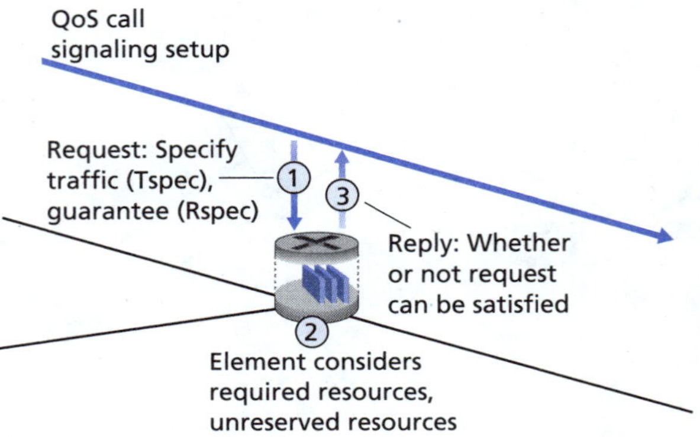

Figure 13.32 ♦ Per-element call behavior

greater than r. The actual delay bound guaranteed under the guaranteed service definition is slightly more complicated, due to packetization effects (the simple b/R bound assumes that data is in the form of a fluid-like flow rather than discrete packets), the fact that the traffic arrival process is subject to the peak-rate limitation of the input link (the simple b/R bound assumes that a burst of b bits can arrive in zero time), and possible additional variations in a packet's transmission time.

Controlled-Load Network Service

A session receiving controlled-load service will receive "a quality of service closely approximating the QoS that same flow would receive from an unloaded network element" [RFC 2211]. In other words, the session may assume that a "very high percentage" of its packets will successfully pass through the router without being dropped and will experience a queuing delay in the router that is close to zero. Interestingly, controlled-load service makes no quantitative guarantees about performance—it does not specify what constitutes a very high percentage of packets nor what quality of service closely approximates that of an unloaded network element.

The controlled-load service targets real-time multimedia applications that have been developed for today's Internet. As we have seen, these applications perform quite well when the network is unloaded, but rapidly degrade in performance as the network becomes more loaded.

13.8.2 Diffserv

The ability to request and reserve per-flow resources, in turn, makes it possible for the Intserv framework to provide QoS guarantees to individual flows. As work on Intserv proceeded, however, researchers involved began to appreciate some of the difficulties associated with the Intserv model and per-flow reservation of resources.

- *Scalability.* Per-flow resource reservation implies the need for a router to process resource reservations and to maintain per-flow state for *each* flow passing though the router. Per-flow reservation processing at a backbone router can thus incur a potentially significant overhead in large networks.
- *Flexible service models.* The Intserv framework provides for a small number of pre-specified service classes. This particular set of service classes does not allow for more qualitative or relative definitions of service distinctions (for example, "Service class A will receive preferred treatment over service class B."). These more qualitative definitions might better fit our intuitive notion of service distinction (for example, first class versus coach class in air travel; "platinum" versus "gold" versus "standard" credit cards).

These considerations led to the so-called Diffserv activity within the Internet Engineering Task Force. The Diffserv architecture aims to provide *scalable* and *flexible* service differentiation—that is, the ability to handle different "classes" of traffic in different ways within the Internet. The need for *scalability* arises from the fact that hundreds of thousands of simultaneous source-destination traffic flows may be present at a backbone router of the Internet. We will see shortly that this need is met by placing only simple functionality within the network core, with more complex control operations being implemented at the edge of the network. The need for *flexibility* arises from the fact that new service classes may arise and old service classes may become obsolete. The Diffserv architecture is flexible in the sense that it does not define specific services or service classes (for example, as is the case with Intserv). Instead, Diffserv provides the functional components, that is, the pieces of a network architecture, with which such services can be built. Let us now examine these components in detail.

Differentiated Services: A Simple Scenario

To set the framework for defining the architectural components of the differentiated service (Diffserv) model, let's begin with the simple network shown in Figure 13.33. In this section, we describe one possible use of the Diffserv components. Many other variations are possible, as described in RFC 2475. Our goal here is to provide an introduction to the key aspects of Diffserv, rather than to describe the architectural model in exhaustive detail. Readers interested in learning more about Diffserv are encouraged to see the comprehensive book [Kilkki 1999].

The Diffserv architecture consists of two sets of functional elements:

- *Edge functions: packet classification and traffic conditioning.* At the incoming edge of the network (that is, at either a Diffserv-capable host that generates traffic or at the first Diffserv-capable router that the traffic passes through), arriving packets are marked. More specifically, the differentiated service (DS) field of the packet header is set to some value. For example, in Figure 13.33, packets being sent from H1 to H3 might be marked at R1, while packets being sent from H2 to H4 might be marked at R2. The mark that a packet receives identifies the class of traffic to which it belongs. Different classes of traffic will then receive different service within the core network.
- *Core function: forwarding.* When a DS-marked packet arrives at a Diffserv-capable router, the packet is forwarded onto its next hop according to the so-called **per-hop behavior** associated with that packet's class. The per-hop behavior influences how a router's buffers and link bandwidth are shared among the competing classes of traffic. A crucial tenet of the Diffserv architecture is that a router's per-hop behavior will be based *only* on packet markings, that is, the class of traffic to which a packet belongs. Thus, if packets being sent from H1 to H3 in Figure 13.33 receive the same marking as packets being sent from H2 to H4, then

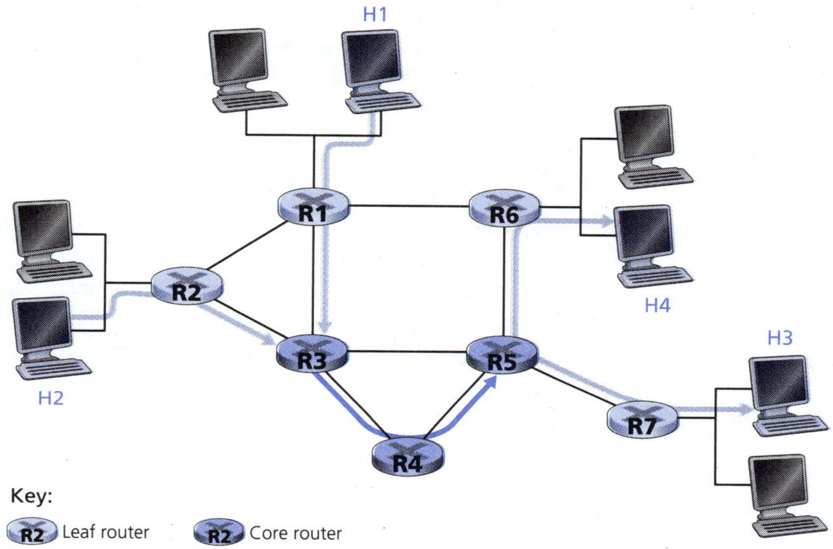

Figure 13.33 ♦ A simple Diffserv network example

the network routers treat these packets as an aggregate, without distinguishing whether the packets originated at H1 or H2. For example, R3 would not distinguish between packets from H1 and H2 when forwarding these packets on to R4. Thus, the differentiated service architecture obviates the need to keep router state for individual source-destination pairs—an important consideration in meeting the scalability requirement discussed at the beginning of this section.

An analogy might prove useful here. At many large-scale social events (for example, a large public reception, a large dance club or discothèque, a concert, or a football game), people entering the event receive a pass of one type or another: VIP passes for Very Important People; over-21 passes for people who are 21 years old or older (for example, if alcoholic drinks are to be served); backstage passes at concerts; press passes for reporters; even an ordinary pass for the Ordinary Person. These passes are typically distributed upon entry to the event, that is, at the edge of the event. It is here at the edge where computationally intensive operations, such as paying for entry, checking for the appropriate type of invitation, and matching an invitation against a piece of identification, are performed. Furthermore, there may be a limit on the number of people of a given type that are allowed into an event. If there is such a limit, people may have to wait before entering the event. Once inside the event, one's pass allows one to receive differentiated service at many locations around the event—a VIP is provided with free drinks, a better table, free food, entry to exclusive rooms, and fawning service. Conversely, an ordinary person is excluded from certain areas, pays for drinks, and receives only basic service. In both cases, the service received within the event depends solely on the type of one's pass. Moreover, all people within a class are treated alike.

Diffserv Traffic Classification and Conditioning

Figure 13.34 provides a logical view of the classification and marking function within the edge router. Packets arriving to the edge router are first classified. The classifier selects packets based on the values of one or more packet header fields (for example, source address, destination address, source port, destination port, and protocol ID) and steers the packet to the appropriate marking function. A packet's mark is carried within the DS field [RFC 3260] in the IPv4 or IPv6 packet header. The definition of the DS field is intended to supersede the earlier definitions of the IPv4 type of service field and the IPv6 traffic class fields that we discussed in Chapter 10.

In some cases, an end user may have agreed to limit its packet-sending rate to conform to a declared **traffic profile**. The traffic profile might contain a limit on the peak rate, as well as the burstiness of the packet flow, as we saw in Section 13.7 with the leaky bucket mechanism. As long as the user sends packets into the network in a way that conforms to the negotiated traffic profile, the packets receive their priority marking and are forwarded along their route to the destination. On the other hand, if the traffic profile is violated, out-of-profile packets might be marked differently, might be shaped (for example, delayed so that a maximum rate constraint would be observed), or might be dropped at the network edge. The role of the **metering function,** shown in Figure 13.34, is to compare the incoming packet flow with the negotiated traffic profile and to determine whether a packet is within the negotiated traffic profile. The actual decision about whether to immediately remark, forward, delay, or drop a packet is a policy issue determined by network administrator and is *not* specified in the Diffserv architecture.

Per-Hop Behaviors

So far, we have focused on the edge functions in the Diffserv architecture. The second key component of the Diffserv architecture involves the **per-hop behavior** (PHB) performed by Diffserv-capable routers. PHB is rather cryptically, but carefully, defined as "a description of the externally observable forwarding behavior of a Diffserv node applied to a particular Diffserv behavior aggregate" [RFC 2475]. Digging a little deeper into this definition, we can see several important considerations embedded within it:

- A PHB can result in different classes of traffic receiving different performance (that is, different externally observable forwarding behaviors).

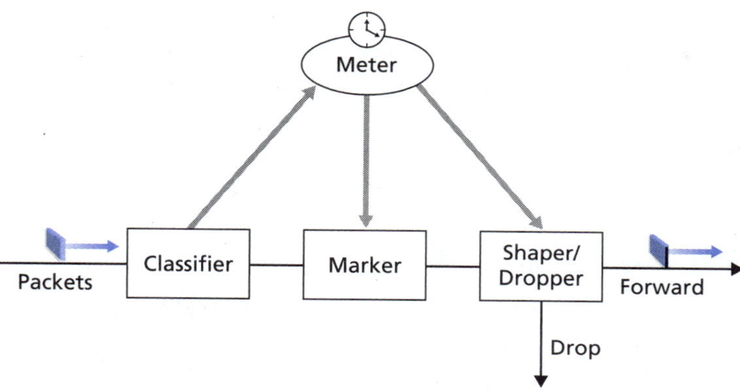

Figure 13.34 ♦ Logical view of packet classification and traffic conditioning at the end router

- While a PHB defines differences in performance (behavior) among classes, it does not mandate any particular mechanism for achieving these behaviors. As long as the externally observable performance criteria are met, any implementation mechanism and any buffer/bandwidth allocation policy can be used. For example, a PHB would not require that a particular packet-queuing discipline, for example, a priority queue versus a weighted fair queuing queue versus a first-come-first-served queue, be used to achieve a particular behavior. The PHB is the end, to which resource allocation and implementation mechanisms are the means.
- Differences in performance must be observable and hence measurable.

Currently, two PHBs have been defined: an expedited forwarding (EF) PHB [RFC 3246] and an assured forwarding (AF) PHB [RFC 2597].

- The **expedited forwarding** PHB specifies that the departure rate of a class of traffic from a router must equal or exceed a configured rate. That is, during any interval of time, the class of traffic can be guaranteed to receive enough bandwidth so that the output rate of the traffic equals or exceeds this minimum configured rate. Note that the EF per-hop behavior implies some form of isolation among traffic classes, as this guarantee is made *independently* of the traffic intensity of any other classes that are arriving to a router. Thus, even if the other classes of traffic are overwhelming router and link resources, enough of those resources must still be made available to the class to ensure that it receives its minimum-rate guarantee. EF thus provides a class with the simple *abstraction* of a link with a minimum guaranteed link bandwidth.
- The **assured forwarding** PHB is more complex. AF divides traffic into four classes, where each AF class is guaranteed to be provided with some minimum

amount of bandwidth and buffering. Within each class, packets are further partitioned into one of three drop preference categories. When congestion occurs within an AF class, a router can then discard (drop) packets based on their drop preference values. See [RFC 2597] for details. By varying the amount of resources allocated to each class, an ISP can provide different levels of performance to the different AF traffic classes.

Intserv and Diffserv Retrospective

For the past 20 years there have been numerous unsuccessful attempts to introduce QoS into packet-switched networks. The various attempts have failed so far more because of economic and legacy reasons than because of technical reasons. These attempts include end-to-end ATM networks and TCP/IP networks deploying Intserv or Diffserv. Will these efforts be successful, or at least partially successful in the long term? Let's take a look at a few of the issues involved.

So far we have assumed that Intserv or Diffserv are deployed within a single administrative domain. The more typical case is where an end-to-end service must be fashioned from multiple ISPs sitting between communicating end systems. In order to provide end-to-end Intserv or Diffserv service, all the ISPs between the end systems not only must provide this service, but most also cooperate and make settlements in order to offer end customers true end-end service. Without this kind of cooperation, ISPs directly selling Intserv or Diffserv service to customers will find themselves repeatedly saying: "Yes, we know you paid extra, but we don't have a service agreement with one of our higher-tier ISPs. I'm sorry that there were many gaps in your voice-over-IP call!"

Another concern with these advanced services is that they need to police and possibly shape traffic, which may turn out to be complex and costly. One also needs to bill the service differently, most likely by volume rather than with a fixed monthly fee as currently done by most ISPs—another costly requirement for the ISP. Finally, if Intserv or Diffserv were actually in place and the network ran at only moderate load, most of the time there would be no perceived difference between a best-effort service and an Intserv/Diffserv service. Indeed, today, end-to-end delay is usually dominated by access rates and router hops rather than by queuing delays in the routers. Imagine the unhappy Intserv/Diffserv customer who has paid for premium service but finds that the best-effort service being provided to others almost always has the same performance as premium service!

13.9 RSVP

We learned in Section 13.8 that in order for a network to provide QoS guarantees, there must be a signaling protocol that allows applications running in hosts to reserve resources in the Internet. The resource ReSerVation Protocol (RSVP) [RFC 2205; Zhang 1993] is such a signaling protocol for the Internet. When people talk about *resources* in the Internet context, they usually mean link bandwidth and router buffers. To keep the discussion concrete and focused, however, we'll assume that the word *resource* is synonymous with *bandwidth*. We note that RSVP has been extended and used as a signaling protocol in other circumstances, perhaps most notably in the form of RSVP-TE [RFC 3209] for MPLS signaling, as discussed in Section 11.8.2. Our focus here, however, will be on the use of RSVP for resource (bandwidth) reservation.

13.9.1 The Essence of RSVP

The RSVP protocol allows applications to reserve bandwidth for their data flows. It is used by a host, on the behalf of an application data flow, to request a specific amount of bandwidth from the network. RSVP is also used by the routers to forward bandwidth reservation requests. To implement RSVP, RSVP software must be present in the receivers, senders, and routers. The two principal characteristics of RSVP are:

1. It provides **reservations for bandwidth in multicast trees** (unicast is handled as a degenerate case of multicast).
2. It is **receiver-oriented;** that is, the receiver of a data flow initiates and maintains the resource reservation used for that flow.

These two characteristics are illustrated in Figure 13.35. The diagram shows a multicast tree with data flowing from the top of the tree to hosts at the bottom of the tree. Although data originates from the sender, the reservation messages originate from the receivers. When a router forwards a reservation message upstream toward the sender, the router may merge the reservation message with other reservation messages arriving from downstream.

Before discussing RSVP in greater detail, we need to consider the notion of a **session.** As with RTP, a session can consist of multiple multicast data flows. Each sender in a session is the source of one or more data flows; for example, a sender might be the source of a video data flow and an audio data flow. Each data flow in a session has the same multicast address. To keep the discussion concrete, we assume that routers and hosts identify the session to which a packet belongs by the packet's multicast address. This assumption is somewhat restrictive; the actual RSVP specification allows for more general methods to identify a session. Within a session, the data flow to which a packet belongs also needs to be identified. This could be done, for example, with the flow identifier field in IPv6.

What RSVP Is Not

We emphasize that the RSVP standard [RFC 2205] does not specify *how* the network provides the reserved bandwidth to the data flows. It is merely a protocol that

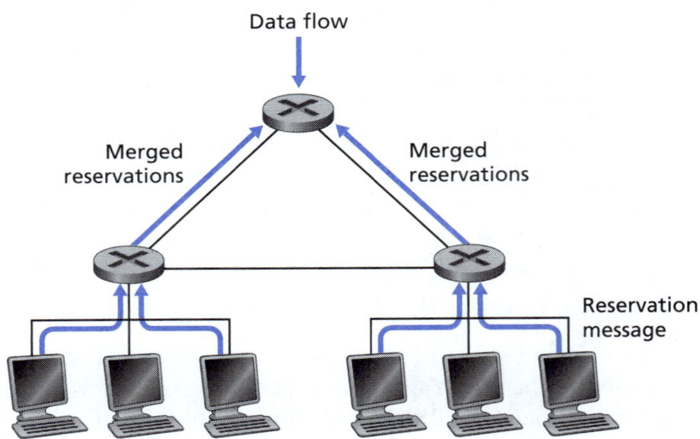

Figure 13.35 ♦ RSVP: multicast- and receiver-oriented

allows the applications to reserve the necessary link bandwidth. Once the reservations are in place, it is up to the routers in the Internet to actually provide the reserved bandwidth to the data flows. This provisioning would likely be done with the scheduling mechanisms (priority scheduling, weighted fair queuing, etc.) discussed in Section 13.7.

It is also important to understand that RSVP is not a routing protocol—it does not determine the links in which the reservations are to be made. Instead it depends on an underlying routing protocol (unicast or multicast) to determine the routes for the flows. Once the routes are in place, RSVP can be used to reserve bandwidth in the links along these routes. (We shall see shortly that when a route changes, RSVP re-reserves resources.) Once the reservations are in place, the routers' packet schedulers must actually provide the reserved bandwidth to the data flows. Thus, RSVP is only one piece—albeit an important piece—in the QoS guarantee puzzle.

RSVP is sometimes referred to as a *signaling protocol.* By this it is meant that RSVP is a protocol that allows hosts to establish and tear down reservations for data flows. The term *signaling protocol* comes from the jargon of the circuit-switched telephony community.

Heterogeneous Receivers

Consider a network in which some receivers can receive a flow at 28.8 kbps, others at 128 kbps, and yet others at 10 Mbps or higher. This heterogeneity of the receivers poses an interesting question. If a sender is multicasting a video to a group of heterogeneous receivers, should the sender encode the video for low quality at 28.8 kbps, for medium quality at 128 kbps, or for high quality at 10 Mbps? If the video is encoded at 10 Mbps, then only the users with 10 Mbps access will be able to watch the video. On the other hand, if the video is encoded at 28.8 kbps, then the 10 Mbps users will have to see a low-quality image when they know they can see something much better.

To resolve this dilemma it is often suggested that video and audio be encoded in layers. For example, a video might be encoded into two layers: a base layer and an enhancement layer. The base layer could have a rate of 20 kbps, whereas the enhancement layer could have a rate of 100 kbps; in this manner receivers with 28.8 kbps access could receive the low-quality base-layer image, and receivers with 128 kbps could receive both layers to construct a high-quality image.

We note that the sender does not need to know the receiving rates of all the receivers. It only needs to know the maximum rate of all its receivers. The sender encodes the video or audio into multiple layers and sends all the layers up to the maximum rate into multicast tree. The receivers pick out the layers that are appropriate for their receiving rates. In order to not excessively waste bandwidth in the network's links, the heterogeneous receivers must communicate to the network the rates they can handle. We'll see that RSVP gives foremost attention to the issue of reserving resources for heterogeneous receivers.

13.9.2 A Few Simple Examples

Let's first describe RSVP in the context of a concrete one-to-many multicast example. Suppose there is a source that is transmitting the video of a major sporting event over the Internet. This session has been assigned a multicast address, and the source stamps all of its outgoing packets with this multicast address. Also suppose that an underlying multicast routing protocol has established a multicast tree from the sender to four receivers as shown in Figure 13.36; the numbers next to the receivers are the rates at which the receivers want to receive data. Let us also assume that the video is layered and encoded to accommodate this heterogeneity of receiver rates.

Roughly speaking, RSVP operates in a two-pass manner, as illustrated in the following simple example. A transmitting source will advertise its content by sending **RSVP path messages** through a multicast tree, indicating the bandwidth required for the content, the soft-state timeout interval (see sidebar on Principle of Soft State), and information about the upstream path to the sender. Each receiver sends an **RSVP reservation message** upstream into the multicast tree. This reservation message specifies the rate at which the receiver would like to receive the data from the source. When the reservation message reaches a router, the router adjusts its packet scheduler to accommodate the reservation. It then sends a reservation upstream. The amount of bandwidth reserved upstream from the router depends on the bandwidths reserved downstream. In the example in Figure 13.36, receivers R1, R2, R3, and R4 reserve 20 kbps, 100 kbps, 3 Mbps, and 3 Mbps, respectively. Thus router D's downstream receivers request a maximum of 3 Mbps. For this one-to-many transmission, router D sends a reservation message to router B requesting that

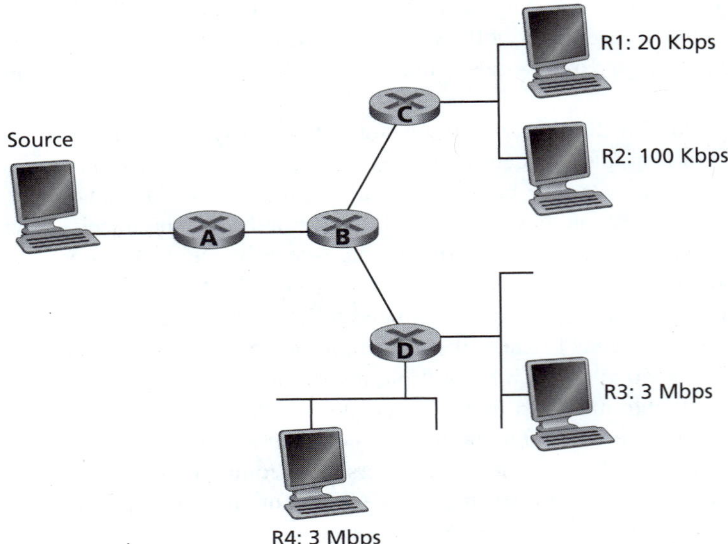

Figure 13.36 ♦ An RSVP example

router B reserve 3 Mbps on the link between the two routers. Note that only 3 Mbps are reserved and not 3 + 3 = 6 Mbps; this is because receivers R3 and R4 are watching the same sporting event, so their reservations may be merged. Similarly, router C requests that router B reserve 100 kbps on the link between routers B and C; the layered encoding ensures that receiver R1's 20 kbps stream is included in the 100 kbps stream. Once router B receives the reservation message from its downstream routers and passes the reservations to its schedulers, it sends a new reservation message to its upstream router, router A. This message reserves 3 Mbps of bandwidth on the link from router A to router B, which is again the maximum of the downstream reservations.

We see from this first example that RSVP is **receiver-oriented;** that is, the receiver of a data flow initiates and maintains the resource reservation used for that flow. Note that each router receives a reservation message from each of its downstream links in the multicast tree and sends only one reservation message into its upstream link.

As another example, suppose that four persons are participating in a video conference, as shown in Figure 13.37. Each person has three windows open on her computer to look at the other three persons. Suppose that the underlying routing protocol has established the multicast tree among the four hosts. Finally, suppose each person wants to see each of the videos at 3 Mbps. Then on each of the links in this

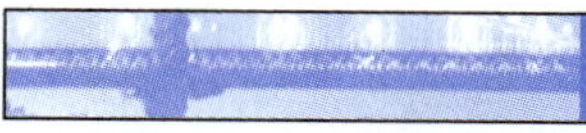

PRINCIPLES IN PRACTICE

THE PRINCIPLE OF SOFT STATE

RSVP is used to install state (bandwidth reservations) in routers, and is known as a *soft-state* protocol. Broadly speaking, we associate the term *soft-state* with signaling approaches in which installed state times out (and is removed) unless periodically refreshed by the receipt of a signaling message (typically from the entity that initially installed the state) indicating that the state should continue to remain installed. Since unrefreshed state will eventually time out, soft-state signaling requires neither explicit state removal nor a procedure to remove orphaned state should the state-installer crash. Similarly, since state installation and refresh messages will be followed by subsequent periodic refresh messages, reliable signaling is not required. The term *soft state* was coined by Clark [Clark 1988], who described the notion of periodic state refresh messages being sent by an end system, and suggested that with such refresh messages, state could be lost in a crash and then automatically restored by subsequent refresh messages—all transparently to the end system and without invoking any explicit crash-recovery procedures:

> ". . . the state information would not be critical in maintaining the desired type of service associated with the flow. Instead, that type of service would be enforced by the end points, which would periodically send messages to ensure that the proper type of service was being associated with the flow. In this way, the state information associated with the flow could be lost in a crash without permanent disruption of the service features being used. I call this concept "soft state," and it may very well permit us to achieve our primary goals of survivability and flexibility . . ."

Roughly speaking, then, the essence of a soft-state approach is the use of best-effort periodic state-installation/refresh by the state installer and state-removal-by-timeout at the state-holder. Soft state approaches have been taken in numerous protocols, including RSVP , PIM (Section 10.7) , SIP (Section 13.4), and IGMP (Section 10.7), and in forwarding tables in transparent bridges (Section 11.6).

Hard-state signaling takes the converse approach to soft state—installed state remains installed unless explicitly removed by the receipt of a state-teardown message from the state-installer. Since the state remains installed unless explicitly removed, hard-state signaling requires a mechanism to remove an orphaned state that remains after the state-installer has crashed or departed without removing the state. Similarly, since state installation and removal are performed only once (and without state refresh or state timeout), it is important for the state-installer to know when the state has been installed or removed. Reliable (rather than best-effort) signaling protocols are thus typically associated with hard-state protocols. Roughly speaking, then, the essence of a hard-state approach is the reliable and explicit installation and removal of state information. Hard-state approaches have been taken in protocols such as ST-II [Partridge 1992, RFC 1190] and Q.2931 [ITU-T Q.2931 1994].

RSVP has provided for explicit (although optional) removal of reservations since its conception.

(*continues*)

ACK-based reliable signaling was introduced as an extension to RSVP in [RFC 2961] and was also suggested in [Pan 1997]. RSVP has thus optionally adopted some elements of a hard-state signaling approach. For a discussion and comparison of soft-state versus hard-state protocols, see [Ji 2003].

multicast tree, RSVP would reserve 9 Mbps in one direction and 3 Mbps in the other direction. Note that RSVP does not merge reservations in this example, as each person wants to receive three distinct streams.

Now consider an audio conference among the same four persons over the same multicast tree. Suppose b bps are needed for an isolated audio stream. Because in an audio conference it is rare that more than two persons speak at the same time, it is not necessary to reserve $3 \cdot b$ bps into each receiver; $2 \cdot b$ should suffice. Thus, in this last application we can conserve bandwidth by merging reservations.

Call Admission

Just as a restaurant manager should not accept reservations for more tables than the restaurant has, the amount of bandwidth on a link that a router reserves should not exceed the link's capacity. Thus whenever a router receives a new reservation message, it must first determine if its downstream links on the multicast tree can accommodate the reservation. This **admission test** is performed whenever a router receives

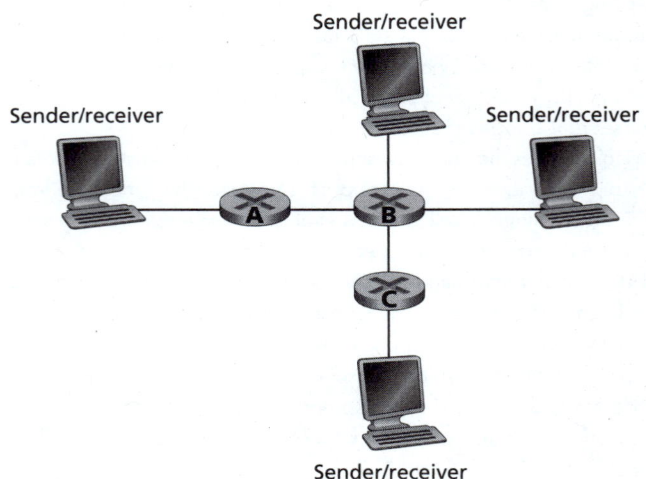

Figure 13.37 ♦ An RSVP video conference example

a reservation message. If the admission test fails, the router rejects the reservation and returns an error message to the appropriate receiver(s).

RSVP does not define the admission test, but it assumes that the routers perform such a test and that RSVP can interact with the test. For addtional material on call admission, you are encouraged to consult [Jamin 1996; Breslau 2000; Roberts 2004].

13.10 Summary

Multimedia networking is one of the most exciting (yet still-to-be-fully-realized) developments in the Internet today. People throughout the world are spending less time in front of their radios and televisions, and are instead turning to the Internet to receive audio and video emissions, both live and prerecorded. As high-speed access penetrates more residences, this trend will continue—couch potatoes throughout the world will access their favorite video programs through the Internet rather than through the traditional broadcast distribution channels. In addition to audio and video distribution, the Internet is also being used to transport phone calls. In fact, over the next 10 years the Internet may render the traditional circuit-switched telephone system nearly obsolete in many countries. The Internet not only will provide phone service for less money, but will also provide numerous value-added services, such as video conferencing, online directory services, voice messaging services, and Web integration.

In Section 13.1 we classified multimedia applications into three categories: streaming stored audio and video, one-to-many transmission of real-time audio and video, and real-time interactive audio and video. We emphasized that multimedia applications are delay-sensitive and loss-tolerant—characteristics that are very different from static-content applications that are delay-tolerant and loss-intolerant. We also discussed some of the hurdles that today's best-effort Internet places before multimedia applications. We surveyed several proposals to overcome these hurdles, including simply improving the existing networking infrastructure (by adding more bandwidth, more network caches, and more CDN nodes, and by deploying multicast), adding functionality to the Internet so that applications can reserve end-to-end resources (and so that the network can honor these reservations), and finally, introducing service classes to provide service differentiation.

In Sections 13.2–13.4 we examined architectures and mechanisms for multimedia networking in a best-effort network. In Section 13.2 we surveyed several architectures for streaming stored audio and video. We discussed user interaction—such as pause/resume, repositioning, and visual fast-forward—and provided an introduction to RTSP, a protocol that provides client-server interaction to streaming applications. In Section 13.3 we examined how interactive real-time applications can be designed to run over a best-effort network. We saw how a combination of client buffers, packet sequence numbers, and timestamps can greatly alleviate the effects of network-induced jitter. In Section 13.4 we explored protocols for real-time interactive multimedia, including RTP, SIP, and H.323. In Section 13.5 we investigated how content distribution networks bring multimedia content to users.

Sections 13.6–13.9 looked at how the Internet can evolve to provide guaranteed QoS to its applications. In Section 13.6 we identified several principles for providing QoS to multimedia applications. These principles include packet marking and classification, isolation of packet flows, efficient use of resources, and call admission. In Section 13.8 we surveyed a variety of scheduling policies and policing mechanisms that can provide the foundation of a QoS networking architecture. The scheduling policies include priority scheduling, round robin scheduling, and weighted fair queuing. We then explored the leaky bucket as a policing mechanism. In Section 13.9 we showed how these principles and mechanisms have led to the definitions of new Intserv and Diffserv standards for providing QoS in the Internet, and an Internet signaling protocol for reservations, namely, RSVP.

Now that we have finished our study of multimedia networking, it is time to move on to another exciting topic: network security. Recent advances in multimedia networking may move the distribution of audio and video information to the Internet. As we'll see in the next chapter, recent advances in network security may well help move the majority of economic transactions to the Internet.

Homework Problems and Questions

Chapter 13 Review Questions

SECTIONS 13.1–13.2

1. What is meant by interactivity for streaming stored audio/video? What is meant by interactivity for real-time interactive audio/video?
2. Three camps were discussed for improving the Internet so that it better supports multimedia applications. Briefly summarize the views of each camp. In which camp do you belong?
3. Figures 13.1, 13.2, and 13.3 present three schemes for streaming stored media. What are the advantages and disadvantages of each scheme?

SECTIONS 13.3–13.4

4. What is the difference between end-to-end delay and packet jitter? What are the causes of packet jitter?
5. Why is a packet that is received after its scheduled playout time considered lost?
6. Section 13.3 describes two FEC schemes. Briefly summarize them. Both schemes increase the transmission rate of the stream by adding overhead. Does interleaving also increase the transmission rate?

7. How are different RTP streams in different sessions identified by a receiver? How are different streams from within the same session identified? How are RTP and RTPC packets (as part of the same session) distinguished?
8. Three RTCP packet types are described in Section 13.4. Briefly summarize the information contained in each of these packet types.

SECTIONS 13.6–13.9

9. In Section 13.6, we discussed nonpreemptive priority queuing. What would be preemptive priority queuing? Does preemptive priority queuing make sense for computer networks?
10. Give an example of a scheduling discipline that is *not* work conserving.
11. What are some of the difficulties associated with the Intserv model and per-flow reservation of resources?

Problems

1. Surf the Web and find two products for streaming stored audio and/or video. For each product, determine:
   a. Whether meta files are used
   b. Whether the audio/video is sent over UDP or TCP
   c. Whether RTP is used
   d. Whether RTSP is used
2. Write a poem, a short story, a description of a recent vacation, or any other piece that takes two to five minutes to recite. Recite and record your piece. Convert your recording to one of the RealNetworks or Microsoft audio formats using one of the free encoders. Upload the file to the same server that holds your personal homepage. Also upload the corresponding meta file to the server. Finally, create a link from your homepage to the meta file.
3. Consider the client buffer shown in Figure 13.4. Suppose that the streaming system uses the third option; that is, the server pushes the media into the socket as quickly as possible. Suppose the available TCP bandwidth >> d most of the time. Also suppose that the client buffer can hold only about one-third of the media. Describe how $x(t)$ and the contents of the client buffer will evolve over time.
4. Are the TCP receive buffer and the media player's client buffer the same thing? If not, how do they interact?
5. In the Internet phone example in Section 13.3, let h be the total number of header bytes added to each chunk, including UDP and IP header.

a. Assuming an IP datagram is emitted every 20 msecs, find the transmission rate in bits per second for the datagrams generated by one side of this application.

b. What is a typical value of h when RTP is used?

6. Consider the procedure described in Section 13.3 for estimating average delay d_i. Suppose that $u = 0.1$. Let $r_1 - t_1$ be the most recent sample delay, let $r_2 - t_2$ be the next most recent sample delay, and so on.

   a. For a given audio application suppose four packets have arrived at the receiver with sample delays $r_4 - t_4$, $r_3 - t_3$, $r_2 - t_2$, and $r_1 - t_1$. Express the estimate of delay d in terms of the four samples.

   b. Generalize your formula for n sample delays.

   For the formula in Part b, let n approach infinity and give the resulting formula. Comment on why this averaging procedure is called an exponential moving average.

7. Repeat Parts a and b in Question 6 for the estimate of average delay deviation.

8. For the Internet phone example in Section 13.3, we introduced an online procedure (exponential moving average) for estimating delay. In this problem we will examine an alternative procedure. Let t_i be the timestamp of the ith packet received; let r_i be the time at which the ith packet is received. Let d_n be our estimate of average delay after receiving the nth packet. After the first packet is received, we set the delay estimate equal to $d_1 = r_1 - t_1$.

   a. Suppose that we would like $d_n = (r_1 - t_1 + r_2 - t_2 + \ldots + r_n - t_n)/n$ for all n. Give a recursive formula for d_n in terms of d_{n-1}, r_n, and t_n.

   b. Describe why for Internet telephony, the delay estimate described in Section 13.3 is more appropriate than the delay estimate outlined in Part a.

9. Compare the procedure described in Section 13.3 for estimating average delay with the procedure for estimating round-trip time. What do the procedures have in common? How are they different?

10. Consider the adaptive playout strategy described in Section 13.3.

    a. How can two successive packets received at the destination have time-stamps that differ by more than 20 msecs when the two packets belong to the same talk spurt?

    b. How can the receiver use sequence numbers to determine whether a packet is the first packet in a talk spurt? Be specific.

11. Recall the two FEC schemes for Internet phone described in Section 13.3. Suppose the first scheme generates a redundant chunk for every four original chunks. Suppose the second scheme uses a low-bit rate encoding whose transmission rate is 25 percent of the transmission rate of the nominal stream.

    a. How much additional bandwidth does each scheme require? How much playback delay does each scheme add?

b. How do the two schemes perform if the first packet is lost in every group of five packets? Which scheme will have better audio quality?

c. How do the two schemes perform if the first packet is lost in every group of two packets? Which scheme will have better audio quality?

12. How is the interarrival time jitter calculated in the RTCP reception report? (*Hint*: Read the RTP RFC.)

13. a. Suppose we send into the Internet two IP datagrams, each carrying a different UDP segment. The first datagram has source IP address A1, destination IP address B, source port P1, and destination port T. The second datagram has source IP address A2, destination IP address B, source port P2, and destination port T. Suppose that A1 is different from A2 and P1 is different from P2. Assuming that both datagrams reach their final destination, will the two UDP datagrams be received by the same socket? Why or why not?

    b. Suppose Alice, Bob, and Claire want to have an audio conference call using SIP and RTP. For Alice to send and receive RTP packets to and from Bob and Claire, is only one UDP socket sufficient (in addition to the socket needed for the SIP messages)? If yes, then how does Alice's SIP client distinguish between the RTP packets received from Bob and Claire?

14. Consider an RTP session consisting of four users, all of which are sending and receiving RTP packets into the same multicast address. Each user sends video at 100 kbps.

    a. RTCP will limit its traffic to what rate?

    b. A particular receiver will be allocated how much RTCP bandwidth?

    c. A particular sender will be allocated how much RTCP bandwidth?

15. a. How is RTSP similar to HTTP? Does RTSP have methods? Can HTTP be used to request a stream?

    b. How is RTSP different from HTTP? For example, is HTTP in-band or out-of-band? Does RTSP maintain state information about the client (consider the pause/resume function)?

16. What are the current Microsoft products for real-time audio/video conferencing. Do these products use any of the protocols discussed in this chapter (for example, RTP or RTSP)?

17. True or false:

    a. If stored video is streamed directly from a Web server to a media player, then the application is using TCP as the underlying transport protocol.

    b. When using RTP, it is possible for a sender to change encoding in the middle of a session.

    c. All applications that use RTP must use port 87.

d. Suppose an RTP session has a separate audio and video stream for each sender. Then the audio and video streams use the same SSRC.

e. In differentiated services, while per-hop behavior defines differences in performance among classes, it does not mandate any particular mechanism for achieving these performances.

f. Suppose Alice wants to establish an SIP session with Bob. In her INVITE message she includes the line: m=audio 48753 RTP/AVP 3 (AVP 3 denotes GSM audio). Alice has therefore indicated in this message that she wishes to send GSM audio.

g. Referring to the preceding statement, Alice has indicated in her INVITE message that she will send audio to port 48753.

h. SIP messages are typically sent between SIP entities using a default SIP port number.

i. In order to maintain registration, SIP clients must periodically send REGISTER messages.

j. SIP mandates that all SIP clients support G.711 audio encoding.

18. Suppose that the WFQ scheduling policy is applied to a buffer that supports three classes, and suppose the weights are 0.5, 0.25, and 0.25 for the three classes.

    a. Suppose that each class has a large number of packets in the buffer. In what sequence might the three classes be served in order to achieve the WFQ weights? (For round robin scheduling, a natural sequence is 123123123 . . .).

    b. Suppose that classes 1 and 2 have a large number of packets in the buffer, and there are no class 3 packets in the buffer. In what sequence might the three classes be served in to achieve the WFQ weights?

19. Consider the leaky bucket policer (discussed in Section 13.7) that polices the average rate and burst size of a packet flow. We now want to police the peak rate, *p,* as well. Show how the output of this leaky bucket policer can be fed into a second leaky bucket policer so that the two leaky buckets in series police the average rate, peak rate, and burst size. Be sure to give the bucket size and token generation rate for the second policer.

20. A packet flow is said to conform to a leaky bucket specification (r,b) with burst size b and average rate r if the number of packets that arrive to the leaky bucket is less than $rt + b$ packets in every interval of time of length t for all t. Will a packet flow that conforms to a leaky bucket specification (r,b) ever have to wait at a leaky bucket policer with parameters r and b? Justify your answer.

21. Show that as long as $r_1 < R\, w_1/(\Sigma\, w_j)$, then d_{max} is indeed the maximum delay that any packet in flow 1 will ever experience in the WFQ queue.

Discussion Questions

1. How can a host use RTCP feedback information to determine whether problems are local, regional, or global?
2. Do you think it is better to stream stored audio/video on top of TCP or UDP?
3. Write a report on Cisco's SIP products.
4. Can the problem of providing QoS guarantees be solved simply by throwing enough bandwidth at the problem, that is, by upgrading all link capacities so that bandwidth limitations are no longer a concern?
5. An interesting emerging market is using Internet phone and a company's high-speed LAN to replace the same company's PBX (private branch exchange). Write a one-page report on this issue. Cover the following questions in your report:
   a. What is a traditional PBX? Who would use it?
   b. Consider a call between a user in the company and another user out of the company who is connected to the traditional telephone network. What sort of technology is needed at the interface between the LAN and the traditional telephone network?
   c. In addition to Internet phone software and the interface of Part b, what else is needed to replace the PBX?
6. Consider the four principles for providing QoS support in Section 13.6. Describe the circumstances, if any, under which each of these principles need not be followed.

Programming Assignment

In this lab you will implement a streaming video server and client. The client will use the real-time streaming protocol (RTSP) to control the actions of the server. The server will use the real-time protocol (RTP) to packetize the video for transport over UDP.

You will be given Java code that partially implements RTSP and RTP at the client and server. Your job will be to complete both the client and server code. When you are finished, you will have created a client-server application that does the following:

- The client sends SETUP, PLAY, PAUSE, and TEARDOWN RTSP commands, and the server responds to the commands.

- When the server is in the playing state, it periodically grabs a stored JPEG frame, packetizes the frame with RTP, and sends the RTP packet into a UDP socket.
- The client receives the RTP packets, removes the JPEG frames, decompresses the frames, and renders the frames on the client's monitor.

The code you will be given implements the RTSP protocol in the server and the RTP depacketization in the client. The code also takes care of displaying the transmitted video. You will need to implement RTSP in the client and RTP server.

This programming assignment will significantly enhance the student's understanding of RTP, RTSP, and streaming video. It is highly recommended. The assignment also suggests a number of optional exercises, including implementing the RTSP DESCRIBE command at both client and server. You can find full details of the assignment, as well as important snippets of Java code, at the Web site http://www.awl.com/kurose-ross.

AN INTERVIEW WITH...

Henning Schulzrinne

Henning Schulzrinne is an associate professor and head of the Internet Real-Time Laboratory at Columbia University. He is the co-author of RTSP, RTP, and SIP—key protocols for audio and video communication over the Internet. Henning received his BS in electrical and industrial engineering at Darmstadt University in Germany, his MS in electrical and computer engineering at the University of Cincinnati, and his PhD in electrical engineering at the University of Massachusetts, Amherst.

What made you decide to specialize in multimedia networking?

This happened almost by accident. As a PhD student, I got involved with DARTnet, an experimental network spanning the United States with T1 lines. DARTnet was used as a proving ground for multicast and Internet real-time tools. That led me to write my first audio tool, NeVoT. Through some of the DARTnet participants, I became involved in the IETF, in the then-nascent Audio Video Transport working group. This group later ended up standardizing RTP.

What was your first job in the computer industry? What did it entail?

My first job in the computer industry was soldering together an Altair computer kit when I was a high school student in Livermore, California. Back in Germany, I started a little consulting company that devised an address management program for a travel agency—storing data on cassette tapes for our TRS-80 and using an IBM Selectric typewriter with a home-brew hardware interface as a printer.

My first real job was with AT&T Bell Laboratories, developing a network emulator for constructing experimental networks in a lab environment.

What are the goals of the Internet Real-Time Lab?

Our goal is to provide pieces for the infrastructure of the Internet as the single future communications platform. This includes the development of protocols, such as SIP and RTSP for signaling or RNAP, YESSIR, and BGRP, for resource reservation, the measurement of performance of Internet protocols and applications, and development of algorithms to increase the quality of service in the Internet. We build prototype applications, such as Internet telephony servers and clients, and have dabbled in hardware, building our own Internet phone.

Recently, we have started to investigate how multimedia and other network services can be located across the Internet. Also, wireless LAN technology offers new opportunities for distributing multimedia content via local replication rather than large-scale peer-to-peer networks or content distribution networks.

What is your vision for the future of multimedia networking?

We are now in a transition phase, just a few years shy of when IP will be the universal platform for multimedia services. We expect radio, telephone, and TV to be up even during snowstorms and earthquakes, so when the Internet takes over the role of these dedicated networks, users will expect the same level of reliability.

To some extent, networking research faces the problem that operating system research has had for a number of years, even more so. While it is still possible to run "boutique" research operating systems in small communities, running a separate network largely defeats its purpose. We will have to learn to design network technologies for an interconnection of competing carriers, with lots of ignorant or malicious end-users.

Visible advances in multimedia networks will largely be driven by factors outside the field itself, namely advances in access and backbone speeds as well as cheap computing power.

Why does SIP have a promising future?

As the current wireless network upgrade to 3G networks proceeds, there is the hope of a single multimedia signaling mechanism spanning all types of networks, from cable modems, to corporate telephone networks and public wireless networks. Together with software radios, this will make it possible in the future that a single device can be used on a home network, as a cordless BlueTooth phone, in a corporate network via 802.11 and in the wide area via 3G networks. Even before we have such a single universal wireless device, the personal mobility mechanisms make it possible to hide the differences between networks. One identifier becomes the universal means of reaching a person, rather than remembering or passing around half a dozen technology- or location-specific telephone numbers.

SIP also breaks apart the provision of voice (bit) transport from voice services. It now becomes technically possible to break apart the local telephone monopoly, where one company provides neutral bit transport, while others provide IP "dial tone" and the classical telephone services, such as gateways, call forwarding, and caller ID.

Beyond multimedia signaling, SIP offers a new service that has been missing in the Internet: event notification. We have approximated such services with HTTP kludges and e-mail, but this was never very satisfactory. Since events are a common abstraction for distributed systems, this may simplify the construction of new services.

Do you have any advice for students entering the networking field?

Networking is almost a classical bridging discipline. It draws from electrical engineering, computer science, operations research, and other disciplines. Thus, networking researchers have to be familiar with subjects well outside their core area.

Work in networks can be immensely satisfying since it is about allowing people to communicate and exchange ideas, one of the essentials of being human. Many areas of engineering have reached a performance plateau; cars, trains, and planes still pretty much work the same as they did 20 or more years ago and probably won't run much faster in another 20. The major change will be in the ability to have these entities communicate and thus improve their performance by making them safer and avoiding gridlock.

APPENDICES

Appendix A

The ISO-OSI Model

The ISO-OSI model was introduced before you learned about the technical details of telecommunications; hence, the explanation about the purpose and functions of the layers of the OSI model was relatively simple. This appendix provides a somewhat more detailed and technical explanation of the functions of the seven layers.

Layer 1: Physical Link Layer Layer 1 defines the electrical standards and signaling required to make and break a connection on the physical link and to allow bit streams from terminals or computers to flow onto the network. It specifies the modem interface between the data terminal equipment and the line. For analog circuits, the most common interface is the V.24 or RS-232-C standard. The standard for the interface to digital circuits is X.21. The physical layer is concerned with voltage levels, current flows, and whether the transmission is simplex, half-duplex, or full-duplex. Besides the interface standards, the physical link layer defines how connections will be established and terminated. Other functions defined in this layer include monitoring channel signals, clocking on the channel, handling interrupts in the hardware, and informing the data link layer when a transmission has been completed.

Layer 1 is the only level of the architecture in which actual transmissions take place. Although we talk about layers 2 through 7 "communicating" with each other, it is important to remember that they must pass the information they wish to communicate down through the layers to layer 1 for transmission to the other correspondent in the communication.

Layer 2: Data Link Layer Layer 2 defines standards for structuring data into frames and sending the frames across the network. It is concerned with the following questions:

- How does a machine know where a frame of data starts and ends?
- How are transmission errors detected and corrected?
- How are polling and addressing handled?
- How are machines addressed?

The answers to these questions make up the data link protocol. The OSI protocol is High-Level Data Link Control (HDLC).

For LANs, the data link layer is divided into two sublayers: the media access control (MAC) layer to define access to the network (the two alternatives are CSMA and token techniques) and the logical link control (LLC), which defines the protocol, a subset of HDLC, for use on LANs.

It is important to know that the IEEE, which establishes the 802 standards for LANs, fully subscribes to the OSI architecture.

Layer 2 is normally located in the front-end processor (if one exists) or server at the host end of the circuit and in a remote cluster controller or intelligent terminal. Layer 2 must work closely with the modem to accomplish its work. Whereas modems ensure that bits are accurately sensed from the communications line at the receiving end, layer 2 groups the bits into characters for further processing.

Layer 2 is also responsible for checking the VRC, LRC, and CRC codes transmitted with the data, for acknowledging the receipt of good frames or blocks, and for requesting the retransmission of those that are in error. Another type of error that layer 2 handles can occur when data is received from the circuit faster than the receiver can handle it. When this happens, layer 2 signals the transmitter to either slow down or stop transmitting until further notice. This is called *pacing*.

Layer 3: Network Layer The primary functions of layer 3 are network addressing and routing. Layer 3 also generates acknowledgments that an entire message has been received correctly. When a message is received from layer 4 for transmission, layer 3 is responsible for breaking it into blocks or packets of a suitable size for transmission. In most packet switching networks, for example, the packet size might be 128 characters. Layer 3 assigns the correct destination address to the packet and determines how it should be routed through the network. Specifically, it decides on which communications circuit to send a packet or block.

At the receiving end, layer 3 reassembles the packets or blocks into messages before passing them up to layer 4. Layer 3 might receive a message from another computer that is not destined for its location. In that case, it turns the message around and sends it back down to level 2 for forwarding through the network to the ultimate destination. This situation occurs in multinode networks where some nodes relay data for others.

Over the past 30 years, countries and companies have established their own standards for layers 1 through 3 (without thinking of them as layers). Many networks have been implemented using these proprietary standards. Therefore, the changeover process to international standards is difficult and time-consuming, even if a country or company wants to make the change.

Layer 4: Transport Layer Layer 4 selects the route the transmission will take between two DTEs. A favorite analogy for layer 4 is to compare it to the postal system. A user mails a letter but does not know (or care) exactly how the letter is transported to its destination as long as the service is reliable. In a telecommunications network, layer 4 selects the network service to be used to transport the message when options exist. For example, if a computer has both leased lines and a packet switching network connected to it, layer 4 decides which of the two services should be used to transport a particular message. To a terminal or computer, layers 4, 3, 2, and 1 together provide the transportation service for the user's message.

Layer 4 also contains the capability to handle user addressing. At the transmitting station, this means that network addresses that are meaningful to the user, such as location codes, terminal names, or other mnemonic codes, are converted to addresses that are meaningful to the network software and hardware. These network addresses usually are binary numbers. On the receiving end, network addresses must be converted back to user addresses.

Another function of layer 4 is to control the flow of messages so that a fast computer cannot overrun a slow terminal. This flow control works in conjunction with the flow control at layer 2, but layer 4 is concerned with controlling entire messages, whereas layer 2 is concerned with controlling the flow of frames. Layer 4 could allow a message to be sent, but the individual frames that make up the message could be delayed by layer 2 because of slowdown signals that it had received from layer 2 at the receiving end.

Layer 4 also prevents the loss or duplication of entire messages. Whereas more detailed checks occur at lower levels to ensure that frames and blocks of data are received correctly, layer 4 must implement controls to ensure that entire messages are not lost and, if necessary, to request their retransmission.

Other functions of layer 4 include multiplexing several streams of messages from higher levels onto one physical circuit and adding appropriate headers to messages to be broadcast to many recipients.

The transport layer is sometimes implemented in the host computer and sometimes in the front-end processor when one exists, or in a higher-level protocol.

Layer 5: Session Layer A *session* is a temporary connection between machines or programs for an exchange of messages according to rules that have been agreed on for that exchange. The session is the first part of the communications process that is directly visible to the user. Users directly request the establishment of sessions between their terminals and computers when they begin the sign-on or log-on process.

Before a session can begin, the machines or programs must agree to the terms and conditions of the session, such as who transmits first, for how long, and so on. Clearly, there will be differences in these rules between interactive sessions and batch sessions and between terminals of different types. Given an appropriate terminal, there is no inherent reason why a user cannot have multiple sessions in progress simultaneously.

Layer 5 establishes, maintains, and breaks a session between two systems or users. If a session is unintentionally broken, session layer must reestablish it. Session layer also provides the ability for the user to abort a session. For example, the BREAK key or ESC key on the terminal may be used for this purpose.

The implementation of priorities for expediting some messages or traffic occurs in this layer, as do certain accounting functions concerning session duration. These are used to charge the user for network time.

The session layer is usually implemented in the host computer access method or server software.

Layer 6: Presentation Layer The presentation layer deals with the way data is formatted and presented to the user at the terminal at the receiving end of a connection. It also performs similar formatting at the transmitting end so that the data from a terminal is presented to the lower layers in a constant format for transmission. An application programmer on the host computer writes programs to talk to a standard virtual terminal, and the layer 6 software performs a transformation to meet the specifications of the real terminal in use. Screen formatting, such as matching the message to the number of characters per line and the number of lines per screen, would also be done.

Other functions that occur in layer 6 are code conversion, data compaction, and data encryption. With the exception of data encryption, which is often implemented in hardware, the rest of layer 6 is almost always performed by software in the host computer.

Layer 7: Application or User Layer Layer 7 is the application program or user that is doing the communicating. This is the layer at which data editing, file updating, or user thinking occurs. This layer is the source or ultimate receiver of data transmitted through the network.

A great deal of effort has been expended to define and standardize some common elements of applications that operate in layer 7. The activity has six major thrusts.

1. Common application service elements (CASE)—this work is aimed at defining standards for such things as log on and password identification as well as checkpoint, restart, and backup processes.
2. Job transfer and manipulation (JTM)—this defines standards for the transfer of batch jobs from one computer to another.
3. File transfer, access, and management (FTAM)—this work is aimed at defining standards for the transfer of files between systems and for providing record-level access to a file on another computer.
4. Message oriented interchange systems (MOTIS)—concerned with defining standards for interconnecting the world's many message exchange systems, this work is also known as the ITU-T X.400 standard.
5. Office document architecture/office document interchange facility (ODA/ODIF)—this work is aimed at providing standards to allow the transfer, edit, and return of documents across systems from multiple vendors.
6. Virtual terminal services (VTS)—this work is concerned with precise definition of the virtual terminal concept, including character, graphics, and image terminals, as well as hard-copy devices.

Telecommunications Trade-Offs

Throughout this book there have been many references to the trade-offs made in planning, designing, or operating a communications system. Trade-offs occur because there are alternate solutions to many communications problems and different ways to design products and provide services. In some cases, the trade-off requires that an absolute *either/or* decision be made. For example, either vendor A or vendor B will be selected to provide the front-end processor. There is no way to buy half of the FEP from one vendor and half from another. In most situations, however, an absolute choice does not have to be made between the alternatives. For example, a company might well decide to have some leased circuits and some switched circuits; it doesn't have to select only one type or the other.

The important thing is to be aware of the options that exist so that you can make a proper selection to solve a problem optimally. Knowledge is the key, for if you don't know that options exist and there are trade-offs to be made, you can't choose between the alternatives.

Many trade-offs are interrelated. For example, the choice of an asynchronous versus a synchronous protocol may be directly related to the choice of terminals to be used for the application. The use of a vendor's proprietary protocol can occur only if that vendor has been selected to provide communications products. Some trade-off decisions are primarily made by the company that is using the communications products. Others are determined by the company in combination with the vendor. Still others are primarily made by the vendors, typically when they are designing their products or services.

The following list itemizes many communications trade-offs and alternatives. Depending on the level of detail, such a list could go on for pages. The trade-offs included here are the most important ones faced by network managers and designers.

CUSTOMER TRADE-OFFS

Network

Mix of LAN and WAN technology, where appropriate
Ethernet versus token ring versus another technology
Type of wiring or cabling for a LAN
Brand of network operating system
Install and maintain the network with employees versus outsourcing the work

WAN Circuits

Private network versus public network
Private versus leased versus switched circuits
Two-wire versus four-wire circuits
Circuit speed versus cost
Point-to-point circuits versus multipoint circuits
Conditioned versus unconditioned circuits
Compressing versus not compressing data transmissions
Multiplexing versus concentrating versus inverse concentrating

Terminals

Intelligent versus smart versus dumb terminals
General-purpose terminal versus application-oriented terminal
VDT versus printing terminal

Applications

Voice mail versus text mail versus both
Teleconferencing versus travel
Encrypting versus not encrypting data
The level of reliability, availability, and responsiveness that is required versus the cost of providing it

Other Trade-Offs

- Custom software versus off-the-shelf programs
- Leasing versus buying hardware
- Vendor A versus vendor B
- Performing certain telecommunications services inside the company versus contracting them to outsiders

CUSTOMER-VENDOR TRADE-OFFS

- Architected versus nonarchitected communications approach
- Terrestrial versus satellite circuits
- Analog versus digital transmission
- Asynchronous versus synchronous transmission

VENDOR TRADE-OFFS

- Front-end processor versus direct connection of WAN circuits to a computer
- Hardware versus software implementation of certain functions
- Entering versus not entering a certain geographic market
- Providing versus not providing a certain telecommunications product or service

Appendix C

Telecommunications Periodicals and Newsletters

The rapid growth of the telecommunications industry in recent years has brought with it an explosion in the number of trade journals and specialized newsletters aimed at providing information to telecommunications professionals. This list contains information about the most widely read telecommunications publications.

Communications News. Published monthly by Nelson Publishing, 2504 N. Tamiami Trail, Nokomis, FL 34275. (941) 966-9521.

Communications Today. Published weekly by Phillips Business Information, Inc., 1201 Seven Locks Road, Suite 300, Potomac, MD 20854. (301) 424-3338.

Datacomm Advisor: IDC's Newsletter Covering Network Management—Products, Services, Applications. Published monthly by International Data Corporation, 5 Speen Street, Framingham, MA 01701. (508) 872-8200.

Internet Week. Published weekly by CMP Publications, Inc., 600 Community Drive, Manhasset, NY 11030. (516) 562-5000.

Network Magazine. Published monthly by CMP Publications, Inc., P.O. Box 2013, Skokie, IL 60076. (800) 577-5356.

Network Strategy Report. Published by Forrester Research, Inc., 400 Technology Square, Cambridge, MA 02139. (617) 497-7090.

Network World. Published weekly by Network World, 118 Turnpike Road, Southborough, MA 01772. (508) 460-3333.

Satellite Communications. Published monthly by Intertec, 6151 Powers Ferry Road, N.W., Atlanta, GA 30339. (770) 955-2500.

Telecommunications. Published monthly by Horizon House, 685 Canton Street, Norwood, MA 02062. (781) 769-9750.

Teleconnect. Published monthly by CMP Publications, Inc., 12 West 21st Street, New York, NY 10010. (212) 691-8215.

Telephony. Published weekly by Intertech Publishing Corporation, One IBM Plaza, Suite 2300, Chicago, IL 60604. (312) 595-1080.

The Voice Report. Published bimonthly by United Communications Group, 11300 Rockville Pike, Suite 1100, Rockville, MD 20852. (301) 816-8950.

Telecommunications Professional and User Associations

This list contains the names, addresses, and telephone numbers of the major national telecommunications associations. Information about membership in these organizations can be obtained by contacting the association at the address listed. In addition to the groups listed here, there are numerous regional, state, and local telecommunications organizations throughout the country.

Association of College and University Telecommunication Administrators (ACUTA)
152 W. Zandale Dr., Suite 200
Lexington, KY 40503
(859) 278-3338

Canadian Business Telecommunications Alliance (CBTA)
161 Bay St., Suite 3650
P.O. Box 705
Trust Tower BCE Place
Toronto, Ontario
Canada M5J 2S1

Communications Managers' Association (CMA)
1201 Mt. Kemble Ave.
Morristown, NJ 07960
(800) 867-8008 or (973) 425-1700

Computer and Communications Industry Association (CCIA)
666 Eleventh Street N.W.
Suite 600
Washington, D.C. 20001
(202) 783-0070

Energy Telecommunications and Electrical Association (ENTELEC)
666 Eleventh Street N.W.
Suite 600
Washington, D.C. 20001
(281) 357-8700 or (888) 503-8700

Institute of Electrical and Electronics Engineers (IEEE)
Council on Communications
3 Park Avenue, 17th Floor
New York, NY 10016
(212) 419-7900

International Communications Association (ICA)
3530 Forest Lane
Suite 200
Dallas, TX 75234
(800) 422-4636

International Telecommunications Users' Group (INTUG)
INTUG Secretary
18 Westminster Palace Gardens
Artillery Row
London SW1P 1RR
England

North American Telecommunications Association (NATA)
P.O. Box 23015
Washington, D.C. 20036
(202) 479-0970

Organization for the Promotion and Advancement of Small Telecommunications Companies (OPASTCO)
21 Dupont Circle N.W., Suite 700
Washington, D.C. 20036
(202) 659-5990

Telecommunications Industry Association (TIA)
2001 Pennsylvania Ave. N.W., Suite 800
Washington, D.C. 20006
(202) 783-1338

The Information Technology & Telecommunications Association (TCA)
74 New Montgomery, Suite 230
San Francisco, CA 94105
(415) 777-4647

United States Telephone Association (USTA)
1401 H St. N.W., Suite 600
Washington, D.C. 20005
(202) 326-7300

Organizations That Conduct Telecommunications Seminars

Many public and private organizations conduct telecommunications education courses and seminars. In addition to those listed here, many colleges and universities have regularly scheduled classes and occasional seminars covering the gamut of telecommunications topics.

BCR Enterprises, Inc.
999 Oakmont Plaza Drive, Suite 100
Westmont, IL 60559
(800) 227-1234

C.M.P. Media, Inc.
12 W. 21st Street
New York, NY 10010
(212) 691-8215

International Communications Association (ICA)
2375 Villa Creek Dr., Suite 200
Dallas, TX 75234
(900) 422-4636

Peregrine Systems
616 Marriot Dr., Suite 500
Nashville, TN 37214
(615) 872-9000

Technology Transfer Institute
741 Tenth Street
Santa Monica, CA 90402-2899
(310) 394-8305

Tele-Strategies
1355 Beverly Road, Suite 110
McLean, VA 22101
(703) 734-7050

Tellabs, Inc.
4951 Indiana Avenue
Lisle, IL 60532
(630) 378-8800

United States Telecom Association (USTA)
1401 H St. N.W., Suite 600
Washington, D.C. 20005-2164
(202) 326-7300

Internet World Wide Web Addresses

There are many sites on the Internet that have valuable information about telecommunications. The following list could never be complete but lists some of the sites the author has found valuable, as well as the addresses of many of the major companies in the telecommunications marketplace. You may want to visit these web sites to gain additional or the most up-to-date information, or to do additional research. The Internet is dynamic, so web addresses do change, but hopefully those on this list will be quite stable.

Organization	Internet WWW Address (URL)
2wire	www.2wire.com
Alcatel	www.alcatel.com
Assistive Technology Industry Association	www.atia.com
AT&T Corporation	www.att.com
Bell South	www.bell-south.com
Cable Modem Information Network	www.cable-modem.net
Cable Modem University	www.catv.org
Canon	www.canon.com
Cisco Systems	www.cisco.com
Comdisco	www.comdisco.com
Competitive Local Exchange Carriers (CLEC)	www.clec.com
Digital Equipment Corporation	www.compaq.com
Dow Corning Corporation	www.dowcorning.com
Ericsson	www.ericsson.com
Federal Communications Commission (FCC)	www.fcc.gov
Fujitsu	www.fujitsu.com
Hewlett Packard	www.hp.com
IBM	www.ibm.com
Internet2 Project	www.internet2.edu
Lucent Technologies	www.lucent.com
Matsushita	www.matsushita.co.jp
Microsoft	www.microsoft.com
Motorola	www.motorola.com
N.V. Philips	www.philips.com

Organization	Internet WWW Address (URL)
Netscape	www.netscape.com
Nippon Electric Company (NEC)	www.nec.com
Nokia	www.nokia.com
Nortel Networks Corporation	www.nortelnetworks.com
North American Numbering Plan	www.nampa.com
Nippon Telegraph and Telephone Corporation (NTT)	www.ntt.com
QWEST Communications International Inc.	www.qwest.com
Ricoh	www.ricoh.com
RSA Security, Inc.	www.rsasecurity.com
SBC Communications, Inc.	www.sbc.com
Siemens	www.siemens.com
Sprint	www.sprint.com
Toshiba	www.toshiba.com
Verizon	www.verizon.com
Who is using the Internet	www.cyberatlas.com
WorldCom, Inc.	www.worldcom.com

Abbreviations and Acronyms in the Text

ACD	automatic call distributor
ACK	acknowledge
ACP	Airline Control Program (IBM)
A/D	analog to digital
ADPCM	adaptive differential pulse code modulation
ADSL	asymmetric digital subscriber line
AHS	American Hospital Supply
AM	amplitude modulation
ANI	automatic number identification
ANSI	American National Standards Institute
APA	all points addressable
API	application program interface
ARPA	Advanced Research Projects Agency
ARQ	automatic repeat request
ASCII	American Standard Code for Information Interchange
ASR	automatic-send-receive
ATM	asynchronous transfer mode
ATM	automatic teller machine
AT&T	American Telephone and Telegraph Company
BALUN	balanced-unbalanced
BCC	block check character
BCD	binary-coded decimal
BELLCORE	Bell Communications Research
BISDN	broadband ISDN
BISYNC	binary synchronous communications
BNA	Burroughs Network Architecture (Burroughs/Unisys)
BOC	Bell Operating Company
bps	bits per second
BSC	binary synchronous communications
CAD	computer-aided design or computer-assisted drafting
CAM	communications access method
CASE	common application service elements
CBX	computerized branch exchange
CCIS	common channel interoffice signaling
CCITT	Consultative Committee on International Telegraphy and Telephony
CCS	centa call seconds
CCU	cluster control unit
CDMA	code division multiple access
CDR	call detail recording
CI–I	Computer Inquiry I
CI–II	Computer Inquiry II
CI–III	Computer Inquiry III
CIO	chief information officer
CIR	committed information rate
CLEC	competitive local exchange carrier
CMIP	Common Management Information Protocol
CODEC	coder/decoder
COE	Council of Europe
CPE	customer premise equipment
CR	carriage return
CRC	cyclic redundancy checking
CRT	cathode ray tube
CRTC	Canadian Radio-television and Telecommunications Commission
CSMA/CA	carrier sense multiple access with collision avoidance
CSMA/CD	carrier sense multiple access with collision detection
CSU	channel service unit
D/A	digital to analog
DAA	data access arrangement
dB	decibel
DBCS	double byte character set
DBS	direct broadcast satellite
DC	direct current

DCE data circuit-terminating equipment
DDCMP Digital Data Communications Message Protocol (DEC)
DDD direct distance dialing
DDP distributed data processing
DEC Digital Equipment Corporation
DES data encryption standard
DID direct inward dialing
DLE data link escape
DNA Digital Network Architecture (DEC)
DOC Department of Communications (Australia)
DOD direct outward dialing
DP data processing
DPAM demand priority access method
DPSK differential phase shift keying
DSL digital subscriber line
DSP digital signal processor
DSS digital satellite service
DSU data service unit
DTE data terminal equipment
DTMF dual-tone-multifrequency
EBCDIC Extended Binary Coded Decimal Interchange Code
EDI electronic document interchange
EIA Electrical Industries Association
e-mail electronic mail
ENQ enquiry
EOA end of address
EOB end of block
EOM end of message
EOT end of transmission
EPSCS enhanced private switched communication service
ESC escape
ESS electronic switching system
ETB end of text block
ETN electronic tandem network
ETX end of text
EUC End User Computing (Dow Corning)
FAX facsimile
FCC Federal Communications Commission
FDDI fiber distributed data interface
FDM frequency division multiplexing
FDMA frequency division multiple access
FDX full-duplex
FEC forward error correction
FEP front-end processor
FIFO first in, first out
FM frequency modulation
FSK frequency shift keying
FTAM file transfer, access, and management
FTP file transfer protocol
FX foreign exchange
GE General Electric Company
GEIS General Electric Information Services
GHz gigahertz
GM General Motors Corporation
GOSIP Government Open Systems Interconnection Protocol
GPS global positioning system
GSM global system for mobile communications
GUI graphical user interface
HBO Home Box Office
HDLC high-level data link control
HDX half-duplex
HTML hypertext markup language
HTTP hypertext transfer protocol
Hz hertz
IBM IBM Corporation
ICC Interstate Commerce Commission
IDDD international direct distance dialing
IEEE Institute of Electrical and Electronic Engineers
ILEC incumbent local exchange carrier
IRM information resource management
ISDN Integrated Services Digital Network
ISO International Organization for Standardization
ISP Internet service provider
IP Internet protocol
IPX internetwork packet exchange (Novell)
ITB intermediate text block
ITT International Telephone and Telegraph Company
ITU International Telecommunications Union
ITU-T International Telecommunications Union-Telecommunications Standardization Sector
IXC interexchange carrier
JTM job transfer and manipulation
kbps thousands of bits per second
KDD Kokusai Denshin Denwa Co. (Japan)
kHz kilohertz
KSR keyboard-send-receive
LAN local area network
LAPB link access procedure, balanced
LAPD link access procedure, D-channel
LAPF link access procedure for frame mode bearer services
LATA local access and transport area
LCD liquid crystal display
LEC local exchange carrier (or company)
LED light-emitting diode
LF line feed
LLC logical link control
LPC linear predictive coding
LRC longitudinal redundancy checking
LU logical unit (IBM)
MAC media access control
MAC moves, adds, and changes
MAN metropolitan area network
MAP Manufacturing Automation Protocol
MAU multistation access unit
Mbps millions of bits per second
MCI MCI Communications Corporation

MFJ	modified final judgment
MH	modified Huffman encoding
MHz	megahertz
MIB	management information base
MIME	multipurpose internet mail extensions
MMR	modified modified read encoding
MODEM	modulator/demodulator
MOTIS	message-oriented interchange systems
MPT	Ministry of Posts and Telecommunications (Japan, Russia)
MR	modified read encoding
MTBF	mean time between failures
MTSO	mobile telephone switching office
MTTR	mean time to repair
MUX	multiplexer
NAK	negative acknowledge
NANP	North American numbering plan
NAU	network addressable unit (IBM)
NCC	network control center
NCP	network control program
NEC	Nippon Electric Company
NECA	National Exchange Carriers Association
NetBIOS	Network Basic Input Output System
NIC	network interface card
NMS	Netware Management System (Novell)
NOS	network operating system
NRZ	nonreturn to zero
NSA	National Security Agency
NTS	Windows NT server (Microsoft)
NTT	Nippon Telegraph and Telephone Company
NUL	null
OCC	other common carrier
OCR	optical character recognition
ODA	office document architecture
ODIF	office document interchange facility
OECD	Organization for Economic Cooperation and Development
OFTEL	Office of Telecommunications (United Kingdom)
ONA	open network architecture
OSI	Open Systems Interconnection
OV	office vision (IBM)
PABX	private automatic branch exchange
PACTEL	Pacific Telesis Corporation
PAD	packet assembly/disassembly
PAM	phase amplitude modulation
PBX	private branch exchange
PC	personal computer
PCM	pulse code modulation
PCN	personal communications network
PCS	personal communications service
PDN	packet data network
PDU	protocol data unit
PEL	picture element
PERT	program evaluation review technique
PFK	program function key
PHS	personal handyphone system
PIN	personal identification number
Pixel	picture element
PM	phase modulation
POP	point of presence
POS	point of sale
POTS	plain old telephone service
PPP	point-to-point protocol
PSC	public service commission
PSK	phase shift keying
PSN	public switched network
PSTN	public switched telephone network
PTT	post, telephone, and telegraph
PU	physical unit (IBM)
PUC	public utility commission
QAM	quadrature amplitude modulation
RBOC	Regional Bell Operating Company
RFP	request for proposal
RFQ	request for quotation
RJE	remote job entry
RMON	remote monitoring
RO	receive-only
RVI	reverse interrupt
SBT	six-bit transcode
SCC	specialized common carrier
SDLC	synchronous data link control (IBM)
SDN	software defined network
SDSL	symmetric digital subscriber line
SLIP	serial line internet protocol
SMDR	station message detail recording
SMTP	simple mail transfer protocol
SNA	Systems Network Architecture (IBM)
SNMP	Simple Network Management Protocol
SOH	start of header
SONET	synchronous optical network
SPX	sequenced packet exchange (Novell)
SS7	signaling system 7
SSCP	system service control point (IBM)
STDM	statistical time division multiplexing
STP	shielded twisted pair
STX	start of text
SWIFT	Society for Worldwide Interbank Financial Telecommunications
SYN	synchronization
TASI	time assignment speech interpolation
TCAM	telecommunications access method
TCM	telecommunications monitor
TCM	trellis code modulation
TCP/IP	transmission control protocol/internet protocol
TDM	time division multiplexing
TDMA	time division multiple access
TNDF	transnational data flow
TOP	Technical Office Protocol
TPF	Transaction Processing Facility (IBM)
TPNS	teleprocessing network simulator (IBM)
TTD	temporary text delay
TWX	teletypewriter exchange system
UDLC	Universal Data Link Control (Sperry/Unisys)
UIFN	universal international freephone numbering
UPC	universal product code

URL	uniform resource locator
UTP	unshielded twisted pair
VAN	value-added network
VDSL	very-high-rate digital subscriber line
VDT	video display terminal
VDU	video display unit
VINES	Virtual Network Integrated Server (Banyan)
VoIP	Voice over IP
VRC	vertical redundancy checking
VSAT	very small aperture terminal
VTAM	Virtual Telecommunications Access Method (IBM)
VTS	virtual terminal services
WAIS	wide area information server
WAN	wide area network
WAP	wireless application protocol
WATS	Wide Area Telecommunications Service
WDM	wavelength division multiplexing
WWW	World Wide Web

Green Grass Case Study

BEGINNING

Setting the Stage Green Grass Wyoming is a small town nestled in the hills of Wyoming that, until recently, saw no need for a telephone company. The residents of Green Grass were content to talk with each other at the local coffee shop, post office, feed mill, church, and the Grange. The change happened rather suddenly on the day of the Big Green Grass centennial. Horace Michaels, mayor of Green Grass, announced that a new company, Flipper.com, was interested in locating in Green Grass. The residents of Green Grass listened intently as the mayor talked about the many amenities a big .com company would bring—money for a new community hall, a traffic light, a new snowplow, and most importantly a memorial to the great grasshopper invasion of 1873. The residents of Green Grass felt a rush of pride as the mayor spoke about the memorial and the significance it had for all Green Grass residents. Green Grass was the only town to have survived the grasshopper invasion and, as such, should be recognized. The memorial would remind all of their grit and tenacity of their forefathers and mothers in the time of hardship.

The mayor then introduced Big Bob Buchman, the town's entrepreneur and funeral director. The mayor explained to the residents that Big Bob had received financing from some progressive-thinking venture capitalists. Big Bob, in turn, had engaged a group of telecommunications consultants to design the Green Grass telecommunications network. Big Bob expressed his great joy at being able to bring communications to Green Grass and explained that he had already hired a telecommunications firm that was going to design the best network in the state.

Throughout the text you will act as the communications consultant hired by Big Bob to design the town's telephone network. Your mission is to build solutions for the different communications needs required by the Green Grass population. At the end of several chapters you will be asked to design a particular portion of the network.

Background Information The following pages contain information about demographic makeup of Green Grass, along with a detailed description of each location that requires special telecommunications services.

- There are 5000 people living in Green Grass according to the last census report. The breakdown of homes is as follows: 2000 households reside within the city limits, 1000 residents and 250 households live within a ten-mile radius around Green Grass.
- Map H–1 (page 689) shows the layout of Green Grass including the street names and topological layout. Map H–2 (page 690) shows the layout of the surrounding township. Map H–3 (page 691) indicates where the businesses, schools, senior citizens' home, county buildings, and churches are located. Map H–4 (page 692) shows where the ranches, homes, and movie stars' residences are located.
- Table H–1 lists each business, school, senior citizens' home, county building, and church along with its reference number.

The following descriptions describe each of the businesses and their telecommunications requirements. You will need to use this information when completing the case studies in each chapter.

- Gertrude Stone's Hardware & Lawn Mower Repair—five employees work at Gertrude's hardware. Chet and Jane work in the hardware and the lawn mower repair service departments. Larry is responsible for stocking shelves and cleaning. Clarence repairs lawn mowers and helps occasionally in the store. Brenda, Gertrude's daughter, works on accounting, manages the employees, and purchases all of the stock. Purchasing stock is one of Brenda's most time-consuming jobs. Every time a product is purchased, Brenda has to manually enter the transaction, mail the inventory request to the distributor, and then track the product through the system.
- Straight or Curled Hair Salon—Violet Tang owns and operates Straight or Curled Hair Salon. At this time Violet employs two hair stylists and one floor girl—Jessie, Janice, and Jennifer. Violet has longed for Internet access that would help her research the newest hair

Table H–1
Locations in Green Grass.

Site	Map Reference No.
Gertrude Stone's Hardware & Lawn Mower Repair	1
Straight or Curled Hair Salon	2
BB's Barber Shop	3
Louden's Department Store	4
Cowboy Clothes	5
Chaser, McDonald, and Rhetorick, Attorneys at Law	6
Mayfair's Five & Dime	7
BookWorm's BookStore	8
Angel's Diner	9
Blessings Insurance Plus	10
Buchman Funeral Parlor	11
Buchman Real Estate	12
Ed's Tattoos & Rug Cleaning	13
Stuff and Stiff Taxidermy	14
Travel Much Travel Agency	15
Kelly's Green Grass Florist	16
Green Grass Grocery	17
Dan's Auto Parts and Car Repair	18
Radishes Ice Cream	19
Pumpkin Stop Mini Marts	20
Five Star Restaurant & Hotel	21
Green Grass Oil & Gas	22
Green Grass Bank	23
Green Grass Municipal Offices	24
Green Grass Municipal Garages	25
Green Grass Library	26
Green Grass Elementary School	27
Green Grass High School	28
Green Grass Community College	29
Green Grass Senior Citizens' Home	30
Green Grass Hospital	31
Wyoming & Western Railway	32
Woodland's Wooden Lawn Ornaments	33
Western Ware Plus	34
Large Ranches	35
Small Ranches	36
Movie Star Estates	37

trends and keep an eye on her stock market investments.

- BB's Barber Shop—Bill Barnes has been running BB's for fifty years by himself. His grandson Bernard recently joined him in running the business. Bernard hopes to improve the efficiency of the shop by adding automatic scheduling.
- Louden's Department Store—Established in 1899, Louden's carries all types of items, ranging from clothes to furniture. It is still owned and managed by the Louden family, including Walden Louden, president; his daughter Carol, vice president of apparel and dry goods; and Walden Jr., vice president of furniture, marketing, and finance. Louden's employs 50 people. 10 work in the office handling mailings, customer complaints, and inventory database. Two of those 10 handle the books. 30 employees serve customers. Five employees work in the warehouse and shipping department, and the remaining five act as supervisors for floor, office, and shipping personnel. Everyone at Louden's is very excited about the new telecommunications network in Green Grass. Currently, information within the store is handled by an old pneumatic system that was installed in 1900. Sales slips, messages, and cash are inserted in a canister that is placed in the enclosed air system that shoots it through to the office.
- Cowboy Clothes—Todd opened Cowboy Clothes three years ago. He employs two salespeople and one assistant manager. The store carries locally-made cowboy boots, cowboy hats, and other western apparel. Todd hopes to begin e-commerce and take advantage of the world's fascination with western wear.
- Chaser, McDonald, and Rhetorick, Attorneys at Law—Bill Chase, Sarah McDonald and Ernest Rhetorick are equal partners in the only law office in Green Grass. In addition to the three attorneys, there are two paralegals, John and Megan, and one legal secretary, Bart.
- Mayfair's Five & Dime—Mayfair's has been running in Green Grass since 1956, when Abby and Brandon Mayfair moved in from New York City. The store carries everything from knick knacks to fabric. A small soda fountain located on one side of the store is run by Laura Jones. Abby and Brandon still run the store every day and employ five floor workers and one stock clerk.
- BookWorm's BookStore—Marian Page started the bookstore within the past year. Her goal was to provide Green Grass with a place to come in, relax, browse, and purchase books. Marian doesn't have any employees at this time. She would like to add an Internet Kiosk once the communications network is up.
- Angel's Diner—The Diner has been running in Green Grass since 1929. Angel started the diner hoping to save their failing ranch. The diner is now open from 6 A.M. until 3 P.M. and serves breakfast and lunch. Angel works every day of the year except for the five that she spends in Las Vegas with Henry Blessing, the local insurance agent. Erma Mudge, Val Littleton, and Henrietta Sprata wait tables and Chris Henley cooks.
- Blessings Insurance Plus—Barbara Blessing runs the only insurance business in Green Grass. She sells auto, home, and life insurance. Barbara employs two agents and one secretary.
- Buchman Funeral Parlor—Big Bob Buchman owns and operates both funeral parlors in Green Grass. Big Bob also owns a funeral parlor in Prairie Corner, a town four miles from Green Grass. He employs three funeral directors and one bookkeeper.
- Buchman Real Estate—Big Bob also owns and runs the only real estate agency in Green Grass. Buchman Real Estate covers all of Green Grass and the surrounding areas. Big Bob was the person responsible for enticing the movie stars to buy estates outside of Green Grass. He employs two real estate agents, Deb Kettle and Horace Buchman, his less-ambitious

brother. Big Bob has decided that the first circuit to be turned up will be an Internet connection to his real estate office. He has high hopes for setting up a Web site to advertise all the beautiful properties for sale in Green Grass.

- Ed's Tattoos & Rug Cleaning—Ed recently attended a seminar in Denver on how to apply permanent tattoos. On his return he quickly added the tattoo business to his established rug cleaning business. He has only applied two tattoos, both on the mayor's prize heifers. Ed employs the Jones brothers as rug cleaners. The Jones brothers run a ranch south of town but often need spare cash to keep up with their tractor-pulling hobby.
- Stuff and Stiff Taxidermy—Stanley Stanowski owns and operates the taxidermy shop. He teaches calculus at the local high school and runs the taxidermy shop during hunting season in the fall. The store also sells antiques and is run by Stan's wife, Arbuta. Arbuta is looking forward to E-bay.
- Travel Much Travel Agency—Kelly Jones runs the travel agency that is currently limited to booking rooms at the local motel or bed and breakfast. Sally is the only person running the business but hopes to expand once the network is in.
- Kelly's Green Grass Florist—Kelly also operates the Green Grass Florist shop out of the same building as the travel agency.
- Green Grass Grocery—Green Grass Grocery is owned and operated by George Hatch. George has two stores—one on the east side of town and one on the west. He employs 30 people at the east side store and 25 at the west side store. George is hoping to link the two stores together and keep a running inventory of all items. He is also planning to place ATM machines in each store, along with credit card validation machines.
- Dan's Auto Parts and Car Repair—Dan runs an auto parts and car repair shop. He employs three mechanics, two salespeople, and one stocker.
- Radishes Ice Cream—Radishes is open for the summer season and is owned and operated by Todd Tillman, the Green Grass grade school principal, and his wife, Mary. Todd and Mary hire several counter people to serve customers.
- Pumpkin Stop Mini Marts—Paul Snyder owns four Pumpkin Stop Mini Marts in Green Grass—one on the east, one on the west, one on the north, and one on the south. The stores located in the north and south are open 24 hours a day while the stores located in the east and west are open only 16. Paul always has two counter workers per store, per shift, and one pump person for the diesel pumps.
- Five Star Restaurant & Hotel—Five Star seats 400 people for banquets, conferences, and meetings. The total number of employees working at Five Star are 20 to 40 waitresses, five janitorial, two events planners, five managers, six hotel clerks, two bookkeepers, one gardener, two executive chefs, five prep cooks, and four dishwashers.
- Green Grass Oil & Gas—Paul Snyder also owns the local oil company. The company offices house all the oil employees and Paul's office. Paul has 10 employees—four office workers, one accountant, three full-time truck drivers, and two part-time truck drivers. Jackie services all of Green Grass and the surrounding territory. He started by supplying gas to ranchers, then expanded to gas and oil for consumers.
- Green Grass Bank—Green Grass Bank, established in 1870, survived grasshopper invasions, the depression, the oil crisis, and the invasion of easterners. The bank now has one main office and two branch offices. It is run by Karl Gordan III. He employs four clerks, one loan officer, and one administrator at the main branch. The two branch offices each have two clerks to serve customers. Karl has been nagging the city council for years for a communications network. He sees the value of tapping into the ATM market and the chance to link their banks into Grass Hoppers Bank, also owned by Karl.
- Green Grass Municipal Offices—The courthouse houses all county employees. The mayor has two offices in the courthouse—one for him-

self and one for his secretary, Karen Jackson. Also located in the courthouse are Judge Gary Keenan, district attorney Steve Stephenson, business planner Bob Wright, and Sheriff Bob French. In addition to the county officers, the courthouse has four clerks in the county records office, two clerks in the justice department, four clerks in the department of transportation office, and two clerks and four deputy sheriffs in the sheriff's office.

- Green Grass Municipal Garages—The municipal garage houses the road crew and road equipment such as graders, snowplows, and mowers. The road crew consists of five road men and one supervisor. A clerk and purchasing agent also work at the garage.
- Green Grass Library—The library was constructed in 1905 from money obtained from a private foundation. Abby and Sarah Keating have run the library for 45 years. Additional community volunteers help to maintain the 5000 books. Abby and Sarah are hoping to add Internet connectivity once the communications network is up.
- Green Grass Elementary School—The elementary school is used for kindergarten through sixth grade. Each grade has two classes, each with one teacher and one teacher's aide. The elementary school has a principal, vice principal, counselor, school nurse, and three office workers. The bus garage for the entire Green Grass system is located across from the elementary school, which has 400 students.
- Green Grass High School—The high school holds grades 7 through 12. Each grade has 2 classes with 1 teacher and 1 aide. The school also has a principal, vice-principal, business director, counselor, school nurse, and four office workers. The administrative office where the superintendent, Hal Hooking, works is located opposite the high school, which holds 350 students.
- Green Grass Community College—The community college has three separate buildings, located on the same campus, and one satellite office at the local high school. The college employs 130 people—50 professors, 30 clerical, 20 administrative, 15 food service, 10 janitorial, and five security guards.
- Green Grass Senior Citizens' Home—The senior citizen home has 100 residents and a staff of six nurses, 10 health aids, and six cafeteria workers. Arliss Abbott is the director of the home.
- Green Grass Hospital—Green Grass Hospital has 50 beds, an emergency room, doctors' offices, an X-ray division, and administrative offices. The hospital employs 150 people—50 nurses, 70 aides, five doctors, five administrators, 10 food service workers, five security officers, and five clerical and employees.
- Wyoming & Western Railway—Wyoming and Western has a depot north of Green Grass near the feed mill. The depot houses two employees who maintain the line between Green Grass and Grass Hopper. Wyoming & Western is interested in selling right of way along the track between Green Grass and Grass Hopper.
- Woodland's Wooden Lawn Ornaments—Woodland's factory is located on the south side of Green Grass. The factory employs 500 people—350 of the employees work on the factory line building the ornaments, 50 are designers, 20 are clerical, 10 are buildings people, 30 are managers, and 40 are sales persons.
- Western Ware Plus—Western Ware Plus designs and manufactures western apparel and sells its products worldwide to major retailers. Western Ware Plus employs 300 people—200 seamstresses, 50 packers, cutters, and go-fers, 30 clerical, 10 designers, and 10 managers.

Locations surrounding Green Grass city limits include the following:

- Jeff Jopkers, million dollar movie star, lives at Rancho Jopkers located west of the city.
- Mabel Currie, half-million dollar movie star, lives on a ranch also west of Green Grass.
- Hal Avery, famous talk show host, has an estate south of Green Grass.

- Emery Luftinkin, owner of three NFL teams, owns 1000 acres east of the city along Green Grass lake.
- Green Grass lake has 75 homes built along the shoreline as shown on the map.
- Buchman estates is a new housing development located east of the city. At this time, ten homes have been completed in the development.
- Rancho Lopez, located five miles from Green Grass, consists of a 5000-acre ranch with five homes and a 50-bed bunkhouse.
- Montana Ranch is a 3000 acre ranch with three homes and six ranchettes.
- Waterford Ranch is a 7000 acre ranch with eight homes, a 70-bed bunkhouse, a restaurant, and a gift shop.
- There are also 20 smaller rancheros scattered around Green Grass. Each of these is shown in Map H–4.

To complete the case studies, you will also need to reference cost and DS-2 line code speed. Table H-2 lists generic costs for equipment and cable. Table H-3 shows DSL speeds.

Table H–2
Costs for equipment and cable, and cost of building cable per mile.

Equipment/Product	Cost
20,000 Port Class 5 Switch	$1,200,000
Fiber-Optic OC48 Multiplexer	$60,000
Fiber-Optic OC12 Multiplexer	$45,000
Fiber-Optic OC3 Multiplexer	$30,000
M13 DS-3 Multiplexer	$3,700
Digital Loop Carrier—500 POTS lines to feed customers and 20 T1 for back-haul	$55,000
Digital Cross Connect—3:1, 256 DS-3s	$200,000
DSX DS-1 84-Position Panel	$2,000
DSX DS-3 16-Position Panel	$2,000
66 Block—100 position	$25
Voice Mail System	$79,000
Fiber-Optic Cable—24 strand	$1/foot
Fiber-Optic Cable—144 Count	$6/foot
Fiber-Optic Cable—288 Count	$12/foot
Fiber-Optic Distribution Panel—100	$1,500
Fiber-Optic Distribution Panel—300 Port	$2,000
Copper Cable—Drop Wire-2 pair per cable	$300/per run
Copper Cable—100 Pairs	$4/foot
Copper Cable—1000 Pairs	$41/foot
Copper Cable—3000 Pairs	$125/foot
Inside 100 Pair Copper Cable	$4/foot
Category 5 Cable	$7/foot
Telephone Pole	$500
Terminal—25 position	$300
Terminal—10 position	$200
Splice Case	$1,000

Table H–3
The standard DSL line code, DMT, speed versus distance.

Wire Guage	Line Code	Speed	KFt.
26 g	DMT	5440 k	9.0
26 g	DMT	1720 k	13.5
26 g	DMT	256 k	17.5
26 g	DMT	640 k	9.0
26 g	DMT	176 k	13.5
26 g	DMT	96 k	17.7
26 g	HDSL2	1.544 M	9.0

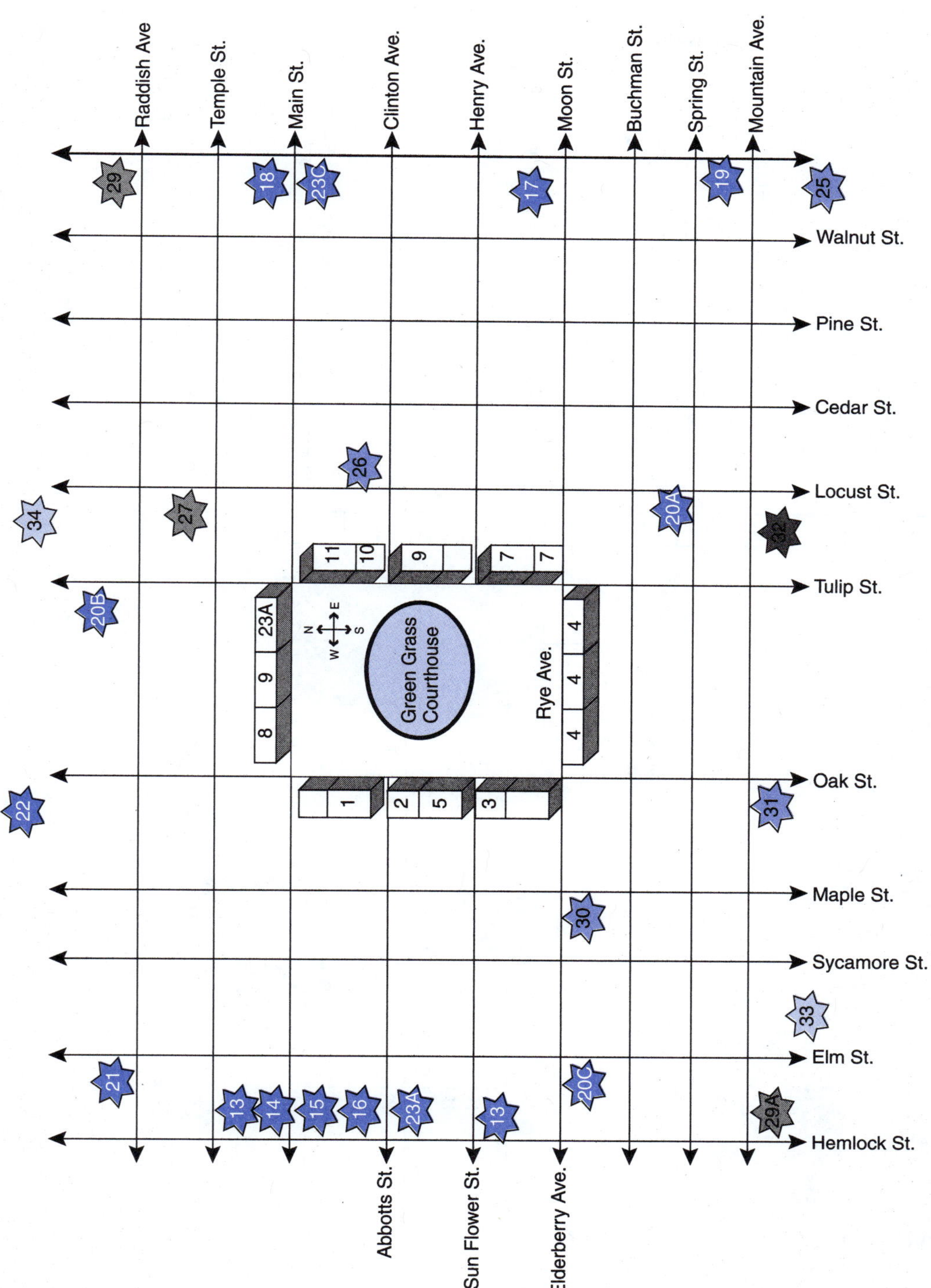

Map H-1 Green Grass Town Layout

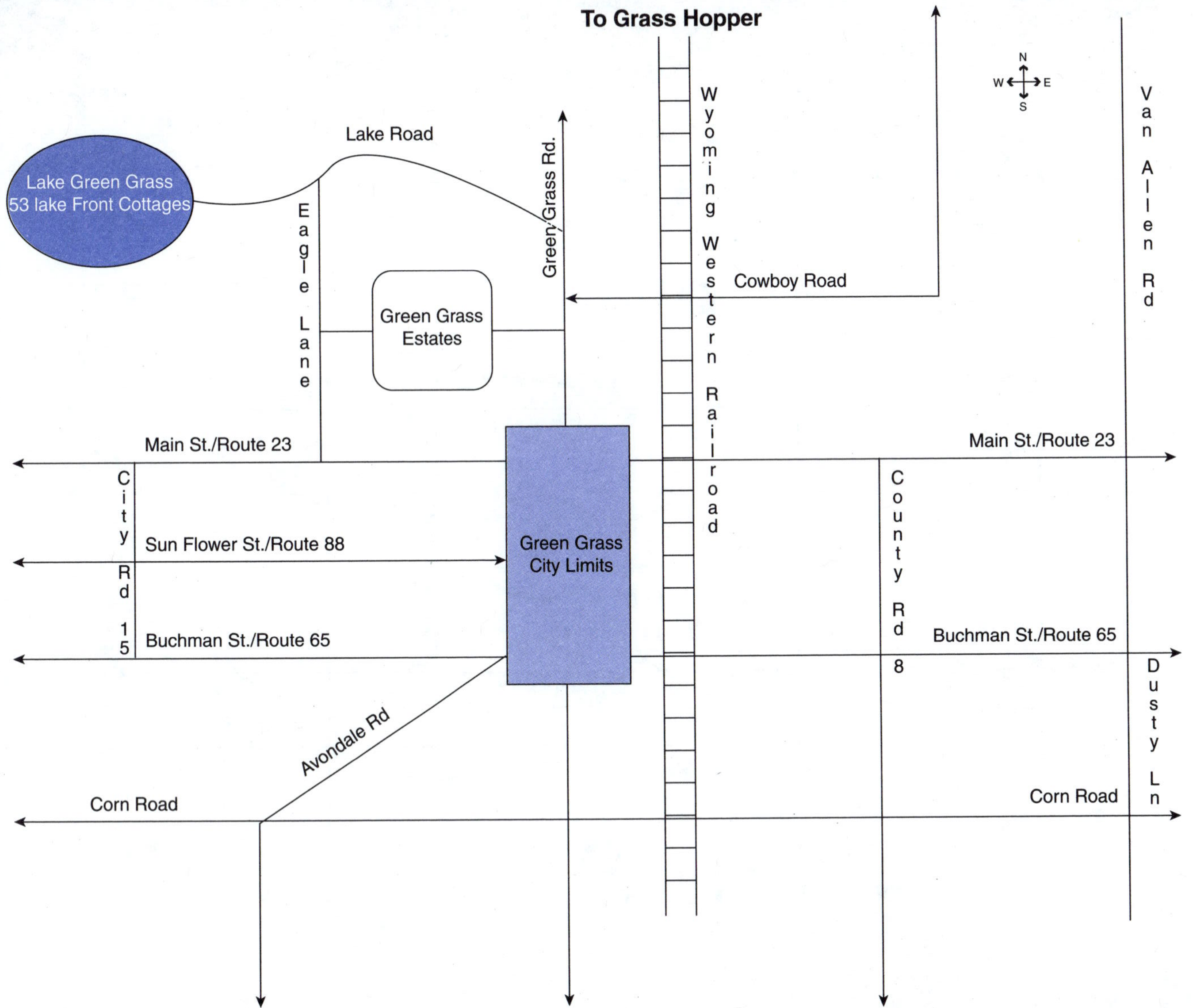

Map H-2 Green Grass Rural Layout

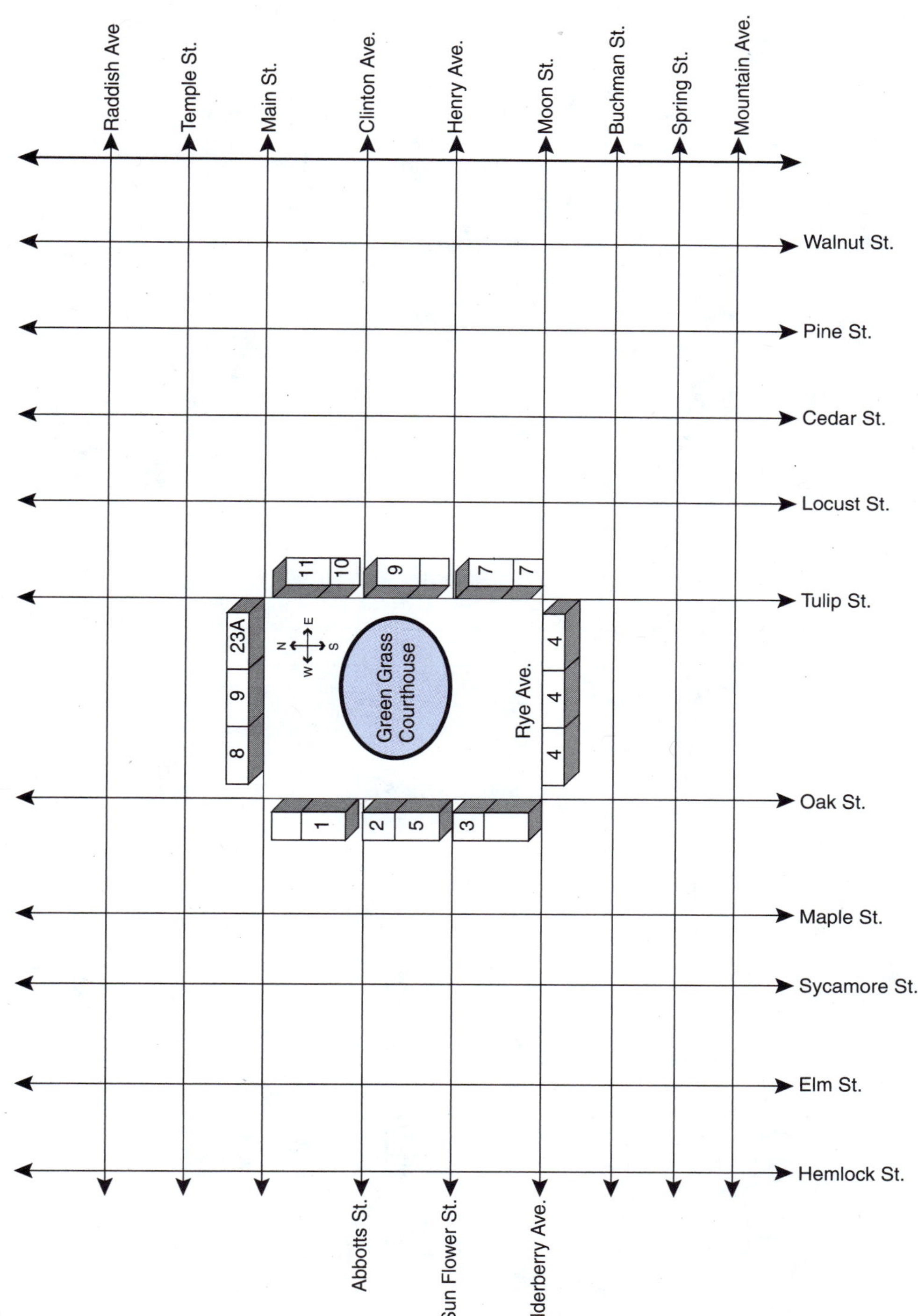

Map H-3 Green Grass Town Layout

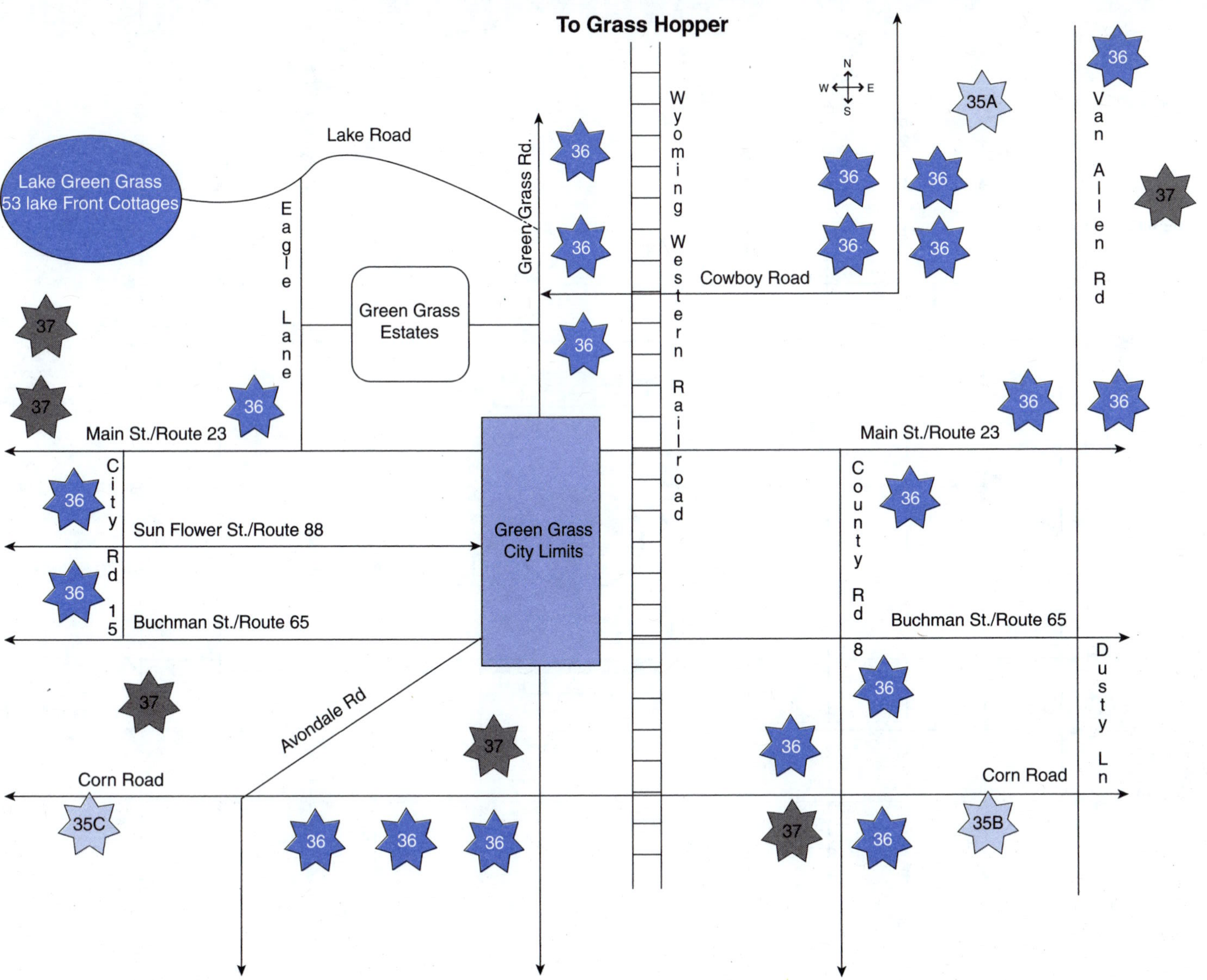

Map H-4 Green Grass Rural Layout

APPENDIX I

Troubleshooting Guide

COPPER CABLE TESTS

POTS Lines

I. Power measurement

1. Voltage measurement

   Using volt/ohm meter (see Figure I–1), measure voltage by

   Measuring between tip and ring = −48 VDC to −52 VDC

   Measuring between ring and ground = −48 VDC to −52 VDC

   Note: − 48 VDC to − 52 VDC source is applied to the ring conductor; tip conductor's job is to be an insulated ground.

2. Current measurement

   Using volt/ohm meter (see Figure I–2), measure current by

   Good measurement

   Measuring between tip and ring = 26 mA @ 52 VDC

   (Varies with loop length due to resistance. Should not be less than 23 mA.)

   Measuring between ring and ground = 42 mA

   (*Ground has 0 resistance*)

   Problem found

   Measuring between tip and ring <23 mA

   Other than very long lines, which may function with as little as 18 or 19 mA, a current measurement less than 23 mA is telling you there is a problem on the line.

   Resolution

   a. Place loop extenders if the loop is too long.
   b. Check the loop characteristics—balance, resistance, ground.

3. Ground measurement

   Using a volt/ohm meter (see Figure I–3), set the dial to DC current

   Measuring between ring and ground = 42 mA

   (*Should be double the current measured between tip and ring*)

   This measurement helps show whether the circuit has a good or bad ground. The current measurement should be double that of the line current.

4. Loop continuity measurement

   Using a volt/ohm meter (see Figure I–4), measure resistance by:

   Idle circuit—Handset in place

   Good measurement

   Measuring between tip and ring = Over 3.5 MOhms

   Measuring between tip and ground = Over 3.5 MOhms

Figure I–1
Measuring between tip and ring.

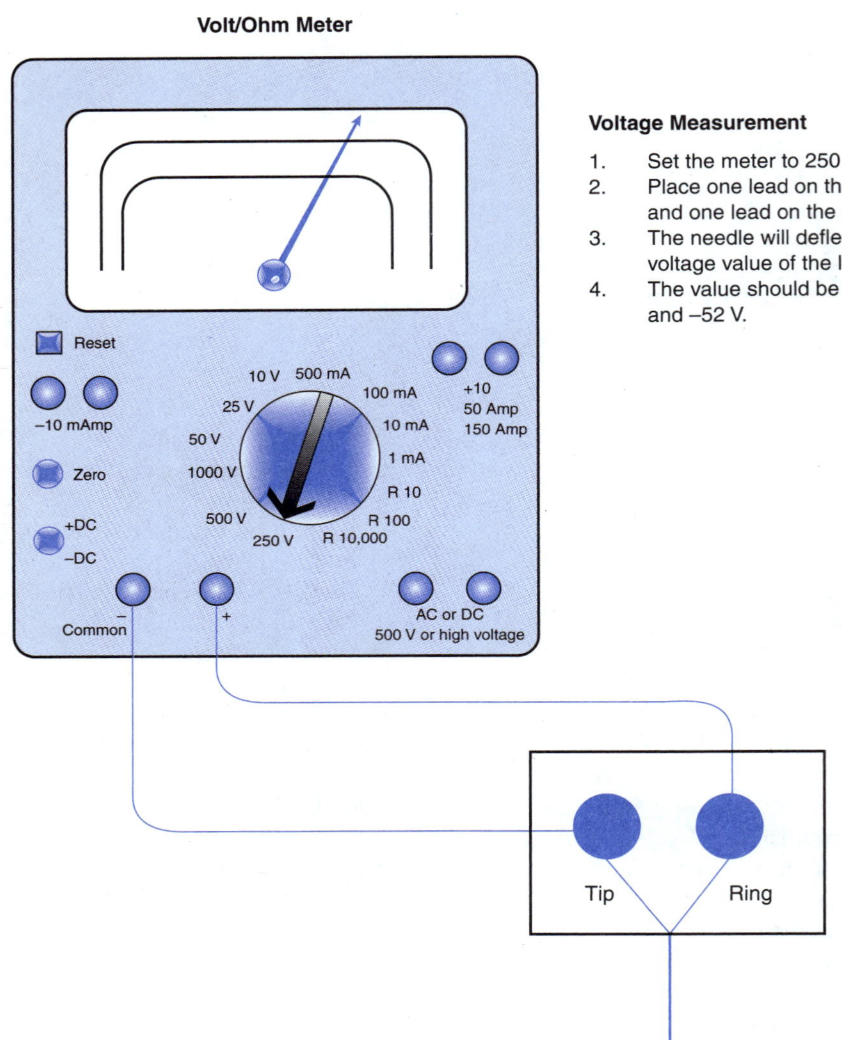

Measuring between ring and ground = Over 3.5 MOhms

Problem found if

Measuring between tip and ring = Less 3.5 MOhms

Telling you there is a short on the line.

Measuring between tip and ground = Less 3.5 MOhms

Telling you a ground exists.

Measuring between ring and ground = Less 3.5 MOhms

Telling you a ground exists.

Figure I–2
Loop current measurement.

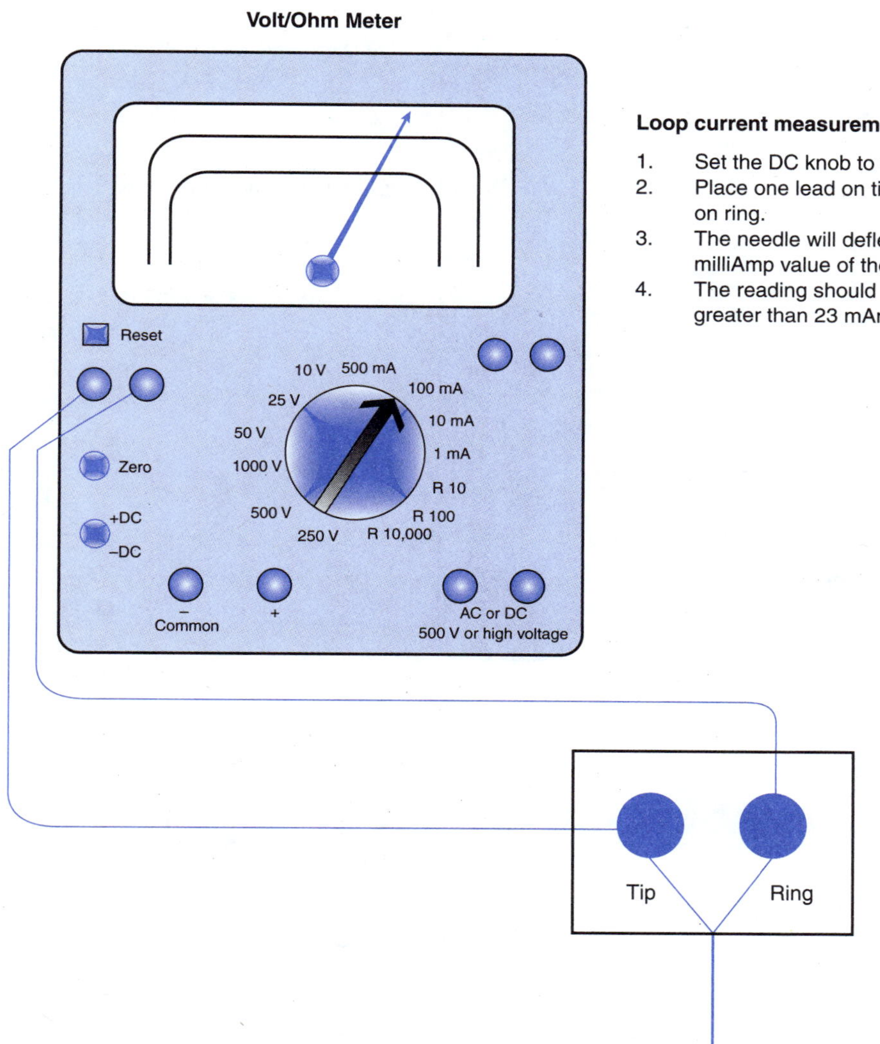

Resolution

If resistance is less than 5,000 ohms, the fault is called a hard short. You may determine the distance to the short by

a. Calculating the resistance value to feet by knowing the cable gauge
b. Using a TDR (time domain reflectometer) or a fault locator to locate the short.

If the resistance is greater than 5,000 ohms, the fault is a highly resistive fault. You may determine the distance to the short by

Figure I–3
Ground Measurement.

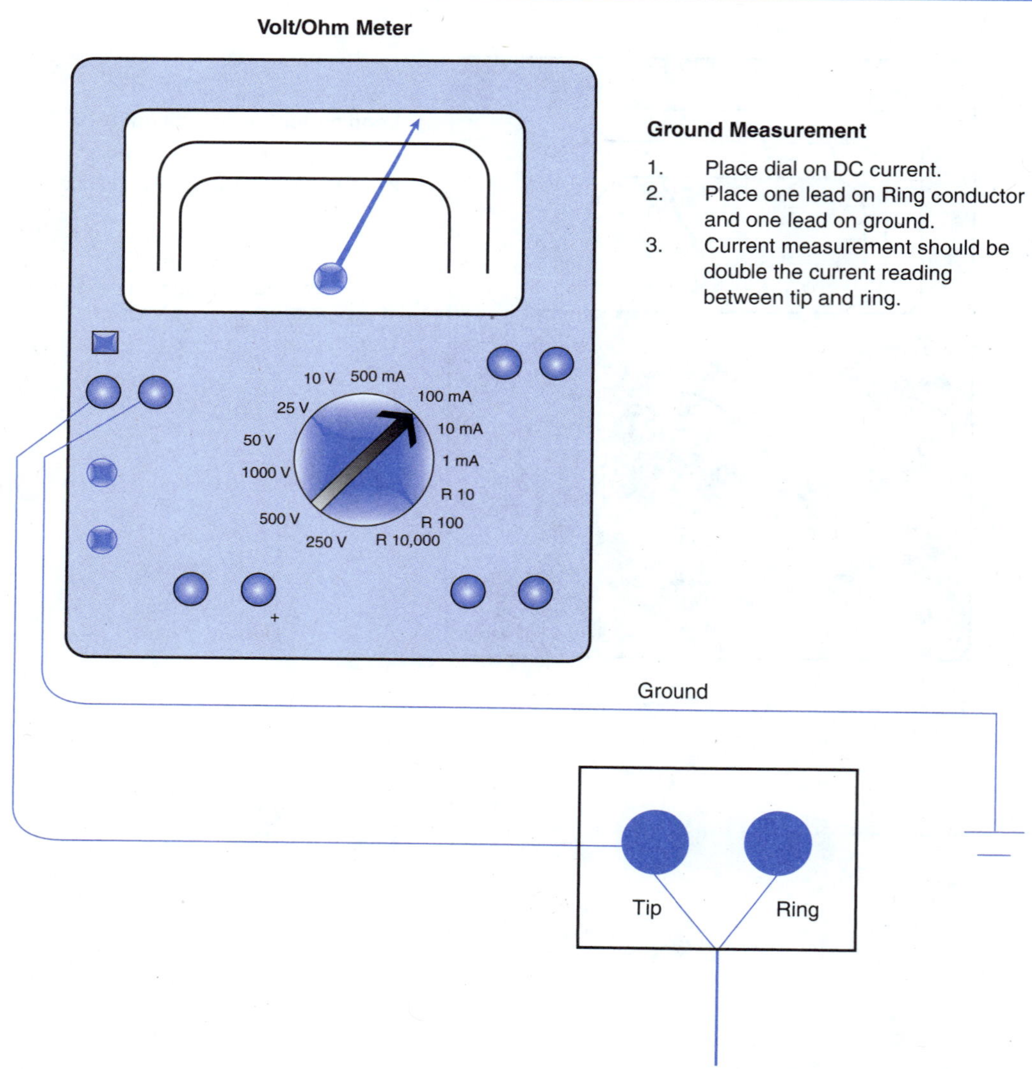

- Using a TDR or fault locator to locate the trouble

5. Balance measurement
   Using the volt/ohm meter (see Figure I–5)
   a. Place the dial on the resistance scale to R × 10,000
   b. Touch one lead to tip and the second lead to ground
   c. Move the AC volts dial from −DC to +DC
   d. Note how far the needle kicks each time you toggle between the +/−

Figure I–4
Loop continuity measurement.

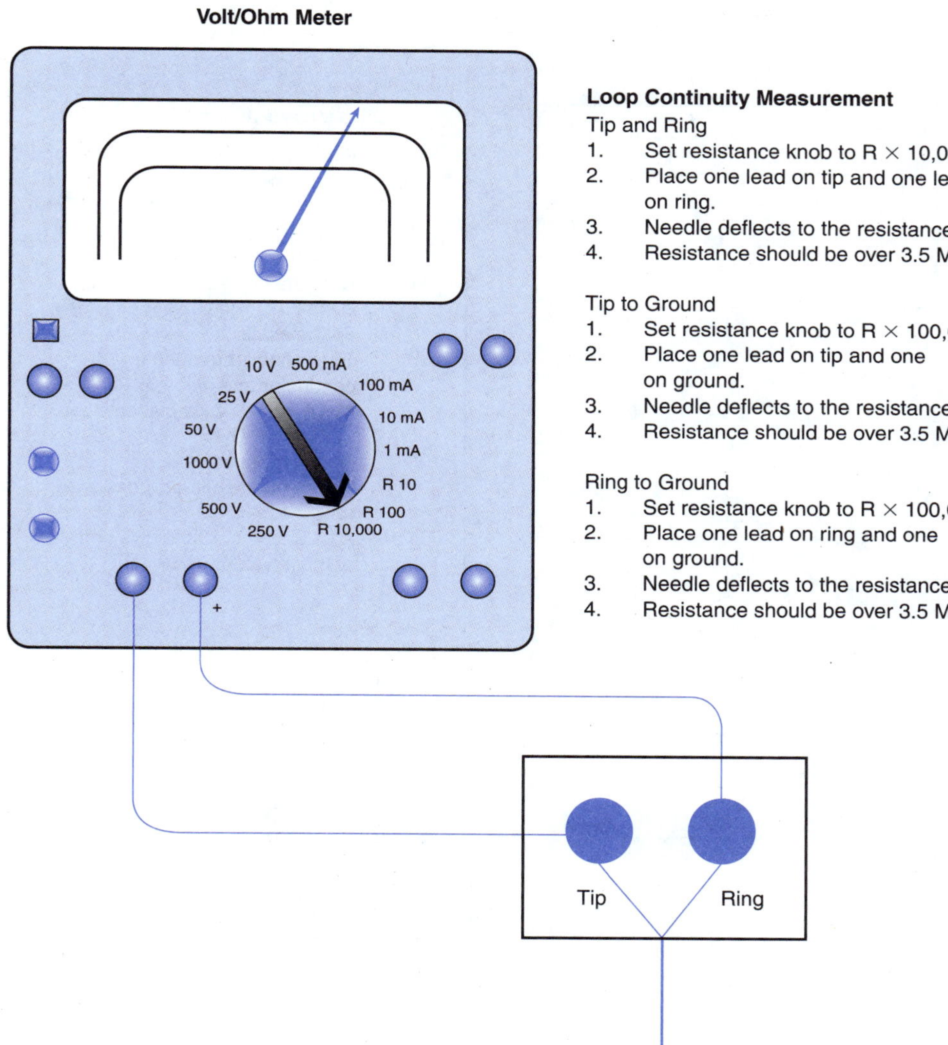

e. Perform the test on each conductor noting the kick value
f. The kick values for the tip and the ring conductor should be the same

Problem found if

One conductor has a much higher or lower kick value than other

Resolution

a. One wire—tip or ring may be coming open

Figure I–5
Balance measurement.

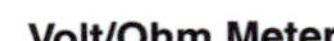

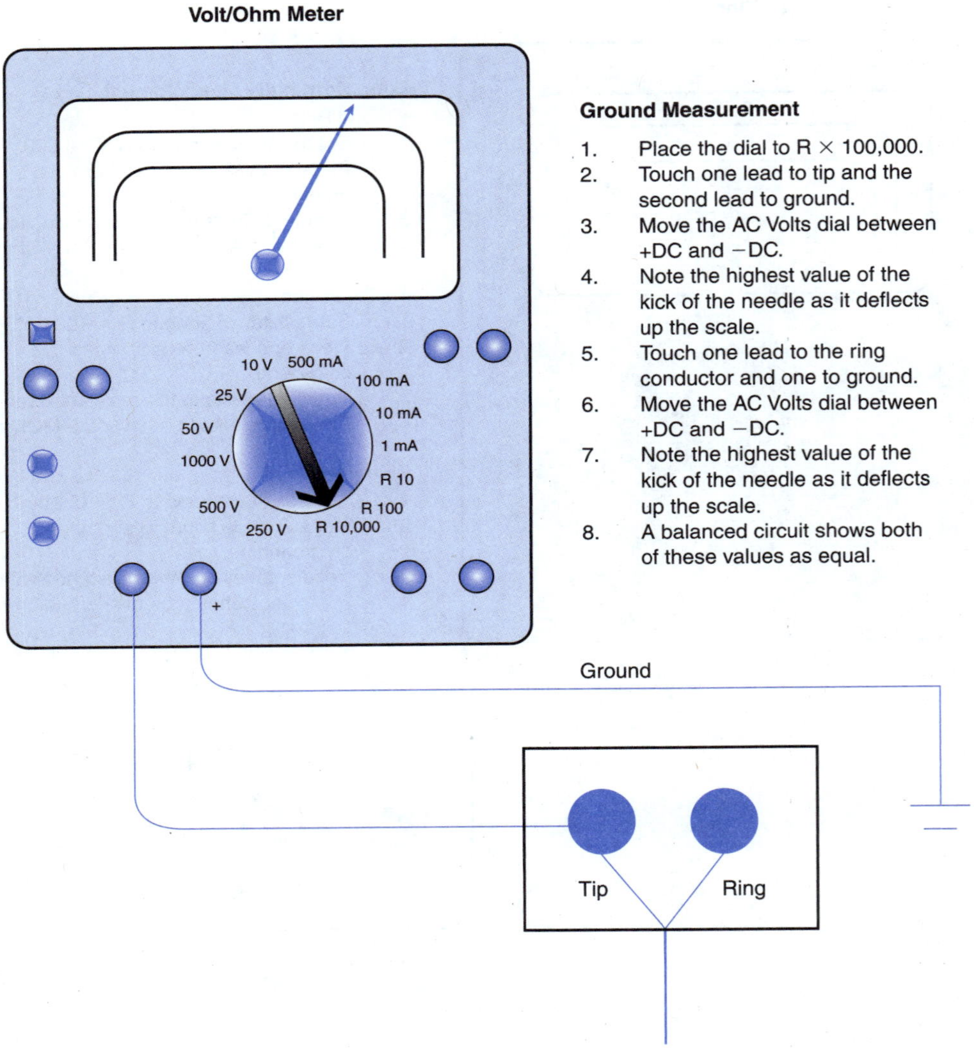
Volt/Ohm Meter
10 V
500 mA
100 mA
25 V
10 mA
50 V
1 mA
1000 V
R 10
500 V
R 100
250 V
R 10,000
+
Ground Measurement
1. Place the dial to R × 100,000.
2. Touch one lead to tip and the second lead to ground.
3. Move the AC Volts dial between +DC and −DC.
4. Note the highest value of the kick of the needle as it deflects up the scale.
5. Touch one lead to the ring conductor and one to ground.
6. Move the AC Volts dial between +DC and −DC.
7. Note the highest value of the kick of the needle as it deflects up the scale.
8. A balanced circuit shows both of these values as equal.
Ground
Tip
Ring

b. Additional wire attached to one wire may cause higher resistance value and thus cause an unbalance between the two conductors
c. Use a TDR to check the line for impairments

II. Noise measurements for voice and data circuits riding on copper medium

Using a transmission test set referred to as a TIMS to perform the following noise tests

1. Loss
   a. Connect the circuit to the test set.
   b. The loss test involves sending a 1004 Hz tone across the circuit. First you will measure for the AML (actual measured loss). Once complete, the AML will be

Figure I–6
Loss test.

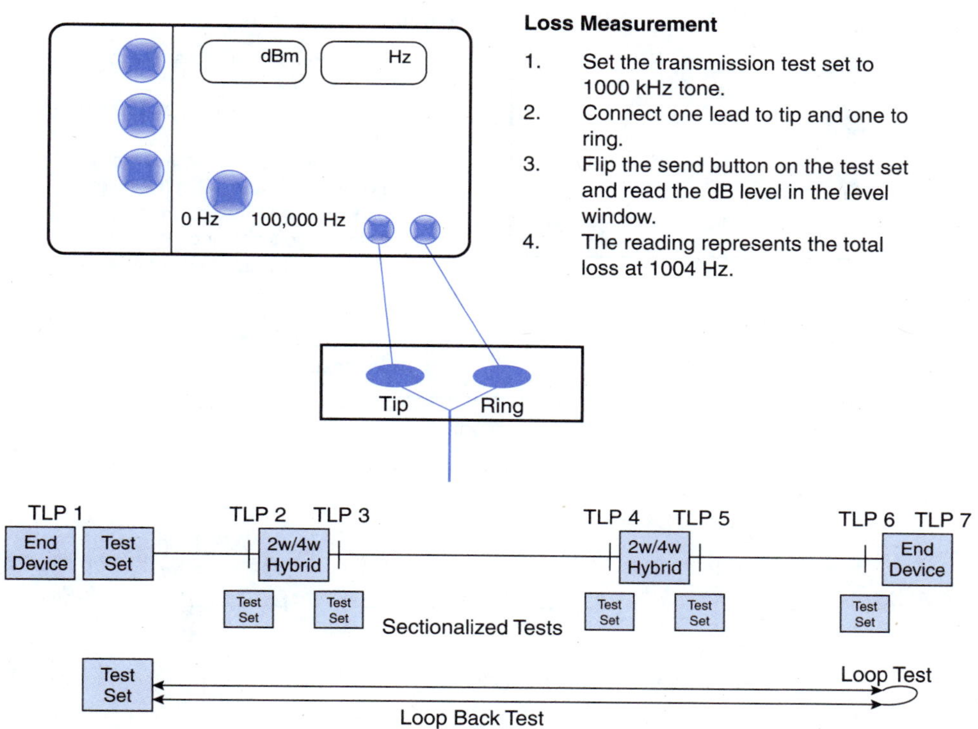

compared to the EML (expected or engineered measured loss) to determine whether the circuit is good or not good.

c. Measure the dB loss at each point in the circuit as shown in the example in Figure I–6 that defines each point that requires testing.
d. Circuit loss for voice circuits is referred to as TLP (transmission level point). The TLP is a method used to reference loss at defined points in the circuit.
e. Circuit loss for data circuits is referred to as DLP (data level point). The DLP, similar to the TLP, issued to reference loss at defined points in the circuit.

2. 3-tone slope
   a. 3-tone slope uses frequencies other than 1004 Hz to uncover problems with circuit balance.
   b. Using a transmission test, set connect the circuit to the test set.
   c. Send 404 Hz tone down the circuit and note the loss.
   d. Send 2804 Hz tone down the circuit and note the loss.
   e. The loss should range from −2 to +7.5 with an AML reading of 16.7 dBm as shown in Figure I–7.

Figure I–7
3-Tone slope test.

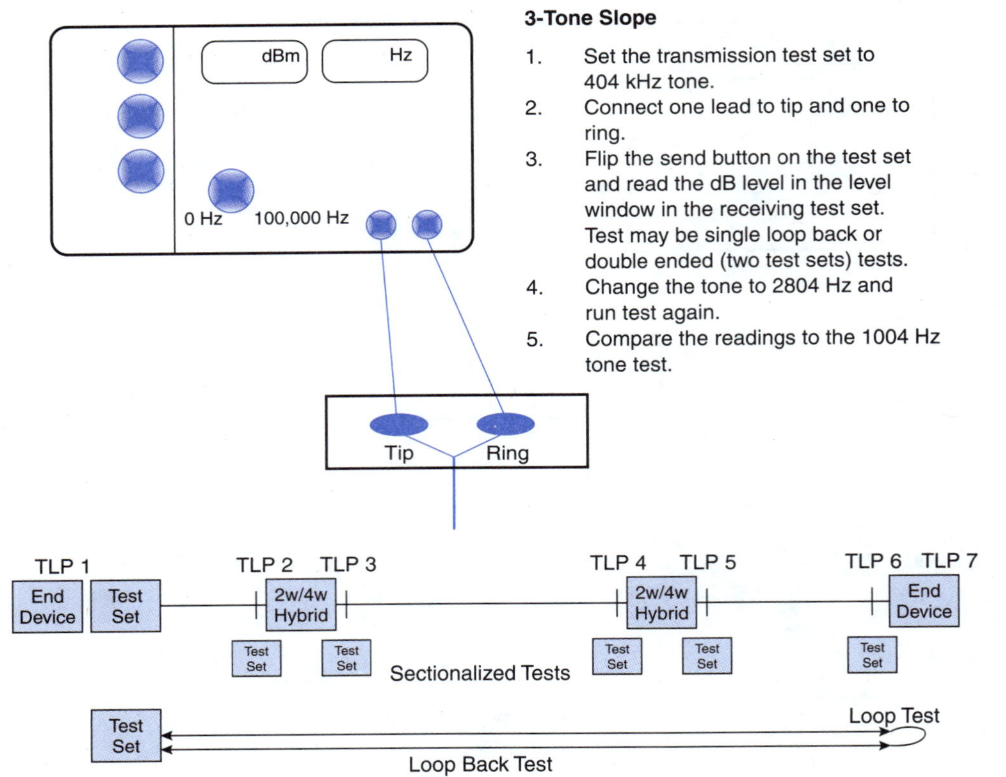

3. C-message noise
   a. C-message noise test measures the white noise level of a voice frequency within a digital circuit.
   b. The far end of the circuit must be terminated—600 ohm termination in order to conduct this test. Using a TIMs test set, test the circuit by terminating each end, then measuring using the message filter that eliminates all frequencies below 250 Hz and above 300 Hz. Looking for noise only within this window.
4. C-notched noise
   a. Measures the noise caused by the data signal.
   b. Using a TIMs test set send out a 1004 Hz holding tone from the distant end at a −13 dBm0 level.
   c. The receiving end notches out the 1004 Hz tone allowing the remaining harmonics to be measured.
   d. A measurement of 45 dBrnc0 TLP shows the signal is good.
   e. Circuit impairments found by C-notched noise test may be caused by the analog to digital converter or analog amplifiers.
5. Signal to noise
   a. S/N ratio test is used to determine whether the loss, slope, and c-notched noise performed properly.

Figure I–8
Signal to noise test.

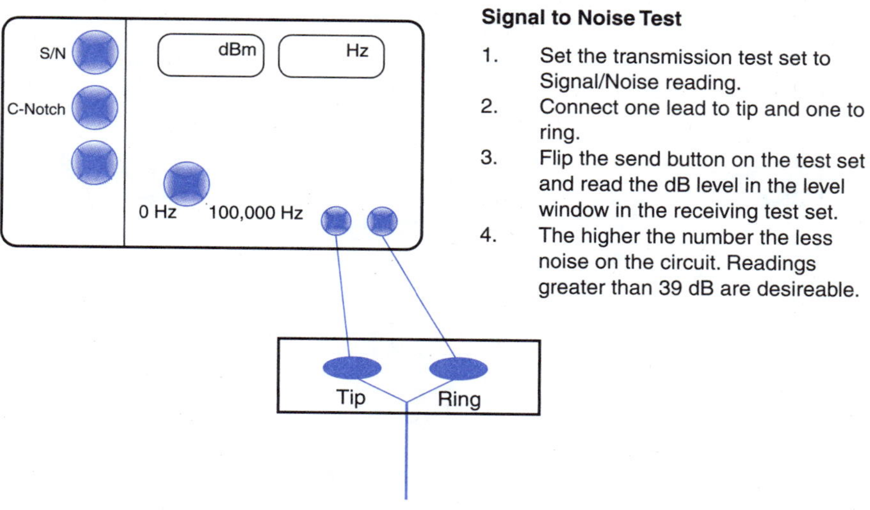

   b. The three tests should be performed and compared as shown in Figure I–8.
   c. The higher the value, the better.
6. Impulse noise
   a. Impulse noise tests look for spikes in the signal such as those caused by lightning or electrical interference.
   b. The first step before testing impulse noise is to set a signal threshold to measure against. A 1004 Hz tone may be used to perform this test.
   c. Monitor the signal for spikes occurring above the defined threshold.

T1 Testing

I. Signal monitoring
1. Setting up the test set
   a. Setting up the test set at a DSX—Refer to Figure I–9
   b. Setting up the test set at a termination block—Refer to Figure I–10
   c. Setting up the test set at a repeater housing—Refer to Figure I–11
2. Read and interpret the output on the test set
   a. The test set should indicate a live signal, frame sync, and if applicable pattern sync. Each value has an associated LED that lights green when it likes what it sees and red when it doesn't. Look first at the LEDs to make sure you are receiving a signal. If the signal LED is not green, you have a real problem.
   b. Look for BPV errors—Bipolar violations are caused by ones of the same polarity arriving consecutively. BPVs may indicate there is a problem at a repeater, there is a cable problem, or a piece of equipment is ready to fail. M13, fiber muxes and microwave equipment corrects BPVs, thus making this test useless on fiber and microwave links.
   c. Look for CRC errors—Cyclic redundancy errors may only be seen on T1 circuits optioned for ESF framing. SF framing does not provide CRC error checks. The CRC error is a robust error-checking

Figure I–9
Monitoring T1 circuit at a DSX panel.

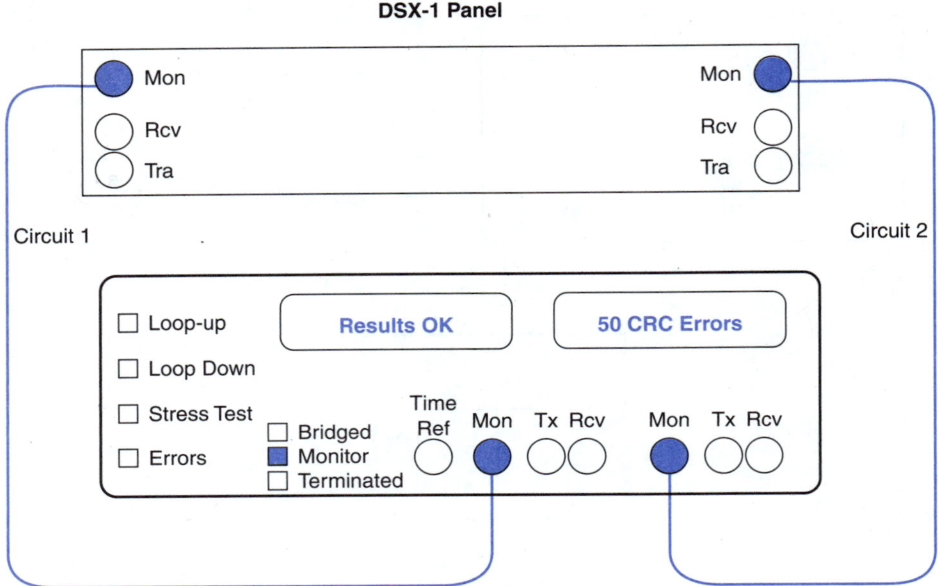

Monitoring T1 Circuit

1. Connect the monitor jack of the DSX to the monitor jack of the test set as shown.
2. Set the test set to monitor.
3. Review the results in the associated window.
4. The illustration above shows two circuits being monitored by one test set. Circuit one shows "Results OK" meaning the signal looks good. Circuit two shows CRC errors meaning the signal has errors.

algorithm that has an accuracy rate of 98.4%. CRC is one of the most reliable monitoring tests available.

d. Look for frame errors—Frame errors occur once every 193rd bit. The information bits are not checked.

3. Timing test
   a. This test may be performed only if you have a stable timing source such as a T1 signal coming from a switch or piece of equipment being referenced back to a stratum 1 clock.
   b. Place the timing reference cord into the monitor jack of the T1 timing source. Set up the test set to show the timing slips. The indicator on the test set should show 0 timing slips. Even slowly recurring slips—1 every 2 or 3 minutes—indicates a timing problem in the network.
   c. Common cause of timing problems
      - Equipment optioned incorrectly. For example, if a channel bank or PBX is optioned as the master clock and the opposite end channel bank or PBX is also optioned as the master clock, timing problems occur. One end of the circuit must be optioned as the slave.

Figure I–10
Monitoring T1 circuit at a termination block.

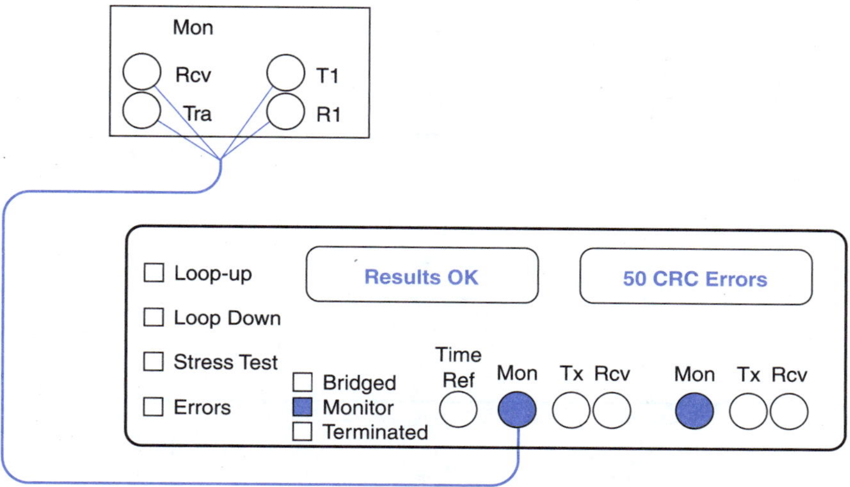

Monitoring T1 Circuit

1. Connect the leads of the termination screws to the monitor jack of the test set as shown.
2. Set the test set to bridged.
3. Review the results in the associated window.
4. The illustration shows two circuits being monitored by one test set. Circuit one shows "Results OK" meaning the signal looks good.

- Equipment on the network timed to different clock references. For example if one multiplexer's timing source references back to a stratum 1 and the second multiplexer is using the internal stratum 3 timing source, timing slips will occur.

4. Loss of signal indicators
   a. Red alarm is telling you that there is a network problem at the near end of the circuit. The incoming pattern loses frame sync and the test set shows an all ones keep alive signal.
   b. Yellow alarm is telling you that the far end equipment is out of service and is shipping you a yellow alarm to let you know there is a problem on the circuit. The test set will show an all ones keep alive signal.
   c. All ones pattern indicates that the framed signal is gone and an all ones signal is being sent to continue synchronization.
5. Monitoring the signaling bits—A B bits
   a. Monitoring the A, B bits in a T1 bit stream can be done by using a T1 test set with drop channel capability. Table I–1 shows the different states of the AB bits according to their state.
   b. Problems associated with signaling may be caused by

      Incorrectly optioned equipment such as robbed-bit signaling not set for that channel.

Figure I–11
Monitoring T1 circuit at a repeater housing.

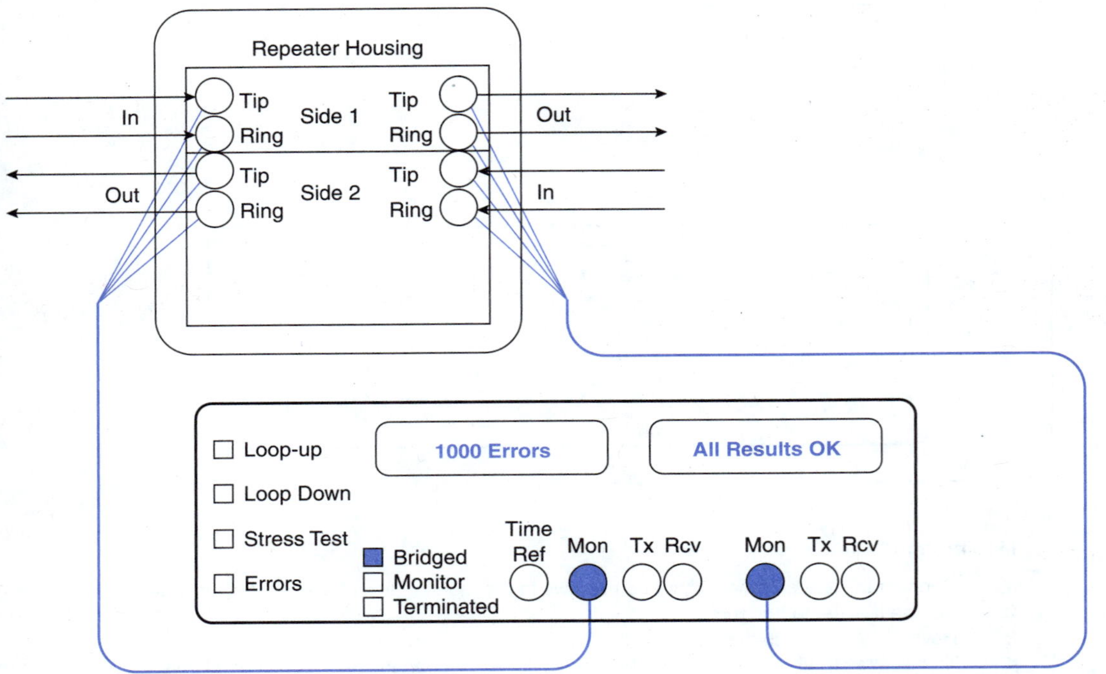

Monitoring T1 Circuit

1. Connect the leads to the pins on the repeater housing and to the Monitor jack of the test set as shown.
2. Set the test set to bridged.
3. Review the results in the associated window.
4. The illustration shows two circuits being Monitored by one test set. Circuit one shows "Errors" showing a problem coming in on side one or going out on side 2. Further isolation is required.

Mismatch signaling type. For example, the channel card in the channel bank may be optioned for ground start signaling and the switch for loop start.

II. Intrusive Tests
   1. Setting up the test set
      a. Setting up the test set at a DSX—Refer to Figure I–12
      b. Setting up the test set at a termination block—Refer to Figure I–13
      c. Setting up the test set at a repeater housing—Refer to Figure I–14
      d. Setting up two test sets at each end of the circuit—Refer to Figure I–15
   2. Stress pattern—stress patterns are used to stress the circuit. Table I–2 lists and defines the stress patterns used to test a T1 circuit. Each tests a particular parameter, such as ones density or excessive zeros.

Table I-1
CAS signaling bits are read by T1 test equipment for the purpose of troubleshooting CAS signaling problems.

Ground Start	**Digital Loop Carrier**				**Foreign Exchange**			
	Station		**CO**		**Station**		**CO**	
	A	**B**	**A**	**B**	**A**	**B**	**A**	**B**
Station called by CO								
On hook	0	0	0	0	0	1	1	1
Off hook	0	0	0	1	0	1	0	1
Ringing from CO	0	0	1	1/0	0	0	0	1
Off-hook-talking	1	0	0	1/0	0	1	1	1
On-hook	0	0	0	1/0	0	1	0	1
CO disconnects	0	0	0	0	0	1	1	1
CO being called								
On-hook	0	0	0	0	0	1	1	1
Off-hook	0	1	0	0	0	0	1	1
Dial tone	1	0	0	1/0	1	1	0	1
Dialing	1	0	0	1/0	1	1	0	1
Talking	1	0	0	1/0	1	1	0	1
On hook	0	0	0	1/0	0	1	0	1
CO disconnects	0	0	0	0	0	1	0	1
Loop Start								
CO being called								
On hook	0	0	1	1	0	1	0	1
Off hook	1	0	1	1	1	1	0	1
Dial tone	1	0	1	1	1	1	0	1
Dialing	1	0	1	1	1	1	0	1
Talking	1	0	1	1	1	1	0	1
On hook	0	0	1	1	0	1	0	1

3. Loopback tests
   a. Two types of loopbacks may be used in a loop back test. The first is a hard loop, which stands for a physically hard loop placed between the transmit and receive jacks at a DSX panel or in the field. The second is a soft loopback initiated by a loopback code sent by the test set to the far end equipment. The equipment bridges the incoming signal to the outgoing port creating a closed loop for the signal to travel around. The benefit of the loopback test is to quickly determine whether the circuit has continuity end to end. Once this is determined, stress patterns can be sent in order to stress the line.
   b. The first test that should be performed once the loopback is established is to send a bit error from the test set and watch for its return in the display of the test set. The bit error returning to the test set ensures that the loopback is in place.

Figure I–12
Intrusive testing of a T1 circuit at a DSX panel.

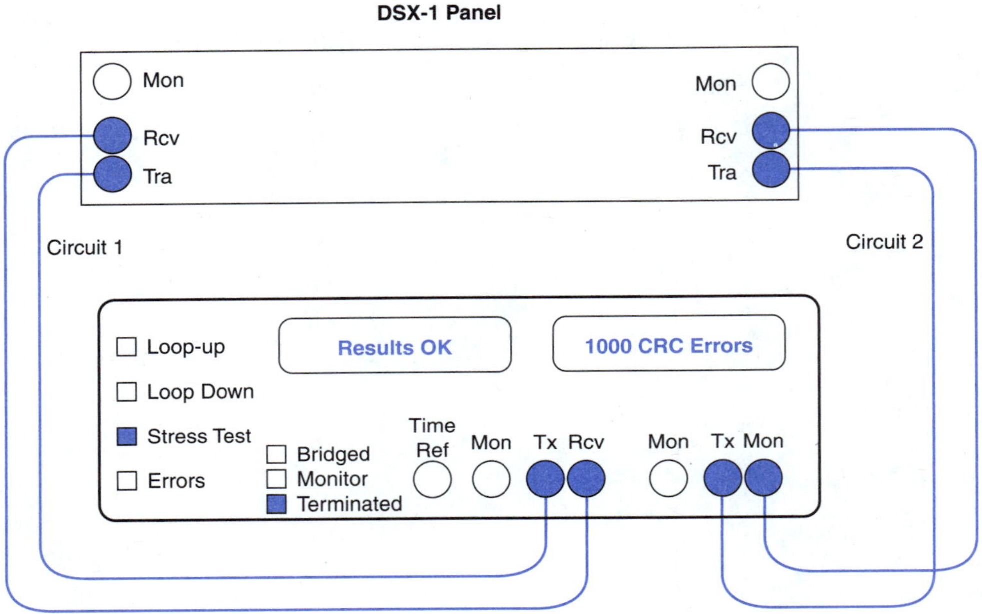

Intrusive T1 Circuit Test

1. Connect the Tx & Rcv jacks of the DSX to the Tx and Rcv jacks of the test set as shown.
2. Set the test set to Terminate.
3. Select a stress patern such as 1:7, 3:24, QRSS, Multilevel test.
4. A loop back or second test set must be placed at the far end of the circuit.
5. Circuit one shows "Results OK" meaning the signal looks good.
   Circuit two shows CRC errors meaning the signal has errors.

c. Once the loopback is verified, stress patterns, as shown in Table I–2, should be run. The circuit should run clean through all of the stress patterns.

4. End-to-end test
   a. Once the loopback test is complete and the loop taken down, you may wish to perform an end-to-end test. At the time of circuit turn-up, the loopback test is performed to ensure circuit continuity. Once the loopback test proves good, an end-to-end test is initiated to truly stress the circuit. An end-to-end test requires that two people physically be at each end of the circuit with test sets.
   b. Similar to the loopback test, stress patterns should be sent between the two test sets and the signal monitored for errors. The stress patterns should remain on the line for at least one hour. Many carriers require twenty-four hour tests. It is important to note that each stress pattern as shown in the table stresses

Figure I–13
Intrusive test at a termination block.

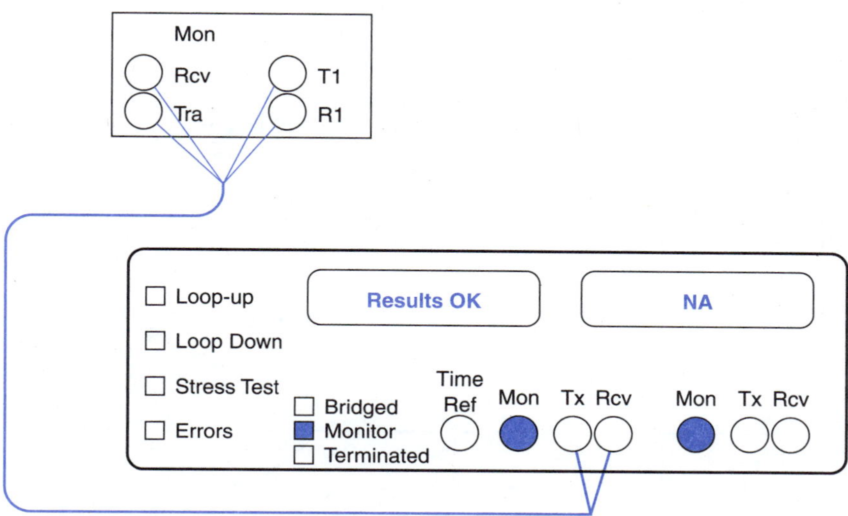

Intrusive T1 Circuit Test

1. Connect the leads to the termination screws and to the Tx and Rcv jacks of the test set as shown.
2. Set the test set to Terminate.
3. Select a stress patern such as 1:7, 3:24, QRSS, Multilevel test.
4. A loop back or second test set must be placed at hte far end of the circuit.
5. Review the results in the associated window.
6. Circuit one shows "Results OK" meaning the signal looks good.

different parameters of the circuit. Troubleshooting can be made simpler if you understand what the stress pattern is stressing.

Note—The errors may be interpreted the same whether they show up during a loopback test or an intrusive test.

DS-3 Testing

I. Nonintrusive tests

1. Setting up the test set
   a. Setting up the test set at a DSX—Refer to Figure I–16
2. The two common nonintrusive tests performed on a DS-3 are a pulse shape test, signal level, and a BPV test. Both help to indicate trouble on the line.
3. Pulse shape test and signal level are performed by
   a. Setting the display on the test set to pulse shape and referencing the value displayed as shown in the example below.
      - Pulse shape = pass (or fail)
      - Pulse width = 11.0 ns
      - Rise time = 8.0 ns
      - Fall time = 11.0 ns
      - Pulse mask = 93 ANSI
      - Power = 17.5 dBm
      - Level = 0.045 V
   b. Cause of the problem

Figure I–14
Instrusive test of a T1 circuit at a repeater housing.

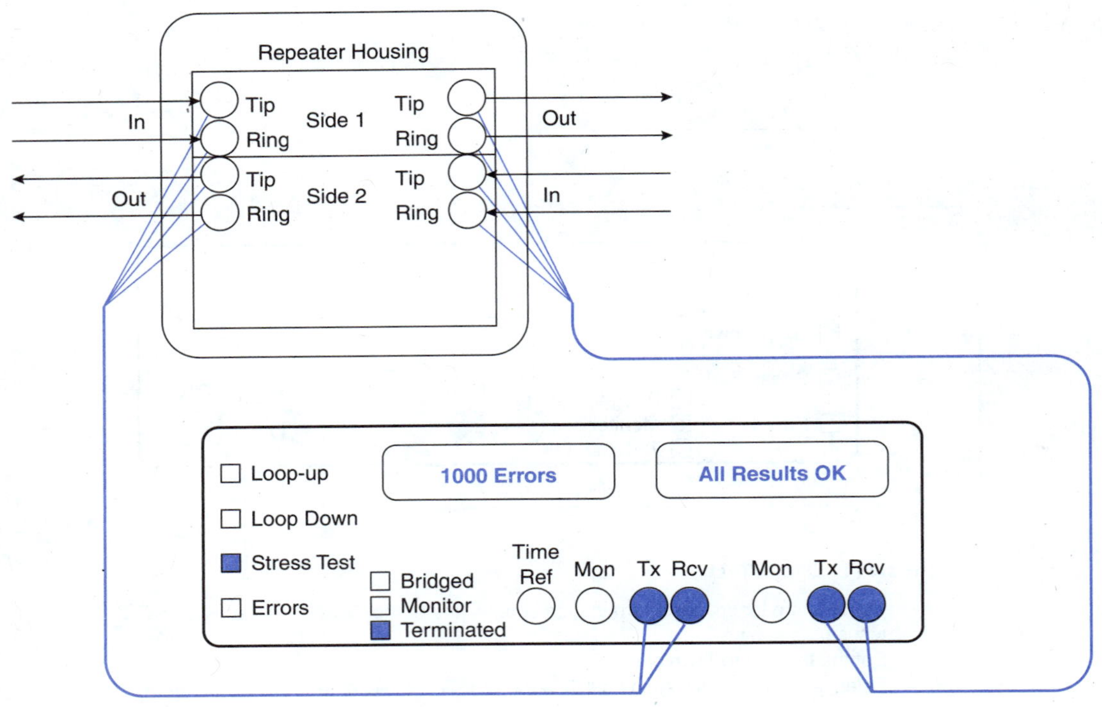

Intrusive T1 Circuit Test

1. Connect the Tx & Rcv jacks of the to the Tx and Rcv pins on the repeater housing and the Tx & Rcv jacks of the test set as shown above.
2. Set the test set to Terminate.
3. Select a stress patern such as 1:7, 3:24, QRSS, Multilevel test.
4. A loop back or second test set must be placed at the far end of the circuit.
5. Circuit one shows "Results OK" meaning the signal looks good.
   Circuit two shows CRC errors meaning the signal has errors.

- Cable length issue
- LBO set wrong for the cable length
- Bad crimps

4. BPV tests can be performed on an in-service DS-3.
5. Reference the display on the test set to determine whether there are BPVs on the line. BPVs indicate the signal is not good normally at the physical level since this is a nonintrusive DS-3 test.
   a. Cause of the problem may be
      - Unterminated plugs
      - Taps on the line
      - Equipment grounded incorrectly
      - Static Charges

Figure I–15
Double ended test of a T1 circuit.

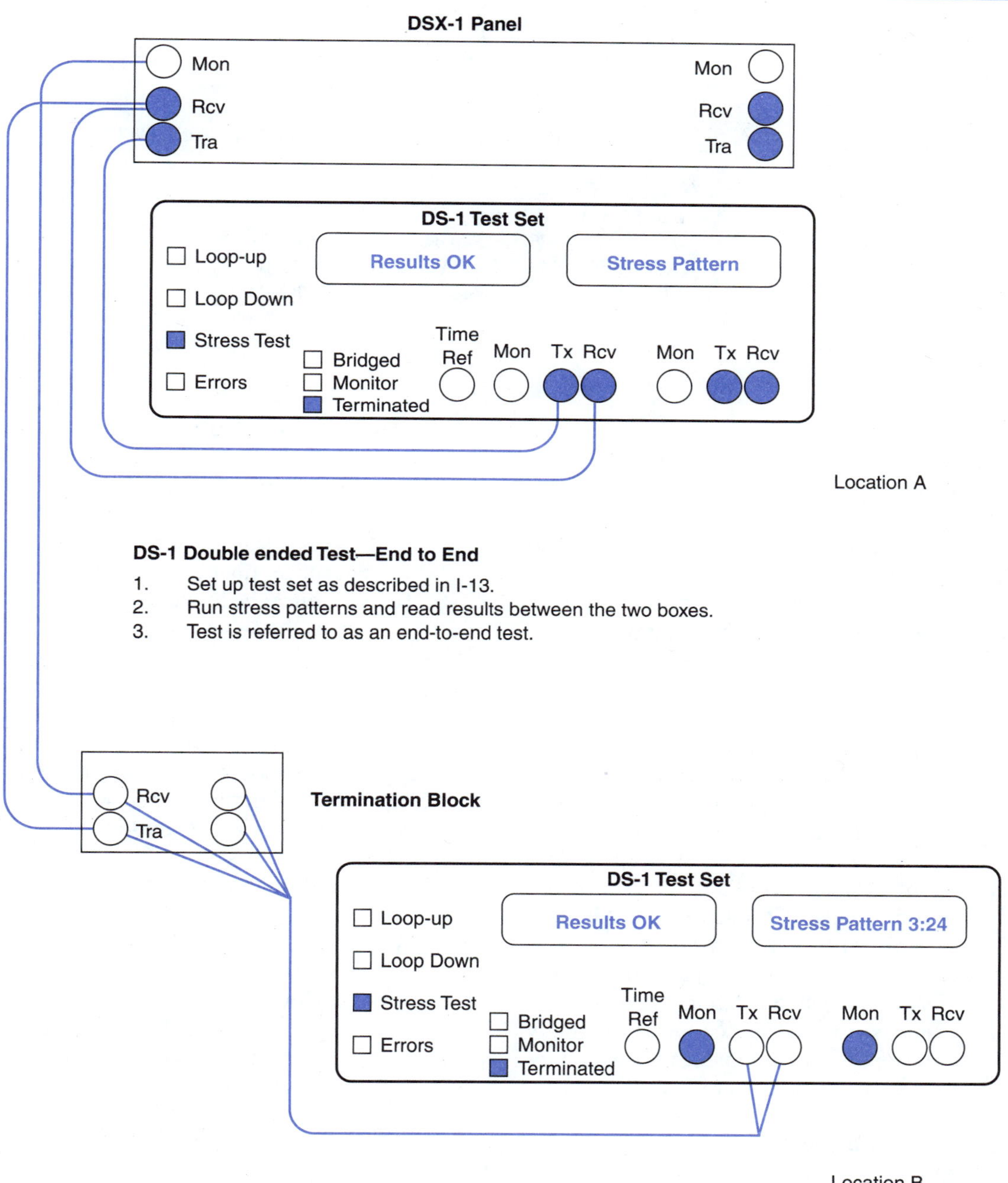

Table I–2
Common stress patterns used to stress a T1 link.

Stress Patterns used on T1 links are:

- QRSS–Pseudorandom sequence generates every combination of patterns to stress circuit.
- 3:24–Stresses ones density and maximum zeros.
- 1:7–Stresses the timing recovery of repeaters.
- 2:6–Used to determine if equipment mis-optioned for B8ZS.
- All Ones–Stresses for DC current problems, repeater problems.
- All Zeros–Stresses for All Zeros rule (Clear Channel).
- 55 Octets–Stress Repeaters.

II. Intrusive tests
1. Two intrusive tests may be performed on the out of service DS-3—jitter test and a BERT test.
2. A loopback may be placed at one of the ends of the circuit, or two test sets one on each end may be used to perform this test. Loopbacks on DS-3 circuits are normally placed at the DSX-3 panel using a coax jumper.
   a. The test set sends a pattern out onto the line to stress the system.
   b. The BERT test calculates the number of bit errors experienced, then converts them into a specific BER value such as $1 \times 10 - 7$. If the circuit complies with this standard, the circuit is deemed good. If the BER rate exceeds this standard, the circuit is considered bad.
   c. Jitter is a second test performed to ensure that network timing is good. If jitter is found, the cause is normally misoptioned equipment or a poor timing source somewhere in the network.

Testing Fiber-Optic Systems

I. Testing fiber for loss
Measurement taken with an OTDR
1. Using a fiber-optic jumper connect the OTDR to the fiber to be tested as shown in Figure I–17.
2. Set up the OTDR to send 1310 nm wavelength.
3. Interpret the test result.
   a. Look for end-to-end fiber distance.
   b. Look for problems on the line such as a bad splice, fiber anomaly.
   c. Reference the loss of the span.
   d. Repeat the above test using the 1550 nm wavelength.

Measurement taken using a power meter
1. This test requires one person with a stable light source at one end of the fiber span and a second person with a power meter at the opposite end of the fiber span.
2. Connect the power meter to the fiber to be tested.
3. Set stable light source to send 1310 nm wavelength.
4. Read the results on the power meter.
   a. No signal indicates the power coming in is too low to read.
   b. Low signal (−25.0 DB to −55 dB)
      - Fibers may need to be cleaned or polished
      - Connectors are not seated correctly
      - May have fault in the fiber span
   c. High signal (−10.0 dB to −15.0 dB)
      - May need to place a pad (attenuator) to reduce signal strength
5. Repeat the test using the 1550 nm wavelength.

Figure I–16
DS-3 test setup.

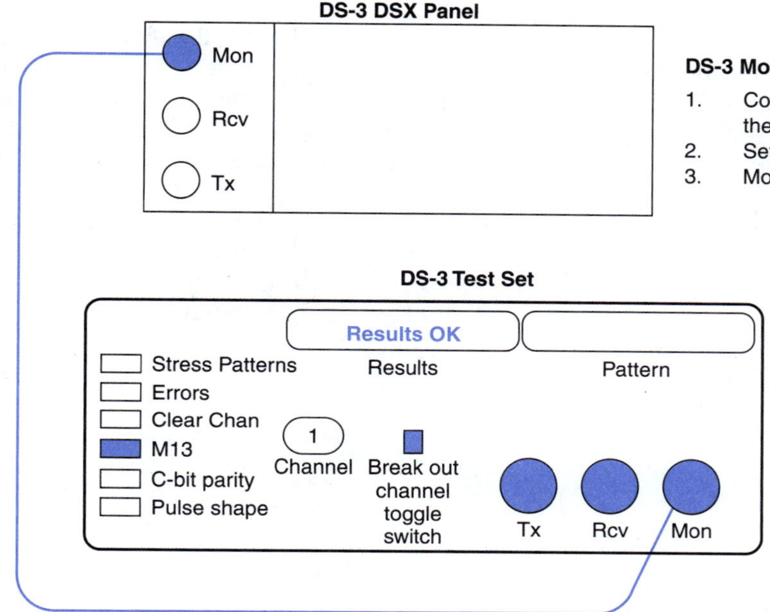

DS-3 Monitor Test Set Up

1. Connect the DS-3 Test set mon port to the mon port on the DS-3 DSX panel.
2. Set the frame type to M13.
3. Monitor results in results window.

Figure I–17
OTDR test.

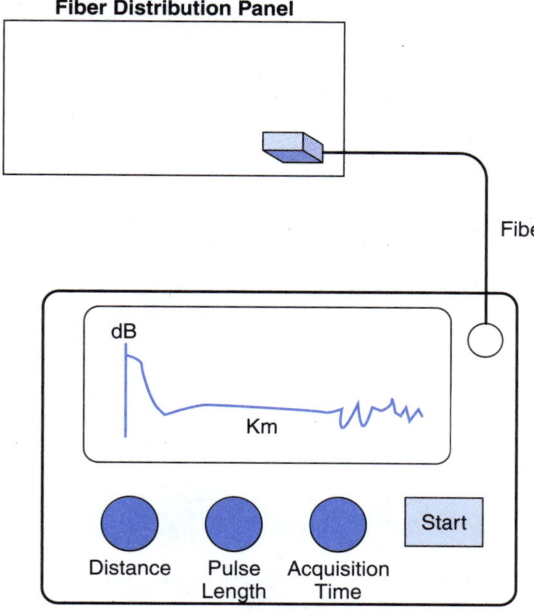

OTDR fiber test

1. Connect the port on the fiber distribution panel to the optical output of the OTDR.
2. Set the distance, pulse length and time on the meter, or press auto for auto configuration.
3. Read the trace in the window for loss, distance, splices and so forth.

Measure the return loss

1. Most OTDRs now have stable power sources plus test for return loss, therefore set up the OTDR to test for return loss measurement.
2. Interpret the test results.
   a. Return loss low (>30dB)
      - Fiber may be partially open at opposite end.
      - Fibers may be dirty or need polishing.
      - Attenuate the reflection by using a mandrel wrap on the fiber. This entails wrapping the fiber around a small object four or five times. If this increases the return loss, the problem is at the opposite end. If the value does not increase, the problem is at your end. Cleaning, polishing, or, if necessary, replacing the connector should solve the problem.

Measure the PMD of the Signal

1. PMD (polarization mode dispersion) tests require a PMD tester.

GLOSSARY

access line. A telecommunications line that continuously connects a remote station to a switching exchange. A telephone number is associated with the access line.
access method. Computer software that moves data between main storage and input/output devices.
acknowledgment. The transmission, by a receiver, of acknowledgment characters as an affirmative response to a sender.
acknowledgment character (ACK). A transmission control character transmitted by a receiver as an affirmative response to a sender.
acoustic coupler. Telecommunications equipment that permits use of a telephone handset to connect a terminal to a telephone network.
acoustic coupling. A method of coupling data terminal equipment (DTE) or a similar device to a telephone line by means of transducers that use sound waves to or from a telephone handset or equivalent.
activation. In a network, the process by which a component of a node is made ready to perform the functions for which it was designed.
active line. A telecommunications line that is currently available for transmission of data.
adaptive differential pulse code modulation (ADPCM). A variation of pulse code modulation in which only the difference in signal samples is coded.
adaptive equalizer. An equalizer circuit in a modem that adjusts itself to the exact parameters of the incoming waveform based on the known characteristics of a standard training signal.
adaptive Huffman coding. A type of character compression in which the text is continuously scanned to ensure that the fewest bits are assigned to the characters appearing most frequently.
add-in circuit board protocol converter. An electronic circuit for converting one protocol to another. Contained on a circuit board, it can be added to a personal computer or other telecommunications device.
address. (1) A character or group of characters that identifies a data source or destination. (2) To refer to a device or an item of data by its address. (3) The part of the selection signals that indicates the destination of a call.
addressing. The means by which the originator or control station selects the unit to which it is going to send a message.
addressing characters. Identifying characters sent by a device on a telecommunications line that cause a particular station (or component) to accept a message sent to it.
aerial cable. A telecommunications cable connected to poles or similar overhead structures.
aeronautical telephone service. Telephone service provided in airplanes to communicate with telephones on the ground.
airline reservation system. An online application in which a computing system is used to keep track of seat inventories, flight schedules, passenger records, and other information. The reservation system is designed to maintain up-to-date data files and to respond, within seconds, to inquiries from ticket agents at locations remote from the computing system.
algorithm. A set of mathematical rules.
all-points-addressable (APA). An attribute of a VDT or printer that allows each individual dot on the screen or spot on a page to be individually addressed for output or input.
alphanumeric character. Pertaining to a character set that contains letters, digits, and usually other characters, such as punctuation marks.
American National Standards Institute (ANSI). An organization formed for the purpose of establishing voluntary industry standards.
American Standard Code for Information Interchange (ASCII). The standard code, using a coded character set consisting of 7-bit coded characters (8 bits, including the parity check), used for information interchange among data processing systems, data communications systems, and associated equipment. The ASCII character set consists of control characters and graphic characters.
amplifier. A device that, by enabling a received wave to control a local source of power, is capable of delivering an enlarged reproduction of the wave.
amplitude. The size or magnitude of a voltage or current analog waveform.
amplitude modulation (AM). (1) Modulation in which the amplitude of an alternating current is the characteristic varied. (2) The variation of a carrier signal's strength (amplitude) as a function of an information signal.
analog. Pertaining to data in the form of continuously variable physical quantities.

analog channel. A data communications channel on which the information transmitted can take any value between the limits defined by the channel. Voice-grade channels are analog channels.
analog signal. A signal that varies in a continuous manner. Examples are voice and music. *Contrast with* digital signal.
analog-to-digital (A/D) converter. A device that senses an analog signal and converts it to a proportional representation in digital form.
analysis. The methodical investigation of a problem and the separation of the problem into smaller related units for further detailed study.
analyst. A person who defines problems and develops algorithms and procedures for their solution.
answerback. The response of a terminal to remote control signals.
application level firewall. A firewall computer that examines and controls data at the application level. The server looks at entire messages and does a more detailed analysis of the appropriateness before making a decision as to whether to let the traffic pass.
application program interface (API). A mechanism for application programs to send data to and receive data from a LAN.
applications server. On a LAN, a computer that provides processing capacity for applications that are shared by many people.
architecture. A plan or direction that is oriented toward the needs of a user. An architecture describes "what"; it does not tell "how."
area code. A three-digit number identifying a geographic area of the U.S. and Canada to permit direct distance dialing on the telephone system.
asymmetric digital subscriber line (ADSL). A transmission technology that delivers high-speed signals over twisted pair telephone wires. Speeds vary, and are normally slower upstream than downstream, but are in the range of 16 to 640 Kbps upstream, and 1.5 to 9 Mbps downstream. *See also* digital subscriber line.
asymmetric key. In an encryption system, the key that is used for encryption and the key used for decryption are not the same. *See also* public key encryption.
asynchronous. Without a regular time relationship.
asynchronous transfer mode (ATM). A packet switching technique that uses fixed-length packets called cells and is designed to operate on high-speed lines. ATM effectively eliminates any delay in delivering the packets, making it suitable for voice or video.
asynchronous transmission (asynch). (1) Transmission in which the time of occurrence of the start of each character or block of characters is arbitrary. (2) Transmission in which each information character is individually synchronized (usually by the use of start elements and stop elements).
attention interruption. An I/O interruption caused by a terminal user pressing an attention key or its equivalent.
attenuation. A decrease in magnitude of current, voltage, or power of a signal in transmission between points. It is normally expressed in decibels.
attenuation distortion. The deformation of an analog signal that occurs when the signal does not attenuate evenly across its frequency range.
audio frequencies. Frequencies that can be heard by the human ear (approximately 15 Hertz to 20,000 Hertz).
audio response unit. An output device that provides a spoken response to digital inquiries from a telephone or other device. The response is composed from a prerecorded vocabulary of words and can be transmitted over telecommunications lines to the location from which the inquiry originated.
audiotex. A voice mail system that can access a database on a computer.
audit. To review and examine the activities of a system, mainly to test the adequacy and effectiveness of control procedures.
audit trail. A manual or computerized means for tracing the transactions affecting the contents of a record.
authorization code. A code, typically made up of the user's identification and password, used to protect against unauthorized access to data and system facilities.
auto answer. *See* automatic answering.
auto dial. *See* automatic dialing.
auto-poll. A feature that allows a piece of hardware to poll stations and accept a negative response without interrupting a higher level piece of hardware or software.
automated attendant. A type of telephone service in which a computer with a voice response unit is programmed to answer a telephone and direct the call to a person, based on input from the caller.
automatic answering. (1) Answering in which the called data terminal equipment (DTE) automatically responds to the calling signal; the call may be established whether or not the called DTE is attended. (2) A machine feature that allows a transmission control unit or a station to respond automatically to a call that it receives over a switched line.
automatic call distribution (ACD) unit. A device attached to a telephone system that routes the next incoming call to the next available agent.
automatic dialing. A capability that allows a computer program or an operator using a keyboard to send commands to a modem, causing it to dial a telephone number.
automatic number identification (ANI). A capability of the telephone system to provide the number of the calling party to the called party as the telephone is ringing. Usually the number is displayed on a small screen on the telephone or on a separate box with a screen that is connected between the telephone line and the telephone.
automatic repeat request (ARQ). An error correction technique. When the receiving DTE detects an error, it signals the transmitting DTE to resend the data.
automatic-send-receive (ASR). A teletypewriter unit with keyboard, printer, paper tape reader/transmitter, and paper tape punch. This combination of units may be used online or offline and, in some cases, online and offline concurrently.
automatic teller machine (ATM). A specialized computer terminal that enables consumers to conduct banking transactions without the assistance of a bank teller.

availability. Having a system or service operational when a user wants to use it.

backbone circuit. The main circuit in a network.
backbone network. The main network in a particular network system.
background noise. Phenomena in all electrical circuitry resulting from the movement of electrons. *Also known as* white noise *or* Gaussian noise.
balun. An acronym that stands for balanced-unbalanced; also the name of a device that connects two different types of wire or cable. The balun is a small transformer that converts the electrical and physical characteristics of one wire type to another, e.g., from coaxial cable to twisted-pair wire.
bandwidth. The difference, expressed in Hertz, between the two limiting frequencies of a band.
bandwidth-on-demand. A concept whereby a person or device can acquire (and presumably pay for) large amounts of bandwidth on very short notice to transmit data at very high speeds, and then relinquish the bandwidth for other uses when it is not needed.
bar code reader. A device that reads codes printed in the form of bars on merchandise or tags.
base group. Telephone company terminology for a 48 kHz signal that contains twelve 4 kHz voice signals.
baseband. A form of modulation in which signals are pulsed directly on the transmission medium. In local area networks, baseband also implies the digital transmission of data.
baseband transmission. Transmission using baseband techniques. The signal is transmitted in digital form using the entire bandwidth of a circuit or cable. Typically used in local area networks.
basic access. A method of accessing an ISDN network in which the user has two 64-kbps B channels and one 16-kbps D channel. This type of access is also known as 2B+D.
basic business transactions. Fundamental operational units of business activity.
basic services. Services performed by the common carriers to provide the transportation of information. Basic services are regulated. *Contrast with* enhanced services.
batch. A set of data accumulated over a period of time.
batch processing. (1) Processing data or performing jobs accumulated in advance so that each accumulation is processed or accomplished in the same run. (2) Processing data accumulated over a period of time.
batched communication. A large body of data sent from one station to another station in a network without intervening responses from the receiving unit. *Contrast with* inquiry/response communication.
baud. A unit of signaling speed equal to the number of discrete conditions or signal events per second. If the duration of a signal event is 20 milliseconds, the modulation rate is 1 second / 20 milliseconds = 50 baud.
Baudot code. A code for the transmission of data in which 5 equal-length bits represent one character. This code is used in some teletypewriter machines, where one start element and one stop element are added.
Bell Operating Companies (BOCs). The 22 telephone companies that were members of the Bell System before divestiture.
Bell System. The collection of companies headed by AT&T and consisting of the 22 Bell Operating Companies and the Western Electric Corporation. The Bell System was dismantled by divestiture on January 1, 1984.
bid. In the contention form of invitation or selection, an attempt by the computer or by a station to gain control of the line so that it can transmit data. A bid may be successful or unsuccessful in seizing a circuit in that group. *Contrast with* seize.
binary. (1) Pertaining to a selection, choice, or condition that has two possible values or states. (2) Pertaining to the base two numbering system.
binary code. A code that makes use of exactly two distinct characters, usually 0 and 1.
Binary-Coded Decimal (BCD) code. A binary-coded notation in which each of the decimal digits is represented by a binary numeral; for example, in binary-coded decimal notation that uses the weights 8-4-2-1, the number 23 is represented by 0010 0011. Compare this to its representation in the pure binary numeration system, which is 10111.
binary digit. (1) In binary notation, either the character 0 or 1. (2) *Synonym for* bit.
Binary Synchronous Communications (BISYNC). (1) Communications using binary synchronous protocol. (2) A uniform procedure, using a standardized set of control characters and control character sequences, for synchronous transmission of binary-coded data between stations.
bipolar, nonreturn-to-zero (NRZ). A signaling method whereby the voltage is constant during a bit time. Most commonly, a negative voltage represents one binary value and a positive voltage is used to represent the other.
bipolar, return-to-zero. Signals that have the 1 bits represented by a positive voltage and the 0 bits represented by a negative voltage. Between pulses, the voltage always returns to zero. *Contrast with* bipolar, nonreturn-to-zero.
bit. Synonym for binary digit.
bit-oriented protocol. A communications protocol that uses bits, singly or in combination, to control the communications.
bit rate. The speed at which bits are transmitted, usually expressed in bits per second (bps).
bit stream. A binary signal without regard to grouping by character.
bit stuffing. (1) The occasional insertion of a dummy bit in a bit stream. (2) In SDLC, a 0 bit inserted after all strings of five consecutive 1 bits in the header and data portion of the message. At the receiving end, the extra 0 bit is removed by the hardware.
bit synchronization. A method of ensuring that a communications circuit is sampled at the appropriate time to determine the presence or absence of a bit.
bits per second (bps). The basic unit of speed on a data communications circuit.
blank character. A graphic representation of the space character.

blink. Varying the intensity of one or more characters displayed on a VDT several times per second to catch the operator's attention.
block. (1) A string of records, a string of words, or a character string formed for technical or logic reasons to be treated as an entity. (2) A set of things, such as words, characters, or digits, handled as a unit. (3) A group of bits, or characters, transmitted as a unit. An encoding procedure generally is applied to the group of bits or characters for error control purposes. (4) That portion of a message terminated by an EOB or ETB line control character or, if it is the last block in the message, by an EOT or ETX line control character.
block check. That part of the error control procedure used for determining that a data block is structured according to given rules.
block check character (BCC). In longitudinal redundancy checking and cyclic redundancy checking, a character that is transmitted by the sender after each message block and is compared with a block check character computed by the receiver to determine if the transmission was successful.
block error rate. The ratio of the number of blocks incorrectly received to the total number of blocks sent.
block length. (1) The number of records, words, or characters in a block. (2) A measure of the size of a block, usually specified in units, such as records, words, computer words, or characters.
blocking. (1) The process of combining incoming messages into a single message. (2) In a telephone switching system, the inability to make a connection or obtain a service because the devices needed for the connection are in use.
Bluetooth. A technology for wireless connectivity within a 33-foot radius.
bridge. A device that allows data to be sent from one network to another so terminals on both networks can communicate as though a single network existed.
broadband. (1) A communications channel having a bandwidth greater than a voice-grade channel and therefore capable of higher speed data transmission. (2) In local area networks, an analog transmission with frequency division multiplexing.
broadband ISDN (BISDN). An enhanced ISDN service that provides full duplex data transmission at either 155.52 or 622.08 Mbps, or an asymmetrical circuit that provides 155.52 Mbps in one direction and 622.08 Mbps in the other.
broadband transmission. A transmission technique of a local area network in which the signal is transmitted in analog form with frequency division multiplexing.
broadcast. The simultaneous transmission to a number of stations.
broadcast routing. A type of routing in which messages are sent to all stations on a network. Stations for which the messages are not intended ignore them.
brouter. A device that provides the functions of a bridge and router.
browser. A program designed to allow easy access to the Internet's World Wide Web including its text, graphic, audio, and visual content. Popular browsers include Microsoft's Internet Explorer and Netscape's Navigator.
buffer. A portion of memory designated as a temporary storage place for data. Buffers are frequently used to hold data arriving from a telecommunications line until a complete unit of data is received, at which time the complete unit is passed to a computer for processing.
buffering. The storage of bits or characters until they are specifically released. For example, a buffered terminal is one in which the keyed characters are stored in an internal storage area or buffer until a special key, such as the CARRIAGE RETURN or ENTER key, is pressed. Then all of the characters stored in the buffer are transmitted to the host computer in one operation.
bus. (1) One or more conductors used for transmitting signals or power. (2) In a local area network, a physical facility from where data is transferred to all destinations, but from which only addressed destinations may read in accordance with appropriate conventions or protocols.
bus network. A network topology in which multiple nodes are attached to a single circuit of limited length. A bus network is typically a local area network that transmits data at high speed.
business machine. Customer-provided data terminal equipment (DTE) that connects to a communications common carrier's telecommunications equipment for the purpose of data movement.
business machine clocking. An oscillator supplied by the business machine for regulating the bit rate of transmission. *Contrast with* data set clocking.
busy hour. The hour of the day when the traffic carried on a network is the highest.
bypass. Installing private telecommunications circuits to avoid using those of a carrier.
byte. An 8-bit binary character operated on as a unit.
byte-count-oriented protocol. A protocol that uses a special character to mark the beginning of the header, followed by a count field that indicates how many characters are in the data portion of the message.

cable modem. A modem that links a DTE to a television system cable.
cabling plan. A document that describes how the wiring and/or cabling will be installed.
callback. A security technique used with dial-up lines. After a user calls and identifies himself or herself, the computer breaks the connection and calls the user back at a predetermined telephone number. In some systems, the number at which the user wishes to be called back can be specified when the initial connection is made and before the computer disconnects.
callback unit. A hardware device that performs the callback function.
call control procedure. The implementation of a set of protocols necessary to establish, maintain, and release a call.
call detail recording (CDR). *See* station message detail recording (SMDR).
call progress signal. A call control signal transmitted from the data circuit-terminating equipment (DCE) to the call-

ing data terminal equipment (DTE) to indicate the progress of the establishment of a call, the reason why the connection could not be established, or any other network condition.

call setup time. The time taken to connect a switched telephone call. The time between the end of dialing and answering by the receiving party.

camp-on. A method of holding a call for a line that is in use and of signaling when it becomes free.

carriage-return character (CR). A format effector that causes the print or display position to move to the first position on the same line. *Contrast with* line feed character (LF).

carrier. (1) A company that provides the telecommunications networks. *See* communications common carrier. (2) A communications signal. *See* carrier wave.

carrier sense multiple access with collision avoidance (CSMA/CA). A communications protocol used on local area networks in which a station listens to the circuit before transmitting in an attempt to avoid collisions.

carrier sense multiple access with collision detection (CSMA/CD). A communications protocol frequently used on local area networks in which stations, on detecting a collision of data caused by multiple simultaneous transmissions, wait a random period of time before retransmitting.

carrier system. A means of obtaining a number of channels over a single circuit by modulating each channel on a different carrier frequency and demodulating at the receiving point to restore the signals to their original form.

carrier wave. An analog signal that in itself contains no information.

cathode ray tube terminal (CRT). A particular type of video display terminal that uses a vacuum tube display in which a beam of electrons can be controlled to form alphanumeric characters or symbols on a luminescent screen, for example, by use of a dot matrix.

CCITT. *See* Consultative Committee on International Telegraphy and Telephony (CCITT).

cell. A fixed-length packet in an asynchronous transfer mode (ATM) system.

cell relay. *See* asynchronous transfer mode (ATM).

cellular telephone service. A system for handling telephone calls to and from moving automobiles. Cities are divided into small geographic areas called *cells.* Telephone calls are transmitted to and from low-power radio transmitters in each cell. Calls are passed from one transmitter to another as the automobile leaves one cell and enters another.

cellular telephone system. A telephone system in which the geographic area to be covered is divided into small sections called *cells.* A transmitter/receiver in each cell relays telephone calls to cellular telephones located within the cell.

centa. One hundred.

centa call seconds (CCS). A measure of equipment or circuit utilization. One centa call second is 100 seconds of utilization.

centi. One hundredth.

central office. In the United States, the place where communications common carriers terminate customer lines and locate the equipment that interconnects those lines.

central office switch. The equipment in a telephone company central office that allows any circuit to be connected to any other.

centralized network. *Synonym for* star network.

centralized routing. A routing system in which the destination of all messages is determined by a single piece of hardware or software.

Centrex. Central office telephone equipment serving subscribers at one location on a private automatic branch exchange basis. The system allows such services as direct inward dialing, direct distance dialing, and console switchboards.

change control. A disciplined approach to managing changes.

change coordination meeting. A meeting held to ensure that changes to a system are properly approved and communicated to all interested parties.

change management. The application of management principles to ensure that changes in a system are controlled to minimize the impact on system users.

channel. (1) A one-way communications path. (2) In information theory, that part of a communications system that connects the message source with the message sink.

channel group. *See* base group.

channel service unit (CSU). *See* data service unit (DSU).

character. A member of a set of elements upon which agreement has been reached and that is used for the organization, control or representation of data. Characters may be letters, digits, punctuation marks, or other symbols, often represented in the form of a spatial arrangement of adjacent or connected strokes or in the form of other physical conditions in data media.

character assignments. Unique groups of bits assigned to represent the various characters in a code.

character compression. A type of compression in which characters are represented by a shortened number of bits, depending on the frequency with which the character is used.

character-oriented protocol. A communications protocol that uses special characters to indicate the beginning and end of messages. BISYNC is a character-oriented protocol.

character set. A set of unique representations called *characters,* for example, the 26 letters of the English alphabet, 0 and 1 of the Boolean alphabet, the set of signals in the Morse code alphabet, and the 128 ASCII characters.

character stripping. A data compression technique in which leading and trailing control characters are removed from a message before it is sent through a telecommunications system.

character synchronization. A technique for ensuring that the proper sets of bits on a communications line are grouped to form characters.

Cheapernet. *See* thin Ethernet.

check bit. (1) A binary check digit, for example, a parity bit. (2) A bit associated with a character or block for the purpose of checking for the absence of error within the character or block.

checkpoint record. The contents of a computer's memory and other control information that are stored on disk or tape at predetermined intervals so that the computer may be restarted after a failure.

checkpoint/restart. The process of recording a checkpoint record on disk or other nonvolatile media and later using that information to restart a computer that has failed.

chief information officer (CIO). A title sometimes given to the highest ranking executive in charge of a company's information resources.

chip. (1) A minute piece of semiconductive material used in the manufacture of electronic components. (2) An integrated circuit on a piece of semiconductive material.

ciphertext. The character stream or text that is the output of an encryption algorithm. *See also* plaintext.

circuit. The path over which two-way communications take place.

circuit grade. The information-carrying capability of a circuit in speed or type of signal. The grades of circuits are broadband, voice, subvoice, and telegraph. For data use, these grades are identified with certain speed ranges.

circuit noise level. The ratio of the circuit noise to some arbitrary amount chosen as the reference. This ratio normally is indicated in decibels above the reference noise.

circuit speed. The number of bits that a circuit can carry per unit of time, typically 1 second. Circuit speed is normally measured in bits per second.

circuit-switched data transmission service. A service using circuit switching to establish and maintain a connection before data can be transferred between data terminal equipments (DTEs).

circuit switching. The temporary establishment of a connection between two pieces of equipment that permits the exclusive use until the connection is released. The connection is set up on demand and discontinued when the transmission is complete. An example is a dial-up telephone connection.

city code. In the telephone numbering system, a single- or multidigit code that is uniquely assigned to a city within a country.

cladding. The glass that surrounds the core of an optical fiber and acts as a mirror to the core.

client. In a client-server computing system, the user or using computer that takes advantage of the facilities or services of server computers.

client-server computing. A type of distributed processing in which certain computers, called servers, provide standardized capabilities, such as printing, database management, or communications, to other computers that are called clients.

clock. (1) A device that measures and indicates time. (2) A device that generates periodic signals used for synchronization. (3) Equipment that provides a time base used in a transmission system to control the timing of certain functions, such as sampling, and to control the duration of signal elements.

clock pulse. A synchronization signal provided by a clock.

clocking. The use of clock pulses to control synchronization of data and control characters.

cluster. A station that consists of a control unit (cluster controller) and the terminals attached to it.

cluster control unit (CCU). A device that can control the input/output operations of more than one device connected to it. A cluster control unit may be controlled by a program stored and executed in the unit, or it may be controlled entirely by hardware.

coaxial cable. A cable consisting of one conductor, usually a small copper tube or wire, within and insulated from another conductor of larger diameter, usually copper tubing or copper braid.

code. (1) A set of unambiguous rules specifying the manner in which data may be represented in a discrete form. (2) A predetermined set of symbols that have specific meanings.

code conversion. A process for changing the bit grouping for a character in one code into the corresponding bit grouping for a character in a second code.

code converter. A device that changes the representation of data, using one code in the place of another or one coded character set in the place of another.

code division multiple access (CDMA). A transmission technique used in digital radio technology that combines time division and frequency division multiple access techniques, yielding higher capacity and better security than either of them.

code efficiency. Using the least number of bits to convey the meaning of a character with accuracy.

code-independent data communications. A mode of data communications that uses a character-oriented link protocol that does not depend on the character set or code used by the data source.

code points. The number of possible combinations in a coding system.

code transparent data communication. A mode of data communications that uses a bit-oriented link protocol that does not depend on the bit sequence structure used by the data source.

codec. A device that converts analog signals to digital signals or vice versa.

coded character set. A set of unambiguous rules that establish a character set and the one-to-one relationships between the characters of the set and their coded representations. *Synonymous with* code.

coding scheme. *See* code (1).

collision. Two (or more) terminals trying to transmit a message at the same time, thereby causing both messages to be garbled and unintelligible at the receiving end.

committed information rate (CIR). The contracted transmission speed on a frame relay circuit. Data sent within the CIR is highly likely to get through the network unless extremely severe network congestion occurs. Data sent above the CIR is subject to discard if the network gets congested.

common carrier. *See* communications common carrier.

common channel interoffice signaling (CCIS). A system for sending signals between central offices in a telephone network.
Common Management Information Protocol (CMIP). An ISO standard protocol for exchanging network management commands and information between devices attached to a network.
communication. (1) A process that allows information to pass between a sender and one or more receivers. (2) The transfer of meaningful information from one location to a second location. (3) The art of expressing ideas, especially in speech and writing. (4) The science of transmitting information, especially in symbols.
communications access method (CAM). Computer software that reads and writes data from and to communications lines. *Synonym for* telecommunications access method (TCAM).
communications adapter. An optional hardware feature, available on certain processors, that permits telecommunications lines to be attached to the processors.
communications common carrier. In the USA and Canada, a public data transmission service that provides the general public with transmission service facilities, for example, a telephone or telegraph company.
communications controller. A hardware device that manages the details of line control and sometimes data routing through a network. *See also* front-end processor (FEP).
communications directory. An online or hard copy document that lists the names and telephone numbers of a company's employees and departments as well as other information, such as terminal names or user IDs, that is pertinent to communications.
communications facility. *See* telecommunications facility.
communications line. Deprecated term for telecommunications line or transmission line.
communications network. A collection of communications circuits managed as a single entity.
communications server. (1) A server on a LAN that provides connections to other computers or networks. (2) A server based telephone system that is attached to both the public telephone network and to a LAN. With time, the capabilities of these two types of communication server are coming closer together.
communications standards. Standards established to ensure compatibility among several communications services or several types of communications equipment.
communications theory. The mathematical discipline dealing with the probabilistic features of data transmission in the presence of noise.
compaction. *See* compression.
compandor (compressor-expandor). Equipment that compresses the outgoing speech volume range and expands the incoming speech volume range on a long distance telephone circuit. Such equipment can make more efficient use of voice telecommunications channels.
competitive local exchange carrier (CLEC). Carriers that have no ties to the old Bell system and are, in general, aggressively promoting new telecommunications services. In some cases these carriers are building their own new digital networks, and in other cases they lease network bandwidth from other LECs.
compression. The process of eliminating redundant characters or bits from a data stream before it is stored or transmitted.
computer-aided design (CAD). The use of a computer with special terminals and software for engineering design and drafting. *Synonym for* computer-assisted drafting (CAD).
computer-assisted drafting (CAD). *See* computer-aided design (CAD).
computer branch exchange (CBX). *See* private automatic branch exchange (PABX) *and* private branch exchange (PBX).
Computer Inquiry I (CI–I). A study conducted by the FCC, concluded in 1971, that examined the relationship between the telecommunications and data processing industries to determine which aspects of both industries should be regulated for the long term.
Computer Inquiry II (CI–II). A study conducted by the FCC, concluded in 1981, that accelerated the deregulation of the telecommunications industry.
Computer Inquiry III (CI–III). A study conducted by the FCC to determine to what extent AT&T and the BOCs are allowed to provide enhanced (data processing) services in the network.
computer network. A complex consisting of two or more interconnected computing units.
computer virus. An executable computer program that causes unwanted events in a computer such as the destruction of data. Most viruses attach themselves to other programs. Viruses are spread when programs to which they are attached are copied or downloaded.
concentration. The process of combining multiple messages into a single message for transmission. *Contrast with* deconcentration.
concentrator. (1) In data transmission, a functional unit that permits a common transmission medium to serve more data sources than there are channels currently available within the transmission medium. (2) Any device that combines incoming messages into a single message (concentration) or extracts individual messages from the data sent in a single transmission sequence (deconcentration).
conditioned line. A communications line on which the specifications for amplitude and distortion have been tightened. Signals traveling on a conditioned circuit are less likely to encounter errors than on an unconditioned circuit.
conditioning. The addition of equipment to a leased voice-grade circuit to provide minimum values of line characteristics required for data transmission.
conducted media. Any medium where the signal flows through a physical entity such as twisted pair wire, coaxial cable, or optical fiber.
configuration control. The maintenance of records that identify and keep track of all of the equipment in a system.

connection-oriented routing. A transmission through a network using a virtual or real circuit between the sender and receiver.

connectionless routing. A transmission through a network when no virtual or real circuit has been established between the sender and receiver. Packets are sent into the network by the sender, and each travels independently to the receiver, which must then reassemble them into a message.

Consultative Committee on International Telegraphy and Telephony (CCITT). The previous name for the International Telecommunications Union-Telecommunications Standardization Sector (ITU-T).

continuous ARQ. An error correction technique in which data blocks are continuously sent over the forward channel, while ACKs and NAKs are sent over the reverse channel. *Contrast with* stop and wait ARQ.

control character. A character whose occurrence in a particular context initiates, modifies, or stops a control operation. A control character may be recorded for use in a subsequent action, and it may have a graphic representation in some circumstances.

control station. A station on a network that assumes control of the network's operation. A typical control station exerts its control by polling and addressing. *Contrast with* slave station.

control terminal. Any active terminal on a network at which a user is authorized to enter commands affecting system operation.

control unit. A device that controls input/output operations at one or more devices. *See also* controller *and* cluster control unit (CCU).

controller. A device that directs the transmission of data over the data links of a network. Its operations may be controlled by a program executed in a processor to which the controller is connected, or they may be controlled by a program executed within the device. *See* cluster control unit (CCU) *and* communications controller.

conversational mode. A mode of operation of a data processing system in which a sequence of alternating entries and responses between a user and the system takes place in a manner similar to a dialogue between two persons. *Synonym for* interactive.

cordless telephones. Telephones in which the base and the handset contain small transceivers, which broadcast to each other and which allow the people using them to move away from the base unit during a conversation.

core. The glass or plastic center conductor of an optical fiber that provides the transmission carrying capability.

cost center. An accounting term used to designate a department or other entity where costs are accumulated. Departments that are cost centers do not make a profit by selling or recharging their services. *Contrast with* profit center.

creeping commitment of resources. A concept of project management that suggests that the resources dedicated to a project should only be increased as the scope of the project becomes better defined. The intention is to minimize the amount of resources spent in case the project is determined to be infeasible or is otherwise canceled.

crossbar switch. A device that makes a connection between one line in each of two sets of lines. The two sets are physically arranged along adjacent sides of a matrix of contacts or switch points.

crosstalk. The unwanted energy transferred from one circuit, called the *disturbing circuit,* to another circuit, called the *disturbed circuit.*

current beam position. On a CRT display device, the coordinates on the display surface at which the electron beam is aimed.

current loop. An interface between a terminal and a circuit that indicates 1 and 0 bits by the presence or absence of an electrical current.

cursor. (1) In computer graphics, a movable marker that indicates a position on a display space. (2) A displayed symbol that acts as a marker to help the user locate a point in text, in a system command, or in storage. (3) A movable spot of light on the screen of a display device that usually indicates where the next character is to be entered, replaced, or deleted.

cursor control keys. The keys that control the movement of the cursor.

customer premise equipment (CPE). Any communications equipment that is located on customer premises, such as telephones, personal computers, fax machines, telephone systems, PBXs, key systems, routers, and hubs.

cut-through switch. A type of switch that reads the destination address of a packet and immediately begins sending the packet to the destination before the entire packet has been received by the switch.

cycle. A complete wave of an analog signal. The frequency is the number of cycles that are completed in one second.

cycle stealing. Interrupting a computer to store each character coming from a telecommunications line in the computer's memory.

cyclic redundancy checking (CRC). (1) An error checking technique in which the check key is generated by a cyclic algorithm. (2) A system of error checking performed at both the sending and receiving stations after a block check character has been accumulated.

data. (1) A representation of facts, concepts, or instructions in a formalized manner suitable for communication, interpretation, or processing by human or automatic means. (2) Any representations, such as characters or analog quantities, to which meaning is, or might be, assigned.

data access arrangement (DAA). Equipment that permits attachment of privately owned data terminal equipment and telecommunications equipment to the public telephone network.

data circuit. Associated transmit and receive channels that provide a means of two-way data communications.

data circuit-terminating equipment (DCE). The equipment installed at the user's premises that provides all the functions required to establish, maintain, and terminate a connection and the signal conversion and coding between the data terminal equipment (DTE) and the line.

data communications. (1) The transmission and reception of data. (2) The transmission, reception, and validation of data. (3) Data transfer between data source and data sink via one or more data links according to appropriate protocols.

data communications channel. A means of one-way transmission.

data encryption standard (DES). A cryptographic algorithm designed to encipher and decipher data using a 64-bit cryptographic key as specified in the Federal Information Processing Standard Publication 46, January 15, 1977.

data integrity. The quality of data that exists as long as accidental or malicious destruction, alteration, or loss of data is prevented.

data link. (1) The physical means of connecting one location to another to transmit and receive data. (2) The interconnecting data circuit between two or more pieces of equipment operating in accordance with a link protocol. It does not include the data source and the data sink.

data link control character. A control character intended to control or facilitate transmission of data over a network.

data link escape (DLE) character. A transmission control character that changes the meaning of a limited number of contiguous following characters or coded representations and that is used exclusively to provide supplementary transmission control characters.

data link protocol. The rules governing the operation of a data link. *See* protocol.

data network. The assembly of functional units that establishes data circuits between pieces of data terminal equipment (DTE).

data PBX. A switch especially designed for switching data calls. Data PBXs do not handle voice calls.

Data-Phone. Both a service mark and a trademark of AT&T and the Bell System. As a service mark, it indicates the transmission of data over the telephone network. As a trademark, it identifies the telecommunications equipment furnished by the Bell System for transmission services.

data processing (DP). The systematic performance of operations upon data, for example, handling, merging, sorting, and computing. *Synonym for* information processing.

data processing system. A system, including computer systems and associated personnel, that performs input, processing, storage, output, and control functions to accomplish a sequence of operations on data.

data security. The protection of data against unauthorized disclosure, transfer, modifications, or destruction, whether accidental or intentional.

data service unit/channel service unit (DSU/CSU). An interface device that ensures that the digital signal entering a communications line is properly shaped into square pulses and precisely timed.

data set clocking. A time-based oscillator supplied by the modem for regulating the bit rate of transmission.

data sink. (1) A functional unit that accepts data after transmission. It may originate error control signals. (2) The part of data terminal equipment (DTE) that receives data from a data link.

data terminal equipment (DTE). The part of a data station that serves as a data source, data sink, or both and provides for the data communications control function according to protocols.

data transfer rate. The average number of bits, characters, or blocks per unit of time transferred from a data source to a data sink. The rate is usually expressed as bits, characters, or blocks per second, minute, or hour.

datagram. In packet switching, a self-contained packet that is independent of other packets, that does not require acknowledgment, and that carries information sufficient for routing from the originating data terminal equipment (DTE) to the destination DTE without relying on earlier exchanges between DTEs and the network.

dB meter. A meter having a scale calibrated to read directly in decibel values at a reference level that must be specified (usually 1 milliwatt equals Φ dB). Used in audio-frequency amplifier circuits of broadcast stations, public address systems, and receiver output circuits to indicate volume level.

dBm. Decibel based on 1 milliwatt.

deactivation. In a network, the process of taking any element out of service, rendering it inoperable, or placing it in a state in which it cannot perform the functions for which it was designed.

decibel (dB). (1) A unit that expresses the ratio of two power levels on a logarithmic scale. (2) A unit for measuring relative power. The number of decibels is 10 times the logarithm (base 10) of the ratio of the measured power levels. If the measured levels are voltages (across the same or equal resistance), the number of decibels is 20 times the log of the ratio.

DECNET. A family of hardware and software that implement Digital Network Architecture (DNA).

deconcentration. The process of extracting individual messages from data sent in a single transmission sequence. *Contrast with* concentration.

decryption. Converting encrypted data into clear data. *Contrast with* encryption.

dedicated hardware protocol converter. Electronic circuitry that has as its sole purpose the conversion of one protocol to another.

delta modulation. A technique of digitizing an analog signal by comparing the values of two successive samples and assigning a 1 bit if the second sample has a greater value and a 0 bit if the second sample has a lesser value.

demand priority access method (DPAM). The media access technique used on 100VG-AnyLAN technology.

demarcation point. The physical and electrical boundary between the telephone company responsibility and the customer responsibility.

demodulation. The process of retrieving intelligence (data) from a modulated carrier wave. *Reverse of* modulation.

demodulator. A device that performs demodulation.

destination code. A code in a message header containing the name of a terminal or application program to which the message is directed.

destructive cursor. On a VDT device, a cursor that erases any character through which it passes as it is advanced, backspaced, or otherwise moved. *Contrast with* nondestructive cursor.

detector. Circuitry that separates a received signal into its component parts, typically the carrier and the modulation.
device control character. A control character used for the control of ancillary devices associated with a data processing system or data communications system, for example, for switching such devices on or off.
dial. To use a dial or push-button telephone to initiate a telephone call. In telecommunications, this action is taken to attempt to establish a connection between a terminal and a telecommunications device over a switched line.
dial backup. A technique for bypassing the failure of a private or leased circuit. When a failure occurs, a switched connection is made so that communications can be reinstated.
dial line. *Synonym for* switched connection.
dial pulse. An interruption in the DC loop of a calling telephone. The interruption is produced by breaking and making the dial pulse contacts of a calling telephone when a digit is dialed. The loop current is interrupted once for each unit of value of the digit.
dial pulsing. A signaling technique used to send a telephone number by generating electrical pulses on a telephone line.
dial tone. An audible signal indicating that a device is ready to be dialed.
dialback unit. A hardware device that performs the function of callback.
dialing. Deprecated term for calling.
dialogue. In an interactive system, a series of interrelated inquiries and responses analogous to a conversation between two people.
dial-up. The use of a dial or push-button telephone to initiate a station-to-station telephone call.
dial-up line. A line on which the connection is made by dialing. *See also* switched line.
dial-up terminal. A terminal on a switched line.
dibit. A group of two bits. In four-phase modulation, each possible dibit is encoded as one of four unique carrier phase shifts. The four possible states for a dibit are 00, 01, 10, and 11. *Contrast with* quadbit *and* tribit.
differential Manchester encoding. A digital signaling technique in which a 0 is represented by the presence of a transition at the beginning of the bit period and a 1 is represented by an absence of a transition at the beginning of the bit period. A mid-bit transition also exists to provide clocking.
differential phase shift keying (DPSK). A modulation technique in which the relative changes of the carrier signal phase are coded according to the data to be transmitted.
digital circuit. A circuit expressly designed to carry the pulses of digital signals.
Digital Data Communications Message Protocol (DDCMP). A byte-count-oriented protocol developed by Digital Equipment Corporation.
Digital Network Architecture (DNA). A communications architecture developed by Digital Equipment Corporation as a framework for all of the company's communications products.
digital satellite service (DSS). *See* direct broadcast satellite.
digital signal. A discrete or discontinuous signal; the various states of which are pulses that are discrete intervals apart. *Contrast with* analog signal.
digital signal processor (DSP). A microprocessor especially designed to analyze, enhance, or otherwise manipulate sounds, images, or other signals.
digital subscriber line (DSL). The generic name for a technology developed to enable telephone companies to deliver digitized signals to subscribers at about 1.5 Mbps over existing twisted pair copper telephone wire. *See also* asymmetric digital subscriber line, symmetric digital subscriber line, *and* very high rate digital subscriber line.
digital switching. A process in which connections are established by operations on digital signals without converting them to analog signals.
digital-to-analog (D/A) converter. A device that converts a digital value to a proportional analog signal.
digitize. To express or represent in a digital form data that is not discrete data, for example, to obtain a digital representation of the magnitude of a physical quantity from an analog representation of that magnitude.
digitizing distortion. *See* quantizing noise.
direct broadcast satellite (DBS). A satellite with the primary purpose of sending signals directly to small antennas in homes or businesses. Because the receiving antennas are small, the satellite normally has a relatively high-powered transmitter.
direct current (DC) signaling. Signaling caused by opening and closing a direct current electrical circuit.
direct distance dialing (DDD). A telephone exchange service that enables the telephone user to call subscribers outside of the user's local service area without operator assistance.
direct inward dialing (DID). A facility that allows a telephone call to pass through a telephone system directly to an extension without operator intervention.
direct outward dialing (DOD). A facility that allows an internal caller at an extension to dial an external number without operator assistance.
direct sequence. A spread spectrum transmission technique in which bits from the original signal are combined with bits generated by a pseudorandom bit stream generator using Boolean math. The receiver, using the same pseudorandom bit stream, can reverse the Boolean math process and recover the original bits. *See also* spread spectrum *and* frequency hopping.
disconnect. To disengage the apparatus used in a connection and to restore it to its ready condition.
disconnect signal. A signal transmitted from one end of a subscriber line or trunk to indicate at the other end that the established connection is to be disconnected.
discussion group. In the context of the Internet, a group of people that meet online to discuss topics of mutual interest and to exchange ideas.
disk server. A server on a LAN that provides simulated disks to other computers.
diskless workstation. A personal computer or other terminal that does not have a hard disk, making it dependent on a server or some other computer for disk storage.

dispersion. The difference in the arrival time between signals that travel straight through the core of a fiber-optic cable and those that reflect off the cladding and, therefore, travel a slightly longer path.

display device. (1) An output unit that gives a visual representation of data. (2) In computer graphics, a device capable of presenting display elements on a display surface, for example, a terminal screen, plotter, microfilm viewer, or printer.

distinctive ringing. A ringing cadence that indicates whether a call is internal or external.

distortion. The unwanted change in wave form that occurs between two points in a transmission system. The six major forms of distortion are (1) *bias:* a type of telegraph distortion resulting when the significant intervals of the modulation do not all have their exact theoretical durations, (2) *characteristic:* distortion caused by transients that, as a result of the modulation, are present in the transmission channel and depend on its transmission qualities, (3) *delay:* distortion that occurs when the envelope delay of a circuit or system is not constant over the frequency range required for transmission, (4) *end:* distortion of start-stop teletypewriter signals. The shifting of the end of all marking pulses from their proper positions in relation to the beginning of the start pulse, (5) *fortuitous ("jitter"):* a type of distortion that results in the intermittent shortening or lengthening of the signals. This distortion is entirely random in nature and can be caused by such things as battery fluctuations, hits on the line, and power induction, (6) *harmonic:* the resultant presence of harmonic frequencies (due to nonlinear characteristics of a transmission line) in the response when a sine wave is applied.

distributed data processing (DDP). *See* distributed processing.

distributed processing. Data processing in which some or all of the processing, storage, and control functions, in addition to input/output functions, are spread among several computers and connected by communications facilities.

distributed routing. A technique of routing messages in a network in which some or all of the nodes maintain tables that show how messages should be directed to destinations.

distribution cable. A subgrouping of individual telephone lines as they approach a central office.

distribution frame. A structure for terminating permanent wires of a telephone central office, private branch exchange, or private exchange and for permitting the easy change of connections between them by means of cross-connecting wires.

domain. In an SNA network, the resources that are under the control of one or more associated host processors.

dot matrix. A printing technique in which a matrix of wires push a ribbon against paper to leave an impression. In a variation of the dot matrix technique, the wires are heated and cause a chemical reaction on specially treated paper.

double byte character set (DBCS). A coding system that has 2^{16} code points that can be used to represent all characters in all languages. DBCSs are usually vendor-specific.

downlink. The rebroadcast of a microwave radio signal from a satellite back to earth.

downloading. The transmission of a file of data from a mainframe computer to a personal computer.

driver. *See* workload generator.

dropout. In data communications, a momentary loss in signal, usually due to the effect of noise or system malfunction.

drop wire. The wire running from a residence or business to a telephone pole or its underground equivalent.

dual-tone-multifrequency (DTMF). A method of signaling a desired telephone number by sending tones on the telephone line.

dumb terminal. A terminal that has little or no memory and is not programmable. A dumb terminal is totally dependent on the host computer for all processing capability.

duplex. *See* full-duplex (FDX).

duplex transmission. Data transmission in both directions at the same time.

dynamic routing. A technique used in data networks by which each node can determine the best way for a message to be sent to its destination.

E&M signaling. A type of signaling between a switch or PBX and a trunk in which the signaling information is transferred via two-state voltage conditions on two wires.

EBCDIC. *See* Extended Binary Coded Decimal Interchange Code.

echo. The reversal of a signal, bouncing it back to the sender, caused by an electrical wave bouncing back from an intermediate point or the distant end of a circuit.

echo check. A check to determine the correctness of the transmission of data in which the received data is returned to the source for comparison with the originally transmitted data.

echo suppressor. A device that permits transmission in only one direction at a time, thus eliminating the problems caused by the echo.

effective data transfer rate. The average number of bits, characters, or blocks per unit of time transferred from a data source to a data sink and accepted as valid.

800 service. A telephone service that lets subscribers make calls to certain zones at discounted rates. Inbound 800 service allows callers to make calls that are paid for by the called party.

electronic document interchange (EDI). The use of telecommunications to transmit documents electronically.

electronic mail (e-mail). The use of telecommunications for sending textual messages from one person to another. The capability of storing the messages in an electronic mailbox is normally a part of the electronic mail system.

electronic mailbox. Space on the disk of a computer to store electronic mail messages.

electronic switching system (ESS). Electronic switching computer for central office functions.

electronic tandem network (ETN). A private telephone network in which software in customer PBXs determines how calls should be routed over leased, private, or public telephone lines.

encryption. Transformation of data from the meaningful code that is normally transmitted, called *clear text,* to a meaningless sequence of digits and letters that must be decrypted before it becomes meaningful again. *Contrast with* decryption.

end of address (EOA). One or more transmission control characters transmitted on a line to indicate the end of nontext characters (for example, addressing characters).

end of block (EOB). A transmission control character that marks the end of a block of data.

end of message (EOM). The specific character or sequence of characters that indicates the end of a message or record.

end of text (ETX). A transmission control character sent to mark the end of the text of the message.

end of text block (ETB). A transmission control character sent to mark the end of a portion of the text of a message.

end of text character (ETX). A control character that marks the end of a message's text.

end of transmission block (ETB). A transmission control character used to indicate the end of a transmission block of data when data is divided into such blocks for transmission purposes.

end of transmission (EOT). A transmission control character used to indicate the conclusion of a transmission that may have included one or more messages.

end office. A local telephone company central office designed to serve consumers or businesses.

end system. In the context of an internet, a subnetwork that supports the users connected to it.

enhanced services. Communications services in which some processing of the information being transmitted takes place. *Contrast with* basic services.

enquiry (ENQ). A transmission control character used as a request for a response from the station with which the connection has been set up; the response may include station identification, the type of equipment in service, and the status of the remote station.

enter. To place a message on a circuit to be transmitted from a terminal to the computer.

envelope delay distortion. Distortion caused by the electrical phenomenon that not all frequencies propagate down a telecommunications circuit at exactly the same speed.

equal access. A part of the modified final judgment that specified that local telephone companies must provide all of the long distance companies access equal in type, quality, and price to that provided to AT&T.

equalization. Compensation for differences in attenuation (reduction or loss of signal) at different frequencies.

equalizer. Any combination of devices, such as coils, capacitors, or resistors, inserted in a transmission line or amplifier circuit to improve its frequency response.

equivalent four-wire system. A transmission system using frequency division to obtain full-duplex operation over only one pair of wires.

ergonomics. The study of the problems of people in adjusting to their environment, especially the science that seeks to adapt work or working conditions to suit the worker.

Erlang. A measure of communications equipment or circuit usage. One Erlang is 1 hour of equipment usage or 36 CCS.

Erlang B capacity table. A table for determining the number of circuits required to carry a certain level of telephone traffic. The Erlang B table assumes that the sources of traffic are infinite and that all unsuccessful call attempts are abandoned and not retried.

error. A discrepancy between a computed, observed, or measured value or condition and the true, specified, or theoretically correct value or condition.

error correcting code. A code in which each telegraph or data signal conforms to specific rules of construction so that departures from this construction in the receive signals can be automatically detected, permitting the automatic correction, at the receiving terminal, of some or all of the errors. Such codes require more signal elements than are necessary to convey the basic information.

error correction system. A system employing an error detecting code and so arranged that some or all of the signals detected as being in error are automatically corrected at the receiving terminal before delivery to the data sink. *Note:* In a packet switched data service, the error correcting system might result in the retransmission of at least one or more complete packets should an error be detected.

error detecting code. A code in which each element that is represented conforms to specific rules of construction so that if certain errors occur, the resulting representation will not conform to the rules, thereby indicating the presence of errors. Such codes require more signal elements than are necessary to convey the fundamental information.

error detection. The techniques employed to ensure that transmission and other errors are identified.

error message. An indication that an error has been detected.

error rate. A measure of the quality of a circuit or system; the number of erroneous bits or characters in a sample, frequently taken per 100,000 characters.

error ratio. The ratio of the number of data units in error to the total number of data units.

error recovery. The process of correcting or bypassing a fault to restore a system to a prescribed condition.

escape character (ESC). A code extension character used to indicate that the following character or group of characters is to be interpreted in a nonstandard way.

escape mechanism. A method of assigning an alternate meaning to characters in a coding system. *See* escape character (ESC).

Ethernet. A local area network that uses CSMA/CD protocol on a baseband bus.

exchange. A room or building equipped so that telecommunications lines terminated there may be interconnected as required. The equipment may include manual or automatic switching equipment.

exchange code. In the United States, the first 3 digits of a 7-digit telephone number. The exchange code designates the telephone exchange that serves the customer.

Extended Binary Coded Decimal Interchange Code (EBCDIC). A coding system consisting of 256 characters, each represented by 8 bits.

external modem. A modem that exists in its own box or cabinet.

facsimile (FAX) machine. A machine that scans a sheet of paper and converts the light and dark areas to electrical signals that can be transmitted over telephone lines.
facsimile (FAX) modem. A modem designed to follow the standards and algorithms required to send facsimiles from a computer to a facsimile machine or another computer that has a facsimile modem.
fast busy. A tone signal that indicates that a telephone call cannot be completed because all circuits are busy.
fast select polling. A polling technique in which a station without traffic to send does not need to return a character to the polling station.
fat client. An application designed such that almost all of the processing is done on the client computer, while little is done on the server. *See also* thin client.
Federal Communications Commission (FCC). A board of commissioners appointed by the president under the Communications Act of 1934. The commissioners regulate all interstate and foreign electrical telecommunications systems originating in the United States.
feeder cable. A grouping of several distribution cables as they approach a central office.
Fiber Distributed Data Interface (FDDI). A standard for transmitting data on an optical fiber.
figures shift. A physical shift in a teletypewriter that enables the printing of images, such as numbers, symbols, and uppercase characters.
file server. A server on a LAN that provides storage for data files.
file transfer protocol (FTP). An application layer protocol designed to efficiently transfer files between two computers. Frequently used on TCP/IP networks.
firewall. In the context of the Internet, a computer with special software installed between the Internet and a private network for the purpose of preventing unauthorized access to the private network.
first in, first out (FIFO) queuing. Queuing in the order that calls or transactions arrive. Calls that arrive first are serviced first.
five-level code. A telegraph code that uses five impulses for describing a character. Start and stop elements may be added for asynchronous transmission. A common five-level code is the Baudot code.
fixed equalizer. Electronic circuitry in a modem that shapes the transmitted wave using the assumption that the communications line has an average set of parameters.
flag. (1) Any of various types of indicators used for identification. (2) A bit sequence that signals the occurrence of some condition, such as the end of a word. (3) In high-level data link control (HDLC), the initial and final octets of a frame with the specific bit configuration of 01111110. A single flag may be used to denote the end of one frame and the start of another.
flat panel display. A technology for VDTs yielding a display that is much flatter and takes up less space on a desk than a CRT.
flat rate service. A method of charging for local calls that gives the user an unlimited number of calls for a flat monthly fee.
foreign exchange (FX) line. A service that connects a customer's telephone system to a telephone company central office that normally does not serve the customer's location.
format effector character. A character that controls the positioning of information on a terminal screen or paper.
formatted mode. A method of displaying output on a VDT in which the entire screen can be arranged in any desired configuration and transmitted to the terminal at one time. *Contrast with* line-by-line mode.
forward channel. The primary transmission channel in a data circuit. *Contrast with* reverse channel.
forward error correction (FEC). A technique of transmitting extra bits or characters with a block of data so that transmission errors can be corrected at the receiving end.
four-wire circuit. A path in which four wires (two for each direction of transmission) are presented to the station equipment. Leased circuits are four-wire circuits.
four-wire terminating set. An arrangement by which four-wire circuits are terminated on a two-wire basis for interconnection with two-wire circuits.
fractional T-1. The subdivision or multiplexing of T-1 circuits to provide circuit speeds that are a fraction of the T-1's capacity.
frame. (1) In SDLC, the vehicle for every command, every response, and all information that is transmitted using SDLC procedures. Each frame begins and ends with a flag. (2) In high-level data link control (HDLC), the sequence of contiguous bits bracketed by and including opening and closing flag (01111110) sequences.
frame relay. A low-overhead packet switching technique—designed to operate on high-speed lines—in which each packet keeps track of the destinations it has passed through.
framing bits. Noninformation-carrying bits used to make possible the separation of characters in a bit stream.
freeze-frame television. A television system in which the picture is only updated as needed, typically every 30 to 90 seconds.
frequency. An attribute of analog signals that describes the rate at which the current alternates. Frequency is measured in Hertz.
frequency division multiple access (FDMA). A transmission technique used in digital radio transmissions in which frequencies are shared among several users.
frequency division multiplexing (FDM). A technique of putting several analog signals on a circuit by shifting the frequencies of the signals to different ranges so that they do not interfere with one another.
frequency hopping. A spread spectrum transmission technique in which the signal is broadcast over a seemingly random series of radio frequencies, hopping from frequency to frequency at split second intervals. *See also* spread spectrum *and* direct sequence.
frequency modulation (FM). Modulation in which the frequency of an alternating current is the characteristic varied.
frequency shift keying (FSK). Frequency modulation of a carrier by a signal that varies between a fixed number of discrete values.

front-end processor (FEP). A processor that can relieve a host computer of certain processing tasks, such as line control, message handling, code conversion, error control, and application functions. *See also* communications controller.
full-duplex (FDX). A mode of operating a data link in which data may be transmitted simultaneously in both directions over two channels.
full-duplex transmission. Data transmission in both directions simultaneously on a circuit.
full-motion television. Television pictures in which 30 pictures are sent every second.
function key. On a terminal, a key, such as an ATTENTION or an ENTER key, that when pressed transmits a signal not associated with a printable or displayable character. Detection of the signal usually causes the system to perform some predefined function.

Gantt chart. A project management tool that shows projects, activities, or tasks (normally listed chronologically) on the left and dates across the top. Each activity is indicated by a bar on the chart that shows its starting and ending dates.
gateway. The connection between two networks that use different protocols. The gateway translates the protocols to allow terminals on the two networks to communicate.
Gaussian noise. *See* background noise.
general poll. A technique in which special invitation characters are sent to solicit transmission of data from all attached remote devices that are ready to send.
geosynchronous orbit. A satellite orbit that exactly matches the rotation speed of the earth. Thus, from the earth, the satellite appears to be stationary.
giga (G). One billion. For example, 1 gigaHertz equals 1,000,000,000 Hertz. One gigaHertz also equals 1,000 megaHertz and 1,000,000 kiloHertz.
global positioning system (GPS). A satellite-based system for precisely locating any point on earth. Receivers on earth pick up signals from three or more satellites and then through triangulation calculate the exact position of the receiver, usually measured in latitude and longitude.
global system for mobile communications (GSM). A cellular telephone technology based on TDMA technology but with a higher capacity and better call quality. It supports both voice and data transmission. GSM is the standard for cellular phone service in Europe and Asia. GSM service is available in the United States but only in limited areas.
Government Open Systems Interconnection Protocol (GOSIP). A U.S. government-specified subset of the OSI model that defines what parts of the OSI model the government will follow and, therefore, what products it will buy.
grade of service. A measure of the traffic-handling capability of a network from the point of view of sufficiency of equipment and trunking throughout a multiplicity of nodes.
graphic character. A character that can be displayed on a terminal screen or printed on paper.
graphical user interface (GUI). A way in which a user can interact with a computer using a pointing device, such as a mouse, to select icons displayed on the screen or indicate an action to be taken.
Gray code. A binary code in which sequential numbers are represented by binary expressions, each of which differs from the preceding expression in one place only.
group. Twelve 4-kHz voice signals multiplexed together into a 48-kHz signal.
groupware. A type of software that allows groups of people to talk to each other or to work together simultaneously.
guard band. *See* guard channel.
guard channel. The space between the primary signal and the edge of an analog channel.
guided media. *See* conducted media.

hacker. A term originally denoting a technically inclined individual who enjoyed pushing computers to their limits and making them perform tasks no one thought possible. Recently, a term describing a person with the mischievous, malevolent intent to access computers to change or destroy data or perform other unauthorized operations.
half-duplex (HDX). A mode of operation of a data link in which data may be transmitted in both directions but only in one direction at a time.
half-duplex transmission. Data transmission in either direction, one direction at a time.
hamming code. A data code that is capable of being corrected automatically.
handset. A telephone mouthpiece and receiver in a single unit that can be held in one hand.
handshake. A security technique, used on dial-up circuits, that requires that terminal hardware identify itself to the computer by automatically sending a predetermined identification code. The handshake technique is not controlled by the terminal operator.
handshaking. Exchange of predetermined signals when a connection is established between two dataset devices.
hardwired. Directly connected by wire or cable.
harmonic. The resultant presence of harmonic frequencies (due to nonlinear characteristics of a transmission line) in the response when a sine wave is applied.
header. The part of a data message containing information about the message, such as its destination, a sequence number, and perhaps a date or time.
help desk. The single point of contact for users when problems occur.
Hertz (Hz). A unit of frequency equal to one cycle per second.
hierarchical network. A network in which processing and control functions are performed at several levels by computers specially suited for the functions performed, for example, in factory or laboratory automation.
High-Level Data Link Control (HDLC). A bit-oriented data link protocol that exercises control of data links by the use of a specified series of bits rather than by the control characters. HDLC is the protocol standardized by ISO.
high-speed circuit. A circuit designed to carry data at speeds greater than voice-grade circuits. *Synonym for* wideband circuit.

hit. A transient disturbance to a data communications medium that could mutilate characters being transmitted.
holding time. The duration of a switched call. Most often applied in traffic studies to the duration of a telephone call.
home page. At a site on the WWW, the top page in a hierarchy. The home page normally indicates what information is available on other pages to which it is connected.
host computer. In a network, a computer that primarily provides services, such as computation, database access, or special programs or programming languages.
hot key. A key or combination of keys that allows the user to switch from one computer or session to view information from another computer or session.
hot standby. A standby computer or telecommunications line in place that is ready to take over automatically in case of failure.
hub. A device that serves as a connection point for all of the wires or cables in a LAN. Some hubs have intelligence and can perform error detection.
hub polling. A type of polling in which each station polls the next station in succession on the communications circuit. The last station polls the first station on the circuit.
Huffman coding. A type of character compression.
hybrid network. A network made up of a combination of various network topologies.
hybrid systems. A term applied to telephone systems that have some of the characteristics of key systems and some of PBXs.
hypertext. A form of text that has highlighted words that can be clicked with a mouse to connect the user with a source of additional information about the word or topic. A tool of the World Wide Web on the Internet.
hypertext markup language (HTML). A formatting tool used to format pages for the WWW.
hypertext transfer protocol (HTTP). The protocol used to carry WWW traffic between a WWW browser computer and the WWW server being accessed.

identification (ID) characters. Characters sent by a station to identify itself. TWX, BSC, and SDLC stations use ID characters.
idle character. (1) A control character that is sent when there is no information to be transmitted. (2) A character transmitted on a telecommunications line that does not print or punch at the output component of the accepting terminal.
idle line. *Synonym for* inactive line.
image. A faithful likeness of the subject matter of the original.
impulse noise. A sudden spike on the communications circuit when the received amplitude goes beyond a certain level, caused by transient electrical impulses, such as lightning, switching equipment, or a motor starting.
IMS/VS. (Information Management System/Virtual Storage). A database-data communications product developed and marketed by IBM. It allows users to access a computer-maintained database through remote terminals.
inactive line. A telecommunications line that is not currently available for transmitting data. *Contrast with* active line.
inactive node. In a network, a node that is neither connected to nor available for connection to another node.
in-band signals. Signal that occurs within the frequency range allowed for a voice signal. *Contrast with* out-of-band signals.
incumbent local exchange carrier (ILEC). Established carriers, many of which were originally part of the Bell system.
information. The meaning that is assigned to data.
information bearer channel. A channel provided for data transmission that is capable of carrying all the necessary information to permit communications, including such information as users' data synchronizing sequences and control signals. It may, therefore, operate at a greater signaling rate than that required solely for the users' data.
information bits. In data communications, those bits that are generated by the data source and that are not used for error control by the data transmission system.
information highway. A popular term for the Internet. However, when thinking of the information highway, people normally envision a network that delivers data at much higher speeds than today.
information interchange. The process of sending and receiving data in such a manner that the information content or meaning assigned to the data is not altered during the transmission.
information processing. *Synonym for* data processing (DP).
information resource management (IRM). An organization of the information-related resources of a company usually incorporating data processing, data communications, voice communications, office automation, and sometimes the company's libraries.
information security. The protection of information against unauthorized disclosure, transfer, modifications, or destruction, whether accidental or intentional.
infrared. Light waves below the visible spectrum. Infrared light can be used for limited distance, line of sight or near-line of sight transmission.
inquiry. A request for information from storage, for example, a request for the number of available airline seats or a machine statement to initiate a search of library documents.
inquiry and transaction processing. A type of application in which inquiries and records of transactions received from a number of terminals are used to interrogate or update one or more master files.
inquiry/response communication. In a network, the process of exchanging messages and responses, with one exchange usually involving a request for information (an inquiry) and a response that provides the information.
integrated circuit. A combination of interconnected circuit elements inseparably associated on or within a continuous substrate.
Integrated Services Digital Network (ISDN). An evolving set of standards for a digital, public telephone network.
intelligent terminal. A terminal that can be programmed.

intensifying. A method for highlighting characters on the screen of a VDT for easy identification by the user. A character, or any collection of dots on an all-points-addressable (APA) screen, that is made brighter than the other characters around it.
inter-LATA. Long distance calls between LATAs. Inter-LATA calls are handled by an interexchange carrier.
interactive. Pertaining to an application in which each entry calls forth a response from a system or program, as in an inquiry system or an airline reservation system. An interactive system may also be conversational, implying a continuous dialogue between the user and the system.
interactive voice response. A type of telephone service in which the caller can obtain varying responses or information from a computer by inputting digits from a Touchtone telephone.
interconnect industry. A segment of the communications industry that makes equipment for attachment to the telephone network that provides customers with alternatives such as decorative telephones and private telephone systems for business.
interexchange carrier (IXC). Long distance carriers. *Contrast with* local exchange carrier (LEC).
interface. A shared boundary. An interface might be a hardware component to link two devices, or it might be a portion of storage or registers accessed by two or more computer programs.
intermediate system. In the context of an internet, subnetworks that provide a communication path and provide necessary relaying and routing of messages.
intermediate text block (ITB). A character used to terminate an intermediate block of characters. The block check character is sent immediately following ITB, but no line turnaround occurs. The response following ETB or ETX also applies to all of the ITB checks immediately preceding the block terminated by ETB or ETX.
intermessage delay. The elapsed time between the receipt at a terminal of a system response and the time that a new transaction is entered. *Synonym for* think time.
internal modem. A modem contained on a single circuit card that can be inserted into a personal computer or other device.
international direct distance dialing (IDDD). A telephone exchange service that enables the telephone user to call subscribers in other countries without operator assistance.
International Organization for Standardization (ISO). An organization established to promote the development of standards to facilitate the international exchange of goods and services and to develop mutual cooperation in areas of intellectual, scientific, technological, and economic activity.
International Telecommunications Union (ITU). The specialized telecommunications agency of the United Nations, established to provide standardized communications procedures and practices, including frequency allocation and radio regulations, on a worldwide basis.
International Telecommunications Union-Telecommunications Standardization Sector (ITU-T). The part of the ITU that deals with global telecommunications standards.
internet. An interconnected set of networks.
Internet. A TCP/IP-based, interconnected set of government, research, education, commercial, and private networks.
Internet service provider (ISP). A company or organization that provides access to the Internet, typically for a fee.
internetwork address. A destination address that contains enough information to route a message to a node on a different network.
interoffice trunk. A direct trunk between local central offices in the same exchange.
intertoll trunk. A trunk between toll offices in different telephone exchanges.
intranet. A private network modeled after the WWW on which browsers and servers are used to provide access to information of use to the particular audience. Many organizations have implemented intranets as a way to disseminate information to employees.
inverse concentrator. Equipment that takes a high-speed data stream, for example from a computer, and breaks it apart for transmission over multiple slower speed circuits.
invitation. The process in which a processor contacts a station in order to allow the station to transmit a message if it has one ready. *See also* polling.
invitation list. A series of sets of polling characters or identification sequences associated with the stations on a line. The order in which sets of polling characters are specified determines the order in which polled stations are invited to enter messages on the line.
isochronous transmission. A data transmission process in which there is always an integral number of unit intervals between any two significant instants.

jack. A connecting device to which a wire or wires of a circuit may be attached and that is arranged for the insertion of a plug.
jitter. Small, rapid, unwanted amplitude or phase changes of an analog signal. Small variations of the pulses of a digital signal from their ideal positions in time.
job. A set of data that completely defines a unit of work for a computer. A job usually includes all necessary computer programs, linkages, files, and instructions to the operating system.
journaling. Recording transactions against a dataset so that the dataset can be reconstructed by applying transactions in the journal against a previous version of the dataset.
joystick. In computer graphics, a lever that can pivot in all directions and that is used as a locator device.
jumbo group. Six 600-channel master groups, giving a total of 3,600 channels. The bandwidth of a jumbo group is 1.440 Mhz.

Kanji. A character set of symbols used in Japanese ideographic alphabets.
key. (1) On a keyboard, a control or switch by means of which a specified function is performed. (2) To enter characters or data from a keyboard.

key-encrypting key. A key used in sessions with cryptography to encipher and decipher other keys.
key system. A small, private telephone system.
keyboard. (1) On a typewriter or terminal, an arrangement of typing and function keys laid out in a specified manner. (2) A systematic arrangement of keys by which a machine is operated or by which data is entered. (3) A device for the encoding of data by key depression, which causes the generation of the selected code element. (4) A group of numerical keys, alphabetical keys, and function keys used for entering information into a terminal and into the system.
keyboard-send-receive (KSR). A combination teletypewriter transmitter and receiver with transmission capability from a keyboard only.
kilo (k). One thousand. For example, 1 kilohertz equals 1,000 hertz.

LAN Manager. Network operating system software for a LAN produced by Microsoft.
laser. A device that transmits an extremely narrow beam of energy in the visible light spectrum.
layer. (1) In the open systems interconnection (OSI) architecture, a collection of related functions that comprise one level of a hierarchy of functions. Each layer specifies its own functions and assumes that lower level functions are provided. (2) In SNA, a grouping of related functions that are logically separate from the functions in other layers. The implementation of the functions in one layer can be changed without affecting functions in other layers.
leased circuit. A circuit that is owned by a common carrier but leased from them by another organization for full-time, exclusive use. *See also* private line.
leased line. *See* leased circuit.
least cost routing. Routing a telephone call so that the cost of the call is minimized.
letters shift. A physical shift in a teletypewriter that enables the printing of lowercase characters.
level. The amplitude of a signal.
levels of support. A concept related to a support organization that suggests that the minimum skills necessary to solve a problem should be used. *See also* problem escalation.
light-emitting diode (LED). A semiconductor chip that gives off visible or infrared light when activated.
lightpen. A specialized input device that is attached to a VDT by cable. It is held by the operator and pressed against the screen of the terminal to mark a spot or indicate a selection from several choices.
line. (1) On a terminal, one or more characters entered before a return to the first printing or display position. (2) A string of characters accepted by the system as a single block of input from a terminal, for example, all characters entered before a carriage return or all characters entered before the terminal user presses the ATTENTION key. (3) *See* circuit.
line-by-line mode. A mode of operation for terminals in which one line at a time is sent to or received from the computer.
line control. *Synonym for* protocol.
line feed (LF). A format effector that causes the print or display position to move to the corresponding position on the next line. *See also* carriage-return character (CR).
line group. One or more telecommunications lines of the same type that can be activated and deactivated as a unit.
line level. The signal level in decibels at a particular position on a telecommunications line.
line load. Usually a percentage of maximum circuit capability that reflects actual use during a span of time; for example, peak hour line load.
line noise. Noise originating in a telecommunications line.
line switching. *Synonym for* circuit switching.
line trace. In the network control program, an optional function that logs all activity on the line.
line turnaround. A process for half-duplex transmission in which one modem stops transmitting and becomes the receiver, and the receiving modem becomes the transmitter.
linear predictive coding (LPC). A technique of digitizing an analog signal by predicting which direction the analog signal will take. LPC samples the analog signal less often than other digitizing techniques, allowing the transmitted bit rate to be lower.
link. A segment of a circuit between two points.
link access procedure, balanced (LAPB). A subset of the HDLC protocol that operates in full-duplex, point-to-point mode. It is most commonly used between an X.25 DTE and a packet switching network.
link access procedure, D-channel (LAPD). A subset of HDLC that provides data link control on an ISDN D channel in AMB mode. LAPD always uses a 16-bit address, 7-bit sequence numbers, and a 16-bit CRC.
link access procedure for frame-mode bearer services (LAPF). A data link protocol for frame relay networks. LAPF is made up of a control protocol, which is similar to HDLC, and a core protocol, which is a subset of the control protocol. The control protocol uses 16- to 32-bit addresses, 7-bit sequence numbers, and a 16-bit CRC. The core protocol has no control field, which means that there is no mechanism for error control, hence streamlining the operation of the network.
liquid crystal display (LCD). A video display technology that uses two sheets of polarizing material with a liquid crystal solution between them. An electric current passed through the liquid causes the crystals to align so that light cannot pass through them.
local access and transport area (LATA). The local calling areas that were defined originally within the United States when divestiture occurred.
local area network (LAN). A limited distance network, usually existing within a building or several buildings in close proximity to one another. Transmission on a LAN normally occurs at speeds of 1 Mbps and up.
local calling. Telephone calling within a designated local service area.
local calls. Calls within a local service area.
local central office. A central office arranged for terminating subscriber lines and provided with trunks of establishing connections to and from other central offices.

local exchange carrier (LEC). The BOCs and the independent telephone companies.
local loop. A channel connecting the subscriber's equipment to the line-terminating equipment in the central office exchange.
local service area. Telephones served by a particular central office and (usually) several surrounding central offices.
Localtalk. A LAN cabling system for Apple computers.
lockout. In a telephone circuit controlled by an echo suppressor, the inability of one or both subscribers to get through because of either excessive local circuit noise or continuous speech from one subscriber.
logical circuit. In packet mode operation, a means of duplex transmission across a data link, comprising associated send and receive channels. A number of logical circuits may be derived from a data link by packet interleaving. Several logical circuits may exist on the same data link.
logical link control (LLC). The data link control protocol defined by the IEEE for use on LANs.
logical unit (LU). SNA's view of a communications user.
log off. The procedure by which a user ends a terminal session.
log on. The procedure by which a user begins a terminal session.
long distance calls. Calls outside of the local service area.
longitudinal parity check. (1) A parity check performed on a group of binary digits in a longitudinal direction for each track. (2) A system of error checking performed at the receiving station after a block check character has been accumulated.
longitudinal redundancy check (LRC). *Synonym for* longitudinal parity check.
loop back test. A procedure in which signals are looped from a test instrument through a modem or loopback switch and back to the test instrument for measurement.
loop network. A network configuration in which there is a single path between all nodes, and the path is a closed circuit.
low speed. Usually, a data transmission speed of 600 bps or less.
low-speed circuit. A circuit that is designed for telegraph and teletypewriter usage at speeds of from 45 to 600 bps and that cannot handle a voice transmission. Used by the public telex network. *Synonym for* subvoice-grade circuit.

main distribution frame. A frame that has one part on which the permanent outside lines entering the central office building terminate and another part on which cabling, such as the subscriber line cabling or trunk cabling, terminates. In a PBX, the main distribution frame is for similar purposes.
management information base (MIB). The database in which the SNMP protocol stores information about the operation of a network.
Manchester coding. A digital signaling technique in which there is a transition in the middle of each bit time. A 1 is encoded with a low level during the first half of the bit time and a high level during the second half. A 0 is encoded with a high level during the first half of the bit time and a low level during the second half.
Manufacturing Automation Protocol (MAP). A communications protocol, based on the OSI reference model, specifically oriented toward use in an automated manufacturing environment.
marine telephone service. Telephone service for boats and ships that uses radio or satellite links to connect from the ship to a shore station.
mark. The normal no-traffic line condition by which a steady signal is transmitted.
master group. Ten supergroups, each of which contains 60 voice channels. The bandwidth of a master group is 2.4 MHz.
master station. *See* control station.
mean time between failures (MTBF). For a stated period in the life of a function unit, the mean value of the lengths of time between consecutive failures under stated conditions.
mean time to repair (MTTR). The average time required for corrective maintenance.
measured rate service. A method of charging for local calls based on the number of calls, their duration, and the distance.
medium. *See* transmission medium.
medium access control (MAC). A technique for determining which of several stations on a local area network can use the network.
medium speed. Usually, a data transmission rate between 600 bps and the limit of a voice-grade facility.
mega (M). One million. For example, 1 megaHertz equals 1,000,000 Hertz. Also 1 megaHertz equals 1,000 kiloHertz.
mesh network. A network configuration in which there are one or more paths between any two nodes.
message. (1) An arbitrary amount of information whose beginning and end are defined or implied. (2) A group of characters and control bit sequences transferred as an entity.
message center. A location where messages are received from a communications network and either forwarded to another location or delivered to the intended recipient.
message queue. A line of messages that are awaiting processing or waiting to be sent to a terminal.
message routing. The process of selecting the correct circuit path for a message.
message switching. (1) In a data network, the process of routing messages by receiving, storing, and forwarding complete messages. (2) The technique of receiving a complete message, storing it, and then forwarding it to its destination unaltered.
message text. The part of a message that is of concern to the party ultimately receiving the message, that is, the message exclusive of the header or control information.
metropolitan area network (MAN). A network of limited geographic scope, generally defined as within a 50-mile radius. Standards for MANs are being defined by the IEEE.
micro. One millionth.
microcomputer. A computer system whose processing unit is a microprocessor. A basic microcomputer in-

cludes a microprocessor, storage, and an input/output facility, which may or may not be on one chip.

microprocessor. An integrated circuit that accepts coded instructions for execution. The instructions may be entered, integrated, or stored internally.

microwave radio. Radio transmissions in the 4 to 28 GHz range. Microwave radio transmissions require that the transmitting and receiving antennas be within sight of each other.

milli. One thousandth.

mobile telephone switching office (MTSO). The central office of a cellular telephone system. MTSOs are typically connected to cellular antenna towers and to the public switched telephone system's central offices by cable.

modem. A device that modulates and demodulates signals transmitted over data communications lines. One of the functions of a modem is to enable digital data to be transmitted over analog transmission facilities.

modified final judgment (MFJ). The stipulation that on January 1, 1984, AT&T would divest itself of all 22 of its associated operating companies in the Bell System.

modified Huffman (MH) encoding. A method of encoding facsimile data before it is transmitted.

modified modified read (MMR) encoding. A method of encoding facsimile data before it is transmitted.

modified read (MR) encoding. A method of encoding facsimile data before it is transmitted.

modulation. The process by which some characteristic of one wave is varied in accordance with another wave or signal. This technique is used in modems to make DTE signals compatible with communications facilities.

modulation rate. The reciprocal of the measure of the shortest nominal time interval between successive significant instants of the modulated signal. If this measure is expressed in seconds, the modulation rate is given in bauds.

modulator. A functional unit that converts a signal into a modulated signal suitable for transmission. *Contrast with* demodulator.

monitor. Software or hardware that observes, supervises, controls, or verifies the operations of a system.

mouse. In computer graphics, a locator device operated by moving it on a surface.

multidrop circuit. *See* multipoint circuit.

multimode. A type of optical fiber with a core approximately 50 microns (.050 millimeter) in diameter.

multiple sessions. Having several connections to different software applications at the same time. The capability is normally provided by hardware or software in the terminal or terminal control unit.

multiplexer (MUX). A device capable of interleaving the events of two or more activities or capable of distributing the events of an interleaved sequence to the respective activities.

multiplexing. (1) In data transmission, a function that permits two or more data sources to share a common transmission medium such that each data source has its own channel. (2) The division of a transmission facility into two or more channels either by splitting the frequency band transmitted by the channel into narrower bands, each of which is used to constitute a distinct channel (frequency division multiplexing), or by allotting this common channel to several different information channels, one at a time (time division multiplexing).

multipoint circuit. A circuit with several nodes connected to it.

multipoint line. A communication line that has several nodes attached.

multiport. *See* split stream operation.

multipurpose internet mail extensions (MIME). An extension to the SMTP mail transfer protocol that overcomes many of the SMTP's limitations, such as its inability to handle foreign characters.

multi-station access unit (MAU). A wiring hub in a token ring LAN.

multitasking. The capability of a computer operating system to appear to run two or more programs simultaneously by rapidly switching back and forth between them.

National Exchange Carriers Association (NECA). An organization of communications carriers that sets North American wide area network standards.

negative acknowledge character (NAK). A transmission control character transmitted by a station as a negative response to the station with which the connection has been set up.

negative polling limit. For a start-stop or BSC terminal, the maximum number of consecutive negative responses to polling that the communications controller accepts before suspending polling operations.

Netware. Network operating system software for a LAN produced by Novell.

network. (1) An interconnected group of nodes. (2) The assembly of equipment through which connections are made between data stations.

network addressable unit (NAU). In SNA, a logical unit, a physical unit, or a system services control point. It is the origin or the destination of information transmitted by the path control network.

network application. The use to which a network is put, such as data collection or inquiry/update.

network architecture. A set of design principles, including the organization of functions and the description of data formats and procedures, used as the basis for design and implementation of a telecommunications application network.

Network Basic Input-Output System (NetBIOS). The part of the DOS operating system that provides the interface between IBM and compatible personal computers and a network.

network computer. A limited-capability computer that allows connection to the Internet but does not have all of the capability of a regular personal computer.

network congestion. A network condition in which traffic is greater than the network can carry, for any reason.

network control center (NCC). A place from which a communications network is operated and monitored.

network control mode. The functions of a network control program that enable it to direct a communications controller to perform activities, such as polling, device addressing, dialing, and answering.
network control program (NCP). A program that controls the operation of a front-end processor or communications controller.
network interface card (NIC). A circuit card in a personal computer that provides the electrical interface to a network.
network management. The process of operating and controlling a telecommunications network so that it meets the requirements of its users.
network node. *Synonym for* node.
network operating system (NOS). The software that controls a LAN's operation.
network operations. The activities required to run a network on a daily basis and to keep it running when problems occur.
network operator. A person or program responsible for controlling the operation of all or part of a network.
network operator console. A system console or terminal in the network from which an operator controls the network.
network simulator. *See* workload generator.
network topology. The schematic arrangement of the links and nodes of a network.
networked society. A vision of the future in which most people have the ability to communicate with each other and with various computer-based systems by several means.
900 Service. A telephone service for which the caller pays the cost of the telephone call.
node. In a network, a point at which one or more functional units interconnect transmission lines. The term *node* derives from graph theory in which a node is a junction point of links, areas, or edges.
noise. (1) Random variations of one or more characteristics of any entity, such as voltage, current, or data. (2) A random signal of known statistical properties of amplitude, distribution, and spectral density. (3) Loosely, any disturbance tending to interfere with the normal operation of a device or system.
nondestructive cursor. On a VDT device, a cursor that does not erase characters through which it passes as it is advanced, backspaced, or otherwise moved. *Contrast with* destructive cursor.
noninformation bits. In data communications, those bits that are used for error control or other purposes which do not directly convey the meaning of the message.
nonswitched connection. A connection that does not have to be established by dialing. *Contrast with* switched connection.
nontransparent mode. A mode of transmission in which all control characters are treated as control characters (that is, not treated as text). *Contrast with* transparent mode.
N-out-of-M code. A coding system in which M bits are used to transmit a character and N of the bits must be 1s.
null character (NUL). A control character that is used to accomplish media-fill or time-fill and that may be inserted into or removed from a sequence of characters without affecting the meaning of the sequence. However, the control of equipment or the format may be affected by this character.
numbering plan. A uniform numbering system in which each telephone central office has a unique designation similar in form to that of all other offices connected to the nationwide dialing network. In one numbering plan, the first 3 of 10 dialed digits are the area code, the next 3 are the office code, and the remaining 4 are the station number.
numeric keypad. Extra keys on a keyboard that function like a 10-key calculator.

off-hook. Activated (in regard to a telephone set). By extension, a data set automatically answering on a public switched system is said to go off-hook. *Contrast with* on-hook.
offline. Pertaining to the operation of a functional unit without the continual control of a computer.
offline system. A system in which human operations are required between the original recording functions and the ultimate data processing function. This includes conversion operations as well as the necessary loading and unloading operations incident to the use of point-to-point or data-gathering systems. *Contrast with* online system.
on-hook. Deactivated (in reference to a telephone set). A telephone not in use is on-hook. *Contrast with* off-hook.
one-way communication. Communication in which information is always transferred in one preassigned direction.
one-way trunk. A trunk between central exchanges where traffic can originate on only one end.
online. (1) The state of being connected, usually to a computer. (2) Pertaining to the operation of a functional unit that is under the continual control of a computer.
online system. A system in which the input data enters the computer directly from the point of origin or in which output data is transmitted directly to where it is used.
open network architecture (ONA). A set of provisions imposed by the FCC on the BOCs and AT&T to ensure the competitive availability of and access to unregulated, enhanced network services.
Open Systems Interconnection (OSI) reference model. A telecommunications architecture proposed by the International Standards Organization (ISO).
open wire. (1) A conductor separately supported above the surface of the ground; that is, on insulators. (2) A broken wire.
open-wire line. A pole line in which the conductors are principally in the form of bare, uninsulated wire. Ceramic, glass, or plastic insulators are used to physically attach the bare wire to the telephone poles. Short circuits between the individual conductors are avoided by appropriate spacing.
operating system. The central control program that governs a computer hardware's operation.

optical character recognition (OCR). The process of scanning a document with a beam of light and detecting individual characters.
optical fiber. A communications medium made of very thin glass or plastic fiber that conducts light waves.
optical recognition. A device that can detect individual data items or characters and convert them into ASCII or another code for transmission to a computer.
OS/2 LAN Server. Network operating system software for a LAN produced by IBM.
oscilloscope. An instrument for displaying the changes in a varying current or voltage.
out-of-band signals. Signals outside of the frequency range allowed for a voice signal. *Contrast with* in-band signals.
out-pulsing. The pulses caused by a rotary dial opening and closing an electrical circuit when the dial is turned and released.
outsourcing. The transfer of some of the activities of an organization to another company, usually for the purpose of obtaining specialized service or lower cost.
overrun. Loss of data because a receiving device is unable to accept data at the rate it is transmitted.

pacing. A technique by which a receiving station controls the rate of transmission of a sending station to prevent overrun.
packet. A sequence of binary digits (including data and control signals) that is switched as a composite whole. The data, control signals, and possibly error control information are arranged in a specific format.
packet assembly/disassembly (PAD). The process of dividing a message into packets at the transmitting end and reassembling the message from the packets at the receiving end.
packet data network (PDN). A network that uses packet switching techniques for transmitting data.
Packet filtering. *See* packet level firewall.
packetizing. The process of dividing a message into packets.
packet level firewall. A firewall computer that examines all network traffic at the packet level and allows or denies packet passage from one network to the other based on the source and destination addresses. This technique is called *packet filtering*.
packet sequencing. A process of ensuring that packets are delivered to the receiving data terminal equipment (DTE) in the same sequence as they were transmitted by the sending DTE.
packet switched data transmission service. A user service involving the transmission and, if necessary, the assembly and disassembly of data in the form of packets.
packet switching. The technique of sending packets through a network, sometimes by diverse routes.
page mode. *See* formatted mode.
parallel transmission. (1) In data communications, the simultaneous transmission of a certain number of signal elements constituting the same telegraph or data signal. (2) The simultaneous transmission of the bits constituting an entity of data over a data circuit. *Contrast with* serial transmission.
parity bit. The binary digit appended to a group of binary digits to make the sum of all the digits either always odd (odd parity) or always even (even parity).
parity check. A redundancy check that uses a parity bit.
patch. (1) A temporary electrical connection. (2) To make an improvised modification.
patch cord. A cable with plugs at both ends that is used to connect two devices.
patch panel. Equipment that allows a piece of equipment to be temporarily connected to other equipment or a circuit using patch cords.
path. In a network, a route between any two nodes.
peer-to-peer. The ability of two computers to communicate directly without passing through or using the capability of a mainframe computer.
pel. *See* picture element (pixel, pel).
performance management. The application of management principles to ensure that the performance of a system meets the required parameters.
permanent virtual circuit. In packet switching networks, a full-time connection between two nodes.
personal communications network (PCN). The European name for personal communication service.
personal communications service (PCS). A type of communication in which a user carries a small telephone-transceiver, which allows him or her to be reached regardless of where he or she is located.
personal handyphone (PHS) system. The Japanese name for their personal communications system (PCS) network.
personal identification number (PIN). A secret code or password that allows a person access to certain facilities or capabilities on a computer system.
phase. An attribute of an analog signal that describes its relative position measured in degrees.
phase jitter. An unwanted change in the phase of the signal.
phase modulation. Modulation in which the phase angle of a carrier is the characteristic varied.
phase shift. The offset of an analog signal from its previous location. Phase shifts are measured in degrees.
phase shift keying (PSK). A modulation technique in which the phase of an analog signal is varied.
physical unit (PU). SNA's view of communications hardware.
picture element (pixel, pel). (1) The part of the area of the original document that coincides with the scanning spot at a given instant and that is of one intensity only with no distinction of the details that may be included. (2) In computer graphics, the smallest element of a display space that can be independently assigned color and intensity. (3) The area of the finest detail that can be effectively reproduced on the recording medium.
pixel. *See* picture element (pixel, pel).
plain old telephone service (POTS). Basic telephone service with no special features.
plaintext. Unencrypted information. *See also* ciphertext.
point of presence (POP). The location within a LATA at which customers are connected to an IXC.

point of sale (POS) terminal. A specialized terminal designed to be used by a clerk in a store and to enter sales transactions into a computer.

point-to-point line. A circuit connecting two nodes. *Contrast with* multipoint circuit.

point-to-point-protocol (PPP). An asynchronous protocol that includes capabilities for line testing, authentication, data compression and error correction. It is primarily used by personal computers to dial into a TCP/IP-based network though it may be used on leased lines as well.

Poisson capacity table. A table for determining the number of circuits required to carry a certain level of telephone traffic. The Poisson table assumes that the sources of traffic are infinite and that all blocked calls will be retried within a short period of time.

polling. (1) Interrogation of devices for purposes such as to avoid contention, to determine operational status, or to determine readiness to send or receive data. (2) The process in which stations are invited, one at a time, to transmit.

polling characters. A set of characters peculiar to a terminal and the polling operation. Response to these characters indicates to the computer whether the terminal has a message to enter.

polling delay. A user-specified delay between passes through an invitation list for either a line or a line group.

polling ID. The unique character or characters associated with a particular station.

polling list. A list that specifies the sequence in which stations are to be polled.

polynomial error checking. An error checking technique in which the bits of a block of data are processed by a mathematical algorithm using a polynomial function to calculate the block check character.

port. An access point for a circuit.

port speed. In the context of a frame relay circuit, the port speed is the maximum transmission speed of the line between the customer and the frame relay carrier.

Post, Telephone, and Telegraph (PTT). A generic term for the government-operated common carriers in countries other than the U.S. and Canada.

presentation services. The processing required to change the format of messages from that required or generated by an application program to or from the format required by a specific terminal.

preventive software maintenance. A philosophy of software maintenance that advocates the application of software corrections, whether the problem being corrected has been seen or not. The intention is to correct software problems before they are seen by users.

primary access. A method of accessing an ISDN network in which the user has twenty-three 64-kbps B channels and one 16-kbps D channel. This type of access is also known as 23B+D.

print server. A server on a LAN that provides the hardware and software to drive one or more printers.

private circuit. A telecommunications line that is owned by a company other than a communications carrier.

private automatic branch exchange (PABX). A private automatic telephone exchange that provides for the transmission of calls to and from the public telephone network. *See also* private branch exchange (PBX).

private branch exchange (PBX). A private telephone exchange connected to the public telephone network on the user's premises.

private key. In a public key encryption system, the key that is kept secret and never distributed.

private line. A communications circuit that is owned by a company other than a common carrier.

private network. A network built by a company for its exclusive use, which uses circuits available from a variety of sources.

problem escalation. The process of bringing a problem to the attention of higher levels of management and/or bringing more highly trained technical resources to work on the problem.

problem management. The application of management principles to ensure that problems are resolved as quickly as possible with the minimum resources.

problem tracking meeting. A periodic meeting to discuss the status of all open problems that have not yet been resolved.

profit center. A department or other entity that generates more revenue than it spends. Profit centers typically sell their services or recharge them to other departments in the company. *Contrast with* cost center.

program evaluation review technique (PERT). A project management technique that shows on a chart the interrelationships of activities.

program function keys. Special keys on a terminal keyboard that direct the computer to perform specific actions determined by the computer program.

project life cycle. A concept expressing the desirability of gradually adding people to a project in order to minimize the cost until the specifications and benefits of the project are known and management's commitment is assured.

project team. A group of people organized for the purpose of completing a project.

propagation delay. The time necessary for a signal to travel from one point to another.

protocol. (1) A specification for the format and relative timing of information exchanged between communicating parties. (2) The set of rules governing the operation of functional units of a communications system that must be followed if communications are to be achieved.

protocol analyzer. Test equipment that examines the bits on a communications circuit to determine whether the rules of a particular protocol are being followed.

protocol converter. Hardware or software that converts a data transmission from one protocol to another.

protocol data unit (PDU). A frame of logical link control protocol.

proxy server. A server that changes the network addresses from one form to another, so that users or computers on one network do not know the actual addresses of nodes on the other network.

public data transmission service. A data transmission service established and operated by an administration and provided by means of a public data network. Circuit-switched, packet-switched, and leased circuit data transmission services are feasible.
public key. In a public key encryption system, the key that is revealed (made public) to anyone who may want to use it.
public key encryption. An encryption technology that uses two keys. One is publicly known and the other is kept private and never distributed. A public-key cryptographic algorithm relies on one key for encryption and a different but related key for decryption.
public network. A network established and operated by communications common carriers or telecommunications administrations for the specific purpose of providing circuit-switched, packet-switched, and leased circuit services to the public.
public service commission (PSC). *See* public utility commission (PUC).
public switched network (PSN). A network that provides circuits switched to many customers. In the United States, there are three: telex, TWX, and telephone.
public switched telephone network (PSTN). *See* public switched network (PSN).
public telephone network. *See* public switched network (PSN).
public utility commission (PUC). An arm of state government that has jurisdiction over intrastate rates and services. *Also known as* public service commission (PSC).
pulse. A variation in the value of a quantity, short in relation to the time schedule of interest, the final value being the same as the initial value.
pulse code modulation (PCM). A process in which a signal is sampled, and the magnitude of each sample with respect to a fixed reference is quantized and converted by coding to a digital signal.
punchdown block. A connector for telephone wiring on which the connection is made by pushing (punching) the wire between two prongs with a special tool.
punched paper tape. A medium used on older teletypewriters. Characters were coded in the tape by punched holes.
push-button dialing. The use of keys or push buttons instead of a rotary dial to generate a sequence of digits to establish a circuit connection. The signal form is usually tones. *Contrast with* rotary dial.
push-button dialing pad. A 12-key device used to originate tone keying signals. It usually is attached to rotary dial telephones for use in originating data signals.

quadbit. A group of four bits. In 16-phase modulation, each possible quadbit is encoded as one of 16 unique carrier phase shifts. *Contrast with* dibit *and* tribit.
quadrature amplitude modulation (QAM). A combination of phase and amplitude modulation used to achieve high data rates while maintaining relatively low signaling rates.
quantization. The subdivision of the range of values of a variable into a finite number of nonoverlapping, and not necessarily equal, subranges or intervals, each of which is represented by an assigned value within the subrange. For example, a person's age is quantized for most purposes with a quantum of 1 year.
quantizing noise. The error introduced when an analog signal is digitized.
queue. A line or list formed by items in a system waiting for service, for example, tasks to be performed or messages to be transmitted in a message routing system.
queuing. The process of placing items that cannot be handled into a queue to await service.

radiated media. Transmission medium that propagates the signal through the air such as radio, infrared, or microwave.
radio paging. The broadcast of a special radio signal that activates a small portable receiver carried by the person being paged.
rate center. A specified geographic location used by telephone companies to determine mileage measurements for the application of interexchange mileage rates.
real enough time. Response time that is fast enough to meet the requirements of a particular application.
realtime. Pertaining to an application in which response to input is fast enough to affect subsequent input, such as a process control system or a computer-assisted instruction system.
receive-only (RO). A teletypewriter that has no keyboard. It is used where no input to the computer is desired or necessary.
reed relay. A switch that has contacts that open or close when an electrical current is applied.
regenerative repeater. *See* repeater.
Regional Bell Operating Company (RBOC). One of the seven corporations formed when divestiture occurred and that comprise the 22 Bell Operating Companies.
regional center. A control center connecting sectional centers of the telephone system together. Every pair of regional centers in the United States has a direct circuit group running from one center to the other.
relative transmission level. The ratio of the test-tone power at one point to the test-tone power at some other point in the system chosen as a reference point. The ratio is expressed in decibels. The transmission level at the transmitting switchboard is frequently taken as zero level reference point.
relay center. A central point at which message switching takes place; a message switching center.
reliability. Trouble-free operation.
remote batch. Data collected in a batch and then transmitted to the computer as a unit.
remote job entry (RJE). The process of submitting a job to a computer for processing using telecommunications lines. Normally the output of the processing is returned on the lines to the terminal from which the job was submitted.

remote terminal. A terminal attached to a computer via a telecommunications line.
repeater. A device that performs digital signal regeneration together with ancillary functions. Its function is to retime and retransmit the received signal impulses restored to their original shape and strength.
request for proposal (RFP). A letter or document sent to vendors asking them to show how a (communications) problem or situation can be addressed. Normally, the vendor's response to an RFP proposes a solution and quotes estimated prices.
request for quotation (RFQ). *See* request for proposal (RFP).
response. An answer to an inquiry.
response time. The elapsed time between the end of an inquiry or demand on a data processing system and the beginning of the response, for example, the length of time between an indication of the end of an inquiry and the display of the first character of the response at a user terminal.
reverse channel. A means of simultaneous communications from the receiver to the transmitter over half-duplex data transmission systems. The reverse channel is generally used only for the transmission of control information and operates at a much slower speed than the primary channel.
reverse video. A technique used with VDTs that reverses the character and background colors for highlighting purposes.
ring. (1) The signal made by a telephone to indicate an incoming call. (2) A part of a plug used to make circuit connections in a manual switchboard or patch panel. The ring is the connector attached to the negative side of the common battery that powers the station equipment. By extension, it is the negative battery side of a telecommunications line. *Contrast with* tip.
ring network. A network in which each node is connected to two adjacent nodes.
ringback tone. An audible signal indicating that the called party is being rung.
roll call polling. The most common implementation of a polling system, in which one station on a line is designated as the master and the others are slaves.
rotary dial. In a switched system, the conventional dialing method that creates a series of pulses to identify the called station. *Contrast with* push-button dialing *and* dual-tone multifrequency (DTMF).
router. A piece of hardware or software that directs messages toward their destination, often from one network to another.
routing code. The name given in some countries to the part of the telephone number known in the United States as the area code.
RS-232-C. A specification for the physical, mechanical, and electrical interface between data terminal equipment (DTE) and data circuit-terminating equipment (DCE). *See also* V.24.
RS-232-D. A 1987 revision and update to the RS-232-C specification that is exactly compatible with the V.24 standard.
RS-336. A specification for the interface between a modem (DCE) and a terminal or computer (DTE). This interface, unlike the RS-232-C, has a provision for the automatic dialing of calls under modem control.
RS-449. A specification for the interface between a modem (DCE) and a terminal or computer (DTE). This specification was designed to overcome some of the problems with the RS-232-C interface specification.
run length encoding. A type of compression in which the input text is scanned for repeating characters, which, when found, are reduced to shorter character strings.

satellite carrier. A company that offers communications services using satellites.
scrambler. A voice encryption device that makes the voice unintelligible to anyone without a descrambler, effectively rendering wiretapping useless.
screen. An illuminated display surface; for example, the display surface of a VDT or plasma panel.
search engine. A program that uses a keyword or keywords to search for information in a database. Most commonly used in the context of the Internet on which search engines allow users to search for information using multiple keywords and Boolean logic.
segment. A portion of a LAN that has been separated because of distance or traffic. Segments are connected to other segments by bridges or switches.
seize. To gain control of a line in order to transmit data. *Contrast with* bid.
serial. (1) Pertaining to the sequential performance of two or more activities in a single device. In English, the modifiers serial and parallel usually refer to devices, as opposed to sequential and consecutive, which refer to processes. (2) Pertaining to the sequential processing of the individual parts of a whole, such as the bits of a character or the characters of a word, using the same facilities for successive parts.
serial line internet protocol (SLIP). A protocol for carrying IP over dial-up or leased lines. SLIP contains little negotiation capability and does not support error detection or correction.
serial system. A system made up of a number of components connected in series. In telecommunications, a terminal, modem, and computer may be connected in a series forming a serial system.
serial transmission. (1) In data communications, transmission at successive intervals of signal elements constituting the same telegraph or data signal. The sequential elements may be transmitted with or without interruption, provided that they are not transmitted simultaneously. (2) The sequential transmission of the bits constituting an entity of data over a data circuit. *Contrast with* parallel transmission.
server. On a local area network, a computer with software that provides service to other devices on the LAN. Typical servers are file servers, print servers, and communications servers.

service level agreement. A set of performance objectives reached by consensus between the user and the provider of a service.
serving central office. A telephone subscriber's local central office.
session. (1) A connection between two stations that allows them to communicate. (2) The period of time during which a user of a terminal can communicate with an interactive system; usually, the elapsed time between log on and log off.
shielded twisted pair. Twisted pair wires surrounded by a metallic shield.
shielding. A metallic sheath that surrounds the center conductor of a cable. Coaxial cable has shielding around the center conductor.
sidetone. The small amount of signal fed back from the mouthpiece to the receiver of a telephone handset.
signal. A variation of a physical quantity, used to convey data.
signal processor. Electronic circuitry that is designed to manipulate a signal.
signal-to-noise ratio. The ratio of signal strength to noise strength.
signal transformation. The action of modifying one or more characteristics of a signal, such as its maximum value, shape, or timing.
signaling rate. The number of times per second that a signal changes. Signaling rate is measured in baud.
Signaling System No. 7 (SS7). A signaling system used among telephone company central offices to set up calls, indicate their status, and tear down the calls when they are completed.
simple mail transfer protocol (SMTP). An application layer protocol used by TCP/IP-based networks for the exchange of electronic mail.
Simple Network Management Protocol (SNMP). A protocol, which originated on the Internet, for exchanging network management commands and information between devices on a network.
simplex circuit. A circuit that carries communication in one direction only.
simplex communication. *Synonym for* one-way communication.
simplex transmission. Transmission on a telecommunications line in one direction only. Transmission in the other direction is not allowed.
simultaneous transmission. Transmission of control characters or data in one direction while information is being received in the other direction.
sine wave. The waveform of a single-frequency analog signal of constant amplitude and phase.
single-address message. A message that is to be delivered to only one destination.
single mode. A type of optical fiber that has a glass or plastic core approximately 5 microns (.005 millimeter) in diameter.
sink. In telecommunications, the receiver.
site license. An agreement, usually for software, that allows its use by an unlimited number of people at the site. The term *site* may be defined in different ways according to the terms of the agreement.
slave station. A data station that operates under the control of a master or control station. *Contrast with* control station.
smart home. A home that uses microprocessors to perform certain functions, such as controling heating, lighting, and security alarms.
smart terminal. A terminal that is not programmable but that has memory capable of being loaded with information.
software defined network (SDN). A bulk pricing offered by telephone companies designed for businesses or others who make large numbers of calls. Standard-switched telephone lines are used to carry the calls.
software metering. A method of keeping track of the number of simultaneous users of a piece of software installed on a server. The usual purpose of software metering is to prevent more people from simultaneously using the software than have been paid for in the software license agreement.
software protocol converter. A computer program that converts one protocol to another.
source. The transmitting station in a telecommunications system.
space. *See* space signal.
space signal. In asynchronous transmission, the space signal is the signal for a zero bit.
speaker cone. The paper-like membrane of a speaker that vibrates in response to the movement of a voice coil. The voice coil movement is caused by the interaction of an electrical signal in the coil with a magnet in the speaker.
specific polling. A polling technique that sends invitation characters to a device to find out whether the device is ready to enter data.
split stream operation. A modem feature that allows several slower speed data streams to be combined into one higher speed data stream for transmission, and split apart at the receiving end. The total data rate of the slower speed data streams must not exceed the capacity of the circuit.
spooling. A technique of queuing input or output between slow-speed and high-speed computer hardware. Print spooling is most common. Output from several computers is queued (spooled) to a disk until a printer is free.
spread spectrum. A radio transmission technique in which the frequency of the transmission is changed periodically.
standard test-tone power. One milliwatt (0 dBm) at 1,000 cycles per second.
star network. A network configuration in which there is only one path between a central or controlling node and each endpoint node.
start bit. *See* start signal.
start of header (SOH). A transmission control character used as the first character of a message heading.
start of text (STX). A transmission control character that precedes text and that may be used to terminate the message heading.

start signal. (1) A signal to a receiving mechanism to get ready to receive data or perform a function. (2) In a start/stop system, a signal preceding a character or block that prepares the receiving device for the reception of the code elements. A start signal is limited to one signal element generally having the duration of a unit interval. *Synonym for* start bit.
start/stop transmission. (1) Asynchronous transmission such that a group of signals representing a character is preceded by a start element and is followed by a stop element. (2) Asynchronous transmission in which a group of bits is preceded by a start bit that prepares the receiving mechanism for the reception and registration of a character and is followed by at least 1 stop bit that enables the receiving mechanism to come to an idle condition pending the reception of the next character.
station. One of the input or output points of a system that uses telecommunications facilities; for example, the telephone set in the telephone system or the point at which the business machine interfaces with the channel on a leased private line.
station extension. An extension telephone.
station features. Features of a telephone system that are activated by the user of the system.
station message detail recording (SMDR). A feature of a telephone system that records detailed information about telephone calls placed through the system.
station selection code. A Western Union term for an identifying call that is transmitted to an outlying telegraph receiver and automatically turns its printer on.
statistical time division multiplexing (STDM). A device that combines signals from several terminals. An STDM does not reserve specific time slots for each device but assigns time only when a device has data to send.
step-by-step switch. A switch that moves in synch with a pulse device, such as a rotary telephone dial. Each digit dialed moves successive selector switches to carry the connection forward until the desired line is reached.
stop and wait ARQ. An error checking technique in which each block of data must be acknowledged before the next block can be sent. *Contrast with* continuous ARQ.
stop bit. In start/stop transmission, the bit that indicates the end of a character. *See also* start/stop transmission.
stop signal. (1) A signal to a receiving mechanism to wait for the next signal. (2) In a start/stop system, a signal following a character or block that prepares the receiving device for the reception of a subsequent character or block.
store-and-forward. An application in which input is transmitted, usually to a computer, stored, and then later delivered to the recipient.
store-and-forward switch. A type of switch that reads entire packets and stores them, if necessary, before sending them to the destination.
Street Talk. A directory service for networks produced by Banyan.
stress testing. Placing a heavy load on a system to see if it performs properly.
Strowger switch. A step-by-step switch named after its inventor, Almon B. Strowger. *See also* step-by-step switch.
subnetwork. (1) In the OSI reference model, layers 1, 2, and 3 together constitute the subnetwork. (2) A portion of the network. (3) In the context of the Internet, one of the interconnected networks that also continues to operate on its own and maintain its own identity.
subordinate station. *See* slave station.
subscriber's loop. *See* local loop.
subvoice-grade circuit. A circuit of bandwidth narrower than that of voice-grade circuits. Such circuits are usually subchannels of a voice-grade line.
supergroup. Five 48 kHz groups of 12 voice channels each. The total bandwidth of a supergroup is 240 kHz.
superhighway effect. A concept that suggests that the capacity of new facilities is often exceeded faster than anticipated because users, finding the capability better than expected, use it to a greater extent or for purposes beyond those for which it was originally designed.
switch. (1) In the context of a LAN, a device that connects two or more LAN segments together and allows all of the connections to operate simultaneously. (2) In the context of the telephone system, a device in the central office that makes the connection for telephone calls. (3) Sometimes a PBX is referred to as a switch.
switched connection. (1) A mode of operating a data link in which a circuit or channel is established to switching facilities, as, for example, in a public switched network. (2) A connection that is established by dialing. *Contrast with* nonswitched connection.
switched line. A telecommunications line in which the connection is established by dialing. *See also* dial-up line *and* leased circuit.
switched telecommunications network. A switched network furnished by communications common carriers or telecommunications administrations.
switched virtual circuit. In packet switching networks, a temporary connection between two nodes established only for the duration of a session.
switchhook. A switch on a telephone set, associated with the structure supporting the receiver or handset. It is operated by the removal or replacement of the receiver or handset on the support.
switching center. A location that terminates multiple circuits. It is capable of interconnecting circuits or transferring traffic between circuits.
switching office. A telephone company location that contains switching equipment.
symmetric digital subscriber line (SDSL). One of the DSL family of services that provides equal speed channels in both directions. SDSL is capable of speeds up to 768 Kbps in each direction and is targeted at business customers. *See also* digital subscriber line.
synchronization character (SYN). In a data message, a character that is inserted in the data stream from time to time by the transmitting station to ensure that the receiver is maintaining character synchronization and properly grouping the bits into characters. The synchronization

characters are removed by the receiver and do not remain in the received message.

synchronous. (1) Pertaining to two or more processes that depend on the occurrences of specific events, such as common timing signals. (2) Occurring with a regular or predictable time relationship.

Synchronous Data Link Control (SDLC). A bit-oriented data link protocol developed by IBM. SDLC is a proper subset of HDLC.

synchronous line control. A scheme of operating procedures and control signals by which telecommunications lines are controlled.

synchronous optical network (SONET). A standard for transmitting data on optical fibers.

synchronous transmission. (1) Data transmission in which the time of occurrence of each signal representing a bit is related to a fixed time frame. (2) Data transmission in which the sending and receiving instruments are operating continuously at substantially the same frequency and are maintained, by means of correction, in a desired phase relationship.

system features. Features of a telephone system that are available to all users and that may be automatically activated on behalf of the user.

Systems Network Architecture (SNA). A seven-layer communications architecture developed by IBM to serve as a basis for future telecommunications products.

T-carrier system. A family of high-speed, digital transmission systems, designated according to their transmission capacity.

tariff. The published rate for a specific unit of equipment, facility, or type of service provided by a telecommunications carrier. Also, the vehicle by which the regulating agencies approve or disapprove of such facilities or services. Thus, the tariff becomes a contract between the customer and the telecommunications facility.

Technical Office Protocol (TOP). A communications architecture, based on the OSI reference model, specifically oriented toward office automation.

telecommunications. (1) Any transmission, emission, or reception of signs, signals, writing, images, and sounds or intelligence of any nature by wire, radio, optical, or other electromagnetic systems. (2) Communication, as by telegraph or telephone.

telecommunications access method (TCAM). Communications software that controls communications lines. *See also* communications access method (CAM).

telecommunications control unit. *See* front-end processor (FEP).

telecommunications facility. Transmission capabilities or the means for providing such capabilities.

telecommunications monitor (TCM). Computer software that governs the overall operation of a network and may provide transaction processing or other services.

telecommuting. Using telecommunications to work from home or other locations instead of on the business's premises.

telediagnosis. Using telecommunications to diagnose a problem from a remote location.

telegraph. A system employing the interruption or change in polarity of direct current for the transmission of signals.

telegraph-grade circuit. A circuit suitable for transmission by teletypewriter equipment. Normally, the circuit is considered to employ DC signaling at a maximum speed of 75 baud.

telephone company. Any common carrier providing public telephone system service.

telephony. Transmission of speech or other sounds.

teleprinter. Equipment used in a printing telegraph system.

teleprocessing. Remote access data processing.

teletex. A standardized communications messaging technology allowing automatic, error-free transmissions between terminals at speeds 48 times greater than telex. Teletex is the logical successor to telex and TWX.

Teletype. Trademark of AT&T, usually referring to a series of teleprinter equipment, such as tape punches, reperforators, and page printers, that is used for telecommunications.

teletypewriter. A slow-speed terminal with a keyboard for input and paper for receiving printed output.

teletypewriter exchange (TWX). Teletypewriter service provided by Western Union in which suitably arranged teletypewriter stations are provided with lines to a central office for access to other such stations throughout the United States and Canada. Both Baudot and ASCII coded machines are used. Business machines may also be used with certain restrictions.

telex. An international message-switching service that uses teleprinters to produce hardcopy of the messages.

telex network. An international public messaging service using slow-speed teletypewriter equipment and Baudot code to exchange messages between subscribers. In the United States, telex service is provided by Western Union.

telnet. A capability of the Internet that allows a person or computer to log on to another computer on the Internet.

terminal. (1) A device, usually equipped with a keyboard and a display device, capable of sending and receiving information over a link. (2) A point in a system or network at which data can either enter or leave.

terminal component. A separately addressable part of a terminal that performs an input or output function, such as the display component of a keyboard-display device or the printer component of a keyboard-printer device.

terminal emulation program. A program that makes a personal computer act like a terminal that is recognized by the host.

terminal session. *See* session.

test tone. A tone used in identifying circuits for trouble location or for circuit adjustment.

text. The part of a data message containing the subject matter of interest to the user.

thick Ethernet. An Ethernet operating on traditional 0.4-inch coaxial cable.
thin client. An application designed such that little or no processing is done on the client computer; most processing is done on the server. *See also* fat client.
thin Ethernet. An Ethernet operating on more flexible 0.25-inch coaxial cable.
think time. The time between the receipt of a message at a terminal until the next message is entered by the user. *Synonym for* intermessage delay *and for* user response time.
tie line. *See* tie trunk.
tie trunk. A telephone line or channel directly connecting two branch exchanges.
time assignment speech interpolation (TASI). A technique of multiplexing telephone calls by taking advantage of the pauses in normal speech and assigning the channel to another call during the pause.
time division multiple access (TDMA). A transmission technique used in digital radio transmission in which the use of a frequency is divided into time slots that are shared among several users.
time division multiplexing (TDM). A technique that divides a circuit's capacity into time slots, each of which is used by a different voice or data signal.
timesharing. (1) Pertaining to the interleaved use of time on a computer system that enables two or more users to execute computer programs concurrently. (2) A mode of operation of a data processing system that provides for the interleaving in time of two or more processes in one processor. (3) A method of using a computing system that allows a number of users to execute programs concurrently and to interact with the programs during execution.
tip. The end of the plug used to make circuit connections in a manual switchboard or patch panel. The tip is the connector attached to the positive side of the common battery that powers the station equipment. By extension, it is the positive battery side of a telecommunications line. *Contrast with* ring.
tip and ring. Telephone company jargon for the two wires that carry a telephone signal. The term is a carry-over from earlier days when the plug at the telephone operator's console had two connection points, the tip and the ring.
token. A particular character in a token-oriented protocol. The terminal that has the token has the right to use the communications circuit.
toll. In public switched systems, a charge for a connection beyond an exchange boundary that is based on time and distance.
toll calls. Calls outside a local service area.
toll office. A central office at which channels and toll circuits terminate. Whereas there is usually one particular central office in a city, larger cities may have several central offices where toll message circuits terminate.
toll trunk. A communications circuit between telephone company toll offices.
tone dialing. *See* dual-tone-multifrequency (DTMF).
tone signaling. Signaling performed by sending tones on a circuit.
topology. The way in which a network's circuits are configured.
torn tape message system. Deprecated name for a teletypewriter-based message switching system in which paper tape was torn off one teletypewriter and read into another.
torn tape switching center. A location where operators tear off the incoming printed and punched paper tape and transfer it manually to the proper outgoing circuit.
total cost of ownership. A concept that tries to identify all of the costs associated with the acquisition and ownership of a device or piece of equipment during its lifetime. The concept of the total cost of ownership was first applied to personal computers by the Gartner Group in the early 1990s.
touch-sensitive. A VDT screen that can detect the location of the user's finger using either a photosensitive or resistive technique.
Touchtone. AT&T's tradename for dual-tone-multifrequency dialing.
trackball. In computer graphics, a ball, movable about its center, that is used as a locator device.
traffic. Transmitted and received messages.
trailer. The part of a data message following the text.
transaction. An exchange between a terminal and another device, such as a computer, that accomplishes a particular action or result; for example, the entry of a customer's deposit and the updating of the customer's balance.
transaction processing system. A system in which the users run prewritten programs to perform business transactions, generally of a somewhat repetitive nature.
transceiver. A terminal that can transmit and receive traffic.
transient error. An error that occurs once or at unpredictable intervals.
transition. The switching from one state (for example, positive voltage) to another (negative voltage).
transmission. (1) The process of sending data from one place for reception elsewhere. (2) In data communications, a series of characters including headings and texts. (3) The process of dispatching a signal, message, or other form of intelligence by wire, radio, telegraphy, telephony, facsimile, or other means. (4) One or more blocks or messages. *Note:* Transmission implies only the sending of data; the data may or may not be received.
transmission code. A code for sending information over telecommunications lines.
transmission control character. (1) Any control character used to control or facilitate transmission of data between data terminal equipment (DTE). (2) Characters transmitted over a line that are not message data but that cause certain control operations to be performed when encountered. Among such operations are addressing, polling, message delimiting and blocking, transmission error checking, and carriage return.
Transmission Control Protocol/Internet Protocol (TCP/IP). A set of transmission rules for interconnecting communications networks. TCP/IP is heavily supported by the U.S. government.
transmission control unit. *See* front-end processor (FEP).

transmission efficiency. The ratio of information bits to total bits transmitted.
transmission medium. Any material substance that can be, or is, used for the propagation of signals, usually in the form of modulated radio, light, or acoustic waves, from one point to another, such as an optical fiber, cable, bundle, wire, dielectric slab, water, or air. *Note:* Free space can also be considered a transmission medium for electromagnetic waves.
transmit. (1) To send data from one place for reception elsewhere. (2) To move an entity from one place to another; for example, to broadcast radio waves, to dispatch data via a transmission medium, or to transfer data from one data station to another via a line.
transnational data flow (TNDF). The transmission of data across national borders.
transparent data. Data that is not recognized as containing transmission control characters. Transparent data is sometimes preceded by a control byte and a count of the amount of data following.
transparent mode. A mode of binary synchronous text transmission in which data, including normally restricted data link control characters, is transmitted only as specific bit patterns. Control characters that are intended to be effective are preceded by a DLE character. *Contrast with* nontransparent mode.
trellis code modulation (TCM). A specialized form of quadrature amplitude modulation that codes the data so that many bit combinations are invalid. TCM is used for high-speed data communications.
tribit. A group of 3 bits. In eight-phase modulation, each possible tribit is encoded as 1 of 8 unique carrier phase shifts. *Contrast with* dibit *and* quadbit.
triple DES. An enhancement to the standard data encryption technique, which doubles the encryption key length to 112 bits.
trouble ticket. An online record or paper form that is filled out to document the symptoms of a problem and the action being taken to correct it.
trunk. A telephone channel between two central offices or switching devices that is used to provide a telephone connection between subscribers.
trunk group. The trunks between two switching centers, individual message distribution points, or both, that use the same multiplex terminal equipment.
tuning. The process of making adjustments to a system to improve its performance.
turnaround time. The actual time required to reverse the direction of transmission from send to receive or vice versa when a half-duplex circuit is used. For most telecommunications facilities, there will be time required by line propagation and line effects, modem timing, and machine reaction. A typical time is 200 milliseconds on a half-duplex telephone connection.
twisted pair wires. A pair of wires insulated with a plastic coating and twisted together that is used as a medium for telecommunications circuits.
two-wire circuit. A metallic circuit formed by two conductors insulated from each other. It is possible to use the two conductors as a one-way transmission path, a half-duplex, or a duplex path.

unbuffered. A terminal in which a character is transmitted to the computer as soon as a key on the keyboard is pressed.
unguided media. *See* radiated media.
Unicode. A standardized coding system that has 2^{16} code points that can be used to represent all the characters of all languages.
unified messaging. A system that allows the handling of e-mail, voice mail, and faxes through one electronic mailbox, so that a person can connect to it and receive all of his or her messages, regardless of how they were originally sent.
uniform resource locator (URL). The address that is used to specify a server and home page on the World Wide Web (WWW).
unipolar. A digital signaling technique in which a 1 bit is represented by a positive voltage pulse and a 0 bit by no voltage.
universal international freephone numbering (UIFN). A worldwide toll-free calling service under which the calls are paid for by the called party. Similar to 800 service in the United States.
universal service. The attribute of the telephone system that allows any station to connect to any other.
unshielded twisted pair (UTP). *See* twisted pair wires.
uplink. The microwave radio signal beamed up to a satellite.
uploading. The transmission of a file of data from a personal computer to a mainframe.
uptime. The time that a telecommunications network is operating and available to be used.
user. (1) The ultimate source or destination of information flowing through a system. (2) A person, process, program, device, or system that employs a user application network for data processing and information exchange.
user friendly. A terminal or system that is easy to learn and easy to use.
user group. In the context of the Internet, groups of people who get together online to discuss particular topics and exchange ideas.
user response time. The time it takes the user to see what the computer displayed, interpret it, type the next transaction, and press the ENTER key. *See also* think time.
user written commands. Control sequences written by users to perform predefined functions.
usenet newsgroup. A type of discussion group on the Internet that notifies registered members of new messages since the last log on.

V.24. An ITU-T specification for the interface between a modem (DCE) and a terminal or computer (DTE). The interface is identical to the RS-232-D. *See also* RS-232-D *and* RS-232-C.
V.32. An ITU-T standard for transmitting data at 9,600 bps, full duplex on a switched circuit.

V.32bis. An ITU-T standard for transmitting data at 14,400 bps, full duplex on a switched circuit.
V.34. An ITU-T standard for transmitting data at 28,800 bps, full duplex on a switched circuit. V.34 assumes that most of the transmission will occur on a relatively error-free digital circuit.
V.34bis. An ITU-T standard for transmitting data at 33,600 bps, full duplex on a switched circuit. V.34bis assumes that most of the transmission will occur on a relatively error-free digital circuit.
V.42. An ITU-T standard for error detection and error correction.
V.42bis. An ITU-T standard that specifies how modems will compress data before transmitting.
V.90. An ITU-T standard for transmitting data at 56,000 bps, full duplex on a switched circuit. V.90 assumes that at least one end of the communications line has a pure digital connection to the telephone network. V.90 transmission is asymmetric, in that the 56 kbps data rate is only achieved on the half of the transmission from the all-digital end of the connection. Transmissions from the analog end follow the V.34bis standard and occur at a maximum rate of 33.6 kbps.
value-added carrier. A carrier that provides enhanced communications services. Normally, some type of computation is provided in addition to the basic communications service.
value-added network (VAN). A public data network that contains intelligence that provides enhanced communications services.
vertical redundancy check (VRC). A parity check performed on each character of data as the block is received.
very-high-rate digital subscriber line (VDSL). One of the DSL family of services that transmits data at speeds of 51 to 55 Mbps over short twisted pair telephone lines of up to 1,000 feet, and as low as 13 Mbps at 4,000 feet. Early versions of this technology are asymmetric, like ADSL, and have an upstream channel of 1.6 to 2.3 Mbps. *See also* digital subscriber line *and* asymmetric digital subscriber line.
very small aperture terminal (VSAT). A satellite system using the Ku band of microwave frequencies, which require small receiving antennas.
video conferencing. Meetings conducted in rooms equipped with television cameras and receivers for remote users' participation.
video display terminal (VDT). A computer terminal with a screen on which characters or graphics are displayed and (normally) a keyboard that is used to enter data.
video display unit (VDU). *See* video display terminal (VDT).
video signal compression. The process of reducing the number of bits required to carry a digitized video signal while maintaining adequate quality.
videotex. An application in which the computer is able to store text and images in digital form and transmit them to remote terminals for display or interaction.
VINES. Network operating system software for a LAN produced by Banyan.
virtual circuit. A temporary circuit built between the sender and receiver of a telecommunications transmission (e.g., for a telephone call).
virtual network. As contrasted with a leased or private network, a virtual network appears to the customer as though it is dedicated for his exclusive use, but in reality it uses the public switched telephone network to provide service.
virtual telecommunications access method (VTAM). IBM's primary telecommunications access method.
virtual terminal. A concept that allows an application program to send or receive data to or from a generic terminal. Other software transforms the input and output to correspond to the actual characteristics of the real terminal being used.
virus. *See* computer virus.
voice-band. The 300 Hz to 3,300 Hz band used on telephone equipment for the transmission of voice and data.
voice compression. The process of reducing the number of bits required to carry a digitized voice signal while maintaining the essential characteristics of speech.
voice-grade circuit. A circuit suitable for transmission of speech, digital or analog data, or facsimile, generally with a frequency range of about 300 Hz to 3,300 Hz. Voice-grade circuits can transmit data at speeds up to 19,200 bps.
voice mail. A messaging service that people use to leave voice messages for others. The system provides a voice mailbox on a computer in which the voice messages are digitized and stored. The voice equivalent of an electronic mail system for textual messages.
voice over IP (VoIP). The ability to send voice signals over a network that uses the IP protocol. This is notable because networks based on the IP protocol were originally designed to handle data transmissions.
voice response unit. Hardware designed to respond to input signals with a spoken voice.

WATS. *See* 800 Service.
wavelength division multiplexing (WDM). A technique used on optical fibers in which many light beams of different wavelengths are transmitted along a single fiber simultaneously without interfering with one another. Each light beam can carry many individually modulated data streams, allowing very high data rates to be achieved.
Web browser. Software that provides access to the World Wide Web and sometimes other parts of the Internet.
white noise. *See* background noise.
wide area network (WAN). A network that covers a large geographic area, requiring the crossing of public right-of-ways and the use of circuits provided by a common carrier.
Wide Area Telecommunications Services (WATS). An older name for 800 service. *See* 800 service.
wideband circuit. A circuit designed to carry data at speeds greater than voice-grade circuits. *Synonym for* high-speed circuit.
Windows NT. Network operating system software for a LAN produced by Microsoft.
wireless application protocol (WAP). A protocol for transmitting WWW pages to cellular telephones. WAP downsizes fat, graphics-rich web pages so that they are usable on small cell phone displays.

wireless communications. Communications in which the media is not wire or cable but the signal is broadcast by radio.

workload generator. Computer software designed to generate transactions or other work for a computer or network for testing purposes.

workstation. (1) The place where a terminal operator sits or stands to do work. It contains a working surface, terminal, chair, and other equipment or supplies needed by the person to do his or her job. (2) A powerful microcomputer that contains specialized software to assist a person in doing his or her job.

World Wide Web (WWW). A collection of servers on the Internet that provide home pages that use hypertext markup language (HTML). The servers are identified by uniform resource locators (URLs).

X.21. A specification for an interface between data terminal equipment (DTE) and a digital public telephone network.

X.21 BIS. A specification for an interface between data terminal equipment (DTE) and an analog telephone network. X.21 BIS is electrically virtually identical to the RS-232-C and V.24 interface specifications.

X.25 standard for data transmission. The first three layers of the OSI reference model. A standard for data transmission using a packet switching network.

X.400 standard for electronic mail. A standard for the transmission of electronic mail.

X.500 standard for network directories. A standard that specifies how to create and maintain a directory of e-mail users and their network addresses.

Xmodem protocol. An asynchronous protocol developed for use between microcomputers, especially for transfers of data files between them.

Ymodem protocol. An asynchronous protocol developed for use between microcomputers, especially for transfers of data files between them.

zero slot LAN. A LAN that connects to personal computers or workstations using the computer's serial or parallel port.

Zmodem protocol. An asynchronous protocol developed for use between microcomputers, especially for transfers of data files between them.

INDEX